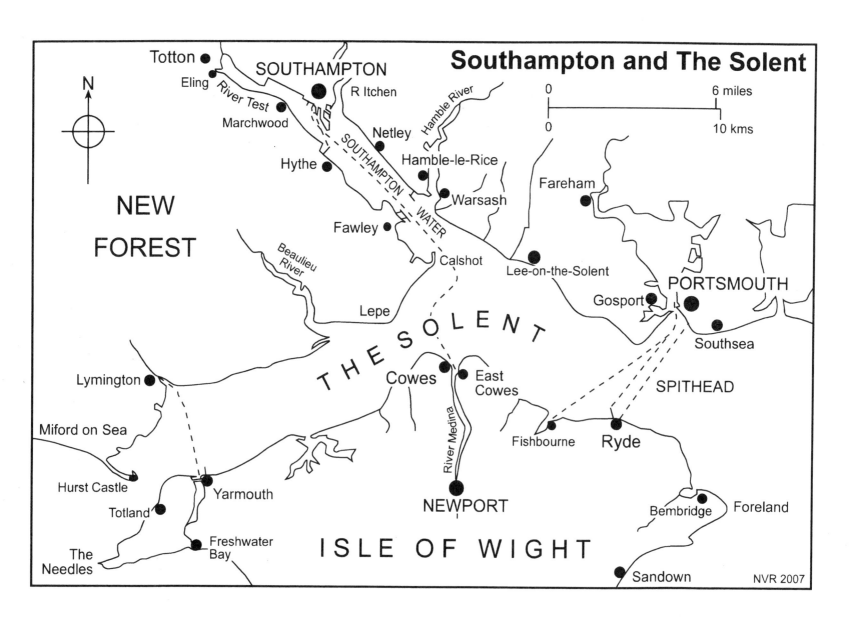

Southampton and The Solent

SOLENT SHIPPING MEMORIES

by

Mick Lindsay and Nigel V Robinson

Successor to the long-lived schoolship **Dar Pomorza**, the 1981-built **Dar Mlodzeizy** was one of six sister ships built at the Gdansk Shipyards (the others being **Mir**, **Druzbha**, **Pallada**, **Khersones**, and **Nadezhda**, all of which came in the late 1980s), distinguished by their squared-off transoms. All have different paint schemes in order to differentiate them. Amazingly, seventy new vessels of the design popularly known as "tall ships" have been built since 1966 and much of the new interest in these superb vessels is due to the Tall Ships Races formerly sponsored by Cutty Sark Whisky. The **Dar Mlodzeizy** is seen here in the Solent on Sunday, 16 April, beginning to unfurl her sails at the beginning of the 2000 Tall Ships' Race, which started at Southampton.

(MAL)

Introduction

This book had its origins in 1995 when we first thought that a colour album of Southampton shipping would be well received. For a variety of reasons the book never materialised and it lay untouched for ten years until Bernard McCall saw its potential for his *Shipping Memories* series. We have attempted to cover a wide variety of the Solent's shipping - it is obviously impossible to include everything within the allowance of 80 pages; hopefully further volumes will give us the opportunity to introduce more of the area's shipping, for there is indeed a vast array from which to choose from - ranging from the world famous Cunard *Queens* to the humblest tug and every conceivable ship type in between.

Southampton like other ports has seen tremendous changes - the passenger liner as such has gone with the notable exception of **Queen Elizabeth 2** (to be withdrawn in November 2008) and **Queen Mary 2**, but cruise ships have more than filled the void. Cargo now moves in huge containerships and the non-too attractive car carriers move thousands of vehicles both in and out of the port. For those who may be tempted to think that it has been all down hill since the "romantic" days of yore, it should be borne in mind that Southampton now handles more cargo and passengers than it ever did in its "heyday". Here, however, we look back to the 1960s, 70s and 80s at the last glorious years of what might be called *traditional* maritime activity in Southampton and the Solent. We have concentrated on merchant ships - perhaps someone would like to tackle the major Naval presence hereabouts?

All the photographs were taken within the Solent area mainly by Mick Lindsay (MAL), and Nigel Robinson (NVR) with a number from the camera of the late W H (Bill) Mitchell (WHM) whose collection was saved through the generosity of Mick Lindsay's late mother. It gives great pleasure to Nigel Robinson to include some photographs taken by his late father Wilfred Robinson. Other photographs are acknowledged individually. We have kept the technical information to the minimum giving generally only the date of build and tonnage - gross tonnage (grt) or, in the case of tankers, deadweight (dwt) - where considered relevant. It should be noted that tonnages and passenger capacities etc can vary considerably over the life of a ship. The date on which the photograph was taken, where known, is also given. This is, however, essentially a picture book so here is a selection to savour - enjoy!

Acknowledgements

Many sources have been consulted whilst researching the captions. Principal amongst these have been *Lloyd's Register* and *Lists of Shipowners* for various years, and the *Southampton Shipping Guide* published monthly by the port authority until 1975. Periodicals have included *Sea Breezes*, *Ships Monthly*, *Shipping Today and Yesterday*, *Marine News* (the monthly journal of the World Ship Society), and *Black Jack* (the quarterly magazine of the Southampton Branch of the World Ship Society). Numerous books in the authors' collections were also referred to, as were various personal records of the shipping scene collated over the years.

Our gratitude is tendered to those friends who have helped with information and advice, but most especially to David Hornsby for casting an eye over the captions for us and Gil Mayes for his usual expert review of the draft and valuable comments. Any errors remain our responsibility. We must thank Amadeus Press for their splendid work. Our respective wives, Wendy Lindsay and Gill Robinson, also deserve our thanks for forbearance over the periods when this work seemed to take over our lives.

Michael A Lindsay   Nigel V Robinson
Southampton, December 2007

Published by Bernard McCall, 400 Nore Road, Portishead, Bristol, BS20 8EZ, England. Website : www.coastalshipping.co.uk
Telephone/fax : 01275 846178. E-mail : bernard@coastalshipping.co.uk
All distribution enquiries should be addressed to the publisher.

Printed by Amadeus Press, Ezra House, West 26 Business Park, Cleckheaton, West Yorkshire, BD19 4TQ
Telephone : 01274 863210; fax : 01274 863211; e-mail : info@amadeuspress.co.uk; website : www.amadeuspress.co.uk

ISBN : 978-1-902953-33-5

Front cover: What can be said about this remarkable ship that does justice to a most amazing career? At nearly 40 years old, the **Queen Elizabeth 2** has travelled more than twice as many miles as her two predecessors, **Queen Mary** and **Queen Elizabeth**, together. She was the result of a major rethink by Cunard, when they were looking to replace the two 'Queens' and abandoned their 'Q3' project. This meant a much more radical ship, at the cutting edge of modern sixties' design. Most of that early panache has gone in favour of a more 'comfortable' look internally, and externally, she has had more face lifts than an ageing American actress. A major refit in 1986/7, including a re-engining, changed her appearance with the originally slim white funnel replaced by a much more substantial design. Originally meant for the dual role of cruising and trans-Atlantic voyages, she now takes it easy and lets her big sister, **Queen Mary 2**, charge back and forth across 'the Pond'. Her days are numbered now, following the announcement from Cunard that the ship had been sold to interests in Dubai as an hotel. She will sail from Southampton for the last time on 11 November 2008, having not quite made her fortieth birthday. A ship's age is measured not from the day of launch, but the occasion of her maiden voyage, which was on 2 May 1969. She is seen here in October 2001, passing the mouth of the River Itchen in dramatic light at the beginning of another cruise. *(MAL)*

Back cover: The late afternoon of a chilly 30 November 1969 finds the Cunard Line *Franconia* swinging prior to backing into the Ocean Dock; the contrast in temperature would have been very apparent to those on board – she was returning from the Caribbean! The *Franconia* started life as *Ivernia*, one of a class of four built for the Canadian trade in the 1950s. Rebuilt for cruising in 1962-63, she became *Franconia* until sold to the Soviet Union in 1973, becoming **Fedor Shalyapin**. She was broken up 2005. *(NVR)*

Cunard Line's **Queen Mary** of 1936 arrives in Southampton on 14 August 1967 towards the end of her active career. She is a famous ship that needs no introduction – a legend in her own lifetime, she has now spent longer in static preservation since 1967 at Long Beach, California, than she did in service. On a very blustery Monday afternoon she is about to begin the turn into the Ocean Dock. Six tugs are assisting her – four are visible here with two more on the port side. The three bow tugs are, left to right, **Formby** and **Brockenhurst** of Alexandra Towing and **Hamtun** of Red Funnel, the first and last named being steam tugs. Just a couple of months later, on 31 October 1967, **Queen Mary** left Southampton for the voyage round Cape Horn to Long Beach.

(NVR)

This busy picture shows the *Iberia, Orcades*, *Canberra* and *Southampton Belle*. It is a sight not too unusual in the 21st century when modern cruise ships tend to depart together at teatime. However, this is 31 August 1968. It is a rather dull Saturday morning and P&O's *Iberia* of 1954 is getting underway having departed from the Ocean Dock. Coming slowly down river from the Western Docks is their *Orcades* of 1948 and visible in the distance at her berth is the 1960-built *Canberra*, also of P&O. *Iberia* and *Orcades* were departing on cruises. Both were scrapped in Taiwan, in 1972 and 1973 respectively. The little boat in the foreground is of note; she is *Southampton Belle*, one of many pleasure boats that operated dock cruises "to view the ocean liners". She had been built in 1909 as the Portsmouth Harbour ferry steamer *Vesta II*. Renamed *Kingston Belle* in 1949, she became *Southampton Belle* in 1963 and it was then that she was converted to diesel. A number of other former Portsmouth ferries were operated in the trade by Blue Funnel Cruises, who still operate in the port with modern vessels offering corporate charters and longer Solent excursions, as well as dock cruises.

(NVR)

Batory was one of the most attractive ships ever to grace the port of Southampton, and she had a long and eventful career. She and her sister, **Pilsudski** (lost at the beginning of World War II), were built by Cantieri at Monfalcone in 1936 for the Gdynia-America Line and each ship was paid for by six shipments of coal for the Italian State Railways in lieu of cash. She was a troopship for this country, returning to Poland in 1946, and the following year sailed on the Gdynia, Copenhagen, Southampton and New York service. This did not last long as politics eventually saw her withdrawn from American ports and change direction to Karachi and Bombay. She eventually returned to the Atlantic, but this time to Canada. She was very popular with the Poles, who preferred her ability to transport large items of personal belongings to the limitations of flying. A refit in 1957 saw her accommodation improved with the deck-mounted lifeboats raised up on gravity davits. In 1969 she started an abortive new career as a hotel ship in Gdansk and was sold for breaking two years later in Hong Kong.

(Mrs K. Lane)

A little while before this picture was taken, the whistles on those massive funnels would have reverberated over Southampton to let everyone know that the **United States** was about to sail. The world's fastest liner, she took the Blue Riband of the Atlantic, the Hales Trophy, on her maiden voyage in July 1952. Withdrawn in November 1969, her history since would take too long to recount here. Suffice to say that there have been many plans to reactivate her, none of which have come to fruition. Her latest owners are the Norwegian Cruise Line who probably have as good a chance as anybody – it was they who took the **France** and converted her into the successful **Norway**. **United States** is depicted here on 27 July 1969 as she backs out of the Ocean Dock assisted by the Red Funnel tugs **Dunnose** and **Hamtun**.

(NVR)

Taken as far back as 1947, this shot shows the **Aquitania**, the "ship beautiful" as she fondly became known, still in her wartime grey, but with her funnels now in Cunard colours, on her way past Dock Head, probably with a passenger list of GI brides heading for a new life in America. When she entered service in 1914, she was Cunard's largest ship at 45,647 grt and was built for comfort, not speed. She may not have been a Blue Riband record breaker, but was the only four-funnelled passenger ship to survive two world wars, so setting her own personal record. World War I saw her in various roles, initially as an armed merchant cruiser, then a hospital ship and finally a troopship. In the 1920s and 1930s she was part of Cunard's mismatched transatlantic fleet and these years represented her heyday. After spending World War II as a troopship, she was employed in an austerity role at the end of hostilities, returning GIs to America, taking emigrants to Australia, relocating displaced persons as well as her usual role as a passenger ship. She left Southampton for the last time on 19 February 1950, arriving at Faslane for her date with the breaker's torch two days later.

(MAL)

Despite appearances, this picture was in fact taken mid-afternoon on 23 June 1967. In pouring rain **Paraguay Star**, of Blue Star Line, is seen arriving in the Ocean Dock to berth at the Ocean Terminal homeward bound from Buenos Aires to London – a brief call probably to disembark passengers and maybe a little cargo. She was one of four sisters built in 1947/48; the others were **Argentina Star**, **Brasil Star** and **Uruguay Star**. They could carry large quantities of frozen meat and in addition had accommodation for just over 50 first-class passengers. **Paraguay Star** herself was completed in 1948 and after a serious fire in London docks on 12 August 1969, she was the first of the four to go for scrap, in the following month.

(NVR)

Achille Lauro is seen outward bound passing Calshot at the entrance to Southampton Water on 29 August 1971. An unlucky ship in many ways, she nevertheless had a long career. She was laid down in 1939 for Royal Rotterdam Lloyd but was not completed until 1947 when she was named **Willem Ruys**. She operated to Batavia (Indonesia's Djakarta) from the Netherlands and then in a round-the-world service jointly with Nederland Lines **Oranje**. After mounting losses, both were sold in 1964 to Italian owner Achille Lauro, **Willem Ruys**

becoming **Achille Lauro** and **Oranje** renamed **Angelina Lauro**. Both worked in the Australian emigrant service then full-time cruising. **Achille Lauro** despite fires, collision and most famously a hijacking by Arab terrorists in 1985, managed to keep going until a final fire off the Somali coast on 30 November 1994, when she burnt out and subsequently sank. **Angelina Lauro** had already been lost by fire in the Caribbean on 31 March 1979.

(NVR)

Seen at night on 22 November 1970 is Union-Castle's **Windsor Castle**, the largest liner ever built for the Cape mail run to South Africa. She too was built in 1960 and served faithfully until the Autumn of 1977 when the weekly mail service, so long a feature of the port, ceased. People still remember "every Thursday at 4 o'clock", although latterly it was every Friday at 13.00 hours. **Windsor Castle** was sold to John H Latsis, renamed **Margarita L** and was converted into an accommodation ship based at Jeddah from 1979 to 1991, before being laid up at Eleusis in Greece. As **Rita**, she eventually arrived at Alang in July 2005 for breaking up.

(NVR)

Two views of liners in the King George V Graving Dock at Millbrook. This dry dock is no longer in use; in fact there is now no dry dock within Southampton Docks. In the past the KGV was host to a multitude of famous vessels undergoing routine annual overhaul or repairs. Two of Southampton's famous ships are depicted here within the dry dock's confines. The **Oriana** seen here on 12 May 1968, was built in 1960 for the Orient Line – she was Orient Lines' largest ship, a logical development from **Orcades**, **Oronsay** and **Orsova**. **Oriana** partnered P&O's **Canberra** in line voyages to Australia. Both latterly became full time cruise ships. After her seagoing days were over **Oriana** went to Japan and then China in ill-fated attempts at static roles but was scrapped in 2005.

(NVR)

One of the most aesthetically pleasing liners of all time is seen arriving at Southampton in the summer of 1965, passing Mayflower Park on her way up to the Western Docks. **Nieuw Amsterdam** was completed in 1938 and at 36982 grt was Holland's largest liner prior to the advent of the **Rotterdam** in 1959. She was affectionately known as "the darling of the Dutch" after her fine Allied war service.

She started life with a black hull, but the grey suited her much better. As transatlantic trade tailed off she turned to full time cruising, mainly in the Caribbean. She retired in December 1973 and early the following year was delivered to shipbreakers in Taiwan.

(Wilfred Robinson)

Queen Elizabeth was one of the truly great liners and, with her sister **Queen Mary**, became one half of the most successful pair of passenger ships ever. She was the largest liner in the world (and arguably still is), with **Queen Mary** officially the fastest. Like her sister, she was built by John Brown at Clydebank, but was still incomplete when she made her now famous dash for safety in New York. After wonderful wartime service, when she carried in excess of 15,000 troops at times, an extensive refit saw her ready for her intended role and her fully booked maiden voyage to New York was on 16 October, 1946. The next 15 years were spectacular for both ships, but the big bird in the sky was looming overhead and starting to eat away at passenger revenues. In 1965 she was extensively refitted for cruising,

given air-conditioning, with an outdoor pool and lido area, the plan being to run her until 1975 alongside the **Queen Elizabeth 2**. One wonders what the new ship would have been called in this situation, Queen Victoria? A change of plan, however, saw her sold to interests in Port Everglades, USA, in 1968, for a similar role to her sister on the West Coast. Far from successful, she was sold at auction to C Y Tung for use as a floating university. She was renamed **Seawise University** (a play on the initials of the new owner), but caught fire in mysterious circumstances on 9 January 1972, burning out and capsizing in Hong Kong harbour. Always in the shadow of her elder sister, she is up there with the best in the ocean liner hall of fame

(WHM)

A classic liner in a classic pose – the splendid **France** at the Ocean Terminal on 30 June 1967. Completed in 1962 for the French Line, this graceful and chic liner was initially a very successful ship on the North Atlantic and endeared herself to passengers and ship-lovers alike. Within ten years, however, she was losing money and despite trying cruising to offset some of the losses, the end came in late 1974 when the French Government withdrew her operating subsidy. After an aborted purchase by Saudi Arabian interests in 1975, she was eventually bought in 1979 by Christian Klosters, owner of Norwegian Caribbean Cruise Lines, who wanted to rebuild her as a full-time cruise ship. He succeeded spectacularly, and renamed **Norway**, she went on to have a very successful second career in the Caribbean, with occasional returns to Europe for refits, when she once again became a transatlantic liner, albeit briefly. Her owners, now restyled Norwegian Cruise Lines, only withdrew her after a serious boiler explosion in 2003, which sadly killed several crew members. She languished at Bremerhaven until a tow out to the Far East and final delivery to breakers at Alang in June 2006 under the name **Blue Lady**.

(NVR)

Britannic is a famous and illustrious name in shipping, but in this instance it only lasted for one day. Originally built in 1969 as the **Hamburg** for Germany Atlantic Line by Deutsche Werft AG, Hamburg, this unusual-looking ship is now something of an icon. Measuring 24,220 grt and having a speed of 22 knots, her passenger capacity was low at 652 and with a crew of 403 it gave a high ratio. She is one of the last of the turbine-powered passenger ships. After five years she was renamed **Hanseatic**, but German Atlantic were in financial trouble and folded the following year. She was quickly snapped by the Black Sea Shipping Company, which renamed her **Maxim Gorky**, but before she came into service, she was day-chartered for a film called "Juggernault", based on the **Queen Elizabeth 2** bomb scare of 1972. Hundreds of locals answered adverts for extras and many of those chosen ended up regretting their decision when the ship went into the English Channel. The weather proved less than smooth and the effects of mal de mer were plain to see as they came off the ship. Since then, **Maxim Gorky** has become one of the great survivors of the steam age, with only minor changes to the spelling of her name and a change of funnel colours. She almost sank after a collision with an iceberg in 1989 off the Norwegian coast - third time lucky for the Russians after the **Admiral Nakhimov** and the **Mikhail Lermontov** both went down. She will be 40 years old in a couple of years, but new SOLAS (Safety of Life at Sea) regulations will see her gone by 2010.

(David T Hornsby)

Southern Cross was a most significant vessel; an engines-aft, passenger-only liner designed for the round the world service of Shaw, Savill & Albion. With no cargo to slow things down she could make four round voyages to Australia and New Zealand in a year, rather than less than three by the combination cargo/passenger liners. She was launched at Harland & Wolff's yard at Belfast by Her Majesty The Queen and entered service in 1955. She was joined in 1962 by the slightly larger **Northern Star**; this latter ship not achieving the success of the earlier vessel and in fact being broken up in 1975 after only 13 years service. **Southern Cross** after cruising for Shaw, Savill went on to have a career of almost half a century with further cruising under the names **Calypso**, **Calypso 1**, **Azure Seas** and **Ocean Breeze**, but with her distinctive profile substantially unaltered. She was finally sold for breaking-up in Bangladesh in 2003. In this photograph, taken on 1 September 1968, she is seen outward-bound, moving down the River Itchen from Berth 30/1.

(NVR)

When William Francis Gibbs built the **America** in 1940, it was with an eye on the future and the stunning **United States**. The advent of World War II meant that she was used for cruising to the Caribbean rather than her intended Atlantic run. She made a significant contribution to the war effort as the troopship **USS West Point**, reputedly carrying over 9,000 troops on one voyage. Beginning her peacetime role in 1946, she was successful for a while, but declining bookings and strikes saw her sold to the Greek Chandris Lines in 1964. Refitted as the **Australis** for the Australian emigrant trade, she was the largest one-class passenger ship afloat. Repainted white (the grey hull came in 1967), she began another highly successful period in her career, until 1977 when she sailed for the last time as **Australis**. Sold for $5million to the American Venture Cruises, two disastrous voyages as **America** (again) saw the ship sold back to Chandris for $1 million (losing $4.5million as they only received a down payment).

(MAL)

After another year as the now one-funnelled **Italis**, she was laid up at Perama, Greece, until sold in 1993 for use as a hotel in Thailand. She was refused passage through the Suez Canal and left under tow for the long trip around the Cape. She broke her line in a Force 12, driving ashore on the western coast of Fuerteventura, in the Canary Islands, breaking in two. The last remains of the ship have recently collapsed into the sea. Above we see **Australis** arriving for the last time on 17 November 1977 and on the right **America** inbound in 1957.

(WHM)

Andes was one of Southampton's best known liners – she spent her entire peacetime career based in the port. Completed in 1939 by Harland & Wolff at Belfast she first served as a troopship and did not take up her designated service to South America until January 1948; she was Royal Mail Lines largest ship. In 1959/60 **Andes** was refitted as a full-time cruise ship at Flushing. She became very popular and was noted for her long distance cruises. After eleven years in this role she was sold for breaking up at Bruges in 1971. She originally had a black hull, but is shown here in her cruising white, worn since 1960, outward-bound off Berth 38/9 on 17 August 1969.

(Wilfred Robinson)

Caribia seen moving astern from the Ocean Dock into the River Test on 6 August 1967, was then nearly 40 years old. She had been built in 1928 as *Vulcania* for the Italian Cosulich Line and with her sister *Saturnia* was one of the largest motorships of her day. She passed to the Italia Line upon the formation of that combine in the 1930s. *Vulcania* served as a US transport in World War II and was returned to Italia in 1946. In 1965 she became the *Caribia* under the ownership of the Siosa Line (Sicula Oceanica S.p.a.), a Palermo-based subsidiary of the Grimaldi Group. It is interesting to note that Grimaldi vessels in the shape of large yellow painted ro-ro vessels are still very much part of the Southampton shipping scene as we write. *Caribia* first operated on the West Indies service as seen here then later turned to cruising. She suffered an engine failure off Cannes in September 1972 and ran aground. After being refloated she was deemed not worth repairing and was sold for scrapping in Taiwan, but sank under tow near Kaohsiung.

(NVR)

Grimaldi-Siosa Line's *Irpinia* was a member of an exclusive club of ships which have passed the 50-year mark. She started life as Transport Maritime's *Campaña* on the South American service. Seized by Argentina in 1943 and named *Rio Jachal*, she returned to France after World War II, going back to her original route and name. Grimaldi-Siosa bought the ship in 1955, renamed her *Irpinia*, increased her length by ten feet and ran her from Genoa to the West Indies. Her first call at Southampton was in 1956 when she still had two funnels. They were replaced in 1962 by a single streamlined stack for her new diesel engines, at which time she started some cruising, going full-time in 1970. She had a starring role in the film "Voyage of the Damned" in 1976 after which there was a rethink on her withdrawal from service and she sailed on until 1983, when she was scrapped at La Spezia in Italy. She is seen here in the River Itchen on 17 July 1972.

(WHM)

In her heyday, **Caronia's** profile was second only to that of the two Queens and she developed an amazing popularity with crew and passengers alike. Of course, the tips were better on the "Millionaire's Yacht", so seamen queued up to get on her and once there tended not to move. A revolutionary ship for Cunard, she had been built purely as a cruise ship and was painted in the now-famous four shades of green, marking her out from the rest of the fleet. Built by John Brown at Clydebank in 1948, she carried 581 first-class passengers and 351 cabin-class at 22 knots on world-wide cruising, occasionally filling in on the Atlantic during refits.

Her modernisation in 1965 proved to be short-lived and she was sold in 1968 to Panamanian interests as **Columbia** and later **Caribia** after a refit at Piraeus. An engine room explosion the following March left her laid up in New York (where she was given a parking ticket) until 1974 when she was sold to Taiwan for scrap, but foundered under tow off Guam and broke up. The picture shows **Caronia** setting off on her maiden voyage on 4 January 1949, with the soon-to-be-scrapped **Aquitania** in the background.

(WSS Southampton)

One of the most enduring and successful of liners, **Rotterdam** is seen on the balmy mid-summer evening of 20 June 1967, gently easing away down river from Berth 38/9. Her maiden voyage was on 3 September 1959 and she was the last and largest of Holland America Line's vessels for its New York service. She had been launched by Queen Juliana on 13 September 1958. Although a two-class liner on the North Atlantic a few hours work was all that was need to convert her to a one-class cruise ship. It was this facility and her beauty, strength of build and thorough maintenance over the years that combined to give **Rotterdam** such a long and successful career. In 1989 Holland-America was bought by Carnival Cruise Line but continues to trade under its old and well-respected name. After sale by Carnival in 1997, she became **Rembrandt**, under which name she did call at Southampton, but her new owners Premier Cruise Lines ceased trading in 2000 and she was laid up. After these problems, few of which can be attributed to the ship herself, she is now being thoroughly restored by Dutch owners as **Rotterdam** to take her place in honourable retirement on Rotterdam's waterfront.

(NVR)

Dedicated troopships have long since disappeared, but were a familiar sight in Southampton during the 1950s. One of the most popular was the handsome **Empire Fowey**, launched by Blohm & Voss, Hamburg, in 1935 as the 17,528 grt **Potsdam** for Hamburg-America Line, but sold to North German Lloyd before completion. After spending World War II as an accommodation ship, she became a war prize and was refitted as the **Empire Jewel** for trooping. She was renamed **Empire Fowey** in 1946 (under P&O management), but boiler problems led to a period of lay-up on the Firth of Forth prior to refit in 1947 at the Alexander Stephens' yard, Glasgow. This was completed in 1950 and included new boilers and turbines as well as reconstruction work which pushed her tonnage up to 19,121. She then went about the business of trooping for the next ten years before being sold to Pan-Islamic Steamship Co of Pakistan as the pilgrim ship **Safina-E-Hujjaj**. During the mid-1960s, she also sailed between Pakistan and Hong Kong and along the coast of East Africa. Her long career ended in 1976 when she was scrapped at Gadani Beach. She is seen here in the Solent in 1957.

(MAL)

Completed in 1953 for Swedish America as the *Kungsholm*, this handsome liner sailed in October of that year from Gothenburg to New York on her maiden voyage. She was notable as the first Atlantic liner to have all-outside cabins and all private facilities. But after only eleven years, she was sold to North German Lloyd and renamed *Europa* for the Bremerhaven-New York service. At the beginning she had the classic black hull, white upperworks and buff funnels, but after NGL amalgamated with Hamburg-America to form Hapag-Lloyd AG in 1970, she was gradually doing more cruising and in 1972 ceased North Atlantic operations. At this point she was given an all-white livery with a broad orange and blue band around the hull. Now full-time cruising, she lasted until 1981 when Costa moved in on the German market and they renamed her *Columbus C*. It was a short-lived career, however, after she hit a breakwater at Cadiz in high winds in 1984, settling on the bottom at her berth. She was towed to Barcelona that year for scrapping. *Europa* is seen here slipping out of the Ocean Dock into the River Test in August 1980

(MAL)

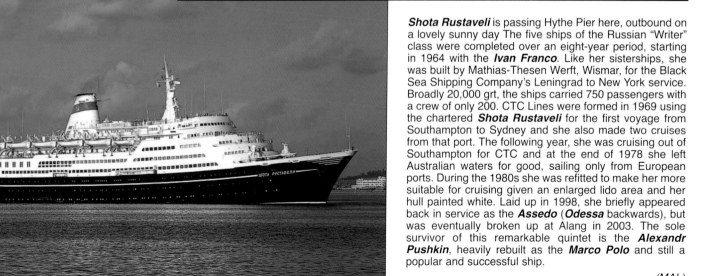

Shota Rustaveli is passing Hythe Pier here, outbound on a lovely sunny day. The five ships of the Russian "Writer" class were completed over an eight-year period, starting in 1964 with the *Ivan Franco*. Like her sisterships, she was built by Mathias-Thesen Werft, Wismar, for the Black Sea Shipping Company's Leningrad to New York service. Broadly 20,000 grt, the ships carried 750 passengers with a crew of only 200. CTC Lines were formed in 1969 using the chartered *Shota Rustaveli* for the first voyage from Southampton to Sydney and she also made two cruises from that port. The following year, she was cruising out of Southampton for CTC and at the end of 1978 she left Australian waters for good, sailing only from European ports. During the 1980s she was refitted to make her more suitable for cruising given an enlarged lido area and her hull painted white. Laid up in 1998, she briefly appeared back in service as the *Assedo* (*Odessa* backwards), but was eventually broken up at Alang in 2003. The sole survivor of this remarkable quintet is the *Alexandr Pushkin*, heavily rebuilt as the *Marco Polo* and still a popular and successful ship.

(MAL)

Fyffes had a long association with Southampton, operating into the Empress Dock to the special banana discharge facilities at Berths 24/5. In the 1950s and 60s amongst the many ships, both owned and chartered, were two particularly handsome liners carrying just over 100 first-class passengers. These were **Camito**, built in 1956, and her older sister **Golfito** of 1949, the latter seen here at Berth 24/5 in the evening glow of 8 August 1967. Given the customary Central American names, they had both been built by Alexander Stephen & Co at the Linthouse yard on the Clyde. Turbine steamers, they were broken up in the early 1970s, **Golfito** at Faslane in 1971 and **Camito** at Kaohsiung in 1973. Fyffes left the port in 1982 and the discharge equipment, clearly seen in this photo, was dismantled in 1983.

(NVR)

For many years United Netherlands Steamship Co's Holland-Africa Line maintained a service from Hamburg, Amsterdam and Antwerp to South and East Africa with a brief call at Southampton. *Randfontein* was the last passenger/cargo liner built for the run and by the mid-1960s was sailing with the *Jagersfontein* of 1950 and *Oranjefontein* of 1940. These last two were scrapped in 1967 and *Randfontein*, which had been completed in 1958, carried on alone until 1971. She then passed to the associated Royal Interocean Lines as *Nieuw Holland* for their triangular Pacific service. In 1974 she went to the Chinese as first *Ya Hua* and in 1981 *Hai Xing*, later subtly amended to *Haixing*. She was finally broken up in India in 1996 as *Herbert*, but never traded under that name. Our view shows her as many will remember her at Southampton, immaculately turned out, departing from the Ocean Dock on 7 March 1970 attended by the Red Funnel tug *Hamtun*.

(NVR)

Between the conventional ships loading cars by crane and the giant roll-on, roll-off car-carriers of today, there were some smaller purpose-built vessels and also some interesting conversions. These photographs depict such a conversion. The **Akaroa**, photographed on 31 July 1971 passing up the River Test bound for Berth 108, started life as the passenger/cargo liner **Amazon**, lead ship of a class of three for Royal Mail Line's South American service; the others were **Aragon** and **Arlanza**, all completed in 1959/60. In 1968 they were transferred within the Furness Withy Group to Shaw Savill, a strange decision given that the latter company apparently had already decided there was no future in combination passenger/cargo liners.

(NVR)

They did not last long and in 1971 all three were sold for conversion to car-carriers. Two went to Leif Hoegh, whilst **Akaroa** went to A/S Uglands Rederi, as **Akarita** seen at Berths 35/6 loading export cars on 26 March 1976. The conversion was very thorough and it is interesting to try and spot the few recognisable bits of the original structure. **Akarita** became **Hual Akarita** from 1977 until 1980 then reverted to **Akarita**. All three ships were broken up by January 1982, **Akarita** arriving at Kaohsiung prior to 8 January 1982.

(NVR)

Savannah's first call at Southampton was in 1962 when she embarked on a series of goodwill calls to ports in Europe before going into service. Like her namesake of 1819, she was a revolutionary ship, the very first nuclear merchant ship; an experiment really, to demonstrate the viability, or otherwise, of nuclear power. Profitability was not an issue initially, which was just as well, as she was always some distance from making money. Built by the New York Shipbuilding Corporation, Camden, New Jersey, she was launched by Mrs Eisenhower, wife of the President. ***Savannah*** had a cargo capacity of 9,400 tons, not a lot for a large ship, but the reactor took up too much room. She could carry up to 60 passengers, though this figure was never more than 25 in practice. Her reactor was charged with 682,000 pellets of enriched uranium, providing the energy for 16,000 hours of full power steaming, or 336,000 miles. Conventional steam power would have used 90,000 tons of oil. Potential commercial users were frightened off by the high maintenance, low revenue situation. Nevertheless, she started her commercial life in late 1964, running to Mediterranean ports from New York, occasionally to northern Europe. In the summer of 1965, management was passed from States Marine Lines to First Atomic Ship Transport (FAST) of Export-Isbrandsen. Increasingly high costs and refusal at some ports meant she was taken out of service in 1970. Her nuclear core was removed in 1971 and the following year she was towed to Savannah, Georgia, and then to Galveston, Texas, as a museum. In 1994 she was moved to the James River reserve fleet, but there are plans for further preservation. The photo sees her at Berth 101 in the Western Docks on a fly-the-flag visit in 1962.

(WHM)

This attractive view of Shaw Savill's handsome **Ceramic** masks the sad truth that she is leaving Southampton in June 1972, for the last time, her career over. One of four sisters (**Athenic**, **Corinthic** and **Gothic** being the others), she was the last by three years to be broken up, in Belgium in mid-1972. It was **Gothic**, though, that was the best known, having been a stand-in Royal Yacht for Her Majesty Queen Elizabeth's round-the-world Coronation tour beginning in November 1953. All four were passenger/cargo ships of just under 16,000 gross tons, sailing from London and North European ports to New Zealand, via the Panama Canal. All Shaw Savill ships were registered in Southampton, despite their offices being in London. **Ceramic**, built in 1948, was yet another in a long line of ships from the great Cammell Laird shipyard at Birkenhead. She had a considerable refrigerated cargo space of 514,386 cubic feet and was capable of 17 knots, carrying up to 85 passengers in first-class-only comfort.

(WHM)

Good Hope Castle (left) and **Southampton Castle** are shown here at Berth 101 on 27 November 1977, laid up and for sale after the closure of the Union-Castle mail service to South Africa. Initially cargo only, they were the last ships built for the mail service and were amongst the fastest cargo liners of the day. They were completed in 1965 by Swan Hunter & Wigham Richardson on the Tyne. Accommodation for 12 passengers was added to each ship in late 1967 by Cammell Laird & Co at Birkenhead so that they could serve St Helena and Ascension Islands following withdrawal of the **Capetown Castle**, which had been calling at the remote South Atlantic islands. **Southampton Castle** led a trouble free existence; **Good Hope Castle**'s only blip, a potentially very dangerous one, came on 29 June 1973 when she caught fire 35 miles off Ascension. She was abandoned, but re-boarded after the fire, caused by a burst oil pipe, had died down. Fortunately no lives were lost and she was eventually repaired at Bilbao. Both were sold to the Costa Line of Italy in February 1978. The **Southampton Castle** became **Carla C** and her sister **Paola C**. Both were broken up in 1984.

(NVR)

To all intents and purposes a Cunard ship, but **Samaria** and her sister **Scythia**, both built in 1965, were actually owned by North Western Line (Mersey) Ltd a subsidiary of their builders Cammell Laird and were on long term charter. There was a third sister, **Scotia**, built in 1966. There were seven similar ships in all, the other four were the slightly smaller **Ivernia**, **Media**, **Parthia**, and **Saxonia** built 1963-64. Containerisation of the North Atlantic cargo trade was by this time on the horizon and the conventional ships quickly became redundant. In 1969 **Samaria** and **Scotia** were sold to T & J Harrison Ltd, another famous Liverpool company,

and became **Scholar** and **Merchant** respectively. After ten years with Harrisons they both went to the Greek flag as **Steel Trader** and **Sisal Trader** respectively, but were soon broken up; the former in 1980 after damage in the Iran/Iraq war and the latter in 1979 after grounding. This photograph shows **Samaria** in her prime on 9 July 1967 coming down the River Itchen from Berth 30. The white building just visible left background is the remains of the former Supermarine factory (since demolished), home of R J Mitchell's famous Spitfire as well as many Schneider Trophy aircraft.

(NVR)

Seen arriving at Southampton in May 1973, Ellerman's City Line-owned *City of Oxford* was the first of a post-war group, having been completed by John Brown in December 1948. Her 7,200 shp turbines gave her a speed of 15.5 knots and she measured 7,593 grt. She had five holds, served by eighteen derricks, one 50-ton, one 20-ton, eight 10-ton and eight 7-ton. One little-known claim to fame was that she was one of a class of several ships used by Sir John Ellerman for use almost as a private yacht. A noted zoologist, he would simply commandeer the passenger accommodation on one of the ships, hand-pick the crew, and set off on field trips wherever took his fancy on the ship's regular route. She gave 28 years service to Ellerman, but only had another two after her sale in 1976. She became *Union Arabia* for Taiwanese owners, but her steam turbine machinery proved uneconomical and she went to Kaohsiung for demolition in 1978 after an impressive 30 years.

(WHM)

It was in 1916 that William Lever of Lever Brothers, Port Sunlight, first went into shipowning with the purchase of H Watson of Manchester's fleet of eight ships. These formed the Brompton Steamship Co. This was to secure cheap supplies of palm oil, but in 1923 he sold his four remaining vessels and moved out of deepsea shipowning. Palm Line itself was formed in 1949 from the 15 ships of the United Africa Line, and named after the commodity so important to Lever Brothers. Cocoa, timber, coconut and wood products were also carried regularly. It was decided to modernize the fleet in 1954 and orders for 14 ships were placed.

Kano Palm was built by Swan Hunter at Newcastle in 1958, and was, at 8,723 grt, one of the larger units of the fleet and not designed for the creek work that the smaller ships did. In the early 1960s, Palm Line had 23 ships, but by 1982 this had dwindled to seven. She was sold to Shanti Shipping of Bombay in 1979 and renamed *Purna Shanti*. Quickly renamed *Island Trader* for Marvia Shipping of Monrovia in the same year, she was eventually scrapped in Bombay in 1982. She is seen here in Southampton in March 1974, catching the last of the late afternoon light.

(WHM)

Clan Line refrigerated ships were a common sight in Southampton during the South African fruit season, but here is one of their general cargo vessels departing from Berth 35/6 on the Itchen Quays on 4 July 1973. **Clan Macintosh** was a single-screw motorship completed in 1951 at John Brown's famous Clydebank shipyard. Clan Line was the trading name of Cayzer, Irvine & Co, founded in 1878 by Charles William Cayzer and his friend, Captain Irvine. Despite Captain Irvine dying almost before the enterprise began, Cayzer kept the company name as a mark of respect. Cayzer had previously worked for the British India Steam Navigation Co and Clan's funnel colours were a play on those of BI – two red bands instead of two white! Clan Line grew eventually into a formidable cargo carrier and amassed a number of notable companies along the way to becoming the parent firm of the British & Commonwealth Shipping Co Ltd, the last and most famous of these being Union-Castle Line in 1956. **Clan Macintosh** herself was sold in 1978 and became **Sanil**, lasting only two more years before arriving at Bombay (Mumbai) for demolition.

(NVR)

A typical Port Line cargo/passenger ship of the immediate post-war period, **Port Pirie** was an attractive vessel of 10,535 grt, with a refrigerated capacity of 536,616 cubic feet in six holds (enough for 350,000 carcasses of meat). She also had accommodation for 12 passengers and her twin Doxford diesel engines gave a speed of 16 knots. They were manufactured under licence by the builder, Swan Hunter & Wigham Richardson of Wallsend and the ship was completed on 30 January 1947. Rough weather prevented her from having any sea trials and she went straight into service serving Australia and New Zealand. Not a common sight in Southampton, she is seen here in Southampton's Western Docks in 1971. It was on 2 July 1972 that she arrived at Castellon for demolition.

(MAL)

Colourful, but rather in need of attention from a paintbrush, is the turbine steamer **Blue Grass State** seen arriving at Berth 34 on the Itchen Quays on 15 February 1970. Owned by States Marine Lines of New York, whose ships were at this time regular callers at the port, she was of the C2-S-AJ3 standard US Maritime Commission design. Completed in 1944 by North Carolina Shipbuilding Co of Wilmington, North Carolina, as **Tolland,** she became **Edgar F Luckenbach** in 1947 before joining States Marine as **Blue Grass State** in 1959. Not long after this picture was taken she passed to the Panamanian flag as **Reliance Cordiality** and was broken up in 1971.

(NVR)

Benalbanach was the first of four specialist heavy-lift ships acquired by Ben Line from the Ministry of Transport (the others were **Benarty**, **Benwyvis** and **Benledi**). Built as the **Empire Athelstan** by Vickers-Armstrong, Newcastle, in 1946, she came to Ben Line in 1947 and served them for 16 years before being laid up. The Ministry of Transport bought her back in 1969, naming her **Camelot**, with British India as managers and sold her later that year to Mercur Shipping Enterprise SA of Panama, becoming **Dragon Castle**. She is seen leaving Southampton on 23 August 1969 as **Dragon Castle** and appears to still be in Ben Line colours (perhaps there was a job lot of paint tucked away in a locker). In 1975 she was sold to Cuatebol Shipping SA, Panama, keeping her name, but went to Yugoslavia in December that year for breaking by Brodospas at Split.

(WHM)

"Better ship Ben Line – faster to and from the Far East" was a slogan used to promote Wm Thomson & Co's Ben Line around the time this photograph was taken. Certainly their ships were fast and always well-presented, as seen here on 29 October 1967 as the 1957-built 17 knot turbine steamer **Benlomond** is eased into Berth 41 on the Test Quays with the assistance of Red Funnel's **Hamtun**. Leaving Southampton, her last loading port, she would have set off for such places as Penang, Port Swettenham, Singapore, Manila, Hong Kong, Osaka and Yokohama, names that conjure up images of the riches of the fabled Orient. As for **Benlomond** herself, she survived for 20 years and in October 1977 headed east for the last time for breaking up in Kaohsiung, Taiwan.

(NVR)

Banana boats, fruit ships, reefers – call them what you will – are always lovely vessels; nice lines and invariably beautifully kept. Here are two such lying at Berth 101 in Southampton's Western Docks. **Geestport** (nearest to us) was built in 1982 and her sister **Geestbay** beyond, in 1981, both at Smith's Dock, Middlesbrough. They delivered their cargoes from the West Indies to the port for a number of years. Geest had moved from Barry and were later, in 1996, to combine with Fyffes and then move to Portsmouth where Fyffes had been since 1988. **Geestport** served as a refrigerated stores ship to the Falklands in 1982.

Both were sold in 1994 - they are seen here on 26 October 1994 shortly after their sale. It can just be discerned that **Geestbay** already has her new name **Magellan Reefer**. The **Geestport** was to become **Bahiana Reefer**. Both ships flew the Panamanian flag, were Greek owned and were managed by a Japanese ship management company; thus showing the true international nature of shipping. **Magellan Reefer** in 2004 became **Nafsica** and later **Estia** and at the time of writing is **Estia 1** - meanwhile **Bahiana Reefer** became **Amfitrite** in 2004 and at present is **Amfitrite 1**.

(NVR Collection)

Seen at the confluence of the River Itchen, Southampton Water and the River Test, just off Dock Head on 7 June 1976, the handsome **Fort Pontchartrain** makes an impressive sight as she turns to head down river after she had left the Fyffes Banana Terminal in the Empress Dock. She was built in 1969 by CNIM at La Seyne as a 9,873 grt general cargo reefer vessel for Compagnie Générale Maritime, Dunkerque. She had five holds served by fourteen derricks and had accommodation for five passengers. She was sold in 1980 and became **Flamar Progress**. Two years later she was renamed **Rainbow Freezer.** After becoming **Rainbow Star** in 1987, she was scrapped at Calcutta seven years later.

(WHM)

Completed in December, 1969, **Atlantic Crown** was a second generation container vessel that combined the carriage of 900 TEU with substantial roll-on, roll-off facilities over three decks. She was built for Atlantic Container Line, a consortium of six companies from five countries formed in 1966 (Cunard, CGT, Holland America, Swedish America, Transatlantic Rederei and Wallenius) and was Holland's contribution to the alliance. Double reduction turbines and twin screws gave her a speed of 24 knots on her usual route between Europe and the United States. It was her British counterpart, **Atlantic Conveyor**, which was so tragically lost in the Falklands conflict. **Atlantic Crown** is seen inbound in June 1973. In 1982/3 she was laid up in Rotterdam and after a further period of lay-up at Liverpool, she was towed to Aviles for breaking in 1985.

(WHM)

Built by Cockerills at Hoboken, **Teniers** would not normally be considered a ship of any note, just another cargo ship really, albeit an attractive one. This rare photo shows the ship arriving in Southampton with the first containers for the brand new container port at the very top end of the Western Docks. Belonging to Cie. Maritime Belge (later part of Dart Container Line), her fifteen minutes of fame were on 27 October 1968, when she tied up for the first time at Berth 201, setting in motion a revolution in Southampton's (and others') maritime history. A year later **Atlantic Causeway** (the first purpose-built container-carrying ship at Southampton) made her maiden voyage from the port and containerisation was on its way.

(MAL)

In March 1970 to help spread some of the enormous cost of containerisation, Ben Line Steamers and Ellerman Lines came together to form Ben Line Containers Ltd to operate in the Far East trade. Three ships were ordered from Germany – steam turbine-driven twin-screw ships capable of 26.5 knots. Named **Benavon**, **Benalder** and **City of Edinburgh**, we see the latter on 7 September 1975, turning at the top end of the Western Docks prior to moving stern first up to her berth. All three ships were re-engined as motorships in 1980-81. They eventually came under the Maersk banner in 1992. **City of Edinburgh** over time became **Benarty**, **Maersk Edinburgh**, then **Edinburgh Maersk**. She became plain **Edinburgh** under the Greek flag in 1999 and was broken up in China in 2002.

(NVR)

This ship was completed in 1950 by Wm Denny & Son, Dumbarton as **Brighton** for the Newhaven – Dieppe service of British Railways Southern Region, although she had been ordered by the Southern Railway prior to nationalisation. Often dubbed the fastest ship in the Channel she was indeed capable of 24 knots. Displaced in 1964 by car ferries she was relegated to no-passport excursions and special trips. Withdrawn in September 1966 she was sold in the December to Jersey Lines, a company owned by the Cowasjee Bros. With some car space and ramps added at the stern (seen clearly in the photograph) and renamed **La Duchesse de Bretagne** she began an ambitious and complicated schedule running to St Malo, Guernsey and Jersey from variously Plymouth, Southampton, Torquay, and Weymouth. Failure was almost inevitable as she was a fast and expensive steamer to run and she was laid up in 1969, eventually going, via H G Pounds of Portsmouth, to ship breakers at Bruges, arriving there on 14 February 1971. She is seen here about to dock at Berth 49 on 12 May 1968.

(NVR)

Definite local interest here as **Sarnia** (the Roman name for Guernsey) and her sister, **Caesarea**, were both built at J Samuel White's yard on the Isle of Wight. They were 2,000 grt more than the Isle class that they replaced and, therefore, a significant step forward in amenity space for the same number of passengers. The **Sarnia** was the last ship specifically built for Channel Islands service and started life at Weymouth in 1961, with **Caesarea** having started in 1960. After fifteen popular years of service, they were replaced by the car-carrying **Maid of Kent**, **Caledonian Princess** and **Earl Godwin**. **Caesarea** was sold to Hong Kong in 1980, by which time **Sarnia** had already become **Aquamart**, a floating supermarket. Unsurprisingly, the venture failed and she was sold in 1979, becoming the Greek **Golden Star** and two years later, Saudi **Golden Star**, before being scrapped in 1987. This photograph taken in July 1974 shows the ship on her way past Berth 38/9, possibly to dry dock.

(WHM)

The three Isle class Channel Island ferries of Southern Railway, **Isle of Jersey**, **Isle of Guernsey** and **Isle of Sark** were familiar sights in Southampton before and after World War II. The first two were built in 1930 and the **Isle of Sark** (the first ship ever to be fitted with Denny-Brown stabilisers) two years later, all by Denny of Dumbarton. They were twin-screw turbine ships of 2,150 grt approximately, with a service speed of 19.5 knots and carried 1400 passengers in two classes. All three performed heroically during the war as hospital ships and **Isle of Guernsey**, still in wartime camouflage, re-opened the post-war cross-channel service from Newhaven to Dieppe on 15 January 1945. Five months later, she re-opened the Channel Islands service, which continued until 1960 when they were gradually withdrawn and sold. **Isle of Guernsey** was the last of the three to go, in August 1961, after a period as a reserve vessel. The service was transferred to Weymouth and operated by the **St Patrick**, with the brand new **Caesarea** and **Sarnia**. **Isle of Guernsey** was sold for scrap to van Heyghan Frères of Belgium in November 1961. This 1957 view shows her turning into the River Itchen inbound.

(MAL)

Viking I of Thoresen Car Ferries arrives in the Princess Alexandra Dock - this was the original Outer Dock of 1842, the first dock opened in Southampton. Otto Thoresen formed his company to fill the void left by the withdrawal of the British Railway's cross-channel services from the port. He revolutionised continental travel with the drive-through concept and with modern attractive ships, efficient service and Scandinavian fare was soon at the forefront. *Viking I* opened the service to Cherbourg in May 1964; *Viking II* arrived in July 1964 and the Le Havre service began. They were joined by *Viking III* in 1965 and by the freight-only *Viking IV* in 1967. A ferry crossing could now be enjoyed rather than endured. These were the forerunners of the giant cruise ferries we take for granted today. The ferries eventually decamped to Portsmouth in the 1980s, as did Vosper Thornycroft in 2003, part of whose shipyard can be seen to the right in this photograph taken on 20 June 1967. To the left in the background is the site of the future Itchen Bridge, completed ten years later (see page 79). *Viking I* became *Viking Victory* in 1976, was sold to Greek owners in 1983 as *Sun Boat* and has since carried the names *Caravan*, *Vasmed*, *Sunny Boat*, *European Glory*, *Neptunia*, *Media II* and *Media V*.

(NVR)

Viking Viscount was one of a group of four ships called the "Super Vikings" that were built to follow in the footsteps of *Viking I*, *Viking II* and *Viking III*. She was built in 1976 by Aalborgs Værft A/S, Aalborg, Denmark, for service between Felixstowe and Zeebrugge, but was transferred to the south coast in 1986 for the route from Southampton to Cherbourg. In December 1987, ownership passed to P&O European Ferries and in 1989 she was renamed *Pride of Winchester* and also spent some time on the Dover-Calais route. In 1994 *Pride of Winchester* was sold to Greek owners Lasithiotiki Anonymi Naftiliaki Eteria (L.A.N.E.) renamed *Vitsentzos Kornaros*, and used on the Lane Lines route from Piraeus to Agios Nikolaos, Crete. She is currently still sailing for Lane Lines. The photograph was taken at Portsmouth in July 1986 on an early morning departure to Le Havre.

(MAL)

Dragon is seen here in the River Itchen on her 11.00 departure from the Princess Alexandra Dock in February 1974, in her original all-white paint scheme, heading for Le Havre. She was one of the new breed of passenger/car ferries that were designed in the mid- to late-1960s and at just over 5,720 grt, somewhat bigger than her predecessors, and could carry 850 passengers, 250 cars or 65 TEU. Built by Chantiers et Ateliers de Bretagne, Nantes, her maiden voyage was on 29 June 1967, inaugurating the Normandy Ferries (a combination of General Steam Navigation Co and the French SAGA, later P&O Ferries) service to Le Havre.

Renamed *Ionic Ferry* in 1986 for European Ferries, she lasted until 1992 (and by then under the P&O flag once more) when she was sold to Marlines as *Viscountess M*, becoming *Charm M* in 1995, operating between Italy and Greece. In 1998 she went to Superferries of London as the *Memed Abachidze* (briefly *Med*) and *Millennium Express II* in 2000 for Access Ferries. Her long career came to an end in 2002 after a fire following a refit. Laid up initially, she went to Turkey the following year for scrap.

(WHM)

The new and very impressive looking car and passenger cruise ferry **Monte Toledo** was introduced in 1974 along with her sister **Monte Granada** by the well known Spanish Aznar Line. They operated a service to Santander in northern Spain. The company soon had problems in other areas of their operations and as a result the sisters were sold. In 1977 **Monte Toledo** became **Toletela** and **Monte Granada** the **Garnata**, of a Libyan company in Benghazi, for service between Libya and Malta. Both were laid up by 2002 - **Toletela** was sold to Indian breakers in March 2005. **Garnata** is still in existence, but laid up. The picture shows **Monte Toledo** in the River Itchen on her maiden arrival in Southampton on 7 May 1974.

(NVR)

This photograph was taken in June 1977 from Portsmouth's Round Tower, a splendid viewing point at the entrance to the harbour. Built in 1973 as the Swedish *Viking 4,* number six in the series of nine Papenburg sisters, the ship was chartered to Sealink in 1980 and served as the *Earl Granville* (after Lord John Carteret, bailiff of Jersey and Earl of Granville) on the service from Portsmouth to the Channel Islands. *Earl Granville* also provided cover on other Sealink routes, including Harwich to the Hook of Holland, Liverpool to Dun Laoghaire and Stranraer to Larne. A plethora of strikes, breakdowns and fires dogged her early days with Sealink and the ship took some time to settle in. After the privatisation of Sealink in 1984, new owners Seacontainers embarked on a series of disastrous changes to the ship and its routes. By the time they got things right, in the late 1980s, the competition (Channel Island Ferries) had cornered the market. In 1990 *Earl Granville* was sold to Greek owners Aegan Pelagos Naftiki Eteria (Piraeus) as the *Express Olympia*. In 1991, owners became Agapitos Express Ferries, which in turn became part of Minoan Flying Dolphins (Hellas Ferries) in 1999. She remains in service with Hellas today.

(MAL)

Carisbrooke Castle was the first purpose-built car ferry for the Red Funnel service from Southampton's Royal Pier to Cowes. Completed in 1959 by John I Thornycroft at their Woolston yard she was based on the successful experience of operating the Norris Castle, a converted wartime landing craft. She was followed by the similar Osborne Castle, Cowes Castle and a second Norris Castle, Red Funnel eventually going for drive-through layout in Netley Castle and all subsequent builds. Indeed Cowes Castle and Norris Castle were converted to drive-through in 1975/76. In the meantime, in 1974 Carisbrooke Castle had been sold to Italy, becoming Citta di Meta, then Giglioespresso Seconda and later Giglio Expresso II. She arrived at Aliaga in September 2007 for breaking up. She is seen here at the Royal Pier on 23 August 1970.

(NVR)

The Southampton, Isle of Wight & South of England Royal Mail Steam Packet Co Ltd's (thankfully now just Red Funnel) Norris Castle of 1942 was something of a ground breaker. Built as an LCT (Landing Craft, Tank), the anticipated post-war increase in traffic to the Isle of Wight prompted Red Funnel to buy and convert her to carry vehicles. Rebuilt at the Northam yard of John I Thornycroft, she entered service on 23 July 1947, could side load and had the all-important bow ramp. She was, however, handicapped by a service speed of only 8 knots and could take up to an hour and a half for the journey. Carrying up to 250 passengers and 30 cars, she was chalk and cheese with her paddle steamer predecessors. Instead of being replaced by the new Carisbrooke Castle in 1959, Norris Castle ran alongside the newcomer until March 1962, when she was sold for service in the Greek Islands, being renamed Nereis. She grounded days after arriving and was badly damaged. Later that year she was renamed Aghios Dionisios. Here we see her passing Calshot towards the end of her Solent career. Still listed in Lloyd's Register, she appears to have had an impressive lifespan of 65 years.

(MAL)

The ferry crossing from Lymington, on the edge of the New Forest, to Yarmouth, Isle of Wight, has seen some interesting vessels over the years. At first there were paddle steamers which later towed barges for vehicular traffic, and then suddenly, in 1938, came the revolutionary double-ended roll-on, roll-off **Lymington** driven by Voith Schneider propulsion units which allowed her to travel in any desired direction or speed at the turn of couple of wheels. Incidentally this system and similar are now commonplace. After Worl War II came what at first sight might be regarded as a backward step – another paddle vessel, but this time a diesel-electric-driven double-ended car ferry. The **Farringford** seen here leaving Lymington on 28 June 1970 was delivered to the Southern Railway in 1947. She served until 1974 and then went north to work the Hull to New Holland crossing on the Humber until she was displaced by the new bridge in 1981. She was sold to Western Ferries in October 1981 but never entered service and was demolished at Hull in March 1984.

(NVR)

Apart from annual visits still made by the preserved **Waverley** to the Solent, **Ryde** was the last paddle steamer in regular operation in the area. She is seen here leaving the characteristic foaming wake as she backs out from Southampton's Royal Pier after a charter cruise on 8 June 1969. Normally employed on the Portsmouth – Ryde ferry service, together with a little cruising, this was her last season in service. She was sold for use as a club on the River Medina, Isle of Wight, where she joined the celebrated **Medway Queen**. **Ryde** still languishes there today in a deplorably decrepit state - the latest news is that her funnel has collapsed – though thankfully **Medway Queen** has long since moved home to the Medway and has a much brighter future.

(NVR)

When she was completed in 1949 by John I Thornycroft at their Woolston works, as an Isle of Wight ferry and local excursion ship, few people could have foreseen that **Balmoral** would still be sailing in the 21st century. She has now given pleasure to thousands of folk round the coastline of Britain. Built for the Southampton, Isle of Wight and South of England Royal Mail Steam Packet Ltd, she had space aft for 10 cars; when on excursions, this area was used as a very sheltered sun deck. She finished Red Funnel service in Southampton in 1968 and was at first chartered, then purchased, by P & A Campbell for their Bristol Channel services. This ended in 1980 and she eventually became a pub in Dundee from where she was rescued in poor condition by supporters of the **Waverley**, refitted and in 1986 put back to work in support of the paddler. The rest is history. She has now visited every corner of Britain, has been re-engined and looks like sailing for many more years. Our picture, taken from **Oriana** at Berth 106, shows **Balmoral** on 19 July 1967 on an excursion from Isle of Wight piers to view Southampton Docks. In the background can be seen a "Sir Lancelot" class logistic ship at Husbands Shipyard, Marchwood; another can be seen in the centre at the Royal Corps of Transport jetty.

(NVR)

Seen approaching Ryde Pier on the Isle of Wight in September 1981, **Brading** was one of three little gems built to replace losses during World War II. **Southsea** and **Brading** were first in service in late 1948 with **Shanklin** arriving three years later. Built by Wm Denny of Dumbarton, these 837 grt, diesel-powered vessels provided a fast service for British Railways on the route between Portsmouth and Ryde until the mid-1980s. They were the first regular screw vessels on this service, providing an economic and successful service for up to 1,400 passengers at a speed of 14.5 knots. When British Railways became British Rail (Sealink) in 1965, **Brading** was the first of the trio to receive the new colours. Although not well received by traditionalists at the time, it was sorely missed after the change to the newly-privatised Sealink white and blue in 1984, with Seacontainers as the owners. Withdrawn from service in 1986, **Brading** supplied her sister, **Southsea**, with spare parts while she had another two years as an excursion ship. Then came the catamarans; efficient, certainly, but not in the same class as their predecessors.

(MAL)

The British Railways Isle of Wight car ferry services from Portsmouth to Fishbourne used to be based at Broad Street, Old Portsmouth, but nowadays operate across the Camber Dock from alongside Gunwharf Quays. One of the present vessels is **St Cecilia**, seen from the Round Tower entering Portsmouth Harbour in her first year in service on 1 July 1987. She is one of four similar vessels built for Sealink between 1983 and 1990 – **St Catherine**, **St Helen** of 1983 and **St Faith** of 1990, are the others. Now owned by Wightlink, the double-ended **St Clare** was added to the fleet in 2001. The passenger services to Ryde Pier from Portsmouth Harbour Station are operated by catamarans.

(NVR)

Amazingly, this 1948-built Gosport ferry is now (according to latest information) a charter yacht called **Venus of Portsmouth**, operating on the Brisbane River and to the Great Barrier Reef. Seventy-three feet long and 74 grt, **Venus** and her many similar sisters were built by Camper and Nicholson for the Port of Portsmouth Steam Launch & Towing Co Ltd ferry service between Gosport and Portsmouth. She was sold in 1968 to the Solent Boating Company and later to Favourite Boats (now Blue Funnel Cruises), converting from steam reciprocating to diesel in 1969 and this July 1969 view shows her just prior to that change. She was sold circa 1983 for conversion to a yacht and this was done on the River Thames by the Jacobait Yard at Blackwall.

(WHM)

Maps from as far back as 1575 show the existence of a Hythe ferry and steamer services started in 1830 with the **Emerald**. The first **Hotspur** was built in 1889, the name from a member of the Percy family (owners of the General Estates Company, which ran the ferries) known as "Harry Hotspur", a name immortalised by Shakespeare. Seen here at Hythe Quay, **Hotspur III** appears to be in the middle of some maintenance work, as her name has been painted out. Built in 1938 by the Rowhedge Ironworks, Essex, she was 56 feet long and carried up to 300 passengers. Initially steam powered, this changed in 1949 when Gardner diesels were fitted. Between 1968 and 1971, all three vessels (**Hotspur II**, **III** and **IV**) were re-engined with Kelvin diesels, increasing their speed from 8.5 to 9.5 knots. **Hotspur III** was scrapped in 1981 after a corroded keel plate was deemed to be beyond economic repair. **Hotspur IV** was still in the fleet in 2007 and **Hotspur II** sails on as the **Kenilworth** on the River Clyde.

(WHM)

Aborted plans for a Red Funnel hovercraft service to Cowes resulted in the arrival of the Italian-built hydrofoil **Shearwater**. She proved fast, but very unreliable. **Shearwater 2** was even more so and clearly a rethink was necessary. A rival manufacturer in Messina built **Shearwater 3**, which was a mainstay of the service for 20 years from 1972. Her 32 knots came from a Maybach Mercedes turbocharged V12 diesel, which sounded most impressive when started from cold. **Shearwater 3** and **4** were sold to operators in the Aegean in 1993, while **5** and **6** provided valuable back-up to the first two Red Jet catamarans for a period.

(MAL)

Sir Christopher Cockerell's genius saw the first sea-going hovercraft sail across the English Channel in 1959; an occasion that was to have a significant effect on the high-speed ferry industry. Because of her size, she was not a particularly useful craft, but was significant in showing the ferry industry the capability of hovercraft with more development. This potential manifested itself when the British Hovercraft Corporation built their large vehicle-carrying craft for the Ramsgate (Pegwell Bay) to Calais and Boulogne routes. Although fast and manoeuvreable, giving quick turnaround times, technical complexity and expensive maintenance has seen the Hovercraft all but disappear from commercial use. At present, the only surviving commercial service in the UK is from Southsea to Ryde, on the Isle of Wight (using AP1-88 craft), fittingly still in the locality of its stunning arrival on the scene in 1959 with the **SRN1**. This shows one of Seaspeed's **SRN6**s on the River Itchen slip of the service to Cowes, Isle of Wight, where this photograph was taken in June 1968. The authors remember the trip as a somewhat boneshaking experience, but you did get there quickly.

(MAL)

Of similar vintage is the **Lune Fisher** completed in Holland in 1962 for James Fisher of Barrow-in-Furness. She was a regular caller to the port, spending a number of years from 1962 on charter to British Railways for their Channel Islands cargo services, from both Southampton and Weymouth, assisting their own vessels such as **Elk**, **Moose** and **Winchester**. She was even known to carry her full quota of 12 passengers when the mail boat was full. She is seen at Berth 27 in the Empress Dock on 25 May 1969. Interestingly in 2006 Fishers took over Everards, something undreamt of when these pictures were taken.

(NVR)

One of the best known names in coastal shipping was that of Everard who were based on the River Thames at Greenhithe. Many of their fleet called at Southampton and here we see the 1963-built **Gillian Everard** leaving Berth 102/3 in the Western Docks, on 13 October 1974, departing after discharging grain to Ranks Solent Flour Mills. In the background is Union Castle Line's **Windsor Castle** at Berth 104. **Gillian Everard** was sold in 1984 and became **Captain Christos G** and in 1987 **Georgios**.

(NVR)

Timber was once a very familiar cargo unloaded not only within the docks but at the Town Quay and at wharves on the River Itchen, as well as the River Test at Eling. In the docks discharge was to a variety of onward transport modes, direct to road or rail transport or overside to lighters for movement to the upriver berths. On 25 September 1971 we see the Russian motorship **Grumant**, built at Rostock in 1967 and registered in Tallinn, at Berth 40 in the Eastern Docks, having already unloaded at least the deck portion of her cargo of timber from the Baltic. In the background can be seen Town Quay, Royal Pier and the Western Docks at which are berthed the **Iberia** and **Oronsay** of P&O. **Grumant** herself retained her port of registry after the break-up of the Soviet Union, although flying the flag of Estonia. She later went under the Russian flag and was broken up in India in 1998.

(NVR)

Owned by the General Steam Navigation Company of London, **Woodlark** was one of forty or so ships used, in the main, on trade routes between London and the continent in the 1950s, sailing principally to Danish ports and Gothenburg. Built by the Grangemouth Dockyard Company in 1956, she was an open shelter decker with three holds and had 'tween deck space. Her British Polar diesels gave her a service speed of just over 11 knots and she measured 933 grt, with a deadweight of 970. Sold in 1969 to the Royal Corps of Transport as the

Marchwood Freighter, she was used for port operations training. She is seen here leaving the Empress Dock assisted by Husband's **Affluence**. The elevators of the old banana berth can be seen in the background, as can Red Funnel's fire-fighting tug **Culver**. The ship was broken up at Sittingbourne in February, 1979, with a former crew member commenting that she was still in pristine condition.

(WHM)

This fine little coaster was built in 1939 as **Badzo** by Gebr. Niestern & Co for J Hulsebos of Holland. Only 213 grt she had a modest speed of seven knots from her 3-cylinder oil engine. In 1959, she was sold to Vectis Shipping Co Ltd, of Cowes, Isle of Wight and became **Vectis Isle**. The vessel was sold to Bob Roberts in 1971. Bob was a renowned singer of nautical folk songs and lived for the sea. This picture was taken in March 1974, at Cowes when in Bob's ownership. In 1978 she was bought by Panamanian flag operators and renamed **Estrella IV**. In 1983, she was reported to be partially sunk beneath the Tagus Bridge in Lisbon after water had entered her engine room because of a broken pipe. She was demolished in situ during the summer of 1985.

(WHM)

Ardingly passes Dock Head on 6 December 1970 after discharging coal at a River Itchen wharf. A motorship built in 1951, she was owned by Stephenson Clarke and named after a Sussex village, as so many Stephenson Clarke vessels were. She was one of a large fleet of coastal ships, mainly colliers, which the company owned, whilst they also managed vessels owned by the public utilities – gas, and electricity - such was their expertise. They had been in the business since 1730 when Ralph and Robert Stephenson started owning shares in sailing vessels. John Clarke's son married Jane Stephenson and so the two names that were to be paired so famously became linked – the title Stephenson Clarke was not however adopted until 1850 after John Clarke's grandson, Stephenson Clarke, took over. In 1971 **Ardingly** passed to the fleet of John Kelly Ltd, Belfast becoming **Ballyrobert**, leaving them in 1977 for Cypriot owners as **Lucky Trader** until broken up in the early 1980s.

(NVR)

Esso ordered six big County class tankers in the late 1950s – big that is for their day at 86,000dwt – for crude oil transport from the Persian Gulf to north European refineries, including Fawley. They were named **Esso Hampshire**, **Esso Lancashire**, **Esso London**, **Esso Pembrokeshire**, **Esso Yorkshire**, and the subject of our picture **Esso Warwickshire**. Delivered between 1961 and 1964, they were driven by steam turbines with a service speed of 17 knots. They had air-conditioned single cabins for the crew and each ship also boasted a swimming pool. In 1975 all left the Esso fleet, mostly direct to shipbreakers, except for **Esso Warwickshire** which was retained for conversion to bow loading from a single point mooring in the North Sea Brent Oil Field. After a 56-day conversion at Birkenhead she lifted her first cargo on 11/12 December 1976 discharging at Fawley on the 18th. She served her owners well until 1988 when sold for breaking up in China. Our illustration shows her outward-bound in ballast from Fawley, off Calshot, on 26 July 1983; a Shearwater hydrofoil of Red Funnel adds a point of scale to the picture.

(Nigel Smith)

In addition to the many Esso-owned tankers, numerous chartered vessels also operate in to Fawley. The Liberian registered *Zaneta III*, a 1953-built motor tanker, is seen in light condition at the Fawley Marine Terminal. She had been built by Götaverken at Gothenburg for Rederi A/B Transmark of the same city as *Camilla*. She is typical of what in the early 1950s was considered a decent sized tanker. She became *Zaneta III* in 1969 when sold to the oddly-named - at least for a ship owner - American Computer Leasing Corp, of Cincinnati, Ohio. In 1971, without change of name, she was sold to Adonis Nav Co Ltd (managed by Atlantic Shipping Co Ltd, Piraeus), but on 27 April 1975 she grounded off the Bulgarian coast in ballast and after being refloated was declared a total loss, the following year being broken up in Greece. Our photograph shows her at Fawley on 7 June 1970.

(NVR)

The Norwegian tanker **Dea Brøvig**, despite appearances in this picture to the contrary, was actually a motorship. Completed in February 1951 by Wm Hamilton & Co Ltd at Port Glasgow for Th. Brøvig, she was of 16,385 dwt and, powered by a 5-cylinder Doxford diesel engine, had a service speed of 14 knots. In 1971 she became the Cypriot **Jan Jan** and in 1974 was broken up at Castellon where she arrived on 28 April. She is typical of the hundreds of ships which serve their various owners well, with few if any incidents of note in their lives. The picture shows **Dea Brøvig** at Fawley on 30 May 1970.

(NVR)

The year of 1977 was the Silver Jubilee of Her Majesty The Queen, and, as is customary on such occasions, a fleet review was held at Spithead on 28 June 1977. Amongst the merchant ships present was the steam turbine Shell tanker **Opalia**, built in 1963 of 31,122 grt and 49,550 dwt. Not a large tanker compared with the mammoth VLCCs, but nevertheless a good representative of tankers generally, and is seen here looking immaculate in the evening light of 27 June. She was sold by Shell in 1984 and renamed **Lady T**, under the Panamanian flag. Struck by an Iraqi missile on 14 March 1985 in the Persian Gulf, she caught fire and was so badly damaged that she was sold for breaking up, arriving at Gadani Beach two months later.

(NVR)

In World War II the T2 tanker was to the oil trade what the Liberty ship was to cargo and altogether there were 525 of these ships built (adapted from a 1930s Esso design). **Esso Glasgow** was one of the first batch of 481 ships (a T2-SE-A1) and was built as the **Wauhatchie** by the Sun Shipbuilding and Dry Dock Co, Chester, Pennsylvania in 1944. Like the Liberty and Victory cargo ships, T2s were prefabricated and produced on the same mass production lines, not meant to last, but they did, some for 40 years or more. They were also very popular with crews because of their sea-keeping qualities, lack of vibration and good accommodation.

Wauhatchie became **Esso Glasgow** in 1947 and the distinctive cowl-topped funnel could be seen at Fawley, at the mouth of Southampton Water (where she is seen here in August 1968), and Milford Haven carrying cargoes of oil, gasoline and other refined products to Esso storage depots around the country. Turbo-electric machinery gave her a speed of 15 knots and gross tonnage was 10,821 tons, with a deadweight of 16,556 tonnes. **Esso Glasgow** was broken up at Bilbao in 1971 after a very respectable 27 years in service.

(WHM)

When **Burmah Endeavour** arrived at Southampton Docks for lay-up, she was, and still is, the largest vessel ever to enter the port. She dominated the skyline from Berth 101 and stayed there from 6 April 1983 until 2 June 1986. This photograph was taken in August 1983. She was built as a ULCC (Ultra Large Crude Carrier), ironically in Kaohsiung, noted then more for ship breaking than construction. Actually launched for the GATX-OSWEGO Corp., she was completed for Burmah Endeavour Ltd in 1977, part of Burmah Oil, and managed by Denholms. She measured 231,629 grt, with a deadweight of 457,841 and steam turbines gave her a speed of 15.5 knots, but this was of no consequence after she left Southampton, for she became a storage vessel in the Persian Gulf. She now became **Stena Queen** for Stena Line and in 2002 **Folk I** for Oceanic Trans Sg, but still Stena owned and managed. She was scrapped in May of the following year and having been built in China, it was fitting that she was broken up there.

(MAL)

A familiar sight in any large port are the bunkering tankers supplying the larger ships with fuel oil. In the late 1950s, Esso had three sisters built by Henry Scarr Ltd at Hessle. They were designed for both coastal work and bunkering duties in Southampton Docks. **Esso Woolston** was completed first in February 1958 – **Esso Lyndhurst** and **Esso Hythe** followed in April 1958 and May 1959. They could each carry 1300 tons of oil in eight tanks. Here we see **Esso Woolston** on 27 March 1971 about to go alongside the **Reina del Mar** at the Ocean Terminal, Berth 43/4. **Esso Woolston** was sold in 1982 becoming the oil pollution recovery vessel **Kinbrace** and was broken up in Spain in 1985.

(NVR)

This very attractive and once familiar coastal tanker was launched in July 1957 and completed in November that year by Philip & Son, Dartmouth, for Esso Petroleum Co Ltd. Of 1082 dwt capacity, **Esso Brixham** served her owners faithfully becoming very well known in many Channel ports, including the Channel Islands, as well as at Southampton. After an uneventful career she was sold to Panamanian interests early in 1980 and renamed **Brixham**. She was quickly resold for breaking up which began at Middlesbrough in May 1980. She is seen here passing Dock Head in July 1974 fully laden and heading up river to bunker a vessel in the Western Docks.

(WHM)

Now hopefully a fixture in Solent waters, the venerable **Shieldhall** is probably only still here because of her outdated machinery when constructed. Lobnitz & Co, Renfrew, were the builders and the ship was commissioned on 16 October 1955 and for 21 years was a "Clyde banana boat" (discretion prevents an explanation here, but she was a sludge carrier!) with a passenger capacity of 80 in summer. Essentially an updated version of a previous design, the installation of steam reciprocating machinery was surprising, with diesel proving to be the power plant of choice at the time. However, it would be instrumental in saving the ship later in life. This photo was taken in July 1985, a couple of days before being taken out of service and laid up. The Solent Steam Packet Ltd bought her on 28 July 1988, and for the last 19 years has done a remarkable job of preserving and maintaining the ship. As well as regular excursions up and down the south coast, she has returned to the Clyde and has visited Dordrecht in Holland; she has also featured in TV programmes and films. The Society has a membership of around 750, with many unpaid volunteers helping to maintain her.

(MAL)

Asperity is seen here in the Solent on 6 August 1987 in ballast inward bound for Fawley. She was another member of the once large fleet of F T Everard & Sons of Greenhithe and was a regular visitor to the area. Built in Holland in 1967 she was a coastal tanker of 1326 dwt and was used widely in the distribution of refinery products. In December 1989 she was sold to Greek owners as **Kastor**, became **Castor** in 1993 and then **Jet V** in 1996 operating as a bunkering tanker in Piraeus, still under the Greek flag.

(NVR)

Southampton has long been involved in the aggregates trade; the dredging for sand and gravel off the coast of the Isle of Wight. An early player was the South Coast Shipping Co, founded in 1946, which like many firms, at first used converted coasters before moving on to purpose-built and nowadays hi-tech vessels. **Sand Serin** was completed in 1974 by Cleland Shipbuilders, Wallsend, and is shown on the fine summer evening of 27 June 1977 coming up Southampton Water with a full load for Leamouth Wharf on the River Itchen. To the left of her foremast can be seen the Chapel of the Royal Victoria Hospital at Netley, all that remains of the once massive Victorian military establishment. The area is now Hampshire County Council's Royal Victoria Country Park.

(NVR)

Seen here heading down river in May 1975, is the 1955-built **Arco Yar** of Amey Roadstone Corp Ltd, a sand dredger of 671 grt, 172 feet long and capable of 9 knots. Built by Ferguson Bros, Port Glasgow, as **Laga II**, as a hopper barge for the British Transport Commission, she was sold in 1968 and converted to a sand dredger. She was renamed **Pen Yar** in 1969 and then **Arco Yar** four years later. Her cargoes of sand would be taken to the Itchen wharves for discharge.

(WHM)

Early aggregate suction dredgers were conversions, as mentioned, and here is one such. **Steel Welder** started life in March 1955 when she was completed by Clelands (Successors) Ltd, Wallsend-on-Tyne, as the 586 dwt coastal oil tanker **Shell Welder**, for Shell, Mex & BP. Sold in 1972 to H G Pounds she was quickly resold to Northwood (Fareham) Ltd who converted her to a suction dredger. As **Steel Welder** she entered service for them in 1974. She was broken up on the River Medway in 1989. Here we see her passing under Southampton's Itchen Bridge inward bound fully laden in June 1980

(MAL Collection)

Westminster Dredging Co's bucket dredger **Afrika** is seen here at work off Berth 34 on 4 July 1973. Before the advent of high-tech suction dredgers the maintenance dredging in the port was carried out by craft such as this. They were noisy and the "screeching and groaning" could be heard over a wide area of Southampton, especially when they were working at night, as they did for instance on the new container berths.

(NVR)

Seen on maintenance dredging, an on-going requirement for any port, is the 1966 built, 2941 grt, twin-screw trailing suction dredger **Swansea Bay**, owned by Associated British Ports. She was built as **Tees Bay** for Costain-Blankvoort (UK) Dredging Co Ltd, her builder being A Vuijk & Zonen at Capelle a/d IJssel. She became **Cap D'Antifer** in 1970 and reverted to **Tees Bay** in 1972. She was renamed **Swansea Bay** in 1980. The photograph was taken in the Ocean Dock on15 September 1985.

(NVR)

A bevy of Alexandra tugs tucked into their usual lay-by, Berth 45, at the inner end of the Ocean Dock seen from the balcony of the erstwhile Ocean Terminal in the summer of 1965. The steam tug *Gladstone* of 1951 is prominent and also in view are the motor tugs *Romsey*, *North Isle*, *North Loch*, *Ventnor* and *Brockenhurst*. *North Isle* completed in 1959 was the first motor tug in the entire Alexandra fleet. The green hull to the left belongs to the Cunard Line's *Franconia* at berth 46. The then-new Customs House seen on the skyline has recently been demolished to be replaced by a block of flats and all the buildings around the head of the dock have long gone. The Ocean Terminal built in 1950 was demolished in 1983.

(Wilfred Robinson)

Pictured on 5 October 1985 is a former London tug which spent some years in Southampton – Alexandra Towing's *Sun XXIV*. She is seen here on the slipway, for maintenance, at Husbands Shipyard, Marchwood, on the western shore of the River Test opposite the Western Docks. Built in 1963 by James Pollock of Faversham for W H J Alexander's Sun Tugs, she was sold in 1992 and renamed *Kingston* and is at present engaged in coastal towage with Griffen Towage who acquired her in 2003.

(NVR)

Southampton's last steam tug in regular service was Red Funnel's twin-screw **Hamtun**. With her sister **Sir Bevois** she was built by John I Thornycroft at Woolston, as were most of Red Funnel's vessels for many years; they both entered service in 1953. Note the patent Thornycroft funnel-top, a device fitted to many vessels in the 1950s. **Hamtun** was withdrawn in October 1970, and, after being sold, was extensively rebuilt as the motor tug **Nathalie Letzer**. In 1987 she went to Klyne Tugs of Lowestoft as **Anglian Lady,** later still going to Canada for work on the St Lawrence Seaway. Our picture shows her coming out of the Ocean Dock on 19 April 1970.

(NVR)

Completed in March 1961 (Red Funnel's centenary year), by John I Thornycroft on the River Itchen at Southampton, **Thorness** and her sister, **Dunnose**, were to have long careers in the port. She was twin screw, powered by twin 6-cylinder Crossley diesels, which gave her a bollard pull of approximately 18 tonnes. She went about her business without fuss or incident for 22 years before she was sold to Canada's J D Irving (Atlantic Towing Ltd) to become **Irving Juniper**. After a career of mainly harbour duties, the prospect of an Atlantic crossing meant that she, and the **Culver** which went with her, had to be modified to carry enough fuel for the journey and this was carried out at The Camber in Portsmouth. She is still in Canada, registered at Saint John, New Brunswick, although her certificate expires in June 2008, so it will be interesting to see if a 47-year-old tug can still hold her own.

(MAL)

Usually stationed at Fawley, **Vecta**, sister of the **Gatcombe**, is further up river here in this October 1978, shot, taken from Hythe Pier. The two tugs were built in 1970 by Richard Dunston at Hessle, something of a departure for Red Funnel, but brought about by Vosper Thornycroft building more warships and consequently having fewer facilities for commercial ships. Specifically built as fire-fighting tugs, both vessels were normally stationed at Fawley refinery, but occasionally used in the docks proper. Notable features included a hydraulic platform able to reach 70 feet in order to spray foam or water on to the decks of tankers and a portable boom for oil dispersal. Their superstructures and exhausts were 'Caronia' green (apparently because it was a restful colour for crews living on board while stationed at Fawley), which distinguished them from the rest of the fleet, but this was later changed to the normal cream, red and black. She was sold in 1999, becoming **Multratug 8**, based at Terneuzen in southern Holland.

(MAL)

Substantially rebuilt in this lovely photograph, Husbands' Shipyard Ltd's **Assurance** looks very different from her initial appearance. She was built as **TID 71** (Tug, Inshore, Dock), for coastal and harbour work, in March 1944, for the US Army. In December that year she transferred to the Admiralty and in 1962 was purchased by shipbreakers H G Pounds of Portsmouth. She was sold in turn to Husbands' Shipyards Ltd in 1964, and they rebuilt her, converting the ship from steam reciprocating machinery to an oil engine, renaming her **Assurance**. As such she became a familiar sight on the River Test and further down in Southampton Water. In 1992 she became **Wyepress** of Itchen Towage and then in 1994 reverted to the name **Assurance**. The photo was taken in May 1975.

(WHM)

Three Alexandra tugs display three ports of registry as they lie at Berth 46 in the Ocean Dock on 2 February 1979. The 1959-built **Sun XXI** came into the Alexandra fleet on the takeover of London Tugs who in turn had absorbed the fleet of W H J Alexander's Sun Tugs. **Victoria** started life in 1972 in Alexandra's 'home' port of Liverpool and later came south with her sister **Albert**. **Brockenhurst** was built in 1964 for the Southampton fleet, hence the local name and registry.

(NVR)

Seen at the top of Ocean Dock in July 1976, *C S Ariel* is awaiting disposal after being superseded by *C S Monarch* (V) in January of that year. She was one of those classic cable ships with the appearance of a private yacht. Built for HM Postmaster General as *Ariel* in 1939 by Swan Hunter, she was 1,479 grt and had triple expansion engines giving her 12 knots from twin screws. She had three cable tanks, all forward of the machinery spaces and these had a maximum capacity of 700 tons of cable. Cones and crinolines were fitted in each tank and forward of number one tank was a hold for cable buoys, grapnels, mushroom anchors and stores. One of her first jobs, in 1940, was to lay a cable from Jersey to Dartmouth, via Guernsey, and most of her subsequent work would be in home waters. The C S prefix came in 1969 after the Post Office became a public corporation. After *C S Monarch* entered service, *C S Ariel* was broken up on the Medway in 1977.

(WHM)

Here is a wonderful steam reciprocating veteran. The cable ship *John W Mackay* dating from 1922 is seen lying at Berth 109 in the Western Docks on 13 November 1975. Owned by the Commercial Cable Co, she was already 53 years old and was withdrawn shortly after this photograph was taken and passed to a trust for her preservation. Sadly the project failed and after a while laid up in Portsmouth Harbour she was sold to Turkey for demolition. She left in tow for Aliaga during March 1994. Some parts were saved and are preserved in an industrial museum in Istanbul. Beyond at the Berth 108 cold store can be seen Royal Mail Lines' *Drina* formerly Shaw Savill's *Cretic* until 1973.

(NVR)

Cable Venture was originally built by Lübecker Flenderwerke AG as **Neptun** for Norddeutsche Seekabelwerke in 1962 and was substantially larger than comparable ships at the time, with a gross tonnage of 8,910. Part of the reason for this was, unusually, a large bulk cargo capacity. Her propulsion was also different, being diesel and diesel-electric powering twin screws at 14 knots. She had four sheaves, three forward and the other aft, all electrically driven. After only three years she was sold to the United States Underseas Cable Corporation. In 1975 she moved again to Cable and Wireless and after a sixteen-month refit at Immingham, she came into service August 1977. Initially she was not suited to the carriage or laying of British repeater systems, but her large hold capacity made her ideal for long transocean multi-channel telephone systems and has an unrivalled installation track record. She was also given a Remotely Operated Vehicle for checking cables on the sea bed. In 1994 she laid the world's longest fibre optic cable (6,676 km and to depths of 9 km, the deepest ever submarine cable) on the Pacific West Rim, including crossing the Marianas Trench. This photograph was taken at Berth 109 in the Western Docks in March 1987 when she had another eleven years to go before being scrapped in Spain as **Able Venture**.

(MAL)

Seen here at Berth 66 at the end of Town Quay in July 1976, **Discovery**, as built, was a very different looking ship compared to her current profile. A 2,568 grt vessel completed in December 1962 by Hall Russell of Aberdeen for the Natural Environment Research Council (NERC), she was a handsome ship, but is now unrecognisable after her rebuilding in 1992. She is 10 metres longer with a new tonnage of 3,008, with the superstructure having been taken down to the main deck level and completely rebuilt, giving a very modern appearance and more in keeping with the demands of research at sea today. The original shapely funnel has given way to a single "uptake", trunked to the port side, giving more room for cranes. There is also more deck space aft, where there is a large "A" frame and a crane. Forward, the original mast and small "A" frame are still there while the bridge now has a view fore and aft. The research vessel **Bransfield** can be seen in the background.

(WHM)

Familiar sights in and around the Solent are the vessels of Trinity House, the lighthouse authority for England and Wales. There is a Trinity House depot at East Cowes and it was from the Cowes yard of J Samuel White that four sisters were ordered. These were the **Mermaid** completed in 1959, **Siren** in 1960 and **Winston Churchill** in1963, as well as the subject of this picture **Stella** in 1961. All were twin-screw diesel electric vessels and they worked from various bases around the coast servicing and relieving lighthouses and attending to the maintenance of navigation buoys. All had been withdrawn by the end of the 1980s, **Stella** finishing her Trinity House service in 1989. **Stella** is seen on 24 November 1979 sailing down the River Test off Berth 38/9.

(NVR)

Seen at Berth 36 pilot station on 4 July 1973, are the Trinity House pilot cutters *Jessica* and *Vectis*. These vessels were used for taking pilots out to board incoming ships off Hythe. The pilots were originally under the jurisdiction of Trinity House but latterly the pilotage has come under the port authority Associated British Ports.

(NVR)

All ports have vessels for maintenance work and here is a once familiar sight, *SHB Seahorse,* a buoy tender. She is passing up the River Test off Berth 38/9 on 25 August 1985. She was built in 1958 by James Pollock at Faversham for the Southampton Harbour Board, passing to the British Transport Docks Board in 1968 when the Harbour Board's functions were amalgamated into BTDB. Later still her owners became Associated British Ports.

(NVR)

Now left sadly neglected in her concrete cocoon in Ocean Village, with an uncertain future, *Calshot Spit* was a familiar and comforting sight to every ship entering or leaving Southampton Water. She was even built locally, at J I Thornycroft at their Woolston yard in 1914. She displaced 140 tons and was 84.5 feet long. For the technophobes, she had a 55mm lamp with a dioptic paraffin vapour burner at an elevation of 32 feet and her Hornsby foghorn could be heard at a range of 12 sea miles. Decommissioned in October 1978, she was sold in January, 1988, to the new Ocean Village complex in the Princess Alexandra Dock. Very little has been done to maintain her and with further development of the site proposed, faces a very uncertain future, although there is talk of her being part of a redeveloped Royal Pier. It is probably colder than it looks in this photograph, taken in January 1961.

(WHM)

Risdon Beazley, born 1903, started his company back in 1926. Always based here in Southampton, by 1944 it had grown into the largest salvage organisation in the world, managing 77 vessels, tugs and lifting craft. Risdon Beazley latterly lived in the village of Twyford, near Southampton, and named some of his vessels after Hampshire villages ending with … ford. *Twyford*, of 1952, was one and *Droxford*, built 1958, another. *Droxford* was one of the most successful salvage ships ever, recovering vast quantities of valuable metals from the cargoes of sunken ships. She and *Twyford* were built by John Lewis of Aberdeen, well-known for trawlers, and as expected, they turned out to be sturdy and workmanlike steam driven vessels. *Droxford* was broken up in 1981. The company also worked on wreck dispersal, one of the most notable being the *Texaco Caribbean*, *Brandenburg*, *Niki* collisions in the English Channel in 1971 off Dover. Sadly there is now little or nothing in Southampton to remind us of such a successful man and his work, partly, it appears, because he was a very private and modest person. *Droxford* was photographed in August 1979, just off the bottom end of the Eastern Docks.

(WHM)

Completed in 1970 for the Natural Environment Research Council by Robb Caledon at Leith, **Bransfield** took her name from Lieutenant Edward Bransfield, who charted the first part of the Antarctic mainland. Ice-strengthened, she was diesel-electric powered and made her first voyage to the Antarctic in 1971 from Southampton. Her routine was to spend the Antarctic summer down south, relieving and supplying British Antarctic Survey bases and then come back home to refit and restore. She spent some of her latter years based at Grimsby. The NERC relocated from Barry to the Empress Dock (Berth 26/7) in Southampton in 1995, in collaboration with the University of Southampton, at what is now the National Oceanography Centre. **Bransfield** is seen here on 22 June 1974, on Town Quay, with her ice-breaker bow very prominent. After completing 28 seasons in the Antarctic she was withdrawn in September 1999 and became **Igen Pearl** for a one-way voyage to shipbreakers in Mumbai arriving there on 25 January 2000.

(NVR)

Famous for all the wrong reasons, **Sir Galahad** (L3005), seen here in August 1977, on her way to her berth at Marchwood Military Port on the western bank of the River Test, was the second of a class of six multi-purpose vessels built to replace the ageing wartime-built LST(3)s. She was 5,675 grt and was built by Alexander Stephen of Glasgow in 1966. Originally built for the army, she was transferred to the Royal Fleet Auxiliary service in 1970. Capable of 17 knots, they were twin-screw ships, Mirrlees diesel powered and 413 feet long. The tank deck runs the whole length of the hull, carrying a limitless variety of military hardware, typically 16 tanks, 25 three-ton and six small lorries, 402 troops, 60 tons of cargo as well as fuel and ammunition. Helicopters had a dedicated pad aft, but could also fly off from the forward deck park. Sadly, **Sir Galahad** became a casualty of the Falklands War on 8 June 1982, when she was attacked while waiting to disembark Welsh Guards at Bluff Cove, being hit in her accommodation and set on fire. Fifty men lost their lives and many were horribly injured. The ship was towed out to sea and sunk as a war grave.

(MAL)

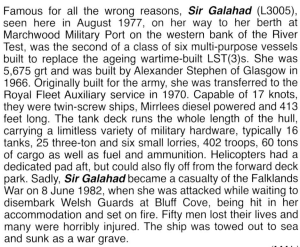

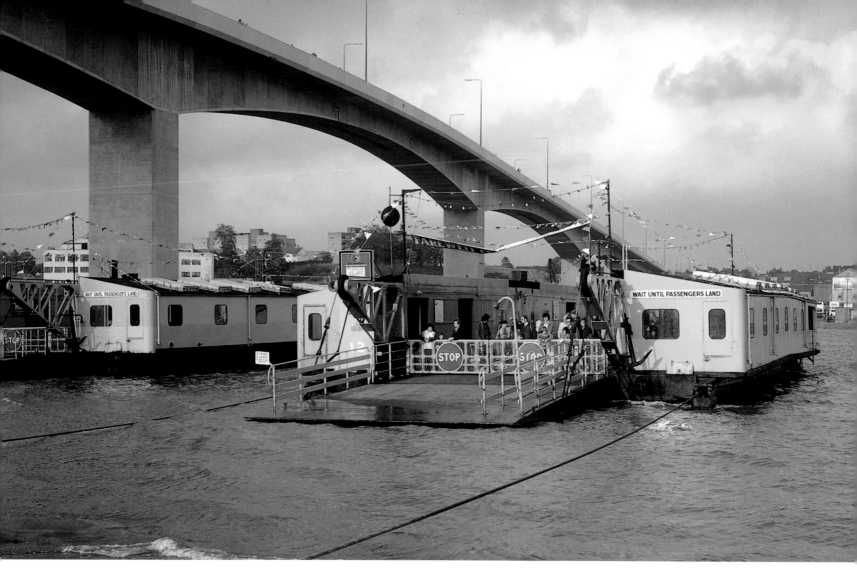

This was one of Southampton's institutions – the crossing of the River Itchen from Crosshouse to Woolston on the floating bridge. This view was taken in June 1977 during the final week of operation – they were replaced by the Itchen Toll Bridge seen in the background. The bridges had been running since 23 November 1836, at first driven by steam, latterly by diesel engines, as they pulled themselves back and forth along their cables. Once run by a private company, in September 1934 the undertaking was bought by the Corporation and operated as part of the transport department along with the trams (until 1949) and buses; many floating bridge drivers were former tram or bus drivers. The last bridges operated on 11 June 1977, the new bridge having opened for traffic on 1 June – the official opening was by HRH Princess Alexandra on 13 July 1977.

(Gill Robinson)

The early career of the **Canberra** was problematic, with instability problems, the threat of scrapping instead of **Orsova** and an abortive attempt to crack the American cruise market out of New York. In 1961, however, she represented a daring experiment in ship design. At 45,733 grt, she was the largest P&O ship built for the Australian market, but not quite the fastest. This accolade went to her Orient Line "sister", **Oriana**. Ironically, it was the Falklands War which raised the bar to a dizzying height for **Canberra**. She earned the nickname of "the Great White Whale" and had an astonishing reception on her return to Southampton, rust-streaked, but proud. Who could forget the banners draped over the railings pronouncing "**Canberra** cruises where **QE2** refuses"? This was a tongue-in-cheek reference to **Canberra** reaching San Carlos Water, while Cunard's flagship only reached South Georgia. It was a public relations dream and **Canberra** never looked back. All good things come to an end, though, and the great ship arrived in Southampton on 30 September 1997, for the last time and left for breakers in India a few weeks later. This atmospheric photo shows the great ship leaving Southampton for her last cruise on 10 September with balloons, fireworks and a stunning sunset seeing her away from Berth 105/6 for the final time in commercial service.

(MAL)

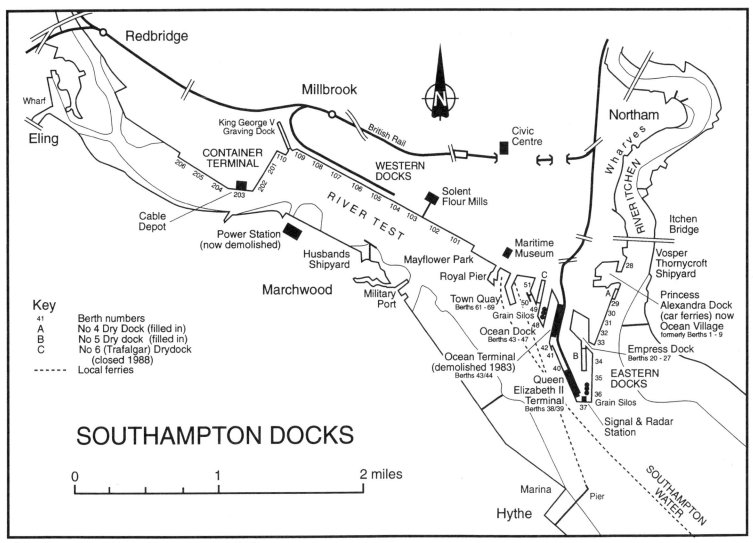

Redbridge

Wharf

Eling

Millbrook

King George V
Graving Dock

CONTAINER
TERMINAL

206 205 204 203 202 201 110 109 108 107 106 105 104 103 102 101

British Rail

WESTERN
DOCKS

N

Civic
Centre

Northam

RIVER ITCHEN
Wharves

Itchen
Bridge

Cable
Depot

Power Station
(now demolished)

Husbands
Shipyard

Marchwood

Military
Port

RIVER TEST

Solent
Flour Mills

Mayflower Park

Royal Pier

Maritime
Museum

Vosper
Thornycroft
Shipyard

28

Town Quay
Berths 61 - 69

Grain Silos

Ocean Dock
Berths 43 - 47

51

C

50
49
48

A

29
30
31
32
33

Princess
Alexandra Dock
(car ferries) now
Ocean Village
formerly Berths 1 - 9

Empress Dock
Berths 20 - 27

Key

41   Berth numbers
A   No 4 Dry Dock (filled in)
B   No 5 Dry dock (filled in)
C   No 6 (Trafalgar) Drydock
            (closed 1988)
- - - -   Local ferries

Ocean Terminal
(demolished 1983)
Berths 43/44

42
41

B

40

Queen
Elizabeth II
Terminal
Berths 38/39

34

35

36
37

EASTERN
DOCKS

Grain Silos

Signal & Radar
Station

SOUTHAMPTON DOCKS

0   1   2 miles

Marina

Pier

SOUTHAMPTON WATER

Hythe

General map of Southampton Docks area - early 1980s

THE
ROOTS & RHYTHM
GUIDE TO

ROCK

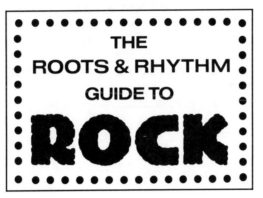

THE ROOTS & RHYTHM GUIDE TO ROCK

Frank Scott, Al Ennis and the staff of *Roots & Rhythm Mail Order*

a cappella books

Library of Congress Cataloging-in-Publication Data

Scott, Frank, 1942—
    The Roots & Rhythm guide to rock / by Frank Scott, Al Ennis,
  and the staff of Roots & Rhythm Mail Order.
      p.   cm.
    ISBN 1-55652-154-5 : $16.95
    1. Rock music—Discography. 2. Rhythm and blues music—Discography.
I. Ennis, Al. II. Roots & Rhythm Mail Order (Firm)
III. Title. IV. Title: Roots and Rhythm guide to rock.
ML 158.4.R6S3   1993
016.78166'0268—dc20

                                              93-8143
                                                CIP
                                                    MN

a cappella books, incorporated
an imprint of Chicago Review Press, Incorporated

5 4 3 2 1
Printed in the United States of America

Cover photo: Chuck Berry, c. 1955, courtesy Frank Driggs collection.
Cover design: Fran Lee
Editorial director: Richard Carlin
Editorial associate: Susan Bindig

Editorial offices:
P.O. Box 380
Pennington, NJ 08534

Sales/business offices:
814 N. Franklin St.
Chicago, IL 60610

Introduction

This book, like our companion book *The Down Home Guide to the Blues*, is not so much a history or scholarly analysis of a musical genre but rather a guide to the vast wealth of exciting music that is available on compact disc, record, and cassette. Like the *Blues* guide, it has grown out of the regular mail-order newsletter started by Down Home Music in 1978 and continuing under our new name of Roots & Rhythm since 1992. Since 1978, we have published several catalogs of rock and roll and R&B, and this book is a considerably expanded and updated version of this catalog.

We cover recordings from what we consider to be the "golden age" of rock music from the early '50s, when R&B and hillbilly boogie rocked the airwaves, to the early '70s, by which time the music had changed so much that it falls out of our realm of interest. In spite of this narrowed focus, we provide information on over 4,000 available recordings, covering rockabilly, vintage rock and roll, R&B, soul, doo wop, swamp pop, surf music, British invasion, and garage-band rock.

Because our primary enthusiasm is for the earlier music, we have given more emphasis to artists who came to prominence in the '50s and early '60s. Such important groups as The Beatles and The Rolling Stones are discussed only briefly—their music is covered at length elsewhere. On the other hand, artists like Big Al Downing, The Fanatics, Joe Clay, James Carr, Mac Curtis, The Spiders, Werly Fairburn, and countless others are rarely discussed outside of specialist magazines or our own newsletter. These "second stringers" might have only peaked on only one or two singles, but oh what peaks! The '50s and '60s are full of such examples, from the Tennessee cool cat with the rockabilly bug to the New York street corner delinquents with a new doo-wop sound to the Texas outcasts who wanted to be The Rolling Stones. Although US reissue companies like Rhino, Relic, Norton, Sundazed, and, to some extent, the major labels are doing a fine job in reissuing vintage recordings, we feel that to get a true picture of this great American music foreign labels, such as Bear Family, White Label, P-Vine, Ace, and Charly, must be included, because they are often the only source for recordings by some of the more obscure artists.

The vast wealth of material presented in these pages may prove to be intimidating to the casual listener. For this reason, we have selected approximately 150 "essential recordings" (indicated by a ✪ next to the title in the text) to offer a balanced overview of the music. Once you've heard these, we hope you'll take the plunge and explore some of the more obscure byways.

The reviews in this book have been written over a period of fifteen years, and a number of people have contributed to them besides ourselves. A particular word of appreciation goes to Gary Mollica who prepared our last rock and roll catalog in 1986 that provided the framework for this book. Other contributors include Myles Boisen, Jeff Colburn, Ray Funk, John McCord, Opal Louis Nations, and Russ Schoenwetter. Thank you all—and, if we have left anyone out, please accept our apologies.

We hope you'll have as much fun as we do exploring the backwaters of '50s and '60s music as well as enjoying the rarest tunes by your favorite legends.

How to Use This Book

The book is divided into two parts: the first part gives listings by artist and forms the heart of the book; the second part lists anthologies, divided into two sections: rock and roll; and R&B/doo-wop.

Artists are alphabetized by last name. In the case of vocal groups, such as "Lee Andrews and The Hearts," they are alphabetized under the last name of the lead singer (ie., under "Andrews," not "Hearts"). Some groups were known under various different names, and we've tried to give cross-references for those interested in tracing their histories.

Under each artist, recordings are arranged alphabetically by label. Within each label, recordings are arranged numerically by catalog number. This means that recordings are not listed chronologically.

The symbols "R," "C," and "L" following a record's catalog number indicate that it is available on record, cassette, or CD, respectively. We have given the full catalog number for each release, but eliminated the often mystifying prefixes and suffixes record companies add to these numbers for internal tracking purposes, or to identify record, cassette, or CD releases.

Although information is given on accompanists and song selection for many listings, they are not meant to give full discographical information.

We have limited ourselves to recordings that are currently in-print. However, in today's rapidly changing world, where LPs are disappearing quickly and being replaced by cassettes and CDs, it is possible that some of these titles may soon disappear to reappear in different configurations, possibly on different labels. Also due to the vagaries of small-label finances, record companies come and go. Even large labels like Motown have had their ups and downs over the years, with releases being recatalogued, dropped, and then reissued in a variety of formats. Most of the recordings in this book are available from Roots & Rhythm Mail Order, located at 6921 Stockton Avenue, El Cerrito, CA 94530, 510-525-2494. Write or call for our latest update.

We have used the following abbreviations in the text:

Musical instruments:

acst (acoustic)
alto sax (alto saxophone)
b (bass)
bar sax (baritone saxophone)
bng (bongos)
clr (clarinet)
drm (drums)
elec (electric)
fdl (fiddle)
gtr (guitar)
hca (harmonica)

kybds (keyboards)
org (organ)
perc (percussion)
pno (piano)
tam (tambourine)
ten sax (tenor saxophone)
trb (trombone)
vcl (vocal)
vibes (vibraphone)
vln (violin)
wshbd (washboard)

Vocal groups:

lead (lead vocalist)
ten (tenor)
alto (alto)
sop (soprano)
bar (baritone)
b (bass)
1st (first)
2nd (second)

THE ACTION

"Mod" group from North London formed in 1963 specializing in blues and R&B covers. Five singles, produced by George Martin, were issued between 1965–1967 and, although none of them were hits, the group have acquired a cult status. After disbanding, the members went on to solo careers or joined other bands.

EDSEL 101 (L)

The Ultimate Action

Fourteen tracks, four not originally issued. I'll Keep Holding On/Never Ever/Since I Lost My Baby/Hey Sha-Lo-Ney/Come On, Come with Me/Shadows and Reflections/The Place/Baby You've Got It/Land of 1,000 Dances.

FAYE ADAMS

Fifties R&B singer best remembered for "Shake a Hand," racial integration's first major anthem, and a million-seller, thanks to her unique high-pitched squalls and gospel-like phrasing. Despite possessing a dynamic, melodious voice, Faye, like many other talented R&B singers of the era, was forced by the economics of the industry to switch from label to label, in search of another big hit. Adams more recently has become a gospel singer.

COLLECTABLES 5122 (RCL)

Shake a Hand

Twelve of Faye's best '50s Herald sides are featured here, including the title track. Great socking and rocking sounds supplied by the fabulous Joe Morris Band. I'll Be True/Your Love (Has My Heart Burning)/Crazy Mixed Up World/Witness to a Crime/Ain't Gonna Tell/Same Old Me.

MR. R&B 110 (R)

I'm Goin' to Leave You

Fabulous album collecting a generous 21 tracks from Adams's best period, 1952–1961. She scintillates on both up-tempo numbers and torch ballads, not to mention the secularized gospel tunes that were her specialty. Shake a Hand/You're Crazy/So Much/It Hurts Me to My Heart/You Ain't Been True/I'll Be True.

JOHNNY ADAMS

New Orleans vocalist Adams is known as the "tan nightingale," because of his unique falsetto. Johnny had his first successes in 1959–1963 and, after recording for a number of labels, he started recording for Rounder in the '80s, resulting in some of his best work. Many of his recordings feature classic New Orleans musicians, including Mac Rebennack (Dr. John). He has also worked in country styles with Nashville producer Shelby Singleton.

ACE (US) 2043 (RL)

Greatest Performance

Eighteen Hep Me label sides, written and arranged by the likes of Allen Toussaint (who also plays Yamaha piano) and Wardell Quezeque. Showcases the balladeering skills of Johnny's magnificent pipes, supported on occasion by Dr. John (pno) and the fast-fingered Jimmy Moliere (gtr). An evenly pleasing collection of soulfully inspired performances, for the most part devoid of disco dirge. After All the Good Is Gone/A Shoulder to Cry On/Love Me Tender/Oh Yes I Cheated/Closer to You/Sharing You/Love Letters (in Kitty Lester's arrangement)/Best of Luck to You.

MAISON DE SOUL 1023 (RC)

Christmas in New Orleans

Excellent R&B versions of mostly traditional Christmas songs, previously issued on the Hep Me label. Silver Bells/Silent Night/Please Come Home for Christmas/Christmas Song.

ROUNDER 2044 (CL)

From the Heart

A truly lovely and moving ten-song collection. Includes the beautiful soulful ballads "From the Heart," "Teach Me to Forget," and "Scarred Knees," and some hot-rockin' bluesy numbers like "Feel Like Breaking Up Somebody's Home," "Roadblock," and "If I Ever Had a Good Thing." Check out the jazzy phrasings of "Why Do I?" and "Laughin' and Clownin'." New Orleans's finest session players enhance this 1983 recording.

ROUNDER 2049 (RCL)

After Dark

Adams croons, warbles, and preaches through ten fine songs from John Hiatt, Doc Pomus, and Paul Kelly. Benefiting from a fine production with tasty guitar from Wayne Bennett, Johnny masterfully updates the classic soul songs "Snap Your Fingers" and "Do Right Woman," as well as giving exquisite interpretations of newer songs such as "Lovers Will" and "Give a Broken Heart a Break." Nice job all around.

ROUNDER 2059 (RCL)

Room with a View of the Blues

Fine, bluesy album with a topnotch band including Walter Washington and Duke Robillard (gtrs), Dr. John (kybds), and Red Tyler (ten sax). Johnny shines on Doc Pomus's jivey "Body and Fender Man," Percy

Mayfield's "The Hunt Is On" featuring his own "mouth trombone," the countryish "Wish I'd Never Loved You at All," the somber "A World I Never Made," and the rockin' title tune. A nice outing from a master. CD has one extra cut.

ROUNDER 2083 (CL)

I Won't Cry

Johnny's eleven singles on Ric Records are prized collector's items today, and are undoubtedly his finest work in terms of raw soulful balladry; only occasional Shelby Singleton sides come anywhere close. Cut in New Orleans between 1959–1963, this material (produced by Mac Rebennack) is supported at times by the great Edgar Blanchard and His Gondoliers. Fourteen cuts in all, with fine sleeve notes from Jeff Hannusch and great digital remastering by Dr. Toby. I Won't Cry/I Want to Do Everything for You/Teach Me to Forget/I Solemnly Promise/Who Are You/Lonely Drifter.

ROUNDER 2095 (RC)

Walking on a Tightrope

This one is devoted to the compositions of the great Percy Mayfield. Adams is backed by a nice group of musicians including Duke Robillard and Wolfman Washington (gtrs). Walking on a Tightrope/Lost Mind/Danger Zone/You're in for a Big Surprise/Baby Please.

ROUNDER 2109 (CL)

Sings Doc Pomus

Johnny's sixth Rounder release and one of his best. He puts his unique vocal stylings to 11 songs penned by the late Doc Pomus. Reflecting the deep emotions of tunes like "Still in Love," "Prisoner of Life," and "The Real Me," Johnny's voice dips to a rich baritone, then soars with his patented falsetto sound. Dr. John provides the fluid and soulful keyboards in the hot backing band. A powerful and emotional recording.

HASIL "HAZE" ADKINS

Billing himself as "Haze Adkins and His Happy Guitar," Haze is a totally crazed one-man band from West Virginia, who has been making tapes since the '50s, all with crummy sound and manic performances. He's gained cult status since The Cramps covered his '50s classic "She Said." You'll love him or hate him, there's no two ways about it; all of his recordings are equally primitive, whether they were made in the '50s or '80s. Norton 201 gives a good introduction to his classic sides; more recent recordings feature a more countryish repertoire, although they still feature his wild playing and singing.

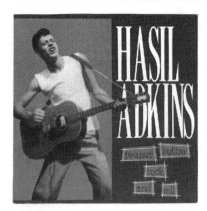

BIG BEAT 34 (R)

She Said

Totally crazed sides, including his classic "She Said." Chicken Twist/DPA on the Moon/Reagan Blues.

DEE JAY JAMBOREE 2043 (R)

Chicken Walk

A cross-section of stuff from the '50s to the present. All songs are primitive and chaotic, including "Ugly Woman" and "Get Out of the Car."

NORTON 201 (R)

Out to Hunch

Billy Miller of Kicks magazine has assembled the ultimate Haze LP. Not only does it contain the original 45 versions of "Chicken Walk" (Air), "She Said" (Jody), and "The Hunch," not only do we get Haze's versions of "Memphis," "Rockin' Robin," and "High School Confidential," we get three previously unissued Haze originals that are among the weirdest songs ever recorded. This trilogy describes Haze's crazed desire to cut off his girlfriend's head. The first, "We Got a Date" and its followup "I Need Your Head (This Ain't No Rock and Roll Show)" are full of growling voices and maniacal laughter. Haze saves the best for last with "No More Hot Dogs," not only featuring the most demented laughter ever on vinyl, but dig the lyrics: "Come on baby, don't be late/I want your head, I want it tonight/I'll cut your head off at half past 8/It'll be on my wall by half past 10." The title refers to the fact that, once her head's cut off, she can't eat "No More Hot Dogs"!

NORTON 203 (R)

The Wild Man

Is the wild man calming down in his old age? This new LP from the folks at Kicks sounds almost calm and country in spots, especially in a fine closing version of Merle Haggard's "Turning Off a Memory." Billy and Mirium's A-Bones back up Haze on "Matchbox" and "Wild Wild Friday Night." Other covers include "Haunted House" and an incredible "Foggy Mountain Top"; wait'll you hear Haze yodel! Punchy Wunchy

Wickey Wackey Woo/Chicken Flop/Do the Scalp/
Big Red Satellite.

NORTON 216 (R)
Peanut Butter Rock and Roll
Recorded by Haze at his West Virginia home during
1956–1963, this mess o' rant'n'roll gives new mean-
ing to the word "primitive." Taken from worn tapes,
acetates, and a cardboard record, the sound quality is
as rugged as the performance, leading Norton to brag
"you can bet your ass there's noise aplenty." So why
do Haze's fans want the Statue of Liberty torn down
and replaced with Haze's likeness? Simple, Adkins is
the cat who would be king, a guitar-hammering, rustic
romeo that would've shot Col. Parker if he was in El's
shoes. Hear what life lived at the speed of sound is like
with "I Wanna Kiss Kiss Kiss Your Lips," "Peanut
Butter Rock and Roll," "The Slop," "Chicken Twist,"
"Stopwatch Baby," and too much more. Inspirational
liner notes by the man who knows everything worth
knowing, Nick Tosches.

NORTON 217 (R)
Moon over Madison
Even a hunch-crazed wildman like Haze drifts into a
dreamy midnight mood when the sun disappears behind the West Virginia hills. These 16 homemade
country-oriented numbers represent the pensive side
of Adkins, although he still finds a way to keep the
rhythm just a step below overdrive. The country tag
owes more to the vocal twang and lyrics than to any
conventional mode of C&W presentation. Much like
"outsider artists" Grandma Prisbrey and Rev. Howard
Finster filtering the world through their rustic visions,
Haze filters the traditions of C&W through his brain
and grinds out pound after pound of "commodity
meat" music. Approach with care, it bites. Blue Velvet
Band/This A.D.C./By the Lonesome River/Lonely
Love/I'm Alone.

STEVE ALAIMO
They say that Steve, the pride of Rochester, NY,
was accepted to three medical schools but
chucked it all to become a pop singer. Steve was
actually one of the very best White pop-soul
singers of the '60s, possessing a pleasant voice
with some bite. He was a regular on TV's "Where
the Action Is," and was one of the first Americans
to travel to Jamaica, helping to popularize ska on
these shores.

TEENAGER 606 (R)
The Very Best
The production here is pretty sparse for pop tunes,
letting Alaimo's vocal talents shine. You'll probably
remember the tunes "Every Day I Have to Cry" and

"I Don't Wanna Cry." "Happy Pappy" is a dopey title
for a good song; Alaimo does a nice version of "Boppin'
the Blues"; but the highlight for me was hearing him
do a good impression of a "rude boy" on "Everybody
Likes to Do the Ska" to the tune of Sam Cooke's
"Everybody Likes to Cha Cha Cha." I guess he liked
it so much he even does a fun ska version of "Stand
by Me" and a bunch of other ska tunes too!

ARTHUR ALEXANDER
Superb R&B/soul singer, and one of those who
successfully wedded black R&B and white country sensibilities. Alexander was worshiped in England and almost unknown here. He was one of
John Lennon's heroes; The Beatles covered his
"Anna" and "Soldier of Love," The Stones did
"You Better Move On," and every British beat
group did "A Shot of Rhythm and Blues."

ACE 922 (L)
The Greatest
All 21 fine cuts made by Alexander for Dot, combining
12 cuts from *A Shot of Rhythm and Blues* (Ace 66)
and nine cuts from *Soldier of Love* (Ace 207), two
out-of-print LP reissues. While Peter Guralnick likes
the later Warner Bros. cuts better (reissued on the
out-of-print Ace 272), I find the simpler arrangements
and the more tentative vocals of these cuts from the
earlier part of Alexander's career immensely appealing.

JOHNNIE ALLAN
One of the prime purveyors of swamp rock, a
Southern Louisiana phenomenon that's a cross
between cajun and Fats Domino, Johnnie and his
band The Krazy Kats recorded mostly for Jin in
the '50s and '60s, with a brief spell in the early
'60s on Viking. His two "hits" were covers of
Chuck Berry's "Promised Land" and a reworking
of Johnny Horton's "North to Alaska" as "South
to Louisiana." Ace 380 or Jin 4001 are the best
single introductions.

ACE 380 (L)
Promised Land
A career-spanning 28-track compilation with numbers
recorded between the late '50s and early '80s pretty
much in chronological order. The tracks were selected
by the illustrious John Broven, author of the book
South to Louisiana. A fine collection that attests to the
heartfelt power of both this artist and swamp pop,
produced with the usual Ace committment to quality.
Fine sound, excellent notes, discographical information, and great photos. A winner. She's Gone/Cry

Foolish Heart/Cajun Man/Somewhere on Skid Row/
I'm Missing You/South to Louisiana.

FLYRIGHT 551 (R)
Good Timin' Man
Fine 1979 Jin and Swallow recordings made at Jay
Miller's Master-Trak studio in Crowley, LA. Backing
is by a seven-piece studio band including two saxes
and accordion. Twelve tunes including Dave
Edmund's "I Knew the Bride" and "Victim of Life's
Circumstances." Flat Natural Good Timin' Man/Juju
Man/Ain't Your Memory Got No Pride at All/Alliga-
tor Bayou.

JIN 4001 (R)
South to Louisiana
Some of Allan's best late '50s-early '60s recordings.
South to Louisiana/She's Gone/What 'Cha Do/Your
Picture/Do You Love Me/Somebody Else.

JIN 9002 (R)
Johnnie Allan Sings
More good early sides. Somewhere on Skid
Row/Please Help Me I'm Falling/Secret of Love/The
Life I Live.

JIN 9006 (R)
Dedicated to You
A Woman Left Lonely/Sweet Dreams/I Cried/Look
at All the Loneliness/A Stranger to You/Sittin' and
Thinkin'.

JIN 9012 (R)
A Portrait of Johnnie Allan
Somewhere to Come When It Rains/I Don't Feel at
Home in Your Arms Anymore/Knock on Wood.

JIN 9015 (R)
Another Man's Woman
Another Man's Woman/Big Fool of the Year/All by
Myself/Conscience I'm Guilty/Come Sundown/I
Was a Fool.

ERNESTINE ALLEN
Ernestine Allen started her recording career in
1945, and for most of her career went under the
name of Annisteen Allen. She was a good, jazz-
flavored singer. She retired from the music business in the '60s.

ORIGINAL BLUES CLASSICS 539 (RCL)
Let It Roll
A reissue of Tru-Sound 15004 from 1961. Allen is
accompanied by a fine band, including King Curtis
(sax) and Al Casey (gtr). The material is strongly
oriented toward pop songs like "Lullaby of Broadway," "Baubles, Bangles, and Beads," and "Tea for
Two," although there are also some good blues perfor-

mances like "Mean and Evil" and "Miss Allen's
Blues."

LEE ALLEN
Tenor-sax player Allen was one of the cornerstones of New Orleans R&B. His hard-driving
playing was featured on hundreds of sessions cut
in the Crescent City from the '50s on. He had a
brief flurry of success under his own name when
his rocking instrumental "Walking with Mr. Lee"
became a hit in 1958. He subsequently returned
to session work, as well as touring with Fats
Domino's band, which he continues to do today.

COLLECTABLES 5083 (CL)
Walkin' with Mr. Lee: Golden Classics
Walkin' with Mr. Lee/Short Circuit/Ivy League/Hot
Rod Special/Promenade/Strollin' with Mr. Lee/Lee's
Blues.

MILTON ALLEN
BEAR FAMILY 15357 (R)
Don't Bug Me Baby
Eleven cuts from 1957. Don't Bug Me Baby/Jambo-
ree/It's Simply Grand/Half Loved/It's Love and It's
Real.

THE RANCE ALLEN GROUP
Rance Allen helped pioneer singing gospel lyrics
to pop/soul tunes. In fact, his biggest hits were
re-written versions of two big pop hits: Archie
Bell and The Drells's "There's Gonna Be a Show-
down" and The Temptations's "Just My Imagination," redone as "Just My Salvation," which
earned his band a coveted spot opening for such
huge-drawing acts as Isaac Hayes.

STAX 8540 (RC)
The Best of The Rance Allen Group
Their biggest early '70s singles made for Stax's Truth
and Gospel Truth subsidiaries, and late '70s recordings
done for the revived Stax. Hot Line to Jesus/Ain't No
Need of Crying/I Belong to You/I Know a Man Who.

THE ALLISONS
John and Bob Allison were brothers from Ful-
ham, England who had a bit of success in Britain
after they won the right to represent England in
the Eurovision Song Contest of 1961. If you like
the lighter side of The Everly Brothers or Buddy

Holly, then you might find these well-mannered popsters your cup of tea.

DIAMOND 515 (R)

Are You Sure

Eighteen cuts, about half original material ("Are You Sure," "Words," "Blue Tears"), and half cover versions ("It Doesn't Matter Anymore," "That'll Be the Day"). Lot's of rockin' strings and even a vibe break on "Be-Bop-a-Lula"!

THE ALLURES

The (NY) Allures a-cappella quartet was formed in 1983, with top second tenor and off-target falsetto lead Ted Ziffer who sang in The Chessmen (Relic 7019), Rosemary and Charles Gaskin who both served in the Bronx-based Lovenotes during the early '60s, and Mike Pia.

STARLIGHT DISCS 19912 (L)

Doo-Wop Memories A Cappella

Average renditions of 24 standards and swansongs culled from notable doo-wop ensembles.

ANDY ANDERSON

Jackson, Mississippi's Anderson cut an unissued LP for Sun with legendary producer Jack Clements in 1956. He released his first single in 1957, "Johnny Valentine" b/w "I-I-I Love You," the first US rock record to be simultaneously released in Europe. Achieving cult status for his work in the late '50s and early '60s, he continued to record sporadically with his band, The Dawnbreakers.

UNION PACIFIC 006 (R)

One Man's Rock and Roll

Classic rockabilly recorded for Zynn, Hermitage, and Anderson's own Century Ltd. labels from 1960–1965. Tough Tough Tough/Sit Right Down and Cry Over You/All by Myself/Chop Suey.

RUBY ANDREWS

Andrews was a Chicago-based soul singer who had a big hit with "Casanova" for the Zodiac label in 1967, and several minor hits over the next few years. After a long absence, she has recently started recording again for Ichiban.

COLLECTABLES 5201 (CL)

Casanova

Includes the title hit. Help Yourself Lover/Gotta Break Away/Casanova 70/You Can Run, but You Can't Hide/Since I Found Out.

LEE ANDREWS and THE HEARTS

Excellent Philadelphia harmony group from the late '50s who specialized in smooth beautiful ballads, both standards and their own compositions. Andrews (b. Arthur Lee Andrew Thompson) was the son of Beechie Thompson who sang with the famed Dixie Hummingbirds. He formed his first vocal group in high school, called The Dreamers, and featuring Roy Calhoun (1st ten), Butch Curry (2nd ten), Jimmy McCalister (bar), and John Young (b). They changed their name when they discovered another group was already known as The Dreamers, and they spent the early '50s performing on local radio and searching for success on records. They initially recorded for Rainbow and Gotham records, but neither label was successful in promoting their sides. They signed to Mainline in 1957, and their two biggest hits, "Long Lonely Night" and "Teardrops" were sold to Chess. In 1958, they went to United Artists with another hit, "Try the Impossible." The group continued to record sporadically with various lineups through the early '80s.

COLLECTABLES 5003 (CL)

Gotham Recording Session

Thirteen sides, mostly previously unissued, including their first recording of "Long Lonely Nights."

COLLECTABLES 5028 (CL)

Biggest Hits

Twelve songs. Teardrops/The Clock/Try the Impossible/Long Lonely Nights/The Fairest/Maybe You'll Be There.

BOBBY ANGELO

An English singer who idolized Elvis, Gene Vincent, and Eddie Cochran, helping him to stay on the rockin' side of the notoriously wimpy British pop-rock scene of the early '60s.

DEMAND 0070 (R)

Baby Sittin' with Bobby Angelo

Pop-rock classics that are as good or better than other British recordings of the era. His first 45, "Baby

Sittin'," is one of the best early British rockers I've ever heard. "Skinny Lizzie," the flip, is also very strong with the same excellent guitar work featured on the A-side. "Cupie Doll" is another good one, but he gets in over his head on Little Richard's "Rip It Up," which is barely saved by some hot guitar.

THE ANGELS

The Allbut sisters, Jiggs and Barb, of Orange, NJ, had a hit on Caprice with "'Til," with Linda Jansen singing lead. In 1963, under the guidance of Feldman/Goldstein/Gottehrer, they moved to Smash, with a new lead singer Peggy Santiglia, and recorded the girl-group classic "My Boyfriend's Back." The toughest of the '60s girl groups, there's no way these New Jersey natives would pass up an evening of leather jackets, motorcycles, or the pursuit of happiness! Regrettably, save for their biggest hit, their music seldom achieved the toughness inherent in their publicity pictures.

COLLECTABLES 5085 (CL)
My Boyfriend's Back: Golden Classics
Fourteen sides. And the Angels Sing/Welcome to the Floor/River of Love/Cotton Fields/'Til/Blow Joe/Thank You and Goodnight.

THE ANIMALS

British R&B/blues band of the mid-'60s led by legendary vocalist Eric Burdon. Their biggest hit was a cover of "House of the Rising Sun." Later in the decade, the group switched gears and recorded more psychedelic sounds. Heavy drug use took its toll on band members, with lead guitarist Hilton Valentine so strung out that he quit music and retreated to his room through most of 1967, imagining that he was Jesus Christ reincarnated, and refusing to speak to anyone except the local grocery store owner. Burdon formed the group War in 1970, and performed as a solo artist later in the decade and in the '80s. Interest was renewed by the publication of his autobiography, *I Used to Be an Animal*, in the late '80s.

DECAL 72 (L)
Trackin' the Hits
Eighteen mid-'60s hits. House of the Rising Sun/Boom Boom/Dimples/Talkin' about You/Mess

Around/Bright Lights Big City/Don't Let Me Be Misunderstood/We've Gotta Get Out of this Place/It's My Life.

POLYDOR 849 388 (CL)
The Best of Eric Burdon and The Animals, 1966–1968
Hits the high points of the band's final years. Leaving the blues covers behind him (except for a rocked-out "C.C. Rider"), Eric kept a shifting lineup together to do such psychedelic anthems as "San Franciscan Nights," "A Girl Named Sandoz," "When I Was Young," "Monterey," and "Sky Pilot." These 15 tracks come from the *Animalization, Animalism, Eric Is Here, Winds of Change, The Twain Shall Meet, Every One of Us, Love Is*, and *Best of* LPs.

⊙ SEE FOR MILES 244 (RL)
The EP Collection
This is actually better than a greatest hits collection because it covers the prime period of The Animals when everything they cut was super-tough blues and R&B. Twenty cuts taken from five EPs released in 1964–1965: *The Animals Is Here, The Animals, The Animals 2, The Animals Are Back*, and *Animal Tracks*. An utterly fantastic collection! House of the Rising Sun/I'm Crying/Boom Boom/Around and Around/I'm in Love/Club a-Go-Go.

SEQUEL 153 (RCL)
Inside Looking Out: The 1965–1966 Sessions
Twenty-two vintage cuts from 1965–1966. This was a good period for Eric Burdon and company; the band was tight, had enjoyed a good dose of fame with "House of the Rising Sun" and "We Gotta Get Out of this Place," and managed through all of this to keep their manic R&B sensibilities intact. Most of these tracks come from the *Animalisms* LP, rounded out by singles sides, one cut from Burdon's solo album (Randy Newman's "Mama Told Me Not to Come"), and four expendable blues covers from a rare EP. The pace here is set by the hair-raising intensity of the title cut, plus "Maudie" and "Squeeze Her, Tease Her."

PAUL ANKA

Canadian-born Anka became an overnight star with his hit "Diana," written when he was just 15. He remained a top-drawing teen idol for ten years, before settling down into lounge-singing heaven. In the late '50s and early '60s, he scored with "Lonely Boy," "Put Your Head on My Shoulder," and "Puppy Love." He has also penned hits for other crooners, from Buddy Holly ("It Doesn't Matter Anymore") to Frank Sinatra's anthemic

"My Way," and made big bucks in residuals from "*The Tonight Show* Theme."

BEAR FAMILY 15613 (L)
In Deutschland

RHINO 71489 (L)
30th Anniversary Collection
Twenty-four hits in chronological order from 1957–1978, his best recordings from the ABC-Paramount, RCA, Buddah, and United Artists labels. Diana/Put Your Head on My Shoulder/Puppy Love/My Way/Having My Baby.

PAUL ANKA/NEIL SEDAKA

RCA (JAPAN) 1014 (L)
Paul Anka and Neil Sedaka
Seven cuts each by these pop legends, lovingly compiled for CD in the meticulous Japanese way. Anka does "Diana," "Put Your Head on My Shoulder," and "Cinderella," while Sedaka renders "Happy Birthday," "Sweet Sixteen," "Breaking Up Is Hard to Do," and "Calendar Girl." Squeaky clean and sugary sweet '60s crooning; not for diabetics.

ANN-MARGRET
Sixties-era actress-turned-singer.

TEENAGER 604 (R)
Hits and Rarities
You'll flip when you get a gander at this LP cover with Ann flippin' her wig in a classic torrid pose. She sings some gently sultry tunes like "C'est Si Bon" and "Begin the Beguine," tries some torch ballads like "Fever" and "That Old Black Magic," and plenty of the old red-hot mama numbers like "Thirteen Men" and "There'll Be Some Changes Made." I like her best on sleazy soundtrack tunes like "The Pleasure Seekers" and "The Swinger," though. There's even a sexy version of her good friend Elvis's "Heartbreak Hotel" among the 18 tunes.

THE AQUATONES
Late '50s New York group, featuring the plaintive lead vocals of Lynn Dixon, who had an enormous hit with "You" for Fargo in 1958. Most of their songs were written by vocalists Larry Vannata and David Goddard. They disbanded in 1960, although Vannata formed a new Aquatones to perform in revival shows in the early '70s.

RELIC 5033 (R)
Just for "You"
Eighteen cuts, including an alternate take of "You."

LLOYD ARNOLD
Average Memphis-area rockabilly performer who played some excellent rockin' guitar.

WHITE LABEL 8921 (R)
Memphis, Vol. 7
"Red Coat, Green Pants and Red Suede Shoes" and "Hangout" were Lloyd's two best recordings, done for Myers and Record-O-Rama respectively, and they're both here. His cover of Chuck Berry's "School Days" is pretty good, and must have shown promise at the time because it was released on three different labels in a couple of different versions. There are some previously unissued and alternate takes along with a selection of his lesser known tunes on Republic, Sharp, and Memphis. Tennessee Twist/Go Go Go/Sugaree.

P.P. ARNOLD
P.P. went to England in 1961 with Ike and Tina Turner's backing group The Ikettes and wound up staying on. She hit England at a good time, hooking up with Andrew Loog Oldham's fledgling Immediate label and becoming the reigning queen of soul there. The high point came quickly with her impassioned hit version of "The First Cut Is the Deepest." While not a sensational voice, she did have the power and dynamics to contend with the Spectoresque arrangements so beloved by Oldham.

SEE FOR MILES 235 (L)
Kafunta: The First Lady of Immediate
Very interesting and fine. (If You Think) You're Groovy/Born to Be Together/The First Cut Is the Deepest/Treat Me Like a Lady/Speak to Me/Eleanor Rigby.

THE ARTWOODS
One of the more "authentic" British R&B bands led by Art Wood, Ron's brother, and featuring Jon Lord (org) and Keef Hartley (drm).

EDSEL 107 (L)
100 Oxford Street
Sixteen sides recorded for British Decca in 1964–1966, with a nice Stax R&B-influenced sound. The CD comes with a four-page pullout section featuring the history of the band in words and pictures. Features the ever-popular "I'm Looking for a Saxophonist Doubling French Horn Wearing Size 37 Boots." One More Heartache/Down in the Valley/Big City.

THE ASSOCIATION

Folk-rock group who enjoyed a brief period of popularity in the late '60s. Formed around guitarist/vocalist Terry Kirkman (who had performed in coffeehouses as a duo with the then-unknown Frank Zappa), the group's first hit was 1967's "controversial" "Along Came Mary" on the tiny Valiant label (some older critics thought the song was about—gasp!—marijuana). Other hits included "Cherish," "Windy," and "Everything That Touches You." The group branched out into more psychedelic sounds in the early '70s, but almost no one wanted to hear these sunny harmonizers get groovy. They split up soon after.

PAIR 1061 (L)
Songs That Made Them Famous

WARNER BROS. 1767 (CL)
Greatest Hits

THE ASTRONAUTS

Early '60s surf group from Denver, originally known as The Stormtroopers. They had never even heard of surf music when RCA signed them in 1963, but they learned fast and went on to become one of the top instrumental bands of the '60s with eight LPs plus several movie appearances. Their big hit was "Baja."

BEAR FAMILY 15442 (L)
Surfin' With/Competition Coupe
Reissues two RCA LPs, originally RCA 2760 from 1963 and RCA 2858 from 1964. Baja/Miserlou/Suzie Q/Kuk/Baby Lets Play House/Batman/Competition Coupe/55 Bird/Happy Ho Daddy.

BEAR FAMILY 15443 (L)
Everything's A-OK/
Astronauts Orbit Campus
Reissues two RCA LPs, originally RCA 2782 and RCA 2903, both from 1964. Bo Diddley/It's So Easy/Wine, Wine, Wine/Big Bossman/Shortnin' Bread/What'd I Say/Be-Bop-a-Lula.

BEAR FAMILY 15556 (L)
Rarities
A cool collection of Astros rarities, from crunchin' surf numbers to later tracks produced under the guidance of songwriters Steve Venet, and Tommy Boyce and Bobby Hart, which, along with the group-penned "Buy Me a Round" and some R&B covers, shows what a great beat/punk group the As could be, too. Come Along Baby/Tryin' to Get to You/Surfs You Right/Surf Softly and Carry a Big Board/Surf Party/Firewater/Tomorrow's Gonna Be Another Day/The Tables Have Turned.

LYNN AUGUST

Blind since birth, August was raised on Chuck Willis and Johnny Ace 78s. By the age of 12, he was playing drums for Esquerita, and in 1964 (at age 15) was scheduled to join Sam Cooke in California before Cooke's untimely demise. Eventually he turned to the accordion and zydeco.

BLACK TOP 1074 (CL)
Creole Cruiser
August's second zydeco album shows him to be one of the finest singers in the genre. He combines zydeco and blues effortlessly, on covers of R&B tunes, traditional zydeco numbers, and good original compositions. Blind Man/Don't You Know I Love You/That Train Is Gone/Bernadette/Tanten Nana/Hippy Ty O.

MAISON DE SOUL 1027 (R)
It's Party Time
Nice collection of cover versions of Louisiana-flavored R&B with a solid backup band featuring the sax of Willie Tee. Having a Party/Whole Lotta Woman/Kansas City/I'd Rather Go Blind/Party Time.

FRANKIE AVALON

One of the first squeaky-clean teen idols, Frankie scored big with a series of hits before becoming Annette Funicello's main squeeze on the silver screen. Like Fabian and Bobby Rydell, Frankie hailed from Philadelphia and recorded for Chancellor records, gaining lots of exposure from his appearances on Dick Clark's Philadelphia-based *American Bandstand.*

COLLECTOR SERIES 240 (L)
The Frankie Avalon Collection
Twenty-four gems of pop simplicity. Venus/De De Dinah/Gingerbread/I'll Wait for You/Bobby Sox to Stockings/A Boy without a Girl/Why/Don't Throw Away All Those Teardrops/Togetherness.

LAVERN BAKER

One of the major R&B singers of the '50s, LaVern started her recording career under the nom-de-disc of "Little Miss Sharecropper" on Okeh in

1948. After four hitless years there and a hitless year on King in 1952, she switched to Atlantic in '53, scoring a major hit with "Tweedlee Dee." In 1956, she crossed over to the rock and roll crowd with even bigger hits like "Jim Dandy" and many others over the next ten years. In 1966 she moved to Brunswick where she had her last hit, a duet with Jackie Wilson on "Think Twice." She went into semi-retirement, but has returned to performing in the last few years and still has a lot of her old magic.

⊙ ATLANTIC 82311 (CL)

Soul on Fire: The Best of LaVern Baker

Excellent 20-song collection of hits and misses recorded between 1953–1962, digitally remastered by Stephen Innocenzi. Uncharted misses, but cool nonetheless, include "Soul on Fire," written by Ahmet Ertegun, from her initial Atlantic recordings, "You Said," "Tomorrow Night," and "How Often" (featuring LaVern, Ben E. King, and King Curtis on tenor sax for kicks). Essential listening for anyone interested in the development of rock and roll, or for anyone who likes to dance around in their socks with the volume turned up loud. Is that Doc Severinson blowing his trumpet on "Shake a Hand"? Yup. Thank Nick Tosches for the fine notes. Tweedlee Dee/Bop Ting a Ling/I Cried a Tear/Play It Fair/Jim Dandy/Still/I Can't Love You Enough/Jim Dandy Got Married/I Waited Too Long/C.C. Rider.

ATLANTIC 90980 (L)

Sings Bessie Smith

Accompanied by a fine jazzy group with Buck Clayton, Paul Quinichette, and Danny Barker, LaVern sounds right at home singing some of Smith's best-known songs. Nobody Knows You When You're Down and Out/Baby Doll/Empty Bed Blues/There'll Be a Hot Time in the Old Town Tonight.

RHINO 70565 (CL)

Live In Hollywood '91

"To view Baker as a nostalgia act is a grave disservice" say the notes on this CD box. With a hefty helping of old classics like "Tweedlee Dee" and "Shake a Hand," she is bound to attract a nostalgia market—as if Rhino didn't know. But who cares, as long as she sounds good? Baker not only sounds good for someone who's been recording for over 40 years, but her blue banter between the songs is fun too; she has her stage stuff down cold. These 17 songs were recorded at the Cinegrill nightclub in Hollywood in front of a pretty enthusiastic crowd. You should sing so well when you're over 60.

HANK BALLARD and THE MIDNIGHTERS

Excellent Detroit vocal group, who started out as The Royals in 1950 (original members included Jackie Wilson and Levi Stubbs). Ballard joined in 1953, and the band changed their name in '54. Guitarist Cal Green joined in '55 and stayed throughout the '50s. Their "Annie" double-entendre jump records and later dance-craze sides kept the group working throughout the '60s. Ballard was truly ahead of his time in the '50s, making frankly sexual records, even for the more open-minded R&B audience, let alone the nascent teenage pop market. Led by Hank's soaring gospel-tinged vocals, The Midnighters were the kind of group that could stand your short hairs on end. Ballard wrote "The Twist" in 1958, but it did nothing for him; it took Chubby Checker to make it a monster hit and dance craze in 1960. Many of their King LPs have been reissued exactly on CD, bringing joy to the heart of collectors.

CHARLY 240 (L)

Let 'em Roll

Twenty tracks, including ten of their fourteen '50s hits from the King/Federal vaults, plus the stompin' "Tore Up over You" (featuring a stinging guitar solo from Cal Green), the soulfully beautiful "In the Doorway Crying," and "Rock and Roll Wedding" (with its wild Louis Stevens tenor-sax break). Let 'em Roll/Crazy Lovin'/Deep Sea Blues/Sugaree/Look at Little Sister/I'm Gonna Miss You/Daddy Rolling Stone.

⊙ KING 541 (RL)

Sing Their Greatest Juke Box Hits

You probably have everything on this greatest-hits collection if you have two or three of their King LPs already, but if you're an R&B collector and have seen the original around for years at big bucks, how can you resist? Exact repro of the colorful cover and liner notes on the back with a band photo showing Hank in action. Work with Me Annie/Annie Had a Baby/Tore Up over You/Sexy Ways.

KING 581 (R)
Hank Ballard and The Midnighters
Hank, wearing shades, peers knowingly from the cover, beckoning the righteous on numbers like "Open up the Back Door," "Stay by My Side," "In the Doorway Crying," "Daddy's Little Baby," and "Is Your Love for Real?"

KING 618 (RL)
Singin' and Swingin'. . . The Twist
Teardrops on Your Letter/Let Me Hold Your Hand/Whatsoever You Do/Ashamed of Myself/The Twist/Sweet Mama Do Right/Tell Them/I'll Be Home Someday.

KING 674 (RL)
The One and Only
Reissue of 1960 LP with typical ultra-cool, full-color cover photo. You couldn't afford this when you were a kid and you didn't want to part with the C-note that the collector's shop wanted, so now's your big chance. Worth the price even if all 12 cuts were "Sugaree," the R&B classic with the devastating guitar solo. I'm Crying Mercy, Mercy/Kansas City/Rain Down Tears/Cute Little Ways/Move, Move, Move.

KING 700 (L)
Mr. Rhythm and Blues

KING 740 (L)
Spotlight on Hank Ballard
Twelve cuts. Let's Go Let's Go Let's Go/Mona Lisa/The Hoochi Coochi Coo/These Young Girls.

KING 759 (RC)
Dance Along
This LP was Hank Ballard and The Midnighters's last big fling. They placed four tunes on the rock-and-roll charts in 1961. The last three—"The Continental Walk," "The Switch-a-Roo," and "Nothin' but Good"—are the cornerstones of this album, but there's still plenty of great stuff built around that trio to make for a classic R&B collection. Tunes like "Daddy Rolling Stone" and "Keep on Dancing" are right up there with the best of them, and we shouldn't overlook one of the weirdest numbers of the era, "The Float," with an Indian war-whoop chorus and what sounds like a Theremin solo! The liner notes prophesy that this music will still sound fresh in 1971. Let's change that to 2001 at least.

KING 950 (L)
24 Hit Tunes
Twenty-four King sides at a budget price, including "The Twist," "The Coffee Grind," "Finger Poppin' Time," and "The Float." Sadly, this doesn't contain his earlier hits for Federal (the Annie songs and "Sexy Ways") or other King-label hits like "Teardrops on Your Letter," "Kansas City," or "Let's Go." So if you were expecting a greatest-hits package, this ain't it.

MACK BANKS/CHARLIE BROWN
Two early Southern rockabilly stars.

WHITE LABEL 8804 (R)
Charlie Brown/Mack Banks
Thirteen tracks. Charlie Brown wasn't really a rockabilly cat, but one of the early country singers who mixed many of the southern musical styles into his upbeat repertoire. Both sides of his two Rose releases are here, recorded at Jim Beck's Dallas Studios. The earlier boppin' hillbilly "Mean Mean Mama" b/w "My Hungry Heart" combo edges out "Have You Heard the Gossip" b/w "Boogie Woogie Mama." Mack Bank recorded a bit later on, in the mid-'50s, and his style is closer to pure rockabilly while still maintaining a strong rural influence, best shown on the catchy "They Don't Come in Droves like Me." His rare (450 copies pressed!) "Be Boppin' Daddy" is prime stuff.

THE BAR-KAYS
The Bar-Kays have a long, involved history. They began as the Number 2 Stax house band (Number 1 was Booker T and the MGs/The Mar-Keys). Their big hit was 1967's "Soul Finger." Original band members Jimmy King (gtr), Ronnie Caldwell (org), Phalon Jones (ten sax), and Carl Cunningham (drm) were killed with Otis Redding in a plane crash; survivors James Alexander (b) and Ben Cauley (tpt) started a new version that replaced the MGs as the Stax house band in the early '70s. They gained fame as Isaac Hayes's original backing group (that's them on "Shaft"), and for their instrumental hits. In later incarnations, the band added Commodores-influenced funk and vocals. They had a 1976 hit with the disco-esque "Shake Your Rump to the Funk."

RHINO 70298 (CL)
Soul Finger
The band's first LP, originally released in 1967 as Volt 417. It contains their Number 3 R&B hit, "Soul Finger," plus "Knucklehead," another top-40 shaker.

Soon after this LP was released, the group (minus two members) was killed in the crash that took Otis Redding's life; at 30 minutes, the music here, like the group itself, is gone all too soon. With a Child's Heart/Don't Do That/I Want Someone/House Shoes.

STAX (UK) 962 (L)

Gotta Groove/Black Rock

Nineteen tracks from two LPs, originally Volt 6004 from 1969 and Volt 6011 from 1971, respectively. *Gotta Groove* is a surprisingly good 11-cut instrumental package that, along with earlier Bar-Kays sides and the best Meters and Booker T. tracks, withstands the ravages of time very well. "Don't Stop Dancing" is a two-part assault of thunderous funk, matched by the tight arrangements of "Humpin'" and "Funky Thang," and the unabashedly psychedelic "Street Walker." Of course, there are a few dated clunkers, particularly their takes of "Yesterday" and "Hey Jude." *Black Rock* shows the Bar-Kay's moving into different territory, obviously influenced by the jazz-tinged successes of Blood Sweat and Tears and Chicago, and even dabbling in some expansive Hendrix-like black acid-rock! Not an essential disc, but an interesting cross-cultural document of those mind-expanding times.

STAX 8542 (RCL)

The Best of The Bar-Kays

This set by the second-generation Bar-Kays includes their instrumental hits—"Son of Shaft" and "Copy Cat"—a sound-alike of the original band's "Soul Finger," plus a few early vocal hits like "Holy Ghost" and "Don't Stop Dancin' (to the Music)."

RONNIE BARRON

Pianist/vocalist Barron was a one-time session man for Paul Butterfield.

LINE 9.00594 (L)

Blue Delicacies

New Orleans standards and originals originally issued by the Japanese Vivid label in 1980. Barron is no Dr. John, but he's pretty good. Covers of Percy Mayfield's "River's Invitation," Joe Liggins's "Pink Champagne," and Earl King's "Trick Bag" are all worthwhile. And while his tendency toward a strained falsetto can be genuinely annoying, it manages to be endearing most of the time, as on songs like "Singing in My Soul." Worried Life Blues/Big Chief/Doing Something Wrong/Lights Out/Hey Now Baby/Happy Tears.

BARRY and THE REMAINS

Barry and The Remains, from Boston, were one of America's top groups in the '60s, even earning the opening slot on the Beatles's 1966 tour. At a time when most kids were having a tough time

learning the chords to "Louie Louie," The Remains were already craftsmen building three-minute masterpieces like "All Good Things" and "Don't Look Back," the latter being perhaps the greatest American garage rocker of the '60s (Number 1 in my book for sure).

EPIC 46926 (1398) (L)

The Remains

Of the 21 tracks here, seven have been remixed in stereo. There's also an early, previously unreleased version of the wonderful "Say You're Sorry." Some studio chatter is also left in on some tracks. Why Do I Cry/Lonely Weekend/You Got a Hard Time Comin'/My Babe.

JOE BARRY

Louisiana-born pianist/vocalist Joe Barry didn't have to look far for his influences. The "fat man" loomed large on the horizon for Joe and he tapped into Domino's success bigtime. He slavishly imitates Fats in his singing and arrangements, but he does it so well for a white boy that it comes off as endearing.

PRINCESS 4000 (R)

I'm a Fool to Care

With the incredible wealth of musical talent in Louisiana, Barry's backup bands work up every tune into a viable, polished swamp-pop hit. Side 2 sometimes finds Joe straying from his formula with mixed results (bad and awful), but there's plenty to enjoy nonetheless among the 18 selections. I'm a Fool to Care/Teardrops in My Heart/Little Papoose/Secret Love.

DAVE BARTHOLOMEW

New Orleans producer, arranger, singer, trumpet player, and talent scout Bartholomew is best remembered for sides he produced with Fats Domino on Imperial, but he also recorded for Imperial, De Luxe, and King under his own name. Although little more than an average vocalist he was an engaging one, and he could blow breathtaking solos. Many star instrumentalists passed through Dave's band, including Frank Fields (b), Earl Palmer (drm), Todd Rhodes (pno), Herb Hardesty (ten sax), and Ernest McLean (gtr).

CHARLY 273 (L)

In the Alley

Twenty cuts in all, with some duplication with the out-of-print Sing 1158. Tommy Ridgely contributes some exciting vocals on "Lawdy Lawdy Lord, Pts. 1 and 2."

EMI (JAPAN) 7293/96 (L)

Dave Bartholomew Plays with Fats Domino

Four-CD set, featuring 32 tracks by Bartholomew released under his own name, and 48 tracks by his most popular protege Antoine "Fats" Domino recording with Bartholomew's band. Only 16 of the 48 Domino tracks are duplicated on the US EMI box set (see Fats Domino listing), and they focus on his early career before any of his hits, featuring all of his recordings made between December 1949 (his first session) and February 1953, with selected items from later sessions through February 1955. The earliest sides are pretty much mainstream urban blues, though his distinctive vocal styling soon came into play and the material is fine and varied. Bartholomew's recordings are quite a mixture, including straight blues, jump, pop, and jazz-flavored instrumentals. The set includes the infamous "Little Girl Sing Ding-a-Ling," which later became better known as "My Ding-a-Ling." Bartholomew's whimsical sense of humor is shown on "Ah Cubanos," "Who Drank the Beer while I Was in the Rear," and "An Old Cow Hand from a Blues Band." Excellent!

FONTELLA BASS

St. Louis R&B singer and keyboard player, Bass's mother Martha was a gospel singer and member of The Clara Ward Singers. She originally recorded for Ike Turner's Prann label and then moved to Checker where she duetted with Bobby McClure. Her first solo, the driving "Rescue Me," was a big hit, and was followed by a number of lesser hits.

CHESS 9335 (CL)

Rescued: The Best of Fontella Bass

Collects much of Fontella's best material recorded for the Checker label between 1964–1968, including her only Number 1 hit "Rescue Me" and the moving "The Soul of a Man," often touted as her finest recording. Four duets with Bobby McClure are here, including "Don't Mess Up a Good Thing" and "You're Gonna Miss Me," and two of her biggest hits, the often overlooked gem "Don't Jump" and Jimmy Reed's "Baby What You Want Me to Do." Many of the cuts are previously unreleased in the US, or not on US LP, or in the case of the stunning and mysterious "Joy of Love," just plain unreleased.

THE BEACH BOYS

The archetypical sun-and-fun group of the '60s that lapsed into the drugged-out-paranoia of the '70s. The Wilson brothers (Brian, Carl, and Dennis), cousin Mike Love, and neighbor Al Jardine created some of the most memorable American pop music ever waxed, under the able production hand of Brian Wilson. The story of their tragic childhood, misadventures with drugs, Brian Wilson's long exile from life followed by his "recovery" under the hands of Svengali-doctor Eugene Landy has become an integral part of the group's legend. They soldier on today, without Brian or Dennis (who drowned in the early '80s), still banking on the hits of the '60s. Although Capitol has reissued their recordings under new catalog numbers, we've kept this entry in chronological order.

CAPITOL 93691 (CL)

Surfin' Safari/Surfin' USA

The Boys's first two Capitol LPs in their entirety, featuring Brian Wilson's sunniest, most innocent odes to girls, surf, sand, and sun.

CAPITOL 93692 (CL)

Surfer Girl/Shut Down Vol. II

The third and fourth Beach Boys's outings, the first two produced by Brian Wilson, and therefore the first worthy of owning. Although the sound is still primitive, there are forebodings of the angst to come in Wilson's "In My Room," perhaps the eeriest ode to childhood ever made. Finishing his surf trilogy, Wilson was ready to tackle cars in *Shut Down Vol. II.* Capitol had shamelessly issued an anthology LP of various car songs, called *Shut Down,* featuring the Beach Boys with other artists. That's how this LP came to be called Vol. II even though there was no Vol. I by the Boys alone. Alternate tracks include "In My Room" recorded with German lyrics for the European market!

CAPITOL 93693 (CL)

Little Deuce Coupe/All Summer Long

The Boys' fifth and sixth LPs reissued in their entirety. The first consists of Brian's classic collaborations with Roger Christian on a series of songs celebrating America's love affair with hot wheels, from "Shut Down" to "Little Deuce Coupe" to "409" (written with Gary Usher) to "Spirit of America." Christian was an LA DJ who had written a number of "poems" celebrating his favorite cars; he formed a fast friendship with Wilson, and the pair wrote dozens of songs together. The second LP features a wider variety of material, opening with the classic "I Get Around," and featuring "All Summer Long" (used in the film *American Graffiti*), "Little Honda," and the first of Brian's wistful ballads, "We'll Run Away," "Wendy," and "Don't Back Down." Bonus tracks include the single version of the goofy "Be True to Your School," featuring full marching band and cheers by The Honeys (the sister act featuring Brian's then-wife Marilyn Rovell), and alternates of "Little Honda" and "Don't Back Down."

CAPITOL 93694 (CL)

The Beach Boys Today!/ Summer Days and Summer Nights

Two classic LPs on one CD, remastered from original mono recordings of 1964–1965. By this time, lead Beach Boy Brian Wilson was really hitting his stride as writer, arranger, and producer. *Today!* has the edge as the better of the two albums, with cuts like the almost symphonic "Kiss Me Baby," the anthemic cover of Bobby Freeman's "Do You Wanna Dance?," the introspective vulnerability of "When I Grow Up," the kinda weird "Don't Hurt My Little Sister," plus the interesting early version of "Help Me Ronda," later redone more effectively as a single (with different spelling). That version is also included here on *Summer Days*, as well as the sublime "California Girls." Of the five bonus tracks we get the haunting "Little Girl I Once Knew," released as a single but not included on LP at the time, alternate takes of "Dance, Dance, Dance," "I'm So Young," and "Let Him Run Wild," and a studio version of The Four Freshmen's "Graduation Day."

CAPITOL 93695 (CL)

Beach Boys Concert/Live in London

Though the Beach Boys freely used a myriad of studio musicians on their recording sessions, the two albums included in their entirety on this disc offer proof they were a fine live band. *In Concert* was recorded in late '64 in Sacramento just months before Brian Wilson quit touring with the band. The majority of the cuts are covers of hits by other groups: "Monster Mash," "Little Old Lady from Pasadena," "Let's Go Trippin'," "Papa Oom Mow Mow," in addition to originals like "I Get Around," "In My Room," and "Little Deuce Coupe." Audience hysteria is evident throughout. *Live in London*, culled from two different late '68 concerts, shows the much-improved band on a program of mostly hits like "Good Vibrations" and "California Girls," but also obscurities like "Wake the World" and the a cappella "Their Hearts Were Full of Spring." Of course, most of these can't measure up to the studio classics, but as a live album it's just fine. As a bonus we get "Don't Worry Baby" from the '64 show, and a "Heroes and Villains" from '67 in Honolulu.

CAPITOL 91008 (CL)

The Beach Boys' Christmas Album

Sixteen songs for all you surfin' Santas—"Merry Christmas, Baby," "Frosty the Snowman," "We Three Kings," "Santa Claus Is Comin' to Town," and "White Christmas"—plus masters and alternate takes of "Little Saint Nick" and "Auld Lang Syne." The Brian Wilson penned songs are the best, featuring his usual inventive arrangements, while the standards often feature the lamest of studio musicians.

❂ CAPITOL 48241 (CL)

Pet Sounds

The most celebrated album produced by Brian Wilson, this ranks with the all-time classics of rock. Lyricist Tony Asher was one of Brian's most sympathetic partners, and together they created some of his most sophisticated songs. Almost every track is memorable, including the beautiful ballads "God Only Knows" and "Caroline No" (released as a solo single by Brian Wilson, the only recording released under his own name at the time), the up-tempo but wistful "Wouldn't It Be Nice," and the complex arrangement of the folk classic "Sloop John B." The CD includes three bonus tracks, the most interesting of which is the instrumental "Trombone Dixie" reflecting Wilson's far-ranging musical tastes. "Unreleased Backgrounds" is just that, a fragment of background vocals, and "Hang On to Your Ego" is the slightly weird original version of the song reworked as "I Know There's an Answer" on the LP.

CAPITOL 93696 (CL)

Smiley Smile/Wild Honey

After spending months in the studio working on the ill-fated *Smile* project, Brian Wilson (a) destroyed the tapes when he feared his fire symphony had touched off a series of mysterious LA fires; (b) withdrew from the project because of undue pressure to create a more commercial LP; (c) retreated into a psychotic, drug-induced haze that would not end until nearly a decade later; or (d) all of the above. Out of the ashes of *Smile* came *Smiley Smile*, a wacky, uneven collection featuring the Boys's biggest hit, "Good Vibrations," an ode to vegetarian living ("Vegetables"), and the Van Dyke Parks/Wilson opus, "Heroes and Villains." And who can forget the "Woody Woodpecker Suite"?? With Brian beginning his long-days-journey-into-night, the other Boys scrambled to create *Wild Honey*, a much simpler production with an uneven collection of songs, including Carl's minor blue-eyed soul hit, "Darlin'."

CAPITOL 93697 (CL)

Friends/20/20

Lesser efforts from the Boys. *Friends* was a fairly simple production, as the Boys tried to return to their roots. *20/20* featured the minor nostalgia hit penned by Mike Love, "Do It Again," and two tracks salvaged from the *Smile* sessions, "Cabinessence" and "Our Prayer."

CAPITOL 93698 (CL)
Party/Stack O' Tracks
The *Party* record was a quickie effort made by the Boys and their girlfriends to fill the gap between *Summer Days* and *Pet Sounds*. It's a truly fun LP, drawing on the Beach Boys' catalog, Beatles's songs, and surf classics. "Barbara Ann" even featured Dean Torrance of Jan and Dean who wandered in from a recording session down the hall, and scored as a fluke Number 1 hit! *Stack O' Tracks* is Capitol's most shameless exploitation of the Beach Boys's catalog; it consists of backing tracks from various LPs. The original recording came with a songbook so you could join in on the fun! Bonus tracks are extra backing tracks never before issued without vocals (wow!).

CAPITOL 46467 (CL)
Endless Summer

CAPITOL 46324 (CL)
Made in the U.S.A.

CAPITOL 46618 (CL)
Spirit of America
Three greatest-hits anthologies with selections from the Boys's Capitol years (1962–1969).

CAPITOL 92639 (CL)
Still Cruisin'
A few new tracks from 1989, including the minor hit "Still Cruisin'" and Brian Wilson's truly strange "In My Car," along with previously issued material from the '60s.

DCC COMPACT CLASSICS 054 (L)
Lost and Found (1961–1962)
At last, a CD for the most rabid Beach Boys fan. Gathered on one disc are twenty-one takes of eight different tunes, making up The Boys's earliest sessions, complete with demos, numerous outtakes, and studio chatter. As we hear on the three tedious versions of "Surfin'," the Princes of California Corn had yet to develop a head of steam under their boards, so to speak. Includes three not-festive-enough takes of "Luau" and one of the abominable "Barbie," named after the then-new doll and rushed out under the name of Kenny and The Cadets to fill a contractual obligation.

DEAN BEARD
Beard is best-known for "Rakin' and Scrapin'" recorded at Sun studios in 1956. He recorded sporadically for a number of labels over the next few years.

REVIVAL 3008 (R)
Rakin' and Scrapin'
Eighteen tunes originally released on a variety of labels, including a couple of takes of the great "Party Party," three takes of his big hit "Rakin' and Scrapin," plus a rockin' "Villa Acuna." Holding on to a Memory/Stand by Me/Long Time Gone/When You're Gone/Sing, Sing, Sing, Sing/Keeper of the Key.

THE BEATLES
Legendary leaders of the British invasion. Originally, their LPs were issued in the US by Capitol (although their first LP was passed on by that label, and came out on Vee Jay), who often eliminated tracks from the British releases. Starting in 1988, the original British LPs were reissued in this country by Capitol on LP, cassette, and CD. EP tracks and other single tracks not on the original British LPs were released under the *Past Masters* name. We're listing those releases in chronological order. Difficulties among the surviving Beatles and EMI records has kept BBC material, unissued alternates, live tapes, and other material out of circulation, except on bootleg issues.

CAPITOL 46435 (RCL)
Please Please Me
Legendary first LP recorded in a single session following the success of their second single, the title cut. Originally issued in the US on Vee Jay as *Introducing the Beatles*. Twist and Shout/Anna/A Taste of Honey/Love Me Do/I Saw Her Standing There.

CAPITOL 46436 (RCL)
With the Beatles
Second Beatles's LP, issued stateside in abbreviated form as *Meet the Beatles* on Capitol. I Want to Hold Your Hand/It Won't Be Long/All My Loving/Till There Was You/Money.

CAPITOL 46437 (RCL)
A Hard Day's Night
Soundtrack to the classic first film by the Fab ones. Originally issued in the US on United Artists records, including soundtrack music that is not on this version. The first Beatles LP made up entirely of Lennon/McCartney numbers. Boys/Can't Buy Me Love/I Should Have Known Better/If I Fell/And I Love Her/I'll Cry Instead.

CAPITOL 46438 (RCL)

Beatles for Sale

Beatles's fourth LP in Britain was originally issued in different form as *Beatles '65* by Capitol. Features the first recording of feedback, according to Mr. Lennon, on the opening of "I Feel Fine." No Reply/I'm a Loser/Baby's in Black/Honey Don't.

CAPITOL 46439 (RCL)

Help!

UK version of film soundtrack. Original US release had soundtrack music by George Martin that is not included here. I've Just Seen a Face/Yesterday/You've Got to Hide Your Love Away.

CAPITOL 46440 (RCL)

Rubber Soul

Folkesque LP showing influence of Dylan, particularly on Lennon's "Norwegian Wood," which also includes the first appearance of George Harrison's sitar on record. Some tracks omitted on original US release appeared on US-only LP, *Yesterday and Today.* Michelle/Drive My Car/In My Life/Girl.

CAPITOL 46441 (RCL)

Revolver

Heavily psychedlic-influenced LP, tracks as on original British release (some not included on the US version). Dr. Robert/Taxman/Yellow Submarine/Tomorrow Never Knows/Eleanor Rigby.

✪ CAPITOL 2653 (RC)/46442 (L)

Sergeant Pepper's Lonely Hearts Club Band

Original British and US releases of this LP were identical for the first time. Landmark conceptual LP that launched an entire era of psychedelic music, as well as making the album an accepted artform, not just a hodgepodge release of earlier singles and B-sides. A Little Help from My Friends/Fixing a Hole/A Day in the Life/She's Leaving Home.

CAPITOL 101 (RC)/46443 (L)

The Beatles

The so-called "white album" is more a collection of solo spots by the various Beatles backed up by the other band members. Noteworthy tracks include The Beach Boys's parody "Back in the USSR," the folkie takeoff "Rocky Raccoon," John Lennon's first collaboration with Yoko Ono on the tape montage "Revolution Number 9," the original version of "Revolution" (slower than the single version), Eric Clapton's guest spot on Harrison's "While My Guitar Gently Weeps," and Ringo's countryesque "Don't Pass Me By."

CAPITOL 153 (RC)/46445 (L)

Yellow Submarine

Soundtrack to animated feature. Includes George Martin's atmospheric soundtrack music. Highlight is Lennon's "Hey Bulldog."

CAPITOL 383 (RC)/46446 (L)

Abbey Road

Last completed Beatles's LP, a return to simpler recording techniques. Includes McCartney's second-side megamedley, plus Harrison's two biggest hits, "Something" and "Here Comes the Sun." Come Together/Maxwell's Silver Hammer/Because/She Came In through the Bathroom Window.

CAPITOL 11922 (RC)/46447 (L)

Let It Be

After recording hundreds of hours of tape while making a documentary film, The Beatles were unable to complete what was to become their final LP (although it was recorded before *Abbey Road*). Producer George Martin was dumped in favor of legendary recluse and "wall-of-sound" man Phil Spector, who added heavy-handed strings and choruses to these cuts. Two of Us/Across the Universe/For You Blue/The Long and Winding Road.

CAPITOL 91135 (RC)/90043-44 (L)

Past Masters

The 33 tracks released by The Beatles that were not originally included on British LPs (although many came out on LPs released in this country, including *Beatles V, Yesterday and Today, Hey Jude,* and *Magical Mystery Tour,* among other places). She Loves You/I Feel Fine/I Want to Hold Your Hand/Hey Jude/Lady Madonna/Paperback Writer.

CAPITOL 91302 (RCL)

Boxed Set

All of the British LPs plus the two *Past Masters* collections in a boxed set.

CAPITOL 11638 (RC)

Live at The Hollywood Bowl

Concerts recorded in 1964–1965 but not released at the time.

CAPITOL 12060 (RC)

Rarities

Hodgepodge collection of oddities not previously issued, disappointing considering what's languishing in the vaults.

CAPITOL 15901 (L)

Singles Collection

Utterly shameless 22-CD set that could easily have been fit on a couple of CDs. Each CD contains just the A and B-sides of each of the original Beatles singles. Next, Capitol plans to release just the first line of each

Beatles song, each on its own gold-plated CD suitable for framing . . .

POLYDOR 823701 (L)
Early Tapes of The Beatles
Recordings made in Germany backing singer Tony Sheridan in 1962 when The Beatles were performing at The Star Club, including their first single on their own (released as by The Beat Brothers) on the immortal "My Bonnie."

SONY MUSIC SPECIAL PROJECT 48544 (CL)
Live at the Star Club, 1962, Vol. 1

SONY MUSIC SPECIAL PROJECT 48604 (CL)
Live at the Star Club, 1962, Vol. 2
Oft-reissued tapes of The Beatles with original drummer Pete Best performing at Berlin's famous Star Club. Intersting glimpse of the group at the dawn of their career.

THE BEAU BRUMMELS
One of the first folk-rock groups, the San Francisco-based Beau Brummels began recording in the mid-'60s for Autumn, and then switched to a more countryish format on Warner Brothers.

EDSEL 151 (R)
Bradley's Barn
Reissue of Warner Bros. 1760 from 1968. The original band was down to just two members, Sal Valentino (vcl) and Ron Elliot (gtr). They went to Nashville to record a beautiful LP, featuring the younger Nashville sessionmen, including Jerry Reed, Norbert Putnam, Wayne Moss, David Briggs, and Kenny Buttrey. Recorded at Owen Bradley's Bradley's Barn studio, each song features four acoustic guitars. Deep Water/Cherokee Girl/I'm a Sleeper/Long Walking Down to Misery.

RHINO 70171 (C)/RHINO 75779 (L)
The Beau Brummels
Lots of hard-to-find stuff here, 13 tracks on cassette and 17 on CD. It has their great 1965 pop classics, produced by Sly Stone, including "Laugh Laugh," "Just a Little," and "You Tell Me Why." Also includes their more rare folk and country-rock sides, such as "One Too Many Mornings," "Here We Are Again," and "Deep Water."

THE BEAU-MARKS
The Beau-Marks were a popular four-piece group out of Montreal, Canada in the early '60s best known for their hit "Clap Your Hands."

QUALITY 1683 (R)
One By One! Rock and Roll Has Got a Beat
Fifteen of their ballads and rockers. Singer and piano player Joey Frechette has a pleasant pop voice but doesn't add too much excitement to the up-tempo numbers. No worry though, because lead guitarist Ray Hutchinson and the crew carry the load on rockers like "Little Miss Twist," "Rock and Roll Has Got a Beat," "Be-Bop-a-Lula," and "What Did I Say?" They do a cool rockin' version of fellow Canadian Hank Snow's "I'm Movin' On," as well as a muddy sounding reprise of "Clap Your Hands."

WILLIAM BELL
Vastly underrated Southern soulster from Memphis who brought a strong country feel to soul. He was a protege of Otis Redding, and recorded for Stax/Atlantic. His first recording for Stax, "You Don't Miss Your Water" (1961), while not a hit, was an important and much-covered song. After a stint in the military, he returned to recording in 1966 when he had a number of hits. He continues to be popular to this day.

ATLANTIC 82252 (CL)
The Soul of a Bell
Reissue of the 1967 Stax classic. Includes his first two self-penned hits, which came five years apart—"You Don't Miss Your Water" (from 1961!) and "Everybody Loves a Winner"—plus his wonderful version of "Do Right Woman-Do Right Man." Then You Can Tell Me Goodbye/You're Such a Sweet Thang/It's Happening All Over/Nothing Takes the Place of You.

STAX 8541 (RC)
The Best of William Bell
The best of Bell's post-Atlantic Stax hits, recorded in 1968–1975. Many tunes were cowritten by Booker T, who produced these sides along with Al Bell. Includes a funky remake of the Jones-Bell classic "Born Under a Bad Sign," and his two hits with Judy Clay ("Private Number" and "My Baby Specializes"). 'Til My Back Ain't Got No Bone /I'll Be Home/I Forgot to Be Your Lover.

STAX 8566 (CL)
A Little Something Extra
The most amazing thing about this collection is that the 20 songs were all previously unissued before coming out recently on British Stax. After hearing "Let's Do Something Together," "You're Never Too Old," and "She Won't Be Like You," you'll wonder how the folks at Soulville USA determined which songs to issue. These tracks were laid down between

1961–1967, and Otis Redding's influence is strong, but the material here represents a variety of styles. Most were presumably demos, although you'd never know it from the vocals, although the instrumental parts are a little sparse and ragged. When you hear Bell's "Will You Love Me Tomorrow?" you'll probably throw out your Shirelles's record. Recommended.

STAX (UK) 970 (L)

Bound to Happen/Wow

Twenty-two tracks, originally issued on Stax 2014 from 1974 and 2037 from 1975, including the hits "I Forgot to Be Your Lover" and "My Whole World Is Falling Down." Everyday People/By the Time I Get to Phoenix/Born under a Bad Sign/I Can't Make It/ I'll Be Home.

WILBE 3007 (R)

On a Roll

Recent recordings.

THE BELMONTS

When Dion DiMucci left the Belmonts in 1960, the group continued to record with Carlo Mastangelo taking the vocal leads in 1961–1962, replaced by Frank Lyndon through the early '70s. They moved to Sabrina Records in 1961 (later mysteriously renamed Sabina Records), and United Artists in 1964. After a brief reunion with Dion and Carlo in 1966, the group soldiered on with Lyndon on Dot Records. In 1972, they had a hit with the LP *Cigars, A Cappella, Candy*, leading to another reunion with Dion, the famous Carnegie Hall concert issued on Warner Bros. Records. A few years later, Warren Gradus had taken over lead vocals, and the group was recording for Strawberry Records. 1981 brought the hit single "Let's Put the Fun Back in Rock 'n' Roll" with Freddie Cannon (who had had solo hits in the early '60s with "Palisades Park" and "Tallahassee Lassie") now taking the lead. (See separate Dion/Dion and The Belmonts listing for other reissues of their work.)

CRYSTAL BALL 102 (R)

Just for You

Fourteen post-Dion sides from the early '60s, recorded for the Sabrina/Sabina labels. Tell Me Why/Come Back Little Angel/Don't Get Around Much Anymore.

ELEKTRA 60989 (L)

Cigars, A Cappella, Candy

Reissue of Buddah 5123 from 1972. The Belmonts's Frank Lyndon (lead), Fred Milano (2nd tenor), and Angelo D'Aleo (1st tenor) perform nine flawless a-cappella numbers, including The Channels's hit "That's My Desire," a new and improved "wow-what's-this" version (without Dion) of the standard "Where or When," a tasty cover of Robert and Johnny's "We Belong Together," plus a finger-snapping reading of "Street Corner Symphony" (a melding of various '50s hit tunes). Recorded and remixed with great skill by Gary Chester and Eddie Smith, it includes lyrics to all songs and a detailed group history annotated by Greil Marcus. Short, but sweet.

JESSE BELVIN

Mellow R&B balladeer who recorded for Specialty, Modern, and RCA, best known for "Goodnight My Love" and for writing "Earth Angel." He died in a car crash in February 1960. His pre-RCA recordings are the best, with the Earth Angel label reissue holding the edge in terms of production quality and packaging.

ACE 336 (L)

Goodnight My Love

The perfect compliment to the Specialty and Earth Angel reissues of Belvin's pre-RCA material. Ace has done its usual high-quality job, offering all 26 cuts that were made for the Bihari brothers's Modern Records in 1956–1957. "Goodnight My Love" is here in two versions. The three previously unreleased cuts include a version of his earlier Cash Records release "Beware," plus two other worthy ballads. Not to be missed.

EARTH ANGEL 900 (R)

Hang Your Tears Out to Dry

Collects Belvin's 1951–1957 material, most made for tiny LA labels, with loose harmonies and plenty of smoochy sax. A beautiful package, including a gatefold cover loaded with liner notes, photos, interviews, and even a reproduction of the news article on Belvin's death. Includes "Dream Girl," Jesse's first solo single recorded in 1951 for Dolphin, "Only a Fool" done in 1952 for Money, a few of his 1952–1953 Specialty sides, "Dear Heart" and "Betty My Darling" for Hollywood with backup by one of my fave LA groups, The Feathers featuring Johnny Otis on vibes, plus lots more done for Modern, Cash, and Aladdin. Highest recommendations.

SPECIALTY 7003 (RCL)
Legends of Specialty:
Jesse Belvin, The Blues Ballad

Early-to-mid-'50s Specialty sides. Belvin is supported by Bobby Relf and The Laurels on the seductively tender "Gone," the bouncy "Love, Love of My Life," the hypnotically beautiful "Where's My Gal," and the moody classic "One Litle Blessing." Also features four duets with Marvin Phillips from 1953, including an alternate of "Dream." There's a duet with Eugene Church and a stunning demo of "Love of My Life" accompanied by the prettiest piano figures I've heard in a while. The CD has ten additional cuts, including five previously unissued takes and three songs recorded for Cash and Recorded In Hollywood in 1952. Superlative collection with informed notes by Steve Propes.

BOYD BENNETT and THE ROCKETS

Early Tennessee rocker who recorded with his band The Rockets for King in the mid-'50s where he had his only two hits "Seventeen" and "My Boy Flat Top."

CHARLY 282 (L)
Tennessee Rock and Roll

Twenty-four honkin' and stompin' King recordings from this underrated group. Ron Ayres on guitar and Bobby Jones on tenor sax were uniformly fantastic, and Boyd, with occasional help from Big Moe, was a pretty good singer with a good ear for rockin' R&B songs to cover. They stick with the same groove on too many tunes but there's hardly a clinker here. Seventeen/Mumbles Blues/Oo-Oo-Oo/The Most/The Groovy Age/My Boy Flat Top/Boogie at Midnight.

BRIAN BENNETT

Former drummer for the popular English instrumental group, The Shadows.

SEE FOR MILES 205 (L)
Change of Direction with The Best of The Illustrated London Noise

Eighteen tracks reissuing Bennett's first solo LP from 1967 and half of his second from 1969, both featuring a mixture of instrumental versions of rock hits and Bennett's jazz-flavored originals. *Change of Direction* (Columbia UK 6144) featured once-and-future Shads Alan Hawkshaw (org, pno) and John Rostill (b), along with sessioneers Big Jim Sullivan and Alan Skidmore, on the title tune, "98.6," "Sunshine Superman," and nine others. *The Illustrated London Noise* (Studio Two 268) is represented here by six tracks, including "Chameleon," "Love and Occasional Rain" (both on Hank Marvin's first LP on See For Miles 210), and "Ticket to Ride."

BROOK BENTON

Smooth R&B balladeer who began as a songwriter (he cowrote "A Lover's Question" for Clyde McPhatter) and had lots of hits on his own. His best material was recorded for Mercury from 1959–1965, including some classic duets with Dinah Washington. He still records and has occasional hits, his last being 1974's "Rainy Night in Georgia." Rhino 71497 gives the best overview of his career.

MERCURY 830 772 (L)
Best of Brook Benton

Fourteen smooth soul stylings from the slick side of the '60s. Kiddio/Endlessly/Frankie and Johnny/Fools Rush In.

RCA 9597 (L)
This Is Brook Benton

This generous 20-track budget CD signals a new era for Bentonphiles. Brook's RCA output was heavily ballad-oriented, with tunes like "Love Is a Many-Splendored Thing," "Call Me Irresponsible," "Moon River," and "I Only Have Eyes for You."

RHINO 71497 (C)
The Brook Benton Anthology

Two-cassette set, featuring recordings from 1959–1970, 19 from Mercury and four from Cotillion. All your favorites are here, including his two hits with Dinah Washington: "Baby (You've Got What It Takes)" and "A Rockin' Good Way." It's Just a Matter of Time/Hurtin' Inside/Kiddio/Hit Record/Endlessly/Rainy Night in Georgia.

WALT BENTON

BISON BOP 2013 (R)
Walt Benton and The Diplomats

Mid-to-late '50s recordings by teen band, about half previously unreleased.

ROD BERNARD

Excellent Southern Louisiana swamp-popster who recorded the classic "This Should Go On Forever" with his band, The Twisters.

JIN 4007 (R)
Rod Bernard

Some of his best sides. This Should Go On Forever/Colinda/Fais Do-Do/I Might as Well/Diggy Liggy Lo.

JIN 9008 (R)
Country Lovin'
Teach Me to Forget/Don't You Think I've Had Enough/On Bended Knee/Mathilda/Just One More Chance.

CHUCK BERRY

By now, everybody in the world knows the importance of this former St. Louis hairdresser. He invented a whole new vocabulary for the guitar, making it THE rock and roll instrument, plus he wrote some of the best, wittiest, and most original lyrics in rock and roll.

Berry's best material was recorded for Chess between 1955 ("Maybelline") and 1964 ("Promised Land"), and again in the '70s ("My Ding-a-Ling"). In between, he signed to Mercury and re-recorded his hits over and over again. For a while, these inferior remakes, released on "greatest hits packages," flooded the market, but now they have virtually disappeared with just the genuine Chess material remaining. Many of his Chess LPs have been reissued in their original forms, plus there are various good anthologies.

CHESS 9171 (CL)
New Juke Box Hits
Reissue of Chess 1456 from 1960, a great collection emphasizing the blues. 13 Question Method/I'm Talkin' 'Bout You/Don't You Lie to Me/Little Marie/Sweet Sixteen/Stop and Listen.

CHESS 9256 (RC)/CHESS 31260 (L)
Is on Top
Reissue of Chuck's third LP, originally Chess 1435 from 1959. Forget *Sergeant Pepper's*, this is the greatest rock album of all time! Maybelline/Almost Grown/Little Queenie/Johnny B. Goode/Roll Over Beethoven/Around and Around.

CHESS 9259 (CL)
Rockin' at the Hops
Reissue of Chuck's fourth LP, originally Chess 1448 from 1960. Chuck gets into some cool blues standards on this one, including "Worried Life Blues," "Driftin' Blues," and "Confessin' the Blues," along with the usual slew of solid hits. Bye Bye Johnny/Too Pooped to Pop/Let It Rock/I Got to Find My Baby/Down the Road Apiece.

CHESS 9295 (RCL)
The London Sessions
Chuck didn't get the big British stars for his LP (as did Howlin' Wolf) but it turned out pretty good anyway. Side 1 is a studio session from 1972 backed by Derek Griffith (gtr) and Ian McLagan (pno) and Kenny Jones (drm) from The Faces (Jones later joined The Who). They run through five lesser-known tunes including a nice instrumental "London Berry Blues" and a bluesy cover of Little Walter's "Mean Old World." Side 2 is part of a live show from 1972 where Berry and the group do three long versions of "Reelin' and Rockin'," "My Ding-a-Ling," and "Johnny B. Goode."

CHESS 9318 (RCL)
Missing Berries: Rarities Vol. 3
Ten rare sides from the vaults (12 on CD), seven previously unreleased in the US, one single B-side, one cut from the "live" *Chuck Berry Onstage* LP, and one unreleased track, an early demo of the instrumental "Rockin' at the Philharmonic." Not particularly essential material here, but fun for those who enjoy hearing Chuck's classic backing tracks with new sets of lyrics and cover tunes. To be fair, we should note the presence of a couple of collectible vocal-group sides: "Do You Love Me" (possibly with The Moonglows) and "Let Me Sleep Woman" featuring The Ecuadors with C. B. as sideman.

CHESS 80001 (RCL)
The Chess Box
A whole lotta Chuck; this fantastic six-LP set (also available as three double-length cassettes and CDs) is the ultimate Berry collection, covering Chuck's entire Chess career from 1955–1973. Everything you'd want is here, in chronological order: the major hits "Johnny B. Goode," "Maybelline," "Roll Over Beethoven," "Rock and Roll Music," "School Days," and "Almost Grown"; the minor hits "JoJo Gunne," "Tulane," "I'm Talkin' 'Bout You," "You Two," and "Jaguar and Thunderbird"; the great LP cuts "13 Question Method," "Bio," and "Confessin' the Blues"; and even the full ten-and-a-half minute "Chuck's Beat" with Bo Diddley on second guitar. There are a mess of tunes making their first US LP appearance, including "I've Changed," "Sad Day, Long Night," and "Ramona Say Yes," and some never before released, like "Crazy Arms," "I'm Just a Lucky So and So," "Crying Steel," and a slow version of "Time Was." Includes a beautiful 32-page slick-paper booklet with liner notes, a new interview with Chuck, albumography, full discographical info on each tune, and loads of pictures. Highest recommendations.

⊙ CHESS 92500 (RCL)
The Great 28

The very best collection of his hits; all meat and no filler. Every important cut from "Maybelline" through "I Wanna Be Your Driver" arranged in chronological sequence and remastered from original tapes in crystal-clear mono. Roll Over Beethoven/You Can't Catch Me/Brown-eyed Handsome Man/School Days/Reelin' and Rockin'/Johnny B. Goode/Carol/Memphis/Little Queenie/Back in the USA/Bye Bye Johnny/Come On/No Particular Place to Go.

CHESS 92521 (CL)
Rock and Roll Rarities

Twenty-tune set. Most of the unreleased versions aren't even in the Chess discography, including alternates of "Johnny B. Goode," "Rock and Roll Music," "Little Queenie," "Beautiful Delilah," and "Come On," plus stereo remixes of such greats as "Promised Land," "No Particular Place to Go," "Nadine," and "You Never Can Tell," and a few tunes such as "Oh Yeah," "Betty Jean," and "Run Rudolph Run" that only appeared on the long out-of-print *Golden Decade, Vols. 2 and 3*. No liner notes, but personnel listings, great photos of Chuck, and great sound. High recommendations!

CHESS (FRANCE) 600085 (L)
Two Dozen Berries

Twenty-four Chess classics; a full 63 minutes of music. Though the cover and title suggest this contains the *One Dozen Berries* LP, it is in fact, a total cross-section mixing the hits—"Nadine," "Brown-eyed Handsome Man," "School Days," "Rock and Roll Music"—with choice LP tracks including "Downbound Train," "No Money Down," "Berry Pickin'," "I'm Talkin' Bout You," and "13 Question Method." Sound quality could be better.

CHESS (FRANCE) 660501 (L)
Chuck Berry Story 1955–1958

Two-CD set offering 36 tracks culled from Chuck's early Chess sessions. This is not a particularly well-organized or great-sounding set, and provides only minimal notes, but you do get rarities, alternate takes, and big hits in an inexpensive package. Maybelline/Thirty Days/You Can't Catch Me/Too Much Monkey Business/Roll Over Beethoven/School Days/Rock and Roll Music.

MCA 6217 (CL)
Hail! Hail! Rock and Roll

Soundtrack to the movie produced by Keith Richards. Mostly just a run-through of the same old Chuck tunes, but this time with a crack backup band including Keith Richards, NRBQ bassist Joey Stampinato, and Chuck's original pianist Johnnie Jones. Plenty of guest stars appear with mixed results. Robert Cray does a masterful "Brown-eyed Handsome Man" and

Etta James romps on "Rock and Roll Music." Linda Ronstadt is listenable on "Back in the USA," Eric Clapton sings "Wee Wee Hours" proving that as a singer, he's a great guitarist, and Julian Lennon proves why his LPs are all in the cutout bin in an embarrassing "Johnnie B. Goode." The LP has a version of "Around and Around" not in the movie and perhaps the best thing, Chuck crooning the standard "I'm Through with Love," done during rehearsals.

CHUCK BERRY/BO DIDDLEY

CHESS 9170 (L)
Two Great Guitars

Reissue of an all-instrumental LP originally issued as Checker 2991 in 1964. Includes a short solo number by each (Chuck, "Liverpool Drive"; Bo, "When the Saints Go Marching In"), plus two extended jams featuring Bo's band as backing group ("Bo's Beat" and "Chuck's Beat")

DAVE BERRY

British pop rocker who changed his surname from Grundy to Berry in honor of his hero Chuck. He had a number of moderate hits in England in the mid-'60s and a Number 1 hit in Holland with "This Strange Effect" written by Ray Davies of The Kinks. He was also famous for his eccentric stage act. He continues to perform on the revival circuit.

DERAM (UK) 820 633 (L)
Berry's Best

Hits and misses. The Crying Game/Little Queenie/Don't Gimme No Lip Child/Baby It's You/Little Things/Not Fade Away/Mama/He's with You.

SEE FOR MILES 122 (R)
This Strange Effect

Twenty Decca ballads and rockers from 1964–1966, most featuring Jimmy Page on guitar. Don't Give Me No Lip/Diddley Daddy/Baby It's You/The Crying Game.

MIKE BERRY

Back in pre-Beatles England, Mike Berry signed up with producer Joe Meek to "carry on where Buddy Holly had left off." He's a fine singer in the Holly style, never stooping to the hiccupping histrionics of other slavish imitators. There's lots of intrusive strings and senseless girly choruses, but all in all one could believe Buddy might be doing tunes like this in early '60s New York.

ROLLER COASTER 2016 (R)
Sounds of the Sixties
Fifteen tunes. Tribute to Buddy Holly/My Baby Doll/Set Me Free/Will You Still Love Me Tomorrow/Little Boy Blue.

RICHARD BERRY

Deep-voiced R&B singer best known for writing "Louie Louie" and singing lead on The Robins's classic "Riot in Cell Block #9." Along with Bobby Day and Jesse Belvin, he formed the elite core of southern California's contribution to the then-developing R&B sound. He recorded with a variety of groups, most notably The Dreamers and The Pharaohs on Flair (1953–1955), RPM (1955–1956), and Flip (1957–1959). The Ace and Earth Angel LPs both offer excellent selections with no duplication.

ACE 355 (L)
Get Out of the Car
Twenty vintage cuts from the Flair and RPM labels. An easy-to-listen-to mix of jump tunes and ballads, some done as a part of a group, all presented in Ace's usual first-rate manner. Good notes, good sound, good music. The Big Break/I'm Still in Love with You/Jelly Roll/Angel of My Life/Yama Yama Pretty Mama.

⚙ EARTH ANGEL 901 (R)
Louie Louie
The first LP to collect Berry's non-Flair '50s sides, highlighted, of course, by the title milestone, recorded with The Pharaohs for Flip in '55. Eleven of the 19 tracks are with The Pharaohs, who, after leaving Berry, became The Satellites, recording for Class. Berry first went into a studio in 1953 with an unnamed quintet featuring Cornelius Gunter and Young Jessie. When this group became The Flairs on Modern, this early tune, "Tell Me You Love Me," was released on the Cash label as by "The Hollywood Blue Jays." While with The Flairs, Berry recorded some solo tunes for Modern, including "What You Do to Me" backed by The Crowns (with Gunther) and "Don't Cha Go" backed by The Cadets. "Baby Please Come Home," recorded for Empire under the nom-de-disc of "Ricky," cowritten by and featuring Jesse Belvin, and three tunes, including "The Mess Around," backed by the girl group The Lockettes, are also included.

THE BIG BOPPER

Texas-born DJ, singer, and songwriter, Jiles P. ("Jape") Richardson, aka The Big Bopper, had country-western roots like Buddy Holly, but was bitten by the rockabilly bug in the mid-'50s. He was famous for his droll songs and equally light-hearted delivery that made him a favorite on the package-show circuit. His big hit was the self-penned "Chantilly Lace." He was also a fine songwriter; his "White Lightnin'" was a big country hit for George Jones and "Running Bear" a Number 1 pop hit for Johnny Preston. He died in the same plane crash that took the life of Holly and rocker Richie Valens.

RHINO 71064 (CL)
Hellooo Baby: The Best of
The Big Bopper (1954–1959)
I was pleasantly surprised to hear that Richardson had recorded some fine R&B for Mercury during the late '50s, including the doo-wop sounding "Walking through My Dreams," the pretty country ballad "Beggar to a King" (accompanied by The Japetts) from 1957, the rocking "Crazy Blues," and the amazing previously unreleased "Bopper's Boogie Woogie" recorded during a practice session at Jay Miller's studio in 1954. Includes his hits "Chantilly Lace" and "White Lightnin'." Good sound quality and informed notes by Jim Pewter. CD contains five bonus tracks: "Old Maid," "Strange Kisses," "The Clock," "Teenage Moon," and, best of all, "Purple People Eater Meets the Witch Doctor."

BILLY and THE ESSENTIALS

White Philadelphia quartet led by "Little" Billy whose musical repertoire spans the entire '60s. Billy's first group, the unrecorded Crystals, later became The Dovells of "Bristol Stomp" fame. The Essentials recorded for Cameo, Jamie, Landa, Mercury, and Smash. The bulk of their material is either insipid or commercially "pop" in nature. They were a group who might have made memorable records had they not suffered from the whims of overzealous commercial record producers.

CRYSTAL BALL 127 (R)
Lonely Weekends

BILL BLACK'S COMBO

Bill Black first gained notoriety as Elvis's bass player starting with Presley's first Sun recordings. However, eventually he and Scotty Moore left the King because, while Elvis was making millions, they were still on their $125-a-week salary. Black returned to Memphis where he put together a funky band, which became Hi Record's alternative to Booker T and The MGs. The band featured Black (switching over to electric bass), rockabilly pianist Carl McAvoy, Reggie Young (gtr), Martin Wills (ten sax; not Ace Cannon as is sometimes stated), and Jerry Arnold (drm). Their instrumentals "Smokie" and "Smokie, Pt. 2" from 1959 topped the US and UK pop charts and the US R&B charts. This set the stage for numerous instrumental hits with a trademark chunky rhythm. In 1961, Bob Tucker replaced Young on guitar, and Black gave him the leadership of the band. When Black died in 1965, Tucker continued the band, replacing the piano with pedal steel in the mid-'70s. They continue to perform country instrumentals to today. Hi 410 is the best introduction to their music.

HI (UK) 112 (L)
Solid and Raunchy/Movin'

This CD pairs Black's third and fourth Hi LPs from 1960 and 1961. With these two dozen tracks, they manage to work their way through a big chunk of the '50s hit parade. There's some piano and organ playing, a little guitar pickin', and a whole lot of "yakety" sax. Don't Be Cruel/Honky Tonk/Tequila/Raunchy/Bo Diddley/Be-Bop-a-Lula/Torquay/Witchcraft.

HI (UK) 115 (L)
Greatest Hits/Play Tunes by Chuck Berry

Twenty-four more sax-led tunes from Black's band. *Greatest Hits* came out in 1963, and was chockful of the hits that the combo had been racking up since 1959: "Smokie, Pt. 2," "Hearts of Stone," "White Silver Sands," and "Josephine." *Bill Black's Combo Play Tunes by Chuck Berry* came out the next year, continuing their basic formula of organ and sax-oriented, rockin' covers of '50s hits. However, this LP also features a whole lot more rockin' guitar than before (played by Reggie Young?), so it holds up a lot

better now than the older stuff. School Days/Sweet Little Sixteen/Little Queenie/Nadine/Thirty Days.

HI (UK) 410 (R)
The Untouchable Sound

Their biggest hits done between 1959 and Black's death in 1965. White Silver Sands/Smokie, Pt. 2/Memphis, Tennessee/ Movin'.

BILL BLACK/WILLIE MITCHELL

HI (UK) 102 (L)
Memphis Rock and Soul Party

A whopping 32 tracks of tough instrumentals from the Hi vaults, 16 from each performer.

BLUE CHEER

Named for a popular brand of LSD, this late '60s power trio was San Francisco's loudest and raunchiest band, the godfathers of all heavy-metal acts who followed. Their repertoire was a mix of classic blues, rock oldies, and their own psychedelized compositions, all played with an eardrum-exploding intensity.

MERCURY 834030 (L)
Good Times Are So Hard to Find

Retrospective of all of their six LPs. After the ear-assaulting power of their first records, The Cheers lapsed into hippie-esque doodling. A little of both is provided on this anthology.

RHINO 70130 (C)
Louder than God:
The Best of Blue Cheer, 1967–1969

Play this cassette loud and bother your friends. Summertime Blues/Out of Focus/Parchment Farm/Babyfinger/Fruit & Icebergs.

THE BLUE JAYS/THE HI TENSIONS

Vocal group led by the smooth-as-silk tenor of Leon Peels, originally known as The Blue Jays (1961–1962), later renamed The Hi Tensions (1964). They had a hit in 1961 with "Lover's Island."

RELIC 5064 (R)/7014 (L)
Lover's Island

Sixteen soul and doo-wop songs at their best. Standouts like the title track, "Tears Are Falling," and the classic "Casual Kiss" from the Milestone and Whirleybird labels are legally reissued here for the first time. "So Long Lovers Island" will take your breath away. Highly recommended.

THE BLUE NOTES

Long-lived group, though it has undergone many personnel changes over the years. Formed by Harold Melvin in Philadelphia in 1954, they recorded for a number of labels before scoring several doo-wop hits in 1959 and 1960 for the Brooke and Value labels ("I Don't Know What It Is" and "My Hero"). They switched from doo-wop to '60s soul and had another hit in 1965 with "Get Out." Teddy Pendegrass joined the group as lead singer and drummer in 1970, and they continued to have hits for the Philadelphia International label. After Pendegrass left to pursue a solo career in the mid-'70s, the group changed their name to Harold Melvin and The Blue Notes; they continue to perform today.

COLLECTABLES 5006 (C)
The Early Years
The group in their doo-wop phase. My Hero/Blue Star/Oh Holy Night/Hey Doc/The Letter/A Good Woman.

THE BLUES PROJECT

NY conglomeration of ex-folkies and session players who played a mixture of blues, rock, jazz, and folk-rock. Members included Danny Kalb and Steve Katz (gtrs), Al Kooper (kybds, gtr, voc), Andy Kulberg (flt, b), Tommy Flanders (voc, hca), and Ray Blumenfeld (drm). They had FM radio hits with "No Time Like the Right Time" and "Flute Thing." Kooper and Katz left to form the first Blood, Sweat and Tears.

RHINO 70165 (CL)
The Best of The Blues Project
Best single overview of their work; CD has four bonus tracks. No Time Like the Right Time/I Can't Keep from Crying/Wake Me Shake Me/Flute Thing/Steve's Song/I Want to Be Your Driver.

VERVE 83346 (CL)
Live at the Cafe Au Go-Go
Reissue of their first LP, Verve Forecast 3000 from 1966. Great live set of blues, rock, and jazz-influenced music.

VERVE 87918 (L)
Projections
Their first studio LP, originally Verve 3008 from 1967.

EDDIE BO (EDWIN BOCAGE)

Edwin Bocage—aka "The Maharajah" (for his loudly colored turbans) and Eddie Bo—is one of the more talented in a long list of New Orleans musicians who missed scoring that elusive big hit. Writer of "I'm Wise" (recorded for Apollo in 1956 and a precursor to Little Richard's "Slippin' and Slidin") and chief producer and writer for Joe Ruffino's Ric label, he came close to hitsville with his ode to Popeye's nautical moves.

ROUNDER 2077 (RCL)
Check Mr. Popeye
Sixties recordings from the Ric label. Eddie performs bluesy ballads (witness the lovely "It Must Be Love" or "I Need Someone"), catchy second-line rompers ("Hey There Baby" or "Tell It Like It Is" [not Aaron Neville's tune]), and just fine tunes ("You Got Your Mojo Working" and "Every Dog Has His Day"), all accompanied by his excellent piano and New Orleans's inexhaustible pool of fine musicians.

TOOTER BOATMAN

Excellent rockabilly singer/guitarist/drummer from Texas. His first band, The Chaparrals, played rock and roll from 1956–1961. He later played drums for the country band Sonny Rister and The Rainbows, and was in one of Willie Nelson's early road bands. He was killed in a hit-and-run accident in 1965.

WHITE LABEL 8879 (R)
The Tooter Boatman Sound
Thirteen tunes from recently discovered tapes made by Boatman in the '50s with Danny Wolfe, who wrote a lot of the songs Boatman and Huelyn Duvall sang. "Life Begins at 4 O'Clock" and "They Won't Let Me In" are two of the best, the latter being a clever tune about an abortive trip to Dick Clark's *American Bandstand*. There's a little bit of country ("Wayward Wind"), R&B ("Stagger Lee"), blues ("Depression Blues"), and even polka ("Beer Rock, Pts. 1 and 2"). The best tune besides the Wolfe tunes is the hot instrumental, "Rock It Up, Yeh."

WHITE LABEL 8895 (R)
For Tooter Boatman Fans Only
The title of this LP should be *For Rock-and-Roll Fans Only*, because that's what Tooter Boatman was all

about. The liner notes by Tooter's drummer Clay Glover are fascinating, the 20 photos are amazing, and the music is as boisterous as a Texas roadhouse at closing time. Susie's House/Big Deal/Thunder and Lightnin'/The Will of Love/Whole Lotta Shakin' Going On.

BOB and LUCILLE

Vancouver husband-and-wife team of Bob and Fern Regan, best-known for "Eeny Meeny Miney Mo" from the King Federal Rockabilly LP. Fern, aka Lucille Starr, sings in a hiccuppy, Janis Martin-type voice. "Eeny" was originally done for the LA label Ditto in the late '50s and later was leased to King.

DITTO 100 (R)
The Canadian Sweethearts
Their original Ditto and King recordings, plus Soma recordings from the '60s. I'm Leaving It Up to You/Rocky Mountain Special/Don't Let the Stars Get in Your Eyes/No Help Wanted/What's the Password/The Flirtin' Kind/Demon Lover.

THE BOBBETTES

The Bobbettes were one-hit, teenaged (11-to-13 years old at the time of their first recording) wonders of the '50s, scoring big on their "tribute" to "Mr. Lee," their junior-high-school English teacher, an energetic, charming little ditty about shooting the teacher. The group, originally called The Harlem Queens, consisted of leads Heather Dixon and Emma Pought with Janice Pought (sop), Helen Gunthers (alto), and Laura Webb (ten). They kept trying for another hit, recording more silly but danceable tunes like "Zoomy" and "Rock and Ree-Ah-Zole." As their voices changed, they moved on to tougher material, like "Come-A Come-A" and even a good cover of Billy Ward's rockin' "Have Mercy Mercy Baby." They were adept at ballads as well, but except for "Untrue Lover," their backup could not match their vocals. Trivia for film buffs: In 1964, The Bobbettes recorded "Love that Bomb" for Stanley Kubrick's *Dr. Strangelove*!

REVIVAL 3011 (R)
Mr. Lee And Other Big Hits
I Cried/I Shot Mr. Lee/Loneliness.

EDDIE BOND

Excellent rockabilly/country rocker from Memphis who was turned down by Sun Records in 1956 (only to finally record for them in 1962), so he went to Mercury and scored with the classic "Rockin' Daddy." Active throughout the years, he enjoyed renewed popularity in Britain in the mid-'80s.

STOMPER TIME I (L)
Rockin' Daddy
Thirty-one tracks drawn from Eddie's own labels including Stomper Time, Diplomat, and Millionaire, mostly featuring hard-core honky tonk. Does not include his classic Sun or Mercury sides. Aside from three or four duds, this is some powerful brew. So Long Darling/When the Jukebox Plays/Someday I'll Sober Up/Can't Win for Losin'/Rockin' Daddy/Monkey and the Baboon/My Bucket's Got a Hole in It/Double Duty Lovin'.

SUNJAY 574 (R)
Early Days
Not necessarily early (it includes recordings from 1958–1975), this excellent set has 20 tunes taken from Eddie's small label recordings. Includes rockabilly and rockin' country 1958–1959 Stompertime sides ("Can't Win for Losin'," "Boo Bap Da Caa Caa"); a 1962 session of mostly unissued tunes including a remake of "Rockin' Daddy"; '60s sessions for Millionaire, Tagg, and Diplomat; 1958 "D" label sides; a 1975 3 Stars side; and unissued demos.

WHITE LABEL 8876 (R)
Rare Early Recordings
Sixteen early rockabilly and country recordings. Tunes like "Rockin' Daddy," "I've Got a Woman," "Flip, Flop Mama," and "Slip, Slip, Slippin' In" rock with a savage grace not found every day. Other tunes like "Backslidin'" and "Double Duty Lovin'" show Eddie's country roots. One of the best.

JOHNNY BOND

A country-western star with roots longer than an oak tree's, stretching back to the '30s, including long stints with Jimmy Wakely and Gene Autrey, and appearances in over 50 Hollywood "horse operas." Bond came to rock and roll naturally in the mid-'50s.

REVIVAL 3010 (R)
A Lotta Rock and Roll
Seventeen-tune collection of Bond's more rockin' material. "Hot Rod Lincoln" is included here along with

"X-15" (hot roddin' in a jet plane!). My Bucket's Got a Hole in It/Wildcat Boogie/Brown's Ferry Blues.

GARY "U.S." BONDS

Exciting Florida singer who made wonderfully noisy party music for Frank Guida's LeGrand label, most of which has been reissued thanks to the label's return in the '80s. A fan from New Jersey named Bruce helped stage his comeback in the early '80s. The Rhino compilation is the best place to start.

LEGRAND 1001 (R)

U.S. Bonds's Greatest Hits

Twelve recordings from 1960–1967, including all his best-known songs along with a few obscurities. New Orleans/Quarter to Three/Dear Lady Twist/School Is Out/I Dig this Station/Workin' for My Baby.

LEGRAND 1002 (R)

Quarter To Three

Reissue of LeGrand 3001 from 1961 with extra tracks, making fourteen songs in all. Features real stereo versions of "A Trip to the Moon," "Cecilia," "School Is Out," "One Million Tears," "Please Forgive Me," and "Don't Go to Strangers."

LEGRAND 1003 (R)/LINE 9.00723 (L)

Twist Up Calypso

Reissue of LeGrand 3002 from 1962 with original cover and liner notes and additional songs, making 14 in all. The LP contains rock and twist versions of calypso songs or, as the liner notes say, the songs are "Americanized, de-patoised, and cleaned up." Wonderful noisy Frank Guida production, newly remixed and remastered by Little Walter. This is simply one of the rowdiest party/dance craze discs of all time. Bonds's band used trombone, maracas, and unconventional R&B arrangements to backup his half-sung, half-shouted, and in-your-face vocals; the effect is rude, crude, and totally irresistible. Guaranteed to turn any party into grounds for eviction! Sorta like Sam The Sham's head grafted onto Chubby Checker's gyrating torso, then injected with a whopping dose of dangerous stimulants, if you can dig that. Three songs appear here in real stereo for the first time: the hit "Dear Lady Twist," "Mama Look a Booboo," and "Man Smart Woman Smarter." Completely essential. Day-O/Naughty Little Flea/Coconut Woman.

LEGRAND 1004 (R)

Warning: For Health's Sake

Thirteen mostly unissued and alternate LeGrand sides, including real stereo versions of "School Is Out," "Havin' So Much Fun" "Seven Day Weekend," "Gettin' a Groove," and "Where Did the Naughty Little Girl Go?"

LEGRAND 17001 (L)

Greatest Hits

Nineteen raucous party hits, duplicating a fair amount of the Rhino CD. New Orleans/Quarter to Three/School Is Out/Dear Lady Twist/Do the Bumpsie/Soul Food/Monkey, USA.

LINE 9.00715 (L)

The Gary U.S. Bonds Collection

Twenty-six song compilation of Bonds's raw, early efforts for the LeGrand label, most originally issued as singles. New Orleans/Quarter to Three/School Is Out/Satan Go Away/Food of Love/Twist Twist Senora.

⊛ RHINO 70971 (CL)

The Best of Gary U.S. Bonds

One simple phrase comes to mind here: contagious party atmosphere. This is indeed Bonds at his best: eighteen dance tunes with the rowdy U.S. Bonds sound. CD has unique clock-face graphic and four bonus cuts. New Orleans/Quarter to Three/Seven Day Weekend/School Is Out/No More Homework/Havin' So Much Fun/Do the Bumpsie/Not Me.

THE BONZO DOG BAND

The original Dada-rock band, led by Neil Innes, the Bonzos were the first to puncture holes in rock's pomposities, paving the way for the Rutles (featuring Monty Python's Eric Idle and Innes), Weird Al Yankovic, and Spinal Tap.

EDSEL 209 (R)

The Doughnut in Granny's Greenhouse

Reissue of their second British LP, which was released in the US as *Urban Spaceman* (Imperial 12432 from 1969), with the addition of the title track. (In other words, "Spaceman" ain't on this one.) The Kings of Dada rock go full force on this, with the wild ramblings of Viv Stanshall, Neil Innes, Legs Larry Smith, Roger Ruskin Spear, and Rhino Rodney Slater. This doesn't have the booklet from the original, but the gatefold cover has lots of the original pictures and, of course, the lyrics, so you can sing along with "We Are Normal," "Trouser Press," "Humanoid Boogie," "Can Blue Men Sing the Whites," and "My Pink Half of the Drainpipe." Not for the sensitive or the squeamish. Highest possible recommendations?

EDSEL 235 (R)

Keynsham

Reissue of the classic LP originally released as Imperial 12457 in 1970. The Bonzos do their version of a rock

"Tutti Frutti" ("she's my little cookie, Yesiree!"). Yeah man!

CURB 77298 (L)
Greatest Hits
Golly gee, what a swell treat. Ten hits including original versions of "Love Letters in the Sand," "April Love," "Remember You're Mine," "Moody River," and "I'll Be Home." Put on your white bucks (not included at this low, low price) and rock gently to these Booney toons.

EARL BOSTIC
Tulsa-born alto sax player Bostic began his career in Lionel Hampton's jazz band, and released numerous instrumental hits from 1946–1958. He died in 1965 leaving behind a wealth of jazz, R&B, and Latin-flavored recordings. His toughest sides were recorded for Gotham and King during the late '40s and early '50s with such luminaries as Lowell "Count" Hastings and John Coltrane on tenor saxes. He is best-remembered for his hits "Flamingo" (1951) and "Sleep" (1952). Just a few years back, there was almost nothing available by Bostic, but now a slew of his King LPs from the '50s have been reissued in exact reproductions of the original releases.

✪ CHARLY 241 (L)
Blows a Fuse
Twenty cuts focusing on Bostic's classic recordings from the '40s and '50s, including the breathtaking "8:45 Stomp," the jumpin' "Cherokee," with great vibe fills from Gene Redd, and the finger-snapping "Moonglow." Informed notes and great pictures enhance your listening pleasure. Flamingo/Sleep/Mambostic/Seven Steps.

HOLLYWOOD 298 (L)
16 Sweet Tunes of the Fantastic '50s
Reissue of Starday 3022, originally cut in the '60s. Bostic pours plenty of smooch and syrup into remakes of familiar pop ballads. Three Coins in the Fountain/Canadian Sunset/Autumn Leaves/Tammy/ Your Cheatin' Heart/Unchained Melody.

KING 500 (RCL)
The Best of Bostic
Exact reproduction of Bostic's first album put out by King during the '50s. This set of 12 ballads, including his enormous 1951 R&B hit "Flamingo," is considered Bostic's best King album collection. Bostic's smooth, sometimes "quirky" tenor solo work sounds commercially acceptable on these sides, as opposed to the uninhibited efforts displayed on his earlier Gotham

sides available on Charly 241 (and previously reissued on Oldies Blues 8007).

KING 503 (RCL)
For You
Reissue of King 503 from 1956, Bostic's second LP. A dozen 1950–1954 classics, including his hit version of "Sleep." Lots of stellar names in various bands including Blue Mitchell, Stanley and Tommy Turrentine, Count Hastings, Benny Golson, Mickey Baker, and, on an April 17, 1952 session, John Coltrane. Velvet Sunset/Moonglow/Linger Awhile/Cherokee/Smoke Gets in Your Eyes.

KING 529 (CL)
Let's Dance with Earl Bostic
Lover Come Back to Me/Cracked Ice/Danube Waves/Blue Skies/Cherry Bean/Liebestraum.

KING 597 (RCL)
Alto Magic in Hi Fi
The most rockin' of all of Bostic's King LPs, featuring two sessions from 1958, mixing mostly uptempo R&B tunes with a few cheesy pop numbers. Nice vibes by Gene Redd (especially on "Wee-Gee Board"), raw, exciting guitar by Allen Seltzer, and, of course, Bostic's unmistakable tone, at once lush and sleazy. Fans of the Las Vegas grind should give this one a listen; it's stripable! Rockin' with Richard/Pinkie/C Jam Blues/The Wrecking Rock.

JIMMY BOWEN
Bass player and singer Jimmy Bowen formed The Rhythm Orchids in 1955 while at West Texas State College, with Buddy Knox (gtr, vcl), Don Lanier (gtr), and Dave Alldred (drm). Initially produced by Norman Petty, their recordings were issued on small labels until they were picked up by Roulette. Bowen, who was a pretty undistinguished singer, had a big hit in 1957 with "I'm Stickin' with You"—the flipside of Knox's "Party Doll"—and minor hits with other songs. He later became a producer, initially working for Frank Sinatra's Reprise label, and is now one of the most highly regarded country producers in Nashville.

COLLECTABLES 5406 (CL)
The Best of Jimmy Bowen
Reissue of his only Roulette album. I'm Sticking with You/Stop Wasting My Time/Money Honey/Raggedy Anne/Way Back Home/Last Night.

THE BOXTOPS

Excellent white-soul group formed in Memphis in 1965 featuring 15-year-old Alex Chilton (lead voc, gtr, b, hca), Bill Cunningham (kybd), and Garry Talley (gtr, b). In 1967 they had a big hit with "The Letter" produced by Dan Penn; after that, Tom Boggs (drm) and Rick Allen (org) joined the band. Later hits included "Cry Like a Baby" and "Soul Deep." When the group split up in 1969, Chilton became lead singer for the critically acclaimed band, Big Star, until their demise in 1978.

RHINO 70161 (R)
Greatest Hits
Fourteen hits featuring the excellent Muscle Shoals production and songs by Dan Penn, Spooner Oldham, Tommy Cogbill, and Chips Moman. The Letter/Neon Rainbow/Sweet Cream Ladies/Forward March/Cry Like a Baby/Soul Deep/Choo Choo Train.

WARNER BROS. 27611 (L)
Ultimate Boxtops
The last thing I expected to see on Warners, since the Tops recorded for Bell/Mala, now owned by Arista. Interesting collection of tunes, with hits by Wayne Thompson ("The Letter," "Neon Rainbow," and "Soul Deep") and Dan Penn and Spooner Oldham ("Cry Like a Baby" and "I Met Her at Church"), plus some non-hit Chilton originals ("Together" and "I Must Be the Devil"), along with "Sweet Cream Ladies," "She Shot a Hole in My Soul," and even a nine-minute "Rock Me Baby."

TINY BRADSHAW

Raspy-voiced singer/pianist who started his career in the '30s with various swing bands, forming his own band in 1934. In the postwar era, he adapted to the burgeoning R&B style, and led tuff little jump bands on King in the '50s where he had a number of hits including "Well, Oh Well," "Walking the Chalk Line," and "Heavy Juice." He was apparently one of Buddy Holly's favorite artists. He recorded the original version of "The Train Kept a' Rollin'" which was covered by Memphis rockabilly hero Johnny Burnette, and later by The Yardbirds. Bradshaw died in 1958 at the age of 53.

JUKEBOX LIL 621 (R)
I'm a High-ballin' Daddy
Concentrates on the beginning and end of Tiny's postwar career as an R&B bandleader and vocalist. Features all four of his 1944 big-band sides for Manor with Sonny Stitt, Big Nick Nicholes, and Billy Ford (including "Bradshaw Bounce"), two of his 1945 Manor sides, and three out of his four 1947 Savoy sides (including "I've Been Around"). From the other end of his career are four of his later King sides, cut after Tiny's stroke, with such a crack band (including Red Prysock, Rufus Gore, and Sil Austin) that Tiny isn't even on the recordings (including "Spider Web" and "Strange")! In between, there's his classic exuberant King sides, including the title rocker.

KING 653 (RCL)
The Great Composer
Reissue of King 653 from 1959. Sixteen jumpin' sides, all written by Tiny, including 14 classic instrumentals. After his mid-'50s heart attack, Tiny was present in name only. However all but two cuts here are from 1950–1954, so the music is great with fine tenor from such stars as Rufus Gore, Red Prysock, Sil Austin, and Noble "Thin Man" Watts. Tiny sings "Train Kept a' Rollin'" and "Well Oh Well."

JIM BREEDLOVE

Jim Breedlove made a career out of recording tunes for song pluggers. He was more than adequate as a singer, his backup is terrific, and the songs are mostly rock and roll cornerstones. Jimmy also recorded with The Cues (see Bear Family 15309).

BEAR FAMILY 15327 (R)
Sings Rock and Roll Hits
Demo recordings of many '50s rock classics. It's very interesting (as well as entertaining) to hear what the songwriter's original intention was on "Rock and Roll Music," "Whole Lotta Shakin' Goin' On," "C.C. Rider," "Hound Dog," "Jailhouse Rock," and "Long Tall Sally." Super rock and roll!

TERESA BREWER

Excellent pop singer who recorded for years on Coral and had numerous hits between 1950–1961 in a sprightly, happy vein ("Music, Music, Music" being her biggest). Though not strictly a rock and roll singer, her recordings often have a light rock beat. She's currently active as a jazz vocalist working for her husband, jazz producer Bob Thiele.

BEAR FAMILY 15440 (L)
Teenage Dance Party
Twenty Coral tracks, including a couple previously unissued takes. The Hula Hoop Song/Why Baby Why/Tweedle Dee/Rock Love/Lula Rock a Hula/Gone.

BILLY BROWN

Billy Brown was a very strong singer and (from all accounts) an accomplished guitar player too. His '50s rockabilly tunes are some of the toughest ever waxed. They were closer to raunchy rock and roll than pure rockabilly, with pounding drums and the occasional wailin' sax solo.

STAR CLUB 8033 (R)
Did We Have a Party
Half of the 12 tunes here are pop rock and ballads. Meet Me in the Alley Sally/Flip Out/Run 'em Off/Lost Weekend.

JAMES BROWN

"The Godfather of Soul," "The Hardest Working Man in Show Business," and "Soul Brother Number 1" are just three of the many monikers that Brown has earned through a long career. He is perhaps the most influential and successful black performer in rock and roll. He recorded vocal-group material with The Famous Flames on Federal in the mid-'50s, soul hits in the early '60s, black pride in the late '60s, and black awareness in the '70s. Brown did a lot of experimenting with funk grooves and polyrhythms (many of which have been sampled by today's rap stars), so that it's impossible to hear any modern black pop that doesn't owe something to him. He went from Federal to parent company King in 1960, recording the classic, million-selling *Live at the Apollo* LP in 1962 (reissued on Polydor). He became hero to Britain's Mods in the mid-'60s. In 1971, he switched to Polydor. Alumni from his band include Jimmy Nolen (gtr), Bootsy Collins and St. Clair Pinckney (bar sax), Clyde Stubblefield (drm), and Fred Wesley, Maceo Parker, and Bobby Byrd (ten sax). His dance steps have been copied by such megastars as Michael Jackson and Prince. Of late, Brown was in the spotlight again, this time because of a run in with the police, leading to a brief prison term. He has returned to performing and recording, although his moves show the toll of many years of hard performing.

Polydor owns the entire Brown back catalog, and has been rereleasing a lot of it, particularly in Japan and France. There are numerous anthologies, including Polydor's *20 All Time Greatest Hits* and *Star Time* that are well worth owning. The now out-of-print *Roots of a Revolution* (Polydor 817 304) is well worth looking for. It is a fabulous, 43-cut compilation of early material, including unreleased alternate takes and studio dialogue, as well as a chronological selection of his strongest recordings for King/Federal from 1956–1964.

POLYDOR 314 511 326 (CL)
20 All-Time Greatest Hits
I Got You/Sex Machine/I Got the Feelin'/Mother Popcorn/Give It Up or Turn It Loose/Make It Funky/Papa's Got a Brand New Bag/Think/It's a Man's World/Try Me/Night Train/Cold Sweat/Get on the Good Foot/Papa Don't Take No Mess/The Payback/Say It Loud/Super Bad/Hot Pants/Get Up Offa That Thing/Please, Please, Please.

POLYDOR 823 001 (CL)
"Live" at the Apollo
The 1967 Apollo show on one CD or two casettes with "Cold Sweat," "I Got You," "Try Me," "Think," "That's Life," and so many more. Not the classic 1962 show, but still well worth a listen! Total time not listed, but it's gotta be pushing an hour and 15 minutes!

☉ POLYDOR 843 479 (CL)
Live at The Apollo, 1962
In case you haven't heard, this is quite likely the finest live recording ever made. Ranking right up there with Sam Cooke live at the Harlem Square Club in 1963, Elvis's sit-down Burbank 1968 sessions, and maybe The Sex Pistols live at Winterland in January 1978, James leads his super-tight band through all his hits. Few releases document the feel and intensity of a performance as hot as this one; listening to this show answers any questions about whether Brown is truly the Godfather of Soul. Highest recommendations. I'll Go Crazy/Try Me/Think/I Don't Mind/Please, Please, Please/You've Got the Power/I Found Someone/Why Do You Want Me/I Want You So Bad/I Love You, Yes I Do/Why Does Everything Happen to Me/Bewildered/Night Train.

POLYDOR 849 108 (CL)

Star Time

Gathers 72 of JB's best sides, covering 28 of his prime years as a latter-day R&B hitmaker, soul sensation, and godfather to today's hip-hop/rap generation. The cuts, chronologically ordered over four CDs, are simply his best and biggest hits, some as alternate, live, or re-mixed/re-edited versions, but mostly the original takes from the King/Federal, Dade, Try Me, Smash, Polydor, People, TK, and Tommy Boy labels. An incredible five hours of music and an essential purchase for anyone with even a measurable amount of soul! Please, Please, Please/Try Me/Bewildered/Good Good Lovin'/I'll Go Crazy/It's a Man's World/I Got You/Papa's Got a Brand New Bag/Cold Sweat/Say It Loud/Funky Drummer/Get Up/Sex Machine/Super Bad/Soul Power/Get on the Good Foot.

POLYDOR (JAPAN) 1847 (L)

Please, Please, Please

Limited edition Japanese reissue of King 610. This is one of the strongest of the early period JB packages, with the rollicking "Chonnie on Chon," "I Feel that Old Feeling Coming On," and "That Dood It," and all-time classic crooners "Just Won't Do Right," "Please, Please, Please" (a top-ten hit in 1956), and "Try Me," which hit Number 1 on the R&B chart in 1958. Sixteen slices of rockin' rhythm and burnin' blues.

POLYDOR (JAPAN) 1848 (L)

Think!

CD repro of super hits collection, 12 classic tracks! Think/Good Good Lovin/I'll Go Crazy/This Old Heart/Bewildered/You've Got the Power/Baby, You're Right.

POLYDOR (JAPAN) 1849 (L)

Prisoner of Love

Limited edition Japanese CD reissue of King 851. Twelve cuts from the early '60s, when Soul Brother Number 1 was churning out hit after hit. Includes these top ten chart-toppers: the title cut, "Lost Someone," "Bewildered," and "Try Me," plus "Signed, Sealed and Delivered," "Waiting in Vain," and "How Long Darling."

POLYDOR (JAPAN) 1850 (L)

Pure Dynamite! Recorded at the Famous Royal Theater

Limited-edition Japanese CD reissue of King 883. Along with the various Apollo sets, this launched a prolific string of hysterical live recordings that became a staple of the Godfather's recorded output over the years. Eight selections, including seven early '60s hits. Oh Baby Don't You Weep/Please, Please, Please/Like a Baby/Signed, Sealed and Delivered/These Foolish Things/Good Good Lovin'/Shout and Shimmy.

RHINO 70194 (CL)

Santa's Got a Brand New Bag

Culled from three long out-of-print LPs by Soul Brother Number 1, James Brown belts out 12 soul Christmas classics and knee-dropping originals. CD contains four extra tunes, including "Santa Claus Is Definitely Here to Stay" and "Hey America." Santa Claus Go Straight to the Ghetto/Go Power at Christmas Time/Let's Make Xmas Mean Something This Year.

RHINO 70219 (C)

Greatest Hits

Twelve solid tunes mostly from the mid-'60s. Despite the respective 1964 and 1965 release dates given on "Please, Please, Please" and "Try Me," these are indeed the original '50s recordings. The rest are from the golden years of 1964–1968 including "Out of Sight," "Papa's Got a Brand New Bag," "I Can't Stand Myself (When You Touch Me)," "I Got the Feelin'," and "Cold Sweat," with the only remake being the version of "I'll Go Crazy" from *Live At the Apollo.* Great liner notes by Don Waller, including numerous words of wisdom from an interview with Brother James.

JOE BROWN and THE BRUVVERS

Popular British singer and outstanding guitarist. He started as a skiffler, moved to rock and roll, and then concentrated on a more pop-oriented, music-hall approach, which his bright and cheerful personality is eminently suited for.

DIAMOND 500 (R)

Joe Brown and The Bruvvers

Eighteen enjoyable tracks, some of them in the Buddy Holly vein, recorded in the early '60s for Piccadilly and Golden Guinea. Surprisingly most of the songs are originals and British music-hall adaptations as opposed to American covers. In fact, the only cover is a Paul Anka tune, appropriately titled "Everybody Calls Me Joe." Henry VIII/A Picture of You/Sea of Heartbreak/The Other Side of Town.

MAXINE BROWN

Outstanding soul singer from South Carolina who started singing in gospel groups and hit it big in 1961 with her incredible and intense "All in My Mind" for the small Nomar label. She later moved to Wand where she had a number of hits including the first recording of "Oh No, Not My Baby," a Goffin/King composition that was later covered by many others.

COLLECTABLES 5116 (CL)
Golden Classics
Twelve-tune collection including Maxine's two classic soul standards "All in My Mind" and "Funny," originally released by Nomar in 1961. Both songs seem to lose impact in their transfer to long play; gone are the pounding bass figures on the original singles. Also included are three gut-wrenching duets made with Chuck Jackson: the "bad" "Something You Got" (1965), "Baby Take Me" (1965), and the hip-shaking "I'm Satisfied." Contains a tasty cover version of James Ray's "If You Gotta Make a Fool of Somebody." Worth purchasing if you missed out on previous reissues.

KENT (UK) 028 (R)
One in a Million
Best of Maxine's Wand material, culled from 11 45s and three LPs recorded between 1963–1967. Includes remakes of her two Nomar hits, "Funny" and "All in My Mind." Oh No, Not My Baby/Since I Found You/Little Girl Lost/Put Yourself in My Place.

KENT (UK) 949 (L)
Oh No, Not My Baby
A great 28-track collection of Wand material recorded between 1963–1967, previously reissued on two Kent LPs, numbers 028 and the out-of-print 047. Included are remakes of her two Nomar hits "Funny" and "All in My Mind" plus Wand hits like "Coming Back to You," "Oh No, Not My Baby," and "It's Gonna Be Alright." The disc also features seven tracks not originally issued by Wand, including the fine "Baby Cakes" written and produced by Otis Redding in 1967.

RUTH BROWN

Ruth Brown started her career as a jazz and blues singer in the '40s, when she was spotted by Cab Calloway's sister Blanche who took her to the up-and-coming Atlantic label in 1949. Over the next seven years, she had hit after hit on the R&B charts with her powerful vocals accompanied by some of New York's top sessionmen. In 1957, she crossed over into the pop market with "Lucky Lips" and continued her string of hits in the pop and R&B charts over the next six years. She made a comeback in the '80s, appearing on Broadway in the hit show *Black and Blue*, and has recorded a number of albums for Fantasy in a jazz/blues vein. She also appeared in the film *Hairspray* and serves as host of NPR's *Bluesstage*.

❂ ATLANTIC 82061 (L)
Miss Rhythm: Greatest Hits and More
Two-CD set featuring 40 of her most memorable Atlantic recordings, including her big hits and four unreleased cuts. Wow!! So Long/I'll Get Along Somehow/Sentimental Journey/Teardrops from My Eyes/I'll Wait for You/It's All for You/5-10-15 Hours/Mama, He Treats Your Daughter Mean/Love Contest/Somebody Touched Me/As Long As I'm Moving/Lucky Lips.

DCC COMPACT CLASSICS 602 (L)
Help a Good Girl Go Bad
Reissue of a 1964 Mainstream album, which tried to place her in the role of a big-band singer, with lush strings and "mainstream" songs. The material ranges from good to ... well, did you really want to hear Ruth do "On the Good Ship Lollipop" as a slow ballad? The best seems to be the Nellie Lutcher tunes "He's a Real Gone Guy" and "Hurry on Down" with Clark Terry (tpt) and Hank Jones (drm) in the band.

FANTASY 9661 (RCL)
Have a Good Time
Powerful comeback LP recorded live at the Cinegrill, Hollywood, in 1989. Ruth, in her first LP in six years, is backed by her working band, an organ and sax quartet, with Bobby Forrester (bar sax), Charles Williams (alto sax), and guest star Red Holloway (ten sax). Ruth does great new versions of "5-10-15 Hours," "Mama, He Treats Your Daughter Mean," "Teardrops from Your Eyes," the title tune, and "Yes Sir, That's My Baby."

FANTASY 9662 (CL)
Blues on Broadway

STOCKHOLM 202 (L)
Takin' Care of Business
Nine 1980 live and studio recordings with able backup by Charles Brown, Preston Love, Chuck Norris, and a cast of enthusiastic Scandinavians. Takin' Care of Business/Oh What a Dream/5-10-15 Hours/I Can See Everybody's Baby.

ED BRUCE

Arkansas singer who recorded some great rockabilly for Sun Records (issued as by Edwin Bruce). Fine as they are, these cuts went nowhere, and many tracks were unissued. He temporarily quit the music business but moved to Nashville in the mid-'60s where he began a long and succesful career as a country singer.

BEAR FAMILY 15194 (R)
Rock Boppin' Baby
Ed's complete Sun recordings, 14 tunes, out of which only two singles (1957's "Rock Boppin' Baby" b/w "More Than Yesterday," and "Part of My Life" b/w "Sweet Woman") were released. The unissued material includes five demos with just Bruce and his guitar, including "Sweet Woman," "King of Fools," and "Just Being with You," along with completed versions of "King of Fools," "Eight Wheel Driver," "Ballad of Ringo," and "Baby That's Good." To round out the LP, there's his rare 1961 RCA single "Flight 303" b/w "Spun Gold." Liner notes by Colin Escott.

TOMMY BRUCE
Tommy Bruce was the British version of Fabian and the rest of those guys—"come here boy, I'm gonna make you a star." He was a handsome cockney laborer who filled the bill for pop stardom on that particular day, even though he couldn't sing and was perfectly happy throwing around crates of grapefruits and melons. His voice sounds like your cousin Joey's feeble attempt to imitate the Big Bopper after a few drinks.

TEENAGER 612 (R)
I'm on Fire
Bruce croaks his way through 18 tunes with "Horror Movies" and "Monster Gonzales" coming across as the most listenable. Ain't Misbehavin'/It's You/Glad Rag Doll/Babette.

DON BRYANT
Soul pyrotechnician Don Bryant hails from Memphis, and sang with his brother James in The Four Kings, who toured with The Willie Mitchell Combo in the late '60s (see Hi 439).

HI 116 (L)
Doin' the Mustang
Twenty-six tune collection featuring Wilson Pickett sound-alike covers, demos, singles, some duets with Marion Brittman, and unissued material. I fail to understand why Bryant, one of the finest soul men around Memphis, was wasted on cutting covers of hit sides by others. But still, the set does please with outstanding purifiers including "For Your Precious Love," "Try Me," "It Ain't Easy," "I Can't Go On (Suffering Like This)," and "Clear Days and Stormy Nights." Detailed notes by Clive Anderson.

THE BUCKINGHAMS
Chicago-area rock band with a British-sounding name, ugly suits, and Beatles's hairdos who turned out well-crafted, horn-heavy hits, most famous for the chart-toppin' "Kind of a Drag."

COLUMBIA 47718 (CL)
Mercy, Mercy, Mercy
Eighteen songs, including their early USA label material, six of them in remixed form. Many of the other songs appear in previously unreleased stereo mixes. Their minor hit "Susan" is a bizarre period piece that will no doubt elicit tears of one kind or another. It's a good show all around, right down to the liner notes. Lawdy Miss Clawdy/I've Been Wrong Before/I Call Your Name/Hey Baby/Don't You Care/Where Did You Come From.

MILT BUCKNER
R&B/jazz organist.

BLACK & BLUE 59.087 (L)
Green Onions
Freewheeling mid-'70s sessions featuring Buckner's fervent fingerwork. The title track opens it up in high style, then Milt switches to vibes on "Sleep." "Since I Fell for You" is a beautifully mellow guitar feature for blues fretter Roy Gaines, leading into a chugging organ boogie and the fast-paced swinger "After You've Gone." After these hot numbers, Milt takes it home with mellow vibes (played very competently, by the way) on "That's All."

BUFFALO SPRINGFIELD
Folk-rock outfit featuring Stephen Stills, Richie Furay, Neil Young (vocs, gtrs), Bruce Palmer (b; replaced by Jim Messina on the band's last LP), and Dewey Martin (drm). Lasting a scant two years, band members have had a long-lasting impact on rock music.

ATCO 33200 (RC)
Buffalo Springfield
For What It's Worth/Nowadays Clancy Can't Even Sing/Sit Down, I Think I Love You/Go and Say Goodbye.

ATCO 33216 (CL)
Again
Highlights are the two, longer tracks, typical of the extended jams of the day, Neil Young's classic "Expecting to Fly" and Stephen Stills's "Bluebird," both of which became staples of late '60s FM radio. Also includes the minor hit, "Mr. Soul."

BEAR FAMILY 15545 (L)

Great Shakin' Fever

Twenty-five mid-'60s recordings.

HANK C. BURNETTE (SVEN-AKE KENNETH HOGBURN)

Through the magic of overdubbing, Sven-Ake Kenneth Hogburn has produced some of the most listenable European rockabilly. His stage name is taken from this three idols: Hank Williams, Chet Atkins, and Johnny Burnette. He plays all of the instruments on his recordings, which first came out in the mid-'60s in the US.

ROCK & COUNTRY 1003 (R)

The Original One Man Rockabilly Band

Twenty sides recorded between 1967–1979.

STAR CLUB 1973–74 (R)

Rock-Ola Ruby

These recordings, from 1973–1974 I think, showcase the Swedish one-man band at his rockin' best. His vocals are deep in a Sleepy LaBeef-style but only adequate, so the mid-tempo tunes don't really cut the mustard. But, except for two numbers, these 16 tunes bop like crazy and feature stunning guitar. Rock-Ola Ruby/16 Chicks/Crazy Baby/Riverside Jump/Rock Town Rock/Hey Mr. Presley.

STAR CLUB 8013 (R)

Spinnin' Rock Boogie

Fourteen cuts. This is a reissue of a 1974 Southern Sound LP featuring sides from the '60s and early '70s. Spinnin' Rock Boogie/Driftin'/I'll Be Around/Fury/I've Got the Blues/Hands Off/Rakin' and Scrapin'.

STAR CLUB 8014 (R)

Multisided

Reissue of Burnette's first LP, a mixture of rockabilly, rock and roll oldies, and original songs.

WILDCAT 5008 (R)

Bop Till I Drop

Thirteen previously unreleased recordings made between 1975–1982. My Bucket's Got a Hole in It/Hop Skip and Jump/From a Jack to a King.

JOHNNY BURNETTE

Elvis's coworker at Crown Electric, Burnette formed the pioneering Rock 'n' Roll Trio with himself on rhythm guitar, brother Dorsey on standup bass, and Paul Burlison on blistering lead. They recorded extensively for Coral in the '50s (reissued on Bear Family). After the trio disbanded, Johnny and Dorsey wrote songs for Rick Nelson. In the '60s, Johnny went solo and had a successful pop career on Liberty (his big hit was "You're Sixteen") until his death in 1964 at 30 in a car crash; most of these recordings are in the teen-pop vein and are marred by syrupy strings and girl choruses.

❂ BEAR FAMILY 15474 (L)

Johnny Burnette Trio: Rockabilly Boogie

The definitive edition of Johnny and The Trio's Coral recordings presenting all 25 songs recorded by them in 1956 and 1957 along with alternate takes of three songs. Superb high-quality sound thanks to Bob Jones, and a great 32-page booklet with detailed notes by Colin Escott, full discographical information, many photos, and newspaper clippings.

DEMAND 0060 (R)

Please Don't Leave Me

Sixteen of Johnny's later teen-pop recordings, probably from his post Liberty and Freedom years when he bounced around from label to label looking for another "You're Sixteen." All but two tunes have girly chorus and/or string sections, which wouldn't necessarily be all that bad except that the violins usually take a solo too! There are two great alternate takes from the trio years of "Lonesome Train" and "Please Don't Leave Me." The Fool/Mona Lisa/Settin' the Woods on Fire/You're So Fine.

EMI (UK) 1324 (R)/792 924 (L)

The Best of Johnny Burnette

Sixteen pop rockers from the early '60s Liberty sessions replete with girly choruses and strings, ten previously unissued (but believe me, none are rockabilly). CD has four bonus cuts. Walk on By/Little Boy Sad/Fools Like Me/Clown Shoes/Girls.

ROCKSTAR 1017 (R)

We're Havin' a Party

Fabulous 20-track LP collecting Johnny's Freedom and Imperial recordings, some other major label cuts, as well as unreleased tracks. Johnny's surrounded by some pretty fair bandmates on these sides: brother Dorsey, Paul Burlison, Eddie Cochran, James Burton, Earl Palmer, Barney Kessel, and Joe Maphis!! This album, along with the Trio material, forms a cornerstone in any rockabilly collection. Boppin' Rosalie/Do Baby Do/That's All I Care/Honey Tree/My Destiny/Speak No Evil/Little Miss Shy/Cincinnati Fireball/Sweet Baby Doll/My Honey.

SAM BUTERA

Hard tenor-sax player who led Louis Prima's backup band, The Witnesses. Bear Family and Prep are the best issues available.

BEAR FAMILY 15449 (L)
Hot Nights in New Orleans
Nineteen RCA/Groove sides, including some unissued tracks and alternate takes.

JASMINE 313 (L)
Sheer Energy
Due to the lack of useful notes, I can only assume that these are recent recordings made for sale at live shows, probably in Vegas and/or other spots where the Prima legend lives on. Saxophone aficionados know that Sam Butera toted a mean tenor onstage during those countless casino nights with Louis Prima's wild band. A New Orleans native, Sam really had the stompin' sound of the south in his blood, and was about the only white saxman who could hang with the top players of the early rock-and-roll generation. As demonstrated on this release, he also took a few vocal pointers from his boss, and here he delivers faves like "Jump, Jive, and Wail," "Pennies from Heaven," "Let the Good Times Roll," and "Kansas City" with eerie Primaesque precision.

JASMINE 314 (L)
By Request
As on *Sheer Energy*, Sam resurrects Prima's gravelly tones with uncanny accuracy on oft-requested favorites "When You're Smiling," the "Just a Gigolo"-"I Ain't Got Nobody" medley, "St. Louis Blues," and "Closer to the Bone." "You Rascal You" is an astonishing copy of the original, but with so many Prima reissues out now, this is destined to be a "fans-only" curiosity. The fare is rounded out with standards like "Cabaret," "For Once in My Life," some good blues with Sam bending his tonsils in a solid rockin' Wynonie Harris direction, the obligatory Italian dialect number, and a couple of lackluster instrumentals. Two cuts are repeated from Jasmine 313.

PREP 100 (R)
Jump, Jive, and Wail
Sam blows powerfully, sings wonderfully (Prima sings on six cuts), and the rest of the band (The Witnesses?) rocks like hell's bells on these '50s era recordings. The highest recommendation is that black R&B audiences of the era naturally assumed Butera was black and were shocked when they saw him play sax in person. Dig this cool cat on 16 great cuts. Bim Bam/Ton of Bricks/Easy Rockin'/Jump, Jive, and Wail/Don't Knock It.

JERRY BUTLER

Silky voiced Chicago soulster who started out as lead singer of The Impressions (see separate listing), scoring big with his composition "Your Precious Love." He was encouraged to go solo and had a long string of hits, first on Vee Jay (1958–1966) and then Mercury (1967–1978), with a lot of help from Curtis Mayfield, who wrote for him and led his backup band. In 1968, he teamed with fledgling producers Gamble and Huff for the beginnings of the Philadelphia sound, joining them in 1978 on their own Philadelphia International label. He recorded duets with Betty Everett on Vee Jay, and Thelma Houston and Gene Chandler on Mercury.

MERCURY 510 967 (CL)
The Very Best of Jerry Butler
Twelve songs recorded for Mercury between 1966–1972, his best work with producers Gamble and Huff. There aren't any liner notes and the running time is just over 34 minutes, but if the two-CD *Iceman* set is too much for you, this outstanding collection is the way to go. Never Give Up/Hey, Western Union Man/Are You Happy/Moody Woman/What's the Use of Breaking Up/I Dig You Baby/Ain't Understanding Mellow/One Night Affair.

MERCURY 510 968 (CL)
Iceman: The Mercury Years
Two-CD set including the fine out-of-print LPs, *Ice on Ice* and *The Iceman Cometh*, along with all of his top 100 R&B hits recorded between 1966–1973, excluding only a duet with Gene Chandler. Among the other treasures are previously unreleased numbers like "The Right Track" (a hit for little brother Billy in 1966), a longer, stronger "Only the Strong Survive," a radio promo, and some fine non-hits, including "You Walked Into My Life," "Loneliness," and "Beside You," and an unreleased, undubbed live version of "For Your Precious Love" from 1967. Forty-four cuts in all, with good booklet notes. No soul collection could be complete without this music. Do your ears a favor. Recommended twice, once for each disc.

⊙ RHINO 70216 (C)/75881 (L)
The Best of Jerry Butler
Excellent collection featuring 14 (on cassette) or 18 (on CD) of his Vee Jay and Mercury sides. For Your Precious Love/I Stand Accused/Let It Be Me/Never Give You Up/Only the Strong Survive.

THE BYRDS

Sixties folk-rock group formed by Roger (formerly Jim) McGuinn, David Crosby, Gene Clark (gtrs, vcls), Chris Hillman (b, vcl), and Michael Clarke (drm). Their soaring vocal harmonies and twangy 12-string guitar leads made hits out of folk classics "Mr. Tambourine Man" and "Turn, Turn, Turn," and their own compositions "Eight Miles High" and "So You Wanna Be a Rock and Roll Star?" Gene Clark was the first to defect in 1966, followed by David Crosby in 1967 (who went on to be a founding member of Crosby, Stills, and Nash). A new, more country-rock oriented band debuted in 1968 with Gram Parsons joining the fold along with drummer Kevin Kelly, recording the classic *Sweetheart of the Rodeo* LP. Soon after, Parsons and Hillman left to form The Flying Burrito Brothers; McGuinn soldiered on as head Byrdsman through the mid-'70s, with a band featuring ex-bluegrass guitar great Clarence White. The band has made several abortive comebacks, with various members performing in various combinations. Today, Crosby continues with megagroup CSN, McGuinn performs as a solo artist, and Chris Hillman leads the country/bluegrass group, The Desert Rose Band. The Byrds sound has influenced many generations of rockers, particularly Tom Petty.

COLUMBIA 9172 (CL)

Mr. Tambourine Man

Their first LP with the folk-rock title hit. Most impressive are Gene Clark's contributions, the hits "I'll Feel a Whole Lot Better" and "All I Really Want to Do," along with LP tracks "I Knew I'd Want You" and "Here without You."

COLUMBIA 9254 (CL)

Turn! Turn! Turn

The 12-strings really chime on their second LP, with more folk-rock classics from the pens of Pete Seeger (title cut), Bob Dylan, and Gene Clark.

COLUMBIA 9349 (L)

Fifth Dimension

Things start getting trippy on their third LP, as the full flowering of '60s psychedelia took root. Clark left the band, leaving a quartet with McGuinn and David Crosby in charge of writing and arranging the material. This LP combines their folk-rock instincts with more extended solos, showing the influence both of American jazz and Indian classical rajas. Includes the hit "Eight Miles High" (about flying in an airplane, says McGuinn, not drugs, and who are we to argue?) and "Mr. Spaceman."

COLUMBIA 9442 (L)

Younger than Yesterday

More psychedelia, with the title hit, a cover of Bob Dylan's "My Back Pages."

COLUMBIA 9575 (L)

The Notorious Byrd Brothers

Now just a trio (with Crosby gone to join Crosby, Stills, and Nash), this is perhaps the only psychedelic/country-rock fusion LP of the '60s! Highlight is "Wasn't Born to Follow," later used in the film *Easy Rider*.

COLUMBIA 9670 (CL)

Sweetheart of the Rodeo

New member Gram Parsons brought the nascent country-rock sound forward on this classic LP of covers of country standards and originals. The LP that launched a hundred country-rock bands. Highlights are a rousing cover of "You Ain't Goin' Nowhere" by old friend Bob Dylan and Parsons's "Hickory Wind."

COLUMBIA 9755 (CL)

Dr. Byrds and Mr. Hyde

The group is starting to lose altitude on this rock and country-rock collection. "This Wheel's on Fire" is the hit.

COLUMBIA 31027 (CL)

Untitled

Original Byrdsman Roger McGuinn is the sole survivor of the classic band on this uneven half-live/half-studio collection. Notable new member Clarence White's guitar licks are legendary, but can't really save most of this material from sounding tired and dated. Includes the minor hit, "Chestnut Mare."

COLUMBIA 31795 (CL)
Best of The Byrds, Vol. 2
Later hits (from 1969 on); not the classic sounds that made them famous.

⊗ COLUMBIA 37335 (CL)
The Original Singles (1965–1967)
Big hits and B-sides from the golden era of Byrds-dom.

COLUMBIA 46773 (CL)
The Byrds
Columbia really went whole hog on this magnificent four-CD box set. They brought in Roger McGuinn to help with the selections and remixing, making this retrospective one to set future standards by. Basically The Byrds recording chronology is strictly followed with unreleased and alternate takes fleshing out the body of work in a natural manner. Don't trade in your old Byrds LPs, though, because you might not always agree with the alternate takes here, but they should prove to be fascinating to fans all the same. How about a version of "She Don't Care about Time" with harmonica solo, "The World Turns around Her" with bongos, the full guitar introduction to "Psychodrama City," or a country version of "Oil in my Lamp," just to name a few? Gram Parsons fans will love the out-takes included in the *Sweetheart of the Rodeo* portion. Gram sings lead on the gorgeous "Lazy Days," "The Christian Life," "You Don't Miss Your Water," and "One Hundred Years from Now." "Lay Lady Lay" has the useless female choir deleted and "Kathleen's Song" can now be heard as it was recorded, minus the orchestra on the original released version. There are some great live cuts here too: "Roll Over Beethoven" from a Swedish radio broadcast in 1967 and four tunes recorded in 1970 at a college show in New York, featuring a cool version of "Positively 4th Street." The fourth CD includes a couple of classics redone at the Roy Orbison Tribute Show in 1990, "Turn! Turn! Turn!" and "Mr. Tambourine Man," as well as four tunes newly recorded (1990) in Nashville with McGuinn, Crosby, and Hillman from the original Byrds. Comes with a nifty 56-page booklet featuring tons of info, too.

COLUMBIA LEGACY 47884 (CL)
Twenty Essential Tracks from the Boxed Set
For those less deep-of-pocket, this presents the hits from the big box.

RHINO 70244
In The Beginning
For the avid Byrds fanatics and those rock historians who are interested in this band's earliest development. These sessions were made as demos to shop around to major record labels, and these work tapes are raw at times, but contain the spirit that was to propel Crosby, Clark, McGuinn, and company to national stardom in just one year. In 1964 they started as a trio known as The Jet Set, rehearsed at LA's Troubadour club, and were soon making music some called folk-rock. Most of the songs found here were originally released as *Preflyte* on the Together label (1001). The previously unreleased tracks include "Tommorow Is a Long Ways Away," plus alternate versions of "It Won't Be Wrong" and "Please Let Me Love You." There's also their earliest track, "The Only Girl I Adore," recorded as The Jet Set, with more than a tip of the hat to The Beatles. Of the eight tunes found on *Preflyte* and repeated here, "Here without You," "She Has a Way" and "You Won't Have to Cry" hold up best for me, as they have more of an electric sound and the harmonies seem to be fully realized. Fine companion to the excellent out-of-print *Never Before* collection on Reflyte.

THE CADETS
They're two groups in one! As The Cadets, they recorded jump tunes for Modern, with a classic cover of The Jayhawks's "Stranded in the Jungle." As The Jacks (see separate listing), they recorded ballads for RPM. When they broke up in the late '50s, lead singer Aaron Collins and second tenor Willie Davis joined The Flairs; Dub Jones sang bass with The Coasters; and Ted Taylor embarked on a successful solo career.

RELIC 5025 (R)
The Cadets Greatest Hits
Twenty-three songs, including everything on their out-of-print United LP. Don't Be Angry/Ring Chimes/So Will I/You Belong to Me/Fools Rush In.

THE CADILLACS
Excellent Harlem-based vocal group capable of classic harmony and Coaster-esque comedy. Led by Earl "Speedo" Carroll, the subject of their biggest hit ("Speedo"), they had a long string of recordings on Josie until Carroll quit to join The Coasters in 1959. The mid-'50s lineup consisted of Carroll and Earl Wade (formerly of The Crystals) lead vocals, with support by Buddy Brooks, Bobby Phillips, and LaVerne Drake. In addition to their musical skills, they were also noted for their onstage choreography created by famed dancer Cholly Atkins, who later devised the famous Motown moves for groups like The Miracles and The Supremes. After Carroll left, the

group soldiered on through the '60s with various lineups.

COLLECTABLES 8800 (CL)

For Collectors Only

Three-disc/cassette set, a total of 60 tunes recorded for Jubilee/Josie Records between 1954–1960. What is amazing about this collection, and the group, is that it never becomes a labor to listen to. Even the later Coasters-like tunes are a considerable amount of fun . . . well, most of them. The disappointments can be counted on the fingers of one hand. Onomatopoetic titles include "Zoon," "Buzz Buzz Buzz," "Dum De Dum Dum," "Zoom Boom Zing," "Shock-a-Doo," and the Number 9 hit "Peek-a-Boo." For namesakes, there's "Betty My Love," "Gloria," "Romeo," "Rudolph, The Red Nosed Reindeer," "Speedo Is Back," "Oh Oh Lolita," and "Please Mr. Johnson."

DR. HORSE 801 (RL)

Please Mr. Johnson

Nineteen greatest hits recorded for Josie 1955–1959; all are on the Collectables set. Speedo/Gloria/Wishing Well/Tell Me Today/Jay Walker.

⚙ RHINO 70955 (CL)

The Best of The Cadillacs

Twelve-track cassette or 16-track CD. Gloria/Down the Road/Speedo/You Are/The Girl I Love/Speedo Is Back/Peek-a-Boo/Window Lady.

STAR CLUB 8030 (R)

The Solid Gold Cadillacs

Great 20-track collection, including five unreleased tracks and ten in original stereo. These are all on the Collectables set, but this is a less-expensive way to get the best. No Chance/Oh! Whatcha Do/If You Want to Be a Woman of Mine/Yea Yea Baby/Holy Smoke Baby/Oh Oh Lolita/Please Mr. Johnson/Romeo/Frankenstein/Rock and Roll Is Here to Stay.

THE CADILLACS/THE ORIOLES

COLLECTABLES 5412 (CL)

Cadillacs Meet The Orioles

Yet another reissue from the Jubilee 1100 *Rumble* album series featuring six Josie delights by The Cadillacs, including the chart-topping "Speedo" (1956), supported by "Zoom," "The Girl I Love," "Sugar Sugar," "My Girlfriend," and the beautiful "Gloria." Veteran Baltimore harmoneers The Orioles fronted by Sonny Til wail on the second half, with original renderings of "Crying in the Chapel," "It's Too Soon to Know," "Chapel in the Moonlight," "Tell Me So," "I Cover the Waterfront," and "What Are You Doing New Year's Eve" in tearful, laid-back fashion. Fluffy notes, no pix, good average sound.

JO ANN CAMPBELL

Excellent '50s pop-rocker, four feet, 11 inches of high energy. She recorded for Gone in the late '50s, ABC-Paramount in 1960–1961, and Cameo in 1962–1963, and appeared in the late '50s teen flick *Go Johnny Go*.

STAR CLUB 8018 (R)

The Blonde Bombshell

Reissue of *I'm Nobody's Baby* (End 306) with the addition of the rare Gone single "Tall Boy" b/w "Happy New Year Baby" (Gone 5049).

RAY CAMPI

Fine multi-instrumental rockabilly performer. Ray originally recorded for several small Texas labels in the '50s (reissued on Domino), later had a string of LPs on the revival label Rolling Rock in the '70s (two reissued on Bear Family 15501), and more recently he has recorded for Bear Family and Rounder.

BEAR FAMILY 15486 (L)

Wild Side of Life

Twelve songs mostly written by Jimmy Heap; essentially a country release.

BEAR FAMILY 15501 (L)

The Eager Beaver Boy/Rockabilly Lives

Reissue of two Rolling Rock LPs from the mid-'70s, featuring 27 cuts by the man who made a name for himself as a rockabilly revivalist, but was also a struggling hillbilly bopper in the late '50s.

DOMINO 1001 (R)

Give that Love to Ray Campi

Fourteen cuts featuring both sides of Ray's legendary early singles cut for TNT ("Caterpillar" b/w "Play It Cool"), Dot ("Give that Love to Me"), Domino ("My Screamin' Screamin' Mimi," originally written for Little Richard, who never recorded it), and the Holly, Valens, Big Bopper tribute single on the D label ("The Man I Met" b/w "Ballad of Donna and Peggy Sue"). Also includes a later Rolling Rock track, plus The Slades's "You Gambled" single written by Campi with Ray on guitar (also includes the "You Cheated" single that doesn't have Ray), and Jim Lowe singing Campi's composition, "The Crossing."

FLYING FISH 90518 (CL)

With Friends in Texas

On this recording, originally issued on the German Bear Family label, Ray attempts to recreate the all-purpose entertainment bands of his Texas youth that played waltzes, two-steps, western swing, Tex Mex, and anything else that got them a gig. A star-studded recording from Austin with Del Shannon, Lou Ann Barton, Rose Maddox, Joe Ely, and Bonnie Raitt. By overdubbing some basic tracks from the early '70s, he also manages to include Merle Travis and Mae West (listen for her vamping on a groovy duet on "Caterpillar")!

ROUNDER 3046 (RC)
Rockin' at the Ritz
Ray plays all the instruments on this set that is a little less inspired than his first Rounder LP (3047).

ROUNDER 3047 (RC)
Ray Campi and His Rockabilly Rebels
His first LP on Rounder.

CANNED HEAT

Blues-based "ultimate boogie band" of the late '60s and early '70s led by vocalist Bob "The Bear" Hite, harp player and vocalist Alan Wilson (both avid blues scholars), and guitarist Henry Vestine. As the band gained popularity, they extended their solo work to the point where many of their live recordings feature seemingly endless boogie.

BEAR TRACKS 979409 (L)
Live at the Turku Rock Festival, Finland
Don't expect a sensitive, respectful blues set by these boogie beasts. They're even more raucous than on their studio LPs! Hite's voice sounds like he gargles with whiskey and the twin guitars of Henry Vestine and Joel Scott Hill sound like a chainsaw demonstration. They blast through faves like "Let's Work Together," "On the Road Again," and "Canned Heat Boogie," and they even give Hill a chance to show off on his blazing signature tune "Hill Stomp." If you can't appreciate some sloppy drunk blues rockin', kindly step aside.

BGO 12 (RL)
Canned Heat '70: Live in Europe
Reissue of Liberty 5509 from 1970. This show is rife with typical '70s noodling, meandering jams, and general psychedelic hogwash. But there's also a lot to be said for their straight-forward approach on the good tunes, particularly "The Bear's" gruff vocals and Harvey Mandel's raunchy blues guitar. That's All Right Mama/On the Road Again/Let's Work Together.

BGO 83 (RL)
Historical Figures and Ancient Heads
Reissue of 1972 United Artists album, originally UA 5557. Eight songs, including "Rockin' with the King" with Little Richard (voc, pno) and Clifford Solomon (ten sax).

BGO 85 (RL)
The New Age
Reissue of United Artists LA049F from 1973 featuring nine cuts of blues rock-and-biker boogie. Bob "Bear" Hite was still with the band (although singing lead on only five cuts), and Henry Vestine's stinging leads are ever present, but the band's emulation of hard blues seems to have softened and transformed into more of a creative and jocular bar-band sound. Includes Lieber and Stoller's classic "Framed," "Lookin' for My Rainbow," with Clara Ward and her singers, "Keep it Clean," and "Election Blues."

EMI (UK) 2026 (R)/793 114 (L)
The Best of Canned Heat:
Let's Work Together
Really good 16-tune selection of the best of Canned Heat's recorded output, leaving out most of the hippy-dippy nonsense and self-indulgent jams. The contrast between Hite's gruff singing and Wilson's mournful moaning (and great harp) kept things interesting, while Henry Vestine cranked up the excitement level with some very nasty distorted guitar. Boogie children! On the Road Again/Amphetamine Annie/Rollin' and Tumblin'/Going Up the Country/Sugar Bee.

SEE FOR MILES 62 (RL)
Boogie with Canned Heat
Reissue of Liberty 7541 from 1968. This, their second LP, found them masters of the electric John Lee Hooker-inspired boogie, enabling the group to take Floyd Jones's "Big Road Blues," redone as "On the Road Again" to the US and UK Top 10. Includes "Whiskey Headed Woman #2," the anti-drug "Amphetamine Annie," the guitar-and-horn Texas-blues instrumental "Marie Laveau," "Turpentine Moan" with guest star Sunnyland Slim, and their 10-minute "Fried Hockey Boogie." New liner notes by Brian Hogg.

SEE FOR MILES 248 (L)
Hallelujah
Reissue of Liberty 7618 from 1969. Includes the minor hit "Time Was." Same All Over/Change My Ways/Canned Heat/Down in the Gutter.

SEE FOR MILES 268 (R)
Canned Heat
Reissue of Canned Heat's debut album originally released as Liberty 7526 in 1967. This was before their FM radio hits and live concert acclaim, but it's probably still the highlight of their long career. They played with power and vision, unsullied by the later blues bombastics they used live and on record. The Bear and his crew work their mojo on city and country blues alike. Rollin' and Tumblin'/Bullfrog Blues/Catfish Blues/Dust My Broom/Big Road Blues.

ACE CANNON

Misissippi-born saxophonist who worked in the
'50s with Billy Lee Riley and then spent a couple
of years with The Bill Black Combo before forming his own group, joining the fledgeling Hi label,
and having a big hit with the somewhat polite
instrumental "Tuff." Subsequent Hi recordings
fared quite well though not as strongly as the first.

HI (UK) 412 (R)

Tuff!

Besides being the title of one of Cannon's tunes, this
LP has nothing "tuff" about it. It's a pleasant enough
romp through 14 jazz and blues standards featuring
the trademark Ace Cannon/Bill Black Combo sound.
Tuff/St. Louis Blues/Cannonball/Kansas City/Heart-
break Hotel.

FREDDY CANNON

Nicknamed "Mr. Boom-Boom," Freddie had a
series of raucous teen hits for Swan and Warner
Bros. With his uninhibited vocals and raucous
accompaniments with throbbing bass drum, his
music had a lively good-time feel. He's still active
on the oldies circuit.

CRITIQUE 5402 (L)

His Latest and Greatest

Excellent collection of 18 songs, including most of his
Swan and Warner Bros. hits, including "Palisades
Park," "Tallahasee Lassie," "Abigail Beecher," "Buzz
Buzz a Diddle It" (my favorite, with its powerful Bo
Diddley sound), "Way Down Yonder in New Or-
leans," "Humdinger," "Everybody Monkey," and
"Okefenokee." Also includes a couple of recent songs,
including a version of "Hanky Panky" with some new
lyrics. Some of the material here can be considered
teen schlock but, in general, this is an entertaining set.

THE CAPITOLS

Detroit-based band, originally formed in 1962 by
drummer and lead singer Samuel George and
guitarist Donald Storball. They scored a big hit
with 1966's "Cool Jerk." Other rug cutters followed, but failed to chart.

COLLECTABLES 5105 (CL)

Golden Classics

Twelve great Karen-label sides from 1966 with fine
vocals by the late Sam George. Cool Jerk/I Got to
Handle It/We Got a Thing That's in the Groove/Let's
Go Get Stoned/Please Please Please.

THE CAPRIS

Not to be confused with the '60s white group
who recorded "There's a Moon Out Tonight"
(see below); these Capris were a black group from
Philadelphia who recorded for Gotham between
1954–1958.

COLLECTABLES 5000 (CL)

Gotham Recording Stars

Includes their hit "God Only Knows" plus previously
unreleased sides and alternate takes.

THE CAPRIS

Fine white New York City-based group led by
Nick Santo. The group was formed in 1957 and
recorded a few unsuccessful numbers for the tiny
Planet label. During the 1960–1961 doo-wop
revival, their original Planet recording of
"There's a Moon Out Tonight" was rediscovered
by pop DJ Murray the K, and it was rereleased on
Hy Weiss's Old Town label and became a Number 3 hit. In 1980, Santo revived the group with
two other original members, and they released
excellent material on Ambient Sound.

COLLECTABLES 5016 (C)

There's a Moon Out Tonight

Ten beautiful Planet sides, including some previously
unreleased numbers, featuring their spine-tingling hit.
My Island in the Sun/Tears in My Eyes/Stars in the
Sky.

CARLO and THE BELMONTS

The Belmonts were Carlo Mastangelo (who took
Dion [DiMucci]'s place after Dion left to pursue
a solo career in 1961), Freddie Milano, and
Angelo D'Aleo. They were all Bronx- born (Bel-
mont Ave. area), second-generation Italian
Americans. (See separate listings for THE BEL-
MONTS and DION/DION AND THE BEL-
MONTS.)

ACE 251 (RL)

Carlo and The Belmonts

Half of this Laurie collection features the Belmonts's
1961 material of average quality, and the other half
features songs cut by Carlo as a soloist in 1962. All,
except the great rocking rendition of "Kansas City,"
are of minor interest and not nearly as exciting as their
Sabina sides cut in 1961 and available on Crystal Ball
102. The CD includes the insipid "Santa Margherita,"

the Belmonts's very first record (1957) for Mohawk, plus eight rarities not on the LP. Rare pix and informative notes.

JAMES CARR

In the mid-to-late '60s, Memphis soul singer James Carr recorded a string of singles for the Goldwax label that are considered to be among the very greatest deep-soul recordings. His expressive and intense vocals reflect his gospel background and the material, often from white writers like Dan Penn and Chips Moman, has a country quality that is part of the Southern soul sound. Songs like "You've Got My Mind Messed Up" and "The Dark End of the Street" are justifiably considered masterpieces and have been covered by everybody from Clarence Carter to Linda Ronstadt. In 1991, Carr recorded again for the reactivated Goldwax label and this new recording, while excellent, is not in the same league as the '60s sides. Curiously Goldwax shows no inclination to reissue the earlier recordings that are only available as expensive but essential Japanese imports.

GOLDWAX 5002 (L)

Take Me to the Limit

A 1991 recording. Of these ten cuts, about half recall the classic sound of his glory days, especially the unadorned arrangements and laid-back intensity of the title cut, "You Gotta Love Your Woman," "She's Already Gone," and "I Can't Leave Your Love." Granted, the voice is a little ragged, and even the better songs lack the poignant perspective that made his mid-'60s waxings so highly prized. But even the more contemporary numbers are on par with the stuff coming out of the South these days on labels like Malaco and Ichiban, with only a couple of real disco/country clunkers.

❂ VIVID SOUND 002 (L)

You Got My Mind Messed Up

Twenty-two great songs recorded in Memphis for Goldwax in the mid-to-late '60s with top Memphis sessionmen at Sam Phillips's studios. In addition to the definitive version of Dan Penn and Chips Moman's classic "The Dark End of the Street," it includes many other gems, including a stunning version of the Bee Gee's "To Love Somebody." She's Better Than You/You've Got My Mind Messed Up/Love Attack/Forgetting You/Lovable Girls/These Ain't Raindrops/Please Your Woman.

VIVID SOUND 005 (L)

A Man Needs a Woman

This superb package, a companion to Vivid Sound 002, includes all 12 selections from his first LP, plus nine more, which come from the *Freedom Train* LP. Unforgettable classics. I'm a Fool for You/More Love/You Didn't Know It but You Had Me/Sowed Love and Reaped a Heartache/Love Attack/Pouring Water on a Drowning Man.

VICKI CARR

Sixties chanteuse born Florencia Bisenta de Casillas Martinez Cardona. She began as a rocker before mellowing out and hitting the lounge circuit.

EMI 93450 (CL)

It Must Be Him

Twenty-four songs drawn from her hit-making years, 1962–1971. Includes the early rockers "He's a Rebel" and "I Got My Eye on You." My Heart Reminds Me/So Nice (Summer Samba)/It Must Be Him/A Bit of Love/Can't Take My Eyes Off of You/The Lesson/For Once in My Life/She'll Be There/Your Heart Is Free Just like the Wind/With Pen in Hand/Eternity.

JOHNNY CARROLL

Excellent Texas rockabilly singer who recorded for Decca and Phillips International in the '50s (reissued on Sunjay). He starred in the cult movie classic, *Rock Baby Rock It* (the soundtrack has been reissued on Rhino; see the compilation section). He staged a comeback in the '70s, recording several LPs for Rolling Rock (one of which has been reissued on Magnum Force), and enjoying new popularity in England.

MAGNUM FORCE 054 (R)

Texabilly

Fine material recorded in '78 for the Rolling Rock label. 16 Tons Rockabilly/Is It Easy to Be Easy?/People in Texas Like to Dance.

SUNJAY 581 (R)

Rockin' Roll Rarities

Reissue of classic '50s performances. The first four songs are from the *Rock Baby Rock It* movie soundtrack, including an amazing 1957 performance by Carroll on "Rockin' Maybelle," "Sugar Baby," "Crazy Crazy Lovin'," and "Wild Wild Women." Also included from the film are two so-so tunes by the Belew Twins, because Johnny's band, The Hot Rocks, back them; lead guitarist Jay Salem stings it but good on "Love Me Baby." The highlight of the LP turns out to be seven demos from 1955 (six previously unissued) cut at Top Ten Studios in Dallas. There's not a ballad in the bunch, either, they're all rockers. Essential for rockabilly fans. This LP duplicates four tunes from the out-of-print *Crazy Hot Rock* (Charly 30241) album released a few years back. Sexy Ways/Crazy Little Mama/Hearts of Stone/Stingy Thing/Cut Out.

CLARENCE CARTER

Incredible, underrated blind soulster who was one of the originators of the Muscle Shoals sound. His early recordings with Calvin Thomas were released as by Calvin & Clarence and C&C on Duke. His first solo recordings were made at Rick Hall's Fame studios in Muscle Shoals; he was one of the first artists to work there. Carter is also an excellent songwriter, whose works include Etta James's "Tell Mama."

ATLANTIC (JAPAN) 2375 (L)
This Is Clarence Carter
Budget Japanese CD of Carter's classic first LP, originally issued as Atlantic 8192 from 1968. One of the best LPs to emerge from Muscle Shoals, it features all of the stellar sidemen who worked for the Fame studios, with tunes from the pens of Carter, Rick Hall, Quin Ivy, Dan Penn, and Spooner Oldham. Includes his first smash hit "Slip Away," plus "Thread the Needle," "Funky Fever," "Looking for a Fox," "She Ain't Gonna Do Right," and a great version of Clay Hammond's "Part Time Love"

ICHIBAN 1001 (RCL)
Messin' with My Mind
1985 LP recorded in Muscle Shoals. Clarence shows he's still in fine voice and his evil laugh is still intact. The only problem is that the material is a bit too weak; most of the tunes were written by either Carter or Malaco's George Jackson. There's still plenty to recommend to the Carter fan, and the deep-soul numbers are quite good. Highlight is Clarence's testifying on his remake of "Wrong Too Long," about the breakup of his marriage to Candi Stanton. Also excellent are the title tune, "Love Me with a Feeling," and "I Was in the Neighborhood."

ICHIBAN 1003 (RCL)
Dr. C.C.
This 1986 LP is a one-man show. Clarence does everything except background vocals, playing all drums, keyboards, synthesizers, bass, guitar, percussion, and horns! Surprisingly, it mostly sounds like vintage Carter except for those darn synthesizers. Includes a fine remake of "I Stayed Away Too Long," "Left over Love" (cowritten with Sam Dees), and six more Carter originals, including "You Been Cheatin'

on Me," "If You Let Me Take You Home," and the title tune.

ICHIBAN 1016 (RCL)
Hooked on Love
Another one-man show, with Clarence playing all the instruments and performing all vocals (except background parts). Carter's sly humor is still strong, especially on what should be this LP's most popular cut, "Grandpa Can't Fly His Kite" ("cuz grandma won't give him no tail"). Eight tunes all written by Carter except a fair version of "What'd I Say" and a fine remake of his biggest hit, "Slip Away."

✪ RHINO 70286 (CL)
Snatching It Back
This greatest-hits package from his Atlantic years (1965–1971) will send listeners searching for Carter's out-of-print albums. Every song is a piece of classic Southern soul with singer/guitarist Carter's expressive baritone leading the way. He deals in love and infidelity; if he's not "Looking for a Fox," he's claiming "I Smell a Rat." All his top 10 hits are here, including "Slip Away," "Patches," "I Can't Leave Your Love Alone," "Doin' Our Thing," "The Feeling Is Right," and the title track. But some of his best cuts never even charted. The gospel-flavored "I Stayed Away Too Long" captures the sound of pure regret as few other songs have done. Likewise the preaching "Making Love (at the Dark End of the Street)," which bears little resemblance to James Carr's version, is a bit of uncharted genius. Great photos, and notes from rockcritic Dave Marsh. Best title: "Back Door Santa." Unambiguously recommended.

THE CASANOVAS

Chester Mayfield and The Casanovas (aka the gospel group The Jubilee Kings) of High Point, NC, are, to my mind, the most neglected major vocal quintet of the '50s. Members included brothers Frank and Willie McWilliams and Chester and L.D. Mayfield, their nephews. Their style, although akin to The Five Royales, was smooth, pretty, and finely polished.

RELIC 5073 (R)
The Best of The Casanovas
Sixteen cuts, four unreleased (one being the beautiful a cappella "Listen to the Bells"). Includes three of their blues-based 1955 ballads, "That's All," "It's Been a Long Time," and "Sleepy Head Mama" that are unsurpassed in beauty and conviction. Fascinating notes and rare pix. Highly recommended.

AL CASEY

Surf-era guitarist.

STACY 100 (R)

Surfin' Hootenanny

Stereo repro of his rare 1963 LP, complete with "surf-colored" vinyl. Casey's attempt to meld the surf sound to folk is (fortunately) limited to "Guitars Guitars Guitars" and the title tune with vocals by The K-C-Ettes. The rest is pure surf-instrumental heaven, produced by Lee Hazelwood, with backing probably provided by studio regulars Larry Knechtel, Steve Douglas, and Hal Blaine. Includes "Ramrod" and "Caravan" (Casey is the guitarist on the original hit version, though Duane Eddy's name was put on the record), plus "Surfin' Blues, Pts. 1 and 2," "Lonely Surfer," and "Baja."

THE CASTELLES

One of the earliest of the Philadelphia groups, featuring the high, lead vocals of George Grant. They recorded for Herb Slotkin's Grand label, whose other main employee was Jerry Ragovoy, who wrote, produced, and played on their records. The Castelles scored with "My Girl Awaits Me" and "Over a Cup of Coffee," before becoming one of the first groups signed to Atco in 1956. Ragovoy moved to New York and began working with uptown soul singers like Garnet Mimms and Erma Franklin.

COLLECTABLES 5002 (CL)

The Sweet Sound of The Castelles

Fourteen excellent Grand sides recorded in 1954–1955. My Girl Awaits Me/Over a Cup of Coffee/This Silver Ring/Over the Rainbow.

JOEY CASTLE

Joey Castle, who also recorded under the name of Cliff Rivers, was actually a stocky teenager from New York City named Joseph Castaldo. Rockabilly fans have been going nuts for years over his handful of waxings, including "Rock and Roll Daddy-O" on Headline, "True Lips" on Thanks (released under the name of Cliff Rivers), and "That Ain't Nothin' but Right" on RCA. He sounded as much like Elvis as anyone else, with a deep, rich voice that could dip down into that kind of little growl that made the girls squeal.

BEAR FAMILY 15560 (L)

Rock and Roll Daddy-O

Includes all of his hit tunes along with their flip sides, plus three tunes from a 1958 demo session, a couple of unissued numbers done for Vik in '58, a trio of '60s demos, and his last single on Out Of Sight, "That's My Secret" b/w "(I'm the) Phantom Lover." A nice booklet is included with some real cool pix.

THE CELLOS

The Cellos, whose ballad B-sides have long been cherished by doo-wop collectors, hailed from West Manhattan, and included Alton Campbell (lead), Billy Montgomery (1st ten), Clifford Williams (2nd ten), Bobby Thomas (bar), and Alvin Williams (b). They struck paydirt with their first single, the novelty "Rang Tang Ding Dong (I Am the Japanese Sandman)" for Apollo in 1957, but never repeated this success. Campbell and Montgomery left the group in 1959 to join The Channels.

RELIC 5074 (R)/7029 (L)

The Best of The Cellos:
Rang Tang Ding Dong
(I Am the Japanese Sandman)

All four of their singles cut in 1957–1958 appear here, plus three unissued sides, two alternates, and the bluesy "Don't Wait" on which the group accompanies Dolly Lyon. Although The Cellos's ballad sides are good, they never really came "alive" except on the novelty hits.

THE CHAMPS

Long-lived instrumental group who began their life as a studio band centered around guitarist Dave Burgess and saxophonist Danny Flores's (aka Chuck Rio) trio with a session bassist. "Tequila," a throw away written by Rio, was a Number 1 hit for Challange, and a group was formed. After an unsuccessful followup, Rio left to form The Originals; a new "Champs" was formed with Burgess, Jimmy Seals, Dash Croft (of later Seals and Croft fame), and Dean Beard for more hits including the followup to their first hit, "Too Much Tequila." Final versions of the group had Burgess (as the owner of the name) running the band with Glen Campbell on guitar, which produced the original "Limbo Rock."

ACE 227 (R)
Tequila
Twenty-two instrumental greats from the various incarnations of the band. Must have sounded great coming out of a late '50s convertible cruising Sunset Strip! Tequila/Too Much Tequila/Le Cucaracha/El Rancho Rock/Limbo Rock/Train to Nowhere/Experiment in Terror/Beatnik.

CHALLENGE 3500 (R)
Go Little Go Cat
When is a Champs LP not a Champs LP? Well, grasshopper, it's when the Tequila-soused band used The Champs name, but also took a shotgun approach when the times were tough to release a whole bunch of singles under many different names in hopes of a hit. Most of the time they go for the raunchy sax-led instrumentals that made them famous, but there are some surprises like the rockin' "Sneaky Pete" where the guitar fights it out with the sax on a mean boogie beat, or the red-hot rockabilly backup on The Four Teens tunes "Spark Plug" and "Go Little Go Cat." Sixteen tunes originally released under the names of The Contenders, The Originals, Jimmy Seals, and Dave Burgess, as well as The Champs. Worth every penny.

LINE 9.00380 (L)
Go Champs Go

LINE 9.00382 (L)
Everybody's Rockin'

LINE 9.00597 (L)
The Champs Collection

LINE 9.01040 (L)
Greatest Hits
How many ways can Line repackage their Champs tracks? The first two CDs each feature twelve short tunes by the champions of the Latin-flavored instrumental. Normal people will wonder why they didn't put both of these collections on one CD (with room to spare). The third and fourth releases give us more generous helpings of Champ tracks, but each duplicate the first two (and each other!) to some degree. Tequila/El Rancho Rock/Night Beat/Turnpike/Bandido/Ali Baba/Mau Mau Stomp/Sombrero/Limbo Rock/Alley Cat/Too Much Tequila/Midnighter/Go Champs Go.

GENE CHANDLER (EUGENE DIXON)

One of the deans of Chicago soul, Eugene Dixon joined the Chicago vocal group The Dukays in 1960. The group recorded for Vee Jay, and were handled by ace producer Carl Davis. On one of the Dukays's sides, "The Duke of Earl," Davis pushed Dixon to the front and changed his last name to Chandler. Gene quickly hit with "Duke" and, working with Curtis Mayfield, produced a long and excellent string of hits for Vee Jay from 1961–1964 (including "Man's Temptation"), Constellation from 1964–1966 ("Just Be True" and "Rainbow '65"), Checker from 1966–1967 ("To Be a Lover"), Brunswick from 1967–1969 ("From the Teacher to the Preacher," a duet with Barbara Acklin), and Mercury from 1970–1974 ("Groovy Situation"). While at Mercury, he also recorded duets with Jerry Butler. He worked on and off as a producer, most notably producing Mel and Tim's *Backfield in Motion* LP in 1969 and working for A&M Records from 1974–1977. He served time in prison for heroin possession, but by 1979 was back on the charts with "Get Down." His fine Brunswick sides have been reissued on *Anthology of Chicago Soul* (Epic/Brunswick 39895; see R&B collections).

CHESS 91561 (C)
The Duke of Soul
Reissue of Checker 3003 from 1967. Twelve sides, the cream of the crop of his Vee Jay and Constellation 45s issued between 1961–1965. This has quite a bit of duplication with the now out-of-print Solid Smoke 8027, the best anthology of his classic recordings, but it also has "Check Yourself" and "A Tear for a Tear," which have not been reissued on any other collection. Man's Temptation/Duke of Earl/Just Be True/Rainbow '65.

BRUCE CHANNEL

TEENAGER 601 (R)
Hey Baby!
It's not too often that the session harmonica player on a Number 1 hit goes further than the singer, but it happened to Bruce. (The harp player was Delbert McClinton!) "Hey Baby" had a unique sound for its time and had much-deserved success. Channel's self-penned tunes are by far the best tracks here. "Run Romance Run," "Sorry Baby," "Number One Man," and "Now or Never" are really good tunes and not overly similar to his hit. His cover versions can be really awful though, especially "Breakin' Up Is Hard to Do" and "Baby, It's You." He does do a fine version of the classic "Goin' Back to Louisiana" that rocks pretty good. Hey Baby/C.C. Rider/Mine Exclusively/My Baby.

THE CHANNELS

Harlem-based doo-wop group with Earl Lewis on lead. They worked mainly with Bobby Robinson, their first manager, with several minor hits on his Whirling Disc (1956's "The Closer You Are"), Fire (1958's "Bye Bye Baby"), and Fury (1959's "The Girl Next Store") labels, with a break in 1957 to score a hit with George Goldner's Gone Label with "That's My Desire." The original group broke up in 1959, but the early '60s doo-wop revival brought a new group together, without Lewis, to record a few more singles between 1963–1965, including 1963's "Sad Song" for Robinson's Enjoy label. Lewis started a new band by the end of the '60s to perform on the rock-revival circuit. Lewis founded his own Channel Records in 1971, which has released new recordings, showing that his high tenor is still in great shape.

RELIC 5086 (R)/7002 (L)
The Channels' Greatest Hits
Their best sides "The Closer You Are" (1956), "All Alone" (1958), and the gorgeous "My Love Will Never Die" (1959) are all included here in peerless fidelity with info-laden sleeve notes by the incomparable Donn Fileti.

THE CHANTAYS

The Chantays were a surf band from Santa Ana, CA that had one of surf music's biggest hits with "Pipeline" in 1963. Formed by high-school buddies Bob Spickard (lead gtr), Brian Carman (gtr), Warren Waters (b), Bob Marshall (pno), and Bob Welch (drm), they were discovered by DJ Jack Sands while playing a dance at The Big Bear, a local club. LA label Downey Records, who had scored with The Rumblers's "Boss," picked up their demo record of "Pipeline," hoping to score another surfing hit. The song raced up the charts, thanks to national distribution by Dot, but the high-school students were unable to tour to support its success. They churned out a few LPs, featuring a few standards along with the surf numbers, before disbanding in 1964.

DOT 7756 (R)
The Best of the Chantays
A generous 19 tracks of surf sounds featuring lots of manic guitar-string contortions. Pipeline/Beyond/Continental Missile/Torquay/Tragic Wind/Space Probe/Banzai/Move It.

REPERTOIRE 4114 (L)
Two Sides of the Chantays/Pipeline
German CD reissue of the Chantays's two Dot LPs: Pipeline (originally on Downey) from 1963 and Two Sides of the Chantays from 1966. Twenty-four primo waxings. Beyond/Space Probe/Retaliation/Tragic Wind/Runaway/Banzai.

THE CHANTELS

One of the earliest and best girl groups, spearheaded by the soulful lead vocals of Arlene Smith. Smith was only 16 years old when the group hit the charts with her incredible original song, "Maybe," released by End in 1958. The group continued to record for End for several years and had smaller hits. They joined Carlton in 1961, by which time Smith had left the group, and had another big hit with "Look in My Eyes."

COLLECTABLES 5423 (CL)
The Chantels
Twelve great songs, a reissue of Roulette 59032, including their monster hit "Maybe." Some duplication with the Rhino collection. Come My Little Baby/Prayer/I Love You So/Whoever You Are/Sure of Love.

COLLECTABLES 8802 (CL)
For Collectors Only
Two-CD/cassette set. Most of this material was recorded for End Records between 1957–1962, with some cuts from the Gone and Carlton labels. Includes their big hit "Maybe" along with lesser charting songs, including "I Love You So," "Summer's Love," and "Look in My Eyes," but this collection is primarily desirable for the "collector's only" stuff. No fewer than nine songs are alternate takes, including "Memories of You," "I'm the Girl," "Goodbye to Love," "I've Lied" (featuring The Tunemasters), and "If You Try." "So Real" and the boring instrumental (?!) "Peruvian Wedding Song" are previously unreleased. With 40 tracks in all, the songs sound a bit similar if taken in one sitting—sort of like listening to two hours of "Maybe"—but fortunately they can be listened to in smaller doses.

⊕ RHINO 70954 (CL)
The Best of The Chantels
Fourteen-track cassette or 18-track CD. CD bonus tracks include one with Richard Barrett. Maybe/Look in My Eyes/I Love You So/Well, I Told You.

PAUL CHAPLAIN and THE EMERALDS

Seven-piece band from the suburbs of Chicago formed in 1957, with Chaplain on vocals, and the other personnel unknown, but there's piano and a couple of booting saxes. The group put out some singles on the NY Harper label, and "Shortnin' Bread" was big enough to be issued in England.

WHITE LABEL 8915 (R)
Mr. Nicotine
This set has seven originally issued tunes, three previously unissued alternate takes, and four never-before issued tunes. "Nicotine," the rockin'-est here and flip side of "Shortnin' Bread" is heard in two different takes. The unissued tunes sound like unfinished demos. Also includes their second hit "Swingtime in the Rockies." Caldonia/Baby Please Don't Leave/Time Time/I Get the Bug.

RAY CHARLES

The Genius! Ray Charles is one of the greatest musical talents of the 20th century, a magnificent and creative singer, songwriter, piano and sax player, arranger, and producer. Blind since the age of six due to glaucoma, Ray has had a long, successful career. Born Ray Charles Robinson, he learned piano as a Florida teen, and in the late '40s moved to Seattle. Ray, now known as R.C. Robinson, was singing and playing in a soft Charles Brown/Nat King Cole vein, and he started a piano trio with G.D. McGhee (gtr) and Milt Garred (b). Called the McSon Trio (for Robinson and McGhee), later slurred to The Maxim Trio, the group started recording for Downbeat/Swingtime in 1949, placing a couple of tunes on the R&B charts. This material has been constantly reissued, and is currently available on Ebony.

When Downbeat/Swingtime went under in 1952, Ray (now Ray Charles, to avoid confusion with boxer Sugar Ray Robinson) signed to Atlan-

tic. In the beginning, he worked in a combined talking blues and jump-blues style, which yielded his first hit "It Should've Been Me" in 1954. He took a bit of a sabbatical, playing piano (as R.C. Robinson) behind New Orleans bluesman Eddie "Guitar Slim" Jones, appearing on the million-selling "Things I Used to Do." By 1955, Ray experimented with a combination of gospel and secular music on "I Got a Woman," which got him in trouble with the Church but was the beginning of modern soul music. By 1956, Atlantic was recording him as a jazz pianist, often with Milt Jackson of The Modern Jazz Quartet. As an LP title, Atlantic president Ahmet Ertegun came up with a Turkish/Muslim phrase, "Soul Brothers," for them (Charles's jazz sides are available on a number of reissues from Atlantic and DCC Classics).

By 1957, Ray finally hit the pop charts with "Swanee River Rock," and topped the R&B charts with "What'd I Say," also a pop hit. By 1960, he had left Atlantic to join ABC, and also formed his own label, Tangerine, which was distributed by ABC. An experiment with recording country music paid off with the two-million selling "I Can't Stop Loving You," plus two *Modern Sounds in Country and Western* LPs. He had several big C&W hits, including "Georgia on My Mind" (which he performed in the Georgia state legislature when it was made the state's song in the late '80s), "Hit the Road Jack," "Let's Go Get Stoned," and "Busted." By 1973, he was back at Atlantic, where he again got his own label, Crossover, where he mainly recorded country, pop, and show tunes. Since the '80s, he's been recording for Columbia as a country artist.

Ray's fine ABC material has finally been reissued by DCC Compact Classics, and is also available from Rhino; his Atlantic material has been reissued in a million forms, from exact duplications of older LPs to anthologies. *The Birth of Soul* (Atlantic 82310) is particularly recommended for these classic sides.

ATLANTIC 1312 (CL)
The Genius of Ray Charles
Big band/jazz ballad LP originally issued in 1959. Twelve cuts with Zoot Sims, Paul Gonsalves, Clark Terry, David "Fathead" Newman, and Bob Brookmeyer. Let the Good Times Roll/It Had to Be You/Come Rain or Come Shine.

ATLANTIC 1259 (C)/81731 (L)
The Great Ray Charles
His first two jazz sessions in chronological order with arrangements by Quincy Jones. Eight tracks on cassette, 14 on CD.

⊙ ATLANTIC 82310 (CL)
The Birth of Soul:
Complete Atlantic R&B Recordings
Many of these 53 tracks are easily available elsewhere, but the cumulative experience of hearing Charles make amazing discovery after discovery about nascent soul's possibilities, reaching over three CDs (although this could have fit on two) is extraordinary. While others' versions of soul were exclusive, Charles's was adamantly inclusive. His interests ranged far beyond even the broadest definition of soul or R&B, and he crossed musical borders as emphatically as Elvis or Jerry Lee. What's most phenomenal on *The Birth of Soul* is his ability to take notions that purists might consider antithetical to the R&B form—like big-band arrangements—and harness them in the service of great, church-influenced, soulful songs. All the landmark soul-gospel hits are here, like "I've Got a Woman," "Drown in My Own Tears," "Hallelujah I Love Her So," and the full-length "What'd I Say"— nearly half of these songs hit the R&B Top 20—and everything appears in its best sound ever. Comes in a six-by-twelve box, and includes a 32-page booklet with scholarly notes by Robert Palmer. Highly recommended.

ATLANTIC (JAPAN) 2381 (L)
Ray Charles
Nine cuts, an exact reproduction of Ray's first LP, Atlantic 8006, from 1957. Drown in My Own Tears/ Hallelujah I Love Her So/Mess Around/This Little Girl of Mine/I Got a Woman.

ATLANTIC (JAPAN) 2382 (L)
What'd I Say
Eleven tracks, reissue of Atlantic 8029 from 1959. What'd I Say, Pts. 1 and 2/What Kind of Man Are You/Tell All the World about You/That's Enough.

COLUMBIA 39415 (L)
Friendship
Country sides with Hank Williams, Jr., Merle Haggard, George Jones, Willie Nelson, and Johnny Cash.

COLUMBIA 40125 (CL)
The Spirit of Christmas

COLUMBIA 40703 (L)
Just Between Us

DCC COMPACT CLASSICS 036 (L)
His Greatest Hits, Vol. 1
Hallelujah! Though Ray's great Atlantic sides are always in print, his ABC sides (recorded between 1959–1972), probably much better-known, have long been out-of-print, mostly due to the fact that they were owned by Ray and not a record company. This CD (and its companion 037) feature 40 tunes, digitally remixed and remastered by The Genius himself for exquisite sound, and the selection is faultless. This first volume has an hour playing time with 20 hits. Georgia on My Mind/Unchain My Heart/Born to Lose/Here We Go Again/Crying Time/Let's Go Get Stoned/I Don't Need No Doctor.

DCC COMPACT CLASSICS 037 (L)
His Greatest Hits, Vol. 2
Another 20 great ABC sides including many never before on LP. Busted/Hit the Road Jack/Ruby/I Can't Stop Loving You/Makin' Whoopie/Baby It's Cold Outside/America the Beautiful/Take These Chains from My Heart.

DCC COMPACT CLASSICS 038 (RCL)
Genius Plus Soul = Jazz
This is a reissue of Ray's Impulse LP of the same name in its entirety plus three cuts from *Genius Hits the Road.* This is all big-band jazz material, featuring Ray on organ and some outstanding playing by sidemen Joe Newman, Thad Jones, Clark Terry, Budd Johnson, and Freddy Green. Arrangements by Quincy Jones and Ralph Burns. Digitally remixed and remastered. From the Heart/One Mint Julep/Strike Up the Band/New York's My Home/Let's Go/Mister C./Basin Street Blues.

DCC COMPACT CLASSICS 047 (L)
Ingredients in a Recipe for Soul
Reissue of 1963 album (originally ABC 465) with four extra cuts originally only on singles. This reissue has been compiled, digitally remixed, and mastered by Ray and Steve Hoffman. Over the Rainbow/In the Evening (When the Sun Goes Down)/Busted/That Lucky Old Sun/Where Can I Go/You'll Never Walk Alone/Something's Wrong/Worried Life Blues.

EBONY 8001 (L)
The Birth of a Legend 1949–1952
Hallelujah! A comprehensive, intelligent collection of this American immortal's 1949–1952 recordings for the Down Beat and Swing Time labels, including titles recorded but not released by them. The full 41 tracks are here, on two CDs in a hinged single CD case with a cardboard slipcover. A 32-page booklet is included, with a biography, discography with alternate titles, session notes, and complete lyrics. All in all, an attractive and detailed portrait of a major artist discovering his musical identity, moving from his early attempts to walk in the footsteps of Nat King Cole to the beginnings of genuine Ray Charles soul. The sound, clearly dubbed from earlier discs, is generally quite good. A compilation of major importance to fans of R&B, blues, and jazz alike. Very highly recommended. Confession Blues/Let's Have a Ball/Don't Put All Your Dreams in One Basket/She's on the Ball/I'll Do Anything but Work/All to Myself/The Snow is Falling/Back Home.

RHINO 75759 (L)
Anthology
Twenty classics, the same titles and versions that were on the out-of-print Rhino *Greatest Hits, Vol. 1 and 2* LPs, which reissue 26 ABC-Paramount recordings in all. CD contains "Hallelujah I Love Her So," which is not on either album.

RAY CHARLES and BETTY CARTER

DCC COMPACT CLASSICS 039 (RCL)
Ray Charles and Betty Carter
Reissue of a duet session (originally ABC 385), one track from *Have a Smile with Me*, and two titles that apparently have not been out on LP before. The duet material is a bit disappointing. Charles and Carter work well together, but the big-band and string/vocal-group accompaniments I found to be too brash and too saccharine respectively. Digitally remixed and remastered. Arrangements by Marty Paich. Ev'ry Time I Say Goodbye/Cocktails for Two/For All We Know/But on the Other Hand Baby/You and I/Side by Side/It Takes Two to Tango/I Never See Maggie Alone.

THE CHARTS
Fine Harlem doo-wop quintet who recorded for Bobby Robinson's Everlast label in 1957. Original members Joe Grier (lead), noted for his yodel-like falsetto, Leroy Bims (1st ten), Steven Brown (2nd ten), Glenmore Jackson (bar), and Ross Buford (b) met as members of a Harlem street gang. They scored their big hit with Grier's "Deserie," a song that got them booed off the stage at the Apollo because of its unusual structure (unlike most other pop songs, it has no chorus or bridge, but rather features three, slow-paced, long verses). It became a New York classic, selling three-and-a-half million copies.

COLLECTABLES 5029 (CL)
The Charts Greatest Hits
Why Do You Cry/I Told You So/You're the Reason/Baby Be Mine.

CHUBBY CHECKER
Legendary chicken-plucker Ernie Evans, who was given his famous nom-de-disc by Dick Clark's wife as a takeoff on "Fats Domino." Chubby took the old Hank Ballard song, "The Twist," and started a national dance craze. It hit the top of the charts twice: in September 1960 and January 1962. Besides all his twist hits for Parkway in the early '60s, he also started the Limbo craze with "Limbo Rock" and "Let's Limbo Some More," and fueled other dances from the Popeye ("Popeye the Hitchhiker"), the Swim ("She Want's t' Swim"), and even picked up on the Freddie ("Do the Freddie," recorded in 1965). He rode the surf craze with 1963's "Surf Party." He stayed with Parkway until 1966, then went to Buddah where he had his last hit, 1969's cover of The Beatles's "Back in the USSR." He was featured in the flick *Let the Good Times Roll* and is still very active on the oldies circuit. Amazingly enough, none of his recordings are currently available in English on a collection devoted to him!

BEAR FAMILY 15339 (R)
Twist Doch Mal Mit Mir
This is the one you have been waiting for: early '60s recordings by the Chubby one singing in German.

Includes "Der Twist Beginnt" which you might know as "Let's Twist Again"!

THE CHECKERS

The excellent Checkers quartet was formed to rival The Dominoes, whose notable bass lead Bill "60 Minute Man" Brown sang in both outfits. They even recorded for the same record company and utilized the same basic harmonies. High-tenor lead Little David Baughn went on to sing with The Harps and to temporarily replace Clyde McPhatter in The Drifters.

SING 503 (R)
The Checkers
Listen to Little David's emotionally touching pipes on the beautiful "House without Windows" and "I Promise You"; you'd swear you were listening to Clyde McPhatter. Includes "Don't Stop Dan," a clone of The Dominoes' "60 Minute Man." No sleeve notes, but good, average sound.

THE CHESSMEN

Mid-'60s a cappella group from Manhattan featuring James Myers (lead voc), Bill Ramirez (1st ten), Ted Ziffer (2nd ten), Tommy Reyes (bar), and Art Crank (b). They built quite a formidable reputation in clubs and on radio around NY and NJ.

RELIC 106 (R)/7019 (L)
A Cappella Showcase/All Nite Long
Twenty fine sides, mostly originals. CD has two bonus cuts. Dance Gypsy/A Teardrop Fell from My Eyes/Don't Have to Shop Around/There Goes My Baby.

THE CHI-LITES

Late '60s through early '70s soul quintet led by Eugene Record, who also cowrote most of their songs. They were originally called The Hi-Lites, but, after discovering another group had already been using this name, added the "C" to become Chi-Lites. Although the group was together since the early '60s, they did not score any hits until late in the decade.

KENT (UK) 911 (L)
The Best of The Chi-Lites
The most extensive Chi-Lites collection ever. Nineteen tunes from 1969's "Give It Away" to 1976's "You Don't Have to Go," running over 74 minutes long. Most tunes cowritten by Eugene Record and Barbara Acklin (they'd started out by writing "Love Makes a Woman"). All the biggies are here and sound great. Have You Seen Her?/(For God's Sake) Give More Power to the People/Homely Girl/Let Me Be the Man My Daddy Was/A Letter to Myself/Stoned Out of My Mind.

THE CHIFFONS

Judy Craig, Barbara Lee, Patricia Bennett, and Sylvia Peterson, four Bronx teenagers, formed The Chiffons in 1960, and after they joined the Laurie label in 1963 enjoyed one of the best strings of success in girl-group history with "He's So Fine," "Stop, Look and Listen," and "One Fine Day." Craig had a voice as rich and complex as fine wine, and when linked with the consummate pop lyrics and arrangements at Laurie, all of their songs were at least catchy and interesting.

ACE 293 (RL)
Greatest Recordings
Value-packed 20-tune collection of the hits and more, digitally transferred from the original Laurie mastertapes. If you like the big hits, you'll be pleasantly surprised at the quality of the rest of their output, especially minor classics like "Mystic Voice," "Up on the Bridge," and "My Block."

COLLECTABLES 5042 (C)
16 Golden Classics
Originally Laurie 4001. He's So Fine/Sweet Talking Guy/I Have a Boyfriend/A Love So Fine/My Boyfriend's Back/Open Your Eyes.

LAURIE (JAPAN) 22056 (L)
Single Collection
Japanese CD, duplicating material on the Ace 293. Twenty-one girl-group rockers about boys, girls, and what happens when they get together. Includes a post-litigation version of the "He's So Fine" soundalike, George Harrison's "My Sweet Lord." One Fine Day/He's So Fine/Sailor Boy/Sweet Talking Guy/My Boyfriend's Back/When the Boy's Happy.

THE CHORDETTES

The Chordettes, favorites of America's maltshops, had a string of pop hits from 1954–1962. The four teen gals from Sheboygan, WI—Lynn Evans (lead), Margie Needham (ten), Carol Buschman (bar), and Janet Ertel (b)—brought together many of the non-teenage styles of the era—barbershop quartet, The Andrews's Sisters, and movie, stage, and TV music—and repackaged them for the teenage market. Winning a talent contest gained them a regular slot on Arthur Godfrey's TV show and a contract on Cadence Records. Their hits include the novelty classics "Lollipop," "Zorro," and "Mr. Sandman." There is much duplication among the reissues listed below.

ACE 934 (L)
Mainly Rock and Roll

Thirty-two Cadence sides from 1954–1962, including their big hits. Mr. Sandman/Eddie My Love/Born to Be with You/Lay Down Your Arms/Just between You and Me/Lollipop/Never on Sunday.

CADENCE (JAPAN) 32 (L)
Lollipop

Twenty mid-'50s pop songs with a light rock-and-roll touch. Mr. Sandman/Lollipop/Born to Be with You/Never on Sunday/Eddie My Love/Lay Down Your Arms/Teenage Goodnight/A Girl's Work Is Never Done/Soft Sands/Faraway Star/The Wedding/Adios.

RHINO 70849 (CL)
The Best of the Chordettes

All the hits are here and more. Do you remember their version of "Zorro"? A couple of the tunes here are almost rock and roll: "A Girl's Work Is Never Done" and "No Wheels," with a King Curtis sax solo. CD has four extra tracks.

LOU CHRISTIE

Christie (real name Lugee Sacco), known for his striking falsetto, first hit on the local Pennsylvania label C&C with "The Gypsy Cried" (1962), which sold so well that it was picked up for national release by Roulette. He stayed with Roulette until 1965, scoring with "Two Faces Have I." He next went to MGM, where he had his biggest hits, "Lightnin' Strikes" (1965) and "Rhapsody in the Rain," which was banned by many radio stations because the couple in the song were "making out in the rain." After short stints at Co & Ce, Colpix, and Columbia, he signed with the bubblegum-infested Buddah label in 1969, and got his first Top 10 hit in three years with "I'm Gonna Make You Mine." He had a spotty recording career in the '70s, and still occasionally hits the oldies circuit.

RHINO 70246
The Best of Lou Christie: En-Lightnin'-ment

Fourteen tunes from 1962–1969, including a few that weren't on the out-of-print Raven reissue. Includes hits for C&C ("The Gypsy Cried"), Roulette ("Two Faces Have I"), MGM ("Lightnin' Strikes" and "Rhapsody in the Rain"), Columbia ("Shake Hands and Walk Away Crying" and "Back to the Days of the Romans"), and Buddah ("I'm Gonna Make You Mine"). Extensive liner notes by fan club prez Harry Young.

THE CHURCH STREET FIVE

Gary "U.S." Bonds's backup group, led by tenor saxman Gene "Daddy G" Barge, previously known for his solo on Chuck Willis's "C.C. Rider." The band had the unorthodox lineup of two tenor saxes (Barge and Earl Swanson, though usually only one played at a time), trombone (Leonard Barks), piano (Willie Burrell), upright bass (Jr. Fairley), and one of the noisiest drummers of all time, Nabs Shields.

LEGRAND 1007 (R)
A Nite with Daddy G

God, what a noisy album! Fourteen pounding tunes, never before on LP, with four in real stereo. Includes the two-part title tune, which is a blazing instrumental version of "Quarter to Three." Church Street Battle/D.C. Shuffle/Everybody Do the Ska/Fallen Arches.

JIMMY CLANTON

Smooth teen singer from New Orleans who hit it big with the R&B ballad "Just a Dream" in 1958, and produced further hits over the next five years. Top-notch accompaniments by New Orleans session musicians and a decent choice of material made his recordings somewhat more interesting than his Philadelphia counterparts, Fabian and Frankie Avalon, despite the anemic quality of his vocals.

ACE (US) 1011 (R)
My Best to You

Reissue of Clanton's fourth LP, a twelve-cut greatest-hits affair. Did you know that "each of his original songs has in its own way reflected the experiences of every teenager"? Me neither. Just a Dream/A Letter to an Angel/Little Boy in Love/Go, Jimmy, Go.

ACE (US) 2030 (R)
Just a Dream
US issue of Ace 93. Fourteen tracks feature Clanton accompanied by fine New Orleans musicians. Just a Dream/You Aim to Please/Go, Jimmy, Go/Another Sleepless Night/It Takes a Long Time/Ship on the Stormy Sea/I Feel These Tears.

ACE (US) 2042 (L)
Jimmy's Blue/Jimmy's Happy
Twenty-four tracks from two LPs (originally Ace 1007 and 1008) on one CD. When Jimmy was blue, he sang "I Wanna Go Home," "Love Me Tonight," "Don't Look at Me," and "I Feel Those Tears Coming On," and when the clouds lifted, you could hear him crooning "A Kiss to Build a Dream On," "Sleepy Time Gal," and "I'm Beginning to See the Light."

CLAUDINE CLARK
Philadelphia teen crooner whose big hit was "Party Lights."

CHANCELLOR 5029 (R)
Party Lights
"Party Lights" was a huge favorite in the Philly area. Poor Claudine captures the mood of teenage frustration as she watches a party from afar, knowing that she's not invited and that all of her friends are having a great time! The sweet but powerful voice of Clark could only propel her to one hit, but these 16 numbers show a very talented young woman who got lost in the shuffle. She makes it to the party later on and sings about it on "Dancin' Party," "Party Time," "Havin' a Party," plus some heartfelt ballads for good measure.

DEE CLARK
Though he was something of a vocal chameleon, capable, for example, of sounding like Little Richard when he wanted to, Delecta Clark enjoyed a string of hits in the late '50s and early '60s for Vee Jay and Constellation using his own high-tenor voice.

FAN CLUB 108 (L)
The Dee Clark Show
A live concert recording made in 1981, featuring The Reddings as a backup band. Though the accompaniment is barely adequate, Clark is in reasonably good voice throughout his performance. The audience, however, seems to be indifferent to his efforts, and the quality of the recording is rather amateurish.

VEE JAY 703 (CL)
Rain Drops
Twenty-five tracks, including all his Top 40 Vee Jay hits, lots of B-sides and album cuts, plus two of his earlier vocal-group efforts with The Kool Gents and The Delegates. Excellent sound and informative liner notes. I Just Can't Help Myself/Seven Nights/Just Keep It Up/Hey Little Girl/How About That.

SANFORD CLARK
Excellent pop/rock/country singer. Clark hit big with his first recording "The Fool," originally on MCA and leased to Dot. His records were produced and mostly written by Lee Hazelwood and featured the great Al Casey on guitar. He spent the rest of his career trying for a second hit.

BEAR FAMILY 15198 (R)
Rockin' Rollin' Sanford Clark

BEAR FAMILY 15199 (R)
Rockin' Rollin' Sanford Clark, Vol. 2
These two Bear Family releases feature all of Sanford's Dot and Jamie recordings, including all his unreleased material. Most tunes were cut in Phoenix, though there are a few that were made in Hollywood, including some with the legendary Duane Eddy on rhythm guitar. Vol. 1 features the best of the Dot material, 18 tunes including six never-before-released masters. The tunes were made between 1956–1958 and include the followup to his lone hit "The Fool," called "A Cheat," and "Ooo Baby," "Modern Romance," "Usta Be My Baby," "Travelin' Man," and a previously unreleased "Ain't Nobody Here but Us Chickens." Vol. 2 gives the rest of the story, opening with all ten tunes done for Jamie 1958–1960, all of which bombed, including still another attempt at "The Fool" called "New Kind of Fool" sung in his distinct Ricky-Nelson-meets-Johnny-Cash style, plus "Son of a Gun," "Pledging My Love," "Run Boy Run," and "Bad Luck." As a bonus, all four solo tunes cut by Al Casey in 1957 for Dot are included, and boy are they terrible, especially when he sings! The best is another version of "The Fool," an instrumental called "Fool's Blues." The set ends with Clark's final five Dot sides, including "Glory of Love," "Darling Dear," and three previously unissued masters. Excellent liner notes on both volumes by Rich Kienzle.

BEAR FAMILY 15549 (L)
The Fool
CD reissue of Clark's MCA, Dot, and Jamie recordings, previously collected on Bear Family LPs 15198 and 15199. The 36-page booklet reprises Rich Kienzle's excellent liner notes from the LPs, along

with a reproduction of a magazine article from the period and some great photos.

THE CLASSICS

Early '60s vocal-harmony group led by Emil Stucchio similar to The Mystics, The Passions, and other "sparkless" harmony groups. They recorded 22 sides between 1960–1967 for Bed-Stuy, Dart, Mercury, Musicnote, Streamline, Stork, Josie, and Piccollo, and briefly re-formed in 1971–1972 to cut four more sides.

CRYSTAL BALL 114 (R)

Greatest Hits

Nearly all of their released sides appear on this album. Cuts like the previously unissued "Portrait of a Fool" and "Sincerely" are quite skillfully sung and arranged but, in the main, the material suffers from lack of excitement and originality. This is indeed sad, as Emil Stucchio and the boys can sing well. Nice pix and good sound reproduction.

JOE CLAY

Rockin' mid-'50s artist who made only two moderately successful singles, both for the RCA subsidiary Vik, released in 1956. After an *Ed Sullivan Show* appearance, Clay was soon forgotten stateside, but he became a legend in Europe, thanks to his blazing version of Rudy Grayzell's "Ducktail" and an appearance on the *Louisiana Hayride* with Elvis Presley (a photo of the two men together circulated throughout Europe's rockabilly community).

BEAR FAMILY 15224 (R)/15516 (L)

Ducktail

Collects all of the rockin' tunes and alternates from Clay's only two sessions. From April 25, 1956 with Hal Harris and Link Davis (gtrs) come "Ducktail," "16 Chicks," "Slipping Out and Sneaking In," "Doggone It," and "Goodbye Goodbye." From May 24 with an R&B band featuring Mickey Baker and Skeeter Best (gtrs) there are two takes of "Get on the Right Track" and "You Look Good to Me," and single takes of "Cracker Jack" (including a false start) and the great "Did You Mean Jelly Bean (When You Said Cabbage Head)?" Includes an eight-page booklet with notes, rare photos, and discography. This is some of the most powerful rockabilly ever recorded.

OTIS CLAY

Wonderful southern deep-soul singer. Otis Clay was born in Waxlaw, MS, and honed his chops singing in a legion of gospel quartets, notably The Christian Travelers who recorded for Peacock in the '50s, and The Gospel Songbirds on Nashboro in which he shared the lead vocal role during the early '60s. In 1964, Clay signed with George Leaner's One-der-ful label, on which he cut a handful of prime tear-dripping soul ballads and hard-driving jump numbers. He spent the '70s recording some of his finest material for Hi with producer Willie Mitchell and, along with Al Green and O.V. Wright, he was one of the few artists performing in the Southern soul sound throughout the '70s and '80s. With Green's "retirement" and the death of Wright, he emerged as the final torchbearer for this style. He is very popular outside of the US and revered in Japan. The P-Vine CD features a great cross-section of his pre-Hi recordings.

BULLSEYE BLUES 9513 (CL)

Soul Man: Live in Japan

1983 concert. Recorded with his own band of Hi Records's vets, these eight extended soul jams (there were ten cuts on the original two-LP issue) are highlighted by a tribute to his late friend O.V. Wright ("A Nickel and a Nail") and a 13-minute medley of Al Green's "Love and Happiness" with "Soul Man." Precious Precious/Love Don't Love Nobody/Hard Workin' Man.

BULLSEYE BLUES 9520 (CL)

I'll Treat You Right

Ten-tune collection cut a while back in Memphis, featuring none other than Little Jimmy King on lead guitar and soul-kids Don Bryant and Percy Wiggins on backing vocals. Particular faves include the righteous "Children Gone Astray" and "Gonna Take My Heart's Advice," a soul-man's talk with his conscience. Right and tight support from the Memphis Horns and the Hi rhythm section.

HI (UK) 110 (L)

That's How It Is

Much of the best of his Hi recordings are here, including his biggest hit "Trying to Live My Life Without You." Oddly, his only other chart success for Hi, "If I Could Reach Out," is missing, but Clay's excess of talent, frequently reminiscent of label-mate O.V. Wright, is apparent throughout. His second album for Hi, *I Can't Take It*, is here in its entirety. Recommended. Precious, Precious/That's How It Is/Too Many Hands/Let Me Be the One/I Die a Little Each Day/I Can't Take It.

P-VINE 2195 (L)

Otis Clay

Nineteen pre-Hi label tunes, once available on long-gone P-Vine wax. Heavy duty soul incineration. Booklet includes complete lyrics for soulful singing along. Wrapped Up in Her Love/Cry, Cry, Cry/A Flame in Your Heart/I'm Satisfied/This Love of Mine/That's How It Is/Don't Pass Me By.

WILLIE CLAYTON

P-VINE 1251 (L)

Forever

THE CLEFTONES

Fine New York vocal group featuring the powerful lead vocals of Herb Cox. Unlike many other groups, they had their greatest success with up-tempo items. They only had two national hits: 1956's driving "Little Girl of Mine" and 1961's update of the standard "Heart and Soul." The group disbanded in 1964 but reunited in the '70s to perform sporadically at revival shows.

COLLECTABLES 8806 (CL)

For Collectors Only

Recorded between 1955–1962 for Gee Records (with a few Roulette sides thrown in), this two-CD/cassette 40-cut compilation has about every Cleftones song anyone could want, with the notable exception of their first single, "You Baby You." The majority of the material is rockin', including their two hits "This Little Girl of Mine" and "Heart and Soul," but ballads like "I Was Dreaming," "She's Gone," and "You're Driving Me Mad" are inserted for contrast; the sweet-and-slow "Please Say You Want Me" with Pat Span singing

lead is one such praiseworthy insert. The alternate version of "Can't We Be Sweethearts" is quite similar to the released version; the alternate of "Neki Hokey" is slower and less interesting than its sister release. "Honey Bun," "Slippin' and Slidin'," and the Coasterish "Cool It Fool" are all issued here for the first time, though only the first is up to snuff. Heed the album title.

🌀 RHINO 70951 (CL)

The Best of The Cleftones

Fourteen-track cassette or 18-track CD featuring all their classic original recordings from the master tapes. Reproduces cuts from the Collectables set, but gives a better general introduction to this group. Heart and Soul/Little Girl of Mine/For Sentimental Reasons/You Baby You.

BUZZ CLIFFORD

Born Reese Francis Clifford III in Illinois, Buzz won a talent contest at New Jersey's Morris County Fair performing cowboy songs. This led to a contract with Columbia records, and his smash hit in 1961 with the novelty classic "Baby Sittin' Boogie." Further novelty numbers failed to chart, and Buzz spent the mid-'60s as a record producer and recorded in a folk-rock vein for RCA and Dot.

BOW 8420 (R)

Baby Sitting with Buzz

Reissues Columbia 8416 from 1961 in real stereo. Baby Sittin' Boogie/Long Tall Sally/Golly Gosh Oh Gee/Three Little Fishes.

THE CLOVERS

The Clovers of Washington, DC began performing as a trio in 1946. After one 78 for Eddie Heller's Rainbow Records, the group signed with Atlantic in late 1950. The original lineup included John "Buddy" Bailey (lead), Matt McQuater (tnr), Harold Lucas (bar), Harold Winley (b), and Bill Harris (gtr). The group was very versatile, boasting three singers who could all sing lead and the fine guitar of Bill Harris. At Atlantic, they had the first crack at all the hippest songs and also were fortunate to be backed up by the finest sessionmen of the time, including Floorshow Culley, Harry Van Walls, Gatortail Jackson, and Mickey "Guitar" Baker.

Atlantic head Ahmet Ertegun didn't like the group's sweet vocal sound, preferring big-band jump, so he paired them in the studio with Frank Culley's group, with Culley on sax, and wrote a jumpin' tune for them called "Don't You Know I Love You" that immediately hit. The group soon became Atlantic's most consistent seller, releasing close to two dozen classics between 1951–1959 including "One Mint Julep," "Your Cash Ain't Nothin' but Trash," "Down in the Alley," "Devil or Angel," and "Blue Velvet." After leaving Atlantic in 1959, they went to United Artists where they scored one more major classic with "Love Potion #9."

They had remarkably consistent personnel. The first major change came when Bailey was drafted in 1954. He was briefly replaced by Charles White of The Dominoes, followed by Billy Mitchell. When Bailey was discharged from the Army, he returned to The Clovers, but they liked Mitchell so much that the two shared lead vocal chores through 1961, when they disbanded. Their Atlantic material is represented on several reissues, the best being Atlantic 82312; the United Artists material has been reissued by EMI.

🌑 ATLANTIC 82312 (CL)

Down in the Alley

Twenty-one track collection, including ten of their biggest hits. Good, accurate booklet notes, great photos and promo pix with shots of singles' labels. One Mint Julep/Good Lovin'/Crawlin'/Lovey Dovey/I've Got My Eyes on You/Your Cash Ain't Nothin' but Trash/Devil or Angel/Blue Velvet/Love Bug.

DR. HORSE 807 (R)

All Righty, Oh Sweetie (1951–1959)

Nineteen tunes emphasizing the non-hits and B-sides. Wonder Where My Baby's Gone/I Confess/Hey Doll Baby/Comin' On/Honey Bun/Rock, Moan and Cry.

EMI 96336 (CL)

Love Potion #9:
The Best of The Clovers

Despite the presence of the great Leiber and Stoller at United Artists, The Clovers suffered after leaving Atlantic for their new label, issuing a tide of forgettable pop standards. But in among the insipid tunes were a bunch of notable releases, including "Rock and Roll Tango," "Stay Awhile," "So Good, So Good," "I'm Confessin' That I Love You," "Yes It's You," the single

and album versions of "Love Potion #9" that stormed the charts during Christmas 1959, plus the remake of their 1952 success "One Mint Julep." Twenty-three singles and album cuts spanning the years 1959–1961. Some minor sparks, but little glow of former glory.

THE COASTERS

Extremely popular novelty R&B group. They began as The Robbins working out of LA with bass singer Bobby Nunn on lead. By 1954, the group had lost a "b" to become The Robins, featuring Carl Gardner on lead. They signed to Leiber and Stoller's Spark label, where the famed songwriting duo crafted memorable "playlets" for the group, including "Riot in Cell Block #9" and "Smokey Joe's Café" (see separate listing for The Robins). The latter became such a big hit that it was picked up for distribution by Atco (an Atlantic subsidiary). Atlantic enticed Gardner and Nunn to New York, renaming the group The Coasters, and matching them with new vocalists Leon Hughes and comedian Billy Guy. The original group only recorded four sides, including "Down in Mexico." Hughes left to be replaced by former Flair Young Jessie. The big hits started to come, with "Searchin'," "Youngblood," and "Yakety Yak," many featuring sax solos by King Curtis.

By mid-1958, both Jesse and Nunn had left to be replaced by new members Cornell Gunter from The Flairs and bass Dub Jones from The Cadets. This was the most popular Coasters incarnation, lasting from 1958–1961, and having hits with "Charlie Brown," "Along Came Jones," "Poison Ivy," and "Little Egypt." Gunter was replaced by Earl "Speedo" Carroll from The Cadillacs to form the longest-lasting Coasters ensemble from 1961–1968. They had hits with "Speedo's Back in Town" and "D.W. Washburn" (later covered by The Monkees). Dub Jones left in 1968, replaced by Ronnie Bright of The Valentines, best known as the bass man on Johnny Cymbal's "Mr. Bass Man," and the group had one last hit in 1968 with "Love Potion #9." In 1972, original member Billy Guy left, replaced by Jimmy Norman. The Coasters, still with Carl

Gardner, continue to go strong on the oldies circuit.

ATLANTIC 33111 (L)
Greatest Hits
CD reissue of the twelve wackiest and rockin'-est Coasters' sides. Great! Poison Ivy/Along Came Jones/Charlie Brown/Young Blood/Searchin'.

C5 579 (L)
Just Coastin'
Ten songs presumably recorded by one of the two or three groups known as The Coasters over the years, which may or may not contain any of the original members. Running only 28 minutes, this collection of remakes sticks pretty close to the originals, so, unless you're a Coasters completist, it's tough to come up with a compelling reason to own it. Searchin'/Poison Ivy/Charlie Brown.

FAN CLUB 110 (L)
Featuring Cornell Gunther
This one's a bit sneaky. On the cover is a vintage Coasters photo taken from their greatest hits LP. And the back cover makes no mention of a recording date, but does mention "intros" and "medleys." What we have is a live recording from 1969 when the only original Coaster left was Cornell Gunther. The singing is bad, with lyrics poorly ad-libbed, the band is weak, and the audience is largely indifferent. For absolute zealots only.

MR. R&B 102 (RL)
What Is the Secret of Your Success
Superb album featuring 16 great sides, none of which have been on LP before. Excellent notes and full discographical information

◉ RHINO 71090 (CL)
50 Coastin' Classics
This fantastic two-CD/cassette set traces the history of the band from their original recordings as The Robins through their big Atlantic hits. Also includes more obscure sides ("Brazil," "What Is the Secret of Your Success," "Stewball," and "Wake Me Shake Me"), some of their later unsuccessful songs recorded for Date, plus a couple of unissued songs ("Hey Sexy," "Shake 'Em Up and Let 'Em Roll," and an early unreleased version of "The Climb" called "The Slime"). Their wonderful vocals are accompanied by top West Coast or NY musicians like Chuck Norris, Adolph Jacobs, Barney Kessell, or Mickey Baker (gtrs), Gil Bernal or King Curtis (ten saxes), and often Mike Stoller (pno). The sound is superb and Rhino has wisely chosen to remaster from original mono single masters. The accompanying booklet has some fine photos and useful discographical information though the text is a bit disappointing; the essay by Robert Palmer has little to say about the group and indulges

in some rather dubious armchair sociology, and the interview with Leiber and Stoller about the songs has interesting moments but is frequently trivial. This is a minor quibble though; the music is what counts, and it's terrific! Riot in Cell Block #9/Framed/Hatchet Man/Smokey Joe's Cafe/Down in Mexico/Young Blood/Idol with the Golden Head/Yakety Yak/Along Came Jones/I'm a Hog for You/Run Red Run.

EDDIE COCHRAN
Excellent singer/songwriter/guitarist from Minnesota who came to LA in the early '50s and helped establish West Coast rockabilly. In 1954, Eddie joined with future country star Hank Cochran (no relation); after teaming up with songwriter Jerry Capehart, the trio recorded several singles on Ekko under The Cochran Brothers (sic) name, mostly in a hillbilly style. Later in 1955, Eddie and Capehart moved to Nashville, releasing "Skinny Jim" on Crest. In early '56, Eddie landed a contract with Liberty, moved back to LA, and produced a four-year string of hits with a loose-knit group called The Kelly Four, featuring bassist Guybo Smith. On "Summertime Blues" and a few others, Eddie sang and played everything through the miracle of overdubbing! He apparently had access to LA's Gold Star Studio (later the home of master producer Phil Spector), because many tapes have surfaced with him jamming with and backing up such artists as Bo Davis and The Four Dots. In 1960, Eddie toured England with buddy Gene Vincent, and the duo appeared together on the BBC. While driving a car with Gene and Sharon Sheely, a tire blew out and the car crashed, killing Eddie and injuring Sheely and Vincent.

Cochran's pre-Liberty material has been reissued on a slew of releases, primarily from Rockstar, while his Liberty material can be heard on EMI 92809.

ACE 237 (L)
The Early Years
Twenty early rarities by The Cochran Brothers, Jerry Capehart, Albert Stone, Darry Weaver, and of course Eddie himself in the spotlight.

⊙ EMI 92809 (CL)
Legendary Masters Series: Eddie Cochran, Vol. 1

Twenty tracks covering the period from Cochran's early Crest recordings in April 1956 to his last Liberty session in January 1960, three months before his tragic death. It includes his hits plus songs that didn't surface until after his death. Excellent sound and nicely packaged with a fold-out booklet with detailed photos, photos of memorabilia, and a nice reproduction of the old Liberty label on the disc. Pink Pegged Slacks/Cotton Picker/Drive-in Show/Jeanie, Jeanie, Jeanie/Summertime Blues/C'mon Everybody/Teenage Heaven/Three Stars/Somethin' Else/The Fourth Man Theme/Three Steps to Heaven.

EMI (FRANCE) 252 687 (L)
Blue Suede Shoes

What's the difference between "C'mon Everybody" and "Let's Get Together"? About two seconds. No matter, they're both here, as are 14 other great ones, including "Something Else," the best thing Mr. Cochran ever recorded, energy-wise. Authentic rock and roll from a guy who never saw the age of 22. 20 Flight Rock/Milk Cow Blues/Cradle Baby/Summertime Blues/Cut Across Shorty/Pink Pegged Slacks/Jeanie, Jeanie, Jeanie.

HYDRA 7706 (R)
Record Date

Eddie's non-Liberty sides leased from Rockstar for German release. Nothing new, and Eddie's own sides are some of his weakest. The best stuff here is by Eddie the Session Guitarist, playing guitar along with Howie Roberts on Troyce Key's first single, "Drown in My Own Tears" b/w "Baby Please Don't Go," and on Bob Denton's 1957–1958 Dot sides, including the hit version of Lefty Frizzell's "Always Late" and "Skinnie Minnie," "24 Hour Night," and "Playboy." Includes a large poster with the reverse filled with liner notes and photos, and a cheesy looking hand-colored front cover.

MUSIDISC 108282 (L)
The Early Eddie Cochran, Vol. 1

MUSIDISC 108292 (L)
The Early Eddie Cochran, Vol. 2

Two CDs each collecting 18 early Eddie Cochran tunes, formerly on various Rockstar LPs and EPs. Almost everyone is familiar with these mid-'50s tunes done for Ekko and Cash, with Hank Cochran and Jerry Capeheart. Vol. 1 highlights include the rockers "Don't Bye Bye Baby Me," "Slow Down," "Fool's Paradise," and "Pink Pegged Slacks," with strong singing and flash guitar playing by Eddie. Cochran especially shines on the blazin' instrumentals "Guybo" and "Pushin'." I don't doubt that others have more of a fondness for his hiccuppy ballads than I do, so let's leave it at that. I'd much rather crank up "Latch On" again anyway, than hear Eddie meander his way through "Yesterday's Heartbreak." Vol. 2 features instrumentals that show Eddie's ability to handle a variety of styles: on "Chicken Shot Blues," he demonstrates his phenomenal blues-guitar playing, "Country Jam" is in a hotshot country-picker style, and "Shotgun Wedding Theme" is in a rockin', jazzy style. That boy could do it all! Well, almost. He couldn't sing a ballad to save his soul, proved again here more than once, but let's hear it for the rockers like "Skinny Jim," "Jelly Bean," and "Latch On," and the rockin' country of "Guilty Conscience" and "Mr. Fiddle."

ROCKSTAR 001 (L)
Rock and Roll Legend

Twenty non-Liberty tracks, including most of the tunes (and a few demos) done for Ekko with Hank Cochran as The Cochran Brothers. Four previously unavailable alternates made their first appearance on this CD: a version of "Guybo" without the final guitar overdub; take 5 (and false start 4) of "Jellybean"; an alternate of "Take My Hand" by The Four Dots with Eddie on guitar; and a finished alternate, with hand claps, of "Don't Bye Bye Baby Me." Excellent sound. Pink Pegged Slacks/Skinny Jim/Latch On/Let's Coast Awhile/Chicken Shot Blues.

ROCKSTAR 1005 (R)
Words and Music

Lots of rare Cochran, including the first appearances on reissue LP of "My Love to Remember," "Half Loved," "Dark Lonely Street," and a version of "Chicken Shot Blues" complete with false starts. Also includes a 14-minute interview with Eddie from Denver in 1957.

ROCKSTAR 1006 (R)
The Young Eddie Cochran
Sixteen tracks recorded in 1955–1956 including the Cochran Brothers sides recorded with Hank Cochran. Latch On/Slow Down/Guilty Conscience/Your Tomorrows Never Come/Slow Down.

ROCKSTAR 1008 (R)
Portrait of a Legend
Remarkable LP featuring 16 cuts, ten in real stereo (only three of these had ever been reissued in stereo before), and six alternate takes, including a totally different "Cut Across Shorty" with a laid-back country flavor. Emphasis here is on rockers; ballads (thankfully) are at a minimum. Great sound by Bob Jones, who also did the informative liner notes. Alternates include "Nervous Breakdown," "My Way," and "Teenage Heaven," and stereo releases include "Three Steps to Heaven," "Jeanie, Jeanie, Jeanie," "Weekend," and "Hallelujah I Love Her So."

ROCKSTAR 1009 (R)
The Hollywood Sessions
Draws on some of the original master tapes from Gold Star Studio, containing unreleased material, alternate takes, false starts, and lots of studio chat. Two previously unknown Cochran songs were first reissued on this collection, both penned by Eddie's buddy Cash McCall: "Jelly Bean" and "Don't Bye Bye Baby Me." They were both recorded during Cochran's 1957 sessions with The Johnny Mann Singers, and they feature numerous false starts along with the complete masters. Four cuts are by The Four Dots with Jewel Aikens on vocals and Eddie on guitar and bass, that were released here for the first time: "Hide and Go Seek"; "Fontella"; "Take My Hand" (with false starts); and "Once More" (with false starts). Two tracks were found at the end of a reel, "Bad Baby Doll" and "Itty Bitty Betty," with a vocalist identified only as Derry! Also includes different versions of "The Fourth Man Theme" and "Bread Fred," extended versions of "Guybo" and "Strollin' Guitar" with outtakes, an unissued version of "Dark Lonely Street," and an unissued acetate of "Kiss and Make Up" by Ray Stanley.

ROCKSTAR 1019 (R)
Thinkin' about You
An amazing 24 tracks including not only unissued studio tunes but a selection of songs that Eddie was believed to have played on. Listening to some of the "vocalists" Cochran backed can be torturous at times, saved only by Cochran's live-wire guitar attack. There's some real hot stuff here, especially instrumentals like "Pushin'" and "Scratchin'," and the R&B blaster, "Quick Like," recorded at Goldband by Elroy Peace. Annie Has a Party/I Hates Rabbits/Rollin'/Fast Jivin'/My Lovin' Baby.

ROCKSTAR 1021 (R)
Yesterday's Heartbreak
Sixteen-tune selection culled from Rockstar's extensive Eddie Cochran reissue program. Six of these were released here for the first time. (I know you have 77 Cochran LPs already but you'll need this one too.) There's the 1956 version of "Skinny Jim" that came out on Crest and the demo version of "Pink Pegged Slacks" to boost the overall standard here; we wouldn't want all unreleased ballads on a 30th-anniversary tribute, now, would we? Four of the previously unissued tunes are ballads: "My Love to Remember"; "Little Angel"; "Half Loved"; and, with Cochran on guitar, the doo-wop ballad "It's Heaven" by Jerry Stone and The Four Dots. More exciting are two unissued instrumentals: the backing track to "Jelly Bean" and "The Fourth Man Theme" where Eddie is heard sending Guybo out for a pack of Salems! Milk Cow Blues/Hammy Blues/Jam Sandwich.

ROCKSTAR 1022 (R)
Eddie and Hank
Twenty recordings from 1955–1956, featuring the Cochrans's Ekko and Cash sides. In keeping with the times, we get a mix of country and rockers, with some nice guitar work from Eddie. Collectors are fortunate to have this document of the rising star's roots, before his success broke up the "family" act.

SEE FOR MILES 271 (RL)
The EP Collection
Twenty of Cochran's British EP releases on Liberty and London from 1959–1964, which basically serve as a greatest-hits package in a new wrapper. The album cover reproduces all of the original EP covers. The music is mostly uptempo rockabilly and covers the well-known and the lesser-known tunes. Skinny Jim/20 Flight Rock/Pink Pegged Slacks/Nervous Breakdown/C'mon Everybody/Summertime Blues/Milk Cow Blues.

SUNJAY 571 (R)
The Hollywood Rocker
A fine collection of Eddie's pre-Liberty material with a beautiful color front photo. All of these tracks are available on other LPs for much less, especially on the fine Rockstar compilations. Latch On/Tired and Sleepy/Chicken Shot Blues/Instrumental Blues/Jelly Bean/Don't Bye Bye Baby Me.

EDDIE COCHRAN and GENE VINCENT
ROCKSTAR 1004 (R)/MUSIDISC 108192 (L)
Rock and Roll Heroes
Recordings from 1959 BBC radio shows accompanied by Marty Wilde's Wildcats. Some of this material has

THELMA COOPER/DAISY MAE and HER HEP CATS

KRAZY KAT 822 (R)

Thelma Cooper/Daisy Mae and Her Hep Cats

Most of Side 1 features the chirpy, sultry pipes of Thelma "Baby Doll" Cooper who recorded for Gotham and Coleman in 1949. It's amazing how closely her voice matches that of namesake Dolly Cooper. Her scat singing (with Doles Dickens) on "Cute Papa" is a classic. Side 2 features the mid-'50s Gotham, Richloy, and 20th Century sides of singer/drummer Daisy Mae Diggs, whose band The Hep Cats can blast up a storm. Daisy has a fine bluesy voice and, on "Woman Trouble," she shows how well she can handle vocal comedy routines. Buy this album for The Hep Cats; they burn like a house on fire.

DON COVAY

Don was one of Atlantic's most neglected soul artists, better-known for the songs he wrote than for his renditions of them. He started out in the '50s with The Rainbows, a Washington, DC harmony group that also included his neighbors Billy Stewart and Marvin Gaye. His first solo recordings were released under the name "Pretty Boy" on Atlantic in 1957. He recorded for numerous labels, big and small, through the late '50s. His songs, covered by other artists, did better than he did, including "Letter Full of Tears" by Gladys Knight and "You're Good for Me" by Solomon Burke. He released "Pony Time" on Arnold in 1960, but the song was beat to the charts by Chubby Checker's cover version of it. "Mercy Mercy" (Rosemart records, 1964) got him resigned to Atlantic, and was soon covered by The Rolling Stones. Aretha Franklin scored with his "Chain of Fools" and "See Saw" and even Steppenwolf covered his "Sookie Sookie." By the '70s, he was label hopping again, and in the '80s was still occasionally touring with The Soul Clan (Solomon Burke, Wilson Pickett, and other '50s R&B singers).

EDSEL 127 (R)

Mercy

Sixteen wonderful and hard-to-find Atlantic sides including six from 1965's *Mercy* (Atlantic 8104) and eight from *See Saw* (Atlantic 8120). Mercy Mercy/See Saw/Sookie Sookie/Take This Hurt Off Me/Boomerang.

BILLY "CRASH" CRADDOCK

Originally, Craddock was signed to Columbia in 1959 as a Fabian-esque pop singer. His records bombed here, but three made the top ten in Australia! In the '60s and '70s, he became a popular country music star.

COLONIAL 711 (R)

Crash's Greatest Hits

An exact reproduction of his 1962 LP, containing 14 of his early Columbia pop hits in stereo. Boom Boom Baby/I Want That/Good Time Billy/Well Don't You Know/Letter of Love.

BEAR FAMILY 16510 (L)

Boom Boom Baby

Craddock's 21 earliest efforts, recorded between 1958–1960, including several like "Ah, Poor Little Baby" and "Little Ole You" on which he sounds a lot like Elvis Whatshisname. And, despite frequent trips to teen town ("School Day Dreams" and "Report Card of Love"), there are a surprising number of credible rock and roll and rockabilly performances among these recordings. Session talent like Grady Martin (gtr) and Floyd Cramer (pno) add authority to the proceedings. Notes from Jimmy Guterman, discography from Richard Weize. I Want That/Am I to Be the One/Sweetie Pie/Treat Me Like You Do/Heavenly Love.

JIMMY CRAIN

Rockabilly hopeful from Ohio who wanted to follow in Elvis's footsteps. Jimmy was an excellent guitarist, but his vocals weren't all that great.

WHITE LABEL 8809 (R)

Rockin' with Jimmy Crain

Includes obligatory crazy dance number, "Shig-a-Shag," originally on the Spangle label, and "Why Worry," where Jimmy takes a page from Alfred E. Newman's book. Among the previously unissued material are some dynamite instrumentals like "Spooky Village" and "London Fog," as well as some cool rockers like "Guitar Playin' Son of a Gun." Sound quality varies on the 13 tracks.

WHITE LABEL 8845 (R)

Rocks On

More excellent guitar-based rockabilly by Jimmy Crain, including "We're Goin' Rockin'," "Learning to Rock and Roll," and "She Loves Rock and Roll." These 14 cuts were all recorded in Crain's home studio in 1959 and were never issued at the time. When you get a load of Crain's heavyweight guitar playing, you'll know why he was too tough for the wimpy charts of the time, especially on instrumentals like "Mixin' It Up," "Crusin'," and "You Name It Rock."

CREAM

The original power trio, the group that launched a thousand heavy metal bands, Cream was a short-lived experiment uniting British blues guitar *wunderkind* Eric Clapton with bassist Jack Bruce and manic drummer Ginger Baker. Originally a blues-based band that dabbled in psychedelia, Cream became famous for their live shows, with extended solos that were either brilliant or tedious (or both) depending on the level of intoxicants in your bloodstream.

POLYDOR 811639 (CL)
Strange Brew: The Best of Cream

POLYDOR 823636 (CL)/MOBILE FIDELITY 552 (L)
Disraeli Gears
Their second LP with the hit "Strange Brew" and the FM radio fave "Sunshine of Your Love." Relive those psychedelic days of your youth!

POLYDOR 823660 (CL)
Goodbye
The group was already history when their record company issued this compilation of live cuts and studio stuff. The Eric Clapton/George Harrison penned "Badge" is the best thing on this lackluster set.

POLYDOR 823661 (CL)
Live Cream, Vol. 2

POLYDOR 827576 (CL)
Fresh Cream
Their debut LP has more of a blues base than their other work, including covers of Robert Johnson's "Four Til Late" and reworkings of blues vamps on "Cat's Squirrel," and the British hit "I Feel Free." Also features the first recording of Baker's mega drum solo, "Toad."

POLYDOR 827577 (CL)
Live Cream, Vol. 1

POLYDOR 827578 (CL)
Wheels of Fire
Half studio, half live cuts. The hit "White Room" with its wah-wah guitar work is the highlight, along with an ultimate-boogie workout on Howlin' Wolf's "Spoonful," fifteen minutes of live wailin', and of course the 17-minute version of "Toad," guaranteed to give your parents a headache.

CREEDENCE CLEARWATER REVIVAL

Originally formed in El Cerrito Junior High School as The Blue Velvets in 1959, with brothers Tom (lead voc and gtr) and John Fogerty (gtr), they recorded under this name in 1961–1962 for the local Orchestra label. In 1964, coming under the British invasion influence, they changed their name to The Golliwogs. They were signed to Saul Zaentz's jazz label, Fantasy, in 1967; he encouraged them to adopt an American swamp-pop sound, putting brother John's songwriting talents and rough-hewn vocals in the spotlight. The band scored with hits on covers of R&B and rockabilly songs, along with Fogerty's creative recreations of these sounds on songs like "Proud Mary," "Bad Moon Rising," and "Down on the Corner." John Fogerty left the band in 1972, leaving it a much-reduced trio that soon dissolved without his creative leadership.

Fantasy has packaged and repackaged their late '60s/early '70s hits in the original LP formats along with many different "greatest hits" sets.

FANTASY 4512 (RC)/8382 (L)
Creedence Clearwater Revival
First LP, originally issued as Fantasy 8382 in 1967. Includes the covers of Screamin' Jay Hawkins's "I Put a Spell on You" and Dale Hawkins's "Suzie Q."

FANTASY 4513 (RC)/8387 (L)
Bayou Country
1969 LP featuring the hit "Proud Mary," which became the theme song for Ike and Tina Turner in 1971. Born on the Bayou/Penthouse Pauper/Bootleg.

FANTASY 4514 (RC)/8393 (L)
Green River
The classic here is "Bad Moon Rising." Green River/Lodi/Wrote a Song for Everyone/Tombstone Shadow/The Night Time is the Right Time.

FANTASY 4515 (RC)/8397 (L)

Willy and The Poor Boys

Concept LP celebrating American roots music. Down on the Corner/Fortunate Son/Midnight Special/Cotton Fields/Poor Boy Shuffle.

FANTASY 4516 (RC)/8402 (L)

Cosmo's Factory

Includes Fogerty's chilling "Run Through the Jungle" along with covers of "Ooby Dooby" and "I Heard It through the Grapevine."

FANTASY 4517 (RC)/8410 (L)

Pendulum

1971 LP, the last with the original quartet. Mindless jams seem to have taken over on long numbers including "Pagan Baby," "Born to Move," and their all-time low-point, "Rude Awakening #2."

FANTASY CCR2/CCR3 (RCL)

Chronicle, Vols. 1 and 2

All the big hits and more on these two-record/cassette/CD sets.

THE CRESTS

Fine white Brooklyn/Staten Island-based vocal group featuring the soaring lead vocals of Johnny Maestro (born Mastrangelo). They had some minor hits on Joyce in 1957, and finally hit it big the next year when they moved to Coed, with several smashes including "16 Candles" and "The Angels Listened In." Johnny went solo in 1961, but had no big hits. In 1969, at the beginning of the '50s rock revival, he joined The Del-Satins, Dion's uncredited backup group. The Del-Satins joined forces with a seven-piece band called The Rhythm Method and became The Brooklyn Bridge, with smash hits including "The Worst That Can Happen" and "Your Husband, My Wife" in the '70s. They're still active on the oldies circuit.

ACE 322 (L)

The Best of the Rest Of

Twenty-nine song collection complementing Rhino 70948; includes eight unissued songs and four alternate takes.

COLLECTABLES 5009 (RCL)

The Crests Greatest Hits

Eighteen hits and misses (only 12 on LP) from the late '50s/early '60s. 16 Candles/Six Nights a Week/Flower of Love/The Angels Listened In.

RHINO 70948 (CL)

The Best of The Crests, Featuring Johnny Maestro

Fourteen tracks from 1958–1961, many remastered in true stereo, including all of their Coed hits. Excellent sound, discography of all their recordings, and detailed notes by album's compiler Bob Hyde. Pretty Little Angel/16 Candles/Six Nights a Week/Flower of Love/The Angels Listened In/A Year Ago Tonight/Step by Step/Trouble in Paradise.

THE CREW CUTS

The Crew Cuts started off as The Four Tones, which split in half; two members formed The Crew Cuts, the other two formed The Four Lads. Though Canadian, they had to go to Cleveland to be discovered. Like other white vocal groups of the time, they made their living by covering R&B tunes.

BEAR FAMILY 15206 (R)

Rock and Roll Bash

Thirteen Mercury sides from 1954–1957, just about all R&B covers, plus three never-before-released tracks, "Party Night," "Ring-a-Rosie Rock," and "Music Drives Me Crazy." Sh-Boom/Earth Angel/Ko Ko Mo/Two Hearts, Two Kisses/Don't Be Angry.

BRUNSWICK 1306 (R)

Surprise Package

Reproduction of the Crew Cuts' late '50s LP homage to college life. The squeaky clean but talented quartet cover some good-time, campus-oriented tunes about school and young love. The Varsity Drag/Collegiate/My Blue Heaven/Button Down Winsocki.

THE CRICKETS

Original backup band for Buddy Holly, with various personnel over the years; not to be confused with the vocal group of the same name (see separate listing). After Holly left for New York, drummer Jerry Allison kept the band going with Sonny Curtis and Glen D. Hardin (gtrs), Jerry Naylor (b), and Earl Sinks or David Box singing lead. They continued to record with Norman Petty's Coral records. In the '60s, they went to Liberty, recording an LP with Holly soundalike Bobby Vee and appearing in the Leslie Gore/Beach Boys's movie *Girls on the Beach.* They regrouped in the '70s with new members Ric Grech and Albert Lee, performing in a country-rock vein. Glen Hardin left to join Elvis, and later played in Emmylou Harris's backup band, as did Lee. The band reformed in '77 with original bassist Joe Mauldin for Buddy Holly Week, and still play every year. Sonny Curtis writes most of their material, including "I Fought the Law." (He also wrote *The Mary Tyler Moore Show* theme!)

BEAR FAMILY 15599 (L)
Still in Style

EMI 95845 (CL)
The Liberty Years:
EMI Legends of Rock and Roll
A whopping 31-song collection of the 1961–1971 Crickets's recordings, with most tracks appearing in stereo for the first time, plus unreleased stuff. Includes the minor hits "He's Old Enough to Know Better" and "My Little Girl." Love Is Strange/Surfin' Special/Lonely Avenue.

ROLLER COASTER 2014 (R)
Three Piece
Ten demos cut in Nashville in January 1987, 30 years to the month of the first Crickets's demo, with the perennial Crickets's rhythm of Joe Mauldin and Jerry Allison fronted by Gordon Payne, who also cowrote a bunch of the tunes. Material is relatively lightweight but enjoyable, and as these were intended as demos, there's minimal overdubbing (Allison plays guitar and drums), and no studio tricks. Includes new recordings of the band's 1978 coupling of "Cruise in It" and "Mulholland Drive." Rockin' Socks/Your M-M-Memory Is T-T-Torturing Me.

SEE FOR MILES 79 (RL)
The Crickets File, 1961–1965
Twenty-track collection (seven in real stereo) of the group's Liberty singles and LP cuts. Most of the tunes were written by Jerry Allison and Sonny Curtis. Don't Try to Change Me/A Fool Never Learns/My Little Girl/I'm Not a Bad Guy/ California Sun.

THE CRICKETS

One of the smoothest and best vocal groups of the early '50s. Led by the distinctive tenor of Dean Barlow, at their best The Crickets rank with The Flamingos and The Harptones as masters of the romantic ballad. The original group recorded for Joe Davis's Jay-Dee label, with 1953's "You're Mine" leased to MGM and becoming a national hit. While it was on the charts, the group broke up after an intragroup rumble. A new group was formed by Barlow, Fred Barksdale of The Cadillacs, Jimmy Bailey of The Velvetones, and original member Harold Johnson. After some more hits on Jay-Dee, the group broke up, with Bailey joining The Cadillacs and Johnson teaming with Lillian Leech to form The Mellows.

RELIC 5040 (R)
The Crickets featuring Dean Barlow
Seventeen sides recorded in 1953 and 1954, produced by Joe Davis for MGM and his own Jay-Dee label, featuring almost their entire recorded output.

RELIC 7022 (L)
Dreams and Wishes
Their Jay-Dee and MGM tracks. Excellent sound quality and fine notes. Be Faithful/You're Mine/Changing Partners/Are You Looking for a Sweetheart/I'm Going to Live My Life Alone.

STEVE CROPPER, POPS STAPLES, and ALBERT KING

STAX 8544 (RL)
Jammed Together
Reissue of Stax 2020 from 1969. To cash in on the *Super Session* craze, Stax took their three big guitar guns, put them in front of Booker T and The MGs (well, I guess Steve was already there), and produced a very satisfying session of mostly instrumental jams, with Roebuck "Pops" Staples providing vocals on "Tupelo," Albert singing "What'd I Say," and Steve singing "Water" by Eddie Floyd. Big Bird/Knock on Wood/Baby, What You Want Me to Do/Opus de Soul/Homer's Theme/Trashy Dog/Don't Turn Your Heater Down.

CROSBY, STILLS, NASH (and YOUNG)

David Crosby (ex-Byrds), Stephen Stills (ex-Buffalo Springfield), and Graham Nash (ex-Hollies) formed this first "supergroup" in 1969, producing a laidback, folk-rock sound notable for their soaring vocal harmonies. Neil Young, raunch guitarist extraordinaire, joined to beef up their sound from 1970–1971. Soon after, the group was more or less history, thanks to internal bickering and drug and alcohol abuse, although they have continued to record together sporadically to today.

ATLANTIC 19117 (CL)
Crosby, Stills and Nash
Suite: Judy Blue Eyes/Marakesh Express/Wooden Ships.

ATLANTIC 19118 (CL)
Deja Vu
Their best-seller, with a tougher sound than their debut LP thanks to Neil Young. Woodstock/Our House/Almost Cut My Hair/Carry On.

ATLANTIC 82408 (CL)
Four Way Street
Two-CD/cassette live set that showed that this super group suffered from super ego problems! CD has four bonus tracks not on the original LPs.

SCATMAN CROTHERS

TV/movie actor (remember *The Shining*?) who enjoyed a brief career as a jumpin' scat singer.

TOPS 1511 (R)
Rock and Roll with Scat Man
This jumping scat-jazz collection is an exact reproduction of his original '50s album. The set does not match his earlier work for Capitol or Recorded In Hollywood, although the gutsy "Nobody Knows Why" stands out by virtue of its solid, relentless R&B drive. Scat's voice is a cross between Louis Armstrong and Louis Jordan. For swingsters only.

THE CROWS/THE HARPTONES

COLLECTABLES 7004 (L)
Echoes of a Rock Era
Reissue of a Roulette double album from circa 1972, featuring material recently regurgitated on out-of-print Murray Hill collections (1071 and 1098). Classic uptown doo-wop, featuring 12 cuts by each group. Harlem's alleyway harmonizers The Crows quartet included Daniel "Sonny" Norton, William Davis, Harold Major, and Gerald Hamilton. They recorded over a dozen sides during a two-year period, principally on George Goldner's Rama label. Their most remembered swansongs were "Gee" and "Baby." Although their style was not particularly unique, the excitement that they generated during live concerts could not be matched. Harlem's Harptones, on the other hand, had a distinctly "soft" harmonic sound made renowned by Willie Winfield. The quintet sing all of their heaviest requests—"Sunday Kind of Love," "My Memories of You," "That's the Way It Goes," and "The Shrine of St. Cecilia"—all arranged by the great Raoul Cita.

THE CRYSTALAIRES

Doo-wop revival quintet from Germany!

CRYSTAL BALL 137 (R)
Sing
Fourteen mostly original songs, including two a cappella numbers.

THE CUES

The Cues stretch back into the early '50s, when, as a backing vocal group, they recorded for Atlantic under different names behind Ruth Brown, LaVern Baker, Charlie White, Ivory Joe Hunter, Carman Taylor, and Joe Turner; they backed up both versions of the hit "Tweedle-Dee," which was written by band member Robie Kirk. The original 1954 group was composed of ex-Raven Ollie Jones (lead ten), Abel DeCosta (2nd ten), Robie Kirk (bar), and Edward Barnes (b). In 1955, led by Jones and Jimmie Breedlove (who later enjoyed a modicum of success as a soloist), they signed with Capitol/Prep and, as The Cues Quintet, cut 12 (issued) pop-oriented, rocking sides, including the memorable "Why." The group suffered terribly from lousy A&R; most of their repertoire was made up of novelty and lightweight pop-oriented mush.

BEAR FAMILY 15309 (R)
Crazy Crazy Party
Includes their Capitol/Prep material, notably their hit "Why." This set also contains four of five previously unreleased cuts, most notable being the high-octane "Killer Diller" with sensational guitar licks from Mickey Baker. Some fine rocking material here. Definitive sleeve notes by Pete Grandys.

BEAR FAMILY 15510 (L)

Why

Twenty-eight-cut collection, covering their entire Capitol, Lamp, Prep, and Groove output, plus previously unreleased Capitol sides and one single for Jubilee. Nice booklet with great rare pix, notes, and discography.

MAC CURTIS

Texan Mac Curtis is one of the big names in rockabilly due almost as much to his recording longevity as to the high quality of his early recordings. His band had the classic slap-bass/Sun sound down to an art. Charly 264 and Kay 5046 reissue his early sides (with much duplication between the two).

CHARLY 264 (L)

Blue Jean Heart

Eighteen tracks recorded for King records in 1956 and 1957, including three unissued, alternate takes. Not much filler here, either, with one great rocker after another. Grandaddy's Rockin'/Goosebumps/Half-hearted Love/That Ain't Nothin' but Right/Little Miss Linda.

KAY 5046 (R)

Grandaddy's Rockin'

Eighteen-track collection of rare rockabilly, mostly from the '50s. Grandaddy's Rockin'/If I Had Me a Woman/You Ain't Treatin' Me Right/Half-hearted Love/Little Miss Linda/Don't You Love Me/You Are My Very Special Baby.

BOBBY CURTOLA

Curtola was a Canadian pop singer who apparently had tremendous success in Canada during the late '50s and early '60s for Tartan records, logging nine hit singles. His American recording career resulted in modest success with "Fortune Teller" and "Aladdin."

TARTAN 1000 (R)

16 Tickets to Cloud 9

Canadian fans might have fond memories of these 15 pop-rock numbers, including his hit "Fortune Teller" and a groovy cover of "Wildwood Days." Devil Lips/Sandy/Without Your Love/Tattle Tale Heart/Midnight.

THE CYRKLE

The Cyrkle were three (later four) enterprising young men who captured the hearts and imaginations of the folk-pop world for a brief moment in 1966. During that time, they exhibited a fierce commitment and zest for living the "Young Life." Not as gutsy as The Critters; not as nasty and macho as The Association; and not as raunchy as The Fifth Dimension, The Cyrkle nonetheless carved a tiny niche with their successive hits "Red Rubber Ball" (cowritten by Paul Simon and a member of The New Seekers, Bruce Woodley) and "Turn Down Day" before fading in early '68 to write ad jingles.

COLUMBIA 47717 (CL)

Red Rubber Ball

Eighteen tunes sure to bring back teary-eyed memories for the '60s folkie crowd. All the trappings of the period are here: sitars, quavering flutes, swirly organ, harpsichord, and wimpy but confident three-part harmonies. Includes two previously unreleased cuts. Turn Down Day/Red Chair Fade Away/Cloudy/Straighten Out My Messed Up Life.

DICK DALE

The King of Surf Guitar. Not only did Dale invent surf music, he named it. An active surfer, he tried to duplicate on guitar what he felt on his surfboard. Influenced by Duane Eddy's "twang," Dale played a heavy staccato on the bass strings with the reverb turned up high. He played to thousands of surf fans every weekend at the Rendez-vous Ballroom in Balboa, CA from 1960–1961. He was finally unseated in 1961 by The Beach Boys who added vocals and teen appeal to surf music. Beach Boy guitarist Carl Wilson (as well as almost every other Southern California guitarist of the era) was heavily influenced by Dale, and the early Beach Boy LPs featured covers of his songs including "Let's Go Trippin'" and "Miserlou"; the Bobby Fuller Four also did a note-for-note cover of "Miserlou," including the middle section that quotes "Havah Nagila." Hard times and personal injuries brought Dick down, but he's come back on the oldies trail. The Rhino anthology is the best place to hear his classic recordings, with Surf reissuing many lesser-known items for the true twang aficionado.

GNP 2095 (RCL)

Greatest Hits

Expanded, twenty-one cut version of an LP originally issued in 1975 as a collection of remakes of Dale's hits and misses. You'll have to get the Rhino collection for the early '60s originals of "The Wedge," "Miserlou," and "Let's Go Trippin'," but don't think there's anything "wrong" with these '70s versions; they smoke! With three exceptions, these tracks just burst with reverb excitement. Miserlou/Surf Beat/Sloop John B/King of the Surf Guitar/The Wedge/Those Memories of You/Let's Go Trippin'.

⊗ **RHINO 70074 (C)/75756 (L)**

King of the Surf Guitar:
The Best of Dick Dale

Believe it or not, this was the first-ever hits collection featuring Dale's original recordings. Includes the original Deltone single versions of such all-time greats as "Let's Go Trippin'," "Miserlou," "Surf Beat," "Mr. Peppermint Man," and "Shake'n Stomp" from 1961–1962, and his original Capitol singles of "Havah Nagila," "King of the Surf Guitar," "The Wedge," "Night Rider," and "The Victor." Deltone and Capitol LP cuts are also here, including the Steve Douglas classic "Banzai Washout." Great notes by Surf expert John Blair. CD has four additional songs: "Mr. Eliminator"; "Taco Wagon"; "One Double One Oh!" (an instrumental); and a duet with Stevie Ray Vaughn on "Pipeline."

SURF 4940 (R)

Rarities

Eighteen Dale tunes, including most of the Deltone B-sides left off the Rhino retrospective. Only the curious would want to hear some of these efforts, but your patience is rewarded with monsters like "Del-Tone Rock," "Secret Surfin' Spot," and "Jungle Fever." Heck, you even get "Taco Wagon" in a "tromet version"; I think that's Luxembourgese for "trumpet version." Jessie Pearl/Watusi Jo/Surf Beat

SURF 4950 (R)

Surfer's Guitar

The album cover resembles Dick's classic *Surfer's Choice* LP from 1962, but the material is collected from a variety of early sources. The good news is that it's all primo stuff with stinging guitar playing throughout on a woodie load of 16 instrumentals, both surf and hot-rod titles. Only "Mr. Eliminator" appears on the Rhino collection. Break Time/Surf Buggy/Mag Wheels/Death of a Gremmie/Nitro Fuel.

SURF 4960 (R)

Draggin' and Surfin'

Sixteen more nitro-powered, hot-rod tunes and pipeline-runnin' surf numbers, including all of the vocal tracks from *Surfer's Guitar*, except for the epic "Surfin' Drums" (almost five minutes long!). It's too bad he didn't take more guitar solos on these, as he does on "426 Super Stock"; it would have really put them a notch above the Jan-and-Dean-type novelties. Dick Dale Stomp/The Grudge Run/Glory Wave/Hot Rod Alley/Blond in the 406.

DAMITA JO

Pop R&B singer, born Damita Jo DuBlanc, vocally somewhere in between Dinah Washington and Jo Ann Campbell. She started out in 1951 with Steve Gibson (later her husband) and The Red Caps, and, after a while, went solo. She had several hits between 1958–1962.

DOLLY 6202 (R)

I'll Save the Last Dance for You

Her greatest years, 1958–1962. All of Side 1 has tunes with the word "dance" in the title, including the title hit, which was the answer song to The Drifters's hit, "Dance with a Dolly" (a big hit in Sweden) and "When You Dance." Side 2 highlights include "Mr. Blues," "I Burned Your Letter," and "Do What You Want."

THE DANLEERS

Brooklyn's Danleers were initially a quintet, groomed by Mercury Records to be a second-string Platters, the label's most successful black vocal group. But the outfit differed in approach; they had a tougher, less sappy edge to their material, and excelled on jump numbers and ballads. Led by Jimmy Weston, the original harmoneers included Johnny Lee (1st ten), Willie Ephraim (2nd ten), Nat McCune (bar), and Roosevelt Mays (b). They recorded for Amp, Mercury, Epic, Everest, and Smash from 1958–1962. Their big hit was 1958's "One Summer Night," a summer-time anthem that sold over a million copies. They re-formed in 1988 to hit the oldies trail.

BEAR FAMILY 15503 (L)

One Summer Night

Covers their total output of two dozen sides, including their debut recording backing Pearl Galloway, and their best-known ballads "One Summer Night" and "Half a Block from an Angel." Six cuts duplicate the Mercury *Vocal Group Album* collection. Sixteen-page book with fine, rare pix and discography.

DANNY and THE JUNIORS

Philadelphia-based white harmony group led by Danny Rapp. The brains behind the group was actually Dave White, who formed the original "Juvenairs" in high school with Rapp, and wrote their two best-known hits "At the Hop" and the anthemic "Rock and Roll Is Here to Stay." The group recorded for Singular in 1957, ABC-Paramount in 1957–1959 (where they had their big hits), and Swan from 1960–1962. They were launched by Dick Clark on his *American Bandstand* show; Clark also suggested that they change the name of their first song, "Do the Bop" to "At the Hop," because he foresaw that the bop dance craze was already fading. The early '60s group recorded some other dance classics, including "Twistin' USA," "Back to the Hop" (a followup to their first hit), and "Doin' the Continental Walk." Group saxophonist Lenny Baker cofounded the rock revival doo-woppers, Sha Na Na, in the '70s. Danny continued to put together various "Juniors" until he committed suicide in 1983; in the '90s, original group members Joe Terry and Frank Maffei put together a Danny-less Juniors to hit the oldies circuit.

ROLLERCOASTER 3005 (L)

Back to the Hop

Twenty-seven, mostly energetic tracks comprising virtually their entire Swan sessions from 1960–1962. There are plenty of twist recordings, reflecting the times, like "Twistin' USA," "Twistin' Italy," "Twistin' Germany," and "Twistin' England" (what, no "Twistin' Portugal"?), other dance numbers like "Doin' the Continental Walk" and "Do the Mashed Potatoes," and some fabulous tunes featuring the guitar work of Roy Buchanan.

SINGULAR 569 (R)

Rock and Roll Is Here to Stay

Their best sides from 1959–1962.

BOBBY DARIN

Versatile Bronx-born singer, whose real name was Walden Robert Cassotto. Bobby signed to Decca in 1956, releasing such flops as "Blue-eyed Mermaid." He signed to Atco, producing three more flops in a row. Afraid he was going to be dropped by the label, he wrote and recorded a song called "Early in the Morning," releasing it on Brunswick under the name The Rinky Dinks. However, Atco found out about the Brunswick recording, stopped them from releasing it, and instead released it themselves. In retaliation, Brunswick quickly had Buddy Holly cover the song, scoring a major hit.

Bobby's next song on Atco was "Splish Splash," which was a huge hit. Bobby's next few releases were all teen-oriented numbers, including "Dream Lover" and "Queen of the Hop." In 1959, he had a smash with "Mack the Knife," switching his career to finger-snappin', Sinatra-esque standards. He started his own production company in 1963, discovered Wayne Newton, and released both his and Newton's recordings through Capitol. In 1966, he returned to Atlantic and switched from pop to folk-rock, scoring hits with covers of songs by Tim Hardin ("If I Were a Carpenter" and "Lady Came from Baltimore") and The Lovin' Spoonful ("Lovin' You" and "Darlin' Be Home Soon"). In 1968, he worked on Bobby Kennedy's campaign and freaked out after the assassination, growing long hair and a mustache, and dropped out for a year in Big Sur. He returned as Bob Darin on his own Direction label doing slightly politically oriented rock. By the '70s, he had signed with Motown, was back to "Bobby," and was singing pop tunes in Vegas. He died in 1973 during open-heart surgery. The two-volume Atco retrospective is the ultimate gift for the Darin fanatic.

ATCO 131 (CL)

The Bobby Darin Story

Best of his Atco sides. Splish Slash/Mack the Knife.

ATCO 91794 (CL)

Splish Splash:
The Best of Bobby Darin, Vol. 1

ATCO 91795 (CL)

Mack the Knife:
The Best of Bobby Darin, Vol. 2

Two-volume, 42-song collection. Packaged and sold separately, the first release focuses on the rock-and-roll side of his career. Includes his original recordings of "Splish Splash," "Dream Lover," "Things," and "Queen of the Hop." The sound quality of these 1958–1971 recordings is excellent. Darin sounds energetic and sharp, but I think his vocal style is more suited to the ballads and dance music featured on the second collection. Vol. 2 covers the period from 1958–1961. Here is Darin's cheesy-Vegas-slick-crooning-schmaltzy style that we love, exemplified by his classic version of "Mack the Knife," and an incredibly bouncing and happy version of a very sad song, "Artificial Flowers." Both volumes include a 16-page booklet with good liner notes and photos. Black Coffee/Bill Bailey Won't You Please Come Home/What a Difference a Day Makes/Guys and Dolls/Skylark.

ATLANTIC 91772 (CL)
The 25th Day of December
Fourteen holiday hummables from Atlantic's entry in the teen idol market. O Come All Ye Faithful/Ave Maria/Go Tell It on the Mountain/Silent Night/Christmas Auld Lang Syne.

WARNER BROS. 27606 (L)
The Ultimate Bobby Darin
Seventeen of Bobby's biggest hits. Splish Splash/Plain Jane/Mack the Knife/Bill Bailey Won't You Please Come Home/You Must Have Been a Beautiful Baby/Things/Early in the Morning/Somebody to Love.

BOBBY DAVIS
Obscure rockabilly performer.

RUNDELL 007 (R)
Rockabilly and Country from Memphis, Vol. 1
Here's a real obscurity for you. I can't turn up a thing on Davis, although he apparently had one 45 out in 1959, "Troubles, Troubles," a pretty good rocker backed with a pop ballad. Most of the rest of the LP is taken up with radio-station recordings, probably from the late '60s. The first four are very poorly recorded but the next six sound OK. He does a nice job on Clyde Beavers's "Here I Am Drunk Again" and the oft-covered "Truck Drivin' Man," but holy smokes folks, a lot of you can sing as well as this guy! These Four Walls/Matchbox/Pass Me By.

HANK DAVIS
NY rockabilly artist who recorded for several small labels from 1959–1964, and staged a comeback in the '70s. Redita 115 has the best selection of early material.

REDITA 115 (R)
I'm Hank Davis
Fourteen rare tracks, a cross-section of Davis's entire career with sides recorded between 1959–1964 and one from 1976. Mojo Workout/I Don't Care Who Knows/Real Soon/Salamay.

REDITA 120 (R)
Rock in the Woods
A nice mixture of rockabilly, rock and roll, and rockin' country recorded between 1959–1977. Move on Down the Line/Part of All These Troubles/Old New Orleans Rhythm and Blues/I'm Not Sure.

TYRONE DAVIS
Excellent Mississippi soulster who began his performing career as "Tyrone, The Boy Wonder." As a teenager, he was Freddie King's chauffeur and valet. He recorded for a number of small labels in the '60s, including Ray Charles's Tangerine label where he first recorded "Can I Change My Mind." In 1968, he hooked up with famed Chicago producer Carl Davis's new label, Dakar. His first single "A Woman Needs to Be Loved" flopped, but the flipside, a re-recording of "Can I Change My Mind" started getting airplay, eventually reaching the top five. He had a long string of hits for Dakar until 1974, including "Turn Back the Hands of Time" and "Turning Point." These great recordings have been reissued on Rhino 70533. He signed with Columbia in 1975, scoring a bit hit with 1976's "Give It Up (Turn It Loose)." In the '80s, he signed to the small Highrise label and hit the national charts again in 1982 with "Are You Serious?"

KENT (UK) 037 (R)
The Tyrone Davis Story
Fifteen of his best-selling sides from 1968–1975, including three titles that hit Number 1 on the US soul charts ("Can I Change My Mind," "Turn Back the Hands of Time," and "Turning Point"). One Way Ticket to Nowhere/I Had It All the Time/So Good/After All This Time.

RHINO 70533 (CL)
Greatest Hits
His great Dakar recordings. Davis likes lyrics about fouled-up love affairs. In song, he is man enough to admit when he's wrong and secure enough to seek forgiveness. In "Let Me Back In" he actually pounds on the door begging to be let in. Davis also possesses a versatile voice, as capable of a convincing shout as a hoarse whisper. CD has five bonus tracks. Can I Change My Mind/Turn Back the Hands of Time/Turning Point/There It Is/I Had It All the Time/It Is Something You've Got/Could I Forget You/One-Way Ticket/Without You in My Life.

MARTHA DAVIS and HER TORRID TRIO

You might have seen big, exuberant Martha on a *Showtime at the Apollo* video, singing and playing the piano with her long, tall bassist husband, Calvin Ponder, as Martha Davis and Spouse. Though she was on TV a lot in the '50s, she only cut 28 sides between 1946–1951, and then two LPs in the '60s before disappearing. Most of the tunes feature Martha, who had piano lessons from Fats Waller, backed by an unknown rhythm section, including '46 cuts for Urban, '47 sides for Jewell and Decca, and some fine '51 Coral sides with Ponder, future Nat King Cole vet John Collins, and drummer Art Blakey.

JUKEBOX LIL 1104 (RL)

The Right Track Baby

Eighteen of her best sides. Title tune is one of two recorded with Louis Jordan and The Tympany Five. Kitchen Blues/Sarah, Sarah/Be-Bop Bounce/Ooh-Wee.

RONNIE DAWSON

Ravin' rockabilly star who recorded in the '50s under many different names. Recent comeback LP shows he still has got the sparks in him.

NO HIT 001 (R)

Rockin' Bones

Includes both sides of five singles recorded under a variety of names, including "Rockin' Bones" by Ronnie Dawson, "Action Packed" by Ronnie Dee, "Do Do Do" by Commonwealth Jones, and even a version of "Riders in the Sky" by The Banjo Band from the Levee, along with "Jump and Run" with Delbert McClinton on harp. Also includes six wild unreleased tunes including "Who Put the Cat Out," Chuck Berry's "Reelin' and Rockin'," and Gene Summer's "Straight Skirts."

NO HIT 002 (R)

Still Alot of Rhythm

I'm not a big fan of promoters diggin' up half-dead, rock-and-roll relics and parading their weary ol' bones for a final go-round, but every once in a while it pays off in spades. The Blonde Bomber, Ronnie Dawson, proves he can still rock circles around the younguns. Backed by a tight little trio, Ronnie blasts through a dozen tunes. His singing is great and his lead guitar playing is tremendous. Has anyone ever made a better revival record? Every tune is a winner. This Is the Night/Hillbilly Blues/Fool about You/Rockin' Dog/Come Back Uncle John.

BOBBY DAY

Bobby Day (born Robert Byrd) was an excellent R&B-oriented rocker who had several hits in the mid-to-late '50s. He moved from his native Fort Worth, TX to LA in 1947, and then formed The Hollywood Flames with David Ford, Willie Ray Rockwell, and Curley Dinkins. The group recorded for just about every small West Coast label until hitting it big with Byrd's song, "Buzz-Buzz-Buzz." He remained with the group until 1957 through several personnel and name changes (see separate listing for reissues of their recordings).

His first solo recording was made in 1955. In 1957, he released his own song, "Little Bitty Pretty One," which was a chart-topper for Thurston Harris on Aladdin, and was covered in the following years by Frankie Lymon (1960), Clyde McPhatter (1962), and The Jackson Five (1972). In 1958, recording as a soloist with The Hollywood Flames (now called The Satellites) as backup, Day hit it big with "Rockin' Robin," and followed it with three minor hits in the following year. His song, "Over and Over" was a Number 1 hit for The Dave Clark Five in 1965. In the early '60s, he formed a duo with ex-Flame Earl Nelson to form Bob and Earl, scoring a minor hit with the original "Harlem Shuffle" (1964). In the mid-'60s, he formed his own label, Birdland, continuing to plug away. Discouraged by his lack of recognition, he moved to Australia and New Zealand in the '70s, returning to Florida and songwriting in the '80s. He died of cancer in 1990. The Ace collection is the best place to start for his '50s hits.

ACE 200 (L)

The Original Rockin' Robin

Reissue of tracks from the Class, Collectables, Ace, and Rendezvous labels. Includes the flip side to Class 207, "Roll on Seven," a rollin' tune in the West Coast style of the time. He cut a swingin' version of "My Blue Heaven" with The Blossums in 1958, "Beep Beep," another B-side, utilizes the newfangled space-program lingo, and "Life Can Be Beautiful" reprises the "Rockin' Robin" riff one more time. Mr. and Mrs. Rock and Roll/Three Young Rebs from Georgia/Little Bitty Pretty One.

CLASS 5002 (R)
Rockin' with Bobby Day
His big '50s hits. Bippin' and Boppin'/Mr. and Mrs. Rock and Roll/Sweet Little Thing.

COLLECTABLES 5074 (CL)
Rockin' Robin
The Bluebird, the Buzzard and the Oriole/My Blue Heaven/Come Seven/Beep Beep/I Don't Want To/Life Can Be Beautiful/Rockin' Robin/Mr. and Mrs. Rock and Roll/Three Young Rebs from Georgia/Little Bitty Pretty One.

MARGIE DAY and THE GRIFFIN BROTHERS ORCHESTRA
Margie Day and The Griffin Brothers of Norfolk, VA were one of the very first important innovators of emerging urban R&B in the early '50s.

MR. R&B 109 (R)
I'll Get a Deal
The Dot sides not included on the out-of-print English Ace 136 collection, plus a smattering of later, more pop-oriented sides cut for Decca, Cat, and De Luxe. Many rare photos and extensive sleeve notes add much to the historical appreciation of these seminal R&B recordings.

JACKIE DE SHANNON
Fringe-jacketed flower child of the '60s and '70s whose excellent recordings have often been overshadowed by other artists' cover versions of her songs. She began as a songwriter, penning such hits as Brenda Lee's "Dum Dum" and Marianne Faithful's "Come Stay with Me." She recorded for Imperial as a folk-rocker in the early '60s, with two of her sides, "Needles and Pins" and "When You Walk in the Room" hitting it big in cover versions by The Searchers. She herself earned gold records for 1965's "What the World Needs Now is Love" and 1969's "Put A Little Love in Your Heart." In the '70s, she recorded in a slick, countryish vein for a number of labels, returning to the spotlight when Kim Carnes cut a note-for-note cover of her song "Bette Davis Eyes" in 1981.

RHINO 70738 (CL)
The Best of Jackie De Shannon
Twenty CD cuts, 14 on tape that are sure to bring nostalgic tears to your eyes, including the songs that brought her little recognition as a performer but lots of royalty checks in the mail. Put a Little Love in Your Heart/What the World Needs Now Is Love/Needles and Pins/Bette Davis Eyes/When You Walk in the Room.

TEENAGER 609 (R)
Trouble with Jackie Dee
Fabulous early '60s tunes. There's a bit of rock and roll, R&B, and the girl-group sound here, but in the end everything comes down to De Shannon's dynamic and beautiful voice. These 16 tunes might very well be the best-kept secret in rock-and-roll history; they're that good! Buddy/Trouble/So Warm/Lonely Girl/Teach Me/Maybe Baby/Oh Boy.

CARL DEAN
Rockabilly pianist.

WHITE LABEL 8944 (R)
Carl Dean and His Piano
While Dean won't make anyone forget Jerry Lee or even Mickey Gilley, he's a pretty good hand at rockabilly-style key plunkin'. These are recent recordings of him playing solo piano, about half "live"; the sound on these is enthusiastic albeit a bit on the muddy side. And like Jerry Lee and Gilley, he mixes in lots of honky-tonk drinking tunes in his repertoire, most of which he writes (and writes well). Milwaukee Here I Come/Jenny Jenny/Little Queenie/Another Skid Row Joe/When the Next Round's Bought.

JIMMY DEAN
Jimmy Dean's the kind of singer that falls through the cracks of categorization; nobody claims him. After "Big Bad John" hit so massively in 1961 and he got a TV show, he fell into bland MOR limbo, doing stuff like "P.T. 109." But this ol' pork-sausage eatin' boy has roots. He knocked around for years before any success, charting only once before 1961, in 1953 with a cover of T. Texas Tyler's "Just Bummin' Around" on Four Star.

DEMAND 0050 (R)
Country Rockers
Sixteen good boogie and rockin' country tunes. Bummin' Around/Nothing Can Stop Me/Walkin' the Dog/Why Don't You Shut Your Mouth/Smoke that Cigarette.

JOEY DEE and THE STARLIGHTERS
Twistin' dance-craze band.

RHINO 70965 (CL)
Hey Let's Twist
Let's twist again like we did in 1961 and 1962 with Joey Dee and the Boys. Fourteen cassette tracks, 18 on the CD. Peppermint Twist, Pts. 1 and 2/Roly Poly/Shout, Pt. 1/Crazy Love/What Kind of Love Is This?

THE DEEP RIVER BOYS
Harry Douglas and The Deep River Boys were one of the founding R&B vocal quartets of the post-World War II period. Most of this jubilee-based outfit's material has remained long out of print.

DOO WOP DELIGHTS 104 (C)
The Deep River Boys
Thirty-six cut collection includes rare transcriptions, cuts from their a cappella gospel album, and later commercial recordings. Sound quality is excellent, but their pop-oriented material has been excluded.

THE DEL VIKINGS
One of the first interracial groups, The Del Vikings have a very complicated 17-year history; even the spelling of their name is confusing, with "Del" sometimes spelled with one or two Ls. The original group, made up of Air Force buddies stationed in Pittsburgh, was all black. There was a little personnel shuffling until 1956, when Corinthian "Kripp" Johnson and Norm Wright (leads and tens), Don Jackson (bar), and Clarence Quick (b), and white member Dave Lechery (2nd ten, formerly of The Meadlowlarks) cut their first demos (reissued on Collectables and Flyright). Jackson was shipped to Germany and was replaced by another white vocalist, Gus Bakus. The group signed to Pittsburgh's Fee Bee label and recorded the classics "Come Go with Me" and "Whispering Bells," released nationally by Dot. Their early Fee Bee/Dot sides have been reissued by Flyright.

Mercury enticed the group away from Fee Bee, but since Johnson was the only member over 21 when they signed their original Fee Bee contract, he could not leave the label. There were now *two* Del Vikings, the group on Mercury with Johnson replaced by William Blakely, and Kripp Johnson's all-black group on Fee Bee, with Don Jackson

returning from Europe and rejoining the group and future soul star Chuck Jackson also coming into the fold. The Fee Bee Del Vikings changed their name to The Versatiles.

The Mercury group went two years without a hit, but as soon as Kripp Johnson's Fee Bee contract ran out in 1958, he rejoined the group for such hits as "Down in Bermuda" and "Sunday Kind of Love" before they broke up in 1960. These Mercury recordings have been reissued by Dee Jay Jamboree. Later, Johnson formed *another* Del Vikings that recorded for Alpine, ABC, and Gateway.

COLLECTABLES 5001 (CL)
1956 Audition Tapes
Nine cuts from this fine group's first recording session, including the first version of their classic "Come Go with Me." Most of these tunes were reissued in 1957 with overdubbed band accompaniments on the Luniverse label. These versions are the originals with only guitar-and-drums backup.

COLLECTABLES 5010 (C)
The Best of
Fourteen tracks. Come Go with Me/What Made Maggie Run/Willette/You Say You Love Me/Whispering Bells/I'm Spinning/A Sunday Kind of Love.

DEE JAY JAMBOREE 2060 (R)
The Swinging, Singing Del Vikings Record Session
Reissue of Mercury 20353 with extra tracks, 16 wonderful Mercury sides in all, featuring the beautiful lead of Norm Wright and basser Clarence Quick who wrote most of the material here. None of their giant hits are here, but the material is uniformly excellent, a blend of harmony, jump, and novelty numbers. Check out the ultra-cool back cover photo of Gus Backus! Includes a cover of Fats Domino's "The Big Beat." There I Go (Falling in Love Again)/The Bells/The Voodoo Man/Pretty Little Thing Called Girls/Friendly Moon.

DEE JAY JAMBOREE 2063 (R)
They Sing ... They Swing
The Del Vikings's 1957–1959 Mercury recordings, featuring the lead vocals of Norman Wright and, after 1958, original vocalist Kripp Johnson. This set reproduces the cover of their first LP (Mercury 20314 from 1957). It has 14 great tunes, including a never-released alternate take of "You Cheated" and the hit version of "A Sunday Kind of Love" and "Down in Bermuda." White Cliffs of Dover/Somewhere Over the Rainbow/Your Book of Life.

DEE JAY JAMBOREE 2064 (R)
Cool Shake
Completes their 1957–1959 Mercury recordings. Fourteen more great sides, including such hard-to-find greats as "Flat Tire," "Cool Shake," "Jitterbug Mary," "Snowbound," plus alternate takes of "Somewhere over the Rainbow" and "There I Go," and two tunes never before issued: "No Ho Ho" and "Gates of Paradise."

FLYRIGHT 34 (L)
Come Go with Me
Twenty-one song collection containing much of the quintet's pre-Mercury Fee Bee (1956–1957) output, plus a smattering of Dot and Luniverse sides (1957). The collection features the group's 1956 initial nine-song, basement audition session, the original Fee Bee version of "Come Go with Me," plus the beautiful "Willette" and "I Want to Marry You," both led by Chuck Jackson. Long-time lead singer Kripp Johnson demonstrates his vocal skills on "When I Come Home." Detailed sleeve notes by John Broven of *Juke Blues* magazine.

FLYRIGHT 53 (L)
The Dell Vikings, Vol. 2
Twenty tracks from the group's Fee Bee recordings; half of them are previously unreleased takes or titles. Most of these tracks are tantalizingly obscure. It's all solid material, mixing jumps, mid-tempo numbers, and ballads. The sound quality is good, even though four cuts come from the "only surviving acetates." Fine notes by Bill Millar, and a great cover photo of lead singer Kripp Johnson decked out in a white jacket and a plaid bow tie. Woke Up This Morning/Hurricane Woman/Billy Boy/Please Say You'll Be Mine/Stay Here With Me/Baby Let Me Be.

THE DELFONICS
One of the originators of the Philly Sound of the '70s, this group was originally formed as The Four Gents in 1965. In the late '60s and early '70s, they had a number of hits on the Philly Groove label owned by their manager Stan Watson. Their recordings are noted for the lovely tenor leads of William Hart and the lavish arangements of Thom Bell.

COLLECTABLES 5109 (C)
Golden Classics
A dozen great Philly Groove sides from 1968–1973, produced, written, and arranged by Thom Bell with beautiful Bill Hart vocals. La La Means I Love You/Didn't I (Blow Your Mind)/Ready or Not.

THE DELLS
Long-lived Chicago vocal group. The original group featured Johnny Funches on lead vocals with Marvin Junior (1st ten), Verne Allison (2nd ten), Mickey McGill (bar), and Chuck Barksdale (b). They first recorded as the El Rays in 1953 for Chess. In 1956, they changed their name to The Dells and began a long association with Vee Jay that included their classic hit, "Oh What a Nite."

In 1958, the group was involved in a car crash that killed Funches and seriously injured McGill. The rest of the group lay low for a while, mostly singing background for pop artists Jerry Butler, Gene Chandler, and Dee Clark. Barksdale left for a while to sing bass in Harvey Fuqua's New Moonglows. By the early '60s, the group was back together on Vee Jay with Funches replaced by former Flamingo Johnny Cart. They began scoring hits again, but then Vee Jay folded in 1964. They signed with Chess-subsidiary Cadet, scoring some of the best Chicago soul hits of the late '60s/early '70s, including "Stay in My Corner," "There Is," and a gorgeous remake of "Oh What a Nite." They left Cadet in 1975, moving first to Mercury then to 20th Century Fox. They continue to perform on the oldies circuit.

CHESS 9103 (RC)
The Dells
Their greatest hits recorded for Chess in the mid-'60s. Stay in My Corner/There Is/Love Is Blue (I Can Sing a Rainbow)/Oh What a Nite/Give Your Baby a Standing Ovation.

CHESS 9288 (RL)
There Is
Reissue of Cadet 804 from 1968. The best Dells LP (besides *The Best of The Dells*), this one started their comeback as a powerful Chicago soul group. Includes three smash singles ("Stay in My Corner," "Wear It on Our Face," and the title tune), a few lesser hits ("Show Me," "Run for Cover," and "O-o I Love You"), and some beautiful covers of "Close Your Eyes" and "Higher and Higher."

CHESS 9333 (CL)
On the Corner: The Best of The Dells
Album and single sides from 1966–1974, beginning with their remake of "Oh What a Nite," featuring the blend of doo-wop and soul that made The Dells so popular. The powerful baritone of Marvin Junior and the silky falsetto tenor of ex-Flamingo Johnny Carter

are showcased on this excellent collection of hits. Also included is the previously unreleased ballad "Since I Found You," which no Dells fan will want to be without. This collection was compiled by *Goldmine's* R&B Editor Robert Pruter, whose excellent notes make this attractive package irresistible. There Is/Stay in My Corner/O-O I Love You/Nadine/Give Your Baby a Standing Ovation/I Miss You/My Pretending Days Are Over.

VEE JAY 701 (CL)
Dreams of Contentment
Vee Jay cuts recorded between 1955–1965, including seven tunes not released by the label at the time, but previously available on Charly and Solid Smoke reissues from the '80s. Excellent sound quality and appreciative notes by Billy Vera. Great music, but you may well wonder, as I do, with all of the fine Dells's material available, why they chose to include the group's ill-considered cover of Tom Jones's "It's Not Unusual." Oh What a Nite/Jo, Jo, Dry Your Eyes/ Wedding Day/Stay in My Corner.

THE DELTA RHYTHM BOYS

The Delta Rhythm Boys were one of a handful of important early black vocal groups instrumental in shaping the development of popular quartet singing. The Deltas, whose sound was at first styled on that of The Mills Brothers, got their start at Oklahoma's Langston University in 1933. Group members of the 1941–1960 period were Carl Jones (1st ten/arranger), Traverse Crawford (2nd ten), Kelsey Pharr (bar), and Lee Gaines (b).

DOO WOP DELIGHTS 102
Delta Rhythm Boys
Spans the 1941–1950 period and touches upon some of the close-harmony quartet's finest sides on various labels, as well as featuring some of their best accompaniments behind Ella Fitzgerald, Mildred Bailey, and Ruth Brown.

THE DEMENSIONS

The Bronx High School choir nurtured this vocal group, best-known for their 1960 cover of the pop standard, "Over the Rainbow." Leaders Lenny Dell and Howie Margolin formed a group with two local friends and, coached by Lenny's father (a professional musician), they landed a contract with Mohawk, recording their lone hit.

RELIC 7032 (L)
Over the Rainbow
Includes all four of their singles recorded for Mohawk, as well as various demos. "I've Been Searching," "Searching," and "Take My Love," for example, are all versions of the same song. "Seven Days a Week," issued by Coral, is here in stereo. Alas, the demo for "Come with Me" sounds like a demo in the worst way, but most of the stuff here is pretty good. Nursery Rhyme Rock/China Girl/Theresa/Zing Went the Strings of My Heart.

TERRY DENE

Terry was one of the first British rock-and-roll stars, starting out in the London coffee bars that were popular in the '50s. He was discovered by Jack Good while singing in between wrestling matches, and was known for his raucous fights and drinking binges. He had a good-sized hit with his first recording, a cover of Marty Robbins's "A White Sport Coat," and was actually called Britain's answer to Elvis Presley. (Britain's Pat Boone would be closer to the truth.) Mostly saddled with saccharine choruses and strings, Dene nevertheless did break out with a couple of good rockers: "This Is the Night" and especially "Baby She's Gone." His downfall came when he joined the army in 1959 and, within two days, had a major nervous breakdown.

CHARM 001 (R)
The Terry Dene Story, Vol. 1
Twenty cuts, including his hit "A White Sport Coat" and two previously unissued takes. Charm/Start Movin'/Teenage Dream/Thank You Pretty Baby.

STAR CLUB 8024 (R)
London Rock
Sixteen tunes from British Decca from his peak years, 1957–1959, when he was a regular on the British TV show, *6/5 Special.* Includes a rare live track from a *6/5 Special* compilation LP, and a complete discography. Pretty Little Pearly/Start Movin'/Come and Get It/Stairway of Love.

ARNIE DERKSEN

Derksen was a young Canadian singer/guitarist who got his big break, like so many others, by being the young stud in a C&W band when rockabilly took off. He handled the rockers for Vic Siebert's Sons of the Saddle out of Winnipeg,

Canada, singing on TV there, and cut a few records for London and Decca.

CHESS 9106 (RC)

His Greatest Sides, Vol. 1

Fourteen classic recordings cut between 1955–1962; great sound and tremendous cover photo. Bo Diddley/Mona/Road Runner/Crackin' Up/I'm a Man/Diddley Daddy/Say Man.

BEAR FAMILY 15362 (R)

My Dancin' Shoes

Ten tunes recorded at Decca in 1958–1959, a mixture of rockabilly, pop, and country. "She Wanna Rock," written by soul great Arthur Alexander and "My Dancin' Shoes" are by far his best work, both featuring some good guitar. Derkson also does a fair job covering Webb Pierce's "There Stands the Glass" and John D. Loudermilk's "K4WO," a ham-radio love song!

CHESS 9194 (RC)

Bo Diddley

Reissue of Bo's first album (Chess 1431) from 1959 featuring some of his most famous songs.

CHESS 9264 (RCL)

In the Spotlight

Reissue of Bo's fourth LP, Checker 2976 from 1960. A dozen tunes recorded between September 1959–April 1960, many with Otis Spann on piano. Contains the immortal "Road Runner," plus "Signifying Blues" (a tune in the "Say Man" vein), instrumentals "Travelin' West" and "Scuttle Bug," and "Craw-Dad."

BO DIDDLEY

A rock-and-roll legend, Bo's "shave-and-a-haircut" beat has become a standard in rock as have dozens of his songs. Discovered by Chuck Berry, Ellas McDaniel, with his harp-player Billy Boy Arnold, attempted to record McDaniel's song "Dirty Motherfucker." Of course, that couldn't be done, so Arnold suggested substituting the nonsense words "Bo Diddley," which became the name of the song *and* the performer. Bo's best material is his early Chess sides with an incredible band, including his guitar and Arnold's harp with Jerome Green (b and maracas), Otis Spann (pno), Frank Kirkland (drm), and Bo's half-sister "The Duchess" (gtr, vcl). Fortunately most of this material has been reissued by Chess. He's still active, constantly touring and recording (mostly in France).

A number of Bo's original LPs have been reissued in exact reproductions; his first two LPs, virtually "greatest-hits" collections, are available on a single rockin' CD. The Chess box is available for dedicated fans, and there are also a couple of collections of rare and unissued material.

CHESS 9285 (RCL)

Bo Diddley Is a Gunslinger

Reissue of Checker 2977 from 1960 with two never-before-issued cuts. The wild and wacky adventures of the true King of Rock and Roll continue with the classic title tune, and, keeping with the Western theme, Bo dishes us up "Cheyenne," "16 Tons," "Whoa Mule (Shine)" (the further adventures of Shine from "Mule Skinner Blues"), along with "Ride on Josephine," "Diddling," "Cadillac" (covered by The Kinks on their first LP), and the first-ever issue of the raw "Working Man" and "Do What I Say."

CHESS 9296 (RCL)

The London Sessions

I guess the London Philharmonic was all booked up when Bo was in town for these 1972 sessions. They had to make do with only 13 people as the backing group, later adding five more in Chicago (where most of this "London" session was recorded)!! The famed Diddley beat is totally lost in this "sym-phoney." A real period piece. Don't Want No Lyin' Woman/Bo Diddley/Bo-Jam/Do the Robot.

CHESS 9331 (CL)

Rare and Well Done

Finally we're treated to a full-blown collection from the vast unreleased legacy of Bo Diddley at Chess. Bo admittedly has a limited repertoire, but even if you've heard most of these riffs before on other tunes, they are great riffs that bear repeating. To open, there's a full 4:21 minute undubbed version of "She's Alright." "Heart-O-Matic Love" chugs along, helped considerably by Billy Boy Arnold's boss harp. Guess what Bo plays on "Blues Blues" backed by Otis Spann and Willie Dixon? Then guess what he does on "Rock and Roll," both previously unreleased and both great. "Cookie-headed Diddley" will surely bring forth a

⊕ CHESS 5904 (L)

Bo Diddley/Go Bo Diddley

It don't get any better than this! Bo's first two LPs together on one CD, 24 tunes with nearly 65 minutes of playing power. Bo's first could almost be a greatest-hits album, including "Bo Diddley," "Diddley Daddy," "I'm a Man," "Who Do You Love," "Pretty Thing," and "Bring It to Jerome," while his second LP has "Crackin' Up," "I'm Sorry," "Dearest Darling," and "Say Man."

smile, "Moon Baby" is an interesting piece of fluff, "I Want My Baby" is nothing special due to the poor recording, but "Please Mr. Engineer" is a revelation with Bo hamming it up on some wild vocals while the guitar player (unknown) runs through every train riff in the book and then some. You're gonna love these 16 tracks, almost all unreleased or never before on LP.

CHESS 19502 (RCL)
Bo Diddley
The Bo Diddley boxed set is here and, although it's certainly not what I'd hoped for, it's still a must have. There are 45 songs on three LPs or two cassettes or CDs, ten never before released, and a couple never released on American Chess. The material here covers the period of his first recordings in 1955 on up to "Bo Diddley 1969," a tune only released as a single (Checker 1213). Let's check the alternate takes: "Bring It to Jerome," without Jerome's vocals, is pretty bland. The alternate of "Hush Your Mouth" though is pretty exciting with a much more trebly sound on Bo's guitar and some rough vocals. On "Dearest Darling," you can hear Bo working up the tune with the band. The alternate of "Say Man, Back Again" has Bo and Jerome trading the same old "dozens" but with slightly different results. A real treat is "Spend My Life with You," a straightforward blues tune recorded at Bo's home in 1959 with (probably) Lafayette Leake (pno), Clifton James (drm), and Jerome Green (maracas). "Signifying Blues" from 1960 could be called "Say Man, Back YET Again"; the dozens are really flying fast and furious on this extended take that was never released. Bo does some fine singing on "You Know I Love You" with The Flamingos on backup vocals. "Look at My Baby" and the "Untitled Instrumental" are both prime Diddley. Add these unreleased tunes to the other odds and ends here, and you get one indispensable boxed set. And don't forget the ultra-cool, photo-filled, 24-page booklet, either.

EDSEL 318 (L)
The 20th Anniversary of Rock and Roll
Mid-'70s RCA album, half of which is devoted to superstar jams on old Bo songs, featuring the likes of Elvin Bishop, Joe Cocker, Billy Joel, Albert Lee, Roger McGuinn, Keith Moon, and Leslie West.

NEW ROSE 34 (L)
Ain't It Good to Be Free
CD issue of the 1985 LP, featuring ten new Bo compositions. There's a good funk groove throughout with little of the old Bo Beat, including songs about freedom, welfare, love, and Bo Diddley! Bo Diddley Put the Rock in Rock and Roll/Mona, Where's Your Sister/Stabilize Yourself/I Don't Want Your Welfare.

VARETTA DILLARD
One of the great R&B vocalists, right up there with Ruth Brown or LaVern Baker, although she never achieved their fame. She started singing during a long hospital stay to treat a bone ailment. She entered talent shows at The Apollo Theatre in Harlem where she was discovered by Savoy Records. She recorded for Savoy from 1952–1955 and for Groove and RCA from 1956–1961.

BEAR FAMILY 15431 (L)
Got You on My Mind

BEAR FAMILY 15432 (L)
The Lovin' Bird
Her complete recordings from 1956–1961, remastered from the original master tapes. This is another Bear Family extravaganza with great clean sound, good notes by Norbert Hess, lots of rare photos, and a complete and detailed discography. The music is rockin' R&B at its best. The first volume (29 cuts, 71 minutes) is the one that I'll probably play more, because the bands tend to be kicking hard with King Curtis (sax) and Mickey Baker (gtr), and the arrangements seem tighter. The second volume (22 cuts, 53 minutes) is still great. If you have to choose, go with Volume 1 first. Gotta warn ya, tho: If you spring for Volume 1, you'll be ordering Volume 2 real soon!

DION/DION and THE BELMONTS
Dion DiMucci, a young Bronx-born singer, recorded two singles for Mohawk in 1956 with his first group, The Timberlanes. The Belmonts (named for Belmont Avenue in the Bronx), consisting of Angelo D'Aleo, Freddie Milano, and Carlo Mastangelo, also recorded for Mohawk, and the two groups paired for "We Went Away" in 1957. Later that same year, they signed to Laurie for a string of hits, including "I Wonder Why," "Teenager in Love," and "Where or When" from 1958–1960. Laurie groomed Dion for solo stardom by releasing an LP of pop standards, and in 1960 he split from The Belmonts for a solo career (See separate listing for THE BELMONTS and CARLO AND THE BELMONTS for their later recordings). Dion had a number of hits on Laurie, including "The Wanderer," "Runaround Sue," and "Lovers who Wander," backed by the uncredited Del-Satins. He signed to Columbia in 1963, but after "Donna the Prima

Donna," he mostly recorded unsuccessful covers. In 1967, he reunited with The Belmonts for a couple of singles and an LP on ABC. After taking a sabbatical from recording to kick a drug habit, Dion re-emerged as a folk-rocker, again recording for Laurie, scoring with the protest anthem, "Abraham, Martin, and John." He later signed with Warner Bros., scoring a minor hit with the anti-drug song, "Clean Up Your Own Backyard," and reunited with The Belmonts for a live LP. After years on the oldies circuit, he re-emerged in the late '70s for an abortive comeback and then again in the late '80s with another comeback LP, featuring Lou Reed and Paul Simon.

Dion's early material has been reissued and re-reissued on Ace and Collectables. The Columbia years are documented on an excellent release (46972), including many previously unissued blues numbers. The wonderful concert reunion LP from Warners has been reissued by Rhino.

ACE 148 (R)/COLLECTABLES 5027 (RC)
Runaround Sue

Reissue of Laurie 2009 from 1961. Ace version has extra cuts, 14 in all, and includes real stereo versions of the hits. Runaround Sue/The Wanderer/The Majestic/Dream Lover/I'm Gonna Make It Somehow/Little Star.

✪ ACE 176 (CL)
Dion Hits

Eighteen incredible-sounding Dion/Dion and The Belmonts Laurie hits, digitally remastered from the master tapes. Sound is so crisp and clear, you can almost count the handclaps! Comes with a nice booklet with liner notes, lots of photos (color and b&w), and chart positions. My only complaint: the disc is only 43 minutes long! Includes four early songs in mono—"I Wonder Why," "Don't Pity Me," "Where or When," and "No One Knows"—with the rest in beautiful digital stereo, including five more by Dion and The Belmonts (including "Teenager in Love" and "In the Still of the Night"), and nine by Dion, including "The Wanderer," "The Majestic," "Runaround Sue," and "Lovers Who Wander."

ACE 204 (R)
Abraham, Martin and John

Reissue of his 1968 comeback LP, originally issued as Laurie 2047. Dion's got long hair and is playing an acoustic guitar, and boy is he wimpy! Lovers of novelty tunes: get this just to hear Dion's sensitive acoustic version of "Purple Haze," which even came out as a single. Folkies may like his thoughtful interpretations of Fred Neil, Joni Mitchell, and Leonard Cohen songs, but lovers of Bronx raunch, stay away!

ACE 294 (R)
Return of The Wanderer

Reissue of 1978 Lifesong album. Nine songs, six of them cowritten by Dion, one from Tom Waits, one from Dylan, and one from John Sebastian.

ACE 295 (R)
Fire in the Night

Reissue of 1979 recordings intended for issue on Lifesong but unissued up to now.

ACE 915 (L)
Runaround Sue: The Best of the Rest

Twenty-four tunes, most making their first appearance here. Many are alternate takes, some from *So Why Didn't You Do That the First Time?* (Ace 155, now on CD as Ace 943), but many were never previously issued anywhere. Includes two takes of the title tune, plus "The Wanderer," "Little Diane" (without the kazoo solo), and "Lonely Teenager," all in real stereo, as are the tracks here from *Alone with Dion,* never before issued in stereo, taken from recently discovered master tapes.

ACE 936 (L)
Return of the Wanderer/ Fire in the Night

Ace 294 and 295 on one CD.

ACE 943 (L)
Lovers Who Wander/So Why Didn't You Do That the First Time?

Two LPs on one CD, the original 1962 album *Lovers Who Wonder* and Ace's 1985 compilation of alternate takes and unissued songs. Thirty tracks in all.

ACE 945 (L)
Wish upon a Star/Alone with Dion

Two LPs on one CD, 28 cuts in all, both from Laurie Records's vaults circa 1960. *Wish upon a Star* (with The Belmonts) is a sentimental stroll through 14 numbers like "Still of the Night," "All the Things You Are," "It's Only a Paper Moon," "Fly Me to the Moon," and, yes, even "When the Red Red Robin Comes Bob Bob Bobbin' Along." You get the picture. *Alone with Dion* paints Mr. DiMucci as the suave songster, complete with ascot, crooning his way through "P.S. I Love You," "Save the Last Dance for Me," "Fools Rush In," and "The Kissin' Game."

ACE 966 (L)
Presenting Dion and The Belmonts/Runaround Sue

Two LPs on one CD: the first Dion and The Belmonts album and Dion's second solo album.

COLLECTABLES 5025 (C)
Presenting Dion And The Belmonts
Reissue of their first LP, Laurie 2002 from 1960. I Wonder Why/You Better Not Do That/I Got the Blues/A Teenager in Love/A Funny Feeling/That's My Desire.

COLLECTABLES 5026 (C)
Wish upon a Star
Reissue of their second LP, Laurie 2006 from 1960, with original cover and notes. Also reissued on Ace 945.

COLLECTABLES 5041 (RC)
20 Golden Classics
Everything you ever wanted to hear by Dion and The Belmonts is featured on this 20-song set of hits in perfect, peerless fidelity. If you don't have any of the previous reissues, buy this one. The Wanderer/Majestic/Runaround Sue/A Teenager in Love/Where or When.

COLUMBIA 46972 (CL)
Bronx Blues: The Columbia Recordings, 1962–1965
Twenty songs recorded between 1962–1965, including unissued songs and alternate takes digitally remixed and remastered. Includes his big hits "Ruby Baby," "Drip Drop," and "Donna the Prima Donna," covers of doo-wop classics like "Little Girl of Mine" and "A Sunday Kind of Love," some fine original songs ("Gonna Make It Alone," "Flim Flam," and "Sweet Baby"), and most surprisingly some down-home blues. He recorded a whole series of blues songs with a small blues/jazz group including Buddy Lucas (hca) and Panama Francis (drm). Most of these were not originally issued and they are making their first appearance here, including the Buddy Lucas original "Sweet Papa Di," Sonny Boy Williamson's "Don't Start Me to Talking," and Willie Dixon's "Spoonful." Dion wouldn't have given Muddy Waters or Howlin' Wolf much cause for concern, but his blues covers don't sound half bad. The album ends up with a previously unissued hard-rocking version of Bob Dylan's "I'm in the Mood for You." The set comes with an excellent booklet with detailed notes and rare photos. A most worthwhile collection.

LAURIE (JAPAN) 22054 (L)
Original Classics
Japanese CD, duplicates material issued on various Ace packages. Nine by Dion and The Belmonts and sixteen from Dion's solo career. I Wonder Why/A Teenager in Love/A Lover's Prayer/In the Still of the Night/Lovers Who Wander/Runaround Sue/Come Go with Me/Lonely Teenager/Purple Haze/Abraham, Martin and John.

RHINO 70228 (CL)
Dion and The Belmonts Reunion
Reissue of *Dion and The Belmonts Live at Madison Square Garden 1972*, Warner Bros. 2664 from 1973. Seems to be something magical about this album. Dion had been wimping along as a folkie on Warner Bros., having a minor hit with "Clean Up Your Own Back Yard." The three original Belmonts were back together and had done the magnificent *Cigars, Acapella, Candy* LP for Buddah. The four finally reunited for a June 2, 1972 oldies show at Madison Square Garden. The harmonies are a bit rough but quite fine, especially on "That's My Desire," "Where or When," and an incredible scat in "Little Diane," and you can tell everybody is having fun. Rhino's new packaging is pretty mediocre, with only early photos and nothing from the show. I Wonder Why/The Wanderer/No One Knows/Teenager in Love.

CARL DOBKINS, JR.
One-hit wonder (1959's "My Heart Is an Open Book") in a countryish/rockabilly style.

BEAR FAMILY 15546 (L)
My Heart Is an Open Book
Twenty-eight songs, very much in the pop-rock style, with choruses and orchestral backing, a few previously unissued. Highlight is "Love Is Everything," penned by Carl and given a full-tilt arrangement, complete with torrid sax, that must have caused young Jr. to take to his bed for a week afterwards. My Heart Is an Open Book/Class Ring/Lucky Devil/A Fool such as I.

DR. JOHN
Mac Rebennack (aka Dr. John) started out as a New Orleans session pianist and guitarist backing up Professor Longhair, Frankie Ford, and Joe Tex. (Recordings of this material are now available on Ace.) Rebennack moved to LA, taking the name Dr. John The Night Tripper, bringing New Orleans voodoo music to the hippies with the aid of Jessie Hill and Harold Battiste. His early hippie-tinged experimentations have been reissued on Atco Japan. He produced the classic *Gumbo* LP in 1972 (reissued by Alligator on vinyl and tape and by Atlantic on CD), full of New Orleans standards, and had a huge pop hit with 1973's "Right Place, Wrong Time." Since the death of Professor Longhair and Tuts Washington, The Doctor has become one of the foremost exponents of New Orleans piano.

ACE (US) 2020 (RL)
Dr. John and His New Orleans Congregation
Wonderful collection featuring various '50s and '60s recordings that Dr. John had a hand in. It opens with a sloppy "New Orleans" by Big Boy Myles, but quickly shifts gears with the fantastic "Storm Warning," a blazing instrumental originally on Rex, with the good doctor on rockin' guitar and Alvin "Red" Tyler on baritone sax. Dr. John also plays guitar on the two following tunes, really cutting loose on his solo on Frankie Ford's "Morgus the Magnificent"; "Bad Neighborhood" is a duet with Ronnie Baron. Also includes some early productions where Dr. John helped launch the careers of Joe Tex and Lee Dorsey. Chick-a-WaWa/Rock/Roll On/Down the Road.

ALLIGATOR 3901 (RC)/ATLANTIC 7006 (L)
Gumbo
Perhaps his best-known LP, originally issued as Atlantic 7006 from 1972. This spicy recipe blends Dixieland jazz, R&B, and indigenous rock and roll into a form best described by Mac as "basic good-time New Orleans blues and stomp music." The horn arrangements by Harold Battiste smoke. Includes "Iko Iko," the Creole romp that epitomizes the spirit of Mardi Gras, "Blow Wind Blow" featuring Fats Domino's premier saxman Lee Allen, "Mess Around" (a spirited shuffle and a tip-of-the-hat to Ray Charles), "Junko Partner," a brilliant rendition of a New Orleans anthem, and "Tipitina" a great reading of the 1953 Professor Longhair gem. Dr. John contributes the liner notes on this reissue.

ALLIGATOR 3904 (RC)
Gris-Gris
This recording, his first for Atlantic (Atco 234, 1968), has been the most readily available over the years, and has acquired mythic status due to its heavy voodoo themes and startling musical creativity. Songs like "Gris-Gris Gumbo Ya Ya," "I Walk on Gilded Splinters," "Danse Kalinda Ba Doom," "Danse Fambeaux," and "Croker Courtbullion" never fail to conjure up images of bubbling cauldrons full of potent herbs and misty bayou rites. These are rounded out by more upbeat fare like the chipper "Mama Roux" and "Jump Sturdy."

ATCO (JAPAN) 231 (L)
Remedies
This 1970 effort (originally Atco 316) relies on an uncredited band to score Rebennack's weird (i.e. "supernatural") imagery, kicking off with "Loop Garoo" ("primitive zombies come bursting past, walking with the queen through the hoodoo dream"). Wow. Also an early version of "What Goes Around Comes Around," the New Orleans anthem "Mardi Gras Day," and "Wash, Mama, Wash," "Chippy, Chippy," and the 17-minute epic "Angola Anthem."

ATCO (JAPAN) 232 (L)
The Sun, Moon and Herbs
Originally Atco 362 from 1971, this is one of the more obscure musical swamp rituals from "The Night Tripper," featuring Eric Clapton (gtr), The Memphis Horns, studio vet Bobby Keys (ten sax), and Mick Jagger (backing voc). Seven haunting cuts, some of which are a little dated now but still full of swirling dark magic. Black John the Conqueror/Where Ya At Mule/Craney Crow/Familiar Reality (Opening and Reprise)/Pots on Fiyo/Zu Zu Mamou.

ATCO (JAPAN) 235 (L)
Desitively Bonaroo
As the incense smoke cleared, Mac Rebennack glided into the mid-'70s, shedding the Night Tripper appellation and making a 360-degree turn back to his Crescent City roots. He enlisted long-time pals Allen Toussaint and The Meters to do his tunes "Quitters Never Win," "Stealin'," "What Comes Around," "Me-You=Loneliness," "Mos' Scocious," "Rite Away," "RU 4 Real," "Sing Along Song," "Can't Git Enuff," and the title track, plus producer Toussaint's "Go Tell the People" and Earl King's "Let's Make a Better World." Originally Atlantic 7043.

ATLANTIC 7018 (L)
In the Right Place
Along with *Gumbo* and *Gris Gris,* this is one of Dr. John's greatest early-'70s recordings. Mac, backed up by the always funky Meters and producer Allen Toussaint, does "Right Place, Wrong Time," "Such a Night," "I Been Hoodood," "Cold Cold Cold," and seven more. If this don't get your mojo workin', don't blame me! Reissue has amazing sound.

BGO 62 (RL)
Hollywood Know Thy Name
Ten cuts on the reissue of this rare 1975 LP, originally UA 552. Reggae Doctor/The Way You Do The Things You Do/Yesterday/I Wanna Rock.

CLEAN CUTS 705 (L)
Plays Mac Rebennack
1981 solo piano album album now on CD with extra tracks. Dorothy/Memories of Professor Longhair/Delicado/Big Mac/Saints.

EDSEL 128 (R)
I Been Hoodooed
A slice of the Doc from his most commercial period, this recording contains eight songs from 1973's *The Right Place* and 1974's *Desitively Bonaroo,* both available in their entirety on Atlantic reissues. Lots of jumping New Orleans R&B with backing by Allen

Toussaint and The Meters. Right Place, Wrong Time/ Such a Night/Cold Cold Cold.

THUNDERBOLT 066 (R)

Loser for You Baby

Eleven tunes. The Time Had Come/The Ear Is on Strike/I Pulled the Cover Off You/Two Lovers/Go Ahead On/Bring Your Love/Bald Head.

WARNER BROS. 25889 (CL)

In a Sentimental Mood

Classy 1991 LP, recreating the toney big-band productions of Ray Charles, especially on such numbers as "Don't Let the Sun Catch You Crying," "Candy," "Love for Sale," and "Makin' Whoopee" (a duet with Ricky Lee Jones). While emulating The Genius of Soul, as well as Charles Brown, The Doctor also gives us a helping of his own unique piano and voice, especially on "Accentuate the Positive." Not a groundbreaker, and a little slow at times, but mighty tasty.

WARNER BROS. 26940 (CL)

Goin' Back to New Orleans

Dr. John calls this recording "a little history of New Orleans music." He's taken music from the 1850s to today and assembled what may be the finest collection of Crescent City performers ever to record for this set. Among the 18 songs are longtime favorites like "Careless Love," Jelly Roll Morton's "I Thought I Heard Buddy Bolden Say," Leadbelly's "Good Night, Irene," and the Joe Liggins title track. The liner notes contain histories and memories of each song by Dr. John himself. The lengthy list of legendary musicians lending a capable hand or two includes Al Hirt, Pete Fountain, The Neville Brothers, Danny Barker, Alvin "Red" Tyler, Chief "Smiley" Ricks, and Chuck Carbo. Not a bad fix 'til Mardi Gras rolls around again.

WARNER BROS. 27612 (L)

The Ultimate Dr. John

Fourteen-cut compilation concentrating on the "hit" years, with 11 of the cuts coming from the classic *Gumbo* LP. The other three tunes are "Mama Roux," "I Walk On Gilded Splinters" from *Gris Gris*, and "Mardi Gras Day" from *Remedies*.

DR. JOHN and CHRIS BARBER

GREAT SOUTHERN 11024 (CL)

On a Mardi Gras Day, with Chris Barber's Jazz Band

1983 live recording, a jamboree of Dr. John favorites ("Such a Night" and "Right Place, Wrong Time"), Mardi Gras songs (the title cut, "Lil' Liza Jane," and "Iko Iko"), and New Orleans jazz. The street-parade material is the Chris Barber Band's specialty, and they really go to town on Paul Barbarin's "Bourbon Street Parade" and "The Wicked Shall Cease," a fascinating

slow dirge. Dr. J sings most of these 12 cuts, and although his voice is a bit ragged, it sounds like a good time was had by all.

BILL DOGGETT

Bill Doggett made hundreds of danceable R&B sides in the '50s, as a leader (cutting over 200 numbers with his own group) and also as the King studio's primary organ-pumper. He started his career in the '30s and '40s with the Lucky Millender and Lionel Hampton bands. He formed his own R&B band in 1951, and started his long tenure with King in 1953. In 1956, Doggett hit it big with "Honky Tonk," which topped the R&B charts and reached Number 2 on the pop charts. He followed this with a number of other hits over the next few years. Part of his success can be attributed to his flair for arranging and adapting different styles to a jazzy small-band format. Many of his King LPs have been reissued in their original format, while the Charly CD gives a good overview of his boppin' numbers.

✪ CHARLY 281 (L)

Leaps and Bounds

Nineteen cuts, a fine cross section of Doggett's work. His "big-organ" sound blasts through on the opening "Bo-Do Rock," and on the instrumentals "Big Dog" and "Leaps and Bounds," where his crack soloists get to shine. Saxophonist Clifford Scott (Charly 280) is featured on "Hippy Dippy," and "Big Boy" showcases brilliant chording by guitarist Billy Butler. These same sidemen made "Honky Tonk" the smash hit of the decade; the mandatory jukebox anthem is presented here in both original parts, as well as the Tommy Brown vocal version. Doggett got a lot of mileage out of the "Honky Tonk" groove: witness the clones "Shindig" and "Yocky Dock" here! Some of his other specialties were the "smoochy" slow dance number, represented by "Blue Largo," and horny late-night numbers like the bump-and-grind treatment of "In the Wee Hours." Mildred Anderson's sassy vocals are spotlighted on "You Ain't No Good" and "Your Kind of Woman."

KING 523 (RCL)

As You Desire Me

A dreamy-eyed young miss holding a glass of vino graces the cover of this reissue, no doubt grooving to the lush, romantic sounds of Doggett's mellow organ. The original Muzak-meister does "Alone," "Yesterdays," "As Time Goes By," "Dedicated to You," "Dream," and other pop standards. Previously reissued as an import on Sing.

KING 557 (RCL)

Doggett Beat for Dancing Feet

Reissue of King 557 from 1957. A dozen rockin' tunes recorded 1953–1957 with Clifford Scott (ten sax, flute) and Billy Butler (gtr), with Percy Francis and Skinny Brown on tenor for the '53 and '54 sides. Includes his classic hit "Ram-Bunk-Shush" with Ray Baretto on percussion, and the hits "Soft" and "Shindig."

KING 585 (RCL)

Dance Awhile

Nearly everything I like about Bill Doggett is found on this disc, served up in tasty, but moderate portions. The emphasis is on R&B-inflected combo jazz ranging from the soft (but not sappy) sound of Doggett's ethereal organ on "Misty Moon" and "Autumn Dreams" to the straight-ahead swing of "Bone Tones" and "The Song Is Ended." Of course, this wouldn't be a complete smorgasbord without a touch of the exotic, supplied on "Passion Flower" and "Chelsea Bridge." As always, there's plenty of grits-and-gravy saxophone ("Tailor Made" and "Smooche"), great guitar (isn't that Bill Jennings?) showcased on "The Kid from Franklin St.," and even some real soulful flute playing on "Flying Home" and "How Could You." A+ rating.

KING 778 (RCL)

The Many Moods of Bill Doggett

Bill has many moods for sure, but thankfully most of them here are of the swingin' variety. "Eleven O'Clock Twist" and "George Washington Twist" are just right for living-room twisting, with deft guitar and honkin' sax. "Ready Mix" has a great jazz feel and "Real Gone Mambo" will have you steppin' better than Ralph Cramden. There's even a vocal version of "Honky Tonk."

RAY DOGGETT

Doggett was a Texan who started off in 1956 on Benny Hess's Spade label out of Houston. He wasn't really a rockabilly singer per se, more of a pop rocker if anything. After a couple of releases on Spade, Ray took his triple-threat talents (singing/guitar playing/songwriting) to a series of labels, including TNT, Ken-Lee, Pearl, Kix, and Top Rank.

HYDRA 7709 (R)

Doggone It Doggett

There's some nice stuff here, both rockers like "No Doubt about It" and ballads like "So Lonely Tonight." Only a couple have been out before on compilations. Beach Party/Whirlpool of Love/Go Go Heart/High School Wedding Ring.

FATS DOMINO

The most popular of the New Orleans R&B stars, Fats started off on Imperial in 1949 recording in a pure blues/R&B style. By the mid-'50s, he had successfully made the transition to rock and roll, being one of the few black artists to continually make the pop charts, altogether selling over 65-million records, including 23 gold singles. His band was never less than magnificent, led by veteran bandleader/trumpeter Dave Bartholomew (who also cowrote with Fats most of his material), Fats on piano, and the cream of New Orleans session musicians including tenor blowers Herb Hardesty and Lee Allen, Roy Montrell (gtr), and Smokey Johnson (drm). Fats stayed with Imperial from 1949–1963. EMI has reissued a healthy cross section of this material on an excellent four-CD box set, along with a single CD for those who want just a taste of The Fat One. He later signed to ABC, who added choruses and strings to the basic formula. There are numerous releases featuring live sides from the '70s and '80s of varying quality.

ATLANTIC 81751 (C)

Live at Montreux

Fourteen tunes recorded May 1, 1973 with a nine-piece band including Roy Montrell, Walter Lastie, and a five-piece sax section. Besides the normal hits set, Fats pays tribute to his hometown sound with "Stagger Lee" and Professor Longhair's "Mardi Gras in New Orleans," and closes with an instrumental version of "Sentimental Journey." Hello Josephine/Jambalaya/Blueberry Hill/Blue Monday.

COLUMBIA 35996 (L)

When I'm Walking

EAGLE 901006 (R)

It's Not Over 'Till the Fat Man Sings

Fats Domino live from I know not where and recorded I know not when. There isn't much info but this set is probably from the '80s. There's a note on the sleeve that says this was leased from Triumph Records, so it could possibly have had a previous release. The show isn't very well-recorded, the band isn't very tight (surely not New Orleans cats), and Fats is ... well, Fats. One for the fans only. Blueberry Hill/The Fat Man/I Want to Walk You Home/Your Cheatin' Heart.

⊛ EMI 92808 (CL)

My Blue Heaven: The Best of Fats Domino, Vol. 1

Twenty vintage hits from the Imperial vaults with excellent sound (some in true stereo for the first time) and detailed notes. My Blue Heaven/Please Don't Leave Me/I'm in Love Again/Blueberry Hill/I'm Walkin'/The Big Beat/Whole Lotta Lovin'/I'm Gonna Be a Wheel Someday/Be My Guest/Let the Four Winds Blow.

EMI 96784 (L)

They Call Me The Fat Man: Legendary Imperial Recordings

Four CDs, 100 tracks, nearly all of them spectacular, representing just under half of Domino's rollicking 1949–1962 recordings for Imperial. Domino was probably not the greatest of the New Orleans pianists who pushed R&B toward rock and roll (that title belongs to Huey "Piano" Smith), but his catalog of top-rank songs wasn't equaled, at least in quantity, by anyone else in the Crescent City. Fats had 58 R&B hits (all but seven are included here) from his first smash "The Fat Man" to his last one "Let the Four Winds Blow." This set suffers from an occasional speed abnormality—as with Little Richard, all of Fats's Imperial sides were sped up for release—but at no point do these minute inconsistencies detract from the considerable pleasures of the loping music. Detractors have often pointed to the similarity of Domino's approach but, like his contemporary and fellow pioneer Chuck Berry, Domino used his chosen stylistic base as a common ground from which he could leap in all directions. This is sly R&B of the highest order—throughout "They Call Me The Fat Man" Fats makes lecherousness sound like friendliness—and the box's 84-page, luxurious 6X12 booklet includes some fantastic photos. Highly recommended.

INSTANT 5043 (L)

Be My Guest: Live!

Eighteen-song live set of unknown vintage. Blueberry Hill/Let the Four Winds Blow/Ain't That a Shame/I Want to Walk You Home/I'm Gonna Be a Wheel Someday/Whole Lotta Lovin'/I'm in Love Again/Be My Guest/Goin' Home.

TOMATO 269663 (L)

Antoine "Fats" Domino

Double-CD set featuring "The Fat Man" recorded live in concert in Texas in the '80s. An enjoyable set, nearly two hours long, with Fats accompanied by a band of New Orleans musicians including Lee Allen and Herb Hardesty. Although not prime Fats, his warm, friendly vocals are as appealing as ever, and his piano playing and the band accompaniments are solid if not exceptional. I'm Walkin'/That Fat Man/Please Don't Leave Me/Margie/Goin' to the River/What a Price/Valley of Tears/Blueberry Hill/Whiskey Heaven/Tuxedo Junction/Red Sails in the Sunset/Another Mule.

DON (HARRIS) and DEWEY (TERRY)

Don and Dewey started their musical career while still in high school in Pasadena, CA, forming The Squires in 1954. The group was fairly successful, recording for several LA labels, and scoring a hit with "Sindy" on Vita. The two decided to split off and perform as a duo, with Don on guitar and Dewey on piano; Don also experimented with electric violin, using a phonograph cartridge for amplification. They recorded for Specialty between 1957–1959, and reformed in 1964 after Dale and Grace scored a Number 1 hit covering their "I'm Leaving It Up to You." They also backed Little Richard during his 1964 comeback, and became part of his band during his Vee Jay days. Don, now known as Sugarcane Harris, toured with the Johnny Otis Show. He even joined the Mothers of Invention in 1970, gaining admiration among the rock audience for his electric violin pyrotechnics. He reteamed with Dewey as part of John Mayall's Bluesbreakers, and they also performed as a duo for a couple of years.

The duo has been unfairly neglected. They are best known for penning songs that were hits for other groups, including The Olympics ("Big Boy Pete"), The Premiers ("Farmer John"), and Dale and Grace. In fact, not only did The Righteous Brothers cover many of their songs ("Justine" and "Ko Ko Joe," to name two), but The Brothers's early sound and stage act were direct copies of the duo's work. Not only did Don and Dewey turn out some of the best rockin' R&B of the '50s, their ballads like "The Letter" and "Kill Me" are still being played regularly by the Southwest's low-riding empire.

SPECIALTY 2131 (RC)

They're Rockin' 'til Midnight, Rollin' 'til Dawn

Ko Ko Joe/Leavin' It All Up to You/Big Boy Pete/Mammer-Jammer/When the Sun Has Begun to Shine/Justine.

⊛ SPECIALTY 7008 (CL)
Jungle Hop
Twenty-five rockin' tracks. Farmer John/Mammer-Jammer/Justine/Big Boy Pete/Bim Bam/Pink Champagne.

LONNIE DONEGAN

Influential British "skiffle" star of the late '50s. Skiffle was a combination of blues, jazz, and traditional folk that paved the way for British rock and roll. Donegan is best-known for his cover hit of Leadbelly's "Rock Island Line" and the immortal "Does You Chewing Gum Lose Its Flavor on the Bedpost Over Night?"

MUSIC FOR PLEASURE 5917 (L)
1956–1958
Twenty cuts, mostly country-folk standards, including Donegan's first certified American hit, "Rock Island Line." Draws on material from the same period as the See For Miles CD. In spite of the hit and the greater number of tracks here, I'd still give the nod in quality to the See For Miles reissue. There are no notes at all here, and the arrangements are less effective. Tom Dooley/Stewball/Puttin' on the Style/Grand Coulee Dam/My Dixie Darling.

SEE FOR MILES 331 (L)
The Originals
A fine reissue of material from Donegan's first two Pye LPs. Seventeen cuts, recorded between 1956–1958, derived from stateside country and blues. Unfortunately, his best known pop hit, "Does Your Chewing Gum Lose Its Flavor on the Bedpost Over Night?," is not included. Nonetheless, an enjoyable collection by this relentlessly enthusiastic, brassy tenor, featuring original photos and sleeve notes. Wabash Cannonball/How Long Blues/I Shall Not Be Moved/Wreck of the Old '97/Frankie and Johnny.

RAL DONNER

Considered to be the first successful Elvis imitator, who parlayed his "talent" into a long career, culminating in his voice being used in the documentary film *This is Elvis*. In 1961, he had his first hit for Gone with a cover of Elvis's "Girl of My Best Friend," and subsequently went to Number 4 on the charts with "You Don't Know What You've Got," followed by several lesser hits in the early '60s. He continued to record for a number of labels and was quite popular through

the '60s, though he never hit it big again. He died of lung cancer in 1984.

SEQUEL 190 (L)
The Complete Ral Donner 1959–1962
Donner's hommage to the RCA '50s-era Elvis, leaning heavily on ballads and mid-tempo pop tunes. We are served up some good rockers like his covers of The King's "Girl of My Best Friend," "It's Been a Long, Long Time," "Nine Times Out of Ten," and "Creampuff." Actually, Donner sounds more like Conway Twitty (with that little growl) than Elvis on the better mid-tempo numbers like "Pray for Me," "I Don't Need You," and "She's Everything." His best record was probably his first 45 on Scottie, "Tell Me Why" b/w "That's Alright with Me." It's too bad that the master for this record has been lost, because the disc used to dub these two songs sounds like it's shot. All in all though, this isn't half bad. A must for Donner fans, including six previously unreleased tunes.

HAROLD DORMAN

Rockabilly star whose first and only hit was "Mountain of Love" issued by Rita, which was later a big hit when covered by Johnny Rivers. He recorded with Sun guitarist/bassist Roland Janes, who played bass along with Rita's house band, Billy Lee Riley's Little Green Men, including Riley (gtr, hca), Martin Willis (sax), and J.M. Van Eaton (drm).

BEAR FAMILY 15262 (R)
Mountain of Love
Sixteen sides, only three previously issued, primarily from the Rita and Sun labels. The title track is great, heard here in its undubbed state (no chorus and strings) for the first time. "I'll Come Running" and "Moved to Kansas City" are the other two cuts that were issued at the time; among the unissued, my faves are "Soda Pop Baby" and "Sweet Sweet Love."

LEE DORSEY

No one has ever summed up Lee Dorsey's appeal better than his associate Allen Toussaint, who said "If a smile had a sound, it would be the sound of Lee Dorsey's voice." Long-time New Orleans R&B star, Dorsey was originally from Portland, OR. He was a successful boxer, fighting under the name Kid Chocolate, and was a contender for the lightweight championship. He settled in New Orleans, working in his auto-body shop and singing on the side. His first record, "Lottie Mo," on ABC-Paramount, led to his discovery by Marshall Seehorn who thought the record was actually by Ray Charles. He connected Dorsey with Bobby Robinson, who signed him to his Fury label, scoring a couple of hits in 1961 with "Ya Ya" and "Do-Re-Mi."

Dorsey began working with Allen Toussaint in the mid-'60s; this material was sold to Bell Records's subsidiary Amy. He had massive hits with "Working in a Coal Mine," "Holy Cow," "Ride Your Pony," and "Get Out of My Life Woman." In the late '60s, his contract was sold to Polydor, where he made "Yes We Can" (covered by The Pointer Sisters), "Freedom for the Stallion" (covered by Boz Scaggs), and "Sneaking Sally thru the Alley" (covered by Robert Palmer). He went to ABC in the late '70s, where he recorded "Night People." Since then, he has mostly worked in his shop and played around New Orleans, but got back in the public eye in the '80s when he opened an extensive US tour for British punksters, The Clash!

CHARLY 3 (L)
Great Googa Mooga
Two-CD set of 40 good-time New Orleans tunes, including such classics as "Lottie Mo," "Ya Ya," "Ay-La-Ay," "Great Googa Mooga" (do I detect a pattern here?), "Ride Your Pony," "Get Out of My Life Woman," "Working in a Coal Mine," "Holy Cow," "Everything I Do Gonh Be Funky," "Yes We Can," "Sneakin' Sally thru the Alley," and "Night People." The first disc reissues recordings from Dorsey's best years, 1960–1968, showing a positive Ray Charles influence atop those loping Crescent City beats. The second saucer covers 1969–1978, and is more concerned with smooth soul à la Allen Toussaint. Excellent!

RELIC 7013 (L)
Ya Ya

THE DOVELLS

Philly favorites The Dovells were five homeboys famous for their big hit "Bristol Stomp" in 1961 for Parkway. Lead singer Len Barry had a very juvenile (but nice) sounding voice, but fortunately they mostly stuck with up-tempo dance numbers in The Teenagers mode.

DOMINO 1006 (R)
The Dovells
Twenty-cuts, including covers of some nice teen jivers. You really have to be young and foolish to have the audacity to cover the Dells's opus "Oh What a Nite," but they do turn in a nice job on "Two People in the World" and a really good cover of Bobby Bland's "36-22-36." I Want You to Be My Girl/The Clock/This Little Girl of Mine/No No No.

JOE DOWELL

Crewcut all-American boy Joe Dowell had a big hit on Smash in 1961 with "Wooden Heart." Although Presley sang it in the film GI Blues, RCA didn't put it out until after Dowell's cover became a hit. He has a deep, pleasing voice, but all his recordings are strictly pop renditions with all the frills that entails.

TEENAGER 602 (R)
Wooden Heart
Nineteen tracks. Young Love/Moody River/Lonesome Town/100 Pounds of Clay.

BIG AL DOWNING and THE POE-KATS

The Poe-Kats were a unique rockabilly band boasting both black (Downing, who also played piano) and white vocalists (Bobby "Poe" Brant), along with hot guitarist Vernon Sandusky. They backed Wanda Jackson on many of her classic rockabilly sides including "Let's Have a Party" and "Mean Mean Man."

JUMBLE 1111 (R)
Big Al Downing and The Poe-Kats
Collects the Poe-Kats's own recordings for the first time. Side 1 has both sides of four singles released under Al's name, including the classic "Down on the Farm" and a great "Lucille" ripoff called "Miss Lucy," both cut for White Rock, and two singles in a Fats Domino vein cut for Carlton. Side 2 has four tunes released on White Rock under The Poe-Kats's name including "Rock and Roll Record Girl" and "Piano Nellie," plus a Len session by Vernon Sandusky released as by "Spic and Span," and a cut featuring the band backing singer Clyde Stacy.

ROLLER COASTER 2015 (R)
Rockin' 'n' Rollin' with Big Al Downing
This is bound to be the definitive Al Downing collection, much better than the haphazard Jumble LP, with brilliant sound quality. Big Al was equally at home

with R&B and rockabilly, pounding the 88s and lending vocal support on Bobby Poe and The Poe-Kats's three tunes included here: "Rock and Roll Boogie"; "Rock and Roll Record Girl"; and "Piano Nellie." Of course, the great tunes Big Al recorded for White Rock are also included—"Down on the Farm," "Oh Babe!," "Miss Lucy," and "Just Around the Corner"—as well as his scorching remake of Jimmy McCracklin's "Georgia Slop." Side 2 is reserved for his later more soul-oriented material and contains some powerful performances.

THE DRAMATICS

Smooth Detroit group, featuring lead vocals by Ron Banks. They signed to Volt in 1970, having a huge hit with "Whatcha See Is Whatcha Get." In 1974, they cut an LP on Cadet with The Dells and then went to ABC.

STAX 8523 (RCL)
Dramatically Yours
Reissue of Volt 9501 from 1974. And I Panicked/I Dedicate My Life to You/Highway to Heaven.

STAX 8526 (RCL)
The Best of The Dramatics
Nice budget collection of early '70s Stax hits, starting with 1971's smash "Whatcha See Is Whatcha Get." In the Rain/And I Panicked/The Devil Is Dope.

STAX 8545 (RCL)
Live
Previously unissued live recordings from 1972 and 1973.

RUSTY DRAPER

Although born in Ohio, Rusty moved to San Francisco in 1942 with his family. He was signed to Mercury Records in 1953, and enjoyed a long and prosperous relationship with them into the '60s. Rusty was certainly one of the best pop rockers from the '50s. He had a strong voice and wasn't afraid to tackle wild tunes like "Pink Cadillac" or "Mule Skinner Blues," usually giving fine rockin' readings of country-esque standards.

MERCURY 20117 (R)
Rock and Roll
Eighteen-track collection, with Rusty rockin' up Roy Acuff's "Wabash Cannonball," trying some R&B ("Buzz, Buzz, Buzz" and "Hip Monkey"), cajun ("Big Mamou"), Hawaiian ("No Huhu"), and whatever else catches his fancy.

THE DREAMLOVERS

Philadelphia doo-wop group originally formed in high school in 1956 and known as The Romancers. The original group included William Johnson and Tommy Ricks (leads and 1st tens), Cleveland Hammock, Jr. (2nd ten), and the brothers Clifton (bar) and James Ray Dunn (b). Early in their career, lead singer Johnson was murdered; after a few replacements, Don Hogan took over his vocal chores in 1960. Their big break came that same year when they backed Chubby Checker on his recording of "The Twist." They sang backup on many other of his hit recordings, always without credit. This led to a contract with Heritage and 1961's hit "When We Get Married," fitting in quite well with the early '60s doo-wop revival. They had a hit on End with "If I Should Lose You," and then signed to Swan. They made single sides for Columbia, Casino, Warner Bros., and Mercury between 1963–1966 before their recording career ended. The original group remains active in the Philadelphia area today.

COLLECTABLES 5004 (CL)
Best of The Dreamlovers
Twelve fine sides including their big hit "When We Get Married." Mother/Time/While We Were Dancing/Home Is Where the Heart Is.

COLLECTABLES 5005 (RCL)
Best of The Dreamlovers, Vol. 2
Twelve more fine sides. You Gave Me Somebody to Love/Anna Belle Lee/Pretty Little Girl/Zoom, Zoom, Zoom.

THE DRIFTERS

Long-lived, highly influential, extremely popular group with a complicated history of personnel changes. The original group, put together by Clyde McPhatter for Atlantic Records in 1953 after he left The Dominoes, lasted only for the first recording session. The first "stable" group consisted of Clyde on lead with Andrew "Bubba" Thrasher and Bill Pinckney (tens), Gerhart "Gay" Thrasher, Andrew's brother, (bar), and William Ferbie (b), with Jimmy Oliver on guitar. Pinckney dropped to the bass part when Ferbie was taken ill. They became the most popular vocal group on the R&B charts with such exciting material as "Money Honey," "Honey Love," and "Such a Night."

McPhatter was drafted in 1954 and was replaced briefly by Little Davy Baughn, a member of the ill-fated original group, who only recorded "Honey Bee" (unreleased until 1961) before being replaced by Johnny Moore in 1955. (Baughn later led Little David and The Harps on Savoy.) Moore gave The Drifters some more big hits including "Adorable." Meanwhile, Andrew Thrasher was replaced by Charlie Thomas in 1956, and Bill Pinckney left in the same year to be replaced briefly by Tommy Hunt before rejoining the group in 1957. Also in 1957, Johnny Moore was replaced by Bobby Hendricks, who led them in 1958's "Drip Drop" before going solo and hitting it big with "Itchy Twitchy Feeling."

In 1959, manager George Treadnell, who owned the "The Drifters" name, fired the *entire* group and hired The Five Crowns to become the "new" Drifters. This group included James "Poppa" Clark, Benny Nelson, and Charlie Thomas, each of whom could take the lead with the other two sharing tenor chores, Dock Green (bar), and Elsbeary Hobbs (b). Nelson soon changed his name to Ben E. King, and the group worked with Lieber and Stoller and Phil Spector to produce the big hits "There Goes My Baby," "Save the Last Dance for Me," and "This Magic Moment." In 1963, King went solo and was replaced by Rudy Lewis, who continued the hit streak with "On Broadway" and "Up on the Roof." On the day they were to cut "Under the Boardwalk," Lewis died and was replaced by Johnny Moore of the mid-'50s group; Tommy Hunt, who had sung with the group in 1955, also rejoined. Moore led the group through the '60s with 1964's pop hits "Under the Boardwalk," "Sand in My Shoes," and "Saturday Night at the Movies," and soul hits "Baby What I Mean" (1966) and "Ain't That the Truth" (1967). The group finally left Atlantic in 1972, and split in two, with former Turbans lead Al Banks teaming with Elsbeary Hobbs, Charlie Thomas, and Dock Green. Lead singer Moore, who had legal rights to the name, formed a new Drifters with Clyde

Brown, Grant Kitchings, and Butch Lecke, and moved to England. They teamed with writer/producers Roger Cook and Roger Greenaway (aka David and Jonathan), producing 1974's UK hits "Kissing in the Back Row of the Movies" and "Down on the Beach Tonight." Meanwhile, the "fired group," tired of the '60s slick sound, reformed as "The Original Drifters," consisting of Bill Pinckney, Gerhard Thrasher, Bobby Hendricks, and Bobby Lee Hollis, and are still active on the oldies circuit.

ATCO 375 (C)

Their Greatest Recordings: The Early Years

The best of the original Drifters recorded between 1953–1959. There Goes My Baby/Money Honey/ Ruby Baby/Why Do Fools Fall in Love.

ATLANTIC 8153 (CL)

Golden Hits

Greatest hits, concentrating on the '60s group. On Broadway/Under the Boardwalk/Sand in My Shoes/There Goes My Baby/Up on the Roof/I Count the Tears.

ATLANTIC 81927 (CL)

Let the Boogie-Woogie Roll: Greatest Hits, 1953–1958

Thirty-two, mid-'50s golden goodies, a few of which have appeared on other reissues. An absolutely essential collection. The Way I Feel/Gone/Such a Night/Don't Dog Me/Honey Love/Bells of St. Mary's/There You Go/Try Try Baby/Honey Bee/Ruby Baby/Adorable.

✪ ATLANTIC 81931 (CL)
All Time Greatest Hits and More, 1959–1965

Thirty-two cuts from the "new" Drifters, 14 of which hit the Billboard R&B charts. Much of this material has surfaced over the years on other collections, but many B-sides appear here in album format for the first time in a while. With detailed sleeve notes by expert Colin Escott.

THE DU DROPPERS

Early '50s Harlem group with roots in Southern gospel music. Lead vocalist J.C. "Junior" Caleb Ginyard was an alum of The Royal Harmony Singers (who became The Jubalaires), and later The Dixieaires; brothers Willie and Harvey Ray (who alternated on tenor and baritone) had performed with The Southwest Jubilee Singers. With bass Eddie Hashew, they first hit it big in 1953 with an answer song to "Sixty Minute Man" called "Can't Do Sixty No More" on Red Robin. Hashew was replaced by Bob Kornegay, who had had a solo career, and the group quickly went to RCA where they had hits with "I Wanna Know (What You Do When You Go Round There)" and the answer song, "I Found Out (What You Do When You Go Round There)" also in 1953. They moved to Groove, RCA's new R&B subsidiary, and hit with "Dead Broke" and "Talk that Talk." After a few hitless years and various personnel changes, the group disbanded; Kornegay recorded some novelty solos for Herald and King, and Ginyard returned to gospel music with The Golden Gate Quartet.

DR. HORSE 805 (RL)
Can't Do Sixty No More

Seventeen sides from 1952–1955. The group can do up a ballad as well as swing, as witnessed on the beautiful "Blues of Desire" and "How Much Longer." The set includes two cuts with female vocalist Sunny Gale who scored with "Wheel of Fortune" in 1952. Great accompaniment by the likes of Ben Webster and Sam "The Man" Taylor (ten sax), plus occasional licks by Mickey Baker (gtr). Learned sleeve notes.

THE DUBS

Harlem quintet whose smooth style captured the magic of church-based doo-wop. Richard Blandon's sweeping lead tenor borrowed from Ray Pollard of The Wanderers. The Dubs are still around playing the occasional oldies revue.

COLLECTABLES 5402 (CL)
The Best of The Dubs

CD reissue of the out-of-print Murray Hill 1187, featuring some of this quintet's best songs, which were only available before on Roulette reissue singles. Includes 14 tracks recorded for Johnson, Goldner, and Jubilee, including two in true stereo. Meticulous sleeve notes by Marv Goldberg and John Neilson. Could This Be Magic?/Don't Ask Me to Be Lonely/Chapel of Dreams.

DORIS DUKE

Fine Southern soulstress who recorded for producer Jerry Williams (aka Swamp Dogg) in 1969–1970, scoring a top-ten soul hit with "To the Other Woman (I'm the Other Woman)."

P-VINE 902 (L)
I'm a Loser

Also reissued as half of Charly 302 (see next entry).

DORIS DUKE and SANDRA PHILLIPS

CHARLY 302 (L)
Deep Soul Queens

Two long out-of-print classic soul albums (Doris Duke's I'm a Loser and Sandra Phillips's Too Many People in One Bed) on one CD. Life is just too damn good! Both these talented but neglected singers recorded this, their best stuff, around 1970 for Canyon Records under the direction of producer/songwriter/musician/eccentric genius Jerry Williams, Jr. Williams cowrote most of the songs with Gary U.S. Bonds, and yet almost all are "my man done me wrong" numbers like "He's Gone," "Divorce Decree," and "After All I Am Your Wife." Sometimes Duke's phrasing even sounds a little like Swamp Dogg's; listen to "I Don't Care Anymore." The biggest hit here is Duke's version of "To the Other Woman (I'm the Other Woman)," which Phillips also covers, but every one of the 24 tracks is at least good if not great. Highly recommended.

JOHNNY DUNCAN

Johnny was England's only American skiffle star. This guitar player from Tennessee, stationed in England while in the army, was given an audition by Chris Barber solely because of Duncan's physical resemblance to skiffle star Lonnie Donnegan.

BEAR FAMILY 15169 (R)
Last Train to San Fernando
His English skiffle and country hits recorded 1957–1963 for the British Columbia label. Contains excellent guitar breaks by guitarist Denny Wright. Rock-a-Billy Baby/Dang Me/Itching for My Baby/Geisha Girl.

THE DUPREES

White doo-woppers form Jersey City, NJ, led by Joey Vann (b. Joseph Canzano). They signed to Coed in 1962, scoring a hit with a cover of Jo Stafford's "You Belong to Me." The original group specialized in slow ballads. A half-a-dozen hits followed before Vann left and was replaced by Mike Kelly. They scored a final hit on Columbia with 1965's "Around the Corner," sounding a lot like Jay and The Americans. After a few hitless years, they attempted to jump on the psychedelic bandwagon with their final single, released as by "The Italian Asphalt and Paving Company"!

COLLECTABLES 5008 (CL)
The Best of The Duprees
Twelve sides from the early '60s. You Belong to Me/Why Don't You Believe Me/Exodus/Have You Heard/Where Are You/It Isn't Fair.

RHINO 71004 (CL)
The Best of The Duprees
Fourteen tracks on cassette, 18 on CD, Including unissued songs and obscure B-sides. You Belong to Me/(It's No) Sin/I Wish I Could Believe You/Have You Heard/Take Me As I Am/The Things I Love/Exodus

HUELYN DUVAL

Excellent but obscure Texas rockabilly guitarist who recorded for Challenge in the late '50s, and Major Bill Smith's Twinkle label in the early '60s.

BEAR FAMILY 15200 (R)
The Challenge Masters
First-ever reissue of Duval's 1957–1958 Challenge recordings, including both sides of his five singles issued by that label and unreleased material. These are the fruits of three sessions: two in Nashville with all-star backup (Grady Martin, lead guitar on the 1957 session, Hank Garland in 1958) and one at Goldstar with the Challenge house band, soon to call themselves The Champs, as the backup group. There's an unreleased take of "Teen Queen," but most important is three versions of the unissued "Fool's Hall of Fame,"

written by Duval's manager Danny Wolfe and also recorded (but not released) by Johnny Cash.

WHITE LABEL 8864 (R)
Huelyn Duvall and The Tight Strings
Fourteen previously unissued tracks. There's a nice sparse sound to these tunes that should appeal to lovers of classic-sounding rockabilly. There are alternate takes of his first two Challenge releases "Comin' or Goin'" and "Hum-Dinger," as well as nice covers of Danny Wolfe's (his piano player, and a recording artist in his own right) "Susie's House" and Jerry Lee's "Whole Lotta Shakin' Goin' On."

WHITE LABEL 8880 (R)
More Huelyn Duvall
Seventeen more homemade recordings, all either alternate takes of his Challenge releases or previously unissued tunes. There's plenty of that driving guitar sound heard on White Label 8864. While not as essential as the first LP, this one does have many good moments, especially on the instrumentals "More Now," "You and Me," and "Just Again." Three Months to Kill/Juliet/Got a Little Girl.

DYKE AND THE BLAZERS

Alester "Dyke" Christian was bass player in the O'Jays's backup group, The Blazers. Legend has it that Dyke was stranded in Phoenix at one point, and he put together his band to raise bus fare home. They recorded Dyke's song "Funky Broadway," originally released by Atco and picked up nationally by Art LaBoe's Original Sound label. The song sold nearly a million, and became a national smash when covered by Wilson Pickett. Dyke and The Blazers's raw soul was too much for the white audience, but they had several R&B hits including "We Got More Soul," "So Sharp" (covered by The J. Geils Band), and "Let a Woman Be a Woman, Let a Man Be a Man." Dyke was shot down on the streets of Phoenix in 1971.

KENT (UK) 004 (L)
So Sharp!
You'll get full points if you can dance all the way through this marathon 24-track funk monster. Funky Walk, Pts. 1 and 2/We Got More Soul/Shotgun Slim/City Dump.

THE EAGLES

The Eagles were a black vocal group that recorded for Mercury in the mid-'50s. They were discovered in Washington, DC, by Fred Foster, who later founded Monument Records. Their big claim to fame is that Elvis covered their song "Trying to Get to You." Roy Orbison also released an earlier cover of the same number on the Je-Wel label. The Eagles weren't a doo-wop group really, but fell into the limbo between older Ravens-type groups and the newer Five Royales/King-label groups.

BEAR FAMILY 15232 (R)
Tryin' to Get to You
A pleasant little R&B footnote. What a Crazy Feeling/Such a Fool/Please, Please

THE EARLS

The Earls, who recorded from 1961–1969, represent the last, white flowering of the doo-wop sound. Formed by Larry Chance (b. L. Figueiredo) in the Bronx in the late '50s, they started recording for the Rome label in 1961 and had a minor hit with their first recording: an up-tempo version of The Harptones's "Life Is but a Dream." They switched to Old Town in 1962 where they had their biggest hit "Remember Then." They never repeated this success, but continued to record for Old Town for another three years, and subsequently for other labels.

ACE 386 (L)
Remember Then:
The Best of The Earls
Their first five cuts are here, originally on the Rome label, along with their less interesting later tracks from Old Town, which either sought to rekindle the success, tempo, or sound of their hit "Remember Then" or aimed for a variety of pop sounds. This is the kind of high-quality job that you'd expect from Ace: brief but decent notes, fine sound quality, and good pix. Looking for a Dream/Without You/I Believe/Cross My Heart

COLLECTABLES 5058 (CL)
Remember Me Baby
Covers the same ground as Ace 386 in a less-expensive format, but without the notes and pix. Many tracks are clearly imitative of their one hit, "Remember Then." Cover art reproduces the original cover from their Old Town LP. Life Is But a Dream/I Believe/Let's Waddle/Out in the Cold Again/Old Man River/Amor.

JACK EARLS

Jack Earls only had one release on Sun, the great raw rocker "Slow Down" b/w "A Fool for Lovin' You" (Sun 240), a 45 released in 1956. But since he had that Sun sound, his legend has grown through the years with rockabilly buffs. He did about a half-dozen sessions for Sam Phillips in 1955–1957 and a number of interesting tunes have appeared scattered over numerous Sun reissue LPs.

BEAR FAMILY 15273 (R)
Let's Bop
All of his Sun recordings, including one cut that is previously unissued, "When I Dream," a pleasant country tune. (The liner notes say that two others are also previously unissued, but they have appeared on Sun Records anthologies!) It is good to have all the cuts together on one LP. Let's Bop/Slow Down/Sign on the Dotted Line/Hey Slim.

DUANE EDDY

Excellent lead guitarist who revolutionized instrumental recordings by adding a bass string to a standard six-string electric guitar, thus creating the "twangy" guitar sound. Eddy's first recordings were done in Phoenix for Jamie Records, produced by Lee Hazelwood and featuring the all-star session band The Rebels (Al Casey [gtr], Larry Knetchel [pno], and Steve Douglas [sax]). He had numerous hits for Jamie between 1958–1962, including "Rebel Rouser" and "Peter Gunn." In 1962, he split from Hazelwood and signed to RCA. His records were still good (including "Dance with the Guitar Man" and "The Ballad of Paladin") but featured treacly choruses and strings. He did an LP of Dylan songs for Colpix in 1965, and a few LPs for Reprise in 1966–1967. He was coaxed out of retirement by Ry Cooder in the mid-'80s and recorded and toured with an all-star band including Cooder and Steve Douglas.

EMI (UK) 796 557 (L)
Twangy Peaks
CD release of two LPs from 1965, *Duane a Go Go* (Colpix 490) and *Duane Does Dylan* (Colpix 494), both produced by Lee Hazelwood. There's plenty of Duane's patented bass string twangin', but he doesn't ignore the other strings either, which makes for a nice

contrast on tunes like "Cottonmouth," "Just to Satisfy You," and "If You've Seen One, You've Seen 'Em All." The sax playing by Jim Horn and the harmonica of Larry Knechtel is too happy and yakety for my taste but some will like it. Something like the extreme fuzz on "House of the Rising Sun," "She Belongs to Me," and "Blowin' in the Wind" is more to the point. Trash/Puddin'/Busted/It Ain't Me Babe/Mr. Tambourine Man.

MOTOWN 8158 (L)
Have Twangy Guitar Will Travel/ $1,000,000 Worth Of Twang
Two Jamie LPs (3000 and 3014) on one CD.

RCA (UK) 90119 (L)
16 Top Tracks
Remakes of his big hits. Rebel Rouser/Shangri-La/ Twangsville/The Marauder/Do It/Rebel Soul/A Fast Friendly Frolic on the Farm/Shindig.

THE EDSELS

A much better group than their track record at hit making would suggest. With one foot in their doo-wop past and another in the soul sound of the future, The Edsels, originally from Youngstown, OH, put out a journeyman mix of ballads and up-tempo tunes for several small labels between 1958–1963, including "My Whispering Heart," "What Brought Us Together," "Could It Be," "Count the Tears," and their best-known song, "Rama Lama Ding Dong" written by lead vocalist George Jones, Jr.

RELIC 5093 (R)
Rama Lama Ding Dong
Sixteen tracks including the hit title song, two unreleased songs, and two alternate versions of previously released numbers. Clean sound, informative notes, and a vintage photo on the cover. This is a definite winner for group harmony fans.

THE ELEGANTS

Excellent, white doo-wop group from Staten Island. Originally called The Crescents, they had a local hit with "Darling Come Home." The renamed band, led by Vito Picone, scored big with 1958's "Little Star." For some reason, they didn't produce a follow-up single until 18 months later, by which time they were already forgotten. Leader Picone went on as a soloist, and finally worked as a used-car salesman, and has since revived the group's name for occasional oldies show.

COLLECTABLES 5420 (CL)
Little Star: The Best of The Elegants
This album duplicates the old Canadian Am-Par release (Apt 1000) but, in addition, offers alternate takes of "True Love Affair" and "Little Boy Blue," as well as the previously unreleased "Rain Rain," all issued on Apt and Ban Cassalin's Hull label in Manhattan.

CRYSTAL BALL 101 (R)
A Knight with The Elegants
Mid-'80s recordings.

LORRAINE ELLISON

Lorraine was one of the best of the "uptown soul" singers, working with writer/producer Jerry Ragovoy. Her biggest hit was recorded while she was signed to Warner Bros. A studio and orchestra were booked for Frank Sinatra, but at the last minute he couldn't make it, so Lorraine used the time to record the chilling "Stay with Me," one of the best, unknown soul songs of all time.

LINE 9.01011 (L)
Stay with Me
Reissue of *Stay with Me* (Warner Bros. 1821 from 1969). Ten of the 11 songs were written by Jerry Ragovoy either alone or with Ellison, Bert Berns, or Mort Shuman. Includes the original version of "Try (Just a Little Bit Harder)," later covered note for note by Janis Joplin. Heart Be Still/I'm Gonna Cry 'til My Tears Run Dry/The Hurt Came Back Again.

THE EMOTIONS

A white, East Coast doo-wop group, The Emotions started out in 1959. The original group included Joe Favale (lead), Tony Maltese (1st ten), Larry Cusimano (2nd ten), Joe Nigro (bar), and Dom Collura (b); Sol Covais of The Hytones replaced Maltese in 1961. The group recorded several singles for PIO, Kapp, Laurie, Twentieth Century, Karate, and Calla before disbanding in 1965. The early '80s doo-wop revival brought Joe and Tony out of retirement with a new set of Emotions.

CRYSTAL BALL 133 (R)

Doo Wop on Your Dial

Recreates an on-air, doo-wop radio show, with '50s-sounding material of recent vintage. The songs are pretty nice, and the overall instrumental sound pleases the ear (even though synthesized strings are used here and there). The lead singing, however, rarely makes for more than average appeal, and lacks zap and vitality. Nineteen cuts with excellent sound quality. Good try boys.

THE ENCHANTERS

Little is known of the Detroit-based Enchanters, except that they came together at Detroit's Pershing High school in 1954 and were discovered by Beatrice Buck (who had close ties with Duke Ellington) at The Flame Show Bar in 1956. The group members, at this time, were: George Wade (lead), Jack Thomas (1st ten), Ulysses Hollowell (2nd ten), Alton Hollowell (bar), and 14-year-old Gerald Hollowell (b). Theirs was a typical '50s Detroit-Chicago sound in the style of The Dandeliers. Their first record and biggest hit, "There Goes," was done for Mercer Ellington's tiny Mercer label in 1956, and reissued by Coral a year later.

STARDUST 102 (R)

There Goes a Pretty Girl and Here Comes The Enchanters

"There Goes" is presented here from one of only two known blue-label promo copies in existence. Most of their Coral/Stardust sides (circa 1956–1957) were backed by The Maurice King Orchestra. Good overall sound, no sleeve notes, but fine, rare cover picture of the quintet.

FRANKIE ERVIN

EARTH ANGEL 902 (R)

Dragnet Blues

Eighteen cuts of West Coast R&B featuring Ervin in front of Johnny Moore's Blazers, Preston Love's Orchestra, and other Los Angeles groups. "Dragnet Blues" was a minor hit that managed to get Ervin and Modern Records involved in a lawsuit with Sgt. Joe Friday himself!

THE ESCORTS

The Escorts were formed in New Jersey's Rahway State Prison while the seven members were serving time. They specialized in intricate interplay like the Philly soul groups and later Curtis Mayfield work, but their work suffered from a repertoire drawn mostly from the pop-rock catalog, and big, melodramatic arrangements.

COLLECTABLES 5167 (CL)

All We Need (Is Another Chance)

After recording "By the Time I Get to Phoenix," "Little Green Apples," and "Ooh Baby Baby," do The Escorts really deserve another chance? Seven cuts in all.

COLLECTABLES 5168 (CL)

Three Down, Four to Go

The title refers to the fact that three of The Escorts had been released while four remained behind bars! Disrespect Can Wreck/Let's Make Love/Corruption/Brother.

ESQUERITA

Eskew Reeder Jr. (aka Esquerita) was one of the wildest performers in rock and roll, a performer even Little Richard could emulate! Listen both to Richard's RCA and Peacock recordings, before he met Esquerita, and to his Specialty recordings, made after the wild men met, for Esquerita's influence. Reeder taught Richard piano and phrasing and, even more important, flamboyance (Richard stole his hairstyle) before being put off as being a mere Richard imitator. Esquerita was probably too wild to make it in the late '50s, but since then his cult status has been perpetuated by reissues of his material on numerous labels. His piano playing alone is the stuff of legend—sometimes in control, sometimes not, but always full of double-fisted intensity—and his alternately growling and shrieking vocals put it totally over the top. You'll never hear anything quite like this. Esquerita died an unknown cult star in 1990 of AIDS.

BEAR FAMILY 15504 (L)

Sock It to Me Baby

Twelve previously unissued tracks. Nobody Wants You When You're Down and Out/Wig Wearin' Baby/Get Along, Honey, Honey/Never Again/At the Dewdrop.

CAPITOL 91871 (L)

Collectors Series

Twenty-eight 1958–1959 Capitol recordings, piano-poundin', pompadour-pumpin', whoopin,' flailin', and wailin' winners from the man Little Richard called "one of the greatest pianists."

NORTON 202 (R)

Vintage Voola

An essential purchase! These nine tracks ought to win some kind of Grammy. Esquerita, aka The Magnificent Malochi, was "rediscovered" by Blue Cap guitarist Paul Peek and toured with Gene Vincent, who got him a Capitol contract in 1958. Includes an incredible Paul Peek single from 1958 on NRC—"Sweet Skinny Jenny" b/w "The Rock-a-Round"—which, besides being Esquerita's first recordings, also feature Jerry Reed, Ray Stevens, and some frantic sax. The other seven tunes on this very short LP come from Esquerita's Capitol demo session from 1958, never before reissued (the sound's a bit rough in places). Includes absolutely devastating versions of three of his best songs ("Rockin' the Joint," "Oh Baby," and "Please Come Home") and four others that were never rerecorded.

THE EVERLY BROTHERS

Very influential country-pop duo. Don, the older brother with the dark hair, began as a country songwriter (he wrote "Thou Shalt Not Steal" for Kitty Wells). In 1955, the duo recorded a single for Columbia, and, in 1957 they signed to Cadence Records where they had numerous hits with their trademark country harmonies and strummed acoustic guitars ("Wake Up Little Susie" and "All I Have to Do Is Dream," to name two). They recorded in Nashville using top sessionmen. In 1960, they signed with Warner Bros., scoring their biggest hit with "Cathy's Clown." Soon after, their career started going downhill. They joined the Marine reserves in 1962, and, in 1963, Don suffered a nervous breakdown during an English tour. They struggled through the rest of the '60s and early '70s before a public fight onstage at Knotts Berry Farm in 1973 ended their duo career for a decade. In this period, Don recorded as a country artist while Phil lived in England and recorded some pop-rock LPs (see separate listings for their solo work). They reformed in 1983 with a comeback single, "On the Wings of a Nightingale," written for them by Paul McCartney. They continue to perform and record sporadically to today.

Their vintage recordings have been reissued and re-reissued by so many different labels that it's hard to recommend a single collection. The Bear Family set has the edge for sound-quality and range of material. For the collector, there are numerous exact reproductions of their original LPs plus unissued demos and alternate takes to keep the true fan happy!

Nice Guys

ACE 118 (R)
Pure Harmony
The third LP of the Brothers's classic Cadence recordings reissued by Ace—beautifully remastered for the best possible sound—mostly in mono but some cuts are in true stereo. Bye Bye Love/Oh What a Feeling/I Wonder If I Care as Much/All I Have to Do Is Dream/Devoted to You/Bird Dog.

ACE 194 (RC)/903 (L)
The Everly Brothers Greatest Recordings
Eighteen of their biggest Cadence classics. The LP has a doublefold cover with color front and back, including a photo of Don and Phil being sworn in as Marines! Digitally remastered with six tunes in real stereo. Wake Up Little Susie/All I Have to Do Is Dream/Bird Dog/Bye Bye Love/When Will I Be Loved.

ACE 272 (R)
Hidden Gems
Fourteen Warner Bros. tracks previously only available as singles. It's Been Nice/No One Can Make My Sunshine Smile/Nancy's Minuet/I'm Afraid/The Girl Who Sang the Blues.

ACE 281 (R)
The Warner Bros. Years, Vol. 2
Second volume devoted to the Everly's Warner Bros. years. Includes light psychedelia ("Lord of the Manor" and "My Little Yellow Bird"), folk-protest ("Human Race"), and covers of folk-rock hits (James Taylor's "Carolina in My Mind" and "Love of the Common People.") Their tight harmony always fit best with country and ballads, so tunes like "Cuckoo Bird," "I'm On My Way Home Again," and "Give Me a Sweetheart" are bound to be the most instantly appealing.

ACE 932 (L)
The Everly Brothers/ The Fabulous Style
Two original albums on one CD, originally Cadence 3003 from 1958 and 3040 from 1960, 27 tunes in all. Bye Bye Love/Wake Up Little Susie/Claudette/Let It Be Me/Bird Dog/All I Have to Do Is Dream.

BEAR FAMILY 15618 (L)
Classic Everly Brothers
This is the first set to bring all of the Everly's early material together, starting with their first four, unsuccessful, 1955 country recordings for Columbia, with backing from Carl Smith's band, The Tunesmiths, along with the complete Cadence recordings (with some alternate takes). Bill Inglot's remastering brings out the astounding clarity of the original recordings, particularly on the Everly's trademark acoustic guitars. Though Cadence Records owner Archie Bleyer, a pop-music veteran, produced them, he let Don and Phil, along with Nashville's finest pickers, frame the music. The guitars of Chet Atkins, Ray Edenton, Hank Garland, and songwriter Boudleaux Bryant made all the difference. Also included is a radio show featuring Don and Phil with Jim Reeves, June Carter, and Hank Garland. A detailed booklet with rare in-studio photos and text by Colin Escott provides complete information.

CURB 77472 (CL)
Best of The Everly Brothers: Rare Solo Classics
After going their separate ways in 1973, Don and Phil encountered varying degrees of commercial success before their musical reunion in the '80s. During these years, Don fared slightly better on the charts, scoring with "Yesterday Just Passed My Way Again," "Since You Broke My Heart," "Brother Jukebox," and "So Sad," while the younger Phil hit with "Dare to Dream Again," "Sweet Southern Love," and a remake of "Let It Be Me." In all, this disc presents seven from Phil and 11 by Don in alternating order.

EDSEL 203 (R)
Roots
Reissue of Warner Bros. 1708 from 1968. Throughout the album, we get short excerpts from early '50s radio shows featuring the "Everly Family." (When are we going to get a whole album of this stuff?!) The rest of the material was recorded in 1968. Some of the production is questionable (fuzz guitars, horns, etc.), but the album holds up pretty well. A welcome reissue for all Everly fans. Sing Me Back Home/Mama Tried/Less of Me/Shady Grove.

EDSEL 297 (R)
Two Yanks in England
Reissue of The Everly's 1965 "mod" LP, originally Warner Bros. 1646, in which Ike's boys obfuscate the line of imitation and influence. Their beautiful, close harmony was certainly very evident in the sound of British pop during the "invasion," however, the Everly's were forced to imitate the imitators to stay abreast of fickle fashion. For the most part, they succeeded. A very good LP. Somebody Help Me/So Lonely/Pretty Flamingo/I've Been Wrong Before.

EDSEL 319 (L)
Pass the Chicken and Listen
Early '70s session, produced by Chet Atkins and recorded in Nashville, originally issued in 1973 as RCA 4781. This was a sort of "full-circle" project for the brothers, bringing them back to their country roots on material like Mickey Newbury's "Sweet Memories," the Buddy Holly classic "Not Fade Away," John Prine's "Paradise," Waylon Jennings's "Good Hearted Woman," and "Rocky Top."

ENCORE 3739 (R)

Like Strangers

Unless you're an Everly Brothers fanatic, keep browsing. The good news is that there are 27 tracks here. The bad news is that 14 tracks are alternates of two songs cut in 1960: "Like Strangers" and "When Will I Be Loved." Most of the material here is from the early '60s when they were trying to find the hit-record formula that they had lost. But for every ill-advised tune like "The Sheik of Araby" or "Hernando's Hideway," you'll find a decent song like "Foolish Thoughts" or even a gemlike "Little Hollywood Girl." I love the intro to "Baby Bye-Oh," an unreleased tune, where the producer says "take FX 13089—with FUZZ," and the fuzz guitar kicks in.

KNIGHT 47004 (RCL)

Perfect Harmony

Four-LP or three-cassette/CD set featuring a cross-section of this great duo's musical career from their first recordings for Cadence in 1957 to their 1988 Mercury recordings. It also includes songs from Don and Phil's solo outings. Sixty tracks in all. Skimpy booklet has brief survey of the brothers' career and a number of photos. Bye Bye Love/This Little Girl of Mine/Bird Dog/Take a Message to Mary/Let It Be Me/Cathy's Clown/Lucille/Ebony Eyes/Muskrat/Don't Ask Me to Be Friends/No One Can Make My Sunshine Smile/The Girl Who Sang the Blues/That'll Be the Day/Love Is Strange/Bowling Green/The Air that I Breathe/Snowflake Bombadier/Brother Jukebox/Lay Lady Lay/Arms of Mary.

MAGNUM FORCE 052 (L)

Susie Q

Twelve rare and unissued tunes from the Warner Bros. vaults including a couple sung in German, two previously issued on the out-of-print Warner (UK) *New Album,* an alternate take of 1962's "How Can I Meet Her," and never before released tracks like "To Show I Love You" and "Nothing but the Best" from 1966, "Sheik of Araby" from 1967, and "Love with Your Heart" from 1968.

MAGNUM FORCE 1.028 (L)

Nice Guys

Unreleased Warner Bros. material made during the mid-'60s. The Brothers take a wide range of material and do it Everly style, covering everything from girl groups ("Chains") to blues ("Meet Me in the Bottom"), and they even try Buffalo Springfield's "Mr. Soul" with a country arrangement and lush strings. Much of this material is better than that originally issued by Warners.

RHINO 211 (C)/70211 (L)

The Everly Brothers

Budget-priced reissue of their first Cadence album (3003 from 1958) with bonus track "Poor Jenny."

This Little Girl of Mine/Bye Bye Love/Keep a Knockin'/Rip It Up/I Wonder If I Care as Much/Wake Up Little Suzie.

RHINO 212 (C)/70212 (L)

Songs Our Daddy Taught Us

Budget-priced reissue of their second Cadence album (3016 from 1958), which featured a great selection of traditional country songs. Roving Gambler/Long Time Gone/That Silver Haired Daddy of Mine/Barbara Allen/I'm Here to Get My Baby Out of Jail.

RHINO 213 (C)/70213 (L)

The Fabulous Style of
The Everly Brothers

Reissue of their fourth LP, Cadence 25059 (the third was a greatest hits package) with two bonus tracks. This is the only Everly Brothers LP in real stereo. Since You Broke My Heart/Let It Be Me/Claudette/All I Have to Do Is Dream/Bird Dog/Devoted to You.

RHINO 214 (C)/70214 (L)

All They Had to Do Was Dream

Fabulous collection of unissued recordings and alternate takes from their classic '50s Cadence recordings. CD features three additional tracks: "Problems"; "Let It Be Me"; and an alternate take of "Love of My Life."

⊙ RHINO 5258 (L)

Cadence Classics:
Their 20 Greatest Hits

Bye Bye Love/All I Have to Do Is Dream/Wake Up Little Susie/Bird Dog/Claudette.

WARNER BROS. 1471 (L)

Golden Hits

Twelve Warner Bros. hits. That's Old Fashioned/Crying in the Rain/Don't Blame Me/Ebony Eyes/Cathy's Clown/Lucille/Muskrat/Temptation.

WARNER BROS. 1554 (L)

Very Best Of

DON EVERLY

SUNDOWN 002 (L)

Brother Jukebox

CD issue of Don's long out-of-print, third solo album, originally Hickory 44003 from 1977. This is a straight country LP produced by Wesley Rose, with female chorus and lots of Buddy Emmons's steel guitar. This is from the Magnum Force people who provide typically poor packaging. Not only are no musician credits given, there aren't even songwriting credits. Playing time is just under a half hour. Includes a fine remake of "So Sad (to Watch Good Love Go Bad)." Deep Water/Turn the Memories Loose Again/Love at Last Sight.

PHIL EVERLY

MAGNUM FORCE 053 (L)
Louise
Reissue of the UK-only release *Phil Everly* (Capitol 27673 from 1983), Phil's last solo work before rejoining Don, adding the non-LP single, "Who's Gonna Keep Me Warm" b/w "One Way Love," from 1982. Recorded mostly in London with Mark Knopfler, Christine McVie, Billy Bremner, and Pete Winfield on board. "She Means Nothing to Me" and "I'll Mend Your Broken Heart" are duets with Cliff Richard. When I'm Dead and Gone/God Bless Older Ladies/Oh Baby Oh.

SEQUEL 164 (L)
The London Sessions
Two of Phil's solo LPs released by Pye, 1974's *There's Nothing Too Good for My Baby* (Pye UK 18448), released on these shores as *Phil's Diner* (Pye 12104), and *Mystic Line* (Pye UK 18473/Pye US 12121), the stronger of the two. Twenty-three tunes in all. When Will I Be Loved/Patiently/January Butterfly.

THE EXCELLENTS

The Bronx-based Excellents were formed in 1960, with founding members John Kuse (lead and 2nd ten), George Kuse (1st ten), Phil Sanchez (falsetto), Joel Feldman (bar), Dennis Kestenbaum (lead, bar, and ten), and Chuck Epstein (b). Their basic sound does not set them apart from other white, East Coast, doo-wop revival groups of the time but, unlike most, these guys can sing with conviction and on key.

ON THE CORNER 135 (R)
Go Bob Bob Bobbin' Along
Personal faves include a tight rendition of "Gloria" and the previously unreleased "Helene." Also includes their 1962 hit "Coney Island Baby." Good fidelity and accurate sleeve notes.

THE EXCITERS

New York crooner Herb Rooney had been a member of two failed vocal groups, The Continentals and The Masters, when he met three Queens high-school juniors who performed under the name of The Masterettes, led by brassy vocalist Brenda Reid. Herb was impressed with their swinging sound and introduced them to famed songsters/record producers Leiber and Stoller. The duo shared his enthusiasm for the group, renaming them The Exciters, and asked Rooney to join as bass singer in what would become one of the best girl groups of the early '60s. They hit it big with 1962's "Tell Him," 1963's "He's Got the Power," and the original 1964 vesion of "Do-Wah-Diddy" (later covered by Manfred Mann). Reid and Rooney continued the group through the '70s, scoring minor hits in the UK, and, by the '80s, were performing as the duo Brenda and Herb.

EMI 95202 (CL)
Tell Him: Legends of Rock and Roll Series
Twenty cuts from the United Artists vaults. Includes their smash hits in released and alternate versions. It's Love that Really Counts/Handful of Memories/I Dreamed/Drama of Love/He's Got the Power/Do-Wah-Diddy/If Love Came Your Way.

SHELLEY FABARES

Teenage actress who got a recording career thanks to her weekly exposure on TV's *Donna Reed Show* from the late '50s on. She sang "Johnny Angel" on the show in 1962, making it a Number 1 hit.

COLPIX 431 (R)
The Things We Did Last Summer
Exact reissue of her second LP from 1962 in true stereo. Great cover snapshots and twelve songs about vacations and Johnny, including her followup to "Johnny Angel" called "Johnny Loves Me," plus the title hit and good covers of pop favorites. Johnny Get Angry/See You In September/Vacation/Palisades Park.

FABIAN

Actor and singing teen idol Fabian (born F. Forte, 1943) was discovered by the same recording executive/song-writing team that made Frankie Avalon a big hit. Like Avalon, Fabian was from Philadelphia but, unlike the beach-blanket star, Fabian was hardly a memorable vocalist. Besides his late '50s hits, the Fab one appeared in a number of forgettable films and TV shows through the '60s, and on the revival trail in the '70s and '80s.

ACE 321 (L)
This Is Fabian!
Hey, wait a minute, Fabian wasn't a total wimp! Listen to the hard rockin' "Tiger," and the desperate junior Elvis gyrations of "Turn Me Loose," "I'm a Man," and "Come On and Get Me." These tracks, taken from the early '60s vaults of Chancellor Records, feature some blazing guitar atop sharp rockabilly-styled backup, skillfully disguising the obvious fact that the Fab one couldn't sing his way out of a wet paper bag. Ace wisely put the best material first, filling out the last two-thirds of the disc with teen schlock like "Steady Date," "Stop Thief!," and "Shivers."

CHANCELLOR 5025 (R)
Fabulously Grateful
Eighteen recordings.

THE FABULOUS FOUR
This group can sing, and if it had been offered original material, probably could have made good use of it. As it was, they not only covered other popular recordings, but their vocals were buried under a slew of strings.

CRYSTAL BALL 115 (R)
Fabulous Hits
Sixteen cuts, most of which were recorded for Chancellor between 1960-1962. On songs like "Mr. Twist," we get a somewhat half-hearted attempt at putting out a piece of solid rock and roll, but, for the most part, the voices get lost beneath layers of insipid string arrangements. Nice pix and good sleeve notes.

TOMMY FACENDA
Tommy Facenda, former background singer and "clapper boy" with Gene Vincent and The Blue Caps, was the discovery of Frank Guida (later of LeGrand records and Gary "U.S." Bonds fame). Guida wrote a novelty song that mentioned all the local high schools in the Norfolk, VA area by name, and had Tommy record it. The song became a local hit for the fledgling LeGrand label, and inspired Guida to write 27 high-school opuses covering most major US cities released by Atlantic. Tommy currently plays with the re-formed Blue Caps.

LEGRAND 1008 (R)
High School USA

LEGRAND 1009 (R)
High School USA, Vol. 2
Together, these two albums release all 28 of the novelty high-school numbers recorded by Facenda.

WERLY FAIRBURN
One of the finest, pure rockabilly cats to ever grace vinyl. Fairburn, "The Singing Barber," hailed from Folsom, LA and recorded for Trumpet, Capitol, Columbia, Savoy, and other labels, singing wonderfully on both rockabilly and hillbilly numbers.

BEAR FAMILY 15578 (L)
Everybody's Rockin'
Twenty-six rockers from Trumpet, Capitol, Columbia, Savoy, and Milestone.

WALL 100 (R)
Everybody's Rockin'
A much-expanded, 14-cut version of a long out-of-print, 10-inch album with better sound quality. Werly's Savoy (yes, the famous R&B/jazz label) material is his best by far with great singing, fine lyrics, and brilliant backing musicians on guitar, slap bass, and honky-tonk piano. On hillbilly tunes, Werly's plaintive style is reminiscent of Hank Williams. Prison Cell of Love/I'm a Fool about Your Love/Speak to Me Baby/My Heart's on Fire.

ADAM FAITH
One of England's biggest pop stars of the '50s and '60s, who sang in a Buddy Holly-ish pop vein with orchestral backups.

EMI (UK) 1350 (R)/793 663 (L)
The Adam Faith Singles Collection: His Greatest Hits
Twenty hits, featuring full orchestral backing by the great John Barry Orchestra. Barry provided interesting and exciting arrangements, although Johnny Keating's Orchestra actually tops them on "Don't that Beat All" and "What Now," featuring what sounds like a musical saw! Especially nice are "Made You" from the film *Beat Girl*, where Adam apes Eddie Cochran, and the tunes he recorded with The Roulettes in the Merseybeat era: "The First Time"; "We Are in Love"; and "Someone's Taken Maria Away." His choice of covering The Blues Project's "Cheryl's Goin' Home" was a good decision, too.

THE FALCONS
Black singer Eddie Floyd and white R&B fan Bob Manardo met while working in a Detroit jewelry

shop in 1955. They formed one of the first inter-racial doo-wop quintets, and were "discovered" by Floyd's uncle, Robert West, who owned a number of small record labels. When Manardo was drafted in 1956, he was replaced on lead vocals by Joe Stubbs (Levi Stubbs's [of The Four Tops] brother, who previously sung with The Fabulous Four). Their first hit was "You're So Fine," sung in a raspy, gospelish lead by Stubbs. In 1960, Stubbs left the group to be replaced by a very young Wilson Pickett, who sang lead on their last minor hit, 1962's "I Found a Love." The original Falcons folded in 1963, but producer West enlisted another local group to carry on the name through the late '60s.

⭐ RELIC 8005 (R)/ 7003 (L)

You're So Fine: The Falcons Story, Pt. 1

Sixteen exciting sides, including their Flick, Lupine, and Mercury recordings from 1956–1959. You're Mine/Baby That's It/You're in Love/I Wonder.

RELIC 8006 (R)/ 7012 (L)

I Found a Love:
The Falcons Story, Pt. 2

The Falcons continue with the only person capable of following the departed Joe Stubbs, the wicked Wilson Pickett! They soar to new heights with Wilson and Eddie Floyd on the incredible title track, which later became a solo hit for Pickett. Lots of fine guitar by Lance Finnie. Take this Love I Got/Anna.

RELIC 8010 (R)

The Falcons Story, Pt. 3

A compilation of unissued masters, demos, and re-hearsals, and a welcome addition to the extremely fine first two volumes. Bob West, owner of Detroit's small but influential Lupine Records, rehearsed The Falcons in the late '50s, backed with piano accompaniment, and usually led by Eddie Floyd or the underrated Joe Stubbs, both heard here in full throttle. Also included are Joe Howard, who fronts the fine "Searching for You Baby," two nifty novelties led by female soloist Little Bee, a Sonnie Monroe demo of "I Found a Love," Eddie Floyd backed by The Velours on "Short and Nappy," and the fantastic "You've Got a Friend" accompanied by The Ohio Untouchables. Highly rec-ommended.

THE FANTASTIC BAGGYS

Excellent surf band featuring Phil Sloan and Steve Barri who, besides their own records on Imperial, served as Jan and Dean's backup group.

They were also talented songwriters ("Summer Means Fun" and "From All Over the World"), and when Phil decided to get serious and call himself P.F. Sloan, the team wrote "Secret Agent Man," "Eve of Destruction," "Let's Live for Today," "You Baby," "Where Were You When I Needed You," and "A Must to Avoid."

EDSEL 118 (R)

Surfin' Craze

Fifteen wonderful surf sides. Tell 'Em I'm Surfin'/Big Gun Board/When Surfers Rule/It Was I.

EMI 998939 (CL)

Tell 'Em I'm Surfin'

This 1964 LP was a bomb, except in surf-crazed South Africa, so it hasn't been too easy to get a copy. Too bad, because it's big fun in the sun. This includes all of the LP tracks, along with 10 bonus tracks, some never before issued. Dawn Eden's booklet notes give a wealth of info. Save Your Sundays for Surfin'/Debbie Be True/Anywhere the Girls Are/It Was I/Move Out, Little Mustang.

CHARLIE FEATHERS

Legendary, eccentric, rockabilly pioneer who re-corded wild sides, beginning in 1954 for Sun, King, Meteor, and various small Southern labels, featuring the rockin' rhythm and slap bass of Jody and Jerry. While at Sun, he recorded the original demo of the classic country tear-jerker, "I Forgot to Remember to Forget (about You)." He contin-ues to record a mixture of country and rockabilly up to the present.

⭐ CHARLY 278 (L)

Gone, Gone, Gone

Twenty-four essential tracks of Feathers's classic rock-abilly recordings done for Sun and King in the '50s. With a relentless slap bass and rockin' guitar backing him, Charlie moans and wails seminal tunes like "One Hand Loose," "I Can't Hardly Stand It," "Bottle to the Baby," and "Tongue-tied Jill." His hillbilly numbers remain some of the most passionate and heartfelt tunes in American music, with "Peepin' Eyes," "Wed-ding Gown of White," and especially "Defrost Your Heart," all recorded at Sun's legendary 706 Union Avenue studio, still able to send chills down your spine. A couple of bare-bones sessions, one from the '60s and one from the '70s, are also included, showing a side of Charlie familiar to many rockabilly pilgrims who sought him out in the seedy Memphis bars he played in for the last 20-odd years.

EDSEL 348 (L)

That Rock-a-Billy Cat

Reissue of an old Barrelhouse LP from 1979 that released some late '60s sessions done at Tom Phillips's Select-o-Hits Studio in Memphis. This is prime rockabilly action, despite the late recording date. With the great Marcus van Story slappin' bass and Bubba Fuller pounding drums, Charlie lays down a solid rockabilly rhythm helped out by Troy Jones and Ramon Maupin on guitars. They hammer out 14 tunes, a mixture of rockabilly and eccentric country in Feathers's distinctive style. Gone, Gone, Gone/Tongue-tied Jill/Rock Me/Wild Side of Life/Wide River/Crazy Heart.

ELEKTRA 61147 (CL)

Charlie Feathers

Fourteen 1991 recordings. We applaud Elektra for their efforts in bringing rockabilly into the '90s on their roots-music series. Some familiar titles here—"You're Right, I'm Left, She's Gone," "Oklahoma Hills," and "If Tomorrow Never Comes"—and an update of his classic, now titled "We Can't Seem to Remember to Forget," all delivered with an amazingly authentic sound courtesy of Memphis's Sun Studio. Great backup too, with Roland Janes (gtr) and J.M. Van Eaton (drm). The trademark vocal hiccups, squeals, and weird little nuances have fallen victim to the passing years, but Charlie remains closer to rockabilly's country roots than anyone else from the Sun Records generation.

KAY 5045 (R)

Jungle Fever

Though there's no information on the cover, these appear to be his original, classic '50s sides recorded for Meteor, King, and Sun. Some duplication with the Charly CD. Tongue-tied Jill/Bottle to the Baby/One Hand Loose/Stutterin' Cindy/Can't Hardly Stand/Tear It Up.

ROCKSTAR 1014 (R)

Wild Wild Party

Some fine '70s rockabilly featuring Charlie's son Bubba on lead guitar. Side 1 has five tunes, featuring the title tune and "Milk Cow Blues," cut in May 1977 in London with The Dave Travis Band. These have never been issued and were only recently discovered. Side 2 is a reissue of the long out-of-print Lunar 2, 10-inch LP taken from the soundtrack of a September 1978 appearance on the Houston TV show, *The Little Old Show*, with Charlie, Bubba, and slap bassist Pee Wee Truitte. It features eight tracks, including "Stutterin' Cindy," "Tongue-tied Jill," and "Cootzie Coo."

ZU ZAZZ 1001 (R)

The Legendary 1956 Demo Session

After Charlie's third Sun single sold only 900 copies, he was dropped from the label. In 1956, Charlie was back in Sun studios cutting a final session for Sam Phillips's consideration. Charlie was turned down, but Meteor released "Tongue-tied Jill" b/w "Get with It" from the session, earning Charlie a contract with King. For the first time, the rest of this incredible session is being released on this 12-inch EP. There are only two takes each of four tunes, but they're incredible, with backing by an unknown guitarist and steel-guitar player and probably Charlie's bassist Jody Chastain with Elvis's Sun drummer, Johnny Bernero. Excellent sound, notes by Colin Escott. Highly recommended. Bottle to the Baby/So Ashamed/Frankie and Johnny/Honky Tonk Kind.

ZU ZAZZ 2011 (L)

Rock-a-Billy

Twenty-six tunes from Feathers's various rare and unissued tunes recorded from 1954–1973. Bob Jones did the mastering so you know the sound is great, especially compared to the shoddy bootlegs these appeared on before. Bottle to the Baby/One Hand Loose/I Can't Hardly Stand It/I'm Walking the Dog/Wild Wild Party/Long Time Ago/Gone, Gone, Gone.

ZU ZAZZ 2208 (R)

All Tore Up!

This one's subtitled *The Definitive Edition of Rare and Unissued Recordings 1954–1964* so that should give you the general idea. Duplicates tracks on Zu Zazz 2011. Side 1 has four unissued rehearsal tunes, rockin' versions of "Bottle to the Baby," "I Can't Hardly Stand It," "One Hand Loose," "Everybody's Lovin' My Baby," and the two songs he recorded for Hi, later released on Wal-May: "Dinky John" b/w "South of Chicago." Side 2 starts off with "Corrine Corrina" taken from the only surviving acetate, three more rehearsal takes including a great version of "Defrost Your Heart," and three unissued hillbilly tunes from the mid-'60s: "Wild Side of Life," "Don't You Know," and "Where's She at Tonight."

NARVEL FELTS and THE ROCKETS

Seventies country star who began his career playing rockabilly in the mid-'50s, first as a session man on Sun with Charlie Rich and Harold Jenkins (aka Conway Twitty), and then on his own at Mercury. After failing his Sun auditions, Narvel and The Rockets recorded three sessions for Mercury in May and October 1957 and June 1958, cutting 14 tunes, although only three singles were released. One of them, the instrumental "Rocket Ride," was accidentally played at the wrong speed on a radio station; this slow version became The Diamonds's "The Stroll"!

BEAR FAMILY 15242 (R)

A Teen's Way

Issues all 14 of Narvel's Mercury sides, eight for the first time, full of wild rockabilly, country, and teen ballads, and adds the entire output of Felts's 1960 MGM tenure, including three cuts never before released, with all-star Nashville backing by Floyd Cramer, Grady Martin, and Hank Garland. Cry Baby Cry/Kiss-a Me Baby/Vada Lou.

BEAR FAMILY 15515 (L)

Memphis Days

Twenty-six tracks recorded for Roland Janes between 1962–1965, some originally issued on the Renay, Southern Sound, and ARA labels, but 15 have never been issued before. Includes 16-page booklet with notes, photos, and discographical information.

NARVEL FELTS and JERRY MERCER

ROCKSTAR 1016 (R)

Radio Rockabillies

THE FENDERMEN

Rural Wisconsonians Phil Humphrey and Jim Sundquist met at the University of Wisconsin in 1957. They shared a love for Fender electric guitars, taping a hard-driving version of Jimmie Rodger's classic "Mule Skinner Blues" in the back of a local record store in 1959. The song hit it big on the local Soma label, leading to tours with Johnny Cash and Johnny Horton and appearances on *American Bandstand* and *The Grand Ole Opry*. Follow-up singles failed to chart, and the duo disbanded.

SOMA 1240 (R)

Mule Skinner Blues

Exact repro of the classic 1960 LP (mint originals are valued at $400.00!). Wild covers of everything from their hit versions of "Don't You Just Know It" and the title tune to "High Noon," Duke Ellington's "Caravan," and The Rock and Roll Trio's "Bertha Lou," plus four originals, including the instrumentals "Torture" and "Beach Party."

AL FERRIER

Louisiana rockabilly/swamp-pop performer of the late '50s who is still active today. His distinc-

tive rich voice and knack for the wry tune made him a true contender. Al has been playing and recording almost steadily since the late '40s; his Goldband recordings, in my opinion, were some of the finest rockabilly done in the '50s.

FLYRIGHT 597 (R)

Let's Go Boppin' Tonight

Twelve fine rockabilly and rockin' country sides recorded for Jay Miller between 1957–1959, featuring Al's brother Bryan (gtr), Jimmie Honeycutt (b), and Rod Harbouf (drm). Lots of these versions are alternate takes. Blues Stop Knockin' at My Door/Honey Baby/Love Me Baby/You Win Again/Gunsmoke.

GOLDBAND 7769 (R)

The Birth of Rockabilly

Ten songs from 1956 and four from 1971. No No Baby/My Baby Done Gone Away/It's Too Late.

JIN 9030 (R)

Greetings from Louisiana

This 1989 album finds Ferrier in tremendous voice, probably better than his early years. He presents a gumbo of styles here (some a bit overproduced) with the straight-ahead honky-tonk numbers being the most effective. The rockers are good, too, if you dig the Hank Williams, Jr. style.

THE FI-TONES

New York R&B group, originally known as The Cavaliers. Group member Gene Redd went on to perform in Kool and The Gang.

RELIC 5010 (R)

The Fi-tones

Nineteen Angletone and Atlas sides from the mid-'50s, including the hit "Foolish Dreams," and "It Wasn't a Lie" and "Silly and Sappy," plus four sides by the previous incarnation of the band, The Cavaliers.

THE FIREBALLS

One of the best of the '60s instrumental bands, led by guitarist George Tomsco. His playing is somewhat restrained by today's standards, but his occasional use of distorted tone was well ahead of its time. The Fireballs recorded for Norman Petty's Clovis Records, original home of Buddy Holly, in the late '50s and early '60s, before moving on to a number of other labels, big and small. Unfortunately, wimpy vocalist Jimmy Gilmore, of "Sugar Shack" fame (the Number 1 pop song of 1963, featuring backing by The Fireballs), is featured on some of their recordings.

ACE 418 (L)
The Original Norman Petty Masters

Cut in Norman Petty's studio between 1958–1964, these 25 streamlined pieces qualify as rambunctious guitar-picking treats ... in moderation, of course. Their biggest hits (without Jimmy Gilmore) are here—"Torquay," "Bulldog," and "Quite a Party"—along with a nice mix of Tex-Mex and other infectious instrumentals. The bluesy "Blacksmith Blues" takes the boys off the beaten path, as do the worthwhile "Long Long Ponytail" and "Cry Baby," the only vocal tracks. Ace has picked the best releases where there was a choice between mono and stereo versions, so "Tuff-a-Nuff" and "Really Big Time," for example, are in stereo, while "Dumbo" and others have been left in mono. Coherent notes make the frequent label and band member changes seem almost, well, coherent.

NOR-VA-JAK 811 (R)
Rik-a-Tik

Sixteen-tune collection of classic '60s instrumentals. These were originally issued as 45s on Warwick, Top Rank, and United Artists. The album cover only lists 15 tunes, but they give you 16, I guess to make up for the two dreadful tunes that Jimmy Gilmore sings on. You take the good with the bad on LPs like this, so for every "El Gato," "Jetster," "Rik-a-Tik," and "Yankie Doo," you get a flip side cheesy enough to make a macaroni casserole. Las Vegas Scene/Side Winder/Kissin'/True Love Ways.

NOR-VA-JAK 812 (R)
Let It All Out

Eighteen fairly obscure tunes from Top Rank, Dot, and other smaller labels. There's some very, as they used to say, "heavy" guitar bashing here by *wunderkind* George Tomsco. Some of these have noticeable surface noise, but it shouldn't bother you rock and rollers too much. The good news is that wimpy Jimmy Gilmer only has two numbers. Sweet Talk/Almost Paradise/Let It All Out/Love Me Too/Good Soul/The Last Time.

NOR-VA-JAK 814 (R)
In the Mood

Sixteen-tune collection recorded in the early '60s, including ten Norman Petty-produced instrumentals. If you like Jimmy Gilmore, there's the added "bonus" of six songs by him backed by The Fireballs; actually, a couple aren't too bad. The Fool/Boom Boom/Mr. Mean/Mrs. Mean/Campussology/Daytona Drag/Pedro's Pad.

QUALITY 1674 (R)
Bulldog

Generous 18-tune collection recorded for Norman Petty in his Clovis studios in the late '50s and early '60s. You should find quite a few faves here! Torquay/Panic Button/Fireball/Bulldog/Rik-a-Tik.

CHIP FISHER

Chip Fisher came of age in the late '50s and latched onto an angle that appeared to hold great promise: a rock and roller out of the Ivy League, Dartmouth to be exact. He never really went anywhere, but did get to record an LP that became collectible in some circles.

STAR CLUB 8040 (R)
Chipper at the Sugar Bowl

This is basically your standard happy-go-lucky pop-rock fare, although Fisher does have a pleasant deep voice and sings fairly well, when not drowned out by the girly chorus. The backing and production is top notch, so if you like '50s teen pop this would be a good choice. Sugar Bowl Rock/I'm in Love/Oh-Yea Louise/Teenage Blues/Snow Job/Poor Me.

THE FIVE AMERICANS

Excellent Texas rock group led by Mike Rabon, featuring a lot of cheesy organ. They put out an LP for cartoonists Hanna-Barbera's HBR label and later three LPs on the Dallas Abnak label. Their hits include "I See the Light," "Zip Code," "Western Union," and "Sound of Love."

SUNDAZED 11004 (L)
Western Union

Twenty songs, most in stereo, and four in unreleased form, from this popular '60s group, produced by Dale Hawkins. Western Union/Good Times/Reality/Stop Light.

THE FIVE CROWNS

Excellent Harlem-based group. The original group included Wilbur "Yunkie" Paul (lead), the three Clark brothers—James "Poppa," Claudie "Nicky," and John "Sonny Boy"—all tenors, and Dock Green (bar, b). They recorded a handful of singles for Rainbow in 1952–1953, including their first hit "You're My Inspiration." After one extremely rare release on Old Town in 1953, they moved back to Rainbow affiliate Riviera in 1955 for "You Came to Me." Unhappy with the performance of these recordings, the group dissolved. In 1958, they reformed with the final lineup of Benny Nelson, Charlie Thomas, and Poppa Clark (leads and tens), Dock Green (bar), and Elsbeary Hobbs (b). In 1959, the manager of The Drifters hired The Five Crowns to take on The Drifters name. Nelson changed his name to Ben E. King, the group released "There Goes My Baby," and a new Drifters was born (see separate DRIFTERS entry).

RELIC 5030 (R)
The Five Crowns
Fourteen early sides for Rainbow and Riviera, many never on microgroove and four never released before. A Star/You're My Inspiration/Oow Wee Baby/Keep It a Secret.

THE FIVE DISCS

The Five Discs were an interracial group from Brooklyn who first formed in 1958. Originally an all-white Italian ensemble called The Flames, the group added two black members from The Love Notes after this local ensemble broke up. Original members were Mario de Andrade (lead vocals, sometimes referred to as Mario Androtti to mask his black heritage), Paul Albano (1st ten), Tony Basile (2nd tenor), Joe Barsalona (bar), and Andrew Jackson (b). They signed with Gene and Bob Schwartz's Emge label (the forerunner of Laurie Records), scoring a minor hit in 1958 with "I Remember," now considered a doo-wop classic. After Laurie's success with Dion and The Belmonts, the group felt ignored, and black members de Andrade and Jackson left. After some personnel changes, the group, now all white with John Carbone on lead and John Russell on bass, recorded the classic, bouncy "Adios" in 1961. Soon after, their best bass singer, Charlie DiBella, joined, along with new lead Eddie Parducci. DiBella's booming bass sound introduces their last hit, the comical "Never Let You Go," Murray the K's "Boss Record of the Week" in 1962! The group recorded sporadically through the '60s under the names The Boyfriends and Dawn, returning as a revival band in the early '70s under their original name. They continue to perform sporadically at revival shows.

CRYSTAL BALL 119 (R)
Unchained through the Years
Demos, relics, and rehearsal tapes from this fine quintet who have managed to stay together (in various configurations) for 30 years. Includes pretty ballads, doo-wop workouts, and two cuts with Earl Lewis of The Channels. A fascinating but uneven collection of rare a cappella and long-lost accompanied sides stretching back 23 years.

EMGE 1000 (R)
The Best of The Five Discs
Fourteen cuts, including alternate versions of "Roses" and "Chinese Girl," and their minor hits "I Remember," "Adios," and "Never Let You Go."

MAGIC CARPET 1002 (R)
The Five Discs Sing Again
A 1957 a cappella practice session on which the makings of their best-sung songs—"I Don't Know What I'll Do" and "I Remember"—are presented before their final issue on a variety of little labels in the late '50s.

THE FIVE JADES/PLAYGROUND

CLIFTON 2004 (R)
Appearing Tonight
OK recent recordings of two East Coast white doo-wop groups. I Wish You Love/You're the One/Falling in Love/Ronnie.

THE FIVE KEYS

Incredible doo-wop group from Newport News, VA featuring Rudy West's amazing tenor. Formed in 1950 as The Sentimental Four, The Five Keys were basically comprised of the West brothers—Rudy (ten) and Bernie (b)—and Ripley Ingram (bar) and the fantastic lead vocals of Maryland Pierce and Dickie Smith. They recorded highly collectible sides for Aladdin from 1951–1953 that featured gorgeous ballads led by Rudy West including their classic million-seller, "Glory of Love" and excellent jump material led by Pierce. In 1954, they became the first harmony group to sign with a major label, Capitol. Rudy West and Smith left the group in 1953 to go into the army; West returned in 1956. Replacements Ulysses Hicks and Ramon Lopez are heard on the group's great novelty hit, 1955's "Ling, Ting, Tong"; Hicks died shortly after its recording, and was temporarily replaced by

Willie Winfield (of The Harptones), before West returned to the group. West's voice was better than ever, and, although the tracks were over-produced, they still had hits with "Close Your Eyes" and "Wisdom of a Fool." Rudy West left again in 1958 and was replaced by Dickie Threat. In 1960, the group signed with King Records, where their biggest hit was "I Took Your Love for a Toy." Rudy recorded solo for King, and then led various versions of reformed Keys from the mid-'60s on for revival shows.

ALADDIN 806 (R)
On the Town
Swedish reissue of their early '50s recordings. Besides their big hit "Glory of Love," they tackle some standards like "These Foolish Things," soulful ballads like "My Saddest Hour" and "Too Late, Baby," and energetic romps like "Hucklebuck with Jimmy." The tunes would cost you thousands of dollars if you bought the originals. Teardrops/Oh Baby/Be Mine.

CAPITOL 92709 (L)
Collector's Series
Twenty great sides. Ling Ting Tong/The Verdict/She's the Most/My Pigeon's Gone/Wisdom of a Fool/From the Bottom of My Heart/Who Do You Know in Heaven/C'est la Vie/Dream/Emily Please.

CHARLY 265 (L)
Dream On
Covers most of the group's King output (24 sides), featuring the hauntingly beautiful title tune, along with "Wrapped Up in a Dream" and "I'll Never Stop Loving You." The group at this time was comprised of Dickie Threat and Maryland Pierce (ten leads), Ripley Ingram (ten), Dickie Smith (bar), and Bernie West (b). Session men include Gene Redd (vibes, gtr) and the great Sonny Thompson (pno).

✪ EMI 96056 (CL)
The Aladdin Years: EMI Legends of Rock and Roll
Twenty-five sides culled from their seminal Aladdin years (1951–1953), featuring some of the group's finest hours. Notes contain minutely detailed sessionography. Indispensable collection by one of the greatest. The Glory of Love/Red Sails in the Sunset/My Saddest Hour/With a Broken Heart/Rocking and Crying Blues.

THE FIVE RED CAPS

Vocal and instrumental ensemble whose style borrowed from The Mills Brothers and The Ink Spots. Where The Red Caps differed was not so much in harmony but in their highly comic vocals and arrangements. The group was originally known as The Toppers when it was based in LA, with four original members—Steve Gibson (gtr, bass vocals), Jimmy Springs (drm, lead tenor), David Patillo (b, tenor vocals), and Richard Davis (pno, baritone vocals). The group went nowhere, and so came to New York in search of greater sucess, where they met fifth member Emmett Matthews (ten sax, 2nd tenor). Renamed The Five Red Caps, they recorded for Joe Davis's various labels between 1943–1946, gaining a reputation for their comic stage act as well as their combination of jump tunes (sung by Gibson or Brown as lead) or ballads (led by Springs). Their biggest hit in this incarnation was 1944's "I've Learned a Lesson I'll Never Forget." In 1947, they went to Mercury, taking the name Steve Gibson and The Red Caps, recording standards like "Blueberry Hill" and "Are You Lonesome Tonight." In 1950, they moved to RCA, adding Damita Jo (born Damita Jo DuBlanc; later Mrs. Steve Gibson) on vocals, remaining with the label for three years. Different incarnations of Red Caps followed on various labels, including ABC Paramount (c. 1956) and Rose and Hunt (late '50s). The group petered out by the end of the decade.

BEAR FAMILY 15490 (L)
Boogie Woogie on a Saturday Night
Their complete RCA recordings, 28 songs including two unissued, some with Damita Jo. Sixteen-page booklet with notes, rare photos, and discography.

DR. HORSE 806 (R)
Blueberry Hill, 1946–1952
Mercury and RCA label recordings.

KRAZY KAT 799 (R)
Vol. 2: It Feels So Good
Early efforts like "Mama Put Your Britches On" (featured here in an alternate version) and "Grand Central Station" are sung in The Red Caps's own inimitable jump-and-jive style. Recommended. Vol. 1 (Krazy Kat 779, *Lenox Avenue Jump*) is currently unavailable.

THE FIVE ROYALES

Gospel-based quintet who started out as The Royal Sons in 1948. The Royales, who were the model for James Brown's Famous Flames, included founder, guitarist, and songwriter Lowman Pauling (b, gtr), Jimmy Moore (ten), Eugene Tanner (bar, b), Obadiah Carter (ten), and Johnny Tanner (lead). The Royales took NY's Apollo Theater by storm in the mid-'50s. If you dig the blues, you'll love this group. They recorded their best work for Apollo in the early '50s (reissued on Dr. Horse and Relic), later signing with King. Their 1957 release, Pauling's composition "Dedicated to the One I Love," later was a hit for The Shirelles in 1959 and 1961 and The Mamas and The Papas in 1967. The Royales recorded sporadically for several small labels through the mid-'60s.

DR. HORSE 802 (RL)

The Real Thing

Incredible collection by one of the most influential vocal groups. Side 1 contains seven previously unreleased, early '50s Apollo sides, including one gospel tune recorded in 1952 under their original name, The Royal Sons. Side 2 features late '50s/early 60s King sides. Important liner notes finally give correct personnel information. A must!

KING 616 (L)

Sing for You

Your Only Love/Don't Let It Be in Vain/Double or Nothing/How I Wonder/The Feeling Is Real/Do unto You/When I Get Like This.

KING 678 (RL)

The Five Royales

Twelve tunes, not quite on par with their essential Apollo recordings, but still right up there with the best '50s R&B. I Know It's Hard but It's Fair/When You Walked through the Door/Women about to Make Me Go Crazy.

RELIC 8015 (R)/7010 (L)

Baby Don't Do It

The first of two stone-crazy collections. Two of the 14 cuts are by the original group, The Royal Sons. Includes classics like "Crazy, Crazy, Crazy" and "Help Me Somebody." Some duplication with Dr. Horse 802, but none with the out-of-print Charly 1096. An indispensable doo-wop collection.

RELIC 8016 (R)/7011 (L)

Laundromat Blues

Thirteen prime cuts made at Bess Berman's New York-based Apollo studios between 1951–1955. Included are two gospel gems recorded under their original name, The Royal Sons, as well as the blues classic "Six O'Clock in the Morning" and "Too Much Lovin'" featuring the unstoppable "Little Jazz" Fergusson on tenor sax. Amazing sound reproduction, great notes, and two unreleased gems.

THE FIVE SATINS

Probably the best-known doo-wop group. The group's leader, Freddy Parris, left his first band, The Scarlets, to go into the army. In 1956, while on leave, Freddy returned to his hometown of New Haven and recorded a song in a church basement that he had written while on guard duty called "I'll Remember." It was released on the local Standard label with the group known as The Five Satins, now consisting of Parris on lead, Lou Peebles and Stanley Dortch (tens), Ed Martin (bar), and Jim Freeman (b). The song was leased to the larger Ember label with its name changed to "In the Still of the Nite" (spelled "Nite" so as not to confuse it with the Cole Porter song "In the Still of the Night"). Though the song was a hit, Freddy remained in the army. The followup, the equally classic "To the Aisle," was recorded with Bill Baker replacing Parris, who returned to The Satins at the end of his military service in 1958. The group went through many personnel and label changes through the '60s and '70s, and remains popular today on the oldies circuit, with "In the Still of the Nite" being voted the Most Popular Oldie of All Time. Bill Baker formed his own group in the '80s, called Bill Baker's Satins.

COLLECTABLES 5017 (CL)

Sing Their Greatest Hits

Fourteen of their biggest hits. In The Still of the Nite/Wonderful Girl/When Your Love Comes

Along/To the Aisle/A Nite to Remember/Shadows/
Candlelight/I'll Be Seeing You.

⊕ RELIC 5008 (R)/7001 (L)
The Five Satins Greatest Hits
Eighteen great sides, covering the years 1956–1960
when the outfit shone brightly on the Ember, Stan-
dard, and First labels. In the Still of the Nite/The Jones
Girl/Oh Happy Day/Again/A Million to One/Seno-
rita Lolita/When Your Love Comes Along/Weeping
Willow/Zippety Doo/All Mine/Wonderful Girl/
Shadows.

RELIC 5013 (R)
The Five Satins Greatest Hits, Vol. 2
Eighteen more classic sides.

RELIC 5024 (R)
What Might Have Been,
Greatest Hits, Vol. 3
Sixteen outtakes, rehearsal recordings, and previously
unreleased masters, courtesy of Fred Parris. Includes
outtakes of "In the Still of the Nite" and "The Jones
Girl," and a-cappella versions of "The Masquerade Is
Over" and "No One Knows."

THE FIVE STAIRSTEPS

Popular late '60s/early '70s Chicago soul group
featuring The Burke family, under the guidance
of producer Curtis Mayfield. The group consisted
of brothers Clarence, Jr. (lead), Alohe (alto),
James (1st ten), Kenneth (2nd ten), and Dennis
(bar), who sang together in high school. Their
father, Clarence, Sr., championed the group,
who first recorded in 1966 for Mayfield's Windy
C label. They moved to Buddah in 1967, and
added their youngest sibbling, Cubbie (then two-
years-old!) and their dad on bass. Their biggest
hit was 1970's "O-o-h Child" produced by Stan
Vincent. They last recorded together in 1976 for
George Harrison's Dark Horse label. In 1980,
four of the brothers (without Cubbie or Alohe)
formed The Invisible Man Band, scoring a minor
hit on Mango with "All Night Thing," and two
years later Keni Burke went solo on RCA.

SEQUEL 114 (L)
Comeback: The Best of
The Five Stairsteps
Twenty-five tracks from the Buddah, Custom, and
Windy C labels. You Waited Too Long/World of
Fantasy/Comeback/Danger! She's a Stranger/Don't

Change Your Love/Baby Make Me Feel So Good/We
Must Be in Love/Ooh Child/Dear Prudence.

THE FLAMIN' GROOVIES
San Francisco's Flamin' Groovies are one of rock
and roll's greatest bands, but the word "band" is
used loosely. The group has persevered all these
years due to the vision of one man: Cyril Jordan.
Since the '60s, Jordan has not only wanted to
make and play rock and roll, he has wanted to
live rock and roll. In the late '60s, The Groovies
and Creedence Clearwater Revival were probably the only Bay Area groups who weren't psychedelicized, playing good-time '50s and early
'60s influenced rock and roll. At that time, the
group featured great vocals by Roy Loney, who
also wrote their anthemic "Teenage Head," before leaving the group in 1971. They go in and
out of style, and everything isn't always (shall we
say) earthshaking, but the spirit is always there.
For some reason, the group is particularly revered
in France.

SIRE 25948 (CL)
Groovies' Greatest Grooves
Twenty-four track collection drawn from the Sire,
Kama Sutra, and United Artists labels. The critics went
nuts when they first heard "Shake Some Action," the
first tune here, and some even called it the greatest
rock tune ever made. While that is certainly debatable,
"Shake" shouldn't be denied its masterpiece status.
My favorite is the epic "Slow Death," everything a
rock tune should be. Tallahassee Lassie/Teenage
Head/You Tore Me Down/Jumpin' in the Night.

THE FLAMINGOS
Fabulously beautiful Chicago doo-wop group,
perhaps the only group to come out of the city's
black Jewish Church of God and Saints of Christ
Congregation, originally performing Jewish
hymns! The original group in 1952 consisted of
Sollie McElroy on lead vocals (brought to the
group by their manager Ralph Leon), along with
tenors Zeke Carey and Johnny Carter, Paul Wilson (bar), and Zeke's brother Jake (b). Their first
recordings on the Chance label (1953–1954) are
among the rarest of all vocal-group records. In
1955, they recorded three singles for Parrot,
including a fantastic version of "I Really Don't

Want to Know." In 1955, Sollie left the group and was replaced by Nate Nelson; they went to Checker, recording the classics "The Vow" and Nelson's original "I'll Be Home" (reissued on Chess 91560).

After spending 1957 on Decca without a hit and some personnel changes, they went over to End, scoring their biggest hits with the ethereal "I Only Have Eyes for You" and "Lovers Never Say Goodbye." Personnel at this time were Zeke, Nate, Jake, Tommy Hunt, and Terry Johnson. Unfortunately, their End recordings in general (reissued on Collectables and Sequel) are marred by a song selection that tends to favor hoary old chestnuts, recorded in an extremely laid-back style, featuring romantic, sweeping lead vocals against a wash of echoey, angelic-like backups. They regained some of their previous soul when they moved to Philips in the mid-'60s, with the hot, dance-number hit "The Boogaloo Party," and recorded for that label and Polydor through the mid-'70s, scoring some minor hits. The best overview of their great '50s and '60s recordings is on Rhino.

CHESS 91560 (C)
The Flamingos
Reissue of mid-'70s LP Chess 702, itself a reissue of 16 Checker sides from 1955–1956, including several previously unissued takes. The Vow/I Really Don't Want to Know/Ko Ko Mo/On My Merry Way/A Kiss from Your Lips.

COLLECTABLES 5424 (CL)
Flamingo Serenade
Reissue of End 304 from the early '60s. They sing a set of Mantovani-type standards in a wistful, dreamy,

echo-chambered style, a kind of hypnotic trance they snapped themselves out of in the mid-'60s when they hitched up with Philips and started to boogaloo.

COLLECTABLES 5425 (CL)
Requestfully Yours
Reissue of End 308, circa 1960, incorporating original, hip sleeve notes aimed at jukebox operators and record salesmen. So much of the Goldner material from this period in The Flamingos's career smacks of commercial schmaltz. Orchestral arrangements of tired old standards, sung as if by wailing somnambulists in the wee hours on a freeway underpass, do little to match the soul and excitement of earlier Chess masterpieces. The best of the dozen songs include "Beside You," "Everybody's Got a Home but Me," "I Was Such a Fool," plus their best effort on the label "Nobody Loves Me Like You."

COLLECTABLES 5426 (CL)
The Sound of The Flamingos
Reissue of 1962's End LP 316 together with sleeve notes. Evergreen mush consisting of Porter, Gershwin, and Rodgers standards, which may prove more effective than Nyquil but comes nowhere close to the glory days of the past. Only two of ten songs on this album pass muster: the beautiful "I Only Have Eyes for You" and "I'm in the Mood for Love." The rest would even put houseplants to sleep.

COLLECTABLES 5428 (CL)
Flamingo Favorites
Straight reissue of their second End LP from 1960, showing a further suppression of the group's solid R&B roots. Compare, for example, their version of "Dream Girl" with the original by Jesse and Marvin. It's not bad stuff, all in all, just a bit pale in comparison to their earlier recordings. Fine sound quality; original cover and liner notes. Besame Mucho/That's Why I Love You/Mio Amore/Maria Elena/Bridge of Tears.

COLLECTABLES 8803 (CL)
For Collectors Only
Two CD/cassette set. Most everything here was recorded for End Records between 1958–1962, including their biggest hit "I Only Have Eyes for You." Unreleased versions of their only chart successes for Checker, "I'll Be Home" and "A Kiss from Your Lips," are interesting enough, but the liner notes don't mention if these came from Checker or End. Aside from an unissued demo of "Lovers Never Say Goodbye," everything here has been reissued before. The first disc is much better that its companion, which moves from ballad to ballad, and for a change of pace, to another ballad. "Lovers Gotta Cry," which sounds like an Aaron Neville vocal, is fine, but nothing makes up for the overblown "Ol' Man River." Buy it for the great music on the first disc, and throw away the aimless liner notes. Ko Ko Mo/Mio Amore/I Was Such a

Fool/I Shed a Tear at Your Wedding/It's Too Soon to Know.

⊗ RHINO 70967 (CL)
The Best of The Flamingos
Terrific 14-track cassette or 18-track CD featuring a cross section of their Chance, Checker, Decca, and End recordings. Golden Teardrops/I'll Be Home/The Vow/I Only Have Eyes for You/Mio Amore.

SEQUEL 609 (L)
I Only Have Eyes for You: The Best of the End Years
Dwells on their earlier End 45s and substitutes album cuts for later End singles. Alongside Flamingos's classics like "Lovers Never Say Goodbye," "I Only Have Eyes for You," and "Nobody Loves Me Like You," is a remake of "Jump Children" from End 309, a third previously unreleased version of the beautiful "I'll Be Home," and a glorious second unissued version of "A Kiss from Your Lips."

THE FLEETWOODS
Originally called Two Girls and a Guy, this pop-harmony trio from Olympia, WA led by Gary Troxel, recorded for Dolton from 1959–1963. They got their name from their telephone exchange.

RHINO 70980 (CL)
The Best of The Fleetwoods
Wholesome threesome responsible for such hits as "Come Softly to Me," "Graduation's Here," "Mr. Blue," and "Last One to Know."

EDDIE FLOYD
Alabama-born soulster who was the original leader of The Falcons (see separate listing) until he left to pursue a solo career. He had a long string of hits on Stax, starting with the classic "Knock on Wood," followed by "Don't Mess with Cupid," "Comfort Me," and "634-5789."

ATLANTIC 80283 (CL)
Knock on Wood
Reissue of Stax 714 from 1967. This wonderful LP highlights Eddie's great songwriting talents, on the title classic and the follow up, "Raise Your Hand," plus his hit for Wilson Pickett "634-5789." Includes fine covers of "Something You Got," "If You Got to Make a Fool of Somebody," and J.J. Jackson's "But It's Alright."

P-VINE 901 (L)
Gotta Make a Comeback
Ten tunes cut in New Orleans in 1982.

STAX 8527 (RC)
Soul Street
Reissue of Stax 5512 from 1974 with original cover and notes. Nothing earthshattering, just a nice funky set. Eddie is in fine voice and the band and arrangements are good. Stealing Love/I'm So Grateful/Guess Who.

STAX (UK) 010 (L)
The Best of
Twenty-two great tunes recorded for Stax between 1966–1974. The first six are from the original Stax/Atlantic sides and, besides the classic "Knock on Wood," there are "Raise Your Hand," "Things Get Better" (later covered by Delaney and Bonnie), and "Big Bird," which was on the *Jammed Together* LP. The rest are from the easier-to-find later Stax sessions currently owned by Fantasy and include such strong material as "Blood Is Thicker than Water," "Consider Me," and "Oh How It Rained." All tunes were written by Floyd, except for wonderful covers of Sam Cooke's "Bring It on Home to Me" and Clarence Carter's "Too Weak to Fight."

WRC 3005 (R)
Flashback
The "Knock on Wood" man is back with a vengeance. Eddie rejoins with his former, long-time Stax-mate William Bell (WRC = Wilbe Recording Corp.) for a fine new LP of boogiein' down. Recorded in Norcross, GA, coproduced by Bell and Floyd, all tunes are written by Eddie except "Pretty Girls" cowritten with Steve Cropper. My faves are "Soul Is Back Again" and "From Your Head to Your Toes." She Likes the Soaps/Daddy's Coming Home/Gonna Satisfy You.

EDDIE FONTAINE
Though not a household name, Eddie's known for a number of things, including the great "Nothin' Shakin' (but the Leaves on the Tree)," which The Beatles covered, and "Cool It Baby" that he did in the teen flick *The Girl Can't Help It.*

EMI (FRANCE) 93173 (L)
Who's Eddie?
Twenty-five cuts from 1955–1957, featuring Eddie in a variety of settings. There are a few hot items, but most of the cuts are teen weepers, pop jivers, and country-flavored items. An interesting set for completists.

JALO 33102 (R)

Nothin' Shakin'

Twenty rockin' songs from the '50s, including two versions of "Nothin' Shakin'." It Ain't Gonna Happen Again/Goodness It's Gladys/Here 'Tis/Baby You Did This to Me/Nobody Can Handle this Job but Me (with Gerry Granahan).

FRANKIE FORD

Excellent, white New Orleans R&B singer (and second cousin to Mack "Dr. John" Rebennack) who recorded for Ace. Ford's rise to stardom is a typical late-'50s success story. His two biggest hits, "Sea Cruise" and "Roberta" were actually recorded by Huey "Piano" Smith, but Ace label head Johnny Vincent felt the songs needed some "improvement." His solution was a simple one: bring in a good-looking white kid in a suit and tie to rerecord Smith's vocal over the original backing tracks! The result was a smash, international hit that eclipsed Ace's previous chart-topper "Rockin' Pneumonia," by guess who: Huey Smith!! (Some guys have all the luck.) Ford continued with lesser hits on Ace and subsequently Liberty, and recorded for a number of small labels in the '70s. He is currently enjoying renewed popularity in England.

ACE (US) 2036 (RL)

Let's Take a Sea Cruise

Chock full o' goodies, including the 12 selections from Ford's *Sea Cruise* LP plus six more. Ford's better tracks have that patented Crescent City sound, with Ford's surprisingly gutsy singing out in front. Other tracks are clearly reaching for the teen-pop market, exhibiting the "Bobby Darin imitating Frank Sinatra" sound. That's rock and roll, folks! Blow Wind Blow/Alimony/I Want to Be Your Man/Watchdog/Cheatin' Woman.

THE FOUR EPICS

Philadelphia vocal group whose career spanned the late '50s through the early '70s. They recorded under a number of names including The Dreamlovers (for Cameo; not to be confused with The Dreamlovers who recorded for Heritage, also a Philadelphia-based band), The Vespers (for Swan), and in 1972, as Exodus, as well as under their own name on Laurie.

CRYSTAL BALL 107 (R)

Getting High on The Four Epics

Fourteen sides. Mr. Cupid/M&M/Rocket Ride/When I Walk with My Angel.

THE FOUR FELLOWS

Smooth New York group that started out in 1953 as The Schemers, but after their single Derby session, they came up with the more commercial name. In 1955, they signed with Gone, and had their only hit with "Soldier Boy," written by tenor vocalist Davey Jones and featuring the amazing lead of Jim McGowan; Teddy Williams (lead ten) and Larry Banks (bar, b) rounded out the Mills Brothers-like quartet at this time. They continued to record for Gone through 1957 and then disbanded.

DERBY 1000 (R)

The Four Fellows

Nice 18-tune collection. Their one Derby release, the fine "I Tried" b/w "Bend of the River," from 1954, is here, along with many of their fine Gone recordings. Alongside the many ballads, you'll find some good uptempo tunes like "Take Me Back Baby" and "I Wish I Didn't Love You So," and even the obligatory calypso number. Angels Say/Fallen Angel/In the Rain.

THE FOUR LOVERS

The Four Lovers hailed from Newark, NJ, and were originally called The Varietones with Frankie Castelluccio, Hank Majewski, and brothers Tommy and Nick DeVito. They signed with RCA and scored a hit with "You're the Apple of My Eye," recording one very rare LP. Castelluccio changed his name to Franki Valli, and Hank and Nick were replaced by Bob Gaudio (of The Royal Teens) and Nick Massi. The group soon changed their name to The Four Seasons, after a local bowling alley, and the rest, as they say, is history.

BEAR FAMILY 15424 (L)

Joyride

The Lovers's complete RCA recordings, including some previously unissued alternate takes. Joyride/Such a Night/Shake a Hand/You're the Apple of My Eye/White Christmas/San Antonio Rose/Cimarron/This Is My Story/Jambalaya.

THE FOUR SEASONS

Beginning their life as The Four Lovers (see separate entry), Frankie Valli and The Four Seasons were famous for the high-reaching lead vocals of Valli and snappy, danceable hits. They scored 29 hits between 1962–1970, selling 50-million copies worldwide, including five Number 1 hits: 1962's "Sherry" and "Big Girls Don't Cry," 1963's "Walk Like a Man," 1964's "Rag Doll," and 1976's "December 1963 (Oh What a Night)," cut by a later incarnation of the group.

As The Lovers, the group was going nowhere, until they hooked up with producer Bob Crewe, who brought talented songwriter/keyboard player Bob Gaudio into the band. Gaudio supplied the band's first smash hit, "Sherry," and cowrote with Crewe many of their other big numbers. Their hits kept coming, first on Vee Jay, and then on Philips, where hit singles included "Rag Doll" and 1966's "Let's Hang On (to What We Got)" and "Working My Way Back to You." They also had solid LP sales, unusual for a doo-wop group.

In 1967, Valli scored a solo hit with "Can't Take My Eyes Off of You," leading to a change in billing to Frankie Valli and The Four Seasons. In 1968, they attempted a fancy concept album called *Genuine Imitation Life Gazette*, including an eight-page pseudo-newspaper, which flopped with their audience. The group struggled through the '70s, though they did score one fluke megahit with Gaudio's song (cowritten with Judy Parker, later his wife) "December 1963 (Oh What a Night)," their first UK and US Number 1 song. By this time, Gaudio and Valli were the only original members of the group performing under The Four Seasons name. The '80s were marked primarily by performances on the oldies circuit.

RHINO 70234 (CL)

The Four Seasons Christmas Album

Twelve yuletide favorites, originally Philips 223 from 1966. What Child Is This/Little Drummer Boy.

RHINO 70247 (CL)

Working My Way Back to You and More Great New Hits

Reissue of Philips 201 from 1966. A dozen tunes. Interestingly enough, the title tune, the only hit here, was written by the team of Linzer/Randell (not the usual Gaudio/Crewe team), who also contributed "Can't Get Enough of You Baby" which was covered and became a hit for, of all people, ?Question Mark and The Mysterions! Beggars Parade/Show Girl/Everybody Knows My Name/One Clown Cried.

RHINO 70248 (CL)

Sing Big Hits by Burt Bacharach/ Hal David/Bob Dylan

Reissue of Philips 193 from 1965, one of the rarest of their Philips LPs. Apparently, The Seasons had planned to record an entire Dylan tribute LP, but this failed to materialize because Frankie was unhappy with his lead vocals on the tracks that they produced. Frankie wasn't far off the mark in his assessment of this material; their cover of "Mr. Tambourine Man" is only a notch above the quality of William Shatner's infamous version of it. The market was glutted with Seasons's singles, so Philips issued Dylan's "Don't Think Twice" under the name of Wonder Who? It was a fluke Top-Ten hit, leading Philips to issue a few more Seasons's outtakes under this name, and their old label Vee Jay to issue a previously unissued novelty number, "Peanuts," also using the Wonder Who? appellation. The LP was cobbled together from the six Dylan covers that were recorded with six from the Bachrach/David songbook. Walk on By/What the World Needs Now Is Love/Make It Easy On Yourself/Blowin' in the Wind/All I Really Want to Do.

RHINO 70249 (CL)
The Genuine Imitation Life Gazette
1968 concept LP that tried to put The Seasons into competition with The Beatles as "artistes." A resounding floparoo.

RHINO 70973 (CL)
Rarities, Vol. 1
Twenty rare and unusual Four Seasons cuts from 1964–1977, taken from LPs, 45s, and commercials, including two sides released as The Wonder Who? Big Man's World/No Surfin' Today/Do You Wanna Dance/A Sunday Kind of Love/On the Good Ship Lollipop/Good-Bye Girl.

RHINO 70974 (CL)
Rarities, Vol. 2
Eighteen more oddities culled from hard-to-find LPs and singles. Includes such gems as the sought after "Whatever You Say" and "Sleeping Man" sides released only in England, "The Night," "We Can Work It Out," and "I'm Gonna Change" from the years 1967–1977.

RHINO 71490 (CL)
Anthology
All of their big hits and notable LP tracks on two cassettes or CDs. 1964's "Rag Doll" was perhaps their pinnacle: a moralistic opera of unmatchable intensity. Songs like "Walk Like a Man" taught an entire generation the difference between right and wrong (still a source of confusion to this day). Almost every essential piece of Seasonabilia can be found here; our only quibble might be the exclusion of The Seasons's foray into psychedelia, "Watch the Flowers Grow," and the inclusion of two 1975 disco-era entries by Valli at the end of the set. An essential chapter in the '60s pop legacy.

RHINO 72998 (L)
25th Anniversary Collection
Deluxe four-CD box set, including vintage Four Seasons and Valli solo tracks. Carefully remastered from original master tapes with booklet with many rare photos.

THE FOUR TOPS

Excellent Motown group that has been around since 1954 (originally as The Four Aims) without personnel change. Levi Stubbs has a great gravelly voice and a phrasing that earned him the nickname "The Black Dylan." Childhood friends Abdul "Duke" Fakir, Renaldo "Obie" Benson, and Lawrence Payton round out the long-lived lineup. After nine hitless years as a jazz-vocal group with flops on Chess, Riverside, and Columbia, The Tops were finally teamed up with Motown producers/songwriters Holland-Dozier-Holland for a long string of classic hits, including "Reach Out I'll Be There," "Standing in the Shadows of Love," and "I Can't Help Myself (Sugar Pie, Honey Bunch)." After disillusionment with Motown, they signed with Dunhill in 1972 for another string of hits, including "Ain't No Woman like the One I Got," "Are You Man Enough," and "Catfish." After Dunhill folded, they had a couple of hits for RSO before resigning with Motown in 1983 and eventually moving to Arista in 1988.

MOTOWN 809 (CL)
Anthology
Two cassette or two CD set of their "golden greats."

MOTOWN 5122 (CL)
The Four Tops
Reissue of their first LP, Motown 622 from 1964.

MOTOWN 5149 (CL)
Reach Out
Reissue of Motown 660 from 1967, one of their best. Twelve great tunes featuring eight hits, including the title track, "Bernadette," and "Seven Rooms of Gloom," and covers of two Monkees's tunes!

⚫ MOTOWN 5209 (CL)
Greatest Hits
Reissue of Motown 662 from 1967. Twelve biggies by The Tops in their prime. Reach Out I'll Be There/Standing in the Shadows of Love/Seven Rooms of Gloom/I Can't Help Myself/Bernadette.

MOTOWN 5224 (CL)
Still Waters Run Deep
Reissue of Motown 704 from 1970. Still Waters (Love)/Still Waters (Peace)/It's All in the Game/Reflections/Bring Me Together.

MOTOWN 5258 (CL)
Live
Reissue of Motown 654 from 1966. Nice collection of hits and standards recorded live in Detroit. It's the Same Old Song/Reach Out I'll Be There/I'll Turn to Stone/It's Not Unusual/I Left My Heart in San Francisco.

MOTOWN 5264 (CL)
Second Album
Reissue of Motown 634 from 1965 including their hits "I Can't Help Myself" and "The Same Old Song." Something about You/Stay in My Lonely Arms/Since You've Been Good/Love Feels like Fire.

MOTOWN 5363 (C)
Motown Legends
A real loser. Besides the hit "Standing in the Shadow of Love," we're subject to terrible covers of "Honey," "Daydream Believer," and "Light My Fire."

MOTOWN 5428 (CL)
Keeper of the Castle
Reissue of their first Dunhill LP, 50129 from 1972.

MOTOWN 5444 (CL)
On Top
Reissue of Motown 634 from 1966.

MOTOWN 5446 (CL)
Nature Planned It
Reissue of their last Motown LP, 748 from 1972.

MOTOWN 5478 (CL)
Changing Times
Reissue of Motown 721 from 1971.

MOTOWN 8107 (L)
Reach Out/Still Waters Run Deep

MOTOWN 8127 (L)
Four Tops/Second Album

MOTOWN 8146 (L)
Four Tops Live/Keeper of the Castle

MOTOWN 9402 (L)
Compact Command Performances
Hits package from 1965–1972.

THE FOUR VAGABONDS
The Four Vagabonds were the natural offshoots of groups like The Spirits of Rhythm and The Cats and the Fiddle, with a heavier emphasis on tight quartet harmony. The St. Louis-based quartet started singing together in high school in 1933, and stayed together with the same lineup through 1947: John Jordan (lead), Robert O'Neal (ten), Noral Tuborn (bar), and Ray Grant, Jr. (b, gtr). They performed on radio through the '30s and recorded a scant 16 sides for Bluebird in the early '40s, moving briefly to Mercury in 1946, and then to Apollo in 1946–1947. Their 1943 78 "Comin' in on a Wing and a Prayer" b/w "It Can't Be Wrong" is, according to *Billboard*, "one of the few records in history to have its A-side chart Pop while its flip charted only R&B."

RELIC 8012 (R)
Yesterday's Memories
At last, for the first time in 40 years, comes a gatefold album collection by this seminal blues and rhythm vocal group. Some of their original 78s command up to $500 among collectors. These badly promoted Apollo sides cut in New York during 1946–1947 show how well the group was able to blend harmony with hokum and humor. Landmark recordings. Good clean sound.

CAROL FRAN and CLARENCE HOLLIMON
Fran began her career in New Orleans's French Quarter in the mid-'50s, and Hollimon, who toured with Charles Brown from 1957–1960, is also known for his session work with O.V. Wright and Bobby "Blue" Bland.

BLACK TOP 1071 (CL)
Soul Sensation
A nice bluesy set of originals and covers. Fran's vocals are strong, as "My Happiness" and the gospel-flavored "I Had a Talk with My Man" will prove. Instrumentals like Hollimon's own "Blues for Carol" and "Gristle" allow his Gibson guitar to shine, as does the duo's good-time "Box with the Hole in the Middle." Backed by a solid band, with help from James "Thunderbird" Davis and The Kamikaze Horns, Carol and Clarence make their first album a pleasant surprise.

CONNIE FRANCIS
Born Concetta Rosa Maria Franconero in Newark, NJ, the young singer/accordionist (!) got her big break on Arthur Godfrey's *Talent Scouts* show; it was Godfrey who suggested her new name. She starred for several years on the kiddie TV show *Startime* before landing a recording contract with MGM at age 16 that led to a string of hits beginning with a cover of the old chestnut "Who's Sorry Now." From 1958–1962, she scored hit after hit with covers of standards and new songs penned for her by the fledgling songwriting team of Neil Sedaka and Howie Greenfield, including "Lipstick on Your Collar," "Where the Boys Are," and "My Heart Has a Mind of Its Own." She appeared in a string of teen flicks for MGM, beginning with the megahit *Where the Boys Are*, that have become schlock classics. Her career waned in the late '60s, followed by a series of personal tragedies in the '70s

that led her to abandon performing. She hit the comeback trail in the '80s without too much success.

POLYDOR 827 569 (CL)

The Very Best Of

12 early hits. Who's Sorry Now?/Stupid Cupid/ Mama/Lipstick on Your Collar/Among My Souvenirs/Lily Marlene.

POLYDOR 831 699 (CL)

The Very Best of, Vol. 2

A dozen tracks, mostly from the first half of the '60s, with the exceptions of a horrid "God Bless America" from 1959 and "Time Alone Will Tell (Non Pensare a Me)" from 1967. Lots of foreign language recordings. Mama/Al-Di-La/Malaguena/When the Boy in Your Arms (Is the Boy in Your Heart)/Blue Winter.

PANAMA FRANCIS ALL STARS

KRAZY KAT 813 (R)

Panama Francis All Stars 1949

This set really jumps with booting sax licks from Danny Turner on soprano, alto, and baritone and George Kelly on tenor sax. Other cats in the groove include the great Doc Bagby (pno), Herb Gordy (b), and Panama himself (drm), who truly punishes the skin on "Out of Nowhere." Turner and Kelly excel on "Jitterbug Jump" and "Panama's Jump." You'll wear out the carpet in no time with this one! Thorough sleeve notes. Nine of the 16 cuts are previously unissued.

ARETHA FRANKLIN

Daughter of famed preacher Rev. C.L. Franklin, Aretha has truly earned her nickname, "Lady Soul." Her first recordings were gospel tracks cut for Joe Von Battle's JVB label. In 1959, she signed with Columbia, thanks to legendary producer John Hammond, who really didn't know what to do with her, having her record pop, blues, and jazz. In 1967, her big break came with a new label, Atlantic, who sent her down to Muscle Shoals to work with producer Jerry Wexler, and together they redefined soul music. She had an incredible string of hits with Wexler from 1967's "I Ain't Never Loved a Man (the Way I Love You)" to 1974's pop version of the venerable hymn, "Amazing Grace." She left Atlantic in 1980 for Arista, reteaming with former Atlantic producer Arif Mardin for a string of dance-oriented pop hits.

ATLANTIC 906 (CL)

Amazing Grace

Her amazing double gospel set recorded with James Cleveland and The Southern California Community Choir in 1972. Mary Don't You Weep/Precious Memories/Climbing Higher Mountains.

ATLANTIC 8139 (CL)

I Ain't Never Loved a Man (the Way I Love You)

Reissue of her 1967 Atlantic debut album. Respect/Dr. Feelgood/Do Right Woman/Drown in My Own Tears/A Change Is Gonna Come/Baby, Baby, Baby.

ATLANTIC 8176 (CL)

Lady Soul

Budget CD reissuing ten of her better-known hits (originally packaged under this same catalog number in 1968). Chain of Fools/(You Make Me Feel Like a) Natural Woman/Ain't No Way.

ATLANTIC 8295 (C)

Aretha's Greatest Hits

Her late '60s hits. I Say a Little Prayer/Spanish Harlem.

ATLANTIC 81230 (CL)

Aretha's Jazz

Eight songs drawn from her *Soul '69* (Atlantic 8212) and *Hey Now Hey* (Atlantic 7265 from 1973) albums (the latter produced by Quincy Jones).

ATLANTIC 81280 (CL)

The Best of Aretha Franklin

Twelve of her best Atlantic sides. Rock Steady/Chain of Fools/I Ain't Never Loved a Man (the Way I Love You)/Respect/Until You Come Back to Me (That's What I'm Gonna Do).

🌑 ATLANTIC 81668 (CL)

30 Greatest Hits

Double-CD/cassette set of 30 Atlantic classics. I Ain't Never Loved a Man (the Way I Love You)/Do Right Woman, Do Right Man/Save Me/(You Make Me Feel Like a) Natural Woman/Chain of Fools/Think/The House that Jack Built/Share Your Love with Me/Spirit in the Dark/Bridge over Troubled Water/Day Dreaming/I'm in Love.

ATLANTIC (JAPAN) 44 (L)

Aretha Arrives

Aretha's second album (originally Atlantic 8150 from 1970) is a solid sender, featuring King Curtis (ten sax) on several cuts. This reissue has good sound quality. Satisfaction/Night Life/Going Down Slow/Baby I Love You.

ATLANTIC (JAPAN) 66 (L)

Spirit in the Dark

This 1970 Atlantic album (originally 8265) yielded two hot summer hits: "Don't Play That Song" and the title track, with Aretha's torrid version of "The Thrill Is Gone" (the flip side of "Spirit") also garnering some chart action. Twelve ultra-soulful songs on this reissue, which generally is not mentioned as a critic's choice, but is my personal favorite nonetheless.

ATLANTIC (JAPAN) 2373 (L)

Aretha Now

Repro of the ten-track LP, Atlantic 8186 from 1968. Think/I Say a Little Prayer/See Saw/Night Time Is the Right Time/You Send Me.

COLUMBIA 31953 (CL)

The First 12 Sides

This overlooked classic, a compilation of Aretha's first singles, is often overshadowed by her parade of late '60s hits on Atlantic. Only the rollicking first cut ("Won't Be Long") was chartbound, but on purely musical terms, this set stands up to anything she has done since. The program is solidly bluesy, and from songs like "Sweet Lover," "All Night Long," and "Maybe I'm a Fool" it's obvious that she didn't get ALL her schooling in her father's church. By 1960, she had come fully into her own, sounding every bit as sassy as Nina Simone or Esther Phillips, creating a seductive blend of churchified soul pursued by future labelmate Ray Charles. Simply superb, with top-notch accompaniment by R&B/jazz vets Ray Bryant, Al Sears, Warren Lucky, and Milt Hinton.

COLUMBIA 38042 (CL)

Sweet Bitter Love

COLUMBIA 40105 (CL)

Aretha Sings the Blues

After the great promise shown on Aretha's *Her First 12 Sides*, this collection of early '60s tracks is a bit of a disappointment. The soon-to-be soul queen's voice is formidable on this 14-part blues program. Indeed, her singing is too potent to be coupled with the string-heavy arrangements and lounge-act cliches that predominate here. Still, as with any Aretha album, there are enough gems to justify the purchase. Drinking Again/Nobody Knows the Way I Feel This Morning/Muddy Water.

COLUMBIA 40708 (C)

After Hours

Budget compilation of 1962–1965 Columbia sides. Aretha schmoozes her way through 11 hoary standards. Misty/Unforgettable/Just for a Thrill/There Is No Greater Love.

COLUMBIA 48515 (CL)

Jazz to Soul

Good two-CD/two-cassette, 39-track set. Highlights included jazz, blues, and soul-flavored numbers. On the negative side of the scale, at least for me, are some of the violin-backed ballads, particularly Aretha's rather straight reading of "If Ever I Will Leave You." Thankfully, such numbers are the exception rather than the rule here. A nicely put-together package, featuring fine sound quality and a 38-page booklet with lots of vintage photos and some discographical information. Sweet Lover/Once in a While/Muddy Water/Soulville/Runnin' Out of Fools/Every Little Bit Hurts.

MOBILE FIDELITY 820 (L)

Live at the Fillmore West

Reissue of classic, 1971 album, originally Atlantic 7205.

RHINO 71063 (CL)

Queen of Soul: The Atlantic Recordings

This four-disc or cassette set of most of the best of Aretha's Atlantic recordings made between 1967–1976 is indispensible to soul collectors and is final proof (if any is needed) of the greatness of Lady Soul. This collection offers up 86 reasons (over five hours!) guaranteed to convince any doubter of the magnitude of Aretha's talent. Among all the hits are equally wonderful non-hit album cuts as well as non-LP tracks like the phenomenal "My Song," one of the best B-sides of all time. No matter whether she's covering The Beatles, Smokey Robinson, The Band, or Clara Ward, Aretha's originality shines through. Attractively packaged, the set comes with an 80-page booklet filled with photos, session info, chart positions, and an essay by Dave Marsh. I Ain't Never Loved a Man (the Way I Love You)/Do Right Woman/Never Let Me Go/Good to Me as I Am to You/Dark End of the Street/One Way Ticket.

JOHN FRED and THE PLAYBOYS

John Fred Gourrier was born in Baton Rouge, LA and formed his first band at age 15. His first single was 1959's "Shirley" released by the local Montel label, with backing by Fats Domino's band. John toured briefly with The Fat One before taking time off for college. On graduation in 1964, he formed a new version of The Playboys, recording a cover of John Lee Hooker's "Boogie Chillen" for the En-Joy label. After 16 singles, they scored a freak hit in 1968 with the hippie-esque anthem, "Judy in Disguise (with Glasses)" penned by Fred and bandmate Andrew Bernard, who played sax and served as the arranger for the band's material. The band had one minor followup hit, "Hey, Hey Bunny," and continues to perform occasionally throughout the South. Fred now runs John Fred Music and the Sugarcane record label.

PAULA 9000 (L)
The History of John Fred and The Playboys
> Twenty-six song retrospective includes Fred's first effort from 1958 ("Shirley") when he was backed by Fats Domino's band, as well as later efforts. The Playboys popularized horns in rock before Chicago or Blood, Sweat, and Tears, and manage a convincingly soulful sound on tunes like "She Shot a Hole in My Soul," "Boogie Chillen," and even a soulful cover of "Back in the USSR." Over 73 minutes of surprisingly good music.

FREDDIE and THE DREAMERS

Manchester-based British invasion band led by Freddie Garrity, responsible for the brief, 1965 dance craze, "The Freddie." Working as a milkman and engineer in the late '50s, Freddie formed his first group, a skiffle band, called The Red Sox. In 1961, he formed the first Dreamers, drawing on local friends. They cut their first hits in 1963, including their breakthrough record for the US charts (released stateside by the Tower label in 1965), "I'm Telling You Now." The band began to fall apart in 1966, but didn't officially disband until 1972; Freddie formed a new "Dreamers" to play on the oldies circuit in 1976.

CAPITOL 96979 (CL)
The Best of Freddie and The Dreamers
> Twenty-five tracks including hits and misses, many tracks not previously issued in the UK.

BOBBY FREEMAN

Bobby was born and raised in San Francisco. At age 14 he sang with The Romancers, who recorded the widely popular "House Cat" on Dootone. After singing lead with the (West coast) Vocaleers, Bobby signed a solo contract with Josie Records. His first release "Do You Wanna Dance?" sped up the R&B charts during the spring of 1958, peaking at Number 2. (It later was a hit in a cover version by The Beach Boys.) His second success was "Betty Lou Got a New Pair of Shoes," followed by "Need Your Love" in the fall. Reverting back to dance-craze ditties in 1964, Bobby hit the jackpot twice more with "C'Mon and Swim" and "S-W-I-M" on the Autumn label.

COLLECTABLES 5417 (CL)
Do You Wanna Dance?
> Twelve dancin' hits, many culled from his Josie album 1086. No inner pix and scant, almost illegible notes. The Mess Around/Need Your Love/C'Mon and Swim/Little Girl Don't You Understand/S-W-I-M.

JUBILEE 1086 (R)
Do You Wanna Dance?
> Twenty tracks from the '50s and early '60s. Standouts include the rocking "Little Girl Don't You Understand," "Mardi Gras Rock," and "Betty Lou Got a New Pair of Shoes." Great rug-cutting sounds. Excludes some fine Josie ballad B-sides, but this is more than made up for by the inclusion of most of his best stompers. Simulated stereo does not detract from the overall sound.

THE BOBBY FULLER FOUR

Excellent, '60s-era, Buddy Holly-influenced rocker from El Paso, best known for his classic cover of the post-Holly Crickets's song, "I Fought the Law" on Mustang. He recorded for a number of small labels in Texas in the early '60s without much impact, and subsequently moved to Los Angeles and formed his group The Bobby Fuller Four. After the success of "I Fought the Law" in January 1966, he followed with another hit, "Love's Made a Fool of You." He was found dead in his car soon after and, although his death was pronounced a suicide, it has since come out that he was found beat up with gasoline poured down his throat.

ACE 314 (L)
Live at PJ's Plus!

Absolutely stunning, 21-cut live set! I could run through every superlative in the book to try and describe the music captured on this recently discovered live show. The Bobby Fuller Four could do it all: rockabilly ("I Fought the Law" and "Oh Boy!"); R&B ("C.C. Rider," "My Babe," and "Keep a Knockin'"); surf ("My Favorite Martian" and "Thunder Reef"); ballads ("A New Shade of Blue" and "My True Love"); or just about anything else that falls under the rockin' banner. This stuff will stand your short hairs on end. They also perform their sensational original, "Let Her Dance," a true rockin' classic. If you like real rock and roll, you'll love this and, if you're a Fuller fanatic, ya gotta get it.

☻ ACE 388 (L)
The Best of The Bobby Fuller Four

Eighteen-track collection. I Fought the Law/Another Sad and Lonely Night/A New Shade of Blue/Pamela/Never to Be Forgotten/Baby My Heart/Only When I Dream/King of the Wheels/The Magic Touch.

ACE 956 (L)
The Bobby Fuller Four

Essential release of two great Bobby Fuller Four LPs, *I Fought the Law* (Mustang 901) and *KRLA King of the Wheels* (Mustang 900), plus seven extra tracks! Two of the bonus tracks are hot instrumentals: "Thunder Reef," a surf tune, and "Wolfman," an homage to you know who. The other five are "Don't Ever Let Me Know," the fabulous "The Magic Touch" (their last 45), two B-sides ("I'm a Lucky Guy" and "My True Love"), and a boss cover of Buddy Holly's "Love's Made a Fool of You." Twenty-four cuts, including gorgeous ballads, shimmering pop tunes, and wild hot-rod instrumentals. I Fought the Law/A New Shade of Blue/KRLA Top Eliminator/The Lonely Dragster.

RHINO 70174 (CL)
The Best of The Bobby Fuller Four

The best of their 1965–1966 Mustang sides. Mostly the best cuts from their two LPs, *I Fought the Law* and *KRLA King of the Wheels*, plus "I'm a Lucky Guy," and the classic title tunes from both LPs. Duplicates Ace 956. Baby My Heart/Let Her Dance/It's Love, Come What May/Love's Made a Fool of You.

BILLY FURY

Fury is perhaps Britain's greatest pre-Beatles rocker, second only to Cliff Richard. Between 1959–1965, he had 20 British chart hits without even denting the US market. His excellent backup band led by pianist Clive Powell left him in 1962 and became Georgie Fame and The Blue Flames. Soon after, Billy abandoned rock for middle-of-the-road pop. In 1967, after seven years at Decca, Billy went to Parlophone where, though he experimented with a number of styles, he failed to produce any hits. He was plagued by ill health, and a comeback attempt was aborted when he died of heart disease in 1983. Billy's Decca sides have been reissued in various packages from the UK, with interesting, rarer cuts from this period available on See For Miles. His later and less exciting Parlophone sides are available from Magnum Force.

DERAM (UK) 820 924 (L)
Halfway to Paradise

Twenty furious flights, including the chart-worthy title track and the Doc Pomus spinoff sides "You're Having the Last Dance with Me" and "Would You Stand by Me." Fans of snappy reviewer's jargon (such as that which peppers these piquant pages) will love the ultra-glib liner notes. Wondrous Place/A Thousand Stars/Don't Worry/He Will Break Your Heart/I Love How You Love Me.

LONDON (UK) 820 530 (L)
The Billy Fury Hit Parade

Budget import CD with 20 of Billy's best UK Decca sides from 1959. All but three of these tunes made the British top 20 (and those three cracked the top 25). Complete US and UK release and chart information; nine of these sides were issued in the US, but none charted! Maybe Tomorrow/Jealousy/Colette/Halfway to Paradise/Like I've Never Been Gone.

LONDON (UK) 820 627 (L)
The Sound of Fury Plus Ten

Reissue of Fury's 1960 LP *The Sound of Fury* (called Britain's first authentic rock and roll album) with ten additional tracks from this period, when Billy was playing his Elvis-inspired bad-boy role to the hilt. Forty-six minutes.

MAGNUM FORCE 072 (L)
Rough Diamonds and Pure Gems

SEE FOR MILES 59 (RL)
The EP Collection

Twenty rare Decca cuts recorded between 1961–1965 taken from Billy's nine EPs, 14 of which have not been on a single or LP before. These are some of Billy's best and rarest, and though they included a number of covers ("You Got Me Dizzy" "Saved," and "Nobody's Child"), they also included a number of Fury originals ("My Christmas Prayer," "Don't Jump," "What Did I Do," and "Keep Away"). In mono with detailed liner notes.

DON GARDENER and DEE DEE FORD

Philadelphia-born Gardener recorded some rare sides with his group The Sonotones for Gotham and Bruce in the early '50s. He then worked as a solo artist for numerous small labels, all with little success. In 1961, he joined with pianist Dee Dee Ford, and, a year later, the duo scored big with "I Need Your Loving," a screeching, gospel-tinged shouter, and a Top-20 hit. The duo split soon after, and reunited briefly in 1966; later, Don with Jeanette "Baby" Washington had a minor R&B hit with 1973's "Forever."

COLLECTABLES 5155 (CL)
I Need Your Lovin'

Thirteen tracks. I Need Your Lovin'/Nobody but You/You Said/T.C.B. (Taking Care of Business)/I'm Coming Home to Stay/Honey Sweet/Lead Me On.

THE GARRETT/SAHM/TAYLOR BAND

MOBILE FIDELITY 757 (L)/VILLAGE GREEN (JAPAN) 00191 (L)
Live in Japan:
The Garrett/Sahm/Taylor Band

One of Doug Sahm's many side-projects, this 12-cut live disc is headed straight to the top of our "10 best aging hippie bar bands of 1990" list. Before you Sir Doug fans ready your poison pens, let it be known that I mean this as a compliment, with barely a hint of irony. Who but Sahm, guitar alchemist Amos Garrett, and keyboardist Gene Taylor would dare to play such familiar fodder as "T-Bone Shuffle," "Lawdy Miss Clawdy," "Sweet Home Chicago," "Smack Dab in the Middle," and "Shake, Rattle and Roll," making these old chestnuts come alive one more time, and having a natural ball in the bargain? My hat goes off to these never-say-die rockers, and, whaddya know: I've got a bit of a bald spot myself!

VERNON GARRETT

LA soul badman Vernon Garrett has built himself quite a strong reputation in the Bay Area. That's because the man can really get down! Like other contemporary soul stylists, Vernon has surfaced on a multitude of small labels including Venture, ICA, and, most recently, Ichiban.

VIVID 013 (L)
Somebody Messed at the Crossroad

This set borrows heavily from Garrett's Glow Hill and WE label output, and features the driving "Drifting Apart," "If You Can't Help Me Baby," "Lonely Lonely Nights," plus the tough bluesy "Johnny Walker Red." Hard-soul singing with heavy-set instrumentation. Sixteen tracks featuring five different guitar players. Lord have mercy!

DANNY GATTON

Guitar Player's Number 1 "unknown" guitarist of the '80s has a career dating back to the '50s where he honed his skills playing rockabilly and country. He was a legendary player on the Washington, DC club scene, though he rarely recorded until the mid-'80s when he released some recordings on his own NRG label and was subsequently picked up by Elektra. Gatton takes the baton from a long line of country/blues/jazz/rock-influenced super-pickers like Les Paul, Chet Atkins, Jimmy Bryant, and Roy Buchanan.

ELEKTRA 61032 (CL)
88 Elmira St.

Guitar-whiz Danny Gatton finally gets the major label treatment he has deserved for years, and turns in his most polished and tasteful work yet on 11 diverse instrumentals. Highlights include the blazing guitar work on John Patton's Texas shuffle "Funky Mama"; "Elmira St. Boogie," a masterful rockabilly romp in the Les Paul tradition; the "Martin-Denny-goes-to-Nashville" stylings of "Quiet Village"; the Latin-flavored "Red Label"; and a surprisingly effective cover of The Beach Boys' "In My Room." What guitarist besides Henry Kaiser would dare put on such a gleeful display of eclecticism, even adding a new twist to "The Simpsons" theme with screaming sax and blazing banjo?! Gatton still has a problem finding inspired rhythm-section players, often laying his jaw-dropping leads over routine or predictable backing. But the mean, tenor sax of Bill Holloman prevails on a few cuts, and Danny never fails to amaze when he cuts loose.

NRG 02479 (CL)
Unfinished Business
This is one of the hottest, and probably the most sensational, electric-guitar release of the '80s. Gatton is AMAZING on each of these eight numbers, running the gamut from his "Homage to Charlie Christian" to Santo and Johnny's "Sleepwalk" to the blistering blues of his original pieces "Lappin It Up" and "Notcho Blues." A must.

NRG 9646 (C)/NRG 02916 (L)
Redneck Jazz
Gatton's first release pales in comparison to his more recent waxings, but does feature some blazing country-flavored riffs. Unfortunately there are also more than a few hokey country-rock songs like "Truck Driving Romance," "Redneck Jazz," and "Ugly Man" that make listening a bit of a chore. The CD features two bonus tracks, extended workouts on "Ode to Billie Joe" and "Canadian Sunset."

MARVIN GAYE
Excellent popular soulster who began his career as a member of the Washington, DC vocal group, The Marquees. The group was co-opted in 1959 by Harvey Fuqua to become The "new" Moonglows; Gaye can be heard on their hit, "12 Months of the Year." While with The Moonglows, he was discovered by Berry Gordy and signed to the new Motown label as both a singer and drummer (he plays drums on all of the early Miracles sides). Starting in 1964, he amassed a steady supply of hits both by himself and in duet with Motown's stable of starlets, including Mary Wells, Kim Weston, Tammi Terrell (his most frequent, and favorite, partner), and Diana Ross. In the '70s, Gaye's work turned more political, with the seminal LP, *What's Going On*, and sexual (*Let's Get It On*). In 1975, following the breakup of his 14-year marriage to Gordy's sister Anna, he spent six years without a recording contract, finally going to Columbia in 1982. After scoring a Number 1 hit with "Sexual Healing," he was murdered by his father during an argument in 1984.

MOTOWN 5181 (CL)
Live
Reissue of Motown 333 from 1974.

MOTOWN 5191 (CL)
Greatest Hits
Reissue of his 1976 hits package, originally Motown 348. Ten of his later hits, most of which came after the *Anthology* set. How Sweet It Is/Can I Get a Witness/Let's Get It On/I Want You/Trouble Man/What's Going On.

MOTOWN 5192 (CL)
Let's Get It On
Soulful 1973 album (originally Motown 324), which includes some very erotically charged material. You Sure Love to Ball/Please Don't Stay (Once You Go Away)/Just to Keep You Satisfied.

MOTOWN 5218 (CL)
That Stubborn Kinda' Fellow
Reissue of Gaye's second album (Motown 239 from 1963). Includes such great early hits as the title song, "Pride and Joy," and "Hitch Hike," and LP tracks like "Get My Hands on Some Lovin'" and "Soldier's Plea."

MOTOWN 5246 (CL)
Marvin Gaye and His Girls
Reissue of 1969 album, originally Motown 293. Duets with Diana Ross, Mary Wells, Kim Weston, and Tammi Terrell.

MOTOWN 5259 (CL)
Live at the London Palladium
Recorded in 1977 at this famed venue, and originally issued as Motown 352.

MOTOWN 5339 (CL)
What's Going On?
Gaye's classic political/protest LP (Motown 310 from 1971), made as a reaction to the riots that spread through the inner-cities, the anti-Vietnam war movement, and the presidency of Richard Nixon. Depending on your outlook, Marvin's potent raps are either nostalgic or dated, but his messages still apply. What's Happening Brother/Save the Children/Flying High/God Is Love.

MOTOWN 5359 (C)
Motown's Legends
Fourteen vintage tracks with lots of hits. Little Darlin'/I'll Be Doggone/One More Heartache/Ain't That Peculiar/Night Life/One for My Baby.

MOTOWN 6311 (CL)
The Marvin Gaye Collection
Four-CD, 81-song box set. If you are a connoisseur of the many stylistic changes Gaye underwent in an up-and-down 23 year career, you will absolutely love this collection. The four discs are divided by categories (Top-20 hits, duets, rare cuts, and ballads) and then chronologically; over thirty tracks are unreleased, some of which are quite magnificent. Among the

discoveries found in Motown's vaults are four duets with Oma Page (she hoped to be Mary Wells's successor), an unreleased 1978 ballad LP, and original single mixes of his '60s hits from the master tapes. The soulful side of Gaye's personality is not well-represented on this set, brought to life only on a steamy live performance of "Come to Get This" from 1974 and his awesome rendition of "The Star Spangled Banner" from the 1983 NBA All-Star Game, the coolest performance of his career. A 32-page booklet with worshipful notes by David Ritz cap a fine release for the diehard Gaye fan.

🌑 MOTOWN 791 (CL)

Anthology

Two-CD or two-cassette, 46-track set, covering Gaye's career, focusing primarily on his '60s hits. Inner City Blues/Chained/I Heard It Through the Grapevine/Distant Lover/I'll Be Doggone/Once Upon a Time/Hitch Hike/It Takes Two/Pride and Joy/Stubborn Kind of Fellow/Can I Get a Witness/You're a Wonderful One/Baby Don't Do It/Forever/One More Heartache.

RHINO 71182 (CL)

Seek and You Shall Find: More of the Best (1963–1981)

Fourteen tracks.

THE GAYLORDS

Detroit, MI doo-woppers who take the Louis Prima approach a step further (maybe a mile further) by singing rock and roll and R&B hits in Italian. I don't know how the Italian-American audience of the time received them, but you can just picture this routine going down like a storm on the Mafia club circuit of the mid-'50s.

ROCKIN' RECORDS 25017 (R)

The Gaylords Sing 16 Big Hits

Hot jivin' guitar and sax on some of these big "Italian" hits. All Shook Up/Blueberry Hill/Sh-Boom/Yakety Yak/I'm Walkin'/Personality.

PAUL GAYTEN

Paul Gayten was a true giant in the R&B field, already a successful star when he hooked up with the brothers Chess in the mid-'50s. At Chess, he was the New Orleans connection, wearing the hats of A&R man, producer, songwriter, promo man, and recording artist! In addition, his band was a spawning ground for new talent, but fortunately many of the best stuck around at Chess

for a while, including sax greats Lee Allen (ten sax) and Alvin "Red" Tyler (bar sax), and guitar player Edgar Blanchard.

CHESS 9294 (RCL)

Chess King of New Orleans

Eight of the ten tunes are from Chess subsidiaries Checker and Argo, with two previously unissued: "For You My Love" and "Down Boy." Both sides of the Anna 1106 single are also included: "Hot Cross Buns" and "The Hunch," a cover of the Bobby Peterson tune. CD has two extra tracks: "Windy" and the previously unreleased "Get It." Nervous Boogie/You Better Believe It/Music Goes Round and Round.

PAUL GAYTEN and ANNIE LAURIE

SPECIALTY 2169 (CL)

Regal Records in New Orleans

Regal Records was formed in Linden, NJ in 1949 by the Braun brothers as a De Luxe subsidiary. Paul Gayten, the company's Crescent City talent scout, introduced much star talent to the world via the waxeries of Regal, De Luxe, and Chess Records. This CD contains two duets by Gayten and Laurie, and 15 Gayten-fronted solos including the stomping "Yeah! Yeah! Yeah!," "Bear Hug," "Kickapoo Juice," and "Back Trackin'." Annie Laurie's warblings add color to six songs, including "My Rough and Ready Man," "Low Down Feeling," and a cover of Jewel King's "3 × 7 = 21." Two undated demos by the legendary Dave Bartholomew are included, plus Roy Brown's frantic "Riding High" and wee-hours blues weeper "Brand New Baby," both previously unissued. Vintage Crescent City R&B, circa 1949–1951. Great pix and extensive notes by Specialty reissue coordinator Billy Vera.

BARBARA GEORGE

New Orleans's singer popular in the '60s, best known for her 1961 hit, "I Know (You Don't Love Me No More)," with backing by the cream of New Orleans's sessionmen.

COLLECTABLES 5141 (CL)

I Know (You Don't Love Me No More)

These dozen tunes recorded for the AFO label showcase George's range from the very soulful "Love" and "Talk about Love" to the cool balladry of "Since I Fell for You" and "Honest I Do."

GERRY and THE PACEMAKERS

Led by Liverpudlian Gerry Marsden, The Pacemakers quickly followed their compatriots The

Beatles in the British invasion of US charts. This group lacked much of the rocking edge of their fellow Liverpudlians opting for a softer, almost M.O.R. approach. They scored hits with their "Merseybeat" sound from 1962–1966, including "Don't Let the Sun Catch You Crying," "How Do You Do It?" (the song producer George Martin wanted The Beatles to release as their first single instead of their own "Love Me Do"), and "Ferry Cross the Mersey." In the late '60s, Gerry had a brief solo singing and acting career before going behind the scenes as a producer and entertainment promoter.

CAPITOL 96093 (CL)
Best of: The Definitive Collection

SEE FOR MILES 95 (L)
The E.P. Collection
Includes many B-sides and rarities along with the hits. How Do You Do It?/I Like It/You'll Never Walk Alone/You've Got What I Like/Don't Let the Sun Catch You Crying.

GEORGIA GIBBS

"Her Nibs, Miss Georgia Gibbs," as Gary Moore dubbed her, was already a famous TV and recording star before rock and roll really took hold. She made a good living covering R&B tunes and, even though her covers were a blatant attempt to popularize raunchy tunes for adult consumption (usually backed by full orchestra), her delivery was so sincere and energetic it's hard not to like her. She's like Louis Prima with his cornball Vegas routine: You try to maintain your cool, but you're still gradually drawn in just like the rubes from Podunkville.

STAR CLUB 6203 (R)
The Rockin' Lady
Gutsy singing and some hot guitar work enliven this set of classic rockers. Great Balls of Fire/I Want You to Be My Baby/Fun Lovin' Baby/Tweedle Dee/Dance with Me Henry/You're Doin' It.

MICKEY GILLEY

Jerry Lee Lewis's "good" cousin, Gilley has performed a mix of material similar to the Killer, from rockabilly to straight country. He's also the owner of the famed Gilley's Bar, where *Urban Cowboy* was filmed.

ASTRA 101 (R)
Lonely Wine
Eighteen tunes from the late '50s and early '60s. These were done a long way from Nashville, so you know they at least have a chance of being good tunes; and they are. Like cousin Jer', Mickey mixes it up in fine fashion, doin' a little country ("Lonely Wine," "I'm to Blame," and "Valley of Tears"), a dash of rock and roll ("I Ain't Goin' Home" and "That's How It's Got to Be"), and a bit of R&B ("Drinkin' Wine Spo-Dee-O-Dee" and "C.C. Rider"), all with the Gilley piano-pounding touch. Most of these tunes were originally issued in small quantities on little labels, and most have never been reissued on LP before.

MINOR 1006 (R)
Rockin' Rollin' Years
Sixteen of Mickey's rarest, straight-ahead, rock-and-roll cuts, sounding very similar to his cuz', Jerry Lee; in fact, his version of "Down the Line" is a ringer for The Killer's. Includes his first rock hit, "I Ain't Bo Diddley," plus tons of rock-and-roll covers done for small Texas labels as well as his rare Dot single, "Call Me Shorty." My Babe/Little Egypt/Slippin' and Sliddin'/Lotta Lovin'.

GLEN GLENN

LA rockabilly performer who made some good recordings for Era in the late '50s.

ACE 057 (R)
The Glen Glenn Story
Thirteen sides recorded for Era in the late '50s. All tracks are also on Ace 403. One Cup of Coffee/If I Had Me a Woman/Blue Jeans and a Boy's Shirt/Everybody's Movin'.

ACE 403 (L)
The Glen Glenn Story/
Everybody's Movin' Again
Reissues Glenn's work of the late '50s, previously available on two Ace LPs, along with two bonus tracks from 1958. The first 15 selections are his complete recordings for Era, featuring some of the highest quality rockabilly you'll ever hear. There are also some exciting live cuts from the same era. In the early '80s, Glenn was enticed into the studio again (accompanied by guitarist Gary Lambert and bass player Guybo Smith, who both played on his Era sessions). The final 14 tunes come from this session, and are a fine testament to a rockabilly cat who never lost the fire. Everybody's Movin'/If I Had Me a Woman/One Cup of Coffee/Shake, Rattle and Roll/Treat Me Nice/

Down the Line/Come On/Flip, Flop and Fly/Rock and Roll Ruby.

SUNJAY 572 (R)

Rockabilly Legend

Exciting LP of rockabilly and rockin' country, all previously unissued tracks except his 1964 Dore single. Side 1 has out-takes of his Era recordings, recorded in 1957–1958, with Guybo Smith on bass and Wynn Stewart on rhythm, including "One Cup of Coffee," "Everybody's Movin'," and "Kathleen." Side 2 includes his rare 1957 TV appearances as host of *Cal's Corral*, includes "Crazy Arms" backed by Fred Maddox.

LESLEY GORE

Sixties chanteuse who scored a string of hits, including her early teeny-bopper ballads ("It's My Party," "Judy's Turn to Cry," and "She's a Fool"), "tuff"-woman sagas ("You Don't Own Me" and "Maybe I Know" [my favorite!]), 1965 bubble-gum classics ("Sunshine, Lollipops, and Rainbows" and "My Town, My Guy and Me"), and 1967 comeback beach sound ("California Nights" and "Summer and Sandy" [another fave]). She also enjoyed a career as an actress, portraying Catwoman's assistant Pussycat on TV's *Batman* show. The Rhino anthology is the ultimate collection of her big hits.

MERCURY 810 370 (CL)

The Golden Hits of Lesley Gore

Eighteen servings of golden Gore, lots of songs about boys and parties and crying and stuff like that. Digitally remastered from the original tapes, in chronological order, and produced by Quincy Jones (fer chrissakes!), so how can you go wrong?

RAVEN 1011 (R)

Start the Party Again

A fine rival to the recent Rhino double set. This single LP has 25 tunes (!) in a beautiful gatefold sleeve, from 1965's "It's My Party" to 1969's title tune, all Mercury singles. The sleeve features a beautiful cartoon cover and great photos, including a tiny one showing Gore on the *Batman* show. Maybe I Know/Judy's Turn to Cry/You Don't Own Me/California Nights/She's a Fool.

RHINO 71496 (C)

The Leslie Gore Anthology

Two-cassette set, with 26 hits, flops, flipsides, and LP cuts. The ultimate Gore collection. It's My Party/Judy's Turn to Cry/You Don't Own Me/Maybe I Know/Sunshine, Lollipops, and Rainbows/Some-

times I Wish I Were a Boy/Start the Party Again/I Don't Wanna Be a Loser.

CHARLIE GRACIE

Excellent Philadelphia-born rock-and-roll singer and outstanding guitarist who recorded for Cameo-Parkway, a label whose main successes were Bobby Rydell and Chubby Checker. As a result, most of Gracie's studio recordings are over-produced, though some good rock and roll sneaks through. For the real picture, check out the amazing live Roller Coaster LP, where his guitar playing is heard to complete advantage.

REVIVAL 3005 (R)

The Very Best

Limited edition featuring 20 fine sides that were issued some years ago on the English London label.

REVIVAL 3016 (R)

Boogie Boogie Blues and Other Rarities

Stopgap collection of small label recordings by Gracie. Sandwiched around a successful stint with Cameo, producing the hit "Butterfly," Charlie tried his hand with labels like Cadillac, Felsted, President, and 20th Century. The best ones here are the ones that keep it simple like "Boogie Boogie Blues," "Head Home Honey," and "Wildwood Boogie," the last two done in a Bill Haley style. He rocks on a twist tune, "Night and Day USA," and the Porky Pig vocals on "W-Wow" are kind of fun. All the rest are pop outings, with his Buddy Holly-ish version of "Makin' Whoopee" being the most interesting.

ROLLER COASTER 2005 (R)

Live at the Stockton Globe

Excellent 1957 live recording from England. Gracie performs a mixture of originals and covers, including a great version of "Guitar Boogie." Long Tall Sally/Tutti Frutti/Hound Dog.

YEAH 003 (R)
Rockin' Italy

Move over Louis Prima, Philly padrone Gracie went over to the old country in 1991 and cut this LP with an Italian rock and roll band, The Jumpin' Shoes. He puts on the kind of show that would've gone down well at The Latin Casino. He does a few hits like "Fabulous," "I Love You So Much," and, of course, "Butterfly," but a large part of this set is devoted to Prima impersonations on "Caldonia," "Darktown Strutters Ball," "Sheik of Araby," and the "Just a Gigolo"/"I Ain't Got Nobody" medley! For fanatics only.

GERRY GRANAHAN

Granahan was a ball of energy during the rock and roll years, forming popular groups like The Fireflies and Dickie Doo and The Don'ts, singing solo and duet, and producing top acts. Most of his work was aimed at the pop charts, but it wasn't all fluff.

HYDRA 7712 (R)
Kingsize Hits

Sixteen of Granahan's '50s and '60s recordings done for Sunbeam, Swan, Canadian American, Gone, Ribbon, and his own Caprice label. Great teen-oriented rock and roll, including the wacky "Nee Nee Na Na Nu Nu." Stella Got a Fella/King Size/Baby Wait/No Chemise Please/Dance Girl Dance.

DOBIE GRAY

Soul singer from Texas best known for his catchy hit "The 'In' Crowd" recorded for Charger in 1965. He had further minor hits in the '70s for a number of labels in a rock/soul vein.

COLLECTABLES 5072 (CL)
The "In" Crowders

Thirteen tracks from the '60s. The "In" Crowd/Monkey Jerk/Be a Man/Out on the Floor/Mr. Engineer/Broken in Two/Feelin' in My Heart.

RUDY GRAYZELL

Late '50s rockabilly artist who recorded for Starday, Sun, and Award, among other smaller labels.

STARDAY 1321 (R)
Let's Get Wild

Lots of very rare, flat-out rockabilly, with a few helpings of teen jive and straight country, taken from Rudy's three most important labels: his 1957–1958 Starday recordings (some reissued on Mercury), including the classic "Ducktail," "Ji-Ga-Lee-Ga," "The

Moon Is Up," and the title tune; his 1958 Sun sessions, including his classic "Judy" heard in its wild rockabilly version as well as a boogie-ish alternate that was not released until the '70s; and his 1959 Award tracks, including "The FBI Story" and "You'll Be Mine."

THE GREAT GATES

Ed White (aka The Great Gates) was an obscure R&B star of the late '40s and early '50s.

KRAZY KAT 7435 (R)
West Coast R&B

Extremely obscure sides recorded for six independent labels between 1949–1952. Bootin' tenor sax player Marvin Phillips can be heard blasting away on "Rocking Time," "Ain't Got No Money," and "Central Rocks." Ace guitar whiz Jesse Ervin shows us some fancy finger work on "Come Back Home," "Change Your Ways," and "Home Town Boy," while Richard Lewis throws in some neat piano fills, Vic Malone some stomping bass, and Earl Brown lays down some solid drumming. For those who like their R&B solid, mean, ragged, and dirty. Fine sleeve notes and good remastered sound from rare 78s.

AL GREEN

Probably the finest soul singer of the '70s. Green's records have a distinct sound due to the fine house band at producer Willie Mitchell's Hi label, that included former Booker T and the MGs's drummer Al Jackson. A 1974 incident in which a former girlfriend poured boiling grits on him and subsequently shot herself changed the direction of both Green's life and career. He bought a church and became a minister, although he still issued pop LPs. In 1979, he fell off a stage and, considering this a warning, went into the ministry full-time, recording for Myrrh, a religious label. In the '80s, however, he returned to performing pop material.

HI (UK) 111 (L)
I'm Still in Love with You/Call Me

A double play of Rev. Green's early '70s efforts. *I'm Still in Love with You* (Hi 32074, 1972) has ten songs, including the memorable title track, a jubilant "Look What You Done for Me," Roy Orbison's "Pretty Woman," a cover of "For the Good Times," and my personal, Number 1 Green favorite, the churning long version of "Love and Happiness." *Call Me* (Hi 32077, 1973) unfolds in much the same way, featuring a couple of hits with the title tune and "Here I Am," two covers in the country vein in "I'm So Lonesome I

Could Cry" and "Funny How Time Slips Away," the prophetic "Jesus Is Waiting," and five more.

HI (UK) 113 (L)
Livin' for You/Al Green Explores Your Mind

Two LPs on one CD, giving us 18 soulful cuts. 1973's *Livin'* (originally Hi 32082) delivers the smooth title track and "Free at Last," "Let's Get Married," "Unchained Melody," and "My God Is Real." *Explores* (Hi 32087) has the hits "Sha-La-La" and "Take Me to the River."

HI (UK) 119 (L)
Have a Good Time/The Belle Album

1976's *Have a Good Time* features the usual horn, rhythm, and string sections used by the Hi label. Not quite up to the quality of his early '70s material, it nevertheless contains some great performances. "Keep Me Cryin'" is the hit (Number 4 on the R&B charts), but the filler here is worth hearing too. With 1977's *The Belle Album* (originally Hi 6004), Green began writing and producing his own songs in his own studio, as well as playing lead guitar. The result is a classic. Both "Belle" and "I Feel Good" made the R&B and pop charts, but neither has the power of the gospel-fueled "Loving You." *The Belle Album* draws its energy from embracing the religious-sexual dualism that Marvin Gaye spent the better part of his career struggling with.

MCA 42308 (CL)
Love Ritual: Rare and Previously Unreleased 1968–1976

Ten cuts that strike me as little more than rejected album filler. Although Green sings well, the choice of material does not rise above standard Hi-funk, although some of the arrangements are clever. Standouts are an unremixed "Ride Sally Ride" of convincingly high octane and a good, solid, personalized version of The Beatles's "I Want to Hold Your Hand."

MOTOWN 5285 (CL)
Full of Fire

Reissue of Hi 32097 from 1976, one of Al's last good ones. Nine tracks. Glory Glory/Let It Shine/Together Again/There's No Way.

MOTOWN 5286 (CL)
Call Me

MOTOWN 5290 (CL)
Let's Stay Together

Reissue of Hi 32070 from 1972. Nine tracks, with much duplication with other releases.

MOTOWN 5318 (CL)
The Belle Album

GARLAND GREEN

Mississippi-born soulster who relocated to Chicago during his high-school years. He was discovered by Argia B. Collins, who owned a slew of Chicago-area ribs houses and marketed Mambo Bar-B-Que Sauce. Collins sponsored Green's music training at the classy Chicago Conservatory. The owners of the Gamma/Giant labels heard Green perform at a South Side club, and together they produced his one mainstream hit, 1969's "Jealous Kind of Fella," released nationally by Uni. Green continued to score minor hits on the R&B charts through 1983.

KENT (UK) 097 (R)
The Spring Sides

VERNON GREEN and THE MEDALLIONS

Fairly obscure LA doo-wop group who had a minor hit in 1954 for Dootsie Williams's Dooto label with "The Letter" and one of the best R&B "car" songs, "Buick '59." The original group featured Green on lead with Andrew Blue (ten), Randolph Bryant (bar), and Ira Foley (b). The local success of "Buick '59" led them to record a number of other car songs like "Speedin'" and "Coupe de Ville." Ironically, Green was seriously injured in an automobile accident in the '60s! Different Medallions recorded sporadically through 1957 and again in 1959 and 1962.

COLLECTABLES 5047 (RCL)
Golden Classics

Twelve Dooto sides. The Letter/Dear Darling/Give Me the Right/Buick '59/Don't Shoot/Unseen/My Mary Lou.

BIG JOHN GREER

Greer was a heavyweight singer and sax player at RCA Victor and its Groove subsidiary in the early '50s. His singing with the Lucky Millinder band follows the pattern of other blues shouters like Roy Brown and Wynonie Harris. Unfortunately, his recorded output is divided between hot R&B and schmaltzy dinner-club standards.

BEAR FAMILY 15554 (L)
Rockin' with Big John

The long-gone Official LP introduced a lot of us to Big John Greer; now we have a three-CD set to give us a better perspective. Over several 1949 sessions, Greer belts out some early rockin' numbers like "Drinkin' Wine Spo-Dee-O-Dee" and "Rockin' with Big John," but there is also already evidence of his crooning style that would become prevalent in his later years. In fact, about half of the 72 tunes here fall into the pop-schlock category. But hey, that still leaves quite a few rockin' R&B tunes like "I'll Never Let You Go," "I'm the Fat Man," "Play Me Some Loud Music," and "Come Back Maybelline." There are also some powerful blues tunes like "Don't Worry about It" and "Confusion Blues" with Greer bellowing the blues like a master. The sessions really start to heat up when Mickey "Guitar" Baker joins the fray in 1953. The later sessions find Big John mostly just exercising his mighty lungs, with the sax chores handed over to the awesome Sam "The Man" Taylor. One word of warning: Besides the intermingling of dreck and real R&B, the CDs aren't programmed chronologically, so it's a real pain to follow the discography in the otherwise nifty booklet.

BUCK GRIFFIN

This Texan, born in 1923, started off doing country boogie and western swing, but his strong voice and great singing ability made him a natural for the nascent rock market.

DOMINO 1007 (R)
The Party

Ol' Buck showed up years ago on one of the first, long out-of-print rockabilly compilations, featuring MGM performances, but he hasn't been featured very much since then. Now there's an entire LP devoted to a cat who was rockin' before folks had ever heard of rockabilly. Just about all of the good stuff is here, like "The Party," "Bawlin' and Squallin'," "Pretty Lou," "Stutterin' Papa," and "First Man to Stand on the Moon." Nineteen tracks in all, done in a variety of styles; the overall standard is excellent.

TINY GRIMES and HIS ROCKIN' HIGHLANDERS

Inventive four-string guitarist who led a hot R&B/blues outfit featuring many instrumental greats plus vocals by Screamin' Jay Hawkins on some early sides. Tiny was one of the most distinctive and accomplished R&B guitarists, with a forceful horn-like approach similar to T-Bone Walker's but even more inventive and fluid.

BLACK AND BLUE 59.067 (L)
Some Groovy Fours

This is a real treat, featuring 13 hard-swingin' instrumentals, mostly reissued from two Black and Blue LPs recorded in the early '70s. The star-studded cast (including Lloyd Glenn, Jay McShann, Arnett Cobb, and Panama Francis) keep things cooking from beginning to end, and Tiny's distinctive four-string guitar is as potent and inventive as ever. Includes three unreleased cuts, plus "Everyday I Have the Blues" and "Lester Leaps In" among the predominantly original material. Highly recommended.

KRAZY KAT 01 (L)
Tiny Grimes and His Rockin' Highlanders

Highlights from Tiny Grimes's Gotham recordings (issued on Krazy Kat LPs 804 [now unavailable], 817, and 821) are brought forth on this 20-track CD. Sadly the early Screamin' Jay Hawkins cuts are not included, but Gotham vocalists J.B. Summers, George Grant, and Claudine Clark all make appearances, backed up by Tiny, the Rockin' Highlanders, and tenor man Red Prysock (who became an ex-Highlander soon after kilts became the band's standard outfit). The sound on disc is greatly improved, due to the use of master tapes and re-equalization. Look no further if you're after jumpin' early R&B with some of the finest solos and swinging-est East Coast grooves ever heard.

KRAZY KAT 817 (R)
Tiny Grimes and His Rocking Highlanders, Vol. 2

The second LP collection of Tiny's frantic Gotham sides from the early '50s, all instrumentals except for a band vocal on "Ho Ho Ho," one of only four previously released tunes on this set (the others are "Call of the Wild," "Pert Skirt," and "1626 Boogie"). There are four tunes never before issued in any form, including two takes of "Bananas," and hot, never-before-issued alternate takes of four tunes including "Call of the Wild" and "Frankie and Johnny Boogie." Lots of great John Hardee tenor sax.

KRAZY KAT 821 (R)
Tiny Grimes and Friends

Fourteen cuts culled from Gotham's vaults, five previously unreleased and all ostensibly featuring Tiny Grimes. Although the cream of Tiny's recordings for Gotham have already been reissued, this collection still has its moments. Grimes's presence on most of the cuts is questionable at best but he turns in a raucous instrumental and some driving accompaniment on tracks by J.B. Summers and Haji Baba. The fine track by The Cats and the Fiddle (a late incarnation) and three titles by The Dixieaires feature some fine vocals and sax and guitar solos. The collection is rounded out by two tracks by Johnny Davis, drummer for The Cats and the Fiddle, and a cut by the unknown Lionel Robinson.

ORIGINAL JAZZ CLASSICS 191 (RC)

Callin' the Blues

Grimes, Eddie "Lockjaw" Davis, J.C. Higginbotham, and Ray Bryant stretch out on four long blues, including Tiny's tribute to Charlie Christian on "Airmail Special." Fine bluesy playing all around; this remains one of the best Tiny Grimes albums ever.

WHISKEY, WOMEN AND ... 706 (R)

Tiny Grimes and His Rocking Highlanders

Unlike the Krazy Kat (Gotham) reissues, this set concentrates mainly on a more simplified blues and jazz style, as opposed to straight honking, and a more "crazed," effusive type of R&B. Side 1 features the talents of John Hardee or Red Prysock on tenor saxes and a great unidentified guitarist. Side 2 highlights the fine skill of Jimmy Saunders on piano. Extensive sleeve notes and a scatter of rare pix.

BILL HALEY and THE COMETS

The chubby 30-year-old Haley hardly looked the part of teen idol, but he was to become a founding father of rock and roll. He spent most of his life in C&W music, starting in 1948 with The Down Homers, The Saddlemen, and The Four Aces of Western Swing. In 1952, he signed with Essex, changing the name of his band to Bill Haley and Haley's Comets, and finally to just The Comets. He started covering R&B hits, including "Rocket 88" and "Rock the Joint" before recording an original "Crazy Man Crazy," a song some claim is the first rock and roll recording. In 1954, he signed with Decca, releasing "Rock around the Clock," which bombed. In 1955, his cover of "Shake, Rattle and Roll" was a hit, and the rerelease of "Rock around the Clock" (thanks to its inclusion in the film *Blackboard Jungle*), started the first rock riots. A movie was soon built around the song; teens at its showings would tear up the theater seats.

Haley's music was good, featuring Rudy Pompeli on sax and Franny Beecher on guitar, and he racked up a lot of hits. However, three key members of the band split in 1955 to form The Jodimars, and Haley's overexposure on stage and screen showed him to be a pudgy, balding man rather than a young rebellious rocker. The

hits stopped coming except in Europe where he remained a hero. He spent the '60s rerecording his hits for Roulette and Warner Bros. In 1969, he became the hit of the Richard Nader Rock Revival Shows and, when that died down, he moved to Mexico, releasing some LPs there. Psychological problems ended his performing career, and he died in relative obscurity in 1981.

Most of Haley's Essex material is available on Roller Coaster 2009. His Decca material is available as a whole for you completists on a Bear Family box, with the MCA set being all you would really need.

AMBASSADOR 98100 (R)

Rarities

This is from perhaps Bill's most dire period, the early '70s, when he moved to Mexico mainly to do twist records for the Latin market. Twenty tunes here, some in Spanish, plus a duet with Caterina Valente ("Viva La Rock and Roll"), "Adios Marquita Linda" from a German film, and a live version of "Hot Dog Buddy Buddy." Let the Good Times Roll, Creole/The Spanish Twist/Chick Safari.

BEAR FAMILY 15068/5 (R)

Rockin' Rollin' Bill Haley

Five-LP box set featuring all of Haley's recordings made for U.S. Decca between 1956–1959 plus two from 1964. There are 102 performances in all, a few never before issued. Each album comes in a picture sleeve with extensive notes by Haley expert Chris Gardner and the box includes a complete discography of his Decca sessions.

BEAR FAMILY 15506 (L)

The Decca Years and More

Five-CD box set. This set includes all the tracks on Bear family's LP box, newly remastered, plus alternate takes, a complete January 1959 session, two songs from the movie *Rock around the Clock* with Caterina Valente, and two previously unissued demos. Also comes with a new, extensively annotated booklet.

GNP 2077 (RC)

Rock and Roll

1970s recordings cut in Nashville. I'm Walkin'/High-Heel Sneakers/Blue Suede Shoes/Tossin' and Turnin'/Flip Flop and Fly/C.C. Rider.

✪ MCA 5539 (L)

From the Original Master Tapes

This is it! The essential Bill Haley collection, including 20 of his all-time greats, all digitally remastered from the original studio tapes. Rock around the Clock/

Shake, Rattle and Roll/See You Later Alligator/Rip It Up/Don't Knock the Rock.

ROLLER COASTER 3001 (L)

Rock the Joint

Twenty-three fine Essex sides from the early '50s. Tracks have been newly remastered from original master tapes where available, and the package includes an extensively annotated booklet with discography of Bill's Essex sessions. Rocket 88/Live It Up/Fractured/Crazy Man Crazy/Green Tree Boogie/Sundown Boogie/Rock the Joint.

SEQUEL 600 (L)

Bill Haley's Rock and Roll Scrapbook: Live!

Reissue of live recordings from around 1970 originally on the Kama Sutra label. Bill and the boys reprise some of his most famous songs. Rock-a-Beatin' Boogie/Razzle Dazzle/See You Later Alligator/Shake, Rattle and Roll/Crazy Man Crazy/Rock around the Clock.

ROY HALL

Honky-tonk piano player and country singer known as "The Hound." He first recorded in 1945 with Fortune, having a minor hit with "Dirty Boogie." He later opened a honky-tonk in Nashville, playing piano in Webb Pierce's band. He hired Jerry Lee Lewis as house pianist for his bar before The Killer made it big. In 1955, he wrote (under the pseudonym Sunny David to escape income tax) "Whole Lotta Shakin' Goin' On," recorded by Big Maybelle, Hall himself for Decca, and, of course, Jerry Lee who made it a massive hit. Hall died in 1984.

ROCK AND COUNTRY 1008 (R)

Boogie Rockabilly

Fourteen fine '50s recordings by this excellent rockabilly and rockin' country singer. Some cuts have been anthologized elsewhere, but it's good to have a whole album of his sides. Don't Stop Now/Dig that Boogie/Bed Spring Motel/Offbeat Boogie/All by Myself.

ROY HAMILTON

Interesting Georgia singer who had operatic and classical voice training before becoming a gospel singer. He subsequently became a pop singer, recording for Epic, and drew on both his operatic and gospel backgrounds to produce emotionally charged renditions of pop standards like "You'll Never Walk Alone" and "Unchained Melody,"

as well as more driving R&B songs like "Don't Let Go" and 1961's "You Can Have Her," his last hit. He drifted from label to label in the '60s, and died of a heart attack in 1969 at the age of 40.

COLLECTABLES 5150 (CL)

Golden Classics

Twelve tracks, including all his biggest hits. Don't Let Go/Hurt/I Believe/Since I Fell for You/Ebb Tide/You're Gonna Need Magic/You Can Have Her.

THE HARPTONES

Classic New York doo-woppers led by tenor Willie Winfield, along with Nicky Clark (lead and ten), Bill Dempsey (2nd ten), Dicey Galloway (bar), and Bill Brown (b); pianist Raoul Cita provided accompaniment and occasionally sang tenor and baritone parts. They recorded two classics, "A Sunday Kind of Love" for Bruce in 1953 and "Life Is but a Dream" for Paradise in 1954. The Harptones conveyed a smooth, pop-oriented, polished style much revered by East Coast doo-wop fans. While at Bruce, they recorded the original version of "Since I Fell for You," later a hit for Lenny Welch. Winfield continued to lead The Harptones through the early '80s, releasing some fine sides in 1982 for Ambient Sound. If you like The Five Keys, you'll like The Harptones.

COLLECTABLES 5401 (CL)

The Goldner Recordings 1956–1957

Fourteen tracks recorded for George Goldner, first reissued on Murray Hill 1098. All you ever wanted to hear by this legendary street-corner quintet, excluding the ever popular "Sunday Kind of Love," "Life Is but a Dream," and "My Memories of You." Their unique treatment of romantic ballads like "The Masquerade Is Over" and "The Shrine of St. Cecelia" thrilled Apollo Theater audiences in 1957. Raoul Cita, the group's pianist and arranger, deserves much of the credit for the success of their sound. For those who like the sweet and mellow.

RELIC 5001 (R)

The Harptones

Fourteen songs including "Sunday Kind of Love." Shrine of St. Celilia/Ooo Wee Baby/Since I Fell for You/Three Wishes.

RELIC 5003 (R)
The Harptones, Vol. 2
Sixteen songs. I Remember/Mambo Boogie/Sunset/ Gimme Some/Hep Teenager.

✪ RELIC 7021 (L)
Sunday Kind of Love
Twenty cuts, including a live tape from a 1955 concert; duplicates Relic LPs 5001 and 5003. Exhaustive sleeve notes by Don Fileti plus rare pix and trade journal clips. Since I Fell for You/I Almost Lost My Mind/Loving a Girl Like You/Why Should I Love You.

WEE WILLIE HARRIS

In 1957, mild-mannered jazz pianist/singer Charlie Harris was changed overnight into Wee Willie Harris, England's wildest rocker, complete with long pink hair and bright red jacket, later exchanged for a leopard-skin loin-cloth.

ACE 178 (R)
Wee Willie Harris Goes Ape
Includes a wild, cover hit of Neil Sedaka's "I Go Ape," along with his best Decca sides (1957–1960) including Bobby Rydell's "Wild One," "No Chemise Please," and "Love Bug Crawl." For contrast, there's a pre-rock version of "Riot in Cell Block Number 9" with just Wee Willie and his pumpin' piano, and even a 1952 acetate of young Charlie Harris doing "Frankie and Johnny." Fold-out cover with biography and lots of great photos, though none in color.

JET HARRIS and TONY MEEHAN

Bassist and drummer for The Shadows.

DERAM 820 634 (L)
Diamonds and Other Gems
Twenty singles waxed between 1962–1964. Diamonds/Hully Gully/Applejack/The Man with the Golden Arm/Some People.

COUNT "RED" HASTINGS

Lowell Hastings spent most of his years as a sideman and sessionman, including long stints with Earl Bostic, Louis Jordan (on X and Aladdin), as well as playing his big tenor sax on dozens of King/De Luxe sides in the late '50s. He recorded two sessions under his own name.

KRAZY KAT 823 (R)
Count "Red" Hastings
Big sax sound from the Gotham vaults. Ten of the 14 tracks are from Hastings's sessions done under his own

name, one each in 1948 and 1950, including his hits "Begin the Beguine" and "Sugar Cane," plus never-before-issued alternates of "Patches" and "Miner in the Diner." The set is completed by two tracks each by tenorman Danny Turner and unknown saxman Eddie Woodland. Turner was heard previously on Krazy Kat/Gotham with Panama Francis's All Stars, and has been a member of the Basie Orchestra since 1975.

DALE HAWKINS

Excellent Louisiana-born rockabilly performer who had a string of hits for Checker in 1957–1959, including "La-Do-Da-Da," a cover of Little Walter's "My Babe," and his own composition, "Susie Q." Accompanying guitarists included Scotty Moore, James Burton, and Roy Buchanan. Hawkins later moved to Texas and became a producer, having hits with The Five Americans ("Western Union"), Jay and Robin ("Do It Again Just a Little Bit Slower"), and Bruce Channel ("Hey Baby").

ARGO 1429 (R)
Oh! Susie Q
Exact reproduction of Dale's first LP from 1958, featuring 12 classic sides. Susie Q/Juanita/Little Pig/Baby Baby/Take My Heart/See You Soon Baboon.

RONNIE HAWKINS

Veteran Arkansas-born rockabilly star who moved to Canada after serving in the US army in 1958. He formed an incredible backup band, The Hawks, who later became known as The Band after splitting with Hawkins. Hawkins had a string of hits on Roulette including covers of Young Jessie's "Mary Lou" and Chuck Berry's "30 Days" that he called "Forty Days." In 1963, he had a Canadian hit with a cover of "Who Do You Love" and in 1970 scored again with a cover of "Down in the Alley." He performed in The Band's farewell concert, *The Last Waltz*, and had a cameo in the Hollywood megaflop, *Heaven's Gate*. His original classics have been reissued by Rhino and Star Club.

PROVOGUE 70242 (L)
Hello Again ... Mary Lou
Comeback bid by this rockabilly legend. Ronnie's remake of "Mary Lou" sounds good, but it takes more than an old hit and a good lookin' cover model to make

it these days. The rest of the tracks are just average country cowpie-kickers and tired rock efforts.

⚙ RHINO 70966 (CL)

The Best of Ronnie Hawkins and The Hawks

Seventeen Roulette sides (14 on cassette) recorded between 1959–1963, with backup by Robbie Robertson, Levon Helm, Richard Manuel, and other soon-to-be members of The Band. Includes one Cotillion single from 1970 ("Down in the Alley" with Duane Allman). Forty Days/Mary Lou/Come Love/Bo Diddley/Wild Little Willy.

SILVER EAGLE 10873 (L)

Rock and Roll Favorites

Recent recordings. Hawkins is still keeping that rock-and-roll torch burnin'! That's Alright Mama/Chuck Berry Medley/Bony Moronie/Matchbox/Dizzy Miss Lizzy/Bo Diddley.

STAR CLUB 8032 (R)

The Rockin' Rebel

Generous 18-track collection of Ronnie's fabulous early recordings (1959–1963). Duplicates some of the tracks on the Rhino release. There are some real gems in this batch, not to mention Ronnie's more familiar rockers. Essential, I'd say. Need Your Lovin'/Hayride/Horace/Hey Boba Lou/Honey Love/Southern Love/Someone Like You/The Ballad of Caryl Chessman/Forty Days/Mary Lou/Wild Little Willie/Red Hot.

SCREAMIN' JAY HAWKINS

One of the great, eccentric, wild men of rock who popped out of a coffin to open his stage show and had a flaming skull named Henry. He recorded the classic "I Put a Spell on You" while dead drunk (as was the entire studio band!), earning him his originally unwanted, wild reputation. However, he played it to the hilt, and is still touring to ecstatic response. His great Okeh sessions have been reissued by Edsel, Epic, and Red Lightnin'.

BEAR FAMILY 15530 (L)

Spellbound 1955–1974

Double CD of Screamin' Jay rantings recorded for Wing, Decca, Philips, and RCA. With the exception of eight cuts from 1955, most of these 48 tracks are pretty silly (wait: green fluorescent bats begin to flutter menacingly as I quickly proclaim my admiration for Hawkins's demented early Okeh and Gotham sides) and 24 of these, originally on two Philips LPs, are already available on Edsel 252. Besides that, the tracks are in some sort of wacky time-traveling order. The version of "I Put a Spell on You" is not the original as

claimed, not to mention the retread of "You Put the Spell On Me." The 1955 sessions, recorded for Mercury/Wing with the Leroy Kirkland band, are generally good R&B efforts, yielding the classic "She Put the Whamee on Me." The rest is for collectors only (although the booklet is top-notch).

CHARLY 163 (L)

Real Life

Equivalent to Charly LP 1205; recorded in France 1983.

CHARLY 181 (L)

I Put a Spell on You

Reissue of Charly LP, with new versions of title track and "Itty Bitty Pretty One," along with other recent recordings. With two non-LP cuts: "What Good Is It, Pt. 2" and "Same Damn Thing."

EDSEL 104 (RCL)

Frenzy

Fourteen wild sides recorded for Okeh in the mid-to-late '50s. Includes the classic "I Put a Spell on You," a few "straight" tunes ("I Love Paris" and "Deep Purple"), plus lots of insanity. Alligator Wine/Little Demon/Yellow Coat.

EDSEL 252 (RL)

Feast of the Mau Mau

The wild, weird fruits of Screamin' Jay's '60s comeback in one package. This two-LP set reissues both of Jay's 1969 Philips LPs. The first, *What That Is* (Philips 600-319), was recorded live in North Hollywood with a band that included Plas Johnson, Earl Palmer, Herb Ellis, and even Graham Bond, performing such classics as "Feast of the Mau Mau," "Stone Crazy," and "What That Is," a straight gospel tune "Ask Him," and that immortal blues about REAL PAIN, "Constipation Blues." The second LP, *Is in Your Mind,* is a bit (only a bit) more "normal" studio session with Huey P. Meaux, including some fine covers of Fats Domino's "Please Don't Leave Me" and "Ain't Nobody's Business," along with such fine filth as "I Wanta Know

What You Do Down There" and "Bite It" (to the tune of The Mar-Key's "Last Night").

EPIC 47933 (CL)

Cowfingers and Mosquito Pie

Basically a reissue of Jay's classic *At Home with* LP (Epic 3448, 1957) with some welcome additions. We not only get the drunken blaster "I Put a Spell on You" but enough Hawkins mayhem to raise the dead on "Little Demon," the surrealistic tale of Screamin' Jay's "Yellow Coat" (with amazing lyrics), a campy pseudo-Oriental "Hong Kong," and nutty versions of "I Love Paris" and "Take Me Back to My Boots and Saddle." Two Okeh singles are included: "Alligator Wine" b/w "There's Something Wrong with You" and "Frenzy" and its flipside. And if that ain't enough to have you reaching for a glass of "bulldog spine wine," how about four prime alternate takes including "I Put a Spell on You" and "Alligator Wine"? Like snowflakes, no two Screamin' Jay screams are the same.

EVIDENCE 26003 (L)

Live and Crazy

The title tells you all you need to know here. Recorded live in Paris in 1988 before an enthusiastic crowd, Jay energetically performs his favorites, plus hoary rock standards like "Tutti Frutti," "Lawdy Miss Clawdy," and "Ain't That a Shame." Good sound quality. The Whammy/Yellow Coat/Alligator Wine/I Put a Spell on You/Constipation Blues.

52 RUE EST 023 (L)

The Night and Day of

A dozen tunes, representing the calmer side of Hawkins's career, ranging from Cole Porter's moody standard, "Night and Day" to uptempo R&B jumpers from "I Wanna Know," "Your Kind of Love," and "Alright, O.K., You Win," and a smattering of blues numbers. Jay's vocals are rich and powerful throughout. No liner notes, but a nice gap filler for his screamin' fans.

RED LIGHTNIN' 0075 (L)

Screamin' the Blues

CD issue of Red Lightnin' 0025 featuring 16 tracks recorded between 1953–1967 by this wild performer. His "I Hear Voices" must rank as one of the most demented records ever!

RHINO 70556 (CL)

Black Music for White People

The title and cover photo of Screamin' Jay's first new American recording in 15 years would give the KKK a fit, promising the sort of outrageous doin's that get Hawkins fans drooling in a hurry. Unfortunately, on the inside we get the same old mixed bag: some corny bar-band fare ("Is You Is or Is You Ain't My Baby," "I Hear You Knockin'," and "I Feel Alright"), a couple of smutty winky-nudgy numbers ("I Want Your Body"

and a completely over the top "Strokin'"), plus the zillionth version of "I Put a Spell on You." This time around, "Spell" gets a hip-hop treatment, with a guest rapper; it's weird but it works! "Ol' Man River" is the real showstopper, a bewildering blast of light opera, R&B, and free jazz! Is this what white people like? I guess we'll see.

⊗ RHINO 70947 (CL)

Voodoo Jive

Seventeen songs (14 on cassette), including nine of his Okeh sides from 1956–1957, featuring, of course, his all-time classic "I Put a Spell on You." There are two songs from his 1962 Enrica session, including the totally demented "I Hear Voices," and six from his 1969 Philips session featuring his "Constipation Blues," which is funny the first time you hear it, but after that, well ...

SJH 71829 (L)

From Grand and Gotham

The juiciest grab bag of Hawkins obscurities to emerge since Official 6062 (in print for only a few minutes back in '89). Although short—just one half-hour long—we get ten potent musical reasons why Hawkins should have been committed as soon as he first faced a microphone on Tiny Grimes's Gotham cuts "Why Did You Waste My Time," "Coronation Jump," and "No Hug No Kiss," presented here with alternates. "Why" and "No Hug" have appeared on various Krazy Kat reissues, as well as on Official, where the lucky few also heard the 1955 Grand label 45-rpm sides "Take Me Back" b/w "I Is." Other Grand sides here include the earliest "I Put a Spell on You" (previously on Collectables 1068), and "Pauline" and "$10,000 Lincoln" in their released versions and in previously unissued alternates. It's a must-have.

MICKY HAWKS

Wild rockin' pianist and singer.

SUNJAY 583 (R)

Bip Bop Boom

Finally, there's an entire LP devoted to Micky Hawks. His quartet of Profile monsters are here ("Bip Bop Boom," "Screamin' Mimi Jeanie," "Hidi Hidi Hidi," and "Cotton Pickin'"), along with two B-sides. There's an infectious "Gonna Dance Tonight, Pts. 1 and 2" (Lance 005 from 1961) with Moon Mullican singing and playing sax (!) and Hawks playing piano. There are a couple of enjoyable and danceable blue-eyed soul workouts from 1968 released as Piedmont 2044. Eight tracks on Side 2 were recorded in Georgia in 1971, but it sounds like Micky was auditioning for the New Orleans Jazz and Heritage Festival, doing "Ya Ya," "Blueberry Hill," and "Hello Josephine." The last two cuts are from 1989, but Hawks was still rockin' on "Fifties Girls" and "Jumpin' for Joy." Nice collection.

ROY HEAD

Fine Texas singer who started working the clubs in the late '50s with a hard driving blend of rock and roll and R&B. In 1965, he hit it big with the R&B stomper "Treat Her Right" recorded for Backbeat. His subsequent recordings, though fine, achieved only moderate success and by the mid-'70s he had switched to country, achieving moderate success as a country performer through the mid-'80s.

BEAR FAMILY 15307 (R)
Treat Her Right
1965 Scepter and Backbeat recordings, including the big title hit and "One More Time," "Get Back," "Just a Little Bit," and "The Feeling's Gone." There are also six numbers from the mid-'70s recorded for the Crazy Cajun label that are a bit overblown perhaps, but dynamite R&B just the same. Plus, there's a previously unissued take of "Bring It to Jerome." And wait 'til you check out the liner notes by Colin Escott. Roy, my man, ol' Jerry Lee ain't got nothin' on you in the hell-raisin' department.

P-VINE 1610 (L)
Singin' Texas Rhythm and Blues
OK all you Roy Head fans (you know who you are), here's your digital dream come true, a total of 17 cuts including two versions of "Baby Let Me Kiss You Just One More Time" and of course the original version of the hit "Treat Her Right." Bring It to Jerome/Rock Me Baby/Money/Before You Accuse Me.

THE HEARTBEATS

Jamaica, Queens-based vocal group led by James "Shep" Sheppard from 1955–1960 who began their recording career for Hull in 1956, after a single release on Network in 1955. Their wistful "A Thousand Miles Away" written by Shep about his girlfriend who had moved to Texas was a big hit in late 1956 on Rama. They recorded for Rama, Gee, and Roulette over the next couple of years, but disbanded in 1959. In 1961, Shep formed a new group—Shep and The Limelites—scoring a hit with "Daddy's Home," which was a sort-of sequel to "A Thousand Miles Away."

RHINO 70952 (CL)
The Best of The Heartbeats
Fourteen-track cassette or 20-track CD of their best-known songs including sides by Shep and The Limelites. A Thousand Miles Away/Down on My Knees/Crazy for You/Daddy's Home/Ready for Your Love.

CLARENCE "FROGMAN" HENRY

New Orleans vocalist who used three distinctive singing voices: his normal voice; a high falsetto shriek; and a deep voice that he created by inhaling and singing at the same time, earning him the "Frogman" nickname. He started in 1955 as a pianist with Bobby Mitchell and scored his first hit on the Chess subsidiary Argo with "Ain't Got No Home." After five hitless years, he had a string of hits on Argo produced by Allen Toussaint including "You Always Hurt the One You Love" and Bobby Charles's "(I Don't Know Why I Love You) But I Do."

BEAR FAMILY 15278 (R)
Little Green Frog
Excellent collection of 1964–1965 recordings produced by Huey Meaux in Shreveport, New Orleans, and Pasadena, TX. Fourteen cuts, most New Orleans-ized versions of country tunes. Ten were previously released on five singles for Parrot including "Have You Ever Been Lonely," Jimmy Donley's "Think It Over," "Tore Up over You," the title tune, and even a remake of "Ain't Got No Home." Four never-issued tracks are also featured, including "Heartaches by the Number" and "Cheatin' Traces."

BEN HEWITT

New York rockabilly performer who recorded some fine sides for Mercury from 1958–1959. When they were reissued by Bear Family in 1984, Hewitt was coaxed out of retirement to record some new LPs and he toured England.

BEAR FAMILY 15150 (R)
They Would Call Me Elvis
Twelve excellent sides, primarily uptempo songs, featuring some fine guitar by Ray Ethier. Includes three previously unissued tracks and two fine instrumentals by Ethier. Full discographical information, beautiful photos, and an interview with Hewitt are all packaged in an attractive gatefold sleeve.

BEAR FAMILY 15187 (R)
Good Times and Some Mighty Fine Rock and Roll

These sides were recorded in Cardiff, Wales on May 20-22, 1985 during Hewitt's "comeback" tour with members of British rockabilly revival bands Nervous Breakdown and Breathless. All 11 tunes are new Hewitt originals. Title tune is subtitled "Some Auto Bio 'Billy Blues." A Little Elfin Jive/Buster Brown's Got the Blues/Shirley Vee.

HYDRA 7704 (R)
Tore Up!

Fine LP recorded in 1986 in Munich with backing by Munich's Catlegs plus saxist Hannes Wollmann from The Ryan Clan and Christian Christl (aka The Bavarian Boogie Woogie Man) on piano. Unlike other LPs recorded by "marginal US rockabilly artists with a European group" that usually feature hopeless retreads of "Blue Suede Shoes" and "Hound Dog," the dozen tunes here contain only three covers, "Flip Flop and Fly," "Bop a Lena" and the title tune, with nine Hewitt originals. To an Old Friend with Love (The Elvis Song)/Can't Cha Feel It/Shattered/Rock and Roll Fever.

CHUCK HIGGINS

Aka "Motorhead," Higgins is a wild sax player and singer who recorded for Combo in the early '50s, with young Johnny "Guitar" Watson on piano. Higgins claims to have initiated the sustained note style of playing so popular with the hell-raising school of honkers and screamers. We'll leave that argument to the R&B scholars, but I think you'll agree that "Motorhead" was one of the most exciting of the genre all the same. Besides working his hoodoo on the tenor sax, Higgins also contributed crunching baritone sax and guitar to many of his classic recordings.

SAXOPHONOGRAPH 1303 (R)
Yak a Dak

All but one tune, a 1961 remake of "Pachuko Hop," were taken from the 1953–1955 period when Chuck was recording for various small labels like Combo. Both sides of the great Lucky 005 are here ("Greasy Pig" b/w "Candied Yam") as well as R&B 1314 ("Rock" b/w "Chop Chop"). Essential stuff to add to your cruisin' tape. Shotgun Wedding/Wiggle/West Side/Chuck a Buck.

WILLIE HIGHTOWER

Soulster whose voice sounds uncannily like Sam Cooke's. Willie Hightower was born in Gadsden, AL, and comes from a strong church-quartet background. During the early '60s, Willie cut one record for Mercury. In 1964, Willie was signed to Enjoy Records by Bobby Robinson, with whom he cut the ballad classic "It's Too Late" (later reissued on Capitol) and "Let's Walk Together" (Fury, 1966), plus four other songs of merit. A pact was subsequently made with Capitol to issue his records under Bobby's guidance and supervision.

COLLECTABLES 5170 (RCL)
Golden Classics

Only ten songs here, but they are all fine soul numbers gathered from Bobby Robinson's Enjoy/Fire labels. It's Too Late/(Take My Hand) Let's Walk Together/I Love You (Yes I Do)/Nobody but You.

LIBERTY (JAPAN) 6601 (L)
High Quality Soul

Great 12-song collection featuring all of his hits plus other winning soul ballads like "It's a Miracle" and a medley of Sam Cooke cleffings.

JESSIE HILL

New Orleans singer/pianist who scored with Minit Records's first hit, the call-and-response classic "Ooh Poo Pah Doo," the first hit record produced by Allen Toussaint. Hill moved to LA in 1963 and teamed up with another New Orleans expatriot, Shirley Goodman (of Shirley and Lee [see separate listing] and later Shirley and Co. fame), recording as Shirley and Jessie. They both eventually worked with Dr. John.

COLLECTABLES 5164 (CL)
Golden Classics

Essentially the same as the out-of-print LP Charly 1169, featuring 16 sides recorded for Minit between 1960–1962, including his big hit "Ooh Poo Pah Doo." Backing is provided by Hills House Rockers with Eddie Lang, The Lastie Brothers, and Allen Toussaint on the ivories. Unlike the Charly reissue, this does not have any sleeve notes or discographical information.

EDDIE HINTON

Fine Southern rock and soul singer and a veteran session musician in the early '70s Muscle Shoals, AL soul scene.

ZANE 1001 (RCL)
Letters from Mississippi
Previously available on the hard-to-get Swedish Amalthea label. Fine '80s recordings recorded at Muscle Shoals and Birdland Studios in Decatur, AL. Eddie possesses a rough, soulful voice reminiscent of Joe Tex, Ted Hawkins, or a hoarse Delbert McClinton, that is very effective on tunes like "I Want a Woman," "My Searching Is Over," or "Everybody Needs Love." Though marred sometimes by overuse of his Bobby Bland catarrh, fans of his 1978 *Very Extremely Dangerous* Capricorn release and of Southern soul-rock will find these tunes to be just what the doctor ordered.

EDDIE HODGES
Eddie was a child TV and movie star in the '50s and '60s, even playing Frank Sinatra's rug rat in one flick. In 1961, he signed to Cadence records, figuring to notch another lively art to his resume.

DOMINO 1004 (R)
I'm Gonna Knock on Your Door
Twenty-one of Hodges's warbling efforts, from his earliest kiddie tunes to his mid-'60s records. "The Water Is over My Head" and "Let's Go Go" are actually pretty good. I wonder whatever happened to him. He could've given Sinatra a run for his money; Frank Jr., that is. Rainin' in My Heart/Ain't Gonna Wash for a Week/New Orleans/High Hopes/Love Minus Zero.

THE HOLLIES
British invasion group led by singer-guitarists Graham Nash and Allan Clarke. Nash and Clarke were boyhood friends, who performed as a duo called The Two Teens while still in high school. They formed several other bands, before putting together the first Hollies with lead guitarist Tony Hicks, Don Rathbone (b), and Eric Haydock (drm). Their first UK hits were scored in 1965–1966 with "Ain't that Just Like Me," "Searchin'," and "Stay," followed by world hits in 1967 with "Bus Stop," "Stop Stop Stop," and "Carrie Ann." Nash left in late 1968 to join forces with David Crosby and Stephen Stills and was replaced by Terry Sylvester. The group had one more major hit, 1969's "He Ain't Heavy, He's My Brother." The band continued to perform through the '70s and '80s, with success limited to the UK and Europe. Nash rejoined the group in the late '80s for a reunion album and tour.

COLUMBIA 32574 (L)
Hollies
Reissues cuts originally on Epic LPs and singles from 1968–1970.

EMI 46584 (CL)
Best of, Vol. 1

EMI 48831 (CL)
Best of, Vol. 2
All of their UK/US hits through the early '70s.

EMI 92882 (CL)
Best of The Hollies
Reissue of late '60s LP with their hits to that point.

EPIC 46161 (CL)
From the Original Master Tapes
The Hollies first US recordings in 1966–67 appeared on Imperial; the band then switched to Epic. This includes their later hits through 1969's "He Ain't Heavy, He's My Brother."

BUDDY HOLLY
More than 30 years after his tragic death at the age of 22 the star of Buddy Holly's genius burns as brightly as ever. One of the true pioneers and great originals in rock and roll, Buddy was one of the few '50s rockers to write his own material, experiment in the studio, and even to record with strings. Though most of what he has recorded has been reissued at some time, there is very little weak material among the gold.

Buddy began as a member of a "western bop band" with Bob Montgomery in 1953–1955. He went to Nashville several times in 1956 and recorded his first sides for Decca, backed by his band which at that time included Sonny Curtis (gtr), Don Guess (b), and Jerry Allison (drm). The group and the slick Nashville producers did not see eye to eye and although some fine rock and roll was produced, only two singles from the sessions (including "Rock Around with Ollie Vee" and "Blue Days, Black Nights") were issued at the time.

After performing as a duo with Allison, Buddy formed a new band, The Crickets, with Niki Sullivan (rhythm gtr) and Joe B. Mauldin (b). The group teamed up in Clovis, NM, with producer

Norman Petty to produce timeless rock and roll. Petty charged by the song, not the hour, so the boys went into the studios days at a time to experiment. Sullivan left for a solo career, and the trio hit it big with the rockers released as The Crickets on Brunswick ("That'll Be the Day" and "Oh, Boy!"), and the quieter tunes coming out under Buddy's name on Coral ("Peggy Sue" and "Heartbeat"). They topped the charts under both names and moved to New York in 1958.

Tommy Alsop was added on guitar in 1958. Later that year, Joe B. and Jerry got homesick and returned to Lubbock, keeping The Crickets name and recording with Earl Sinks on vocals (see separate listing for further recordings under The Crickets name). Throughout the winter, Buddy composed songs on acoustic guitar, which were later released with overdubbed backups. He started a winter tour in January 1959 with a new band featuring Alsop (gtr), Waylon Jennings (b), and Charlie Bunch (drm). Also on the tour was J.P. "Big Bopper" Richardson and Ritchie Valens; Holly and the other headliners were flying to an engagement on February 3, 1959 when their plane crashed, killing them all and ending a rock era.

Holly's popularity was so great (particularly in England) that, in the years following his death, efforts were made to find any recordings that he was involved in. Over the years, many recordings were discovered including studio recordings, home recordings, and demos, and these were reissued on LP, usually with overdubbed backings to make them sound more "professional."

Holly enjoyed renewed popularity with the release of the film *The Buddy Holly Story* in 1978. His songs were covered by many MOR rock stars, including Linda Ronstandt and James Taylor. Paul McCartney bought the rights to his songs and proclaimed September 7, Holly's birthday, National Buddy Holly Day. In 1979, a six-LP box set was issued by English MCA, featuring all his known recordings plus live performances, interviews, and some of the posthumously discovered recordings in undubbed form. This was complemented by a magnificent book. This set was eventually made available in the US.

In 1983, previously unreleased material was discovered at Norman Petty's studio and released as *For the First Time Anywhere* (MCA 27059, now out-of-print). When Petty died in 1985, more recordings were discovered, mostly undubbed recordings and alternate takes along with a few previously unissued songs. Because of legal entanglements with the Holly and Petty estates, this material remains unissued legally.

Holly's classic sides have been reissued and re-reissued by MCA. The best of these is the digitally remastered *Buddy Holly: Legend from the Original Master Tapes* collection. No complete CD set is available of all of Holly's recordings.

MCA 1484 (RC)
Twenty Golden Greats
Just what the title says. That'll Be the Day/Peggy Sue/Words of Love/Everyday/Not Fade Away/Oh, Boy!/Maybe Baby/Listen to Me/It's So Easy/Heartbeat/Think It Over.

⊙ MCA 4184 (RC)/5540 (L)
Buddy Holly: Legend from The Original Master Tapes
Twenty digitally remastered tracks with marvelous sound, the best Buddy has ever sounded. Two-LP/cassette set priced as a single LP/cassette, or one CD. You get "It Doesn't Matter Anymore" and "True Love Ways," not only in real stereo, but with additional studio chat with Buddy getting his starting note on piano! The rest is in the original mono versions, but sounds great! Fine cross section of his Brunswick and Coral sides. That'll Be the Day/Oh, Boy!/Not Fade Away/Peggy Sue/Think It Over/Rave On/I'm Gonna Love You Too.

MCA 25170 (C)/31182 (L)
The "Chirping" Crickets
Budget reissue of Brunswick 54038 from 1957. Not only was this Buddy's first LP, it was the only one with The Crickets issued in Buddy's lifetime (the only other one was his 1958 "solo" LP *Buddy Holly* on Coral). Includes such classics as "Not Fade Away," "Oh, Boy!," "Maybe Baby," "That'll Be the Day," "I'm Lookin' for Someone to Love," and "Tell Me How," along with Buddy's versions of Chuck Willis's "It's Too Late," Shorty Long's "Rock Me Baby" and Lloyd Price's (via Little Richard) "Send Me Some Lovin'." Detailed discography and new liner notes by Andy McKaie.

MCA 25239 (L)
Buddy Holly
Holly's first solo record without The Crickets, initially Coral 57210 from 1958. Twelve cuts. I'm Gonna Love You Too/Peggy Sue/Ready Teddy/Words of Love/Rave On.

MCA 80000 (RC)
The Complete Buddy Holly
The definitive Buddy Holly collection. Six-album/cassette set featuring 120 songs, including all available versions of his songs and six posthumously discovered performances in their undubbed versions, plus records he produced or played on by Ivan, Waylon Jennings, and Lou Giordano. Also includes his performances on the Ed Sullivan shows and several brief interviews. Set comes with 12-by-12-inch 60-page booklet full of rare pix, press clippings, and other memorabilia. Each LP has its own sleeve with pix and full discography.

MCA (UK) 1717 (L)
Love Songs
Twenty slow and mid-tempo numbers, including common and less frequently reissued material. True Love Ways/Listen to Me/Learning the Game/Love Is Strange/Because I Love You/Heartbeat/Take Your Time/Look at Me/Wishing/What to Do.

MCA (UK) 5003 (L)
Golden Greats
Sixteen Holly hits. Peggy Sue/That'll Be the Day/Everyday/Oh, Boy!/Not Fade Away/Brown Eyed Handsome Man/Maybe Baby/Rave On/Think It Over/It's So Easy/Bo Diddley.

THE HOLLYWOOD FLAMES

See the entry for Bobby Day for the story of The Hollywood Flames.

EARTH ANGEL 905 (R)
The John Dolphin Sessions
The Hollywood Flames were famous for their great Specialty records, but Bobby Byrd (who later changed his name to Bobby Day for a string of solo hits) and his crew were one of the oldest of the LA groups, going back to 1949. They sandwiched a couple of stints with the John Dolphin label around their stand at Specialty. Jumpin' tunes like "Young Girl," "Oooh La-La," and "Fare Thee Well" were the order of the day, but they shined on ballads as well, especially when smooth Gaynel Hodge took the lead vocal on tunes like "I Know" and "Peggy." They even covered one of the all-time great ballads, The Five Keys's "The Glory of Love." Hodge went on to form The Turks, and five of their wonderful tunes are also included here. Not to be outdone, Byrd formed his own spinoff group, The Voices, more of a backup group for his ideas than the group effort of The Flames, although "Santa Claus Baby" and "My Love Grows Stronger" are both energetic and very likeable tunes.

SPECIALTY 2166 (RC)
Buzz Buzz Buzz
These cats could do it all: gorgeous ballads, rockin' R&B, blues, dance tunes, and cool novelty tunes. Fourteen cuts recorded for Ebb records, including three previously unissued items. Buzz Buzz Buzz/Crazy/My Confession/Strollin' on the Beach/This Heart of Mine/Frankenstein's Den.

SPECIALTY 7021 (L)
The Hollywood Flames
All 27 tunes cut by this group for the Specialty and Ebb labels between 1952–1959. Includes The Flames's greatest weeper, "Just for You," penned by Bobby Relf of The Laurels fame. Nice pix and learned booknotes, compiled and produced by Billy Vera. Duplicates all of the material on Specialty 2166. So Good/This Heart of Mine/Strollin' on the Beach/Frankenstein's Den.

THE HONEYCOMBS

The Honeycombs were languishing in the London pubs until they had the good fortune to be signed up by England's hottest producer, Joe Meek, in 1964. They had a big hit right off the bat with "Have I the Right," one of the all-time best pop hits (Number 1 all over the world). They lived off of that one hit for years, touring everywhere. When Joe Meek died, however, The Honeycombs as a group died too.

SEQUEL 125 (L)

It's The Honeycombs/All Systems Go

Both of their LPs are here on one CD (all 28 cuts!). If none of the other tracks quite live up to the catchy, pounding "Have I the Right," there is still a lot to recommend. Nice While It Lasted/It Ain't Necessarily So/She's Too Way Out/I Can't Stop/All Systems Go.

LYNN HOPE

Tenor saxophonist Lynn Hope was a distinctive, instrumental stylist, although not a fire-breathing screamer by any means. More of a mellow balladeer, Hope's luscious tone reveals a sensuous world that rarely sinks down into the depths of corny sentimentality.

SAXOPHONOGRAPH 508 (L)

Morocco

Sixteen cuts from the early '50s. She's Funny That Way/Stardust/Sentimental Journey/Girl of My Dreams.

LYNN HOPE/CLIFFORD SCOTT

CHARLY 280 (L)

Juicy!

Another must for sax-instrumental buffs, with rare wax by Texas tenor Clifford Scott and balladeer Lynn Hope. You and a few million others heard Scott on Bill Doggett's classic "Honky-Tonk"; here he is joined by my main man, Hank Marr (org), Charles Brown (pno), and other session cookers for five solid shufflin' sides. Lynn Hope is a different character, a Moslem who admired the record-selling style of Earl Bostic, and in turn influenced a generation of ska hornsmen. In contrast to his lush romantic sound on "Stardust," "Tenderly," and "Ghost of a Chance," is the bar-walkin' "Shockin'," jazzy "Juicy," swaggering "Little Landslide," and the exotic "Sands of the Sahara." Twenty tooters in total; little duplication with Hope's Saxophonograph disc.

JOE HOUSTON

Unlike many of the jazz vets of his generation, Texas tenorist Houston didn't give a hoot for subtlety. In his frantic solos, he'd choose a climactic note and wring the hell out of it, sending everyone into a rockin' frenzy. He started his career in 1949 recording behind Joe Turner and then consistently turned out tootin' takes of hot R&B for Mercury, Imperial, Combo, Modern, Dooto, and scores of other labels.

SAXOPHOGRAPH 1302 (R)

Rockin' 'n' Boppin'

SPECIALTY 2171 (CL)

Cornbread and Cabbage Greens

Yes friends, if you want R&B honkin', this is it in 26 slices from 1952 recorded for the John Dolphin labels, including a multitude of unreleased takes. His 78 spinners are here, including the hotter than hot "Flying Home" and "Rockin' and Boppin'," the classic squealer "All Night Long," the mouth-watering title track, as well as the jazzy "Sentimental Journey." Houston only had a few tricks in his bag, waxing jazz standards like "Lester Leaps In" and "I Cover the Waterfront" with (as Billy Vera's boss notes reveal) nearly identical arranged solos on each take! This will drive your neighbors crazy, but get it anyway.

TOMMY HUNT

Pittsburgh-born Tommy (Charles) Hunt sang alongside Johnnie Taylor in The Five Echoes during the early '50s, then joined The Flamingos in 1956 and sang with them on Chess and End Records. In 1961, he signed with Wand/Scepter, where he recorded two best sellers, "Human" and "I Am a Witness." Hunt had a very impressive style, too often wasted on poor material. He gained renewed success on Dynamo Records, but in 1967 chucked it all and moved to Wales.

COLLECTABLES 5246 (CL)

Human: Golden Classics

Twelve songs, including his two big hits, and standouts "Your Man" and "Don't Make Me Over." Decent book notes, average sound. Duplicates English vinyl of the recent past.

TAB HUNTER

Tab was a big movie and recording star in the '50s and early '60s, but dropped out of sight until his resurrection on TV's *Fernwoood Tonight* and the films *Polyester* and *Lust in the Dust.*

STAR CLUB 8036 (R)

King of Young Love
Sixteen "classic" recordings from 1957–1960. No, he doesn't sing "Polyester" here, unfortunately, but he does step all over a program of venerable standards. Red Sails in the Sunset/Hey Good Lookin'/Invitation to the Blues/Don't Get Around Much Anymore/ Young Love.

THE HUNTERS

STAR CLUB 8023 (R)

Hits from The Hunters
Twelve tunes by British instrumental group.

FERLIN HUSKEY

Country star who approached the newfangled rockabilly hubbub with tongue firmly in cheek, using his alternate musical personality, Simon Crum, to present a country bumpkin's approach to the style.

DEMAND 0040 (R)

Bop Cat Bop
Brief LP (12 cuts) collects his Simon Crum efforts, including "Bop Cat Bop" and "Don't Be Mad" (the later a fun poke at "Don't Be Cruel"), some hillbilly bop ("Slow Down Brother" and "Stand Up Sit Down Shut Your Mouth"), and other assorted pop efforts from his long career as mostly a country artist. Also includes a song from his TV show *Price Possession,* and "This Moment of Love" from the movie *Mr. Rock and Roll.*

THE IKETTES

Backup vocalists for Ike and Tina Turner in the '60s (see separate listing). Consisting usually of Robbie Montgomery, Venetta Fields, and Jesse Smith on lead, they scored two big hits in '65, "I'm So Thankful" and the classic "Peaches and Cream," before splitting from Ike's Review and becoming The Mirettes.

KENT (UK) 063 (RL)

Fine Fine Fine
Fourteen tunes recorded for Modern in 1965–1966, while they were simultaneously recording and touring with Ike and Tina (Ike sent studio singers out to do The Ikettes's live gigs). "It's Been So Long" and "Camel Walk Blue on Blue" are in real stereo. Sally

Go Round the Roses/Can't Sit Down/Fine Fine Fine/ The Biggest Players.

THE IMAGINATIONS

Fine, white, early '60s doo-wop group from Long Island featuring Bobby Bloom of "Montego Bay" fame (a 1970 hit). The original group recorded in 1961 with Frank Mancuso and Bloom (leads and tens), brothers Phil (2nd ten) and Pete (bar) Agtuca, and Richard LeCausi (b). In 1962–1963, Bloom took the group in a more soulful direction under the name The Expressions. He committed suicide four years after his big solo hit.

RELIC 5058 (R)

The Imaginations
Includes all 16 sides that they recorded for Music Makers, Duel, and Ballad, many never released and all but one in stereo. Their first session featured King Curtis and Mickey "Guitar" Baker in the backup band. Hey You/Guardian Angel/Fannie Brown.

RELIC 7024 (L)

Goodnight Baby

THE IMPALAS

The Impalas were formed in Canarsie, a neighborhood in Brooklyn, NY, and had a hit right off the bat with "Sorry (I Ran All the Way Home)" in 1959. Their next record for the Cub label, "Oh, What a Fool" did OK too, but they faded from the scene before too long. Lead singer Joe "Speedo" Frazier had a beautiful, mellow voice that was most effective on ballads but much too fragile for rockers like "Chum." They recorded some gorgeous doo-wop songs, and the production was often brilliant with great guitar and lonely, distanced sax.

STAR CLUB 8035 (R)

Sorry
Oh, What a Fool/Fool, Fool, Fool/(You Want) Too Much Too Soon/All but the Memory of You.

THE IMPRESSIONS

Singer/songwriter/guitarist/arranger/producer Curtis Mayfield, the mastermind behind this group, developed a new Chicago soul sound based on the gospel tradition of switching leads. The original group, called The Roosters, featured

Jerry Butler on baritone lead, Mayfield (ten), Arthur and Richard Brooks (tens), and Sam Gooden (bar). They released the classic "For Your Precious Love" for Falcon/Vee Jay in 1958. (Early Impressions tracks with Butler were reissued on the now unavailable LP Charly 2023). Butler soon left for a solo career, still under the guiding hand of Mayfield, while Mayfield and his silky high tenor slid into the lead role in The Impressions. In 1961, the group had another hit with "Gypsy Woman" for ABC, followed by two more years of silence while Mayfield worked with Butler. Starting with 1963's "It's Alright," the group had a continuous string of hits for ABC until 1968, and then for their own Curtom label, until Mayfield left for a solo career in 1970. There was always a strong religious and political bent to their songs, including "Amen," "Keep on Pushing," "People Get Ready," "This Is My Country," "Choice of Colors," and "Mighty Mighty (Spade and Whitey)." In the '70s, Mayfield had a long, successful solo career, highlighted by writing the score, performing the music, and appearing in the movie *Superfly*. The Impressions reunited in 1985 for a tour that featured both Mayfield and Butler.

✪ KENT (UK) 923 (L)

The Definitive Impressions
Twenty-eight track collection (74 minutes) featuring almost all of their '60s hits. Gypsy Woman/Little Young Lover/I'm the One Who Loves You/It's Alright/I'm So Proud/I've Been Trying/I Made a Mistake/Amen/Woman's Got Soul/I Need You/You've Been Cheating/I Can't Satisfy/I Can't Stay Away from You/We're Rolling On.

MCA 1500 (RC)/31338 (L)

Greatest Hits
Ten cuts recorded for ABC/Paramount between 1961–1967. Gypsy Woman/We're a Winner/Keep on Pushing.

MCA 10664 (CL)

The Anthology 1961–1977
Two-disc set featuring 26 songs from the group's ABC years, hits from the Curtom catalog, plus the best of Mayfield's early solo career. All the hits and some interesting album tracks, with informative booklet notes from Chicago soul expert Bob Pruter. Gypsy Woman/It's Alright/Keep on Pushing/Meeting over Yonder/Talking About My Baby/Little Young Lover/Fool for You/Freddie's Dead/Superfly/Move on Up/Pusherman/Only You Babe.

THE INDEPENDENTS
Less well-known than The Impressions or The Manhattans, The Independents were no less talented. Originally a trio consisting of Charles Jackson, Maurice Jackson (no relation), and Helen Curry, the group added Eric Thomas after their first LP. They recorded three albums for Wand between 1972–1974.

COLLECTABLES 5245 (CL)

Leaving Me: Their Golden Classics
Most of their best stuff, including their biggest hit "Leaving Me." They primarily specialized in ballads, but they also liked to get a little funky now and again, as "Arise and Shine" and "No Wind, No Rain" prove. Baby I've Been Missing You/Couldn't Hear Nobody Say/Let This Be A Lesson to You/It's All Over/Just as Long as You Need Me.

LUTHER INGRAM
Soul singer/songwriter Luther Ingram was born in 1944 in Jackson, TN. As a teen, he sang gospel with his kin—The Ingramettes—and waxed his first solo sides for Smash in 1965. However, Luther didn't see chart action until 1969. Having signed with Johnny Baylor's Koko label, whose output was distributed by Stax, he scored with "Pity for the Lonely."

CHARLY 303 (L)

If Loving You Is Wrong
(I Don't Want to Be Right)
Reissues Luther's Urgent album, covering all of his later Koko hits (circa 1972–1978), featuring his Number 1 title cut. Personal faves include the bluesy "Always," the tender "Let's Steal Away to the Hideaway," the James Brown-inspired "Sweet Inspiration," the soul anthem "I'll Be Your Shelter in Time of Storm," and the self- penned "Oh Baby, You Can Depend on Me." Go see him in the rentable movie *Wattstax*.

THE INNOCENTS
ACE 375 (L)

The Complete Indigo Recordings
If everything The Innocents recorded sounded as good as "Honest I Do," then the thought of their collected Indigo releases would elicit spirited shouts of "Oh, happy day!" and "We are truly blessed!" But since

nothing—with the possible exception of "Gee Wiz"—ever came close to its quality, a more reserved course of conduct seems appropriate. This CD offers 25 selections, with the only missing selections being "Tick Tock" and the instrumental "The Rat," which were recorded during the "Honest I Do" sessions and later sold to the Transworld label. The masters of these two numbers apparently have been lost. Some cuts, like the cover of Jesse Belvin's "Beware," are reasonably good, but too many are flat, uninspired, and dull. And their attempt at "I'm a Hog for You" is a disaster of unheralded proportions. Honest!

THE ISLEY BROTHERS

Veteran family R&B group, active with giant hits way into the '80s. They began as a gospelesque group in 1959 recording for RCA the classics "Shout" and "Respectable" and, for Wand, "Twist and Shout." They had a few hits for Tamla in the mid-'60s, including "This Old Heart of Mine," before starting their own label, T-neck (the brothers hail from Teaneck, NJ) in 1969. The Rhino release is the best all-around introduction to their biggest hits.

ACE 928 (L)
Shout and Twist with Rudolph, Ronald and O'Kelly
The Isley Brothers trio of the early 1960s created a series of influential hits, including a marvelous pre-Beatles "Twist and Shout" and "Nobody but Me," rerecorded by the Human Beinz in 1967. This great-sounding 19-cut CD (including three unreleased tracks) highlights their attempts to match their initial success, utilizing the percussive production style of Bert Berns in songs like "The Snake," "One Way Love," and a blatant remake of "Twist" with "Hold on Baby." However, nothing would click again for the Isleys until the latter part of the decade.

BEAR FAMILY 15425 (L)
Shout!
Their complete RCA recordings from 1959 and 1960, a total of 21 sides, including three previously unissued takes. Shout/How Deep Is the Ocean/Respectable/Open Up Your Heart/Without a Song/Ring-a-ling-ling.

COLLECTABLES 5103 (C)
Shout!
Exact repro of the Isley's first LP, RCA 2156 from 1959. Includes: the long version of the title hit (pts. 1 and 2); their first RCA single, "Turn to Me"; their second big hit, "Respectable"; and a lot of standards performed in the style of "Shout," including "St. Louis Blues," "How Deep is the Ocean," and "Rock around the Clock."

EMI 95203 (CL)
The Complete UA Sessions: EMI Legends of Rock and Roll
Twenty-song package compiled from United Artists/Veep recordings cut between 1963–1966. The emphasis here is on FUN with a capital F, with lotsa dance numbers and twist spinoffs ("Surf and Shout," "Tango," "What'cha Gonna Do," and "Do the Twist"); covers of James Brown, Hank Ballard, and Little Richard hits ("Please, Please, Please," "Let's Go, Let's Go, Let's Go," and "Long Tall Sally"); and some great original material. An early version of their later smash hit "Who's That Lady" sounds a lot like the old chestnut "Gypsy Woman." Also reissues two unreleased instrumentals with young Jimi Hendrix on guitar (no solos, however). A classic party collection that compares favorably to the Rhino 70908.

RCA 9901 (CL)
Shout! The Complete Victor Sessions
Duplicates material on Bear Family 15425, without the three previously unissued takes.

⊗ RHINO 70908 (CL)
Isley Brothers Story, Vol. 1: Rockin' Soul (1959–68)
Twenty tracks culled from a staggering array of labels—RCA, Atlantic, Wand, United Artists, T-Neck, and Tamla/Motown—including their big hits. Also includes "Who's That Lady" (the original version of their later smash hit "That Lady"), the demented "Testify" with a young Jimi Hendrix on guitar, "Rock around the Clock," and the rocking "Behind a Painted Smile." The Isleys always had their eyes on the top of the charts and their ears on the black and white pop sounds of the day, which, when combined with a solid gospel background, made for some very creative and propulsive sides. Twist and Shout/This Old Heart of Mine/I Guess I'll Always Love You/Got to Have You Back/Take Me in Your Arms.

THE IVY LEAGUE

UK-based The Ivy League, like stablemates The Rockin' Berries, recorded for Pye and Piccadilly in the mid-'60s. They tried to match a beat-group rhythm to a Four Seasons/Beach Boys harmony sound with only partial success.

SEQUEL 179 (L)
The Best of The Ivy League
Twenty-two cuts from this harmony group that does best on slow ballads and standards. They go off the deep end, however, when they try to cover "Don't

Worry Baby"! "Funny How Love Can Be," "In the Not Too Distant Future" and "Running around in Circles" show what they could do with a good tune. The liner notes say that their backing band later became Ten Years After! Strange bedfellows indeed. Tossing and Turning/That's Why I'm Crying/A Girl like You/Lonely Room/Almost Grown.

JACKIE and THE STARLITES

Little Jackie Rue and The NY Starlites are best remembered for their tear-soaked rendition of "Valerie." This extremely talented quartet never received enough recognition and praise for the beautiful ballad weepers they put out between 1960–1965. With the decline of doo-wop, The Starlites's close harmonies and powerfully soulful sides sadly got lost in the shuffle. There was never more downright anguish than when Little Jackie (with tear-stained handkerchief in hand), in knee-drop stance, choked convulsively on the lyrics of their weepy hits. The original lineup included Jackie (lead voc), Alton Jones (1st ten), George Lassu (2nd ten), John Felix (bar), and Billy Montgomery (b). The group's act borrowed from the church, spiced with antics culled from James Brown. Their songs were a Wet-Ones box of heartaches and broken affairs wailed in echo-chambered despair.

RELIC 5090 (R)/RELIC 7018 (L)
Jackie and The Starlites
From Fury, Hull, Mascot, and Sphere Sound sources, including previously unreleased material. Peerless sound quality and learned notes by Don Fileti. Indispensable. Ain'tcha Ever Coming Home/I Found Out Too Late/Don't Be Afraid/They Laughed at Me.

THE JACKS

See THE CADETS for the story of this group.

RELIC 5023 (R)
The Jacks Greatest Hits
Fourteen sides from the RPM label.

BULLMOOSE JACKSON

Tenorman and vocalist who began his career with The Lucky Millinder Orchestra in the early '40s, initially as a member of the sax section and later as a vocalist after substituting for Wynonie Harris. He worked with Millinder's band until 1948 and went out on his own after his King recording of "I Love You, Yes I Do" topped the R&B charts in late 1947. He had more hits for King through the end of the decade and continued recording for them until 1954. He was known for some wonderfully risque jump blues including "Big Ten-Inch (Record)" and "Nosy Joe." In 1961, a remake of "I Love You, Yes I Do" was a hit on the R&B and pop charts. He was pretty much inactive through the '70s but returned to the scene in the mid-'80s, making some new recordings and touring Europe. He died in 1989.

AUDIO LAB 1524 (RC)
Bullmoose Jackson Sings His All-time Hits
A reproduction of the original album, a collection of tunes cut between 1947–1951 for King, containing many ballads from the Eckstine school of smooch. The set includes the storming "Why Don't You Haul Off," the joys and perils of "Sneaky Pete," the jumpin' "Cherokee Boogie," and the comic "Bow-legged Woman." Three songs also appear on Route 66 14.

ROUTE 66 14 (R)
Big Fat Mamas Are Back in Style Again
Reissue of 1945–1956 sides.

SAXOPHONOGRAPH 506 (R)
Moose on the Loose
Moose's early sides (1945–1947) with The Lucky Millinder Orchestra, plus later grooves (1949–1952) backed by Harold "Money" Johnson and Tiny Bradshaw's big bands. Joyful jiving and root-tooting abound on such houseshakers as "Hold Him Joe," "Jammin' and Jumpin'," and the title cut. The set also includes soulful ballad singing on "Sometimes I Wonder" and "End This Misery," plus raunchy double-entendre numbers like "Oh John" and the legendary "Big Ten-Inch (Record)." Star musicians include Bill Doggett, Sam "The Man" Taylor, Red Prysock, and Bernie Peacock.

CHUCK JACKSON

Smooth soulster who began his career in the re-formed Del Vikings from 1957–1959 (see separate entry). Jackson had a string of hits for Scepter's subsidiary label Wand between 1961–1967, including his biggest hits "Any Day Now" and "I Don't Want to Cry."

COLLECTABLES 5115 (CL)
Golden Classics
Twelve tracks, including his big hits. It's unfortunate that "Something You Got" is missing, especially because non-hits like "I'm Your Man" and "I Keep Forgettin'," which are average at best, are here. Jackson's throaty baritone sounds best on uptempo numbers like "The Breaking Point." It's too bad that Wand kept smothering his voice with strings. Still, songs like the unsympathetic "Beg Me" and the horn-punched "Any Other Way" make everything better than all right. Since I Don't Have You/Hand It Over/I Wake Up Crying/Make the Night a Little Longer/Tell Him I'm Not Home.

KENT (UK) 935 (L)
Good Things
Twenty-four of his best recordings made for Wand between 1961–1965, including his biggest hit "Any Day Now," and the original version of "I Keep Forgetting" which was covered by David Bowie note for note. It also includes several cuts that were not originally issued but surfaced on a Kent LP a few years ago, plus a couple of never- before-issued titles, "Where Do I Go from Here" and "What's with This Loneliness." Excellent sound and nice eight-page booklet with informative notes and good photos. I Don't Want to Cry/I Wake Up Crying/Any Other Way/Beg Me.

DEON JACKSON
Detroit soulster discovered by famed producer Ollie McLaughlin. He had a hit in 1966 with his own "Love Makes the World Go Round."

COLLECTABLES 5106 (CL)
Golden Classics
Twelve sides recorded for Detroit's Carla label, produced by Ollie McLaughlin. Love Makes the World Go Round/Love Takes a Long Time Growing/Ooh Baby/S.O.S./I Can't Go On.

J.J. JACKSON
Originally an arranger and songwriter Jackson became a singer in the mid-'60s when his "But It's Alright" was a huge hit on East Coast dance floors. With a vigorous stop-start arrangement and J.J.'s powerful Otis Redding-like vocalizing, it's a soul burner for the ages.

SEE FOR MILES 281 (RL)
The Great J.J. Jackson
I never knew until I read Trevor Swaine's reverent liner notes that Jackson's big hit "But It's Alright" was recorded in London with a group of English jazzbos! In retrospect, it isn't surprising that J.J. brought out a

Memphis soul sound from those guys because he was a top-flight arranger before he ever stepped in front of the mike. Lots of great stuff here, including dance-floor burners "I Dig Girls" with its *Dragnet* horn riffs, "That Ain't Right," and the epic "Come and See Me (I'm Your Man)." Jackson also shows his versatility on soulful ballads like Sam Cooke's "A Change Is Gonna Come," Lou Rawls's "Love Is a Hurting Thing," and "Give Me Back My Love."

JERRY JACKSON
BEAR FAMILY 15481 (L)
Shrimp Boats A-Comin', There's Dancin' Tonight
It seems that we have finally outdone ourselves in the tireless crusade to search out obscure reissues; no one here knows anything about this black crooner who recorded these 24 cuts for Kapp and Columbia in the early '60s. Bear Family puts it pretty bluntly in their liner notes: "Hardly a household name at any time during his brief secular career, Jerry Jackson straddled an uneasy line between black and then-current pop music." His version of "It Hurts Me" inspired Elvis Presley's later version, and a few of these cuts feature The Four Seasons as backup singers. The music is actually pretty good, although his six producers put him in a different "bag" ranging from saccharine, Drifters-type arrangements to peppy, Jackie Wilson settings, a little Brook Benton, and even some James Brown-styled grooves.

MARVIN JACKSON
Marvin Jackson was a rockabilly singer and guitar player from Missouri who is best remembered for his fine Crestwood single "Gee Whiz, Miss Liz," from 1957.

WHITE LABEL 8883 (R)
Ozark Rock-a-billy
His big hit is reissued here, along with 16 unreleased recordings from the '50s. Just about everything rocks along nicely with some very interesting self-penned lyrics on the important teen issues of the day like "Fifty-Six V8 Ford," "He's Just a Cool Man, Cool," "Down at the Roller Rink," and "Keep a Shakin'."

WANDA JACKSON
The queen of rockabilly. Wanda recorded wild, wild sides for Capitol between 1956–1962. While still in high school, she started singing in front of Hank Thompson's band for Decca with the excellent Billy Gray on guitar. In 1956, she signed with Capitol, and her rockabilly sides

were backed by a solid studio band featuring Joe Maphis on lead guitar and Buck Owens on rhythm. With the help of sped-up tapes, these were certainly the wildest female rockabilly recordings ever made. The best collection of her early recordings is available from Rhino. In 1962, Capitol switched her backup to calmer string sections, and the emphasis changed from rockabilly to pure country, particularly on her hit "Right or Wrong." More recently, she has combined gospel and rockabilly in her live shows, and has recorded in her old style (released in this country on Varrick).

EMI (FRANCE) 252 676 (L)
Let's Have a Party
Before she was born again, before she sang honky-tonk flavored country, Wanda Jackson was the "Queen of Rockabilly." This 16-song, 36-minute set collects the best of those sides recorded for Capitol in the late '50s and early '60s. The variety of subjects ranges from the raucous "Let's Have a Party," featuring Gene Vincent's Blue Caps, to the raucous "Man We Had a Party," to the raucous "There's a Party Goin' On" ... you get the idea. Wish there were some liner notes with this release. Fujiyama Mama/Tongue Tied/Mean Mean Man/Whole Lotta Shakin' Goin' On/Honey Don't/Rip It Up.

EMI (FRANCE) 798126 (L)
Legends of Rock and Roll
Eighteen cuts, many of them covers, almost all in the little girlish, whining growl that Jackson made famous. Rhino offers a better collection with a much-easier-to-listen-to mixture of rockabilly and straightforward country tunes.

⊙ RHINO 70990 (CL)
Rockin' in the Country:
The Best of Wanda Jackson
Eighteen cuts, including her sassy early rockabilly sides plus later country recordings. A thoughtfully compiled collection with great sound as always. Let's Have a Party/Honey Bop/Hot Dog! That Made Him Mad/Mean Mean Man/Fujiyama Mama/Right or Wrong/In the Middle of a Heartache/Tears Will Be the Chaser for Your Wine.

VARRICK 025 (RC)
Rock and Roll Away Your Blues
Recorded in Sweden in 1984 with Swedish musicians, this was Wanda's first rockabilly recording in decades and her first pop recording since 1971 when she started singing for The Lord. It features mostly quite good covers of rockabilly and '50s teen pop. Rockabilly

Fever/Breathless/Oh Boy/Rave On/Stupid Cupid/Ain't It the Gospel.

WILLIS "GATOR TAIL" JACKSON
Miami-born tenor blower Willis Jackson could honk as well as Eddie "Lockjaw" Davis or Big Jay McNeely, but (and this is where the other guys get left behind) he could also smooch out the prettiest love ballads in a style that was all his own.

WHISKEY, WOMEN, AND ... 705 (RL)
On My Own
Great collection of 16 instrumental jumpers and weepers from Jackson's pre-jazz period 1950–1955, including the token vocal number "Wine-o-Wine," "Try a Little Tenderness," and the saxman's staple "Harlem Nocturne."

THE JAGUARS
Legendary, central Los Angeles, racially mixed quartet whose mid-'50s Aardell (later R-Dell) singles fetch astronomical prices. The group was formed in Freemont High School, a hot bed of doo-wop activity. (The Meadowlarks, The Medallions, and The [Hollywood] Flames all began their chirpin' careers there.) Originally known as The Miracles, the group included Sonny Chaney (lead), Val Poliuto (ten), Manny Chavez (bar), and Charles Middleton (b), and also recorded for Ebb (1957–1958), Original Sound (1959), and, as The T-Birds, for Chess in 1961. After they disbanded, Poliuto worked as a studio musician in Southern California. *Trivia buffs note:* The "Beach Boys" recording of "Surfin' Safari" b/w "Little Surfer Girl" was actually cut in February 1962 by Brian and Dennis Wilson with Val Poliuto on piano and vocals!

EARTH ANGEL 904 (R)
The Way You Look Tonight
Almost their complete output. Of the 24 cuts in this collection, 11 are memorable ballads of classic proportions, but the remaining 13 either constitute jump novelties or average pop-oriented compositions. However, standouts like "The Way You Look Tonight," "Moonlight and You," and "I Wanted You" make this reissue a worthwhile proposition. Great pix and sleeve notes by Steve Propes and Jim Dawson.

ETTA JAMES

Powerful R&B vocalist whose career spans more than three decades. Etta was only 14 when she was discovered by Johnny Otis, who wrote her first hit, an answer song to The Midnighters's "Work with Me Annie." Originally called "Roll with Me Henry," the title was considered too risque, so the song was released as "The Wallflower" on Modern in 1955 (with Richard Berry singing bass); it enjoyed renewed popularity in the '80s when it was featured in the film *Back to the Future*. Her Kent/Modern material has been reissued by Ace. In 1960, James moved to Chess subsidiary Argo for a long, successful career. By the end of the '60s, she was suffering from a heroin addiction, and eventually was hospitalized for detox. In 1967, she switched to Cadet, another Chess subsidiary, and scored her biggest hits "Tell Mama" and "Security." Many of her original Argo/Cadet LPs have been reissued in their original packaging by Chess, besides the many compilations available on domestic and foreign Chess labels. Her most recent recordings have been issued by Island and Elektra.

CHESS 6028 (RC)/9280-81 (L)

The Sweetest Peaches
(The Chess Years)

Two LPs/cassettes/CDs of Etta's most high-spirited material. Includes the incomparable "If I Can't Have You" with Harvey Fuqua, the show-stopping live rendition of "Baby What You Want Me to Do," the gospel-drenched "Stop the Wedding," the hard-driving "In The Basement (Pt. 1)" with Sugar Pie De Santo, the irrepressible "Tell Mama," plus 15 other soul-nuggets from various singles and albums covering the 1960–1974 period. Nice pix and literate sleeve notes round out this extremely fine collection. Each CD has two additional tracks.

CHESS 9110 (RC)

Her Greatest Sides, Vol. 1

Solid package with 14 great Chess sides recorded between 1960–1968. Tell Mama/I'd Rather Go Blind/Pushover/Stop the Wedding/Sunday Kind of Love/At Last.

CHESS 9184 (RCL)

Rocks the House

Originally released as Argo 4032 form 1963, this set was recorded at The New Era Club in Nashville on September 27 and 28, 1963, when Etta was enjoying her greatest chart success. Although James is a great ballad singer, this show documents her ability to tear the club up with one uptempo R&B tune after another. She wraps her powerful vocal chords around Ray Charles's "What'd I Say," Jessie Hill's "Ooh Poo Pah Doo," and Jimmy Reed's "Baby What You Want Me to Do." The CD has three unreleased bonus tracks including the album's only ballad "All I Could Do Is Cry."

CHESS 9266 (RCL)

At Last!

Reissue of Argo 4003 from 1960. After five hitless years, Etta signed to the Chess subsidiary and immediately scored four smash R&B hits ("All I Could Do Was Cry," "My Dearest Darling," "At Last," and "Trust in Me"), all included here along with such standards as "A Sunday Kind of Love" and "Stormy Weather." Backing is by The Riley Hampton Orchestra, which skirts the line between rocking R&B with booting sax and white pop with strings, flutes, and vocal chorus.

⊛ CHESS 9269 (RCL)

Tell Mama

Reissue of Cadet 802 from 1969, remixed back to original mono (original issue was in electronic stereo). Etta's best and most popular LP recorded at Fame Studios with Spooner Oldham, Jimmy Johnson, Barry Beckett, Dave Hood, and Roger Hawkins. Includes her electrifying title hit, written by Clarence Carter: Try listening to it without dancing! Also featured are her superb hit versions of Otis Reddings's "Security" and "I'd Rather Go Blind," a reworking of Saki's "I'd Rather Be a Blind Man," Jimmy Hughes "Steal Away," a beautiful version of "The Love of My Man," and a blazing version of Rosco Gordon's "Just a Little Bit."

CHESS 9287 (RCL)

The Second Time Around

Reissue of Argo 4011 from 1961 with ten songs. Don't Cry Baby/One for My Baby/Seven Day Fool/Dream/Plum Nuts.

CHESS 91509 (RC)

Come a Little Closer

Reissue of Chess 60029 from 1974, an LP of mid-'70s funk featuring such rock mainstream (and non-Chess) names as Lowell George, Danny Kortchmar, Jim Horn, and Bobby Keys. Produced by former Steppenwolf producer Gabe Mekkler, who brought two Steppenwolf songs with him besides writing six more himself. Also includes a beautiful gospel version of "St. Louis Blues" and Randy Newman's "Let's Burn Down the Cornfield." A nice LP but Etta never really breaks loose.

CHESS (FRANCE) 600175 (L)

On Chess

Twenty-six great Chess sides, starting off with nine from 1960-1964 that mainly appeared on the *Etta James* (Cadet 4013, 1963) and *Peaches* (Cadet 60004, 1973) LPs, including "Something's Got a Hold on Me," "Spoonful," and "Breaking Point." Next is the entire *Tell Mama* LP, probably the best of her career (see Chess 9269). The final tunes are from 1968–1969, and are mostly non-LP singles including "I Got You Babe," "Fire," and "Miss Pitiful."

ELEKTRA 61347 (CL)

The Right Time

1992 release produced by Jerry Wexler, with 11 well-chosen cuts, exuberant liner notes, and four righteous photos. From the sardonic put down of a sub-par lover in "Wet Match," to the splendid meshing of talents in her duet with Stevie Winwood on "Give It Up," to the potent affirmation of "Love and Happiness," Etta shows that she has arrived in the '90s with a vengeance.

FLAIR 91695 (L)

R&B Dynamite

The most comprehensive collection of Etta's Kent/Modern material. Twenty sides recorded between 1954–1961, including the never-before-issued "Be My Lovey Dovey" from the same 1954 session that produced her biggest hit "Roll with Me Henry (The Wallflower)." The first session and a 1957 date that was recorded in New Orleans have backing by The Johnny Otis Orchestra. The rest was done in LA with Maxwell Davis's band, including her other big hit "Good Rockin' Daddy." No dance party is complete without this set! Tough Lover/W-O-M-A-N/Hey Henry/I'm a Fool/Strange Things Happen/Good Rockin' Daddy/That's All/Roll with Me Henry/Baby, Baby Everynight.

ISLAND 842 926 (RCL)

Stickin' to My Guns

Stickin' to My Guns is an apt title for this collection that makes no concession to fashion (save for the unnecessary, but not unsuccessful, appearance by rapper Def Jef on one track, "Get Funky"). Etta is in top form; the backing band is first rate, including musicians from the Muscle Shoals and Hi Records crew. The production has a modern blues/rock sheen, with drums a bit forward in the mix, but the band is funky and totally sympathetic to Etta's cause. Few singers (if any) rock this hard or sing with this much authority and conviction in the '90s. Highlights include "Beware" and "Love to Burn."

ISLAND 842 655 (CL)

Seven Year Itch

Etta's vocals are powerfully spine-tingling, and they're meshed perfectly into the most rockingest, soulful music to have come out of an American studio in I don't know how long. This is a horn-lovers' heaven over a bass-grinders' dream in modern Stax style. Most of these players were around in the heyday of Memphis, so the standards are the tops. The sound is hot, modern, and real, a sensuous pleasure for the ears. Etta's material has been chosen with care and she clearly relishes getting her vocal cords around some meaty lyrics. Her voice is both tough and tender—sometimes at the same time, sometimes by turns—but always strong. This album displays her as improving with age.

ETTA JAMES and "CLEANHEAD" VINSON

FANTASY 9647

Blues in the Night, Vol. 1: The Early Show

FANTASY 9655

Blues in the Night, Vol. 2: The Late Show

Two CDs recorded live on digital equipment in 1986 at Marla's Memory Lane supper club in LA with backup by Red Holloway, Jack McDuff, and Shuggie Otis. Vol. 1 has 9 tracks, including "Kidney Stew," "Misty," and "Something's Got a Hold on Me." Vol. 2 has 10 numbers, including "Cleanhead Blues," "Cherry Red," "Baby What You Want Me to Do?," "Sweet Little Angel," and "I'd Rather Go Blind."

TOMMY JAMES and THE SHONDELLS

Dayton, OH born Tommy James began performing for local dances with his group The Shondells when he was 12-years-old. They released a single called "Hanky Panky" in 1960 for the tiny local Snap label, which went nowhere until, five years later, a Pittsburgh DJ discovered it in the slush pile and played it over the air. The orders piled in—Snap was deluged with 80,000 orders from Pittsburgh alone!—and the single, acquired nationally by Roulette, shot to Number 1 on the charts in 1966. The Shondells went on to chart four more Top-10 hits in that year alone. They produced a total of 26 chart-making hits by 1970, including 1967's "I Think We're Alone Now," 1968's "Mony, Mony" (recently covered by Billy Idol), and 1969's "Crystal Blue Persuasion" and "Crimson and Clover" (a hit in 1982 for Joan Jett and The Blackhearts). In 1970, James collapsed while performing due to a drug overdose, and after a brief retirement to recover, he performed as a solo artist, recording for Roulette through 1974 and then for Fantasy, without achieving his former success.

RHINO 70920 (CL)
Anthology
Twenty-seven chronologically arranged tracks, including everything that matters, from "Hanky Panky" through "Mony Mony," "Crystal Blue Persuasion," "Crimson and Clover," "Mirage," and solid pop creations like "Gettin' Together," "I Think We're Alone Now," and James's solo hits like "Ball and Chain" and "Draggin' the Line."

JAN and DEAN

Jan Berry and Dean Torrence were the clown princes of surf music. They started out as an excellent doo-wop duo, recording "Jennie Lee" for Arwin in 1958 (Dean was temporarily replaced by Arnie Ginsberg while he was serving in the army), and a long string of minor classics for Dore between 1959–1961. They joined Liberty in 1961, still doo-wopping (scoring a minor hit with "Linda"), but friendship with Beach Boys guru Brian Wilson led them to record his "Surf City," their only gold record. They put out an amazing string of surf and hot-rod classics, written with Wilson and by the team of Roger Christian and Gary Usher, also Wilson cohorts. Unlike Wilson and The Boys, however, they never really got beyond the fun-fun-fun of surfing and hot rods in their music. Their backup band, The Fantastic Baggys, recorded their own LPs (see separate listing). In 1966, Jan Berry was driving a car that struck a parked car while traveling at 65 mph; Jan's three passengers died, and he suffered severe brain damage. Dean carried on by himself under the Jan and Dean name, putting out rare material on Warner Brothers and Columbia. In the '70s, Jan, having taught himself how to speak again, put out some solo recordings on A&M. The duo reunited in the '80s.

C5 550 (RL)
Dead Man's Curve/
The New Girl in School
Reissue of Liberty 3361 from 1964. One side of this collection is devoted to their hot-rod tunes and the other to school days. Everyone knows the hit "Dead Man's Curve," but "Bucket 'T'" is the critic's choice, with its great stuttering chorus. Of the rest, "Three Window Coupe" and "My Mighty GTO" are the best, and "'B' Gas Rickshaw" is a nice orchestrated instrumental. The "School Days" songs are not all whitebread dross; there are actually two fine tunes here. Hal Blaine's studio group turns in a boss instrumental "Barons, West LA," and really rock out on Jan and Dean's version of "School Days," featuring blazing guitar.

C5 574 (L)
The Little Old Lady from Pasadena
Reissue of Liberty 3377 from 1964. Twelve tracks dealing with topics as diverse as summer, girls, and cars, including the title track and the skateboard classic "Sidewalk Surfin'." Sure, the topics are limited, but who would want Jan and Dean to sing about nuclear holocaust or poverty? The most charming song titles are "Horace, The Swingin' School Bus Driver," which is everything it promises to be, and "One-Piece Topless Bathing Suit," which is not. It's all too much to think about, probably something no one has ever said about a Jan and Dean LP before. Background vocals provided by The Fantastic Baggys.

EMI 80055 (CL)
Ride the Wild Surf/
The Little Old Lady from Pasadena
Melt those winter blues away with these two classic LPs on one disc, originally Liberty 3368 and 3377 from 1964. Twenty-four slices of surfin', shiftin', and skin cancer. *Ride the Wild Surf* includes the anthemic title cut, "Tell 'em I'm Surfin'," "She's My Summer Girl," "Skateboarding," and "A Surfer's Dream," among other classics. And, when the sunscreen runs out, there's another LP to go! *Little Old Lady* has a more eclectic focus with "Memphis," "Move Out Little Mustang," "Old Ladies Seldom Power Shift," "Summer Means Fun," and two versions of the title track. Rad, dad.

EMI 92772 (CL)
The Best of Jan and Dean
Twenty-two board-waxin', rubber-burnin' churners. A Sunday Kind of Love/Fiddle Around/Linda/She's My Summer Girl/Someday (You'll Go Walking By)/Dead Man's Curve/The Little Old Lady (from Pasadena)/The Anaheim, Azusa and Cucamonga/Sidewalk Surfin'.

ROLAND JANES

Brilliant guitarist from Alabama who was a member of Billy Lee Riley's band The Little Green Men in the '50s. He was also a session guitarist at Sun, playing on dozens of sessions behind Riley, Jerry

Lee Lewis, Teddy Redell, Harold Dorman, Bill Justis, and Charlie Rich. His versatility kept him very busy. After leaving Sun, he continuing performing on and producing for dozens of small Southern labels, eventually opening his own studio in Memphis. He was recently reunited with Riley on Billy's new Hightone album which Roland engineered as well as playing on.

BEAR FAMILY 15340 (R)
Guitarville

JOHNNY JANO

Louisiana rock and roll/rockabilly singer.

FLYRIGHT 531 (R)
King of Louisiana Rockabilly
> Some Other Time/Have You Heard the Word/She's My Baby/Rock and Roll Baby/She's Mine/Rock Me Baby.

THE JARMELS

In the early '60s, one of the most influential sounds was that of The Drifters and their use of Brazillian baion rhythms. Many groups scored big hits with The Drifters's sound, one of the biggest being The Jarmels's "A Little Bit of Soap." This five-member group started their career in Richmond, Virginia in the '50s, and "Soap" was their one-and-only hit though they continued to perform and record for many more years.

COLLECTABLES 5044 (CL)
14 Golden Classics
> Fourteen great Laurie recordings from 1961–1964, with lead vocals by Nathaniel Ruff. Includes their first recording, "Little Lonely One," and the venerable classics "Red Sails in the Sunset" and "The Way You Look Tonight."

JAY and THE AMERICANS

Brooklyn-based, pop vocal group that originally performed under the name The Harbor Lites with lead singer John Traynor. They were discovered by songwriters/producers Leiber and Stoller, who turned them into a white Drifters with their only hit recorded with Traynor (who changed his name to Jay), "She Cried." Leiber and Stoller even gave the group, now with lead singer Dave Black (who also changed his name to Jay!), an

unreleased Drifters track "Only in America" to record as a followup. This was followed with more Drifters's sounds: "Come Dance with Me," "Come a Little Bit Closer" (written by Boyce and Hart), and "Let's Lock the Door (and Throw Away the Key)." The group switched to a new producer, Gerry Granahan (of Dickie Doo and The Don'ts), who gave them a pseudo-operatic sound for their biggest hits "Cara Mia" and "Some Enchanted Evening." Granahan also introduced them to songwriters such as Roy Orbison ("Crying") and gave them the first hit written by a new songwriter named Neil Diamond, "Sunday and Me." In the mid-'60s, they experimented with more modern sounds, recording some nice flops ("Livin' Above Your Head" and "You Ain't as Hip as All That Baby"), before their final smash in 1968 with, ironically, a cover of The Drifters's "This Magic Moment." The group's popularity faded in the early '70s, and they disbanded by mid-decade.

EMI 93448 (CL)
The Best of Jay and The Americans
> Twenty-eight cuts, including foreign-language versions and radio spots.

BILL JENKINS

Memphis-area one-man rockabilly artist who originally recorded in 1965 as one half of The Jenkins Brothers.

REDITA 132 (R)
Bop Like Carl
> Hot rockabilly cut in Memphis 1965–1986. Includes his first single cut with his brother for the Salem Brothers label, "A Shoulder to Cry On" b/w "Open Up Another Bottle." The other 15 tunes are mostly Carl Perkins-influenced originals like "Lust, Hurt and Beer," "Poni-Tail and Bobby Sox" (check out that guitar!), and "Ol' Johnny Cash." A few covers include "Take Out Some Insurance on Me Baby" and Ed Bruce's "See the Big Man Cry."

KRIS JENSEN

Sixties pop-rocker from New Haven, CT who had a hit in 1962 with the John D. Loudermilk song "Torture," which had been previously offerred to The Everly Brothers.

BEAR FAMILY 15023 (R)
Let's Sit Down
Twelve 1962–1969 sides from Hickory

BEAR FAMILY 15031 (R)
Torture
Twelve Hickory sides recorded in Nashville between 1962–1965, with all-star session men (Loudermilk, Cramer, Kennedy, and Robbins). Includes the title hit and the previously unreleased "Wait." Lonely Island/ Cut Me Down (from Your Whipping Post)/Big as I Can Dream.

THE JESTERS

Fine and popular doo-wop group from Harlem formed in 1956 featuring the soaring lead vocals of Lenny McKay and Adam Jackson. They had a minor hit with, "So Strange" b/w "Love No One but You," their first recording for the Winley label in 1957. Their biggest hit was their third recording, a remake of The Chantels's "The Plea."

COLLECTABLES 5036 (CL)
The Best of The Jesters
Fourteen tracks. The Wind/I'm Falling in Love/Uncle Henry's Basement/Please Let Me Love You/Love No One But You/Now that You're Gone/I Laughed.

THE JIVE FIVE

The Jive Five took the Brooklyn doo-wop singing style of the late '50s and shaped it to perfection. Led by Eugene Pitt, who sang in The Genies of "Who's that Knocking" fame in the late '50s, and supported by friends Jerome Hanna (1st ten), Billy Prophet (2nd ten), Richard Harris (bar), and Norman Johnson (b), the original J5 recorded fine ballads and novelties for Les Cahan's Beltone label circa 1961–1963. They were truly a major-league doo-wop group, as proven not only by their all-time classic "My True Story" but also by their many other beautiful and artful tunes.

ACE 76 (RL)
Our True Story
Eighteen outstanding classics from tapes used on the Relics reissues (see below). Includes fine booklet notes by Bill Millar. My True Story/Begging You Please/ What Time Is It/No, Not Again.

COLLECTABLES 5022 (CL)
Their Greatest Hits
Lead singer Eugene Pitt's soulful voice backed by the deep, rich bass of Norman Johnson and the soaring

harmonics of the rest of the group will send chills down your spine on songs like "Begging You Please" and "Never Never." And if you want to knock your sacroiliac out of wack, roll up the rug for their dance tunes, especially "Hully Gully Callin' Time" where Johnson urges you to "do the Frank Sinatra" and "do the Floyd Patterson."

RELIC 5020 (R)
Greatest Hits
Sixteen early '60s Beltone sides, including several not previously released. My True Story/Do You Hear Wedding Bells/Hully Gully Callin' Time/Rain.

☻ RELIC 7007 (L)
The Jive Five
An indispensable collection of black, secular, quartet singing at its greatest. Twenty songs from their golden years, including all of their masterpieces, lovingly transferred from original session tapes. Duplicates Relic 5020 and the out-of-print Relic 5028, plus the Ace collection. My True Story/Hurry Back/What Time Is It/Never Never/No, Not Again/Beggin' You Please/Rain.

THE JODIMARS

Rockin' group formed in 1955 by three former members of Bill Haley and The Comets: Joe Ambrose (ten sax), Dick Richards (voc), and Marshall Lytell (b). Featuring the lead vocals of Richards, they turned out a number of upbeat rock-and-roll songs very much in the Haley vein, although, with the exception of their minor hit "Well Now Dig This," they didn't achieve his success. Although the singing and songs are unexceptional, the instrumental work is very good indeed, particularly from sax player Ambrose and guitarist Charles "Chuck" Hoss.

BULLDOG 1031 (RL)
Well Now Dig This
Twelve sides recorded for Capitol between 1955–1957. Although Bulldog is often thought of as a schlock label, the sound on this CD is superb, and there are brief interesting notes from High McCallum of the Bill Haley fan club.

LITTLE WILLIE JOHN

What Detroit native Little Willie John lacked in stature (he stood five-feet tall), he more than made up for in voice. A cross between Johnnie Taylor and O.V. Wright, Willie John laid the groundwork for soul stylists to come. Willie started singing professionally when he was 11 years old and, in 1951, when he was 14, he sang with Count Basie's Orchestra. After duetting with Paul Williams (of "Hucklebuck" fame) and recording for Prize, Willie signed with King in 1955, scoring a string of hits with them until 1962. In 1966, he killed a man in a brawl and was sentenced to jail; two years later, he died in mysterious circumstances while serving his prison term, some say of pneumonia, others say of head injuries following a beating.

CHARLY 246 (L)

Fever

Collects his King sides recorded circa 1955–1961, a mixture of pop ballads, jumps, and blues, the more memorable of which were his least successful sides. Along with five of the 14 charted hits is the low-down "Suffering with the Blues," the pleadingly delicate "Need Your Love So Bad," the frantic "Uh Uh Baby," the bluesy "You Hurt Me" with Mickey Baker's excellent guitar work, and "Drive Me Home" with its sweet Rufus Gore sax figures. A neatly balanced collection.

DE LUXE 1034 (L)

Little Willie John

Fifteen great King sides, for a total of 40 minutes playing time, including eight tracks not on the Charly reissue. Features his big hits including "Fever," "All around the World," and "Talk to Me." Cottage for Sale/Heartbreak/Sleep/The Very Thought of You/You're a Sweetheart/I've Got Spring Fever/Now You Know/Take My Love.

KING 596 (R)

Talk to Me

A straight reissue of Willie's second LP from the late '50s, reproducing the original cover art and notes. Worth getting because only the title track has been widely reissued; most of the rest are currently available only on this record. An inexpensive way to add some great music to your library, and a great cover to boot. Twelve cuts in all; staunchly recommended. I've Been Around/Drive Me Home/No More In Life/Person to Person/Don't Be Ashamed to Call My Name.

KING 603 (RL)

Mister Little Willie John

It's a treat to see this long out-of-print collection available again. Many of Little Willie's best '50s singles are included here: the joyous "Let's Rock While the Rockin's Good"; the unusual "Spasms," written by Young Jessie; the bluesy "Don't Leave Me Dear"; and "Are You Ever Coming Back?" There is little duplication of previous reissues. Thrill to the sweeping glis-

sandos and hypnotic melismatics of Little Willie's pipes. Recommended.

KING 739 (RL)

Sure Things

Surprisingly, apart from a couple of cuts on Gusto 45s, most of this collection has never been legally reissued up to this point. Gathered from '50s King 45s, the album includes the hits "Sleep," "A Cottage for Sale," and "Heartbreak," along with the outstanding "I Like to See My Baby" (with Hank Ballard and The Midnighters sharing vocal chores) and "You Hurt Me." Great collection.

JOHNNY and THE HURRICANES

Seminal instrumental group from Toledo, OH that were best-known for their cheesy organ sound (courtesy of Paul Tesluk). Johnny Paris led the band on sax, and Dave Yorko contributed some hot guitar runs. They scored several hits for Warwick with rockin' versions of old chestnuts including "Red River Rock" (a redo of "Red River Valley") and "Beatnik Fly" ("Bluetail Fly"). They went to Big Top in 1960, scoring with "Down Yonder" and "JaDa." In the '60s, Johnny formed a new Hurricanes in Europe where they remained popular for a decade, especially in France and Germany.

BIG TOP 222 (R)

Time to Rock

Collects some of their lesser-known tunes. At least a couple of these tunes were left out of Don Riswick's massive *Nothin' but Instrumentals* tome. I can also tell you that at least six tunes here are not even by Johnny and The Hurricanes but were done by The Craftsmen, who took up the slack on Warwick Records in 1960 when Paris took his band to the Big Top label. At any rate, there's some hot rockin' here, plus some ultra-cool photos on the jacket. Time to Rock/Marty's Party/Walkin' on Down/Goofus/Knock Out/Rock-a-Long.

BIG TOP 1302 (R)

The Big Sound of Johnny and The Hurricanes

Stereo repro of the 1959 LP with extra tracks, 18 in all. Great instrumentals with the triple threat front line of Johnny Paris on tenor sax, Paul Tesluk on Hammond organ, and great lead guitar from Dave Yorko. Includes the hits "Beatnik Fly" and "Down Yonder." Like...Rock/Teensville Tonight/Ten Little Indians.

BUBBER JOHNSON

Smooth crooner/composer/pianist/arranger in the Johnny Mathis mold. Johnson opted for the sophisticated lounge market while his raunchy King stablemates raked in the real dough with hard-rockin' R&B.

KING 569 (RL)

Come Home

Lounge-singer heaven. Another martini dear? I Lost Track of Everything/Too Many Hearts/Come Home/ My Lonely Heart.

BUDDY JOHNSON

The Buddy Johnson Orchestra was one of the few important swing bands to carry the Basie sound over into R&B. His sister Ella was certainly a major singing talent, up there with Ella Fitzgerald, Etta Jones, and Betty Carter. The band was active from the '40s through the '60s, with brother Buddy handling piano, arranging, and composing and sister Ella taking most of the vocals.

BEAR FAMILY 15479 (L)

Buddy and Ella Johnson: 1953–1964

R&B fans take note; this is one sizzling slice of music history that you shouldn't be without. Begins with Johnson's first Mercury Records session of February 1953, gliding effortlessly through his famed Wing/Mercury years, making a switch to Roulette in 1958, bouncing back to Mercury for three songs in 1961, and ending up with a 1964 Old Town session. Through 104 selections, BJ never strays far from his "Walk 'em Rhythm" philosohy: "They want to hear a melody ... they come to dance and they want to hear that beat. And we have to play loud!" At its heart, this was a hard-swinging big band, honed on countless tours during the '40s and '50s, and fronted by Buddy's sweet-voiced sister Ella. Her vocal numbers, including "Hittin' on Me," "I'm Just Your Fool," "Any Day Now," "What a Day," "I Don't Want Nobody," "Please Mr. Johnson," and even the unissued "Have Mercy on a Fool" qualify as the hits of this collection. Nolan Lewis, Floyd Ryland, and Lee Thomas were also featured vocalists during these years, with Buddy taking the mike on occasion. The underrated Purvis Henson (ten sax) steals the show on numerous instrumentals, showing that he had what it takes to do battle in his youth with Illinois Jacquet and Arnett Cobb in Texas. In the later years, Buddy tinkered with his style a bit, addressing the teen market, or trying his hand at more artful hi-fi horn arrangements. But, by and large, these cuts weathered the changing styles of '50s pop and, as a result, still sound great today! A beautiful 20-page large-format booklet is included, with photos and discography, of course. Bear Family scores again!

COLLECTABLES 5410 (CL)

Go Ahead and Rock: Featuring Ella Johnson

Reissue of Roulette 25085 (1959) with the rock-and-roll cover photo. A great collection of post-Mercury treasures. Highlights include a remake of the Decca classic "Fine Brown Frame" revamped as "Real Fine Frame," and "Walk 'Em," both from 1946. Sister Ella's smoky interpretation of her 1949 torch song "Down Yonder," the no-nonsense "Get on the Right Road," plus "Don't Fail Me Baby," "Sliding Horns," and a sultry reading of "I'm Tired of Crying over You" make the collection worthwhile. Ends with a bluesy rendition of "My Humble Plea" by Lee Thomas. Essential gravy.

JUKEBOX LIL 624 (R)

I'll Dearly Love You

Seventeen cuts spanning almost 20 years (1942–1961). Some of the singers on these swingin' Decca reissues are Buddy, Ella, and Arthur Prysock. A special treat is the inclusion of three tunes from a 1951 Voice of America radio broadcast from the Savoy Ballroom. Bold and brassy, jazz-flavored R&B. Down Yonder/Am I Blue/Pullamo/Ecstasy/Let's Beat Out Some Love.

MARV JOHNSON

High-tenor vocalist who bridged the gap between '50s R&B and '60s Motown. Johnson recorded for United Artists between 1959–1963, foreshadowing the happy, danceable blend of black and pop styles that would dominate the charts from the early '60s well into the '70s. In 1963, he was among the first artists to sign with Motown, helping to launch the label. He died in 1993 after many years of inactivity.

EMI 98895 (CL)

You Got What It Takes: The Best of Marv Johnson

A fine sample of this transitional performer's better United Artists recordings. These 24 tracks avoid the overtly pop numbers that appeared on Johnson's early '60s LPs. The sound is fine, as are the notes and vintage photos.

SYL JOHNSON

Chicago soul singer. Mississippi-born Syl Johnson first recorded as a guitarist behind Billy Boy

Arnold on Vee Jay in 1956. He spent most of the '50s playing guitar behind such blues greats as Magic Sam, Junior Wells, and Jimmy Reed before shifting gears and embarking on a solo career in 1959. After vocal efforts for Federal, Tempting, and Twinight, Syl signed with Hi in 1971 where he waxed a motherlode of fine ballads and hard-driving stompers arranged, produced, and musically garnished by Willie Mitchell.

HI (UK) 117 (L)
Music to My Ears
Hi singles and album cuts from 1972–1976. Booklet lists 26 songs, but the disc only features the first 25! Syl-salvation. I Hear the Love Chimes/Any Way the Wind Blows/Let Yourself Go/Wind, Blow Her Back My Way/Diamond in the Rough/I Only Have You/'Bout to Make Me Leave Home/Take Me to the River/Steppin' Out/It Ain't Easy/That's Just My Luck.

HI (UK) 404 (R)
The Love Chimes
Fifteen classic slabs of deep soul recorded between 1971–1974, notable not only for Johnson's gritty, soulful singing but for the superb arrangements and playing by the Hi stable (best known as the backing unit on all of Al Green's pre-gospel hits). Back for a Taste of Your Love/I'm Yours/I Hear the Love Chimes/The Love You Left Behind/Feelin' Frisky.

THE JONES BROTHERS

Clyde, Herb, and Max Jones were a popular vocal-harmony trio that thrived on the club circuit. They combined swing and jive with pop and semi-classical tunes, all played with the utmost professionalism.

WHISKEY, WOMEN AND ... 708 (R)
Stop the Sun, Stop the Moon
Their entire recorded output: six tracks from the '40s along with 13 tracks dating from the late '60s taken from radio broadcasts. The brothers are excellent singers and fine musicians (playing piano, trumpet, vibraharp, and drums), and the material, which is a mix of standards and instrumentals, is pleasant enough. Their career is well-documented in photos and the detailed reminiscences of Herb Jones.

LINDA JONES

Perhaps the greatest soul singer you never heard of, Linda was born in Newark, NJ, in 1944 and sang in her family gospel group, The Jones Sing-

ers, from the age of six. She suffered from diabetes throughout her life, leading to her untimely death in 1972. Linda's second waxing (her first was for Cub) was the great soul classic "Take This Boy Out of the Country" on Atco in 1964. In 1967, her producer George Kerr signed her to the Loma label, where she enjoyed four successful recordings, two of which ("Hypnotized" and "What've I Done") shot up to the Top Ten; these are reissued on Collectables 5120. Her last recordings were for the All Platinum label's Turbo subsidiary (reissued on Sequel).

COLLECTABLES 5120 (RL)
Hypnotized and 19 More Golden Classics
An unexpected goldmine for Linda Jones lovers and a must for any true lovers of '60s soul. This set contains her entire *Hypnotized* LP (Loma 5907 from 1967), along with nine single sides never before issued on LP from Loma, Blue Cat, and Neptune, including such classics as "I'll Be Sweeter Tomorrow," "Take This Boy Out of the Country," "For Your Precious Love," and, of course, the wonderful title track. Highest recommendations.

SEQUEL 167 (L)
Your Precious Love
Eighteen Turbo-label sides cut in 1972, including the slower remake of "Hypnotized" (which I personally think is a better version), the gospel-like impassioned "For Your Precious Love," "I've Given You the Best Years of My Life," "Doggin Me Around," "Let It Be Me," and the fabulous "Things I've Been Through."

LUKE JONES and RED MACK

KRAZY KAT 7440 (R)
West Coast R&B 1947–1952
Jump and easy vocal blues recordings by Shreveport's sax-wailing band leader Luke Jones ably supported by horn-blowing vocalist Red Mack who shines on "Feelin' Low Down" (from 1946). Other talent includes notable pianist/comedienne Betty Hall Jones (The Galloping Grandma), the unstoppable Chuck Barksdale on string bass, plus singing drummer George Vann whose vocal chords ache beautifully over "Graveyard Blues" and "Worryin' Anyhow Blues." Culled from sides recorded on Al Scherman's LA-based Atlas label. Other featured vocalists include Helen Andrews, Joe Alexander, and Clarence Williams.

MARGIE JOSEPH

Margie, throughout her long career, was always on the verge of a big breakthrough, and often came near the top of the soul charts, most notably with an 11-1/2 minute testifying version of The Supremes's "Stop! In the Name of Love" in 1971, but never got the one big hit.

STAX (UK) 015 (R)
In the Name of Love
Fifteen of her 1969–1971 Volt sides, including nine of her dozen singles sides. After a couple of flops on Okeh in 1967 and 1968, Margie was teamed up with brothers Earl and Willie Tee Turbington for two fine singles (the first, "One More Chance" b/w "Never Can You Be" is heard here, along with a never before issued cover of "Tell It Like It Is"), both of which flopped. She was then paired with Darrell Carter and Fred Briggs, and the trio also includes the hit "Your Sweet Lovin'." This collection also includes the five-minute single version of "Stop! In the Name of Love." Sweeter Tomorrow/Takin' All the Love I Can/Strung Out.

BENNY JOY

Benny Joy was a '50s rockabilly singer who started out recording on the Tri-Dec label in Florida. He went on to record a fair amount of material for small labels like Dixie, Antler, and Ram. Benny is one of the very best of the second-string rockers, too frantic and wild to have made much of an impact in the '50s, but his legendary status continues to grow with collectors. He was as pure a rockabilly spirit as ever slipped on a pair of blue-suede shoes.

COLLECTOR 4401 (L)
Rockin' and Rollin' with Benny Joy
These 23 cuts are basically the best of the two White Label LPs (8803 and 8825) with an alternate take of "Hey High School Baby" thrown in. Spin the Bottle/Steady with Betty/Wild, Wild Lover/Gossip, Gossip, Gossip.

WHITE LABEL 8803 (R)
Rockabilly with Benny Joy
A dozen of Joy's crude but effective knee knockers. "Crash the Party" (originally on Antler), "Steady with Betty" (originally on Dixie), and "Spin the Bottle" (originally on Tri Dec) are all great, and the original releases would set you back a pretty penny if you ever even found them. Also includes such gems as "Rebel Rock" and "Hey High School Baby."

WHITE LABEL 8825 (R)
More Rock-a-billy with Benny Joy
Fifteen more raunchy, low-fi recordings by Mr. Joy, all previously unissued except for "Stompin'," a tune actually by Benny's musical partner Big John Taylor. Tunes like "Gossip, Gossip, Gossip," "Wild, Wild Lover," and "I'm Gonna Move" rock with primitive fury. Dig the crazy pix on the LP cover too. Button Nose/Dark Angel/Indian Giver.

DON JULIAN and THE MEADOWLARKS

Fine integrated group from Los Angeles featuring the soft ballad leads of Don Julian. They recorded for RPM and Dooto in the mid-'50s and had a hit with "Heaven and Paradise." Further success eluded them and Julian went out on his own. In 1965 he formed The Larks to record his original dance song "The Jerk" that became a big hit.

COLLECTABLES 5046 (RCL)
Golden Classics
Twelve Dooto ballads and rockers. Heaven and Paradise/Oop Boopy Oop/I Am a Believer/This Must Be Paradise/Embarrassing Moments/I Got Tore Up.

THE JUNIOR RAYMEN

Vern Wray, Jr. was the son of Vern (Ray Vernon) Wray and the nephew of Doug and Link Wray. Growing up in the coolest family in America rubbed off on young Vern in a big way. He picked up the guitar at an early age, even writing a tune for The Raymen when he was 11 years old. That's him playing sax on The Raymen's "Dinosaur." At the age of 15, he had his own little combo, The Junior Raymen, carrying on the family tradition. Sadly, Vern Jr. drowned in July 1967, leaving only a handful of recordings as a hint of how good he might have become.

NORTON 213 (R)
Rumble '66
Five-song, mini-LP. I'm Branded/Ace of Spades/The Rat Fink/Jack the Ripper/Rumble '66.

JIMMY JUSTICE

British popster who covered American R&B.

ROCKIN' RECORDS 25101 (R)
His 15 Biggies
Here's a new one for me. No wonder I haven't heard of him; he was a pop artist on Pye, doing mostly covers of R&B ballads for the British market. He's a pretty decent singer, but when he tries to compete with the originals of "Save the Last Dance for Me," "Spanish Harlem," "Loop De Loop," and "A Little Bit of Soap," he's in a no-win situation. However, if you are nostalgic for British pop or want to check it out, Justice will reign. Sorry about that. One/Early in the Morning/Write Me a Letter.

KALEIDOSCOPE
Long before 3 Mustaphas 3 blended rock with Middle Eastern music, a '60s band called Kaleidoscope accomplished the same feat admirably, although hardly anyone noticed at the time. Led by David Lindley (aka El Rayo-X) and Solomon Feldthouse, Kaleidoscope released four LPs (1967–1970) that seem to fascinate any collector who happens to come across them. The five group members played a truckload of instruments including oud, bouzouki, and saz, not to mention more common instruments like banjo, dobro, and mandolin. Their style was just as eclectic as their instrumentation, with all of the American folk musics blended into the soup, but not just as an act of emulation. They remind me of The Band's approach, grabbing a bit of this and that to put across their own unique songs.

EPIC 47723 (CL)
Egyptian Candy
Eighteen tunes presenting a very good sampling of the Kaleidoscope story, but I can't believe Epic didn't include "Seven-ate Sweet," one of their very best, even if it is eleven-and-a-half minutes long. However, the twelve-and-a-half minute "Beacon from Mars" is included. The title tune, "Love Games," and "Sefan" are all previously unreleased and are all great. Cuckoo/Life Will Pass You By/Why Try/Pulsating Dream.

EPIC 48513 (L)
Side Trips
1967 debut LP from one of the most talented and sophisticated groups of the '60s. Egyptian Gardens/Hesitation Blues/Pulsating Dream/Oh Death/Why Try.

THE KALIN TWINS
At the age of 24, these New York twins hit the top 40 with "When," and then spent the next four years trying to repeat that success. One reason for that failure is that the Kalins preferred pop to rock and roll. So, their label's attempt to fit them into the teenage mold often produced half-hearted stuff. Recently, the duo was rediscovered working as bureaucrats in Washington, DC's city government!

BEAR FAMILY 15122 (R)
When
Sixteen late-'50s Decca sides by pop-rock duo. Sweet Sugar Lips/Oh My Goodness/Clickety Clack.

BEAR FAMILY 15597 (L)
When
Thirty cuts, including the aptly named "It's Just Terrible." Excellent notes, great photos, and impeccable sound quality, but the music is too mainstream to qualify as effective rock and roll. Jumpin' Jack/Forget Me Not/Dream of Me/I'm Gonna Knock on Your Door.

RAMSEY KEARNEY
Ramsey Kearney was a pretty fair C&W and rockabilly singer from Tennessee who never had too much success in the '50s. He kept plugging away, however, until he ultimately put together a long career in the music biz. His strong point was his ability to write good songs, so he always seemed to find a job writing for the major Nashville publishers, including Cedarwood and Acuff-Rose.

SUNJAY 591 (R)
Tennessee Rock
Twenty tunes recorded over an 11-year period from 1955–1965 (with a 1989 tune thrown in) at various Tennessee radio stations and studios. You'll recognize a lot of the studio musicians; Roy Orbison was even called on to play guitar on a couple of tunes done at Sam Phillips's studio in 1960. There are a few, decent, countryish rockabilly tunes here, but most of this is straight-ahead country with a beat. Everything is recorded with such a lack of polish that this often sounds like a collection of demos, which ain't so bad when you consider the string sections that marred many finished studio productions of the era. Red Bobby Sox/Rock the Bop/Don't Tease/Goodbye Train/Doin' Hard Time.

THE KEIL ISLES

DOWN SOUTH 9214 (R)
Rock from the Other Side, Vol. 4
Fourteen songs by this New Zealand group who recorded between 1958–1962. They performed mostly covers of US hits with a few originals.

JERRY KELLER

Jerry Keller was a midwestern boy who rose to prominence after his song "Here Comes Summer" hit a nerve with daydreamin' teenagers in 1959. Born in Fort Smith, AR, his family relocated to Tulsa, OK, where he performed with the gospel choral group, The Midwest Boy Singers. Later, he formed a secular barbershop quartet called The Lads of Note while still in high school. In 1956, he relocated to New York, where he worked as an oil company clerk, still searching for fame and fortune. A chance meeting with Pat Boone led to a connection with Kapp Records and his self-penned hit. Soon after, Keller left for England where he had his own TV show. Despite numerous tries with a variety of labels big and small, he never again hit it big as a solo act, although his composition "Turn-down Day" was a hit for The Cyrcle in 1966. His stuff is about as lightweight as you can get, and I'm sure he was loved by the mums and dads as well as their well-scrubbed kids.

TEENAGER 614 (R)
Here Comes Jerry Keller
Likeable fluff, including his big hit "Here Comes Summer." If I Had a Girl/Some Summer/Goodnight Little Girl/True Love/Time Has a Way.

PAUL KELLY

EDSEL 316 (R)
Hangin' On in There
Fourteen superb tracks of Southern soul recorded between 1970–1974 for the Happy Tiger and Warner Bros. labels, spearheaded by Kelly's brilliant and controversial "Stealing in the Name of the Lord." This scathing and witty indictment of certain kinds of preachers was denounced from Southern pulpits, and radio stations that played it were picketed. While the rest of his recordings are not quite as unique, the material, almost all written by Kelly himself, is consistently fine with production by Buddy Killen and superb accompaniments by Muscle Shoals or Nashville sidemen. They provide a rich backdrop to Kelly's gorgeous, gospel-flavored vocals. The songs are a mixture of mid-tempo items like "509" and "Come Lay Some Lovin' on Me" and scorching soul ballads like the title cut, "Love Me Now," and "I Wanna Get Next to You." Detailed notes by John Ridley.

CHRIS KENNER

Splendid New Orleans R&B singer who recorded excellent sides for Imperial and Instant, but who is today remembered as a writer ("Sick And Tired," "Land of 1,000 Dreams," "I Like It like That," and "Something You Got").

COLLECTABLES 5166 (CL)
I Like It like That: Golden Classics
Excellent collection of 16 Instant recordings from 1961–1967 produced by Allen Toussaint. "Land of 1000 Dances" is heard here with a great gospelish call-and-response intro that was chopped off the final release. Also includes the never before reissued "(I Found) Peace" from 1961. I Like It Like That/Shoo-Rah/Gonna Getcha Baby/Something You Got/She Can Dance.

THE KEYNOTES

Central Harlem quintet led for the most part by tenor Sam Kearney who idolized The Five Crowns.

RELIC 5072 (R)
The Best of The Keynotes
The first legal reissue of all six Apollo singles by this group, including the 1955 classics "Zenda," "A Star," and "Suddenly," plus four unreleased and alternate takes. Jump number "Bye Bye Baby" really burns along with Sam "The Man" Taylor featured on tenor sax.

JOHNNY KIDD and THE PIRATES

Probably England's first authentic rock group (formed in 1959 and disbanded in 1966) and the godfather of the power trio. The group featured the fantastic guitar of Mick Green, and excellent songs, mostly written by Kidd, including the original "Shakin' All Over" and "Please Don't Touch." Kidd was killed in a car crash on October 7, 1966. Green, an especially big influence in England's pub-rock scene, re-formed The Pirates in 1976.

SEE FOR MILES 120 (RL)
Rarities
Twenty extremely rare HMV sides, recorded between 1959–1966. Side 1 has ten previously unissued tunes, mostly covers of US hits, with some great guitar from Mick Green and John Weider, including "I Know," "Oh Boy," "Right String But the Wrong Yo-Yo," and "Can't Turn You Loose." Side 2 has nine A and B sides, many never before on LP, plus "Weep No More My Baby," which only appeared on a 1960 Parlophone Saturday Club compilation. Shakin' All Over '65/The Fool/Whole Lotta Woman.

SEE FOR MILES SEE 287 (R)
The Classic and Rare
Jam-packed collection of 22 Pirates's hits and misses from 1959–1966. Includes the previously unreleased "Some Other Guy," recorded in 1963, a real pounding pop tune sounding like early Merseybeat. Next is an alternate take of "Let's Talk about Us," and it's a lot nastier than the released version. "Send Me Some Lovin'" is from 1964 and is in the style of a raunchy Elvis ballad with tremendous singing and guitar playing. Kidd's version of Sanford Clark's "The Fool" is from 1964 and tougher than the 1966 version. The final previously unreleased track is the 1964 remake of "Big Blon' Baby," much stronger than their 1960 version, with staccato guitar work that would be a big influence on guitarists that followed. Lots more in the way of hits and B sides. I Want That/So What/ Feelin'/ Please Don't Touch.

MERLE KILGORE

Merle Kilgore might not be a household name, but he has been smack dab in the middle of country and rockabilly action since the early '50s, performing and recording, writing or cowriting more than 300 recorded songs, acting in movies, and managing Hank Williams, Jr.!

BEAR FAMILY 15544 (L)
Teenager's Holiday
Thirty-tune retrospective covering his Imperial rockabilly tunes including "Ernie" and "Everybody Needs a Little Lovin'," some Fats Domino-like tunes from a New Orleans session with Dave Bartholomew, as well as some folky tunes and teen ballads. There are some good tunes in all of these genres but Kilgore's strong suit is in his great country tunes, including "More and More," "It Can't Rain All the Time," "Seein' Double, Feeling Single," and "Funny Feelin'" (he wrote 'em all!) He really sings the heck out of these songs, too. "Now That You Are Leavin'" and "That's When My Blues Began" were both unissued at the time, but, as you can hear, they're both top-flight hillbilly performances.

DEMAND 0055 (R)
Country Rockers
Eighteen of Kilgore's early recordings. Includes the great "Love Flame," Imperial rockabilly tunes ("Everybody Needs a Little Lovin'," "Dirty Ernie," and "Hang Doll"), a live "Mona Lisa" from 1959, and consummate country tunes like "It Can't Rain All the Time" and "Funny Feeling." Good collection, although his singing style turns hokey on Side 2.

KING CURTIS

One of the last, great, honking tenor-sax men, Curtis Ousley started playing when he was 12 and went directly from high school to Lionel Hampton's band. He spent part of the late '50s in the Nat Adderley Quintet, and played a bit with his own group, but mostly worked as a freelancer for dozens of tiny NY R&B labels. His popularity soared after his famous stuttering sax break on The Coaster's hit "Yakety Yak." His recording of "Soul Twist" for Enjoy in 1962 topped the R&B charts. He led The King Pins and The Noble Knights through the '60s, first on Capitol and then on Atlantic/Atco, and he played on hundreds of Atlantic sessions for everyone from Aretha to Eric Clapton to The Rascals. In 1971, he became Aretha's musical director, but tragically, in August of that year, he was stabbed to death outside of his home while trying to break up an argument. Collectables 5119 is one of the better reissue collections.

ACE 262 (R)
It's Party Time with King Curtis
Reissue of a 1962 LP. Curtis wails up a storm here on a party album that must have livened up many a teenager's rec room in the '60s. There's a few slower numbers here but mostly it's dance music for the hyperactive generation with the King blowin' his brains out, backed up by a tight, little R&B band. On "Hot Saxes," Curtis is joined by Sam "The Man" Taylor in an old-fashioned cuttin' session, a tune so hot they probably had to hose off their axes when they finished. Free for All/The Party Time Twist/Low Down/Keep Movin'/Something Frantic.

BULLDOG 2009 (R)
20 Golden Pieces of King Curtis
Rocking instrumental R&B from 1967 and 1970. Includes remakes of "Tequila," "Night Train," "Harlem Nocturne," "Honky Tonk," "Soul Twist," and 15 more.

⊙ COLLECTABLES 5119 (CL)
Soul Twist and Other Golden Classics

Fabulous NY R&B collection with fellow tenor honkers Willis "Gatortail" Jackson and Noble Watts. Fifteen cuts, mostly instrumental. Exceptional.

COLLECTABLES 5156 (CL)
Enjoy Records ... The Best Of: Golden Classics

Ten Enjoy-label sides, including Curtis's big hit "Soul Twist," already reissued on the plainly superior Collectables 5119. Some of these "classics" sure ain't no 14-karat gold, but I bet you'll gyrate to "Groovin' with the King" and "Sack o' Woe," the instrumental version of "What'd I Say," and the sax-less "Hot Potatoes." "Midnight Blue" is a mellow nocturnal number with oh-so-good solos by Curtis and his guitarist (most likely Mickey Baker, who steals the spotlight more than once on this disc). Forget about the rest of these sides, especially the two vocal numbers.

EDSEL 315 (RL)
Instant Groove

Seven servings from Curtis's greatest period, the late '50s, standing as some of the greatest sax instrumentals ever done, especially the jungle groove of "Castle Rock," a piping hot "Chili," and the regal frenzy of "Restless Guitar" and "Boss." The other nine cuts are from his second Atlantic stint, which lasted from 1965 until his tragic death in 1971. "Rocky Roll" is a tribute number, quoting "Haunted House," "Yakety Yak," and "Maybelline"—cool IF your living room already resembles a scene out of *Beach Blanket Bingo*. The other late '60s waxings, though successful soul formula hits, sound sadly uninspired today. The slow funk "Cookout" and a remake of Big Jay's "There Is Something on Your Mind" are the only tunes that don't tread on Jr. Walker's turf. Anyway, get a couple of copies, and an extra pair of shoes while you're at it, 'cause I bet you'll wear out the whole shebang before you tire of this one!

RED LIGHTNIN' 0074 (R)
Didn't He Play

A real treat. Thirteen extremely rare or never issued tunes produced by Herb Abramson, each with the saxophonist at his best. There are three tunes from January 1959 sessions with saxman Freddy Mitchell that were previously issued on Trip; Triumph-label sides with Curtis backing up Tony Middleton and The Capitols (not the "Cool Jerk" group); 1963 sides backing Derek Martin and Jimmy Breedlove; and some 1967 "comeback" sides with Ronnie Miller that led to Curtis's late '60s success, including "Home Cookin'," a precursor to "Memphis Soul Stew." Solid sax (and, on "Blue Nocturne," guitar) throughout.

KING PERRY

Small jump group similar in style to Louis Jordan's Tympany Five with a rougher, more R&B sound. This sextet featured leader Perry on vocals and alto sax, along with Maxie Ward (ten sax), Ralph Bowden (trb), Earl Payton or Jimmy Beasley (pno), Chuck Norris (gtr, last session only), Ike Brown or Vic Greenwood (b), and Cake Wichard (drm).

KRAZY KAT 7438 (R)
King Perry

Perry sings on the first five cuts, recorded for Excelsior in 1947–1948; backs up singer Duke Henderson on four 1948 Excelsior sides, including the fine jail-bait song "San Quentin Quail"; does "Going to California" for De Luxe in 1949; some swing standards for Lucky in 1954, including "Christopher Columbus"; and four more for Excelsior at the end of 1954, including Lucky Millinder's "Fat Mama."

BEN E. KING

As Bennie Nelson, he was a member of The Five Crowns, which included lead singer Bobby Hendricks who left in 1958 to join The Drifters. In 1958, The Drifters broke up and, in order to fulfill contracts, Drifters's manager George Treadwell turned The Crowns into the "new Drifters," with Nelson, now known as Ben E. King, as lead singer (see separate listing). After three smashes ("There Goes My Baby," "Save the Last Dance for Me," and "This Magic Moment"), King, with the aid of songwriters Lieber and Stoller and producer Phil Spector, had a long string of solo hits for Atlantic including "Spanish Harlem," "Stand by Me," and "I (Who Have Nothing)." When the hits stopped, he quit Atlantic, resigning with them in 1975 and recording "Supernatural Thing" which made the Top 10. In the '80s, he had hits singing with The Average White Band, and enjoyed a comeback as a soloist when the film *Stand by Me* was released. The song was also used in a Levi's commercial, leading to its rerelease, bringing it back into the US Top 40 and the top of the British charts.

ATLANTIC 80213 (L)
The Ultimate Ben E. King: Stand by Me

Twenty-track disc, including three tunes with The Drifters ("This Magic Moment," "Save the Last Dance for Me," and "I Count the Tears"); a rarely reissued track from a 1959 session, "Show Me the Way," performed solo while he was still with The Drifters; and all the greats. All of the tracks are reissued in real stereo. Stand by Me/I (Who Have Nothing)/Spanish Harlem/Amor/Supernatural Thing/Here Comes the Night.

EDSEL 131 (R)

Here Comes the Night

Sixteen fine and seldom reissued Atco sides. Liner notes are from an interview with King. Brace Yourself/Seven Letters/The Record/Jamaica/Tell Daddy/It's All Over.

SID KING and THE FIVE STRINGS

One of the very earliest white rock-and-roll outfits. Texan Sid King started his career in 1952 performing western swing and C&W but, like other teenagers of the time, gradually started incorporating R&B into his sound. King and The Five Strings really hit their stride in 1954 after signing with Columbia, cutting some of the very best rockabilly ever made, mostly at Jim Beck's Dallas studio.

BEAR FAMILY 15048 (R)/15535 (L)

Gonna Shake this Shack Tonight

Twenty great '50s rockabilly sides (29 on CD) by this fine Texas band, including two previously unissued cuts on LP, seven on CD. These are top-notch rockabilly tunes with the classic slap bass, jive lyrics, and red-hot guitar work. CD includes the fine Dot single from 1959 ("Hello There Rockin' Chair" b/w "Once upon a Time"); a 1953 Starday pairing (released as by The Western Melody Makers: "Who Put the Turtle in Myrtle's Girdle" b/w "If Tears Could Cry"); plus five more previously unissued tunes. A super 36-page booklet is also included. I Like It/Drinkin' Wine Spo-Dee-o-Dee/Purr, Kitty, Purr/Sag, Drag and Fall/Let 'Er Roll.

ROLLER COASTER 2006 (R)

Rockin' on the Radio

Fascinating and significant album showing the development of rock and roll in the mid-'50s. Side 1 is a broadcast from 1954, and is pretty straight honky-tonk country with an upbeat flavor. Side 2 is from a year later, and the music is rockabilly with a country flavor. Beautifully packaged with extensive notes.

THE KINGSMEN

The Northwestern garage band whose no-frills approach launched thousands of would-be pre-tenders who could easily approximate the three-chord racket of the naughty "Louie Louie" or the goofy "The Jolly Green Giant." The quintet, led by vocalist/guitarist Jack Ely, was formed in Portland, OR, in 1958. Their reworking of the Richard Berry R&B song "Louie Louie" was originally part of a live album issued on Wand in 1963. When the single was issued it became a Number 2 hit and influenced thousands of garage bands. "Louie Louie" still puts almost every subsequent rock-and-roll song to shame with its simple but effective riff, killer guitar solo, and licentious lyrics. They had several other lesser hits, but friction within the group led to it disbanding in 1967.

COLLECTABLES 5073 (CL)

Louie Louie and More Golden Classics

An even dozen tunes from the rulers of the cool Northwest '60s teen scene. The B-sides of their two big hits are here: "Haunted Castle," a boss instrumental; and "Long Green," a tune too great to have been just a B-side. "Killer Joe," "Annie Fanny," "The Climb," "Little Sally Tease," and the rest of the Wand singles didn't do much on the charts at the time (mid-'60s), but they're all fun, rockin' tunes.

INSTANT 5047 (L)

Louie Louie

Twenty Wand label winners, featuring the vocally indecipherable title track, plus other frat-party essentials, all recorded in genuine full-blast distort-o-phonic sound. Other cuts include a couple of New Orleans standards, The Kingmen's commentary on '60s aesthetics ("That's Cool, That's Trash"), and a personal favorite, the goofy "Jolly Green Giant." If you don't think The Kingsmen are awesome, you just haven't had enough Olympia beer! Money/Little Latin Lupe Lu/Killer Joe/The Climb/Do You Love Me?

RHINO 70745 (CL)

Greatest Hits

All eight of their Wand hits are on this brilliant sounding cassette or CD including "Money," "Little Latin Lupe Lu," and "The Jolly Green Giant," as well as ten other primo cuts like "Haunted Castle" (the B-side to "Louie Louie"), and the way too cool "That's Cool, That's Trash." Don't plan another party until you have this collection to slap in the CD player! Rosalie/Little Sally Tease/Annie Fanny/Killer Joe.

THE KINKS

Ray Davies (1944) and brother Dave (1947) are the prime movers behind this long-lived band, overshadowed somewhat during the British-invasion years by their rivals The Beatles, The Rolling Stones, and The Who. The brothers began playing and writing together during their early teens, forming the band in 1964 originally as an R&B-based outfit. Their first hit was scored during that year ("You Really Got Me"), followed rapidly by "All Day and All of the Night" and "Who'll Be the Next in Line," earning them spots on teen-fave TV shows *Hullabaloo* and *Shindig*. In 1966 and 1967, they scored hits with their nasty put-downs of social snobbery, "Well Respected Man" and "Dedicated Follower of Fashion." The group suffered a few setbacks in 1968 and 1969, but returned with a vengeance in 1970 with "Lola," perhaps the first rock song about transvestite/homosexual love. Despite animosity between the founding brothers, the band soldiered on through the 1970s and 1980s, forging further into areas of artiness verging on the pretentious. Rhino has reissued their first four LPs with their original covers and notes, including bonus singles tracks, for the true Kinks collector.

RHINO 70315 (CL)
You Really Got Me
Reissue of the original British *The Kinks* LP (Pye 18096, 1964), with three additional singles: "Long Tall Sally," "You Still Want Me," and "You Do Something to Me." Ray and the boys bang their way through 14 R&B-based rockers. Their toughest LP, and a rock classic to boot. You Really Got Me/Stop Your Sobbing/Beautiful Delilah/Got Love if You Want It.

RHINO 70316 (CL)
Kinda Kinks
Combines the original British release of *Kinda Kinks* (Pye 18112, 1965) with hits "All Day and All of the Night," "I Gotta Move," and "It's All Right," for a total of 15 kinky kuts. Ray Davies really steps to the fore in a hurry on their second LP release. He wrote ten of the 12 tunes here ("Dancing in the Streets" and "Naggin' Woman" are the covers). Great self-depreciating liner notes, too. Tired of Waiting for You/Something Better Beginning/Wonder Where My Baby Is Tonight.

RHINO 70317 (CL)
Kinks-Size
Another Kinks album (originally Reprise 6158, 1965), with another classic single as the centerpiece: "All Day and All of the Night." It's mind-boggling to realize that thousands of teenagers were all hangin' out in rec rooms and garages around the world memorizing these and earlier Kink's gems! And tell me, is there one guitar solo on MTV that even comes close to the one on "All Day and All of the Night"? I rest my case. Wonderful fan-club type lowdown on the boys for liner notes. I Gotta Move/Long Tall Sally/Louie Louie/Things Are Getting Better/Set Me Free.

RHINO 70318 (CL)
Kinkdom
Ray wrote every song on this one, a reissue of Reprise 6184 from 1966. He plays the Carnaby Street dandy to the hilt with the mincing classics "Well Respected Man" and "Dedicated Follower of Fashion," but also pens some tough garage-band favorites like "Who'll Be the Next in Line" and "I Need You," not to mention the anthemic "I'm Not like Everybody Else." Kinkdom, as the all-time greatest liner notes say, "is a land so wild, so fantastic, so far out that even Rand is scared to tell McNally."

RHINO 75769 (CL)
Kinks-Size Kinkdom
These cuts originally released on British singles and EPs, and were collected on LP solely for the US market. Some of the tracks appeared on British LPs that had more tracks than the US LPs. This set contains all of the EP and 45 cuts that appeared on *Kinks-Size* ("Set Me Free," " "Louie, Louie," "Who'll Be the Next in Line"), as well as on *Kinkdom* ("Well Respected Man," "I Need You," and "See My Friends"; this last song features pseudo-sitar sounding guitars, the first UK hit to show an Indian-music influence!). Also included are "Dedicated Follower of Fashion" (which made its first LP debut on the *Greatest Hits* LP), and two rare B-sides that took years to get to LP: "I'm Not Like Everybody Else" and "Sitting on My Sofa." Highest recommendation.

SEE FOR MILES 295 (R)
The EP Collection
Reissue of the first six Kinks EPs on one LP, a generous 24 tracks in all. Also includes brother Dave's *Hits* EP released in 1967, consisting of his two solo efforts, the

brilliant "Death of a Clown," the thunder strike of "Love Me Till the Sun Shines," and their flip sides. Whether the Kinks were drunkenly bashing away at "Louie Louie" or playing the gentle "Two Sisters" with the demeanor of a baroque quartet, their vision and craftsmanship always labels the finished product with their own stamp. Set Me Free/David Watts/Lazy Old Sun/Well Respected Man/Don't You Fret.

THE KNICKERBOCKERS

New Jersey-based quartet with a strong Beatles flavor to their music. Originally called The Castle Kings, the group was fronted by brothers Beau (gtr) and Johnny (b) Charles, along with Buddy Randell (sax, voc), and Jimmy Walker (drm, voc). The group was signed to Challenge, changed their name to The Knickerbockers (after a street in their hometown), and recorded two duds, "Bite, Bite Barracuda" and "Jerktown," before hitting it big with the Beatles sound-alike, "Lies." Their squeaky clean appearance led to regular appearances on the popular teen show, *Where the Action Is*. They disbanded in the late '60s. Collector's note: Their first LP, *Sing and Sync Along with Lloyd: Lloyd Thaxton Presents The Knickerbockers* was the only LP every issued in "Trick Track" format; the listener never knew exactly what he or she would hear, as any one of five alternate numbers might be played depending on exactly where the needle was dropped on the vinyl!

SUNDAZED 5000 (R)

The Great Lost Knickerbockers Album

Fourteen previously unissued recordings, stereo versions, and demos, including a demo version of their only hit "Lies."

SUNDAZED 11002 (L)

Presenting The Fabulous Knickerbockers

Twenty cuts (eight in stereo). Lies/Rumors, Gossip, Words Untrue/Jerktown.

FREDERICK KNIGHT

Fine soul singer from Alabama who had a hit for Stax in 1972 with "I've Been Lonely So Long." He had a few other minor successes for various small labels and continues to pursue an active career as a singer and producer.

STAX 8564 (L)

I've Been Lonely for So Long

Knight uses his fine falsetto to best effect on the title song, which made it to Number 8 in the R&B charts in 1972. He also plays piano, organ, drums, and percussion all over this self-produced 1973 Stax LP. The album is a little uneven at times, but there are plenty of fine songs. "I Let a Chance Go By" is a wonderful mid-tempo look at regret and misery. The vaguely doo-wopish "Now that I've Found You" is also worth a play or ten. Knight can manage funky sounds, too, on "Your Love's All Over Me," "Take Me on Home Witcha," and "Pick 'um Up, Put 'um Down." His cover of "Someday We'll Be Together" ain't too shabby either.

GLADYS KNIGHT and THE PIPS

Gladys Knight made her debut singing at Mount Maria Baptist Church in Atlanta at age four! Her parents were both members of The Wings Over Jordan Choir, a popular local gospel group. Gladys's fame as a singer quickly spread, leading to a tour of Florida and Alabama with The Morris Brown Choir before she reached the age of five. At seven, she won first prize on *Ted Mack's Amateur Hour*, and continued to tour as a soloist until the age of 12. In the late '50s, Gladys performed with her brother Merald, sister Brenda, and cousins William and Elenor Guest at a family party. Their cousin James Wood, nicknamed Pip, urged them to go professional, and so they took the name Gladys Knight and The Pips. Popular on the R&B circuit in the late '50s and early '60s, they scored their first Top 10 pop and Number 1 R&B hit with Johnny Otis's "Every Beat of My Heart" in 1961, quickly followed by the #3 R&B hit, "Letter Full of Tears." In 1966, they signed with Motown, scoring a year later with a remake of Marvin Gaye's "I Heard It Through the Grapevine." The group continued to score hits through the '70s and '80s, with Knight going solo in the latter decade.

COLLECTABLES 5154 (CL)

Letter Full of Tears

Fourteen early '60s sides made for Fury records. Operator/Come See About Me/Morning, Noon and Night/I Want That Kind of Love.

MOTOWN 5126 (CL)

Everybody Needs Love
Reissue of the Pips's first Motown release, issued in 1967 on the Soul subsidiary (706).

MOTOWN 5148 (CL)

Nitty Gritty
Their fourth LP, originally 1970's Soul 713.

MOTOWN 5193 (CL)

Neither One of Us
Originally issued in 1973 as Soul 737.

MOTOWN 5303 (RCL)

Anthology
Their big hits and album tracks recorded from 1967-1973. Liner notes are less-than-inspiring and CD remastering is poor.

MOTOWN 5388 (CL)

If I Were Your Woman
One of their best Motown LPs, originally issued as Soul 731 in 1971.

MOTOWN 5396 (CL)

All I Need is Time
Originally issued in 1974 as Soul 739.

MOTOWN 5458

Silk n' Soul
Their third LP, originally 1969's Soul 711.

MOTOWN 5467 (CL)

Feelin' Bluesy
Their second LP, originally 1968's Soul 707.

MOTOWN 5470 (CL)

Standing Ovation
Originally Soul 736 from 1972.

P-VINE 2172 (L)

Letter Full of Tears
Twenty early-'60s sides from the Fury label, including seven selections not on the Collectables release. Includes three Pips tracks: "Darlin'," "Linda," and "Hap-

piness." Every Beat of My Heart/Morning, Noon and Night/Guess Who/How Do You Say Goodbye.

RELIC 8022 (R)

Every Beat of Our Hearts
Although this duplicates Fury sides that are currently available on P-Vine and Collectables, it is a superior production in every way, lovingly remastered from the original master tapes wherever possible, along with detailed annotation. These hauntingly beautiful early '60s songs constitute some of the group's finest hours. Every Beat of My Heart/Operator/Letter Full of Tears/Queen of Tears.

RHINO 70756 (CL)

Soul Survivors
Their post-Motown recordings made for Buddah, Columbia, and RCA between 1973-1983. The big hit here is "Midnight Train to Georgia." CD has five bonus tracks.

JEAN KNIGHT
Excellent soul singer from New Orleans who started her career recording for legendary maverick Louisiana producer Huey Meaux. In 1971 she recorded "Mr. Big Stuff" at the Malaco studios in Jackson, MS. Released on Stax, this recording became a giant hit on the R&B and pop charts with its infectious dance rhythms. She continued to record for Stax with only moderate success. She re-emerged in the '80s with a couple of minor hits including a version of the popular Louisiana novelty "My Toot Toot."

STAX 8554 (CL)

Mr. Big Stuff
Reissue of her 1972 album with six extra tracks. Don't Talk About Jody/Take Him (You Can Have My Man)/Why Do I Keep Living These Memories/One Way Ticket.

SONNY KNIGHT
Pop/R&B singer from the LA area who recorded for a number of small labels in the early '50s, and is best-known for "Confidential," originally issued on Vita and leased to Dot. In 1981, under his real name Joseph C. Smith, he wrote a fictionalized expose of R&B life called *The Day the Music Died.*

MR. R&B 107 (R)
Confidential

This soft, melancholic singer's best recordings were made between 1953–1964 for a number of labels, the best material coming from the earliest sides, recorded for Alladin ("But Officer"), Vita ("Confidential"), and Starla ("Dedicated to You"). The usual excellent sound and informative notes by Bill Millar.

BUDDY KNOX

Buddy Holly-flavored rocker from Happy, TX. In 1956, Knox formed a band with Jimmy Bowen and excellent guitarist Don Lanier called The Rhythm Orchids, releasing a record on the local Triple D label. The single was picked up by Roulette, and each side given its own record, resulting in two smash hits: "Party Doll" by Knox and "I'm Stickin' with You" by Bowen. Knox's recordings were immensely appealing with his warm vocals and gently swinging and thoroughly infectious songs with excellent rockabilly guitar from Lanier. He had further hits with "Rock Your Litle Baby to Sleep" and "Hula Love." In 1960, he moved with Bowen to Los Angeles, and began recording teen-pop material for Liberty. In the mid-'60s, he switched to country music, though he continued to perform rock and roll on his European tours in the '70s and '80s. At the present time he lives in Canada.

RHINO 70964 (CL)
The Best of Buddy Knox

A fine cross section of his most popular Roulette and Liberty recordings, including his big hit "Party Doll," and many other fine sides (most of them written by Knox). A highlight is his controversial "I Think I'm Gonna Kill Myself," which Buddy makes sound positively cheerful! Backing his fine vocals are The Rhythm Orchids, including Jimmy Bowen on bass and the excellent Don Lanier on lead guitar. As usual for Rhino, the sound quality is superb, and the package comes with a 12-page booklet with notes by Colin Escott and some fine vintage photos. Rock Your Little Baby to Sleep/Storm Clouds/Somebody Touch Me/Hula Love/Devil Woman/Swingin' Daddy.

ROCKSTAR 1012 (R)
Texas Rockabilly Man

Recorded in England in 1982 with the ubiquitous Dave Travis Band with hot lead from Eddie Jones. Includes four tunes written by Buddy in the '50s but never recorded, plus his versions of Jimmy Merrit's "Too Much Fun," Roy Oribson's "Ooby Dooby," Carl Perkin's "Restless," and Buddy Holly's "I'm Lookin' for Someone to Love."

ROULETTE 25048 (R)
Buddy Knox and Jimmy Bowen

Generous 24-track LP, nine by Knox and 15 by Bowen. Their big hit's—Knox's "Party Doll" and Bowen's "I'm Sticking With You"—are missing, but there are plenty of other good'uns to make up for these omissions. A nice bonus is the great instrumental "Rockabilly Walk" by Buddy and Jimmy and their group The Rhythm Orchids. There's a great cover shot of the boys arm wrestling, too.

THE KODAKS

The Newark-based Kodaks were led by 15-year-old Pearl McKinnon, who took Frankie Lymon's part in the recreated Teenagers touring group. She was accompanied by James Patrick (lead, ten), William Franklin (2nd ten), Larry Davis (bar), and William Miller (b). The quintet borrowed from The Teenagers and The Youngsters for its sound, but don't let that detract you. Their 1957–1958 Fury recordings hold both a spiritual warmth and excitement.

RELIC 5083 (R)
The Best of The Kodaks

Includes "Kingless Castle," "Guardian Angel," and "Teenagers Dream," plus two alternates, and a single Pearl cut with The Deltares (named after Delta Airlines!) in 1961. Rare pix and learned sleeve notes.

SLEEPY LABEEF

Rockabilly and rockin' country artist (more on the country side) who's been putting out recordings since the '50s, when his Starday sides were leased to Mercury. He recorded for Shelby Singleton's revived Sun label in the '70s, as well as in Europe, and currently puts out material on Rounder. He has a very deep and distinctive voice (hence his nickname) and is a powerful guitar player.

ROUNDER 3052 (RC)
It Ain't What You Eat
It's the Way You Chew It

ROUNDER 3070 (RC)
Electricity
Selection of old country and rock-and-roll songs. Not one of his best but still good.

ROUNDER 3072 (RCL)
Nothin' But the Truth: Recorded Live
Nearly an hour of rockabilly and rockin' country recorded in October 1985 at Harper's Ferry, MA. Backed by a five-piece band and occasional backing vocalists, Beef tears through everything from Hank Ballard's "Tore Up over You," Webb Pierce's "How Do You Talk to a Baby," "Milk Cow Blues," Bo Diddley's "Gunslinger," to "Toot Toot"! Also includes a fine Hank Williams medley with "Whole Lotta Shakin' Goin' On" and "Folsom Prison Blues" added for good measure. Relentless rockin', reminds me of Johnny Cash on speed!

THE LADDINS
New York harmony group led by Apollo MC Bobby Jay. They started in 1956, hitting in 1958 with "Yes Oh Baby Yes" for Alan Freed's Grey Cliff label. An unreleased tune from the mid-'50s was put out on the Times Square label during the doo-wop revival of the early '60s, and was a smash hit. Original members John Marcus and Bobby Jay still lead the group.

RELIC 5018 (R)
The Laddins Greatest Hits
Twenty songs.

DON LANG and THE TWISTERS
Rockin' British trombonist of the early '60s.

C5 509 (R)
20 Rock and Roll Twists
If you were living in the UK in the late '50s/early '60s and have fond reminiscences of the "6.5 Special," or are a fan of jive, you'll probably enjoy this reissue of Don's 1962 UK Decca LP. Don performs 20 '50s "oldies" in a "stars-on-45" style, with a constant clap track going through each tune. Besides "twist" arrangements, Don substitutes the word "twist" whenever "appropriate," so we get "Twist around the Clock," "Whole Lotta Twistin' Goin' On," and the immortal lyrics, "every cat in the whole cell block/ was twistin' to the jailhouse rock!"

THE LARKS
Fine R&B quintet founded in 1950 by ex-Selah Jubilee Singer Thurmon Ruth, and featuring Eugene Mumford (who was falsely accused of rape of a white woman and imprisoned for two years in the late '40s), Allen Bunn, better known as Tarheel Slim, (bar and gtr), Ray "Pee Wee" Barnes (ten), Hadie Row, Jr. (ten), and the deep bass of Dave McNeil. Though short lived The Larks were one of the best vocal groups of the early '50s having hits with "Eyesight to the Blind" and "Little Side Car," performing at a large number of venues including many TV shows. Only Billy Ward and His Dominoes (see separate listing) came close to singing as well as The Larks.

RELIC 8013 (R)
The Best of The Larks:
Vol. 1, The Apollo
RELIC 8014 (R)
The Best of The Larks:
Vol. 2, The Apollo
Two collections of their Apollo/Lloyds sides, totalling 32 cuts all legally issued in album form for the first time. Vol. 1 includes the beautiful a-cappella standard "My Reverie," the jumping "Eyesight to the Blind," and the memorable "If It's a Crime." Vol. 2 includes the melancholy "When I Leave These Prison Walls" and "Hopefully Yours," plus the bluesy "I Ain't Fattening Frogs for Snakes." Excellent notes and terrific remastering by Walter DeVene. Highly recommended.

THE LARKS
Group formed in the early '60s by Don Julian (see also Don Julian and The Meadowlarks).

COLLECTABLES 5176 (CL)
The Jerk: Golden Classics

DENISE LASALLE
Aggressive Memphis soulster with a strong C&W influence. She first recorded for Tarpen in 1967 (later acquired by Chess), and then moved to Westbound where she had a number of hits in the early '70s. She subsequently recorded for ABC and MCA, and for the past ten years has been recording for Malaco. In 1985 her version of the novelty "My Toot Toot" (she called it "My

Tu-Tu") was a minor hit in the USA but a massive pop hit in England!

MALACO 7412 (RC)

A Lady in the Street
Eight sides from 1983. This Bell Was Made for Ringing/Come to Bed/Down Home Blues.

MALACO 7417 (RC)

Right Place, Right Time
Excellent 1983 LP. Treat Your Man Like a Baby/Your Husband Is Cheating on Us/Keep Your Pants On/Bump and Grind.

MALACO 7447 (RCL)

Hittin' Where It Hurts
Another winner from Denise. Nine slabs of rappin' (Joe Tex not Fat Boys), testifyin', talkin' lowdown from the queen, with titles that tell it all. Most tunes written by LaSalle or Malaco house-writer George Jackson. Denise even totally redoes the two cover tunes here, "Don't Cry No More" and "Bring It on Home to Me," and makes 'em her own. You've Got to Pay to Play/Caught in Your Own Mess/Write This Off (As a Loss).

BENNY LATIMORE
Soul singer/songwriter from Tennessee who started his career in the early '60s with the Nashville-based group, The Hi-Toppers. He subsequently went solo and recorded for Miami entrepreneur Henry Stone's Dade label in the mid-'60s with little success. In the early '70s, he started recording for Stone's Glades label, by which time he had dropped his first name. He hit it big in 1973 with a soul/blues version of T-Bone Walker's classic "Stormy Monday," and continued with more hits through the '70s. In the early '80s he joined the Malaco label where he has been ever since. His '70s Glades hits are currently unavailable on reissue.

MALACO 7414 (RC)

I'll Do Anything for You
Nine fine sides from 1983. Hell Fire Lovin'/Out to Lunch/Take Me Down/(She Left Me with) One Shirt.

MALACO 7443 (RCL)

Slow Dance
The best in quite awhile from Benny. Every soul fan oughta check out "Careful Man," written by Jimmy Lewis, who wrote five of the eight tracks, including the title tune. Three tunes were recorded at Criteria studios, with a band including Clayton Ivey, Roger

Hawkins, and David Hood. Breakdown/Too Many Lovers/That's the Way That I Do It.

STEVE LAWRENCE
Steven Leibowitz got his big break on *The Arthur Godfrey Talent Scout Show* in the '50s, later becoming a regular, along with his wife Eydie "Blame It on the Bossa Nova" Gorme, on *The Steve Allen TV Show*. He had some good success in the pop charts with tunes like "Pretty Blue Eyes," "Footsteps," and the number-one hit "Go Away Little Girl." Steve and Eydie became big hits on the lounge circuit in the '60s, enter MOR heaven.

COLPIX 8320 (R)

Chartmakers
All of his chart-bustin' hits! Besides the ballads, you can hear Steve jive it a bit on tunes like Leiber and Stoller's "The Chicken and the Hawk" and Buddy Knox's "Party Doll," as well as "Speedo" and "Girls, Girls, Girls."

LILLIAN LEACH and THE MELLOWS
Though commercial success and fame eluded them, The Mellows were a tremendously talented R&B vocal group that sported one of the finest female leads in teenaged Lillian Leach. Group members included Johnny "Tiny" Wilson (1st ten), Harold Johnson (2nd ten, who previously sung with Dean Barlow and The Crickets), and Norman "Polecat" Brown (b). Their first sides were cut for New York's Jay-Dee label in 1954, including the winsome "Smoke from Your Cigarette." The Mellows then moved to Brooklyn's tiny Celeste Records where they recorded some of their best work, including "I'm Yours," "Lucky Guy," "My Darling," and "Sweet Lorraine." Their last single was issued by Candlelight.

RELIC 5039 (R)

Lillian Leach and The Mellows
Sixteen fine sides recorded between 1954–1957 for Joe Davis's Jay-Dee label and the Candlelight label.

RELIC 7023 (L)

Yesterday's Memories
Reissues all the material on Relic LPs 5014 (now out-of-print) and 5039, except for "No More Loneli-

ness" and "Farewell Farewell," which have been replaced by the excellent and unreleased Apollo tracks
"So Strange" and "Be Mine." Nine a-cappella demos
for Celeste are here too, the most endearing being "I'm
Gonna Pick Your Teeth with an Icepick." Highly
recommended.

BRENDA LEE

"Little Miss Dynamite," born Brenda Mae Tar-
pley, Lee started out in 1956 when, at age 11,
she toured with Red Foley. She signed to Decca
and recorded some wild rockabilly-style sides
along with country material, scoring with "Dynamite" and "One Step at a Time." In 1960, she
had hits with two classics, "I'm Sorry" and the
seasonal "Rockin' Around the Christmas Tree."
In the '60s, she switched over to ballads and, by
the '70s, was recording for the country market.
She still has a loyal following and is big in Japan.

BEAR FAMILY 15186 (R)/ 15644 (L)
Wiedersehn' Ist Wunderschon
Brenda Lee tried to bust into the European market by
making these recordings in the early '60s, 12 in
German, and two in Italian and French. Fool Number
One/Anyone but Me/Even Tho'/Kansas City.

MCA 10384 (L)
Anthology 1956–1980
Forty songs, including all the big hits, on two CDs,
from her earliest days in the late '50s as "Little Brenda
Lee" through her pop-rock sides and '60s pop ballads
to her 1970s–1980s country hits. Her early tracks,
recorded with some of Nashville's greatest pickers—
"Jambalaya," "Bigelow 6-2000," "Dynamite," "Sweet
Nothin's," and "Rockin' Around the Christmas
Tree"—wear well over three decades later, as do her
pop-rock and country hits, "All Alone Am I," "As
Usual," "Nobody Wins," and "Big Four Poster Bed."
The packaging is perhaps MCA's best ever, far superior
to their Country Hall of Fame Series, with a better
booklet, including near-complete recording information. With Brenda's help, MCA was able to get hold
of some excellent photos and memorabilia. The well-
researched liner notes by Diana Haig place Brenda's
career in the right context and are truly enjoyable
reading. Also available as two separate cassettes.

MCA 10405 (C)
Anthology, Vol. 1: 1956–1961

MCA 10406 (C)
Anthology, Vol. 2: 1962–1980

CURTIS LEE

Curtis Lee of Yuma, AZ, was one of the first rock
stars to fall under the guidance of future wunderkind producer, Phil Spector. Spector produced his
two big hits, "Pretty Little Angel Eyes" (with vocal
backup by The Halos) and "Under the Moon of
Love," both Lee originals cowritten with professional songsmith Tommy Boyce. Lee was unable
to equal these 1961 hits, and soon returned to
Yuma to enter the construction business.

DUNES 2000 (R)
Pretty Little Angel Eyes
Fourteen 1961 Dunes recordings, including his two
Spector-produced hits, "Under the Moon of Love" and
the title classic, and Tommy Boyce's imitation Gary
"U.S." Bonds's tune called "A Night at Daddy Gee's."
The Wobble/Beverly Jean/Mr. Mistaker/Just An-
other Fool.

DICKEY LEE

Like Johnny Burnette, Dickey Lee was a Golden
Gloves boxing champ who turned to rockabilly
to get his hits. These days he's best known for
the maudlin hit "Patches," but he started off with
the Sun label in 1957, and recorded some good
rockers like "Good Lovin'," but mostly stuck to
teen ballads. "I Saw Linda Yesterday" was one of
the better pop rock tunes of 1962, and the same
could be said of the '63 follow up "Don't Wanna
Think about Paula," although "She's Walking
Away" from 1964, which didn't even click on
the charts, beats both of them.

STAR CLUB 8039 (R)
I Saw Linda Yesterday
Eighteen tunes, including all of his chart-toppers. Stay
True Baby/Dreamy Nights/Fool Fool Fool/Hey
Heart/Life in a Teenage World.

LAURA LEE

Chicago-born Laura Lee Rundless made her
debut in the late '50s on Jubilee, singing with her
mother, the great gospel diva Ernestine Rundless,
and Della Reese in the Detroit-based Medita-
tions. After cutting records with the group on
Hob, Gospel, and Checker, and a moderately
successful soul single on Ric Tic, she was persuaded by Rick Hall to quit gospel and stick to

soul singing. A series of anguish-drenched singles ensued, centering around the misgivings of manhood (notably "Dirty Man" and "A Man with Some Backbone"). Her gritty, late '60s Chess recordings were followed by classic sides in a feminist vein for Holland-Dozier- Holland's Hot Wax and Invictus labels during the '70s, including "Women's Love Rights" and "Rip Off." She's currently back in Detroit and recording gospel music.

CHESS 93005 (CL)
That's How It Is
Twenty-two cuts covering the years 1966–1969. Outstanding booknotes by John Ridley. You Need Me/Need to Belong/That's How It Is/She Will Break Your Heart/It's All Wrong But It's Alright/Love More than Pride/Hang It Up/Uptight Good Man/Sure as Sin/Another Man's Woman.

THE LEFT BANKE

Baroque-flavored rockers from the mid-'60s led by 16-year-old keyboard whiz Michael Brown, whose big hits were the gorgeous "Pretty Ballerina" and "Walk Away Renee."

RHINO 70123 (C)
The History of The Left Banke
Twelve wonderful sides, including their big hits. The rare "Ivy Ivy" b/w "And Suddenly" is also included, which Brown recorded without the other band members, even though it was released under The Left Banke name. The other band members took legal action against Brown, and the record was forced off the market. There are also rare recordings by the band released under singer Steve Martin's name, the previously unreleased "Foggy Waterfall," and as a bonus, two songs by Brown's next group, Stories, including the hit "Brother Louie." Extensive liner notes by all four band members.

THE LEMON PIPERS

The Lemon Pipers—originally known as Ivan and the Sabres— hailed from Oxford, OH, with the exception of their British drummer. The group was heavily into psychedelic sounds, but were convinced by their label, Buddah, to record the bubble- gummy classic "Green Tambourine," hitting Number 1 in February 1968.

SEQUEL 131 (L)
The Lemon Pipers
Break out the love beads, squeeze into your tie-dyed bell-bottoms, and throw flowers in your hair while you "get down" with these twenty very groovy tunes, spanning the years 1967–1969. Green Tambourine/Lonely Atmosphere/No Help from Me/The Shoemaker of Leather Square/I Was Not Born to Follow/I Need Someone/Rice Is Nice/Through with You/Love Beads and Meditation/Jelly Jungle.

BARBARA LEWIS

Creative soul singer, songwriter, and multi-instrumentalist from Michigan, Lewis recorded for Atlantic in the early and mid-'60s, and had a giant hit with the sensual "Hello Stranger." Lesser hits followed, and in 1968 she moved to Stax. Only a few unsuccessful singles were issued, and she retired from music in the early '70s.

COLLECTABLES 5104 (RCL)
Golden Classics
A dozen Atlantic sides. Hello Stranger/Baby I'm Yours/Make Me Your Baby.

BOBBY LEWIS

Rock and roll/R&B singer from Indianapolis who started his recording career in the early '50s. He eventually moved to New York's Beltone label, and had a giant hit with the rocking "Tossin' and Turnin'" in 1961. The followup "One Track Mind" was a smaller hit, but further releases flopped. He subsequently ended up on the oldies circuit.

LINE 00323 (L)
Tossin' and Turnin'
Only 12 cuts here, but they're mostly good ones, and where else can you find them? The raucous title track is the standout, of course, but "Boom-a-Chick-Chick" gives it a run for the money. With a good band providing solid backing, Bobby really wails on the fast tunes like "Head over Heels," "What a Walk," and "Turn over a New Leaf." He also does a great job with Jackie Wilson's "Lonely Teardrops." "Are You Ready" is a wonderful, slow, bluesy ballad that shows Bobby's roots.

JERRY LEE LEWIS

The Killer! Lewis and his pumping piano have been making top-quality rockabilly and country recordings since he came in off the street to audition for Sun Records in 1956. While at Sun from 1956–1963, he recorded an incredible body of work, including the monster hits "Whole Lotta Shakin' Goin' On," "Great Balls of Fire," "Breathless," "High School Confidential," and "Milkshake Mademoiselle" that still sound fresh and powerful today. His backup band consisted of such sterling musicians as Roland Janes and Hank Garland (gtr), Billy Lee Riley (b), and James Van Eaton (drm). Unfortunately, his famous marriage to his 13-year-old cousin in the late '50s destroyed his early career.

In 1963, he left Sun for Mercury/Smash, and, in between redoing Sun tunes and cutting Little Richard covers, he managed to pound out some great sides, including the wild "I'm on Fire" and the incredible live LPs *The Greatest Live Show on Earth* and *Live at the Star Club* (with backing by The Nashville Teens). He still, however, saw little chart action. In 1968, with the aid of producer Jerry Kennedy, Lewis turned his career around and recorded for the country market, achieving over 30 Top-10 country hits (notably "What Made Milwaukee Famous" and "Middle Age Crazy"). In 1978, he signed to Elektra and immediately hit again ("39 and Holding"). He's still quite visible on the concert scene, capable of drawing huge crowds and giving incredible shows, although his health has declined in recent years.

Jerry Lee's massive discography can be divided into three major groups: his Sun recordings, reissued and re-reissued by Bear Family, Rhino, and many others; his Mercury/Smash recordings, massively reissued by Bear Family on three boxed sets (totaling 28 LPs), with selections reissued by Mercury itself; and a whole lotta live recordings from all over the place, mostly recorded in the '80s. These live recordings vary widely in sound quality and sometimes feature rather sleepy performances. For one-stop shoppers, Rhino 71499 is the only reissue to include both his classic Sun recordings and a couple of his later Mercury, countryish sides.

ACE 326 (L)

Live at The Vapors Club

This live performance was recorded on the Killer's 55th birthday in front of friends and fans in Memphis, and originally issued on SCR in the mid-'80s. Mostly concert favorites, these 12 cuts are delivered with his customary high energy. Chantilly Lace/Drinkin' Wine Spo-Dee-O-Dee/Me and Bobby McGee/Whole Lot of Shakin' Goin' On/Will the Circle Be Unbroken.

ACE 332 (L)

Honky Tonk Rock and Roll Piano Man

ACE 348 (L)

Pretty Much Country

Two collections of studio recordings originally issued by SCR in the mid-'80s. Producer Dave Travis has remixed the original tapes, lopping off some instrumentation, and adding new guitar overdubs from Sun specialist Eddie Jones. The changes neither substantially improve nor destroy the originals, although the new mixes place the piano and vocal farther in front, where they belong. The songs aren't all that great (many showed up on two early-'80s MCA LPs), but the performances are a cut or two above Lewis's usual output of the period.

BEAR FAMILY 15210 (R)

The Killer (1963–1968)

The first of three box sets reissuing all of Jerry Lee's Smash/Mercury recordings. This nine-album set features 137 tunes, with eight never-before released and a few that only appeared on compilation albums. It includes reissues of his first nine Smash LPs: *Golden Hits of Jerry Lee Lewis* (Smash 67040, 1964, mostly remakes of Sun hits); *The Greatest Live Show on Earth* (Smash 67056, a July 1, 1964 show from Birmingham, AL, that lives up to its name); *The Return of Rock* (Smash 67063, 1967, covering everything from "Maybelline" to "Sexy Ways"); *Country Songs for City Folks* (Smash 67061, 1965, his first country LP, mostly covers, with "Green Green Grass of Home" and "Detroit City"); *Memphis Beat* (Smash 67069, 1965, great rockin' LP with "Lincoln Limousine,"

"Drinkin' Wine Spo-Dee-O-Dee," and "The Urge"); *By Request (More of the Greatest Live Show on Earth)* (Smash 67086, 1967, another live one from September 7, 1966, recorded in Fort Worth, TX, that mixes country covers with rock- and-roll covers); *Soul My Way* (Smash 67104, 1968, soul covers and new originals); *Another Time, Another Place* (Smash 67104, 1968, the first original country LP with the hit "What Made Milwaukee Famous"); and the incredible *Live at The Star Club, Hamburg* backed by The Nashville Teens. Comes with a 128-page booklet with complete discography.

BEAR FAMILY 15228 (R)
The Killer 1969–72
The second big Bear box, ten LPs of Smash/Mercury material. Includes: The two-volume *Country Music Hall of Fame* (Smash 67117/8, 1969), with an unissued alternate of "You Belong To Me"; the *Together* LP (Smash 67126, 1969), duets with Linda Gail Lewis, including an unissued "My Blue Heaven"; the classic LP *She Even Woke Me Up to Say Goodbye* (Smash 67128, 1970) with three unissued tunes; *In Loving Memory* (Mercury 61338, 1971), with two unreleased tunes; *There Must Be More than Love to This* (Mercury 61323, 1971), International Hotel, Las Vegas recordings, including the entire original LP and 25 additional cuts, from "Smoke Gets in Your Eyes" and "High School Confidential" to "Today, I Started Loving You Again," "When the Grass Grows Over Me," and "Mexicali Rose" done in Gene Autry and Jerry Lee style; the religious LP *Touching Home* (Mercury 61343, 1973); *Would You Take Another Chance on Me* (Mercury 61346, 1972); an unissued religious session from December 1970, including an entire performance of religious tunes recorded live in a church, for a total of 20 sanctified numbers, including "Old Rugged Cross," "I'll Fly Away," and "Looking for a City"; *Who's Gonna Play That Old Piano* (Mercury 61366, 1973) with a couple unissued tracks, including "I Don't Know Why I Just Do"; and the Killer's rockin "comeback" LP *The Killer Rocks On* (Mercury 1-637, 1972) with "Chantilly Lace." Comes with a 128-page photo-filled book written by Colin Escott.

BEAR FAMILY 15229 (R)
The Killer 1973–1977
The final box set, consisting of 11 LPs. The first two are the complete *London Sessions* LPs (Mercury 2-803, 1973) with extra cuts, the same as the previously released Bear Family 15240/41, but without the gatefold covers. The set also includes the complete *Sometimes a Memory Ain't Enough* (Mercury 1-677, 1973), *In Country* (1-710, 1974), *Boogie Woogie Country Man* (1-1030, 1975), *Odd Man In* (1-1064, 1975), *Country Class* (1-1109, 1976), and *Country Memories* (1-5004, 1977) LPs. Also has three LPs from The Killer's return to Memphis that produced the

Southern Roots LP (1-690, 1974), an all-star affair produced by Huey P. Meaux that reunited The Booker T-less MGs on rhythm, plus Carl Perkins, Tony Joe White, Augie Meyers, and The Memphis Horns. Includes ten outtakes and extended versions, and live-in-the-studio cuts with lots of chatter and arguing among White, Jerry Lee, and "that coon-ass bastard" Meaux. The final LP has the Killer's return-to-rock material, featuring lots of unissued cuts. A 112-page book by Colin Escott, many photos, and a discography completes the package.

BEAR FAMILY 15240/15241 (R)
The Revised London Session, Vol. 1/Vol. 2
Reissue of 1973 London sessions. Each volume includes three previously unissued tracks. Vol. 1 offers a great version of "Dungaree Doll" (featuring Jerry alone with his piano), a timid remake of "(I Can't Get No) Satisfaction," and a passable "I Can't Give You Anything but Love," plus previously issued tracks like "Drinkin' Wine Spo-Dee-O-Dee," "Baby, What You Want Me to Do?," and "Sea Cruise." Vol. 2 has a great slow bluesy "Be-Bop-a-Lula," "Singing the Blues," and "Goldmine in the Sky," all previously unissued, plus "Johnny B. Goode," "Early Morning Rain," and "Whole Lotta Shakin' Goin' On." Jerry is backed throughout by a very sympathetic band including Albert Lee and Delaney Bramlett (gtrs), Klaus Voorman (b), and Kenny Jones (drm). Foldout album jackets include complete session details, session photos, extensive liner notes by Colin Escott, and the usual superior Bear Family mastering and pressing. Don't miss this!

BEAR FAMILY 15408 (L)
Up Through the Years, 1956–1963
This incredible CD, featuring 24 of The Killer's Sun sides, misses the mark for being "THE Jerry Lee CD to buy" for one reason: I can *almost* understand not having "Milkshake Mademoiselle," but why leave off "High School Confidential"? Instead, we get stuff like the definitely sub-par, LP cut of "Don't Be Cruel" and such non-important stuff as "John Henry" and "Carry Me Back to Old Virginny." However, the sound is fantastic, and besides the big hits (you know what they are), there are many of my fave minor hits like "Lovin' Up a Storm," "Break Up," "Down the Line," and "Big Blon' Baby," plus lots of pictures from the famed hair-combin' photo session.

BEAR FAMILY 15420 (L)
The Definitive Edition of His Sun Recordings 1956–1963
This is it: rock-and-roll's version of the Rosetta stone, the Blarney stone, Stonehenge, and the Hanging Gardens of Babylon. When you graduate from the greatest-hits collection, this is the forbidding door that

beckons. This eight-CD box set of Sun and Phillips recordings has expanded upon the 209-track LP version, adding a further 35 cuts. Everything is programmed in chronological order so you can hear the way Jerry Lee develops a song, although he tore through most numbers in a single take. The four takes of "High School Confidential" and the three takes of "Milkshake Mademoiselle" is about as indulgent as it gets. It begins with the November 1956 session that produced his first Sun 45, "Crazy Arms" b/w "End of the Road," and ends with a pair of August 1963 dates where Sam Phillips has Lewis rockin' up a variety of music styles on tunes like "Hong Kong Blues," "Love on Broadway," and "Carry Me Back to Ol' Virginia," with strings and chorus, an approach they'd tried throughout the '60s. In between there were close to 200 songs cut, most with the nucleus of Lewis (pno), Roland Janes (gtr), and J.M. Van Eaton (drm). Virtually everything is fascinating, due to Lewis's unique stylistic approach to the wide variety of material he tackled. Who else but Jerry Lee would have the audacity to shake it up on "Old Time Religion," "Hand Me Down My Walking Cane," "Deep Elem Blues," and even "The Marines' Hymn"? You'll get to hear some outrageous studio patter and even the legendary religious discussion with Sam Phillips during the recording of "Great Balls of Fire." In a nutshell, you get 246 songs, original versions of all Sun singles, tons of unissued stuff, all remastered from the master tapes, plus a deluxe LP-size booklet with fantastic vintage photos and an up-to-date (1989) discography of everything in the Sun vaults. Frankie and Johnny/Matchbox/Ubangi Stomp/Ooby Dooby/Settin' the Woods on Fire/Hound Dog/Jambalaya/Sweet Little Sixteen/What'd I Say/Mexicali Rose/Be-Bop-a-Lula.

BEAR FAMILY 15608 (L)
The Greatest Live Shows on Earth
Seventy-two minute disc with two shows, a 1964 Birmingham date and a 1966 Fort Worth gig, originally released as *The Greatest Live Show on Earth* and *More of the Greatest Live Show on Earth*, respectively. At Birmingham, the chosen repertoire was perfect for Jerry Lee (heavy on Chuck Berry and Little Richard tunes), and it features him at his rockin' peak. The Fort Worth date is not as consistently mesmerizing, although the small band is excellent, and the song selection still ideal, with more of a tilt toward country. For anyone who cares about rock and roll or country music, this CD is indispensable.

CHARLY 1 (L)
Ferriday Fireball
Twenty-five classic Sun sides. Lewis Boogie/High School Confidential/Whole Lotta Shakin' Goin' On/Big Legged Woman/Great Balls of Fire/Matchbox/Will the Circle Be Unbroken/Crazy Arms.

CHARLY 70 (L)
Rare and Rockin'
Twenty-five Sun recordings. Includes nine Sun releases never on CD, plus five tunes only available on the Jerry Lee Sun box, and "You Win Again" only available on the *Rockin' Years* box. This also has ten alternate takes of hits and B-sides (also reissued on Bear Family 15420).

CHARLY 185 (L)
Great Balls of Fire!
Thirty-track CD, missing two tracks but otherwise equivalent to the out-of-print LP, Charly 44. His Sun recordings, focusing mostly on the big hits.

ELECTROVERT 3001 (L)
The Killer's Private Stash
Rare Jerry Lee Lewis material, including a very scratchy but fascinating acetate recorded in 1954 at Louisiana radio station KWKH. Lewis sounds somewhat subdued on Hank Snow's "I Don't Hurt Anymore" and "If I Ever Needed You," but shows a lot of confidence and budding talent. There's no info at all regarding where the rest of these tunes came from, but "Lust of the Blood" and "Let a Soldier Drink" probably come from a production of Jack Good's play *Catch My Soul,* a rock-and-roll version of The Bard's *Othello* that had Lewis as a piano-playing Iago. The rest sounds like a live recording without any audience noise, with Jerry Lee doing signature tunes like "Crazy Arms," "Real Wild Child," and some gospel tunes. But the one you really need to hear is the outrageous, X-rated version of "Whole Lotta Shakin' Goin' On." Say no more, wink wink, nudge nudge.

FLASH 9001 (R)
Mona Lisa
These two sessions, one from 1989 in Memphis and the other from 1990 in Nashville, catch the Killer in an extremely loose (some might call it intoxicated) mood with just a bottle of booze and a piano. He sings, curses quite a bit, tells some tall tales and jokes, plays the hell out of the piano, and, yes, even belches into the mike. He staggers through a few rockers like "Lucille" and "Breathless" ("I always hated that damn song ..."), but the real treat is when he makes up a dirty song on the spot called "Jimmy, Mickey, and Me," and then jumps into a backhanded tribute to Jimmy ("The Sawdust Trail") and Mickey ("A Room Full of Roses"). He clowns through a series of takes of the old western-swing number "It Was The Whiskey Talkin' (Not Me)." Bill Mack's rockin' tribute "To Jerry Lee" is thrown in as a bonus.

LIVE GOLD 70007/80008 (L)

A Private Party: Live, Dec. 31, 1978, Dalton, GA

Dismal 1978 live set with 26 songs. The show sounds as if it were recorded in the room next to where Lewis and his band were playing, and in a couple of spots the music "warps" as if the tape were damaged.

MAGNUM FORCE 071 (RL)

Live in Italy

Sixteen tunes taken from a couple of shows in Milan and Rome in April 1987. The muddy recording quality, plus Jerry Lee's mumblin' and stumblin' over the lyrics, contribute to the general humdrum quality. His daughter Phoebe and his sister Linda Gail are the backup singers, the band (uncredited) is pretty good, and the Killer's piano pounding is, as always, impressive. Highlights are "Roll in My Sweet Baby's Arms" with the gals, and a fine honky-tonk tune, "There Must Be More to Love than This." This is fine for collectors, but if you don't have a large Lewis LP collection, stick to the essential. High School Confidential/Jackson/What'd I Say/Mona Lisa/One of Those Things We All Go Through.

MERCURY 836 935 (CL)

Killer: The Mercury Years, Vol. One: 1963–1968

MERCURY 836 938 (CL)

Killer: The Mercury Years, Vol. 2

MERCURY 836 941 (CL)

Killer: The Mercury Years, Vol. 3

Three-volume set covering Jerry Lee's Mercury and Smash recordings. Each volume is a "best of" selection corresponding to the three Bear Family box sets, highlighting his rock-and-roll, country, blues, and gospel work, including both released and (at the time) unreleased material. Respectful liner notes by Hank Davis. Vol. 1 highlights: Corrine, Corrina/Don't Let Go/Skid Row/I'm on Fire/Another Time, Another Place/What Made Milwaukee Famous. Vol. 2: Jambalaya/I Can't Stop Lovin' You/You've Still Got a Place in My Heart/Reuben James/You Went Out of Your Way (to Walk on Me)/You Don't Miss Your Water/Flip, Flop and Fly/Stagger Lee/Shoeshine Man/When He Walks on You (Like You Walked on Me)/I Get the Blues When It Rains/Another Hand Shakin' Goodbye. Vol. 3: Haunted House/Born to Be a Loser/Honey Hush/Boogie Woogie Country Man/Honky Tonk Wine/No One Knows Me/Jesus Is on the Mainline/House of Blue Lights/Lord, I've Tried Everything but You/I Can Help/That Kind of Fool/Crawdad Song/Ivory Tears.

PAIR 1261 (L)

Live

1986 live recording from Italy, featuring 15 songs, for one-hour of music. The sound quality leaves something to be desired, but the performance is energetic as always. Great Balls of Fire/You Win Again/Mona Lisa/High School Confidential/Me and Bobby McGee/Whole Lotta Shakin' Goin' On.

RHINO 70255 (CL)

Original Sun Greatest Hits

His best from Sun, 14 tracks on cassette, 18 on CD. Whole Lotta Shakin' Goin' On/Great Balls of Fire/Breathless/High School Confidential/Crazy Arms.

RHINO 70268 (CL)

"Live" at The Star Club, Hamburg

One of the most exciting rock-and-roll live performances ever recorded. On April 5, 1964, the Killer performed at Hamburg's famed Star Club accompanied by the British band The Nashville Teens and stormed his way through 13 classic rock-and-roll tunes. Also reissued on the first Bear Family LP box set. Mean Woman Blues/Money/What'd I Say, Pts. 1 and 2/Great Balls of Fire/Lewis Boogie/Hound Dog/Whole Lotta Shakin' Goin' On.

RHINO 70656 (CL)

Jerry Lee Lewis

Digitally remastered reissue of Jerry Lee's first album, Sun 1230 from 1958. Don't Be Cruel/Put Me Down/Ubangi Stomp/Jambalaya/Fools like Me/High School Confidential/Matchbox.

RHINO 70657 (CL)

Jerry Lee's Greatest!

Digitally remastered reissue with original cover and notes of Sun 1265 from 1961. Money/Hillbilly Music/Hello, Hello Baby/Let's Talk About Us/Frankie and Johnny/What'd I Say.

RHINO 70899 (CL)

Rare Tracks

Eighteen Sun rarities. Deep Ellum Blues/Night Train to Memphis/Big Legged Woman/In the Mood/Whole Lot of Twistin' Goin' On/Sixty Minute Man/Hong Kong Blues.

✪ RHINO 71499 (CL)

Milestones

Twenty-four cut collection of Jerry Lee's Sun and Mercury recordings. Assembles important landmark recordings, rather than just concentrating on the Killer's biggest hits. Features his best late-'50s to early '60s Sun material, including many classics, plus the less familiar "Lucky Old Sun," "All Night Long," "Down the Line," "Return of Jerry Lee," "Big Blon' Baby," and "It Won't Happen with Me," and some of his better later Mercury cuts.

SEE FOR MILES 307 (RL)

The EP Collection

Just what the world needs: another collection of Jerry Lee's Sun Records hits (and misses), this time as they appeared in England on seven four-track EPs. Great Balls of Fire/Whole Lotta Shakin' Goin' On/Crazy Arms/High School Confidential/Jambalaya/What'd I Say/Money/Good Golly Miss Molly.

SMASH 826 251 (CL)

The Golden Rock Hits of Jerry Lee Lewis

Budget reissue of *Golden Hits of Jerry Lee Lewis* (Smash 67040 from 1964). For the Killer's first Smash/Mercury LP, Jerry Lee re-recorded a mixture of his Sun hits and, despite the title, country tunes. These are energetic and not bad recordings, except for the female chorus. Great Balls of Fire/Whole Lotta Shakin' Goin' On/Breathless/You Win Again/Your Cheatin' Heart.

SPECIAL MUSIC 4811 (L)

Greatest Hits Live

1986 concert recording, 12 cuts in all. Great Balls of Fire/Whole Lotta Shakin' Goin' On/High School Confidential/You Win Again/What'd I Say.

STOMPER TIME 2

That Breathless Cat

1983 recordings made in Nasvhille. The Killer had showed up to overdub a few vocals for what turned out to be a lousy LP; he quickly tired of material like "Send Me the Pillow You Dream On," sat himself before a piano, and promptly did what he's done at every recording session since 1956: He showed off on solo piano, playing parts of songs he fancied at the moment, reminiscing about his past, and bumping into new songs when he ran out of stories. Snippets of Jerry Lee classics like "Meat Man," "Ubangi Stomp," and "A Damn Good Country Song" are three of many high points. Two late-'50s live tracks round out the set.

SUN (UK) 35 (L)

The Alternate Collection

A great idea, but what a mess. The concept was a worthy one: to bring together all the odd Jerry Lee Lewis Sun recordings that weren't on Bear Family's otherwise definitive *Classic* LP boxed set. But several of the cuts identified as alternate takes aren't, and two of the 63 tracks listed on the back cover aren't here in any form. Also, his solo songs from various *Million Dollar Session* CDs are included, for no conceivable reason. Should I mention that the discography in the booklet is frequently wrong, or that the sound quality is a big step down from Bear Family's?

SUN STAR 002 (R)

Outtakes

Twenty-three studio outtakes from the early days, including alternate takes, solo versions, false starts, and other goodies from the vaults. Break Up/High School Confidential/Sweet Little Sixteen/Breathless/Great Balls of Fire/You Win Again/Whole Lotta Shakin' Goin' On/I Forgot to Remember to Forget.

SUN STAR 003 (R)

From London to Hamburg

Listenable (for a change) conglomeration of live and studio tracks. Highlights are 1964 BBC recordings, including "Great Balls of Fire," "You Win Again," "When the Saints Go Marchin' In," "Lewis Boogie," a great version of "I'm on Fire," "Whole Lotta Shakin' Goin' On," "High Heeled Sneakers," and a brief interview. Also includes random live cuts and unreleased studio recordings. All are better quality than the average Killer live sets, which lately has been terrible.

TOMATO/RHINO 70385 (L)

The Complete Palomino Club Recordings

Over two hours and 20 minutes, containing all of the tracks from Tomato/Rhino 70392/70698, plus unissued recordings, for a total of 42 winners.

TOMATO/RHINO 70392 (CL)

Rockin' My Life Away

TOMATO/RHINO 70698 (CL)

Rocket '88

Two fine collections featuring The Killer live and raunchy at the Palomino in Los Angeles recorded in 1979–1981 and 1985, with James Burton (gtr), Kenny Lovelace (gtr, vln), Bob Moore or Joel Shoemaker (b), and Buddy Harmon (drm). Jerry Lee is in good form on a mixture of rock-and-roll and country favorites. Vol. 1 highlights: You Win Again/What'd I Say/Another Place, Another Time/Your Cheatin' Heart/Whole Lotta Shakin' Goin' On/Great Balls of Fire/Harbor Lights/You Belong to Me. Vol. 2: What'd I Say/Roll Over Beethoven/Chantilly Lace/Great Balls of Fire/Whole Lotta Shakin' Goin' On/Johnny B. Goode.

WARNER BROS. 26689 (CL)

Rockin' My Life Away

This collection takes its tracks from just two sessions. The first ten songs, recorded in Hollywood (in just four days!) and produced by Bones Howe in 1978, were originally released as *Jerry Lee Lewis* (Elektra 184). Largely overlooked when it came out, the album rocks harder and better than just about anything he did for Mercury. Fine studio talent (James Burton and Hal Blaine) make tight, punchy music for Lewis to reign over triumphantly. Count "Don't Let Go," "Rockin' My Life Away," and Dylan's "Rita May" among the best tracks. The other ten tracks represent the best of his 1979–1980 Nashville sessions, and appeared originally on the *When Two Worlds Collide* (Elektra 254, 1980) and *Killer Country* (Elektra 291, 1980) LPs. The studio musicians were more plentiful and less talented than their Hollywood counterparts of the year before, but Lewis manages some bright moments anyhow. "39 Years and Holding" and "When Two Worlds Collide" are both fine, though the material tends to be slower and more country flavored. Annotated by Jerry Lee authority Jimmy Guterman.

ZU ZAZZ 2003 (R)

Keep Your Hands Off It!

Another dozen Sun alternates, mainly from the legendary "lost sessions" of January 1960 that produced the instrumental "Hawk" single. The Killer roars off with the double-entendre-filled title tune that is actually about a birthday cake. He does Hank's "I Can't Help It" the way only Jerry Lee can: Instead of a mournful tale of unrequited love, the boastful Killer sings "I can't help it if you're still in love with me!" There's a couple versions of "Bonnie B," one of my fave later singles, piano instrumentals including an alternate of "I Get the Blues When It Rains," both versions of "Mexicali Rose" including the fast take, and a rare "Waitin' for a Train" from September 1962. Beautiful sound and all the studio chat. Get it!

ZU ZAZZ 2004 (R)

Don't Drop It

Another incredible LP of unissued Sun material. Although these sessions date from the 1960–1962 period, Jerry Lee rocks along, impervious to the clean-cut image so popular at the time. Indeed, Colin Escott's entertaining liner notes relate how Sun's promo man set up a meeting with Jerry Lee to talk about improving his image, but The Ferriday Fireball skipped out early; he had to catch a double feature of *Return of the Werewolf* and *The Bride of Frankenstein Meets Godzilla!* Jerry Lee, helped by Roland Janes (gtr) and J.M. Van Eaton (drm), among others, turns in a fabulous version of "Bonnie B," plus solid rock and roll and rockin' hillbilly. Hound Dog/Don't Drop It/What'd I Say/Great Speckled Bird.

EARL LEWIS and THE CHANNELS

One of New York's most popular groups with Lewis on lead. They worked mainly with Bobby Robinson, their first manager, with hits on Whirling Disc (1956's "The Closer You Are"), Fire (1958's "Bye Bye Baby"), Fury (1959's "The Girl Next Door"), and Enjoy (1963's "Sad Song"), with a break in 1957 to score a hit with "That's My Desire" on George Goldner's Gone label. Though the group broke up in 1963, Lewis

started a new band by the end of the decade to play the rock-revival circuit. He owns his own Channel Records and his high tenor is still in great shape.

COLLECTABLES 5012 (L)

New York's Finest

Thirteen sides recorded for Whirling Disc, Fury, and Fire between 1955–1959. The Closer You Are/My Love Will Never Die/What Do You Do/The Gleam in Your Eyes/I Really Love You/My Lovin' Baby.

JOHN LEYTON

Actor Leyton, best known in the States for roles in *The Great Escape*, *Von Ryan's Express*, and *Krakatoa, East of Java*, turned an early '60s TV career into a long string of British teen-pop singles.

SEE FOR MILES 127 (R)

Rarities

Twenty early '60s HMV recordings, some tracks produced by the legendary Joe Meek. You Took My Love for Granted/That's a Woman/Funny Man/Voodoo Woman.

SEE FOR MILES 201 (RL)

The Best of

Twenty tunes done for Top Rank between 1961–1964, notable for the fact that all but five were produced by Joe Meek, including "Johnny Remember Me," both Leyton's and Meek's first Number 1. Wild Wind/Six White Horses/Lone Rider/Lonely City.

TOP RANK 596400 (R)

John Leyton

Twenty Top Rank and HMV tunes, many produced by Joe Meek. Johnny Remember Me/Wild Wind/Son This Is She/Tell Laura I Love Her/Voodoo Woman/Lonely Johnny.

LITTLE ANTHONY and THE IMPERIALS

Smooth Brooklyn-based doo-wop group led by Anthony Gourdine; the group formed in 1957 and recorded with little success as The Duponts and The Chesters. In 1958, they signed with the End label and changed their name to The Imperials while, at the same time, Gourdine was nicknamed Little Anthony by Alan Freed. They had a long string of hits for End including "Tears on My Pillow" and "Shimmy Shimmy Ko-Ko Bop," until Anthony left the group to pursue a solo career in 1960. After three years with no hits, he returned to The Imperials on DCP Records, and they had their biggest hits in a very pop vein with "Goin' Out of My Head" and "Hurt So Bad." In 1966, they went over to United Artists's subsidiary Veep and later to UA in 1969. Anthony went solo in the '70s, and became a born-again Christian in the '80s, recording for Songbird.

COLLECTABLES 5422 (CL)

We Are The Imperials

Reissue of End/Roulette 303 from 1961, featuring the original twelve tracks, cover pix, and inaccurate sleeve-note hype. Includes their million-seller "Tears on My Pillow" (1958), the magnificent "So Much," the smoochy "When You Wish upon a Star," and "The Diary," all from 1959, and the rockin' "Travelin' Stranger" (1961). These are some of the fellas' best work-outs.

COLLECTABLES 8804 (CL)

For Collectors Only

Almost all of their End sides (recorded 1958–1961) are on this 40-track, two-cassette/CD set, as well as selected other cuts including the excellent "Prove It Tonight" and "Somebody" from 1957 (originally released as Royal Roost 627) when they were calling themselves The Duponts. The faves are all here, along with the previously unreleased "I Cover the Waterfront," the alternate takes of "So Much" and "Two People in the World," and the unissued "Count the Hours" by The Duponts. The covers of standards like "Over the Rainbow" and "Love Is a Many Splendored Thing" are better in small doses, which may or may not be why the songs are not even close to being in chronological order. Tears on My Pillow/Shimmy, Shimmy, Ko-Ko Bop/So Much/Formula of Love/Wishful Thinking.

✪ RHINO 70919 (CL)

The Best of Little Anthony and The Imperials

All of their best early material, avoiding the over-productions of later years. These tracks are presented here from first-generation master tapes, some in stereo for the first time. Great loose-leaf liner notes, pix, and sessionography. CD contains four extra tracks including the previously unreleased "It's Not for Me" from 1958. Tears on My Pillow/So Much/Shimmy, Shimmy, Ko-Ko Bop/Going Out of My Head/Hurt So Bad/Take Me Back/Miss You So.

LITTLE EVA

"Little Eva" Narcissus Boyd was born in June 1945 in Bellhaven, NC, and as legend has it, she was launched into temporary stardom in the years 1962–1963 by songwriters Carole King and Gerry Goffin, for whom she babysat. Her first big hit was a song they had just written, "The Locomotion." Eva was also a friend of Earl Jean McCree, lead vocalist for The Cookies, who ended up backing Eva on her bubble-gum-like chirpings for Al Nevin's Dimension Records. She had a few more hits with Dimension ("Let's Turkey Trot") and later became a session singer.

COLLECTABLES 5407 (CL)

The Best of Little Eva

Includes her major sellers "The Locomotion," "Keep Your Hands Off My Baby," and "Let's Turkey Trot," all produced in the Don Kirshner factory to emulate the "Mashed Potatoes" dance-craze success of Dee Dee Sharp. Also includes her duos with Oklahoma's Big Al Downing: "Swinging on a Star," "The Christmas Song," and "Heigh Ho." Miniscule fanzine-type book notes by John Neilson and Chris Huff. Average sound quality; good for cutting rugs.

LONDON (UK) 820 615 (L)

Llllloco-motion

Reissues her 1962 Dimension Records album (6000), plus four extra 45 sides. Plenty of King/Goffin songs like "Some Kind-a Wonderful," "Down Home," "Up on the Roof," "Will You Love Me Tomorrow?," "Old Smokey Locomotion," and of course "The Locomotion," plus an extended disco remix!

LITTLE RICHARD

The Quasar of Rock, the wild man, the real King, "Little" Richard Penniman first recorded as a straight ahead blues shouter for RCA in 1951, and later in 1953 for Peacock, with Johnny Otis producing. In 1955, after meeting Larry Williams, he sent a demo to Specialty Records in LA. After pestering them for awhile, he finally arranged a recording session. After recording some blues, he recorded "Tutti Frutti," a song that originally had obscene lyrics but was cleaned up for recording purposes, which topped the charts. He had a long string of hits until 1958, when he gave up show biz for the ministry. He recorded gospel music from 1959–1963, but returned to rock and roll in 1964 with "Bama Lama Bama Loo" on Specialty. He next went to Vee Jay with a band including Jimi Hendrix (whom he later fired) and Don & Dewey, where he rerecorded his earlier Specialty hits. In 1965, he did the same for Modern, but by 1966 he was recording new material for Okeh with Larry Williams as producer and Johnny "Guitar" Watson in the band. He hit the rock-and-roll revival trail and, by 1970, he was a hit on the TV talk-show circuit. At the same time, he released two fine LPs on Reprise, including the hit "Freedom Blues," but since then, his recordings have been sporadic. He continues to fluctuate between rock and The Rock, so his recordings have been divided between gospel numbers and remakes of his old hits. He's also enjoyed a minor acting career, appearing in *Down and Out in Beverly Hills*.

Ace has reissued his classic Specialty recordings of the '50s in their entirety, and also on individual records, tapes, and CDs. These have been remastered from the original master tapes in "living mono." This material is also available in a less intimidating box set from Specialty, along with numerous of his original LPs reissued in their original formats by Ace and Specialty. A good sampler collection is available from Rhino who, along with Bear Family, also offers a nice selection of his non-Specialty recordings.

ACE 1 (RL)

The Specialty Sessions

Eight-LP or six-CD set of all of Mr Penniman's Specialty recordings. In addition to the original versions of all of his hits, this set includes early demos, radio commercials, and dozens of studio outtakes and alternates for a total of 140 songs. All tracks have been remastered from the original master tapes by Bob Jones. Includes a 32-page book containing in-depth

articles about this phase of his career, together with a complete discography of his Specialty recordings.

ACE 109 (R)

His Greatest Recordings

Sixteen classic, beautifully remastered Specialty sides. All the great sides are here, plus, as a bonus track never before on LP, "Chicken Little Baby," a great bluesy number featuring Richard accompanied by only his piano. Liner notes are by Richard's official biographer Charles White, and the fold-out cover features a great action photo from 1956 with the band all wearing shorts! Ready Teddy/Long Tall Sally/Lucille/Tutti Frutti/The Girl Can't Help It/Good Golly Miss Molly.

ACE 128 (R)/SPECIALTY 2100 (RC)

Here's Little Richard

Exact repro of his first LP, Specialty 2100 from 1957, in mono and digitally remastered. Twelve classics, including a totally different take of "Reddy Teddy." Tutti Frutti/Long Tall Sally/Jenny Jenny/Can't Believe You Wanna Leave.

ACE 131 (R)/SPECIALTY 2103 (RL)

Volume 2

Exact repro of Specialty 2103 from 1957 digitally remastered directly from the master tapes for incredible sound. Includes a version of "Keep a Knockin'" with a totally different verse. Good Golly Miss Molly/Lucille/The Girl Can't Help It/Hey Hey Hey Hey.

ACE 195 (RL)

20 Classic Cuts

Twenty Specialty hits (22 on CD) with superb sound and great music; Ace 109 is a similar collection with four fewer tracks. Long Tall Sally/The Girl Can't Help It/Miss Ann/Lucille/I'll Never Let You Go/Send Me Some Lovin'/Slippin' and Slidin'/Can't Believe You Wanna Leave/Baby Face/By the Light of the Silvery Moon/True Fine Mama.

BEAR FAMILY 15448 (L)

The Formative Years

All of Richard's pre-Specialty recordings for RCA and Peacock on one clean CD. This may be Richard's formative years, but the recordings are still great, ranging from fine blues ballads to Roy Brown-type shouters. With good photos and notes by Rick Coleman, who also did the booklet for the Specialty box.

DEMAND 0025 (R)

The Great Little Richard

Alternate takes of "Long Tall Sally" (titled "The Thing" here), "Birmingham," "Baby Face," "Ooh My Soul," and "Kansas City," and previously unreleased tunes from one of Richard's gospel phases, including "Old Ship of Zion," "It's a Miracle," and "Walk through the Valley." There's a very funny radio bit with DJ Gene

Nobles where Little Richard pushes a ladies hair product, and a live "Hound Dog" from Paris in 1966.

RHINO 75899 (L)

18 Greatest Hits

A-wop-bop-a-loo-bop-a-wop-bam-bam. Little Richard's ecstatic opening yell to "Tutti Frutti" starts off this wonderful collection of 18 classic Specialty rockers, digitally remastered for the best possible sound. All tracks are in pristine mono with the exception of "Bama Lama Bama Loo," a 1964 recording, which is issued here for the first time in real stereo. Wonderful stuff! Tutti Frutti/Slippin' and Slidin'/Ready Teddy/ She's Got It/All Around the World/Send Me Some Lovin'/Miss Ann/Good Golly Miss Molly/Kansas City.

SPECIALTY 2104 (RC)

The Fabulous Little Richard

Thirteen great songs. Shake a Hand/Chicken Little Baby/All Night Long/The Most I Can Offer/Lonesome and Blue/Wonderin'.

SPECIALTY 2111 (RC)

His Biggest Hits

Twelve old favorites. Rip It Up/All Around the World/ Long Tall Sally/Send Me Some Lovin'/True Fine Mama/Tutti Frutti.

SPECIALTY 2113 (RC)

Little Richard's Grooviest
17 Original Hits

Long Tall Sally/Send Me Some Lovin'/Good Golly Miss Molly/She's Got It/Jenny Jenny/Miss Ann.

SPECIALTY 2136 (RC)

Well Alright!

Richard's 1964 Specialty comeback material, with a band including Don & Dewey and Johnny "Guitar" Watson, plus some non-LP '50s Specialty material. Includes his comeback single, "Bama Lama Bama Loo." Poor Boy Paul/Directly from My Heart/Annie Is Back.

SPECIALTY 2154 (RCL)

The Essential Little Richard

Twenty of Richard's greatest songs with all the original versions digitally remastered from the master tapes for especially nice sound. Released in conjunction with Charles White's excellent biography *The Life and Times of Little Richard*, this set sports the same front cover as the book, and includes White's Specialty sessionography/discography. Tutti Frutti/Rip It Up/Long Tall Sally/Lucille/Keep a Knockin'/Ready Teddy.

SPECIALTY 7012 (CL)

The Georgia Peach

If there's anyone out there who doesn't yet have a Little Richard greatest-hits compilation, this is the one for you, with 25 howlers in chronological order. Chances are that every Penniman fave you can name is here, as well as less chartworthy, but equally great cuts like "I Can't Believe You Wanna Leave," "Kansas City," and "Hey Hey Hey Hey." Compiler Billy Vera's notes are astute and usually on the mark.

SPECIALTY 8508 (RL)

The Specialty Sessions

If the Ace box set seems a little intimidating (there are up to five takes of some songs), then the US Specialty reissue will be more manageable (not to mention less expensive!). This five-LP (or three-CD) box contains 73 selections including at least one version of every song Richard recorded for the label. The box exterior is done in black lizard-skin paper, with Richard's image and the set's title hot-foil stamped on the cover in gold and silver. Each LP in the box features a different cover and the set comes with a 32-page booklet (presumably the same as the Ace one) with notes by Rick Coleman, Rob Finnis, and Ray Topping. Includes rare recordings, demos, a few alternate takes, and true stereo versions of his 1964 recordings. There's also a series of radio commercials Richard cut for Royal Crown Hair Dressing in the mid-'50s.

THE LIVELY ONES

The Lively Ones, originally known as The Surfmen, were one of the top surf bands in Southern California. Jim Masoner (lead gtr), Ed Chiaverini (gtr), Ron Griffith (b), Joel Willenbring (ten sax), and Tim Fitzpatrick (drm) were from Orange County and by all accounts really got the surfers a-stompin' at places like the legendary Retail Clerk's Hall in Buena Park.

ACE 957 (L)

Surf Rider/Surf Drums

Reissue of both Lively Ones LPs on one CD, originally released by Del-Fi in 1963. Great sound remastered from the original master tapes on these 24 tunes, and no drippy vocals, either! Surf Beat/Misirlou/Let's Go Trippin'/Happy Gremmie/Tuff Surf/Bustin' Surfboard.

LAURIE LONDON

BEAR FAMILY 15133 (R)

England's 14 Year Old Singing Sensation

It was hard enough hearing this lad's not-quite-changed voice warbling enthusiastically through "He's Got the Whole World in His Hands," but now, besides one LP side worth of such goodies from 1958 as "Gospel Train," "Up above My Head," and "Boom-Lada-Boom-Boom," we get an LP side of German language recordings such as "Mandolino Pling Plang Plong" and "Bum-Lada-Bum-Bum." I demand combat pay!

ROY LONEY and THE PHANTOM MOVERS

NORTON 209 (R)

The Scientific Bombs Away!

Roy Loney, originally a member of The Flamin' Groovies, leads this retro-band. They're helped out by fellow ex-Groovies Cyril Jordan and Mike Wilhelm on 13 rockabilly and pop rockers. Loney's pop craftsmanship comes across best on "Ruin Your Shoes" and "Cry Like the Wind," while his pure rock-and-roll sensibility jumps for the jugular on Mickey Hawks's "Bip Bop Boom," along with "Nobody," "Boy, Man!," and "Feel So Fine." Nothing fancy here, just straight ahead rock-and-roll from a veteran.

LONNIE and THE CAROLLONS/THE DEANS

CRYSTAL BALL 126 (R)

Lonnie and The Carollons Meet The Deans

The Brooklyn Carollons started out as the unrecorded Irving Brosky and The Emeralds, and, during 1958, recorded for Irv Spice's Mohawk label (the same company that gave The Belmonts their start). This collection includes all three of their singles plus a 45 made in 1973 for Street Corner. The Deans were formerly the unrecorded Ralph Maffie and The Four Playboys who signed with Mohawk Records in 1960 where they cut three singles. They then signed with Laurie where they waxed "I Don't Want to Wait" (not included). Of the nine tracks, three are previously unreleased. Some good Caucasian doo-wop here.

TRINI LOPEZ

Trinidad Lopez III, from Dallas, TX, is remembered for his folky stint with Reprise records, but Trini cut a fair amount of rockers and ballads before singing "If I Had a Hammer." Lopez started performing in the early '50s and was encouraged to record by Buddy Holly. He cut his first sides for Columbia in 1958 and then recorded for a number of other labels with little impact. He moved to Los Angeles in 1963 where he was discovered performing at PJ's by Reprise label owner Frank Sinatra and had a lengthy series of hits for the label through the '60s. He recorded for a number of labels in the '70s with little success, and for the past 10 years or so has been a regular on the Vegas scene.

BEAR FAMILY 15427 (L)

Live

No one rocked quite like Trini Lopez, as demonstrated by these 15 cuts recorded live in the early '60s. This CD reissue takes musical eclecticism to new heights, with songs in German, Spanish ("Cielito Lindo" and "La Bamba"), Italian ("Volare"), and English. Wow! If I Had a Hammer/Bye Bye Blackbird/This Land Is Your Land/What'd I Say/America (from *West Side Story*)/Unchain My Heart/Marianne.

VOLK 1101 (R)

Rock On

"The Right to Rock" and "Rock On" (both studio and live versions) show Lopez to be a fine rocker. The other studio recordings are either pop rockers or ballads featuring Trini's smooth vocal style. Eleven of the 18 tracks are from live shows and have Trini backed by a rockin' band with good guitar and sax. Here Comes Sally/Yes You Do/It Hurts to Be in Love.

WARNER BROTHERS 72868 (L)

25th Anniversary

BOBBY LORD

REVIVAL 3006 (R)

Everybody's Rockin'

Fourteen tunes that are mixtures of rockabilly, pop rock, and hillbilly boogie. Bobby recorded for Columbia and Hickory in the '50s and '60s, singing a few Boudleaux Bryant compositions along the way. Everybody's Rockin' but Me/Beautiful Baby/High Voltage/No More No More.

DICK LORY

Dick Lory was the (early) stage name of Dick Glasser, a California singer/songwriter who was a fair vocalist with some cool songs in the teenage mode.

REVIVAL 3013 (R)
Cool It Baby

Many of the rock-and-roll tunes here have one foot firmly in the pop-rock style (corny arrangements and girly choruses), but there's enough good guitar and sax to boost them over the run-of-the-mill pop dreck. Lord doesn't have the voice for the RCA-era Elvis-type boppers, and his ballads are standard teen fare. Dick tries his hand at imitating Neil Sedaka on "I Got over You" and Roy Orbison on "Handsome Guy" with some amazingly faithful results. All in all, Lory probably beats many of the bigger names on the Revival label. Crazy Little Daisy/Wild Blooded Woman/My Ballroom Baby/Crazy Love/Go Girl Go/Loud Perfume.

LOVE

First important LA psychedelic band, led by Arthur Lee, a black vocalist who sounds like Mick Jagger. More hard-edged than other "flowers-in-your-hair" outfits, they were probably the only band to wed whimsical psychedelia with hard-edged soul. Lee first formed the LAGs (short for "Los Angeles Group," modeled after Booker T and the MGs), recording one song for Capitol in 1965 ("Ninth Wave"), before going to Elektra with Love, the first rock group signed to this famous folk label. The original group members were Lee (vcls), John Echols (lead gtr), Ken Forssi (gtr), Bryan MacLean (b), and Alban "Snoopy" Pfisterer (drm). After releasing three LPs, the original band broke up, and Lee recorded tracks for an LP with Jimi Hendrix. This LP was never released, although one track did appear on a later Love LP. Lee formed a second, short-lived Love to record two LPs for Blue Thumb in 1969, with Jay Donnellan (gtr), Frank Fayard (gtr), original bass player MacLean, and George Suranovitch (drm). Since then, Lee has recorded as a solo artist and has also formed several different revived versions of the original band, often with bandmate Bryan MacLean.

ELEKTRA 74001 (L)
Love

Their 1966 debut album was in a folk-rock vein, producing two minor hits, a manic version of Burt Bacharach's "My Little Red Book" and Dino Valenti's "Hey Joe" (a big hit for The Leaves).

ELEKTRA 74005 (L)
Da Capo

This 1967 album features the psychedelic epic "Revelation," that took up an entire side of the LP (19 minutes long), and their major hit "7 and 7 Is."

ELEKTRA 74013 (L)
Forever Changes

This 1967 album is considered the group's masterwork and is their most heavily produced LP, in the vein of The Beatles's *Sergeant Peppers*, using all the studio tricks then in the book.

ELEKTRA 74058 (L)
Revisited

C.P. LOVE and HIS BLUESMATES

C.P. has a long history as a New Orleans soulster, including playing on King Floyd's classic "Groove Me." Relocated to San José, C.P. has a fine group including a funky horn section and guitarist Chris Cain.

SOUTHLAND 25 (R)
An Album of Rhythm and Blues

A poor choice of material—over-recorded, Big-Chill, Yuppie classics in versions that do nothing to improve on the originals—mars an otherwise well-performed collection. Dock of the Bay/Knock on Wood/Stormy Monday/Stand by Me.

THE LOVIN' SPOONFUL

NY-based folk rockers led by singer/songwriter John Sebastian. They scored a number of hits in the mid-'60s featuring Sebastian's wistful vocals, harmonica, and even electric autoharp. Sebastian left the group in 1969 and embarked on a solo career, beginning with a drugged-out appearance at Woodstock, but it soon fizzled out. His last big hit was the theme for TV's *Welcome Back, Kotter* show.

RHINO 70944 (CL)
Anthology

All of their classic hits. Do You Believe in Magic?/You Didn't Have to Be So Nice/Did You Ever Have to Make Up Your Mind?/Younger Girl/Summer in the City/Rain on the Roof/Nashville Cats/Darling Be Home Soon/She's Still a Mystery to Me.

SPECIAL MUSIC 4916 (CL)
Greatest Hits

Similar selection to the Rhino collection.

JIM LOWE

New York DJ best known for his 1956 two-million seller, "The Green Door." He had a few other minor sucesses and then returned to radio work in New York.

DOMINO 1002 (R)

Rock-A-Chicka

Eighteen rockin' Dot jivers, most with honky-tonk piano. These must all be LP cuts because none of Lowe's hit singles are here except "The Green Door." I seem to remember that "The Green Door," listed as by Davie-Moor, was actually written by Esquerita. Oh-Oh-Baby!/I Feel the Beat/Gambler's Guitar.

BUDDY LUCAS

Alabama-born Lucas was a saxophone and harmonica player, who is mostly remembered as the sax player on tons of R&B hits like "Maybe," "Why Do Fools Fall in Love," and "Tears on My Pillow."

REDITA 138 (R)

Hoppin' Bop

Lucas's solo recording legacy is more spotted than his famous stints as a sideman. He tackled the sax instrumental on stuff like "Hoppin' Bop," "Night Train," and "Slow Walk." He also does some of the worst vocal impressions of Fats Domino you're likely to hear outside of a shower stall. These can be overlooked though because he really shines on tuff R&B numbers like "I Can't Go," "So Happy," the C&W-styled "True Love Will Come," and the instrumental "Gee Gee Walk."

ROBIN LUKE

If Robin Luke were any more wholesome looking, he would be a glass of milk. As it is, he was a minor teen idol who played the ukulele and hit it big in 1958 with "Susie Darlin'," a song written about his five-year-old sister! Although he recorded for several more years, this was to be his only hit, and, in the early '60s, he returned to school and eventually became a teacher in the Missouri state school system.

BEAR FAMILY 15022 (R)

Susie Darlin'

Sixteen Dot recordings from 1958–1960. School Bus Love Affair/Chicka Chicka Hony/So Alone/Everlovin'.

BEAR FAMILY 15547 (L)

Susie Darling

Thirty-one songs recorded between 1958–1962, including many demos and other previously unissued stuff. Sure, Luke sounds like an Elvis/Buddy Holly "wannabe" a lot of the time, and yes, he finds the subject of teen romance endlessly fascinating; but despite it all, songs like "Won't You Please Be Mine," "Everlovin'," "Five Minutes More," and "Sugar" have a certain charm. Not surprisingly, the early cuts are better than the '60s tracks, which often suffer from wretched strings and hokey backup singers. As usual, Bear Family has done an excellent job with everything including the liner notes.

BOB LUMAN

Country and rockabilly guitarist/singer/songwriter who moved from straight country to rock after catching Elvis on an early Louisiana Hayride program. His '50s career was spotty, though he recorded the rockabilly classic "A Pink Cadillac and a Black Moustache." In 1960, he signed with Warner Bros. and, at the suggestion of the Everly Brothers, recorded Boudleaux Bryant's "Let's Think about Living," which became his only pop hit. His career ended in the mid-'60s after he was drafted, although he later became a big country star, recording for Hickory and Epic. He died in 1978.

BEAR FAMILY 15140 (R)

Still Rockin'

Sixteen Warner Bros. sides, recorded 1959–1965, including the previously unissued rocker "Lonely Road." Most of the LP is country with an upbeat rock-and-roll flavor. A Lonely Room/Fire Engine Red/You Win Again/Interstate 40/Old George Dickel.

BEAR FAMILY 15268 (R)

Wild Eyed Woman

Luman's red-hot seminal rockabilly material, including his 1955 demo session with The Mac Curtis Band and his 1957 Dallas and Hollywood sessions with the great James Burton-led band. It doesn't get any better than this. Stranger Than Fiction/You're the Cause of It All/In the Deep Dark Jungle/A Pink Cadillac and a Black Moustache/Wild Eyed Woman/Red Hot/Whenever You're Ready/Your Love.

BEAR FAMILY 15345 (R)

Carnival Rock

Seventeen tracks. Try Me/Precious/Svengali/A Lover's Prayer/Instrumental/Saving It for You/So

Happy for You/Almost Persuaded/Love Stay Away from Me.

ROCKSTAR 1015 (R)

Try Me

Twenty Liberty and Capitol sides. Duplicates Bear Family 15268 and 15345.

SUNDOWN 1013 (R)

Let's Think about Living

Twelve songs recorded for Warner Bros. and Hickory between 1962–1968. Mostly pop-country rockers and ballads, including the title hit. Still Loving You/Hey Joe/Louisiana Man/I Love You Because.

THE LY-DELLS

CLIFTON 2002 (R)

The Ly-Dells

Sixteen sides by early '60s Philadelphia doo-wop group who had a minor hit with "Wizard of Love."

FRANKIE LYMON

COLLECTABLES 5421 (CL)

At The London Palladium

Reissue of Frankie's 1957 solo release (Roulette 25013). If Bobby Darin had a kid brother making a Las Vegas debut, the results would probably sound like this. Why anyone would bother reissuing this insipid doo-doo beats me. Strings and choral backgrounds surround these refits of his big hits and other forgettable wincers. Horrible! Goody Goody/Fools Rush In/My Baby Just Cares for Me/Too Young.

FRANKIE LYMON and THE TEENAGERS

Highly influential "kid-sound" group from New York, featuring 13-year-old Frankie on lead vocals. The original group, The Premiers, featured Herman Santiago on lead vocals, with Frankie singing tenor and lead on duets, along with Jimmy Merchant (2nd ten), Joe Negroni (bar), and Sherman Garnes (b). They performed "Lily Maebelle," a song by the local group The Valentines, and were discovered by Valentine singer Richie Barrett. Barrett brought them to George Goldner to record a song that they had written, then called "Why Do Birds Sing So Gay?" Goldner was so taken with Frankie that he forced the group to let him sing lead. He renamed the group Frankie Lymon and The Teenagers and issued the song, now called "Why Do Fools Fall in Love?,"

on his Gee label where it was a smash hit. The song was issued as by "Lymon and Goldner," in the then-common practice of the record company executive taking a cut of publishing royalties by putting his name on a song. Goldner later sold his share of the song to the infamous Morris Levy, manager of many NY pop labels who had strong ties with the mob. Meanwhile, the last two surviving members of the Teenagers, Santiago and Merchant, claimed that they were the real authors of the song, not Lymon, and they finally won their case in 1992, only 36 years after the song originally hit!

The Teenagers's "kid-sound" really caught on, and basser Sherman Garnes, just two years older than Frankie but with an amazingly deep voice, set the standard for dozens of future low-noters. The group recorded for Gee until 1957, when Frankie went solo, but after only two hits ("Goody Goody" in 1957 and "Little Bitty Pretty One" in 1960), his voice changed and he was washed up. He became a junkie and died in July 1968 at the age of 26; Sherman Garnes died in 1978. In 1980, original members Herman Santiago and Jimmy Merchant reformed The Teenagers with Pearl McKinnon of The Kodaks singing lead. She was replaced in 1983 by Rosalyn Moreland. Frankie's falsetto voice influenced countless lead singers in the early '60s girl groups.

INSTANT 5054 (L)

Why Do Fools Fall in Love?

An amalgam of singles and album cuts from the Gee/Roulette catalog covering the years 1955–1957. The

24-song selection features most of the group's best material, and is the strongest CD reissue to date. Those of you who own the now- unavailable Murray Hill box set will be missing "I'm Not Too Young to Dream" and "Silhouettes," both included here. Decent notes by Adam Komorowski, but lousy, xerox-type reproduction of publicity stills. Great sound. I'm Not a Juvenile Delinquent/I Want You to Be My Girl/Paper Castles/Goody Goody/Portable on My Shoulder.

LIVE GOLD 10001 (L)

Live, Rare and Unreleased

This fascinating collection contains "live, rare, and unreleased" material from 1956–1960. Highlights on this 17-cut selection include backstage interviews by Bob Miles and Red Robinson, three super versions of "Why Do Fools Fall in Love?," one version a duet from 1960 performed by Frankie and his brother Lewis of The Teenchords (see separate listing), and two recorded live at The Brooklyn Paramount in April 1956 (one previously unreleased). There are also four previously unissued live gems: "The One Way to Love," "Please Be Mine," "I Promise to Remember," and "I'm Not Too Young to Dream." Also includes unreleased studio solo recordings of Frankie performing "Since the Beginning of Time" and "Blessed Are They." No sleeve notes and good sound quality.

✪ RHINO 70918 (CL)

The Best of Frankie Lymon and The Teenagers

Fourteen of the best from the Gee Records years. This is a nice collection for the casual fan, and fanatics will want it for the terrific insert featuring cool photos and a loving appreciation by Bob Hyde, actually a condensation of the booklet in the (now out-of-print) Murray Hill box set. CD has six additional tracks including "Please Be Mine," "Am I Fooling Myself Again?," and "Thumb Thumb." Why Do Fools Fall in Love?/I Want You to Be My Girl/Goody Goody/The ABCs of Love.

STAR CLUB 8031 (R)

Hits and Rarities

Great 20-track collection including unissued songs and alternate takes (all previously available on the out-of-print Murray Hill box set). A nice complement to the Live, Rare, and Unreleased package. Why Do Fools Fall in Love?/I Promise to Remember/I'm Not a Juvenile Delinquent/Goody Goody/It Hurts to Be in Love/Together/It Would Be So Nice/Diana/The Magic Song/Good Lovin'.

LEWIS LYMON and THE TEENCHORDS

Frankie's younger brother who, unfortunately, did not share Frank's versatile pipes.

RELIC 7028 (L)

I'm So Happy

Kiddie harmony from Frankie Lymon's younger brother Lewis (age 12) and pals. The Teenchords's biggest sellers were cut for Fury in 1957, with less success coming from End and Juanita sides. Everything they released is here, along with outtakes of "Your Last Chance" and "I'm Not Too Young to Fall In Love." But that isn't necessarily good news. While "I'm So Happy" and "Honey Honey" are pleasing enough, too many of the other numbers are bores. Mediocrity from minors.

LEWIS LYMON/THE KODAKS

COLLECTABLES 5049 (CL)

Lewis Lymon and The Teen Chords Meet The Kodaks

BARBARA LYNN

A native of Beaumont, TX, Barbara Lynn Ozen began her musical career playing the Louisiana club circuit. She was "discovered" by Huey Meaux, who, in 1962, began recording her at Cosimo Matessa's New Orleans studio and leasing her material to Jamie Records. Lynn's blend of Texas and New Orleans blues styles, mixed with just a touch of the emerging soul sound, produced solid blues ballads in the tradition of LaVern Baker.

SOUND OF THE FIFTIES 002 (L)

You'll Lose a Good Thing

Among the best are the hit title track, "Lonely Heartaches," "I'm Sorry I Met You," "What I Need Is Love," and "You're Gonna Need Me." There are a couple of unproductive attempts at an early '60s white, teen sound, but the rest of the disc is certainly strong enough to overcome them. Lynn wrote most of the 18 tracks, and both her singing and her writing are fine on these, her earliest recordings. Nice cover photo, with the '60s Jamie label reproduced on the disc itself, vintage notes, and good sound, but not in stereo as the cover booklet claims. Recommended.

GLORIA LYNNE

COLLECTABLES 5138 (CL)

Golden Classics

Gloria goes the torch song route on this 14-track collection backed by syrupy strings, full orchestra, and the inevitable jazz organ gurgling away in the background. She has a nice voice for this kind of supperclub material ("I Should Care," "Perdido," "Stella by

Starlight"), but even when the material calls for a little more soul ("Try a Little Tenderness" and "Tower of Strength"), she still sticks with a pretty straight-laced rendition. I Should Care/I Wish You Love/Impossible.

LONNIE MACK

Cult guitar hero and sometimes vocalist, Mack was backing up singer Troy Seals in 1963 when he recorded two instrumentals, "Memphis" and "Wham," during the last ten minutes of the session. Both were released (initially without his knowledge) on Fraternity and became hits. His *The Wham of the Memphis Man*, a landmark LP which showed the diversity of Lonnie's skills and also revealed him to be a soulful vocalist, was such a cult classic that it was reissued on Elektra in 1969, bringing him out of retirement for several years. Mack re-emerged again in 1985, again with a comeback from Alligator, *Strike Like Lightning*, which was coproduced by blues guitar hero Stevie Ray Vaughan. He has had a number of fine albums released on Alligator since then.

ACE 352 (L)
Lonnie on The Move
Nineteen blazing tracks, equal parts country, blues, and rock and roll, recorded between 1964–1967, that are just a cut below his peak. Mack's singing often takes a back seat to his six-string mastery on these recordings, but he pulls off a broad variety of material, including his own songs and others associated with Ben E. King, Buddy Holly, Barrett Strong, and The Falcons.

ALLIGATOR 3903 (RC)
The Wham of The Memphis Man
Originally issued in 1963 as Fraternity 1014 to capitalize on the two title-hit instrumentals, "Wham" and that great version of Chuck Berry's "Memphis," this LP has become a cult classic. Seven fine instrumentals, plus six sides of Lonnie singing the blues. This new pressing has the original front cover with new liner notes. Suzie Q/Babe What's Wrong/Down in the Dumps/Why.

ALLIGATOR 4750 (RCL)
Second Sight
Ten new Mack tunes with a crack band featuring vets Tim Drummond (b), Jim Keltner (drm), and The Memphis Horns. Lonnie's '60s roadhouse music is brought into the '80s with especially crisp and modern production. Lonnie's voice and especially his guitar are sounding fine, though I'm not really thrilled by the material (eight of ten are cowritten by Lonnie). My

faves are the shuffle "Cincinnati Jail" and the set's only instrumental, "Camp Washington Chili."

ALLIGATOR 4786 (RC)
Attack of the Killer V
Sounds better after a couple of beers. It's a live recording, starring the big humbucker sound of the '58 Flying V guitar that Lonnie's played throughout his 30-year career. There are gospel-styled backup vocals, electric grand piano (placed low in the mix), hard-hitting modern drumming, and Mack's gravelly vocals, which recall Johnny Winter or Stevie Ray Vaughn. When he switches on that treble pickup and starts biting, the sound is pretty irresistible.

THE MAD LADS

Memphis R&B vocal group formed in the early '60s, originally as The Emeralds. They changed their name to The Mad Lads in the mid-'60s. They recorded for the Stax subsidiary Volt and had their first hit with the doo-wop flavored "Don't Have to Shop Around" in 1965. They had several other hits through 1969 when the band split up. They re-formed in 1972, recorded one album, and disbanded again. The group re-formed again in 1984 and recorded a couple of albums for Volt.

COLLECTABLES 5030 (RC)
The Mad Lads Greatest Hits
Their early Stax sides, recorded between 1965–1966, featuring the silky lead vocals of John Gary Williams. This is the material that Atlantic owns (not the '70s sides reissued by Fantasy), and has been out-of-print for years. Includes their beautiful 1965 hits "Don't Have to Shop Around" and "I Want Someone." I Want a Girl/My Inspiration/Patch My Heart/Come Closer to Me.

STAX 8525 (RCL)
The Best of The Mad Lads
The best of their later Volt recordings cut between 1968–1972. So Nice/Seeing Is Believing/Did My Baby Call/I Forgot to Be Your Lover.

JOHNNY MAESTRO and THE BROOKLYN BRIDGE

Maestro, formerly of The Crests (see separate listing), formed this group in 1969 with members of two New York groups, The Del-Satins and The Rhythm Method. They had their first hit that year with Jimmy Webb's "The Worst that Could Happen," and had six further hits over the next 18 months. Maestro continued working with various incarnations of The Brooklyn Bridge into the '90s.

COLLECTABLES 5015 (CL)
Greatest Hits
Twelve tracks. The Worst that Could Happen/Welcome Me Love/Your Kite/My Kite/Minstrel Sunday/Down by the River.

THE MAJORS

The Majors were a Philadelphia quintet produced by Jerry Ragovoy in the early '60s. First known as The Versatiles, the group consisted of Ricky Cordo on high tenor lead, Eugene Glass, Frank Troutt, Ronald Gathers, and Idella Morris. After their 1962–1963 seesions with Ragovoy, they cut one final single as The Performers, which was issued in 1966. Their style was not unlike The Essex, a female-led aggregation of the same era.

COLLECTABLES 5249 (CL)
Meet The Majors:
A Golden Classics Edition
This 12-song collection, reissuing Imperial 9222 (1963), embraces some of the gang's singles sides, including the very pretty "Time Will Tell," "Tra La La," "She's a Troublemaker," and their one-hit wonder "A Wonderful Dream" that climbed to Number 23 on the charts in October 1962. The notes are lifted from the original album, and the sound is average. Pretty soul-harmony.

THE MAMAS AND THE PAPAS

Folk-rock quartet who had smash hits from 1966–1969, and were the moving force behind 1967's Monterey Pop Festival. The group was founded by John Phillips (gtr, voc) and his then-wife Michelle (voc; b. Holly Michelle Gilliam), along with Denny Doherty (gtr, voc) and Cass Elliot (voc; b. Ellen Naomi Cohen). They hooked up with producer Lou Adler, who gave them a folk-popish sound on big hits like "California Dreamin'" and "Monday Monday." The group disbanded in 1969. Cass Elliot had a successful solo career for a while, before dying in mysterious circumstances in 1974 (it was said that she choked on a ham sandwich). John Phillips pursued a solo career also, with less success, and spent much of the later '70s and early '80s battling drug addiction; Michelle became a well-known model and TV actress, as did their daughter Mackenzie. John brought forth a new Mamas and Papas in 1982 with Doherty, Elaine ("Spanky") McFarlane (of the '60s group Spanky and Our Gang), and his daughter Mackenzie; they have performed sporadically through the '80s and into the '90s.

MCA 709 (C)
Farewell to the First Golden Era
Reissue of Dunhill 50025 from 1968, the group's last official LP.

MCA 1657 (C)/5701 (L)
16 of Their Greatest Hits

MCA 10195 (L)
Creque Alley/History of
the Mamas and the Papas
Two-CD set bringing together all of their charting singles, early cuts by pre-Mamas and Papas groups, solo cuts from the early '70s, and studio chatter.

MCA 31042 (CL)
If You Can Believe Your Eyes and Ears
Reissue of Dunhill 50006 from 1966, their first LP with big hits "California Dreamin'" and "Monday Monday."

MCA 31044 (L)
Deliver
Reissue of Dunhill 50017 from 1967.

THE MANHATTANS

The Manhattans, not to be confused with the group who recorded for Dootone in 1959, got their start on Capitol Records in 1962. In 1964, they switched to Carnival where they cut 14 singles, remaining with the label through 1969. The group consisted of George "Smitty" Smith (lead), Edward "Sonny" Bivins (ten), Ken Kelly (2nd ten), Rich Taylor (bar), and Winfield Lovett (b). With several personnel changes, they have continued recording through the '80s having hit after hit in a more contemporary vein for De Luxe and Columbia.

COLLECTABLES 5135 (RCL)
Dedicated to You:
Golden "Carnival" Classics, Pt. 1

COLLECTABLES 5136 (RCL)

For You and Yours:
Golden "Carnival" Classics, Pt. 2

Each volume includes 12 classic 1964–1969 Carnival sides considered by fans as their best work. The group's Carnival style is best described as a mix of The Spinners with the latter-day Impressions. One of the earliest exponents of soul-funk, the group excels on Pt. 1 on such songs as the beautiful "Can I" and "Our Love Will Never Die." And on a livelier note, they get down with "The Philly Dog" and "The Boston Monkey." Pt. 2 includes four chart-toppers: "I Wanna Be (Your Everything)," I Betcha (Couldn't Love Me)," "When We're Made as One," and "I Call It Love." Personal faves include "Alone on New Year's Eve" and "It's That Time of the Year." Great fidelity.

CARL MANN

Jerry Lee Lewis-influenced pianist who recorded for the Sun subsidiary label, Phillips International. Mann had a very solid style, and he hit big with rock versions of pop tunes and standards, beginning with 1959's "Mona Lisa," later covered by Conway Twitty. He disappeared, resurfacing on Dot in the mid-'70s, and continues to work in Europe.

STAR CLUB 8022 (R)

14 Unissued Sides

1959–1960 recordings made for Phillips International. Like most of his hits from this era, these are mostly loping versions of pop and country standards, with Carl providing a solid bass riff countered by Eddie Bush's guitar. Take These Chains from My Heart/Sentimental Journey/Stop the World and Let Me Off/Ain't You Got No Love for Me.

THE MAR-KEYS

In 1957, 16-year-old guitarist Steve Cropper formed The Mar-Keys (not to be confused with The Bar-Kays, the mid-sixties Stax/Volt group that lost most of its members in the plane crash that killed Otis Redding). The group was originally called The Royal Spades, and included Donald "Duck" Dunn (b), Charles "Packy" Axton (ten sax), Charlie Freeman (gtr), Terry Johnson (drm), and sometimes Jerry Lee "Smoochie" Smith (pno); later, Wayne Jackson (tpt) and Don Nix (sax) joined them, among others. They were the house band for the fledgling Satellite label, founded by Estelle Axton and her brother, Jim Stewart. (When a similarly named label out of California threatened legal action, the pair renamed their company Stax [for STewart and AXton], and the Memphis sound was born.) The Mar-keys had a floating membership, working basically as the Stax label backup band. Their only Top-Ten hit was 1961's "Last Night," issued on the Satellite label. By the late '60s, Dunn and Cropper had joined up with Booker T. Jones and Al Jackson, Jr. to form the Stax label's most famous instrumental outfit, Booker T and The MGs. The Mar-Keys, now just a horn section, became The Memphis Horns, and often worked with Booker and company.

ATLANTIC 82339 (CL)

The Great Memphis Sound

Reissue of their 1966 platter (Stax 707), featuring the minor hit, "Philly Dog." There is good dance-floor material in the unique grooves of "Honey Pot," "Plantation Inn," the Junior Walker answer "Cleo's Back," a strutting "In the Mood," and a "Dear James Medley" of solid James Brown-inspired horn work.

STAX (UK) 959 (L)

Damifiknow/Memphis Experience

This CD reissues the group's last two albums from 1969 and 1971 (originally Cotillion 9014 and Stax 2036, respectively), with 18 instrumentals for nearly 70 minutes of hot music, including a nine-and-a-half minute work-up of The Temptations's classic "Cloud Nine." Every song will make you wonder how a band could be this good. Best title: "Creeper's Funkatrations." Soul Man/Knock on Wood/Never Loved a Man/After the Affair/Angel Dust/Mustang Sally/Black.

THE MAR-KEYS/BOOKER T and THE MGs

ATLANTIC 90307 (CL)

Back to Back

This would almost be a genuine, old-fashioned battle of the bands, except for one detail; The Mar-Keys were just three horn players (later featured on countless sessions as The Memphis Horns) backed by Booker T and company! Very energetic all-instrumental live recording from 1967, with 10 wired versions of your favorites, featuring Steve Cropper, Duck Dunn, Al Jackson, and the Bookman ticklin' the keys. Green Onions/Hip Hug-Her/Philly Dog/Last Night/Gimme Some Lovin.

THE MARCELS

Pittsburgh vocal group featuring Cornelius Harp on lead vocals and Fred Johnson (b). They're best known for their dadaistic reinterpretations of standards recorded for Colpix in the early '60s, especially their classic hit, "Blue Moon," featuring the unique bass intro by Johnson, which reached Number 1 in the charts in 1961. They had further hits with their unique interpretations of "Summertime" and "Heartaches."

COLPIX 250 (R)
Heartaches
Twenty great Colpix sides from the early '60s. Besides their big hit, "Blue Moon," there's an emphasis on their surreal versions of the standards including the title tune, "Summertime," "You Are My Sunshine," "That Old Black Magic," and a hilarious version of "My Melancholy Baby."

COLPIX 521 (R)
Rare Items
Seventeen sides in peerless stereo, including Colpix recordings along with not-so-familiar titles made at later dates for Queen Bee (1963) and St. Clair (1975). There are a handful of excellent sides here, but this collection dwells too heavily on the group's cover versions of old standards.

CRYSTAL BALL 111 (R)
The Fabulous Marcels
Twelve, fine, early sides, featuring seven previously unreleased items, six of them a cappella. Two takes of some tunes are included, one sung a cappella and the other with accompaniment. Lucky Old Sun (two versions)/Peace of Mind (two versions)/High on a Hill/Soul Dinner/Save the Last Dance for Me.

RELIC 7030 (L)
Summertime
Twenty of these 24 mostly a-cappella tracks are taken from pre-Colpix rehearsal tapes or demos cut while the group was recording for Colpix. Most of the cuts are covers, and remained unreleased until the 1980s. The famous Fred Johnson bass intro on "Blue Moon" is heard in an earlier version on the similar-sounding "Zoom." A unique opportunity to hear The Marcels before their rise to stardom. Got a Job/Stormy Weather/Spanish Harlem/That Lucky Old Sun/Over the Rainbow.

RHINO 70953 (CL)
The Best of The Marcels
Fourteen pieces of inspired nonsense. The tunes are all taken from their original Colpix master tapes, so you get studio chat, crystal-clear sound, and real stereo. As a bonus, this features the very first release of "Blue Heartache" from 1962. Excellent, informative liner notes and complete sessionography and discography. Includes their big hits "Blue Moon," "Heartaches," and their definitive version of "My Melancholy Baby," along with lesser hits and LP cuts. CD has four additional cuts. Friendly Loans/Summertime/I'll Be Forever Loving You.

LITTLE PEGGY MARCH

Starting her musical career when she was only five years old, Peggy first recorded in the early '60s for RCA and, at the age of 15, had the million seller "I Will Follow Him" (1963), a cover of Petula Clark's French-language recording of "Chariot." After lesser US hits, she moved to Germany in the late '60s where she made further recordings, wrote pop songs, acted on television. She returned to the USA in the '80s and made an appearance in cult director John Waters's film, *Hairspray*.

RAVEN 1017 (R)
Boy Crazy!
Great girl-pop compilation, 20 tunes from her singles and three albums cut for RCA. Includes, of course, "I Will Follow Him," along with "Leave Me Alone" written by Randy Newman, "Can't Stop Thinking about Him" written by Leon Huff, plus the title hit. I Wish I Were a Princess/Johnny Cool/Wind Up Doll.

BOBBY MARCHAN

Former lead vocalist with Huey "Piano" Smith and The Clowns, and a renowned female impersonater in New Orleans, Marchan's intense high vocals contributed to the success of "Rockin' Pneumonia and the Boogie Woogie Flu" and "Don't You Just Know It." In 1960, he went out on his own and had a hit on the Fire label with his version of Big Jay McNeely's "There Is Something on Your Mind." He continued recording through the '70s with minimal success.

COLLECTABLES 5113 (RCL)
Golden Classics
A dozen Fire sides from 1959–1960. This is the only way to get these sides, but Collectables again has provided shoddy packaging (no information on the cover, not even writer credits!) and short playing time. Includes his smash cover of Jay McNeely's "There Is Something on Your Mind, Pts. 1 and 2." Booty Green/

You're Still My Baby, Pts. 1 and 2/All in My Mind/I Miss You So.

HANK MARR

Hank Marr was an obscure blues and jazz organist and piano player who recorded for King and Federal in the early '60s as a sideman and under his own name. He was a first-class key-pounder right up there with better-known organ combo commanders like Jimmy Smith, Jack McDuff, and Milt Buckner.

CHARLY 271 (L)
Greasy Spoon
Twenty toe-tappers, emphasizing jumpin' jazz, along the lines of fellow King-label keyboardist Bill Doggett, but more stripped-down, revved-up, and with barely a whiff of corny commercialism. Marr gives plenty of blowing room to his talented sidemen, coaxing noteworthy sax and guitar leads from bopster Rusty Bryant, Osborne Whitfield, and even bluesman Freddie King! Lots of straight-ahead swing, epitomized by "Let's Cut One," "Wild Shindig," "Sabotage," "The Squash," "Jim Dawg," and "Back Slop." Hot!

MARTHA and THE VANDELLAS

Martha Reeves was originally employed as a secretary at Berry Gordy's fledgling Motown Records. Because she had a decent voice, she often made demo tapes for other artists so that they could learn the words and music to the songs. Reeves and two other Motown backup singers, Betty Kelly and Rosalind Ashford, backed Marvin Gaye on his 1962 hit "Stubborn Kind of Fellow," and toured with him through 1963. The trio recorded "Come and Get These Memories" for the Gordy subsidiary label in 1963, scoring their first of 21 big hits, including 1963's "Heat Wave" and the anthemic "Dancing in the Streets" (1964). Martha left the original group in 1971 to pursue a solo career, and can still be heard in clubs and rock-revival shows.

MOTOWN 778 (C)
Anthology
Overview of their career, originally issued in 1974.

MOTOWN 5145 (CL)
Heatwave
Reissue of Gordy 907 from 1963.

MOTOWN 5204 (CL)
Greatest Hits
The best collection of the group's numerous hits. Come and Get These Memories/Heatwave/Dancing in the Street/Spooky/It's the Same Old Song/I Say a Little Prayer/Come See About Me.

MOTOWN 5265 (CL)
Watch Out
Their fourth LP, originally Gordy 920 from 1966.

MOTOWN 5433 (CL)
Dance Party
Reissue of Gordy 915 from 1965, a chance to groove to the big dance numbers of the day!

MOTOWN 5477 (CL)
Black Magic
Originally Gordy 958 from 1974.

MOTOWN 8149 (L)
Heatwave/Dance Party

JANIS MARTIN

One of the few female rockabilly singers, Martin recorded for RCA in the mid-'50s and was produced by Chet Atkins. She was best-known for her novelty rocker, "My Boy Elvis." She was dropped from the label in 1958, because it was hard to push her as an innocent child star when, at age 17, she was married and pregnant! She still occasionally performs.

BEAR FAMILY 15032 (R)
That Rockin' Gal

BEAR FAMILY 15046 (R)
That Rockin' Gal Rocks

BEAR FAMILY 15406 (L)
The Female Elvis:
Complete Recordings 1956–60
All of Martin's recordings, on two LPs or one CD, including 26 tunes recorded for RCA from 1956–1958, plus four tunes from her 1960 "comeback" on Palette. Typically excellent mono sound from Bear Family. My Boy Elvis/Will You, Willyum/Drug Store Rock and Roll/Ooby Dooby/Teen Street.

THE MARVELETTES

Outstanding early Motown group featuring two lead singers, Gladys Horton and Wanda Young. They had one of the first Motown hits, "Please Mr. Postman," which was a million seller in 1961 and was covered by The Beatles. The group had hits through 1968, many written by Smokey Robinson ("Don't Mess with Bill" and "My Baby Must Be a Magician"), before they broke up in the early '70s.

MOTOWN 827 (C)
Anthology
Retrospective originally put together in 1974. Beechwood 4-5789/The Hunter Gets Captured by the Game/That's How Heartaches Are Made.

MOTOWN 5180 (CL)
Greatest Hits

MOTOWN 5266 (CL)
Please Mr. Postman
Reissue of their first LP with their big hit, Motown 228 from 1961.

MOTOWN 5421 (CL)
The Marveletttes
Reissue of Motown 274 from 1967.

MOTOWN 5430 (CL)
Sophisticated Soul
Reissue of Motown 286 from 1968.

MOTOWN 5473 (CL)
Playboy
Reissue of their third LP, Motown 231 from 1963.

MARVIN and JOHNNY

The R&B duo of Marvin and Johnny featured Marvin Phillips with various other singers in the role of "Johnny" including Jesse Belvin, Johnny Dean, Carl Green, Emory Perry, and even Phillips himself through overdubbing. Perry, who originally played sax, was probably the best of the "Johnnys." They first recorded for Specialty from 1952–1954, and had a hit with 1953's "Baby Doll." They switched to Modern in 1954 and hit again with the double-sided "Cherry Pie" and "Tick Tock."

SPECIALTY 2176 (CL)
Flipped Out
Twenty-six song set recorded between 1952–1956, including "Wine Woogie" and "Old Man's Blues" by Marvin and His Men from Mars, and the Number 2 R&B hit "Dream Girl" by Jesse (Belvin) and Marvin, plus three by the Red Callender Orchestra with Marvin. Of Marvin and Johnny's two biggest hits, "Baby Doll" is here, but "Tick Tock" is missing. Included, however, are many unreleased items like "If I Should Lose You," "What's the Matter Baby," and "I Want

Lovin'," two alternate takes of "Honey," and four unissued demos. The unreleased stuff is every bit as good as the rest, making this collection especially worthwhile. A Hunter Hancock radio ad is also provided.

MARVIN, WELCH and FARRAR

SEE FOR MILES 78 (RL)
Step from The Shadows
In 1968, bespectacled Hank Marvin, guitar hero of The Shadows, did an about face and formed a trio with Shadow Bruce Welch and John Farrar from The Strangers, concentrating on acoustic CSNY-type music, loaded with three-part harmonies. The eighteen tunes are taken from their three LPs for Regal Zonophone, recorded between 1971–1974, plus two singles—"Please Mr. Please" and "Marmaduke"—never before on LP. Lady of the Morning/Music Makes My Day/Skin Deep.

HANK MARVIN

Legendary British guitarist (b. Brian Rankin; Hank was his nickname, and he took Marvin for Marvin Rainwater!) who led the famed group The Shadows (see separate listing) in the '60s backing British star Cliff Richard (see separate listing) as well as recording instrumentals under their own name. After the group disbanded in 1968, Hank pursued a solo career, with hits being separated by long periods of near anonymity. From time to time he would work again with Richard or various other members of The Shadows. His guitar work with The Shadows provided an inspiration for many of today's British rock guitar heroes.

SEE FOR MILES 210 (RL)
Would You Believe It . . . Plus!
The bulk of these 20 tracks comes from the long out-of-print LP *Hank Marvin* (UK Columbia 6352 from 1969), Hank's first solo outing after the 1968 breakup of The Shadows, featuring "Shads" drummer Brian Bennett, who brought along "Chameleon" and "Love and Occasional Rain" from his own solo LP (See For Miles 205). Unfortunately, this is mostly "pretty music" along the lines of covers of MOR standards "Somewhere My Love," "Windmills of Your Mind," and (egads!) "Born Free." What's important here is the first official issue of the often bootlegged tune "Would You Believe It," complete with Marvin's vocals, and a slew of 1969 and 1970 singles making their first LP appearance and their first issue in stereo.

SEE FOR MILES 289
Guitar Syndicate

BARBARA MASON

Philadelphia soul singer Mason first recorded for Crusader in 1964, then switched to Arctic in 1965 where she hit it big with "Yes, I'm Ready." After several successful years with Arctic she moved briefly to National and then in 1972 to Buddah.

SEQUEL 115 (L)
Philadelphia's Lady Love: The Best of Barbara Mason

Sixteen soulful slices from her early '70s Buddah recordings. Includes a remake of her big 1965 hit "Yes I'm Ready." Give Me Your Love/Shackin' Up/We Got Each Other.

SAMMY MASTERS

California-based rockabilly/country singer and songwriter.

HYDRA 7708 (R)
Rockin' Red Wing

Sixteen sides recorded between 1956–1962.

JOHN MAYALL (and THE BLUESBREAKERS)

Second only to Alex Korner, John Mayall was the key figure in the British blues revival of the '60s. A dedicated fan of American R&B and electric blues, Mayall nurtured the talents of many young rockers, including guitarists Eric Clapton, Peter Green, and Mick Taylor during the band's greatest days, from 1966–1969.

DERAM 8000086 (CL)
Blues Breakers: John Mayall with Eric Clapton

Discouraged by the increasingly commercial orientation of The Yardbirds, Clapton joined Mayall in recording this seminal LP of electric blues.

DERAM 820474 (CL)
A Hard Road

1967 LP featuring the debut of Peter Green in the band, along with drummer Aynsley Dunbar, and longtime bassist John McVie. Features original Mayall numbers along with blues and R&B covers.

DERAM 820539 (L)
Blues from Laurel Canyon

Trippy diary of Mayall's 1967 visit to California, featuring guitarist Mick Taylor.

DERAM 837127 (CL)
Archives to Eighties

Reissue of a remixed version of the 1971 LP, *Back to the Roots*, which featured Mayall performing his own material accompanied by ex-Bluesbreakers Clapton and Taylor, along with five late-'80s cuts.

DERAM 844302 (L)
London Blues

Two-CD set featuring early Mayall cuts with various band members.

VAN MCCOY

Van Allen McCoy, singer, producer, and pianist, was born in Washington in 1944, and first recorded with The Marylanders and Ambassadors; he later recorded with The Starlighters, The Four Buddies, and The Pacettes. Van sings in a soft, soulfully romantic, laidback style. He died in 1979.

VAM 4079 (R)
Dedicated to the Memory of Van Allen McCoy

This magnificent set features his three singles cut for End with The Starlighters (recorded between 1958–1960), including the classic "It's 12 O'Clock"; his Philips single with The Four Buddies; and the sides that he made with the female group The Pacettes. Also featured are his solo efforts, including his best-known song, 1960's "Hey Mr. DJ" released on Rockin', plus duets with Norman McCoy, Kendra Spottswood, Paul Comedy, and Freddie Smith. Average sound.

JIMMY MCGRIFF

Philadelphia-born James Harrell McGriff came from a musical family and was bitten by the organ bug when he heard Jimmy Smith playing a Hammond B-2 at a local jam session. His 1962 cover of Ray Charles's "I Got a Woman" was his one big hit, scoring on the pop and R&B charts, combining jazzy stylings with a hot dance beat. He continued to place singles on the charts through the '60s.

COLLECTABLES 5125 (CL)

A Toast to Jimmy McGriff's
Golden Classics

Select cuts from Jimmy's six Sue albums. Includes "Topkopi" with string section, the pretty bluesy "Turn Blue," the sax-frantic "Hello Betty," the soulful "Last Minute," and the unstoppable million-seller "I've Got a Woman, Pts. 1 and 2." Average sound quality. For lovers of early Blue Note and Sue soul-jazz sounds.

COLLECTABLES 5126 (CL)

Jimmy McGriff at The Apollo

Reissue of Jimmy's live album cut in the early '60s for Juggy Murray's NY-based Sue label. Six soul-jazz stylings display the virtuosity of the fine solo work, notably Rudy Johnson's inspired tenor sax on "There'll Never Be Another You" and Larry Frazier's fast-fingered guitar on "Frame for the Blues." Jimmy shines on "A Thing for Jug," a suicide-paced cut where he pulls out all the stops. Behaved drumming from Willie "The Saint" Jenkins. Crowd noise never interferes with music.

COLLECTABLES 5147 (CL)

Blues for Mr. Jimmy

SCOTTY MCKAY

Scotty McKay was the piano player for Gene Vincent and The Blue Caps, playing on ten of their 45s and three LPs, before splitting from the band in 1958 to do his own thing. He recorded for Event, Parkway, Swan, Ace, Dot, and Philips during the '60s, mostly doing pop covers. Soundtrack work and record producing occupied his time after that.

EAGLE 901007 (R)

Scotty McKay

A dozen tunes spanning the years 1958–1966, finding Scotty singing pop versions of "You're So Square," "Be-Bop-a-Lula," and "Lonely Weekend." Some of his later efforts are tougher though, like "Let It Rock," "Who Do You Love," and especially "Train Kept A'Rollin'," with overdubbed guitar by Jimmy Page.

TOMMY MCLAIN

Tommy is a fine swamp pop singer with a distinctive voice. He worked for many years with Clint West and The Boogie Kings. In 1966 he had a surprise hit with his version of Don Gibson's "Sweet Dreams."

ACE 285 (RL)

Sweet Dreams

Twenty fine sides recorded for Jin in the mid-to-late '60s. Tommy and Clint West do a great duet on "Try to Find Another Man" with some great guitar. The collection also includes the title hit, along with covers of country and R&B hits, some original songs, and a medley of Fats Domino songs. Nice! Before I Grow Too Old/Barefootin'/When a Man Loves a Woman/Just Because/Together Again/So Sad (to Watch Good Love Go Bad)/My Heart Remembers.

BIG JAY MCNEELY

One of the giants of the wild, honking style of sax blowing who emerged in the '40s. In addition to his instrumental pyrotechnics, he was also noted for his extroverted stage act, which included rolling on the floor and playing the sax on his back. He had his first hit for Savoy in 1949 with the classic honker's dream "Deacons Hop." A decade later, he had another hit with his self-penned R&B song, "There Is Something on Your Mind," with Little Sonny Warner on vocals. In the '80s he recorded some new albums for his own Big J label and reissued some of his earlier recordings, and remains active today.

❂ COLLECTABLES 5131 (CL)

Live At Birdland 1957

This vintage 1957 Big Jay show recorded at Seattle's Birland Club should be a popular release. The discovery of this tape in 1988 was, for R&B fans, tantamount to the unearthing of King Tut's tomb. This CD version adds six cuts from another Big Jay Records LP, Swingin' (Big J 103). The band opens with the dynamic, raspy voiced Little Sonny Warner singing "I Hope You're All Right," then jumps into prime Big Jay on the wild "Insect Ball." After a soulful rendition of Lynn Hope's "Tenderly" and a swingin' number called "Havana Hop," McNeely really cuts loose on an amazing and exciting version of the old Goodman/Hampton classic "Flying Home," that must have really worn out the dancers; it's eight-and-one-half minutes long! He does his crowd pleasers, "Deacon's Hop" and "There Is Something on Your Mind," and throws in some surprises too, like a fine version of Les Paul and Mary Ford's "How High the Moon."

COLLECTABLES 5133 (CL)

The Swingin' Cuts

Sixteen fine tracks recorded for the Los Angeles Swingin' label between 1957–1961. Lots of hard-driving music, including the unedited version of the hit "There Is Something on Your Mind" with Little

Sonny Warner on vocals, some hot honkin' instrumentals, and even a rockabilly track with a white singer. Includes six previously unissued tracks. Previously issued on Jay's own Big J label.

KING 650 (RCL)

Big Jay in 3-D

Jay's tenor and band will literally tear your socks off on these rockin', mid-'50s instrumentals, great for parties and not bad at home either. Swing through "Whipped Cream" into "Hot Cinders," then to "Ice Water," and finally turn to "Rock Candy," plus eight more. Crazy!

SAXOPHONOGRAPH 505 (L)

Roadhouse Boogie

Features a variety of swing styles, sometimes bop, sometimes Latin, sometimes just wildly frantic. There are eight sides recorded in 1949, including the title tune with screaming vocals by Ted Shirley, and the mellow "Midnight Dreams" featuring the voice of Clifford Blivens. There are also six of Jay's excellent Aladdin cuts plus two from Federal. Junie Flip/Real Crazy Cool/Deac's Blowout

SAXOPHONOGRAPH 1300 (R)

The Best Of Big Jay McNeely, Vol. 2

Big Jay's best booting from the much coveted Federal period, including the jet speed "3-D," the bouncy "Let's Work" with fine Ed Moody piano, and the positively frantic "Nervous Man Nervous." Some duplication with other albums.

CLYDE MCPHATTER

Clyde was born in Durham, NC, in 1933 and died of a heart attack in 1972. Vocally inspired by Robert Harris of The Soul Stirrers, McPhatter became one of the finest high tenor soul-soloists of the '50s. Starting as a choir boy, he graduated to lead the Mt. Lebanon Gospel singers, before joining The Dominoes. He formed the original Drifters for Atlantic records in 1953. He served in the army in 1954, and continued to record through the '50s as a soloist for Atlantic and had many hits. He recorded for MGM and Mercury through the mid-'60s, though these recordings are often of lesser interest. He was inactive in the late '60s, and his 1970 Decca album went nowhere.

⊕ ATLANTIC 82314 (CL)

Deep Sea Ball

Nineteen of McPhatter's big hits, rather than his greatest recordings, covering the 1955–1959 period, and embracing all but one of his charted sides. Omits

the first and finest Drifters recording, "Lucille" (1953), along with many of his masterpieces like "The Way I Feel," "Warm Your Heart," and "Everyone's Laughing." Issued as part of the ongoing Remasters series, with great pix but scanty notes. Rock and Cry/Without Love/Come What May/Lovey Dovey/A Lover's Question/Long, Lonely Nights.

BEAR FAMILY 15271 (R)

Rhythm and Soul

Eight-LP box set containing all of Clyde's MGM (1959–1960) and Mercury (1960–1965) recordings. Clyde has got to be one of my all-time favorite singers, but his MGM sides are among his worst, with the label trying to make him an adult-pop stylist. His Mercury outings were quite a bit better, especially when he was paired with producer Clyde Otis, who had been working with Brook Benton and Dinah Washington. His first Mercury hit was "Ta Ta," followed by the Shelby Singleton produced "Lover Please." He ended his Mercury career with the fine Songs of the Big City and the excellent Live at the Apollo LPs; The Apollo concert features hits from his entire career going back to "Have Mercy Baby" from his Dominoes days. Don't buy this box expecting the youthful exuberance of the '50s, but there are still plenty of sparks to make it worthwhile.

CURB 77417 (CL)

Greatest Hits

Kind of a stingy collection (only 12 tracks), but this is still a welcome addition, considering the relative scarcity of McPhatter discs. Three Drifters tracks are featured ("Money Honey," "Honey Love," and "Lucille") as well as his mid-'50s solo outings ("A Lover's Question," "Treasure of Love," and "Without Love"). Also features his '60s Mercury recordings, including "Lover Please," "Little Bitty Pretty One," "Crying Won't Help You Now," and more finger-poppers. Good liner notes, too.

KING 559 (RL)

Clyde McPhatter with Billy Ward and His Dominoes

Twelve cuts. 60 Minute Man/Don't Leave Me this Way/The Bells.

JACK MCVEA and HIS ALL STARS

Jack McVea was one of many jazz musicians who moved into R&B in the '40s. Prior to forming his own band in 1946, McVea who was a vocalist, saxophonist, and clarinetist who had worked with Lionel Hampton, Dizzy Gillespie, and Charlie Parker. In 1947, he had a hit with the R&B novelty "Open the Door Richard." He had his own band through the '50s and later worked in various bands. By the mid-'60s he was leading a trio at Disneyland, a job he kept into the 1980s.

JUKEBOX LIL 625 (R)

New Deal

Sixteen tunes by Jack McVea and His All Stars. Besides their seminal R&B recordings like "Open the Door, Richard," McVea and company backed artists like T-Bone Walker and Wynonie Harris. Estelle Edson sings the risque "My Business Is C.O.D." and "Baby Make Up Your Mind," and former Ellington singer Betty Roche does a beautiful "Rainy Day Blues." Gene Phillips does a nice job on "You Can Come Back Home," but the two Arthur Duncan tunes are very dated pop ballads. Drummer Rabon Tarrant handles the remaining vocals, including a rockin' "Two Timin' Baby Boogie" and the novelty "Carlos." The musicianship is marvelous throughout with Gene Phillips (gtr) and Jack's fellow Hampton alumnus Marshal Royal (sax, clr). Jack's Boogie/F Minor Boogie/Tatoe Pie.

THE MELLO-KINGS

The Mello-Kings were five white teenagers from Mt. Vernon, NY. They were originally formed in High School after trying out for a school musical, and were known as The Mellotones. Original members were brothers Jerry and Robert Scholl, who shared lead and first tenor chores, with Eddie Quinn (2nd ten), Neil Arena (bar), and Larry Esposito (b). Their first single, "Tonite Tonite," issued by Al Silver's Herald label, was their sole hit, although initially it raised the ire of competitor George Goldner who had his own group known as The Mello-Tones. The group's name changed, but their luck ran out on the charts. They last recorded in 1961.

RELIC 5035 (R)

The Mello-Kings Greatest Hits

Eighteen sides from the late '50s. She's Real Cool/Do Baby Do/Dear Mr. Jock.

RELIC 7008 (L)

The Mello-Kings

Contains all their Herald output, including four songs which did not show up on Relic 5035 (two of these are previously unreleased). The quintet sings well in a smooth, sweet-sounding way, but too often drifts into commercially trite material. Notable songs include "Baby Tell Me," "'Til There Were None," and "Tonite Tonite." Digitally transferred from the original master tapes.

JOE MELSON

BEAR FAMILY 15027 (R)

Barbara

'60s pop rock and ballads reissued from Hickory.

THE MEMPHIS BOYS

Memphis-based sessioneers, led by guitar wizard Reggie Young, who stamped their brand of the "Memphis Sound" on 121 commercial hits in the late '60s and very early '70s. They relocated to Nashville in 1972. Instrumental buffs will appreciate the band's contributions to the hits of Elvis, Bobby Womack, and Joe Tex, along with recent recordings and tours with Delbert McClinton, Smokey Robinson, and The Highwaymen.

VANGUARD 79461 (L)

The Memphis Boys

Ten new mid-tempo Booker T and The MGs-type instrumentals from this premier session quintet, featuring subtle interplay between Reggie Young's guitar and the keyboards and organ of Bobby Emmons and Bobby Wood, all firmly anchored by bassist Mike Leech and drummer Gene Chrisman. Highlights are the mild funk of "Callin' Your Bluff," the haunting "Streets of Soul," and the sprightly "Beale Street BBQ."

THE METERS

The only instrumental funk group that matters (a forerunner of the Neville Brothers), with Art Neville (kybds), Leo Nocentelli (gtr), George Porter (b), and the incomparable Zig Modeliste (drm).

CHARLY 2 (L)

Funky Miracle

Double-CD set featuring 38 slices of steamin' Crescent City funk. Duplicates the now out-of-print Charly LPs *Second Line Strut* and *Here Come The Metermen*, the previously issued single Charly CD *Struttin'*, and Rounder's recent *Look Ka Py Py*. But, as we say in the biz, it's nice to have these all together in one package.

RHINO 70376 (CL)

Uptown Rulers!:
Live on The Queen Mary

A live 1975 set, with the kings of New Orleans funk at the height of their rhythmic powers. The show opens with an incredible "Fire on the Bayou" and then moves quickly into the groove-laden "Africa," a song built like an armored car. As always, Art Neville and company throw some incongruous covers into the show ("I Want to Make It with You"), but, of course, their take of this schlock classic is cooler than Bread's. Other proof of The Meters's greatness includes the classic "Mardi Gras Mambo," "Hey Pocky-a-Way," "It Ain't No Use," "Liar," and a couple of body-shaking medleys. Recommended.

ROUNDER 2103 (RCL)
Look Ka Py Py
Reissue of Josie 4011 from 1970; some tracks are duplicated on the Charly two-CD set, but the sound is superior here. Nothing can compare to the concise clipped funk of The Meters in their prime, and this is it, tight, right, and impossibly laidback. Anchored by the steady cubist strokes of Zig (the world's most angular drummer), they produced a bumper crop of instrumental classics. There are numerous highlights for Art Neville's keyboards and that nasty guitar of Leo Nocentelli. When these guys get cookin', there ain't nothin' tastier! Only a couple of cuts are less than thrilling. Not only recommended; this is REQUIRED for anyone with a soulful bone in their body. Rigor Mortis/Pungee/Yeah, You're Right/The Mob/Dry Spell.

ROUNDER 2104 (RCL)
Good Old Funky Music
Eleven previously unissued cuts from the late '60s to mid-'70s. The title track is a bare-bones boogaloo workout, followed in high style by a New Orleans medley that's just one of the many numbers featuring the singing of Art and (I think) Cyril Neville, credited only as percussionist here. Several of these could be Neville Brothers outtakes, like the covers of "Jambalaya" and the grinding funk "I'm Gonna Put Some Hurt on You," plus a few just barely worth reissuing, like the sappy soul of "Heartache," "What More Can I Do," and (yikes!) "The Riddle Song" ("I gave my love a chicken that had no bone..."). But the real kickers here are strangely seductive nuggets of low-down psychedelia like "Keep on Marching," the cryptic "He Bite Me," and the menacing space-jam instrumental "Voodoo." Pretty good, but get Look Ka Py Py first.

ROUNDER 2105 (CL)
The Meters Jam
Another odds-and-ends reissue, along the lines of Good Old Funky Music, but a good deal more satisfying. The fare gets better after the first pair of expendable funk numbers, and stays on the good foot right up to the final jazzy jam session that gives the disc its name. On the way there, we get Art Neville's soulful cover of "People Get Ready," the churning Mardi Gras fave "Big Chief," and some tasty chicken-scratch instrumentals. Their uptempo version of "Bo Diddley" gets the classic scritchy guitar treatment, too. Good times and good tunes; ten rare singles and unreleased cuts.

MICKEY and SYLVIA
Sylvia Vanderpool began her career in 1950 as 14-year-old "Little Sylvia," recording a couple of sides for various small labels. Four years later, she encountered McHouston "Mickey" Baker, one of the all-time great session guitarists. The duo recorded "Love is Strange" in 1957, a racy rock classic, but split up in 1959. They regrouped for some minor hits in 1961–1962, working with Ike and Tina Turner. Mickey went to Europe to continue as a jazz-guitar virtuoso, while Sylvia married Joe Robinson and worked as a record company executive and producer. She returned in 1973 for the fluke hit "Pillow Talk," another sexy outing.

BEAR FAMILY 15438 (L)
Love Is Strange
A double-CD set featuring all of this duo's Rainbow, Groove, and RCA recordings cut between 1955–1965, 60 tracks in all. It includes several alternate takes and some dozen unissued songs! Their material ranged from bluesy stuff, like their biggest hit "Love Is Strange" and other fine songs ("Rock and Stroll Room," "Baby You're So Fine," "Going Home," and "Where Is My Honey?"), to awful schmaltzy pop like "Mommy Out De Light" and "Love Lesson." Still, you can always skip over the schlock to get to the cream! Sound, of course, is immaculate, and the set comes with a 56-page booklet with extensive notes by Norbert Hess, full discographical information, and lots of great photos including some atmospheric studio photos and a couple of color shots of the duo live on stage!

AMOS MILBURN JR.
Neither related to or stylistically similar to his namesake, Jr. toured once with Amos and just started using his name.

MR. R&B 1000 (R)
You Used Me
Seventeen sides recorded for Major Bill Smith between 1959–1967, featuring King Curtis (ten sax) and Delbert McClinton (hca). An interesting mixture of rock, R&B, country, pop, and blues, including a good rockabilly-styled "Long Tall Sally."

CHUCK MILLER
Country-jiver Chuck hit the Top 10 in 1955 with his cover of "House of Blue Lights" and in

1956 with a cover of "The Auctioneer," both for Mercury.

REVIVAL 3002 (R)

Going Going Gone ...

Eighteen Mercury recordings from 1955–1958, mostly jive and boogie covers of other peoples' tunes. Cow Cow Boogie/Down the Road Apiece/Vim Vam Vamoose/Hupahoola Boogie.

LUCKY MILLINDER

Popular R&B bandleader of the '40s and '50s. The roster of this swingin' dance band included singers Wynonie Harris, Annisteen Allen, Bubber Johnson, and the instrumental talent of Big John Greer, Sonny Thompson, Rudy Powell, Count Hastings, Sam Taylor, and Roomful of Blues's Porky Cohen!

CHARLY 288 (L)

Ram-Bunk-Shush

Covers the man's King years circa 1950–1955, with featured soloists Wynonie Harris, Annisteen Allen, and Brother John Sellers, plus vocal groups The Millinderites and The Admirals. Outstanding selections include the title cut and the off-color "Chew Tobacco Rag." Great swingin' R&B with noted soloists Sonny Thompson (pno), Count Hastings (ten sax), Tyree Glenn (trb), and the incomparable Sam "The Man" Taylor (ten sax). Good, concise, detailed notes by Dave Penny. Silent George/I'm Waiting Just for You/Please Be Careful/Heavy Sugar/It's a Sad, Sad Feeling/Ow.

JUKEBOX LIL 609 (R)

Shorty's Got to Go

Sixteen tunes, mostly new to LP. Includes seven sides from 1942–1946 with vocals by Annisteen Allen, Judy Carol, and Leon Ketchem ("Fare-Thee-Well Deacon Jones," "More More More," and "Are You Ready"). Nine additional sides from 1950–1952 feature Lamar Wright, Rudy Powell, Big John Greer, Sheldon Powell, Tyree Glenn, and Sonny Thompson, with vocals by Greer, Melvin Moore, Harlan Lattimore, Henry Glover, and Hey Jackson ("Who Said Shorty Wasn't Comin' Back," "The Grapevine," and "Chew Tobacco Rag").

JUKEBOX LIL 613 (R)

Let It Roll Again

A mixture of material cut between 1941–1951, including war-propaganda novelties sung with bravado by all the band members. Although much of the vocal work by Trevor Bacon and Judy Carol sounds dated, Arbee Stidham does a fine job on the bluesy "Your Heart Belongs to Me," Big John Greer wails on "Let It Roll Again," Annisteen Allen hollers "The Blues Done Got Me," and Wynonie Harris belts out the Ruth Brown hit "Teardrops from My Eyes."

GARNET MIMMS and THE ENCHANTERS

An excellent performer of early '60s uptown soul, Garnet was born in 1933 in Ashland, WV. He sang in many gospel groups, including the world-famous Harmonizing Four, before turning to secular music and forming his own vocal group, The Gainors, in 1958. After a handful of unsuccessful sides, producer Jerry Ragovoy put him together with The Enchanters (with ex-Gainor Sam Bell, and Charles Boyer and Zola Pearnell), and the combination struck paydirt in 1963 with three great soul anthems on United Artists: "Cry Baby," "For Your Precious Love," and "Baby Don't You Weep." In 1964, while Mimms continued to record for UA and Veep, the other members of The Enchanters were replaced by The Warwick Sisters, who masqueraded as The Enchanters on Garnet's best sides like "A Quiet Place," "The Truth Hurts," and "I'll Take Good Care of You." In 1977, Mimms returned with a disco hit on Arista, fronting The Truckin' Co.'s hit "What It Is."

COLLECTABLES 5248 (CL)

Cry Baby

Although the scant liner notes were lifted from UA 3305 (1963), only five of its twelve songs are included. Little duplication with the out-of-print Charly 1121, and average sound quality on this essential collection of deep soul. Cry Baby/I'll Take Good Care of You/One Girl/For Your Precious Love/Baby, Don't You Weep.

LIBERTY (JAPAN) 6598 (L)

Cry Baby

Fifteen singles and album cuts from the '60s, including all of the hits. Gospel-type soul singing at its very best.

SAL MINEO

Movie cutie Sal cut eight singles and an LP for Epic between 1957–1959, including the modest hits "Start Movin'" and "Lasting Love," letting his good looks and almost pleasant voice sell platters of what we now call "jive" to the kids.

He returned to a full-time acting career in the '60s and was murdered in 1976.

STAR CLUB 8029 (R)
Make Believe Baby
Thirteen tracks, including both sides of six singles and the "A" side to a seventh. Start Movin'/Lasting Love/The Words That I Whisper/Little Pigeon.

BOBBY MITCHELL
Mitchell was a fine New Orleans R&B singer who formed the group The Toppers while still in high school. The group started recording for Imperial in 1952. In 1955, they split and Bobby started his solo career having a modest hit with "Try Rock and Roll." He also recorded the original version of "I'm Gonna Be a Wheel Someday," which was a hit for Fats Domino in 1959. He recorded for a number of small labels in the late '50s and early '60s, and subsequently worked outside the music business. He died in 1989.

MR. R&B 101 (R)
I'm Gonna Be a Wheel Someday
Rockin' R&B and doo-wop ballads. I'm Crying/Wedding Bells Are Ringing/One Friday Morning/Sister Lucy/64 Hours.

FREDDIE MITCHELL
WHISKEY, WOMEN AND ... 712 (R)
The Derby, 1949–55
Nine sessions (18 tunes) from 1949–1955 cut for the small Derby label, after the tenor saxist had put in stints with The Benny Carter and Fletcher Henderson Orchestras, among others. Many of the tunes are scaled down, big-band-type arrangements popular at the time, like a rockin' "Music Makers Boogie" (Harry James) and "Summertime Boogie" (George Gershwin). Mitchell and his band also backed some of the fine female blues "thrushes" (as they were known then) on Derby, and three of those tunes are included: Honey Brown's "Lonesome and Mistreated" and "Rockin' and Jumpin'"; and Sarah "Fat Woman" Dean's "Long Lean Daddy." There's plenty of rock'em, sock'em R&B here, too, especially "Hot Ice," "Three Strikes You're Out," "Preachin'," and "Jersey Bounce."

GUY MITCHELL
Guy Mitchell was an interesting phenomenon: a pop singer who had a great deal of success performing pop-flavored versions of country, rock-and-roll, and even blues songs accompanied by New York studio musicians.

BEAR FAMILY 15454 (L)
Heartaches by the Number
Twenty-five tracks presenting an overview of his career, including almost all his hits, plus non-hit songs like "Crazy with Love," "Sunshine Guitar," "Sweet Stuff," "Take Me Back Baby," and one unissued track, "Notify the F.B.I." ("Please Mr. Hoover/My baby's she's a groover"!). In spite of the pop trappings, Guy is really quite an engaging singer who doesn't sound uncomfortable with the material. As usual for Bear Family, the sound is superb, there is a 24-page booklet with a detailed biography by Peter Grendysa, a few photos, and full discographical information. My Heart Cries for You/Sparrow in the Tree Top/My Truly Truly Fair/Pittsburgh, Pennsylvania/'Cause I Love You (with Mindy Carson)/Singing the Blues/Rock-a-Billy (in spite of the name, it isn't!)/My Shoes Keep Walking Back to You.

WILLIE MITCHELL
Willie is a trumpet-playing band leader, best known for his work with Hi Records. He was born in Ashland, MS, in 1928, formed his own band in the early '50s, and, in 1960, his combo became the house band at the Home-of-the-Blues label. He joined Hi in 1963 and had a nice string of hit funk instrumentals including "Soul Serenade" and "Prayer Meeting." When Hi's president died, Mitchell started doing more production work and took over administrative duties for the label. By 1969, he had abandoned his own career to work with his discovery, Al Green, and became vice-president of Hi. He spent the '70s as a molder of the modern Memphis soul sound by producing and totally overseeing the recordings of his many discoveries, including Green, Ann Peebles, O.V. Wright, and Syl Johnson.

HI (UK) 120 (L)
Solid Soul/On Top
Twenty-four-cut collection that reissues two of Willie's extremely fine instrumental albums. He cut so many fine, groovy Memphis soul instrumentals that you can't lose whatever collection you choose to buy. Superb pix and booklet notes. Prayer Meetin'/Sunrise Serenade/Up Hard/Strawberry Soul/Take Five/30-60-999/I Say a Little Prayer/I Wish It Would Rain.

HI (UK) 408 (R)
That Driving Beat
Sixteen pieces (15 singles and one LP track) of strong instrumental Memphis funk by Willie's great studio band, recorded for Hi during the '60s, and featuring the strong beat of MGs's drummer Al Jackson on most tunes. Includes his biggest hit, a cover of King Curtis's "Soul Serenade." Biographical notes by Roger St. Pierre. The Crawl/20-75/Percolatin'/Buster Browne.

CURLEY MONEY
Rockabilly and rockin' country singer/guitarist from Georgia who led The Rhythm Ramblers.

BISON BOP 2003 (R)
Curley Money
Stop Your Knocking/Lazy Man/Wire Guitar/Hurricane Baby/Shortnin' Bread/Honky Tonk Man.

THE MONKEES
Sixties rock group manufactured to star in a TV sitcom. Their first four LPs, recorded while the show was on the air, are masterpieces of pop, with no expense spared in getting the finest material from writers such as Neil Diamond, Goffin and King, Lieber and Stoller, and other pop tunesmiths, all under the able direction of producer Don Kirshner. Later on, the group began to take itself seriously, the show was canceled, and, with only the team of Boyce and Hart still providing outside material, the band members tried to make up for the slack on their own. With the exception of excellent work from Mike Nesmith, their later LPs are spotty at best.

RHINO 70139 (CL)
The Monkees Live 1967
A dozen live tunes from August 25-27, 1967 recorded in Portland, Seattle, and Spokane. This has the band as a straight-ahead quartet, with Peter on bass and no sidemen, doing tunes from *The Monkees*, *More of*

The Monkees, and *Headquarters*. Sound quality isn't exceptional, but the excitement's all there. CD has four bonus tracks. Last Train to Clarksville/Mary, Mary/Your Auntie Grizelda/Randy Scouse Git/(I'm Not Your) Stepping Stone.

RHINO 70150 (CL)
Missing Links
A dozen tunes never-before released and most never-before bootlegged. These are all finished studio tunes, not demos of TV stuff. Recorded 1966–1969, most tunes were produced by Nesmith or Boyce and Hart. CD has four bonus tracks. War Games/Nine Times Blue/Apples, Peaches, Bananas and Pears/So Goes Love/All of Your Toys.

RHINO 70566 (CL)
Listen to the Band
Four-cassette/CD boxed set commemorating The Monk's 25th anniversary. Covers their entire career from their first recordings through their last gasps; 72 songs.

RHINO 70903 (CL)
Missing Links, Vol. 2
Unreleased numbers plus TV-only versions of their classic songs. CD has four bonus tracks. All the King's Horses/Some of Shelly's Blues/I'll Be Back on My Feet/Circle Sky/Hold on Girl/Mr. Webster/You Just May Be the One.

THE MONOTONES
The Montones first record was one of the true classics of rock and roll, 1958's "The Book of Love." The six members—Charles Petrick (lead), Warren Davis (1st ten), George Malone (2nd ten), Warren (bar) and John (b) Ryanes, and Frank Smith (b)—hailed from the same housing project in Newark, where the group was formed in 1955. They were all exmembers of the church choir that spawned Cissy Houston (Whitney's mom), Dionne Warwick, and The Sweet Inspirations. Group members Patrick (whose brother James sang with The Kodaks), Malone, and Davis penned their big hit after hearing the famous Pepsodent jingle on the radio ("You'll wonder where the yellow went/when you brush your teeth with Pepsodent..."). Released by tiny Hull records in 1957, it was leased for nationwide distribution to Argo a year later and hit it big. The band was unable to produce a followup hit, and only a few random singles and tracks appeared. The original members, minus brothers John and

Warren Ryanes who have both died, still occasionally perform on the revival circuit.

COLLECTABLES 5427 (L)
Who Wrote the Book of Love?

A straight reissue of the solid Murray Hill LP of the same name issued a few years back, newly remastered by Rhino for Collectables. The material here is worthy of a retrospective, with a nice mix of jumps and ballads, including two unreleased numbers, plus four alternate takes. A total of 14 tracks, clean sound, and decent liner notes taken (xeroxed?) directly from the original LP issue. Good stuff. The Book of Love/Dreams/Soft Shadows/You Never Loved Me/What Would You Do If There Wasn't Any Rock and Roll.

MASCOT 1000 (R)
The Best of The Monotones featuring Charles Patrick

All of their released sides (except for "Words of Wisdom" released under the pseudonym of The Terracetones), and alternate takes of "Book of Love," "Tom Foolery," and "Soft Shadows." A total of 20 tracks, making this the ultimate Monotones collection, complete with liner notes, discography, and their only known photo.

CHRIS MONTEZ

Los-Angeles based, Chicano rocker Montez was influenced by the vocal stylings of his idol Ritchie Valens. Discovered in 1961 by Jim Lee, who had just started the Monogram label, he recorded a number of singles that went nowhere. In July 1962 he recorded Lee's composition, the Valens's flavored rocker called "Let's Dance" that became a million seller. The followup "Some Kinda Fun" was also hit. A dry period followed until he was signed to A&M in 1966 and continued to have hits in a more pop-flavored style.

ACE 369 (L)
Let's Dance! The Monogram Sides

Twenty sides waxed between 1962–1964, reflecting then-current pop tastes as much as any originality. His "No! No! No!," sung in Spanish, sounds too much like "La Bamba"; "It's Not Puppy Love" and "He's Been Leading You On" are copped from The Beatles, the latter effort being a rewrite of "You Can't Do That." Also includes four duets with Indigo recording artist Kathy Young, the best being "All You Had to Do (Was Tell Me)," the worst being the surfing paean "Shoot the Curl." Nearly everything else is about dancing, though nothing matches the power of the title track.

DCC COMPACT CLASSICS 056 (L)
All-Time Greatest Hits

His original '60s hits from the Monogram and A&M labels. Twenty-one tracks, including the peppy "Let's Dance." Puppy Love/Time after Time/Because of You/All You Had to Do.

MONOGRAM 100 (R)
Early Recordings

MONOGRAM 1001 (R)
Let's Dance and Have Some Fun

Sixteen fine sides recorded for Monogram between 1962–1963, featuring wonderfully cheesy Farfisa organ. Let's Dance/You're the One/Somebody Loves You/Some Kinda Fun/No! No! No!

THE MOONGLOWS

One of the classic vocal groups, The Moonglows were formed in Louisville, KY, in 1951, and soon moved to Cleveland where they met local DJ Alan Freed. After one release on the local Champagne label, they started recording for the Chance label in Chicago. By the end of 1954, they signed with Chess, producing a long string of hits, including two rock-and-roll classics, "Sincerely" (with Bobby Lester on lead vocals) and "The Ten Commandments of Love" (with Harvey Fuqua on vocals). Under the name The Moonlighters, they recorded for the Chess subsidiary label, Checker. In 1958, the original group broke up, and Fuqua took on the Washington, DC group The Marquees (which featured Marvin Gaye) as The New Moonglows, scoring a hit with "Twelve Months of the Year." In the early '60s, Fuqua and this group (minus Gaye) went over to Motown, where Harvey became a highly successful producer. The rest of the group became The Spinners, and are still recording. Sadly, at the time of writing, none of their classic '50s recordings are currently available, except as odd tracks on anthologies.

RELIC 8001 (R)
One More Time

A live recording with vocalist Bobby Lester leading the '70s-era Moonglows in a-cappella versions of their hits. Sincerely/In My Diary/Whistle My Love/Just a Lonely Christmas.

MERRILL MOORE

Legendary San Diego-based country-boogie singer-pianist who recorded for Capitol from 1952–1958. Along with Moon Mullican, he was one of the fathers of piano-based rock and roll. With his band The Saddle, Rock, and Rhythm Boys, he recorded some classic rockers, including "House of Blue Lights" and "Rock-Rockola." Moore still performs regularly in San Diego.

BEAR FAMILY 15505 (L)

Boogie My Blues Away

Two-CD set brings together all of Moore's Capitol recordings. All the Moore standards are here: "Corrine Corrina," "Bell Bottom Boogie," "Fly Right Boogie," his version of Julia Lee's "Gotta Gimme What You Got," and "Rock-Rockola." His vocal versions of pop and swing numbers like "King Porter Stomp" and "Yes Indeed" hold up well, although a little of Moore's vocals can go a long way. In many ways, the most interesting material is the superb instrumentals, including the previously unissued boogie-woogie version of the pop tune "Nola" (two versions included here) and the 12 songs recorded at his final sessions for a projected Capitol instrumental LP. Backup musicians include some of Capitol's (and southern California's) best players, such as Speedy West, Roy Lanham, Jimmy Bryant, and a very young Howard Roberts. Moore badmouths rock and roll in the liner notes despite the fact he recorded some incredibly stupid songs himself. Anyone responsible for "Big Bug Boogie" with the memorable line, "the bug's got a big ba-zoo" (should this record get a parental advisory sticker?) shouldn't complain about Bill Haley!

ELLA MAE MORSE

CAPITOL 95288 (CL)

Collector's Series

Ella Mae Morse was one of the best singers on Capitol in the '40s and '50s, and this 21-song collection of her greatest hits is long overdue. A fantastic disc at a low price. Cow Cow Boogie/Shoo Shoo Baby/No Love No Nothing/House of Blue Lights/Oakie Boogie/Forty Cups of Coffee.

DANNY MOTE

Rocking piano player from Atlanta who sings in a pleasant, relaxed style reminiscent of Jerry Lee Lewis.

WHITE LABEL 8911 (R)

Rockin' It Out

Danny is heard in solo demos and with four bands: The Gents; The Rhythm Masters; The Downbeats; and The Quick Sand Band, all of which included his dad Bud (pno, drm, gtr), as well as appearances by uncles Robert Mote (gtr) and Pete Bennett (b). Mote released singles on his own Opal label; this set includes his one nationally released single, "Lonesome" b/w "Done You Wrong," released by Vee Jay in 1961. Twistin' Dog/Ditch Digger/Paralyzed/Cold Cold Heart/Since I Met You Baby.

MOON MULLICAN

Aubrey "Moon" Mulligan was born in Polk County, TX, in 1909. When he was eight, his father brought home a pump organ that, within a few years, Aubrey learned to play in a distinctive two-fingered, right-handed style that became his trademark, influencing country and rock stylings (most notably, Jerry Lee Lewis's playing). Around 1930, Mullican went to Houston, supporting himself by working nights, which was apparently how he earned his nickname. He began recording solo in the '40s, and had a hit with the Cajun classic "New Jole Blon'" for King in 1947. He had more hits in the period 1948–1951, several of which were his own compositions. He died of a heart attack in Beaumont in 1967.

BEAR FAMILY 15607 (L)

Moon's Rock

Highlight's Moon's post-King recordings, including 21 sides for Coral and Decca and 11 1962–1964 tracks recorded for the tiny, Texas-based Hallway label (later released on a Kapp LP). His Coral and Decca sides suffer from slick "Nashville Sound" arrangements with occasional sax and vocal choruses. A few bright spots include "Every Which-a-Way," a terrific pop number, and "Pipeliner Blues," which jumps nearly as much as the King version, and his final two unissued Decca recordings, funky numbers done with only a rhythm section. The rest of the material is tepid, at best, and awful, at worst. Rich Kienzle's liner notes feature an interview with Mullican's Decca producer Owen Bradley, a longtime fan, who admits that the label never really handled Moon right. Only a couple of the Hallway tracks, like "I'll Pour the Wine" and "Cajun Coffee Song," are worth it. Moon's poor health in the early '60s, combined with the mediocre musical material, was an underwhelming end to an incredible career. The Bear Family presentation is typically superb, with fantastic sound, photos, and complete dis-cographical data. If someone could only issue the King sides with as much care!!

THE MURMAIDS

The Murmaids were the Fischer Sisters, whose dad was Frankie Laine's musical director, joined by neighbor Sally Gordon. The Fischer's mom brought them to the local Chattahoochie label, where they recorded their one Top-10 hit, "Pop-sicles and Icicles," a tune written by David Gates (later of Bread) and produced by Kim Fowley. The sisters went off to college, but, when the record hit it big, they made a few more singles for Chattahoochie. Different singers (Cathy Brasher and maybe Yvonne Vaughn) were called upon to be "The Murmaids" for the 1968 Liberty single, "Go Away."

CHATTAHOOCHIE 628 (R)

Resurface

Though there is no information on the LP, it sounds like these are all early '60s Chattahoochie recordings. Includes The Murmaids's big hit "Popsicles and Ici-cles," as well as "So Young," "Alone," "Mr. Sandman" (where the boy they want should have "lots of wavy hair like Elvis Presley"), "You Cheated," and the weird "Bull Talk"!

THE MUSIC EXPLOSION

Musical teens from Mansfield, OH, whose 1967 Laurie single "A Little Bit o' Soul" made it to Number 2 on the charts! The group consisted of the distinctive hoarse-voiced Jimmie "Jamie" Lyons (lead vcl), Don "Tudor" Atkins and Rick Nesta (gtrs), Bob Avery (drm, hca), and Burton "Butch" Sahl (b, pno). They originally recorded "A Little Bit o' Soul" for the Attack label, and then re-recorded it under the hands of bubble-gum rock gurus Jeff Katz and Jerry Kasenetz (who later molded the careers of The Ohio Express and The 1910 Fruitgum Company for Buddah). The group's follow-up single, "Sunshine Games," was a minor chart success, but their remaining output failed to catch on. Lyons formed his own group in the early '70s, and then fronted The Capitol City Rockers. Avery remained a house drummer for Buddah, performing in the Katz and Kasenetz created group, Crazy Elephant.

PERFORMANCE 384 (R)

Little Bit o' Soul

Contains all their non-LP singles, including a great version of "Little Black Egg" that was initially issued on Attack. Also featured are their second hit, "Sun-shine Games," and fine LP tracks like a strong version of Terry Knight and The Pack's "Love Love Love." A free flexidisc contains a Lyon's solo single, "Soul Struttin'" plus "Stoney" and "Gonna Have a Good Time" by The Jamie Lyons Group.

THE MYSTICS

White Brooklyn-based group led by brothers Phil and Albee Cracolici. They recorded for Laurie Records from 1959–1961, scoring with the beau-tiful "Hushabye" written for them by Pomus and Shurman. A later recording, "All through the Night" featured "Jerry Landis" (aka Paul Simon) on vocals. The group's sugary pop style resembles a mixture of The Belmonts with The Elegants.

COLLECTABLES 5043 (CL)

16 Golden Classics

Their pleasing interpretations of "White Cliffs of Dover" and "A Sunday Kind of Love," coupled with standouts "Darling I Know Now" and "Adam and Eve," make this 16-cut set a worthwhile purchase. Includes their hit song "Hushabye." No sleeve notes. Great remastering.

THE MYSTICS/THE JARMELS

ACE 929 (L)

The Mystics Meet The Jarmels

Two out-of-print Ace LPs on one beautiful CD. In-cludes both sides of The Mystics six singles, along with four previously unissued tracks (three of them have also been reissued by Crystal Ball). Duplicates their Collectables LP. The Jarmels cuts feature both sides of their six issued singles plus two unissued tracks cut between 1961–1963 for Laurie Records. The Jarmels at this time were produced by Bert Berns, who also produced Johnny Moore and The Drifters on Atlantic. The striking similarity between The Jarmels and The Drifters is much in evidence here. The singing and harmony are fine, and the songs are a mixture of R&B and string-assisted pop. The Jarmels were Laurie's only successful black vocal group, and perhaps one of the best around. Wherever possible, tracks have been remastered from original tapes for crystal-clear sound.

NAZZ

Fine Beatle-esque psychedelic group from Philly led by Todd Rundgren and featuring Stewky

Antoni on vocals. They recorded for the Screen Gems subsidiary SGC (distributed by Atlantic), and had hits with "Open My Eyes" and "Hello It's Me."

RHINO 70116 (C)
Best of Nazz
Includes all their 45s (some never on LP), LP cuts, two unreleased demos ("Train Kept A'Rollin'" and "Magic Me"), and the hilarious "Loosen Up." Open My Eyes/Hello It's Me/Kicks/Under the Ice.

RICK(Y) NELSON

A true child of the media, Ricky was in the public eye since he was eight years old, debuting on his parents' radio show, *The Adventures of Ozzie and Harriet* (later, the show moved to TV). In 1957, his girlfriend told him she was in love with Elvis, so Ricky told her he sang, too. Though he had never sung before, he recorded Fats Domino's "I'm Walkin'" for Verve, and thanks to his TV exposure, the song went to Number 4. He signed a contract with Imperial and recorded a long string of pleasant rockabilly pop tunes, with a band that featured James Burton (gtr) and James Kirkland (b). He premiered many of his hits on the TV show including "Hello Mary Lou," "Travelin' Man," and "Be-bop Baby." In 1963, he signed a 20-year contract with Decca (later MCA), and the hits continued with "String Along" and "Fools Rush In." The TV show was canceled in 1966, and Rick's hits stopped, but his music improved and a strong country influence prevailed. He also changed his name from the child-star's "Ricky" to the more mature "Rick." In 1968, he formed one of the first country-rock bands, The Stone Canyon Band; the band's bassist Randy Meisner later quit to form The Eagles. In 1972, he returned to the charts with a song about how he was booed off the stage at an oldies show in New York ("Garden Party"). He died tragically in a plane crash on New Year's Eve, 1985. Rick's twin sons are the golden-haired leaders of the pop/metal band, The Nelsons.

Nelson's material has been reissued many times, in different formats. EMI's Legendary Masters brings back most of his best Imperial sides. MCA 10098 is a good cross-section of his later Decca recordings. See for Miles has reissued two of his influential country LPs on a single disc. There are numerous reissues of his later concerts and LPs.

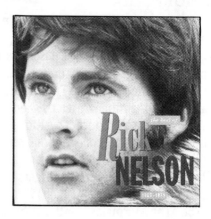

BGO 38 (R)/MCA 31364 (L)
Garden Party
Reissue of Decca 75391 from 1972. The title track sold a million and reached the Top 10. There's a nice country feel from backing Stone Canyon Band, including former Buckaroo Tom Brumley on pedal steel and lead guitar from Alan Kemp. Unfortunately, the spirit of then-superstars CSNY pervades on some tracks for some sickly sweet harmonies. Most tunes are Nelson originals along with an excellent cover of Chuck Berry's "Talkin' 'bout You." So Long Mama/Nighttime Lady/Palace Guard/A Flower Opens Gently By.

◉ *EMI 92771 (CL)*
Legendary Masters Series: Ricky Nelson, Vol. 1
Twenty-track collection featuring some of Ricky's biggest hits from the 1957–1960 period, including nine songs that made the Top 10. Excellent sound and nicely packaged with a fold-out booklet with detailed notes, photos, and a nice reproduction of the Imperial label on the disc. Be-bop Baby/Stood Up/Believe What You Say/Poor Little Fool/I Got a Feeling/It's Late/Sweeter Than You/Mighty Good/Right by My Side/Yes Sir, That's My Baby.

EMI 95219 (CL)
The Best of Rick Nelson, Vol. 2
Twenty-seven Imperial Records sides and rarities. Includes a list of all of Rick's Imperial recording sessions, EPs, and albums. Travelin' Man/Hello Mary Lou/Young World/Teenage Idol/If You Can't Rock Me/It's Up to You/I'm in Love Again.

MAGNUM FORCE 078 (L)

Live at The Aladdin

Twelve live cuts from 1979, recorded to exacting lo-fidelity standards in Las Vegas. Garden Party/Poor Little Fool/Lonesome Town/Hello Mary Lou/It's Late/Mystery Train.

MCA 1517 (RC)

The Decca Years

Ten songs cut for Decca/MCA between 1963–1972. Garden Party/String Along/For Your Sweet Love/For You.

MCA 6163 (RCL)

All My Best

Sixteen 1985 re-recordings of Ricky's old Verve, Imperial, and Decca hits, from "I'm Walkin'" through "Garden Party," plus a new one, Mickey Jupp's "You Know What I Mean." Ricky originally released the album on his own Silver Eagle label, selling it at live shows and via TV ads. When he died, MCA picked up the set. It's well-recorded, with help by The Jordanaires and Jimmy Haskell, and is very faithful to the originals. As far as I know, these are his last recordings. Hello Mary Lou/It's Late/Young World/It's Up to You/Travelin' Man/Teenage Idol/Believe What You Say.

MCA 10098 (CL)

The Best of Rick Nelson, 1963–75

Fifteen tracks. Fools Rush In/There's Nothing I Can Say/Since I Don't Have You/Mean Old World/Mystery Train/Garden Party/Rock 'n' Roll Lady/One Night Stand.

MCA 25983 (CL)

In Concert: The Troubador, 1969

Reissue of Decca 75162 from 1970. One of Rick's best LPs, that forecasts the LA country-rock scene on a dozen songs recorded on December 13, 1969. Backup by The Stone Canyon Band, including Tom Brumley (pedal steel), ex-Millenium drummer Pat Shanahan, and Randy Meisner (b). A beautiful mixture of country, folk, and rock, way ahead of its time. Includes Dylan's "You Belong to Me" and Nelson's own "Easy to Be Free," plus "Hello Mary Lou" and "Violets of Dawn."

MCA 31363 (L)

Rick Nelson Sings "For You"

Reissue of Decca 74479 from 1964. For You/Fools Rush In/A Legend in My Time/The Nearness of You.

PAIR 21191 (C)

Teen Age Idol

Budget set collecting some of Rick's Imperial recordings made after his initial success. There are some fine rockers here ("If You Can't Rock Me," "Boppin' the Blues," "Down the Line," and "Whole Lotta Shakin'

Goin' On") with the great guitar licks that were standard on his early rock-and-roll hits. But mostly he does dreamy-eyed pop covers of R&B tunes like "I'm in Love Again," "Unchained Melody," "You're So Fine," and "I Can't Stop Loving You."

RHINO 71114 (CL)

Ricky Nelson "Live": The Collection

Nelson's last official live album recorded at the Universal Amphitheater, Los Angeles on August 22, 1985, about four months before his tragic death, is mostly a program of his late '50s and early '60s rockers. He also does a couple of surprise tunes, including The Rolling Stones's "Honky Tonk Women" and Micky Jupp's "You Know What I Mean." He only does one of his country-rock numbers, the big hit "Garden Party." Rick, in fine voice, is backed by a very good band that really pound out the rockabilly numbers with hot guitar in the James Burton mode. Stood Up/Waitin' in School/Travelin' Man/Hello Mary Lou/Milk Cow Blues Boogie/That's Alright Mama/Lonesome Town/It's Late.

ROCKSTAR 1010 (R)

Hey Pretty Baby

Sixteen rare Imperial tracks, recorded 1958–1962. The "mono" side has Ricky at his rockin'-est, with "One of These Mornings," covers of Jerry Lee Lewis's "I'm Feelin' Sorry," Carl Perkins's "Your True Love," and Hank Williams's "My Bucket's Got a Hole in It." The stereo side is much mellower, with "A Long Vacation," "My One Desire," and "That Warm Summer Night." Most cuts feature great James Burton solos, except "Your True Love" which features Joe Maphis.

SEE FOR MILES 84 (R)

Country Fever, Bright Lights and Country Music

Twenty-four tunes graced by the genius of James Burton on guitar and dobro on nearly every track. *Bright Lights and Country Music* (Decca 74779, from 1966) contains mostly country covers, including the extremely hot "Night Train to Memphis," the hit "You Just Can't Quit," plus The Jordanaires on background for "Hello Walls," "I'm a Fool to Care," and "Welcome to My World." *Country Fever* (Decca 74827) released in 1967 has the hit "Take a City Bride" with Rick singing cajun-style, plus a hot "Mystery Train" with more fine Burton, and "Take These Chains from My Heart," "Salty Dog," and "Funny How Time Slips Away."

SEE FOR MILES 217 (R)

Rick Nelson Comes of Age

Excellent set of 16 early '70s tunes by Rick and two different incarnations of The Stone Canyon Band, with Randy Meisner and former Buck Owens steel guitarist Denny Lorden, plus future Capt. Beefheart drummer Ty Grimes. Emphasis is on Rick's original tunes, including the first side of *Rick Sings Nelson* (originally Decca 75236 from 1970) and four cuts from *Rudy the 5th* (Decca 75297 from 1971), plus two singles never before on LP: "Try (Try to Fall in Love)" and "Rock 'n' Roll Lady."

THE NEVILLE BROTHERS

The four kings of New Orleans's first family of rock, boogie, and soul: Aaron, Art, Charles, and Cyril. Their recordings have never measured up to their legend. (For more Nevillology, see separate Aaron and Art Neville listings, plus The Meters).

A&M 75021 4866 (CL)

Fiyo on the Bayou

The incredible Nevilles classic. Hey Pocky A-Way/ Brother John/Run Joe.

A&M 75021 5240 (CL)

Yellow Moon

Striking 1988 LP with The Neville Brothers in top form after the ill-advised pop LP, *Uptown*. With Daniel Lanois producing, the sound was stripped down to reveal the Brothers's strengths. They shine on such unabashedly political songs as the anthemic "Sister Rosa" and "Wake Up (Superpowers)." The Caribbean touch of "Yellow Moon" and the classic New Orleans groove of "Fire and Brimstone" and "Wild Injuns" deliver a revitalized Nevilles sound that equals or tops their previous work. And, finally, four sublime efforts from the unearthly voice of Aaron Neville (Sam Cooke's "A Change Is Gonna Come," Bob Dylan's "With God on Our Side" and the chilling "Ballad of Hollis Brown," and an achingly lovely "Will the Circle Be Unbroken") top off a splendid effort—and a good value, with over 50 minutes of playing time.

A&M 75021 5312 (CL)

Brother's Keeper

Follow-up LP to *Yellow Moon*, this finds The Nevs enjoying their new-found popularity and performing a mix of New Orleans and folk-rock standards. Includes a reggae number cowritten with U2's Bono, a guest appearance by aging hippie Buffy Sainte-Marie, and a cover of Leonard Cohen's "Bird on the Wire."

A&M 75021 5384 (CL)

Family Groove

1992 LP with a more pop-oriented selection of material.

BLACK TOP 1031 (RCL)

Neville-ization

Excellent live recordings from the late, great Tipitina's club of New Orleans. Includes hot, uptempo numbers like "Mojo Hannah" and "Big Chief" and smoky ballads like "Tell It Like It Is" and "Why You Wanna Hurt My Heart."

CHARLY 1 (L)

A History of The Neville Brothers: Legacy

Double CD featuring 50 recordings made between 1955–1972, featuring the brothers's solo recordings and tracks with The Hawketts and The Meters. Includes a 16-page booklet.

RHINO 70776 (CL)

Treacherous Too! Vol. 2, 1955–1987

Eighteen more cuts spanning the family's 35-year history. Things get off to a great start with Art's classic vocalizing on The Hawketts's "Your Time's Up" plus his Specialty and Instant singles "Oooh Whee Baby," "What's Going On," "Skeet Skat," and "Hook Line and Sinker." Brother Aaron is also well represented with "How Many Times," "Humdinger," and "Jailhouse." About halfway through the disc, we leave the early period and move into the soul years, which is where my enthusiasm starts to falter, unfortunately. And, then we get into the modern era, typified by the mainstream rock sound of the Capitol *Neville Brothers* LP and their *Uptown* and *Neville-ization* albums. For a quick introduction to the Nevilles's legacy, this Rhino reissue is a good bet, but fans and purists will find at least a few expendable cuts.

RHINO 71494 (CL)

Treacherous: A History of The Neville Brothers

Double CD or cassette set featuring 28 tracks recorded between 1955–1985. This is not quite the same as the earlier Rhino double-LP set; a few tracks have been left off (presumably for contractual reasons), but about a half-dozen have been added.

AARON NEVILLE

Legendary New Orleans vocalist and the heartbeat of The Neville Brothers's band. Aaron began performing with his brothers Art and Charles as The Hawketts in the mid-'50s, scoring a local hit with "Mardi Gras Mambo." When Art entered the Navy in 1960, Aaron went solo, recording another minor hit, "Over You," with Allen Toussaint. 1967 was a banner year for Aaron as a vocalist when he scored a Number 2 hit with "Tell It Like It Is" released by New Orleans's Par-Lo records. He continued to record as a soloist, while brother Art formed The Meters. The brothers reunited in 1977, and have since recorded a number of LPs for A&M. Aaron gained national attention when he won a Grammy in 1990 for his duet with Linda Ronstandt, "Don't Know Much." Ronstandt returned the favor by producing his solo LP, *Warm Your Heart*, with the hit cover of "Everybody Plays the Fool."

A&M 75021 5354 (CL)
Warm Your Heart
With a voice like an angel in the body of a giant, Neville moans, wails, and weaves honey-coated webs around Randy Newman's "Louisiana 1927," The Main Ingredient's "Everybody Plays the Fool," John Hiatt's "It Feels Like Rain," The Drifters's 1961 hit "Don't Go, Please Stay" (supported by The Grace Episcopal Boys Choir of LA), Clyde McPhatter's "Warm Your Heart," the traditional Bahamian gospel ballad "I Bid You Goodnight," plus a magnificent reading of "Ave Maria." Supporting background harmonies and choruses are supplied by Linda Ronstadt, along with such notable talent as Rita Coolidge and Bobby King. A touchingly beautiful collection.

COLLECTABLES 5132 (CL)
Tell It Like It Is
A reissue of Aaron's 1967 Par-Lo album, adding the single-only side "Those Three Words." In spite of its somewhat legendary status, this is a disappointing set. Girlie choruses and slick pop arrangements wipe out whatever soulful dress Neville has to offer. Two redeeming features are his hit "Tell It Like It Is" and a tasty instrumental "Bet You're Surprised." Notes by Clive Richardson discuss Aaron's career but have very little to say about these recordings!

CHARLY 64 (L)
Make Me Strong
CD issue of Charly 1111, featuring 18 tunes recorded at Sansu Studios with Allen Toussaint and released on the Bell, Mercury, and Island labels between 1968–1974. This disc omits "Going Home" from the original LP and adds "Wild Flower," "Feelings," "Nadine," "For the Good Times," and "She's on My Mind." There is an extensive biography of Aaron and The Neville Brothers but no information on the music.

CHARLY 162 (L)
Show Me the Way
CD issue of Charly 1217 with three non-LP alternate takes; 22 cuts in all. Although many of these Minit-label sides from 1960 and 1961 have appeared on other reissues, unissued and alternate takes constitute half the playing time. Standouts include a purer, more soulful alternate version of "Reality," "Show Me the Way," and "Don't Cry," plus 1961's tortuously tearful "For Every Boy There's a Girl."

CURB 77303 (CL)
Greatest Hits
Includes original versions of Aaron's chart toppers "Over You" (1960), "Tell It Like It Is" (1966), and "She Took You for a Ride" (1967), along with other Par-Lo sides. Ten cuts in all, every one a winner.

CURB 77491 (CL)
Tell It Like It Is
This is not the same package as the Collectables *Tell It Like It Is* reissue, but does duplicate his most popular tracks, including "Tell It Like It Is" and "Over You." Thirteen New Orleans classics, mostly '60s material. For your extra bucks, you do get some good liner notes, which are conspicuously absent from Curb's budget releases. I'm Waiting at the Station/Get Out of My Life/Sweet Little Mama/How Could I Help But Love You.

RHINO 70956 (CL)
Orchid in the Storm
Five-song cassete/CD, including a medley with Art Neville on "This Is My Story" and "We Belong Together." Pledging My Love/For Your Precious Love/ The Ten Commandments of Love/Earth Angel.

ROUNDER 2102 (RCL)
The Classic Aaron Neville: My Greatest Gift
The dozen tracks on this best of LP/CD are from the late '60s to the mid-'70s, and are aided by arrangements and production from the fabulous Allen Toussaint. Each cut is a prime example of Aaron's magic. From funky to soulful, he does not disappoint: from his 1967 chart-topper "Tell It Like It Is" to a compelling performance, his personalized rendition of the torch standard "Cry Me a River." Hercules/You Can Give but You Can't Take/Mojo Hannah/The Greatest Love/Where Is My Baby/Waiting for a Bus.

ART NEVILLE
The oldest and funkiest of the Neville crew, keyboardist Art Neville formed the popular New Orleans band The Meters that performed from the mid-'60s to the mid-'70s.

ACE 188 (RL)
Mardi Gras Rock and Roll
Sixteen tracks recorded between 1956–1958 for Art Rupe's Specialty label. Having toured with Little Richard and recorded with Larry Williams, Art's style leans heavily toward early rock and roll. Nevillologists will be pleased to know there are ten previously unreleased tracks; the CD has four bonus tracks. The sound is raw and intense. Extensive notes by Ray Topping. Zing Zing (two takes)/Bella Me/Cha Dooky Doo/What's Going On/Rockin' Pneumonia and the

Boogie Woogie Flu (with Larry Williams)/The Dummy/Let's Rock (two takes)/Please Listen to My Song.

SPECIALTY 2165 (RC)

That Old Time Rock and Roll

Fourteen good cuts covering much of the same ground as Ace 188. Included are his singles "Cha Dooky Doo," "What's Going On," "Zing Zing," and "Arabian Love Call," plus an unissued version of his big hit "Oooh Whee Baby." We also get many unreleased cuts (as of 1987, anyway) in the early rock vein, withheld from the public and later forgotten while Art was in the Navy.

TERRY NOLAND

Terry Noland's biggest claim to fame is that he went to school with Buddy Holly and had minor hits with two decent rockers, "Hypnotized" and "Oh Baby! Look at Me."

BEAR FAMILY 15319 (R)

The Original 1956 Demos

Mini LP of Noland's 1956 unreleased, eight-tune demo session recorded for Brunswick. Puppy Love/ Let Me Be Your Hero/Crazy Dream/Oh Judy.

BEAR FAMILY 15428 (L)

Hypnotized

Features everything Noland recorded for Brunswick in 1957–1958 along with a couple of demos recorded in 1956 with Larry Welborn and Joe B. Mauldin. There are many unissued songs along with alternate takes. The material ranges from nice rocking numbers with good Holly-esque guitars to dreadful pop- rock ballads with The Anita Kerr Singers. The sound is excellent, and there are extensive notes and full discographical details.

NRBQ

The New Rhythm and Blues Quartet (NRBQ) is one of rock's longest-lasting and unusual acts, with a skewered vision of rock's legacy. Although never scoring a hit, they have achieved cult status and command a devoted following for their sound that both celebrates and satirizes the best of rock and R&B. They specialize in wacky covers of standards and in originals that sound like slightly offbeat variants of rock and rhythm formulas. The band has survived numerous label and personnel changes. The Rhino anthology gives an excellent overview of their entire recording career.

RHINO 70770 (CL)

Peek-a-Boo: The Best of NRBQ (1969–1989)

Hats (and all other articles of clothing) off to Rhino Records for making one fabulous two-CD compilation. NRBQ's albums often suffer from excessive cuteness, but this collection sports nothing but great rock and roll. "I Want You Bad" and "Me and the Boys," both covered by Dave Edmunds, are nearly perfect gems, and it is impossible to listen to "Ridin' in My Car" and not be happy. "Magnet," "You Can't Hide," "Never Take the Place of You," and "Rain at the Drive-In" are also near the top of the wonderful scale. For the diehard Q fan, several alternate versions of old favorites are included, the best being "RC Cola and a Moon Pie." And the CD has five bonus tracks, none of which are expendable, as is so often the case. NRBQ has never had a hit record, but their misses are so good it hardly matters.

ROUNDER 3108 (CL)

God Bless Us All

Live recording.

ROUNDER 3109 (RCL)

Live!: Diggin' Uncle Q

Whereas their last live LP, *God Bless Us All*, captured the feeling of a Q concert, this one is more for the fans, drawn from two short 1987 sets from Toads in New Haven and Lupos in Rhode Island, concentrating more on band originals. Weird covers include a rockin' "Rocket in My Pocket," an instrumental "Scarlet Ribbons," and a Karaoke version of "Just the Way You Are," along with originals "It Comes to Me Naturally," "Macho Maria," "Some Kind of Blues," and "Trouble in the Henhouse."

ROUNDER 11506 (L)

Uncommon Denominators

CD sampler from six NRBQ Rounder albums. Twenty-one big tunes from the most talented and whacked-out bar band in the universe. Howard Johnson's Got His Ho-Jo Workin'/RC Cola and a Moon Pie/It Was an Accident/Wacky Tobacky.

RYKODISC 10240 (L)

Honest Dollar

Since they've been together for more than 20 years without ever scoring a hit song, NRBQ has had to survive on a steady diet of touring and more touring. It's what they do. They're good at it. So it should come as no surprise that they sound good on this collection of live material recorded at this place and that between 1984–1991. It should also come as no surprise that there are no surprises here. "Ridin' in My Car" and "Green Lights" still sound like the perfectly crafted rock-and-roll songs that they are; the covers are fun as usual (especially "Batman Theme" and "Deep in the

Heart of Texas"); and the band's slightly odd view of life is still in effect. And for those who accuse NRBQ of being preoccupied with strictly adolescent concerns, the song "I Love Air Conditioning" has been provided.

THE NUTMEGS

Excellent a-cappella doo-wop group from New Haven, originally formed by brothers Leroy and Sonny Griffin as The Lyres. They signed to Herald in 1955, changed their name, and recorded the classic "Story Untold." Leroy died in a smelting-furnace accident in 1969, and was replaced by his nephew Harold Jaynes. The group still performs occasionally.

COLLECTABLES 5018 (C)
Greatest Hits
Twelve classic Herald sides from the mid-'50s, including "Story Untold." The Ship of Love/Gift of Gabbin' Woman/My Story/A Love So True. Duplicates much of Relic 5011.

RELIC 5002 (R)
The Nutmegs Featuring Leroy Griffin
Fourteen songs. Let Me Tell You/Shifting Sands/I Like to Cha Cha/Roseanne/Why Must We Go to School/The Way Love Should Be/Down in Mexico.

RELIC 5011 (R)
The Nutmegs Greatest Hits
Thirteen Herald sides. Story Untold/Key to the Kingdom/Rock Me/Shifting Sands/Gift of Gabbin' Woman/Make Me Lose My Mind.

✪ RELIC 7038 (L)
Story Untold
Includes 12 of the 13 cuts on Relic 5011 (unfortunately, the terrifice a-cappella version of "Shifting Sands" is omitted), plus four additional numbers (two that were previously unreleased and two outtakes). This is all of the material that the group recorded for Herald Records, including the title track, "My Sweet Dream," "Whispering Sorrows," and the unreleased "Hello," "Ship of Love," and "Key to the Kingdom." Ballads alternate with up-tempo numbers throughout the program. The cover reproduces the artwork from the rare Nutmegs EP on Herald. Sound quality is excellent, as are Donn Fileti's informative notes.

THE OLYMPICS

Great novelty group, who recorded around the dawn of the '60s for the Arvee, Demon, and Loma labels. Lead by Walter Ward, this LA vocal group specialized in novelty and dance tunes.

They had an extremely long and successful career on a number of different labels, including 1958's "Western Movies," 1960's "Hully Gully," 1962's "Peanut Butter," 1963's "The Bounce," 1965's "Good Lovin'" (later a monster hit for The Young Rascals), and 1966's "Baby Do the Philly Dog."

ACE 324 (L)
Hully Gully/Dance by the Light of the Moon/Party Time
Landmark CD reissue of three complete LPs (they made 'em short in those days!): the oft-tapped *Hully Gully* (Arvee 423, c. 1960), their follow-up *Dance by the Light of the Moon* (Arvee 424, c. 1960), and the rarely heard ten-cut dance craze spinner *Party Time* (Arvee 429, c. 1961), for a total of 26 nifty novelty numbers. However, faves "Good Lovin'," "Western Movies," and "Peanut Butter" are missing.

SANDSTONE 233078 (L)
All-Time Greatest Hits
Twenty-six picks to click, by this happy-go-lucky vocal group in The Coasters vein. Reissue of DCC 57 that includes several unreleased titles. Western Movies/Big Boy Pete/Workin' Hard/Little Pedro/Boo-Dee Green/Peanut Butter.

THE OLYMPICS/THE MARATHONS

COLLECTABLES 5081 (CL)
Golden Classics
Eight wild songs by each. Big Boy Pete/The Slop/Little Pedro/(Baby) Hully Gully/Peanut Butter/C. Percy Mercy of Scotland Yard/Gee/Tight Sweater/Oink Jones.

ROY ORBISON

Incredible singer/songwriter known for his near-operatic voice and dark glasses. Though originally only into ballads and country music, college buddy Pat Boone convinced him to try pop, resulting in the original version of "Ooby Dooby," recorded by his first band, The Teen Kings, on the tiny Texas Je-Wel label. Johnny Cash told him to send a demo to Sun, who signed him in 1955 where he recorded rockabilly for two years, scoring a hit with a new version of "Ooby Dooby." In 1958, after recording a couple of singles for RCA, he signed as a staff writer for Acuff-Rose, penning "Claudette" for The Everly

Brothers. He moved to Nashville and signed with the local Monument label in 1960, where he scored a couple dozen hits in his operatic ballad style, including "Only the Lonely," "Running Scared," "Crying," "Blue Bayou," and the Number 1 hit, "Oh, Pretty Woman." He signed with MGM in 1965, appearing in the film *The Fastest Guitar Alive* and scoring some country hits. But personal tragedy hit him hard. The death of his wife Claudette in a motorcycle accident and a fire at his house, killing two of his three children, just about ending his career. He recorded sporadically for Mercury and Elektra in the '70s with no success, but a 1980 duet with Emmy Lou Harris, "That Loving You Feel Again" made for the movie *Roadie*, won him a Grammy. A remake of "Crying" with nouveau country singer k.d. lang, and the use of his song "In Dreams" in the spooky film *Blue Velvet*, brought him further attention. These successes were followed by his triumphant return to the pop scene as a member of The Traveling Wilburys. Orbison recorded a comeback LP, *Mystery Girl*, with the help of fellow Wilbury Jeff Lynne, including his last hit, "You Got It." He also appeared in a Showtime special called *A Black and White Night* with luminaries ranging from Bruce Springsteen to James Burton to Elvis Costello. Orbison died of a heart attack in 1990.

Roy's recordings have been reissued and remade many times and are available on many different labels. The CBS Special Products four-CD/cassette set gives the best overview of all of his recordings; Rhino has two excellent CDs, one covering his MGM years, the other his Sun years.

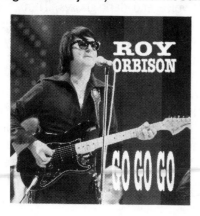

BEAR FAMILY 15019 (R)

Almost Eighteen

Twelve-inch EP featuring six of his seven RCA recordings, including four songs from December 1958 released as 45s (the title tune, "Jolie," "Sweet and Innocent," and "Seems to Me") and two previously unreleased tracks from June 1959 ("The Bug" and "Paper Boy").

BEAR FAMILY 15352 (R)

In Deutschland

This twelve-inch, German-language, 45 rpm was recorded in Hamburg, West Germany in 1963. The flip, "Mama," is nothing special, but "San Fernando" is Roy at his soaring best. I'm ready for some Finnish versions, or maybe Swahili.

BEAR FAMILY 15461 (L)

The Sun Years, 1956–58:
The Definitive Collection

All of his Sun recordings including alternates and demos.

CBS SPECIAL PRODUCTS 21427 (L)

Sings Lonely and Blue

As if you would expect him to sing anything else . . . Reissue of Monument 14002 from 1961. Only the Lonely/I'm Hurtin'/Blue Angel.

CBS SPECIAL PRODUCTS 21428 (L)

Crying

Twelve-cut Monument reissue (originally 14007 from 1962). The Great Pretender/Love Hurts/Running Scared/Crying.

CBS SPECIAL PRODUCTS 21429 (L)

In Dreams

Reissue of 1963 Monument LP 18003, featuring 12 songs. Blue Bayou/Dream/In Dreams/All I Have to Do Is Dream/Beautiful Dreamer.

CBS SPECIAL PRODUCTS 45115 (L)

Rare Orbison

Twelve "rare" (well, at least scarce) Roy O. tunes taken from non-hit 45s and B-sides that were not released on LP, for the most part. Pretty One/Blues in My Mind/Only with You/Drifting Away/Belinda.

CBS SPECIAL PRODUCTS 45404 (L)

Rare Orbison, Vol. 2

The compiler of this album has really dug into the Monument vaults for this collection of Orbison rarities. It includes five previously unissued sides from 1960–1962, three unissued tracks from 1978 when Roy returned to Monument, two tracks recorded with Roy singing in German for the German market, the title songs from the 1970 movie *Zigzag*, and an obscure album track with Roy singing with Larry Gatlin and The Gatlin Brothers. What more can I say? What more dare I say?

CBS SPECIAL PRODUCTS 46809 (CL)
The Legendary Roy Orbison
For anyone who loves the golden voice of Texan Roy Orbison, this four-CD set, with 65 cuts, is your ticket to paradise. It successfully covers almost all of Roy's finest recorded moments. Save for his amazing late 1980s resurgence, we get material from Sun to RCA, Monument, and MGM sessions, covering the years 1956–1976. For me, the "Big O" was never cooler than on "Oh, Pretty Woman," included here in it's original single version. If you're curious to see what Roy did before he became a Wilbury, travel no further. The set also includes a 36-page booklet with notes by Colin Escott and lots of photos, some inexcusably reversed! Tryin' to Get to You/Ooby Dooby/Claudette/Uptown/Blue Angel/Running Scared/Crying/Leah/Blue Bayou/It's Over/Summersong/ Southern Man/Ride Away/Mama (German)/Dance/Wild Hearts.

COLUMBIA 45405 (L)
The Fastest Guitar Alive:
Original Soundtrack
B-movie soundtrack by the Orb and Bill Dees originally issued in 1968. Ten tunes, 27 minutes long.

CURB 77481 (CL)
Best of His Rare Classics
Ten original hits, some not so rare but classic nonetheless. "Ooby Dooby," "Rock House," "Devil Doll," and "It's too Late" are from his Sun Records years; and "So Young," "I'll Remember the Good," and four others come from the MGM label.

ELEKTRA 198 (L)
Laminar Flow
CD reissue of 1979 album with ten songs. Easy Way Out/We're into Something Good/Hound Dog Man.

ENCORE 3688 (R)
Collector's Edition
Twenty selections on this grab bag taken from a variety of sources. "The Eyes of Texas," "Life Fades Away," "Run for the Sun," "Heavy Load," and three others come from some of Roy's later movie work. "Wild Hearts," "Help," "This Little Bird," "Where Have All the Flowers Gone," and "Bridge over Troubled Water" are taken from BBC-TV programs. Add some more TV tunes and rare acetates and you get a bonanza for Orbison fans, although casual fans will be left scratching their heads.

JEWEL 13011/12 (R)
Hillbilly Rock
Fourteen-tune collection aimed at the hard-core collector. In the mid-'50s, Roy and his band The Teen

Kings went into Norman Petty's studio in Clovis, NM, and waxed some seminal rockabilly. "Domino" is a great one; the demo plus a stereo version are included here. "Ooby Dooby" was the other classic, and it's represented by the 1955 version, an alternate take, and a 1956 version. A wild, alternate take of Ray Harris singing "Greenback Dollar" finds Roy on guitar and backup vocals (with Jerry Lee Lewis on piano). Roy also backs Ken Cook on the cool rocker "I Fell in Love" and Hayden Thompson on the near-perfect "Rockabilly Gal." Sound quality isn't very good, but the music is fine.

KNIGHT 47002 (RCL)
The Golden Decade 1960–1969
Four-LP/three-CD compilation from the UK. The set begins with "Only the Lonely" from Monument, stretching across 59 songs, ending with "Penny Arcade" from MGM, which made the British Top 30. Although the musical greatness of Roy's finest material isn't really apparent here, sound quality is very good on all tracks, and there's surprisingly small duplication with CBS 46809. For the fanatic, a 1963 outtake, "Almost," is included, along with a slew of mostly unknown album tracks. I'm Hurtin'/Double Date/Mean Woman Blues/Pretty Paper/Twenty-two Days/Yes/Running Scared/Party Heart/Beautiful Dreamer/Communication Breakdown/Too Soon to Know/In Dreams/Lonesome Number One.

MUSIDISC 107312 (L)
The Legend
Twenty selections from Roy's later years. I'm pretty sure that these were done for Monument and/or MGM, consisting of a lot of Don Gibson songs and other obscurities. I'm Hurtin'/A Legend in My Time/Sweet Dreams/Blue Blue Day/Give Myself a Party/Lonesome Number One.

PAIR 1247 (L)
An Original
Budget two-CD set.

RHINO 70711 (CL)
The Classic Roy Orbison 1965–1968
Fourteen tunes from Roy's first four years at MGM. Although he never enjoyed the success at MGM that he did at Monument, he still made some fabulous records there. As Jim Fahey's liner notes suggest, his commercial failure was almost totally due to the popularity of the "English Invasion" groups, not because of any musical shortcomings on his part. His soaring voice weaves mini-operas on ballad after ballad, most only heard a few times on the radio after release, before their unjust demise. Two of his best up-tempo numbers from this era are included: "Twinkle Toes," a great go-go tune, and the catchy "Claudette." Ride Away/Crawling Back/It Takes One (to Know One)/Breakin' Up Is Breakin' My Heart.

RHINO 70916 (L)

The Sun Years

Rhino complements their excellent MGM collection with this equally fine compilation of Roy's early Sun Records sides, recorded in 1956–1957, including "Ooby Dooby" (his only charted hit from this period) and 19 other tracks. Superb sound, as always. Claudette/Domino/Devil Doll/Chicken Hearted/Rockhouse.

⊘ RHINO 71493 (CL)

For the Lonely

Twenty-four tunes, four from Sun (including "Ooby Dooby" and "Rockhouse"), and 20 from Monument. All the biggies are here including "Oh, Pretty Woman," "Blue Bayou," "In Dreams," "Crying," and, of course, "Only the Lonely." The collection also features a few lesser-known sides, including Roy's own ripoff of "Only the Lonely" called "I'm Hurtin'." A must for everybody!

VIRGIN 90604 (RC)

In Dreams: The Greatest Hits

Re-recordings of 19 of Roy's Monument hits, made after the success of the film *Blue Velvet* (that featured the title track). Blue Bayou/Oh, Pretty Woman/Only the Lonely/Blue Angel.

VIRGIN 91058 (L)

Mystery Girl

Orbison's comeback LP released just after his fatal heart attack. Jeff Lynne produced with an all-star supporting cast. Features the hit single "You Got It."

VIRGIN 91295 (L)

A Black and White Night Live

The tribute to Roy Orbison done shortly before his death. Produced by T-Bone Burnett, Roy is helped out by rock stars like Bruce Springsteen, James Burton, Elvis Costello, Tom Waits, k.d. lang, and many others. Only the Lonely/In Dreams/Crying/Ooby Dooby/Oh, Pretty Woman.

ZU ZAZZ 2006 (R)

Problem Child:
Sun Sessions 1956–1958

A real treasure trove of Sun material for both the fan of Roy Orbison and quality rock and roll. These are the raw tapes, with no overdubs; in many cases, they are unissued alternate takes and demos. There's even an instrumental version of "Chicken Hearted." "Problem Child," "This Kind of Love," and "It's Too Late" are each heard in two versions: the original, released recording (sans overdubs) and a raw alternate. Trying to Get to You/Mean Little Mama/Claudette.

ROY ORBISON/SONNY JAMES

BEAR FAMILY 15407 (L)

Roy Orbison and Sonny James

Two stars performing non-hit material for RCA during career lulls. Roy's material, recorded in 1958–1959 between his Sun and Monument careers, includes seven fine cuts in beautiful stereo, featuring all six cuts from Bear Family 15019, along with the more recently found "I'll Never Tell" also available on the *Rockin' Rollin' High School* compilation. Sonny's 12 tunes are from a brief spell away from Capitol in 1961–1962, including a remake of "Young Love," a vocal version of "Apache," and the excellent "Magnetism," sounding much more pop than country. All tunes are in beautiful stereo.

THE ORIOLES

One of the pioneer black harmony groups, The Orioles were led by Earlington Tilghman, better known as Sonny Til, and specialized in beautiful ballads. Though there were other black harmony groups around when they started in 1957 (the most important being The Ravens), these other groups still had a very white-pop sound. Sonny and The Orioles were the first pure black-sounding vocal group. They started with It's a Natural Records in 1947 (which soon changed its name to Jubilee), releasing the classic "It's Too Soon to Know." The group stayed fairly stable through 1954, releasing classic hits including "What Are You Doing New Year's Eve," "Baby Please Don't Go," and the 1953 original version of "Crying in the Chapel." Sonny remained active recording with different groups of Orioles for Vee Jay in the late '50s, Charlie Parker Records in the early '60s, RCA in the '70s, and Ivory in the '80s. He remained smooth-voiced and a highly magnetic, sexual singer until his death in 1983.

BEAR FAMILY 15682 (L)

The Jubilee Recordings

This beautiful six-CD box set offers every number The Orioles laid down for Jerry Blaine's Jubilee label, drawn almost completely from the original master tapes, totalling 152 tracks. It is dominated by the sinuously slow ballads for which the group is justly famous, but it also reveals their journeyman touch on night-club styled blues and up-tempo numbers. The set features an attractive LP-sized booklet written by Peter Grendysa, rich in studio portraits of both the original group and the later aggregation (Sonny Til and

The Regals), which also made several recordings for Jubilee. Outdoes the Collectables set (8801), which has only 60 tracks and poorly illustrated notes. At Night/Tell Me So/I Cover the Waterfront/(It's Gonna Be a) Lonely Christmas/What Are You Doing New Years Eve?/We're Supposed to Be Through/Oh Holy Night/Don't Tell Her What's Happened to Me/Pal of Mine/See See Rider/Write and Tell Me Why.

COLLECTABLES 5014 (CL)
Greatest Hits
Fourteen songs. Crying in the Chapel/It's Too Soon to Know/Chapel in the Moonlight/Secret Love/I Miss You So/Lonely Christmas/What Happened to You/What Are You Doing New Year's Eve/Wobble.

COLLECTABLES 5408 (CL)
Sing Their Greatest Hits
All the group's finest earlier work is included. Good sound reproduction and detailed notes by Bob Hyde, similar lineup and packaging as the now out-of-print LP Murray Hill 1233; all tracks are on Collectables 8801, as well as Bear Family 15682. Tell Me So (second version)/Forgive and Forget/What Are You Doing New Year's Eve/It's Gonna Be a Lonely Christmas/Crying in the Chapel.

COLLECTABLES 8801 (CL)
For Collectors Only
Three-cassette/disc collection, previously released—with a different song order and notes—on Murray Hill vinyl (1233), containing a staggering 60 tracks. Why "In the Mission of St. Augustine," a substantial hit of 1953, is missing is anybody's guess. Crying in the Chapel/I Cover the Waterfront/Goodnight Irene/I Miss You So (two versions)/Lonely Christmas/It's Too Soon to Know/Tell Me So/A Kiss and a Rose/I Challenge Your Kiss/Forgive and Forget/What Are You Doing New Year's Eve/Baby Please Don't Go.

DR. HORSE 800 (RL)
Hold Me, Thrill Me, Kiss Me
Sixteen Jubilee recordings from 1948–1954. Duplicates other reissues. Shrimp Boats/A Kiss and a Rose/It's a Cold Summer/We're Supposed to Be Through.

ORION
Elvis-influenced rockabilly artist, born Jimmy Ellis.

BEAR FAMILY 15548 (L)
Some Think He Might Be King Elvis
Orion is a rockabilly force to be reckoned with. He has the best "Elvis" voice of anyone, and he's not even an Elvis impersonator. He's a logical extension of the Presley musical persona, performing songs in The King's style that The King never got around to cover-

ing like "Rockabilly Rebel," "Susie Q," "Peggy Sue," "Matchbox," and "I'm Gonna Be a Wheel Someday." Orion even covered the Queen tune "Crazy Little Thing Called Love" in a rockabilly style. The arrangements, for the most part, are rockin' and unencumbered, and the new songs are top-flight.

THE OVATIONS
These Ovations should not to be confused with Louis Williams and The Ovations who recorded for Goldwax. These Ovations are a white quartet from Queens who sound very much like The Four Seasons in both style and choice of material. Their one claim to regional fame came in 1964 with "Who Needs Love" recorded for Jose Records.

CRYSTAL BALL 125 (R)
Highschool Reunion
Much of the material on this collection is bubble-gum and should please lovers of groups like Randy and The Rainbows.

(LOUIS WILLIAMS and) THE OVATIONS
The Ovations trio came together in the early '60s around the delicate soulful lead of Louis Williams, who still comes closest to matching the yodeling acrobatics of the late Sam Cooke. Right up to 1972, when they switched from Goldwax (under the firm direction of Quinton M. Claunch and Rudy Russell) to The Sounds of Memphis label, this outfit cut some fine Southern-soul drippings in a style that would have pleased Sam.

P-VINE 1310 (L)
Hooked on a Feeling
Reissue of 1972 album recorded in Memphis, including most of their The Sounds of Memphis label singles. The Ovations's singing on this collection is every bit as fine as their earlier Goldwax sides. Standouts include a Soul Stirrers-like medley of "Were You There" and "Touch the Hem of His Garment," and a teasingly beautiful version of "Touching Me." One of two worthwhile collections the group produced during this period. Nicely remastered digital sound.

VIVID SOUND 004 (L)
I'm Living Good
Twenty '60s Goldwax cuts in peerless digital audio. Essential. I'm Living Good/Don't Cry/It's Wonderful to Be in Love/Me and My Imagination/Peace of Mind.

VIVID SOUND 016 (L)
Sweet Thing
One of the worst Ovations collections to date; it doesn't come anywhere close to the quartet's best work on Goldwax (see Vivid Sound 004). It's not that Louis Williams rinsed his mouth with Drano; his voice is in fine fettle and still makes you think that Sam Cooke is alive and well. It's the overladen strings, the fancy production, and cute choruses that prevail over soulful leads and simple harmonies that drag these recordings down. Originally recorded in the late '70s for The Sounds of Memphis's XL label, Louis's rendition of Joe Simon's arrangement of "Just Enough to Keep Me Hangin' On" is the only one of 12 songs that remind me of their former glories. Nightclub wallpaper music only.

THE PARAGONS

The Paragons, a Brooklyn-based quintet, recorded for the Winley label during the late '50s. The group's most beloved sides ("Florence," "Twilight," and "Let's Start All Over Again") feature the high-tenor lead of Julius McMichael, a disciple of the Clyde McPhatter school of vocal-drama, harking back to the gospel sound.

COLLECTABLES 5035 (CL)
The Best of
Fourteen songs. Florence/The Vows of Love/Two Hearts Are Better than One/Kneel and Pray/Hey Little Schoolgirl/Give Me Love/If.

RELIC 7006 (L)
The Paragons Meet The Jesters
The Paragons's hit songs (duplicating Collectables 5035) are all here, along with hot wax from The Jesters, a Harlem-based quintet, who also recorded for Paul Winley during the late '50s. Adam Jackson, yet another advocate of the soaring academy of vocal gymnastics, led the group on touching ballads like "So Strange," "The Wind," "The Plea," and "Please Let Me Love You." With good notes and good sound, too.

MACEO PARKER

Sax star who backed up James Brown and George Clinton, making a big comeback as a bandleader in the '90s.

CHARLY 292 (L)
Maceo and All The King's Men: Doing Their Own Thing
In 1970, the James Brown band suffered a mass mutiny. Key members St. Clair Pinckney and Fred Wesley split, and sax star Maceo Parker also jumped ship taking guitarist Jimmy Nolen and most of the other band members with him. James did his best to sabotage the rebels, reportedly paying DJs to keep the newly formed group's early singles off their turntables. In light of this, and seeing their fame eclipsed by the hot new JB band, most of The King's Men eventually returned to the fold, leaving behind only two LPs. This is a reissue of their first record, including lots of solid classic instrumental funk, with two or three dated vocal numbers and a nice Sly Stone medley. Ten tracks in all.

VERVE 314 511 068 (CL)
Mo' Roots
Maceo's 1990 *Roots Revisited* LP made quite a splash, getting him back in the studio pronto. The formula here is the same: no-nonsense roadhouse R&B and funk, but done up slick for the '90s. This time out there are no JB tunes, but the album features instrumental covers of Ray Charles's "Hallelujah, I Love Her So" and Marvin Gaye's "Let's Get It On," and some funk vocalizing on Otis Redding's "Fa Fa Fa." Shep and The Limelighters's "Daddy's Home" is a real treat, as is the original funk of the closing cut "Southwick." Ten tunes with JB bandmates Fred Wesley and Pee Wee Ellis.

VERVE 843 751 (CL)
Roots Revisited
A pure delight. This long-overdue date for Maceo as a leader was one of my favorite releases of 1990. The set ranges from bop to Sly Stone, with nods to Ray Charles and Mingus along the way. It features a stompin' band including fellow JB alums Pee Wee Ellis and Fred Wesley, the one and only Bootsy Collins, and Mingus alumni Don Pullen doing some serious testifying on the Hammond organ. This is music to make you feel better, about everything. Better get it in yo' soul collection!

ROBERT PARKER

New Orleans sax-player-turned-singer Parker had a good thing goin' doing session work for Professor Longhair, Irma Thomas, and Ernie K-Doe. He went solo in 1959 and recorded for Ron and Imperial before signing to New Orleans's Nola label. He must have thought the singing game was a snap when he hit Number 4 on the charts in 1966 with the pounding dance-floor classic "Barefootin'." His "Sneaking Sally through the Alley" and "Let's Go Baby (Where the Action Is)" are also well-known.

COLLECTABLES 5163 (CL)
Barefootin'
Fourteen tunes. Skinny Dippin'/The Hiccup/Disco Doctor/Barefootin'/ A Little Bit Of Something (Is Better than Nothing)/Better Luck in the Summertime.

THE PASSIONS

The much revered, original Passions (originally known as The Sinceres) hailed from Brooklyn and recorded in the late '50s to early '60s. Founders included Jimmy Gallagher (lead), Tony Armato (1st ten), Albie Galione (2nd ten), and Vinnie Acierno (bar). Their first recording for the Audicon label "Just to Be With You" was a hit, and was followed by lesser successes like "I Only Want You" and "Gloria." This is the quartet other white groups on the revival circuit most admired. Too bad most of their material sounds like insipid pop today.

CRYSTAL BALL 138 (R)/RELIC 7031 (L)
Legendary Hits/Just to Be with You
Sixteen-song set of Audicon, Diamond, Jubilee, and Octavia releases and alternates, including their renowned version of "Gloria," the pretty "Just to Be with You" and "This Is My Love," plus the Belmonts-sounding "I Only Want You" and "You Don't Love Me Anymore."

BOBBY PATTERSON

Excellent soul singer and guitarist/drummer from Texas who started working with the group The Royal Rockers in the mid-to-late '50s. He made his first recording for Abnack in 1962, and recorded for a number of labels over the years, scoring some minor successes in the late '60s and '70s.

KENT (UK) 098 (L)
Taking Care of Business
Twenty-nine tracks from the mid-to-late '60s recorded for Jetstar and Abnak.

PAUL and PAULA

Ray Hildebrand and Jill Jackson were a couple of college kids from Texas who instantly captured the collective hearts of malt-shop teens when, as Paul and Paula, they vaulted into the charts with a Number 1 hit in 1962 with the naive ditty "Hey Paula." Their little fling lasted for a couple of years bearing a few more chart singles and two LPs for Philips.

TEENAGER 600 (R)
Hey Paula and Other Big Hits
Eighteen tunes. This is the stuff of mid-American teenage myth; they can even make their R&B covers sound like sunny postcards from Wonderbread land. You Send Me/Pledging My Love/So Fine/Hey Baby/Hey Paula/Young Lovers/First Quarrel.

THE PEARLS

The underrated Howie Guyton and The Pearls come from Detroit. The original group was filled with star talent. Howie sang high tenor lead, and David Clowney, better known as Dave "Baby" Cortez, sang tenor and played piano. The group also included Derek Martin of "You Better Go" solo fame, Coley Washington, and George Torrence. In 1954 the quintet recorded the tenderly beautiful "Please Let Me Know" for Aladdin, and almost topped this with 1955's touching "Shadows of Love." During 1956–1957 the group recorded for Jerry Winston's Onyx label, where they waxed their unbeatable version of "Your Cheating Heart."

ONYX 203 (R)
Zippity Zippity Zoom: Here Comes The Pearls
Twenty magnificent Aladdin and Onyx sides, plus the outfit's On-The-Square single and the pretty "More than the Day Before" (released as by Howie and The Sapphires). No sleeve notes, but good overall sound quality. Highly recommended.

MIKE PEDICIN

Philadelphia-based saxophonist who has had a long career with numerous singles and two LPs, one released in 1959 on Apollo and the second some 20 years later on Philadelphia International.

REVIVAL 3003 (R)
Rock and Roll with Paul Pedicin
Reissue of *Musical Medicine by Mike Pedicin* (Apollo 484) from 1959, with extra tracks, 16 in all. The cuts are Bill Haley-ish, "rockaphilly" jive, featuring a guitarist named Sam Cooke! Includes his hit version of "Shake a Hand." Banjo Rock/Rockin' on a Rocket/Mambo Rock/Large Large House/Hotter than a Pistol.

ANN PEEBLES

Gritty Memphis soul singer/songwriter, originally from East St. Louis, Peebles began her musical career with her family gospel group, The Peebles Choir, when she was eight. Bandleader Gene Miller discovered her singing in a Memphis club in 1969, and took her to Hi Records producer Willie Mitchell. Her first release "Walk Away" was a big hit, and she followed it with many others through the '70s, including many songs written by her (sometimes with her husband, soul singer Don Bryant), including the classic "I Can't Stand the Rain" which has been covered by a number of performers, most recently Tina Turner. Ann kept a low profile in the '80s but has returned to a more active career in the last couple of years with some fine new recordings and a dynamic stage act.

BULLSEYE BLUES 9515 (CL)
Full Time Love
Back after a long "Hi"-atus from recording, Ms. Peebles sheds the tough-talking, homewrecker image (given her by Willie Mitchell) and sings the praises of love and fidelity. She's found a "Full Time Love" in singer/songwriter hubby Don Bryant. When she sings originals like "He's My Superman," "Just You and Me," and "Ain't No Business Like Your Business," she is more convincing than on Delbert McClinton's "Read Me My Rights" or The Stones's "Miss You." The exception is "Fear No Evil," an anthemic love song that should be a hit single. The Memphis Horns and the Hi Rhythm Section provide serviceable accompaniments.

⚙ HI (UK) 100 (L)
Greatest Hits
This isn't greatest hits, its everything great she ever recorded, 26 wonderful Hi sides recorded in the '70s, including almost all of her two UK reissues, *I'm Gonna Tear Your Playhouse Down* (Hi 422) and *99 Lbs* (Hi 402). I Can't Stand the Rain/Dr. Love Power/Old Man with Young Ideas/Part Time Love/I Feel Like Breaking Up Somebody's Home/Somebody's on Your Case.

HI (UK) 105 (L)
Lookin' for a Lovin'
Twenty-one tracks cut between 1969–1981, produced by Willie Mitchell. Respect/It's Your Thing/My Man/What You Laid on Me/Love Played a Game/You're Gonna Make Me Cry/The Handwriting Is on the Wall/Lookin' for a Lovin'/I Didn't Take

Your Man/Be for Me/I'd Rather Leave While I'm in Love.

HI (UK) 402 (R)
99 Lbs
Sixteen Hi single sides, many never before on LP when this was released. Slipped, Stumbled and Fell in Love/I Feel like Breaking Up Somebody's Home/I Pity the Fool/Part Time Love/Somebody's on Your Case.

TRACY PENDARVIS

BISON BOP 2004 (R)
Tracy Pendarvis
Fourteen sides from 1958–1961 by this Florida rock and roller and vocalist; some cuts feature Jerry Reed on lead vocals.

THE PENGUINS

The quintessential LA vocal group formed by Cleve Duncan in 1954, named for Kool cigarette's mascot, Willie the Penguin. They had one of the best-known hits of all time with "Earth Angel," a song written by group member Curtis Williams with Jesse Belvin. After several hits on the local Dootone label, they went to Mercury and Atlantic where they failed to have any further hits. Cleve Duncan is still leading a group of Penguins.

ACE 249 (RL)
Earth Angel
Includes most of The Penguins's best pre-Mercury sides. Hear the original "Earth Angel" without the heavy-handed accompaniment and annoying glockenspiel of later recordings, the bluesy "Kiss a Fool Good-bye," the pretty back-beat piano on "Love Will Make Your Mind Go Wild," and singing guitar solo on "Money Talks." Twenty-one magnificent sides, including three CD bonus tracks. Peerless fidelity and exhaustive sleeve notes by Jim Dawson. Recommended.

BEAR FAMILY 15222 (R)
Earth Angel
This album is a reissue of the Mercury bootleg (Wing 1000) that was long a collector's item. It has four unissued remakes of sides originally issued on Dootone, including an upbeat version of "Hey Senorita." Also featured is a pleasant, simplified version of "Earth Angel" without the heavy drum track as on the Dootone version and glockenspiel as on the later Mercury release. Good sleeve notes, but note that the accompanying picture shows the earlier

Dootone group. Their finest middle-period material. Recommended.

COLLECTABLES 5045 (CL)
Golden Classics
"Earth Angel" and 11 more cuts.

THE PENTAGONS

Early '60s California group who had a Top 40 hit with their first recording for Donna, "To Be Loved," in 1961. "I Wonder," recorded for Jamie in the same year, was a lesser hit.

COLLECTABLES 5093 (RCL)
Golden Classics
Twelve songs. To Be Loved/I Like the Way You Look at Me/I'm in Love/O Wonder/Your Good Lovin'/That's All Over Baby.

CARL PERKINS

One of the best rockabilly performers ever, who has unfortunately been a victim of bad luck. With his beautiful, soulful honky-tonk voice and jangly, bluesy guitar, Carl Perkins epitomized rockabilly like no other artist. Accompanied by the thumping bass and propulsive guitar of brothers Jay and Clayton and the steady drumming of W.S. Holland, he produced exciting, timeless music for Sam Phillips's Sun label between 1954–1957. His song "Blue Suede Shoes" was the first song to simultaneously top the R&B, pop, and country charts. Thanks to its success, Perkins was invited to perform on TV's *Perry Como* show in March 1956, the first rockabilly star to be asked to perform on nationwide TV. Sadly, on the way to the gig, Perkins was in an auto wreck that killed brother Jay and laid Carl up for about a year. During that time, Elvis covered "Blue Suede Shoes," appeared on the *Ed Sullivan Show*, and became a household name. After he recovered, Carl stayed with Sun until 1958, when he signed with Columbia, having hits with "Pink Pedal Pushers" and "Pointed Toe Shoes." He turned to booze in the '60s, recording a bit for Decca before joining up with buddy Johnny Cash. Their association lasted from 1965–1975, with Perkins appearing regularly on Cash's TV and touring shows. He became a giant star in England in the

'70s, and converted to Christianity. Perkins continues to perform sporadically.

Perkins's Sun recordings have been reissued many times, with Bear Family 15246 holding the edge for sound quality, although the domestic Rhino CD is less expensive. Columbia has recently reissued its catalog of his post-Sun recordings for that label, while Rhino also has a CD of his post-Sun recordings for a variety of labels. The Bear Family box set (15494) is the ultimate collection of his '50s and early '60s recordings.

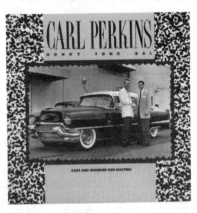

⊕ BEAR FAMILY 15246 (L)
Up through the Years, 1954–1957
Rockabilly as it was meant to be heard. Twenty-four Sun classics that have tremendous punch, presence, and clarity. We can really hear the vibrancy of Carl's vocals, the jangle of his guitar, and the thundering slapped bass of Clayton Perkins. Tracks are featured in chronological order and include all of his gems. Honky Tonk Gal/Turn Around/Let the Jukebox Keep on Playing/Blue Suede Shoes/Tennessee/All Mama's Children/Dixie Fried/You Can Do No Wrong/Your True Love/Put Your Cat Clothes On (with great piano by a certain Mr. J.L. Lewis)/Pink Pedal Pushers/Lend Me Your Comb/Right String Baby.

BEAR FAMILY 15494 (L)
The Classic Carl Perkins
The first two-and-a-half CDs in this beautiful five-CD set feature Perkins's Sun recordings and, although many of these tracks have been reissued before, this collection features several previously unissued takes. In Carl's case, the alternate versions are frequently very different from the more familiar ones; the three different versions of his most famous song "Blue Suede Shoes" are particularly revealing. These recordings have never sounded better, thanks to the remastering wizardry of Bob Jones. The rest of this box is devoted to his recordings made for Columbia and Decca be-

tween 1958–1964, which are generally less interesting, marred by assembly-line Nashville production, thin sound, and often mediocre songs. Nevertheless Carl's beautiful vocals often surmount the obstacles, and he manages to get in a hot guitar solo here and there. Interestingly, the best of these recordings are from a 1964 session in England with the English group The Nashville Teens where Carl sounds more enthusiastic than he had in a long time. The set is beautifully packaged in a sturdy box with a full-color photo of Carl and his band from the late '50s or early '60s. There is a 24-page, LP-sized booklet with notes by Colin Escott and Bill Millar, over two-dozen photos, and full discographical details on all the recordings included.

BEAR FAMILY 15593 (L)
Country Boy's Dream: The Dollie Masters

CAPITOL 90079 (L)
Born to Rock

COLUMBIA 48896 (CL)
Restless: The Columbia Recordings
For much too long, I ignored Carl's Columbia output, being too busy diggin' the earlier Sun Records masterpieces. Don't let it happen to you. I won't argue that these 18 primo cuts are better than the Sun boppers, coz they aren't, but that still leaves them up there with the very best rockabilly recordings. After all Carl was still in his prime when he signed on with Columbia in 1958. Sure, tunes like "Pink Pedal Pushers," "Rockin' Record Hop," and "Pop, Let Me Have the Car," were aimed at the, by then, huge teen market, but they rock like crazy, so, what the hay. Pointed Toe Shoes/Jive after Five/That's All Right Mama.

INSTANT 5019 (L)
Tennessee Bop
Fourteen Sun hits on this budget import. No big surprises, just alotta hot boppin' to the classics. Blue Suede Shoes/Honey Don't/Matchbox/Put Your Cat Clothes On/Everybody's Trying to Be My Baby/Dixie Fried/Boppin' the Blues.

RHINO 70221 (C)/RHINO 75890 (L)
Original Sun Greatest Hits
The Sun era has been over-reissued, but this album's as good as it gets (except for the Bear Family CD). Fourteen of Carl's biggest and best, recorded between 1955–1957. Blue Suede Shoes/Honey Don't/Dixie Fried/Put Your Cat Clothes On/Matchbox/Lend Me Your Comb/Everybody's Tryin' to Be My Baby.

RHINO 70958 (CL)
Jive after Five: The Best of Carl Perkins, 1958–1978
Fourteen of Carl's best post-Sun recordings (18 on CD), including tracks from Columbia, Decca, Mer-

cury, and Jet, ranging from hot rockers to country weepers. Shows just how good Carl could be even if he didn't quite scale the heights of his Sun recordings. Great sound, informative notes by Jimmy Guterman, and some great photos. Where the Rio De Rosa Flows/The Unhappy Girls/Let My Baby Be/Restless/Help Me Dream/Goin' to Memphis/Standing in the Need of Your Love/I'm in Love Again.

ROUNDER 27 (RCL)
Honky Tonk Gal: Rare and Unissued Sun Masters

SUN (UK) 2 (L)
The Sun Years
Unlike the elaborate Bear Family package, this three-CD set comes in a simple fold-out package with a 48-page, CD-sized booklet. Features all the Sun recordings that are in the Bear Family set, plus several songs from the legendary Million Dollar Quartet session (with Elvis, Jerry Lee, and Johnny Cash) on which Carl is prominently featured. The arrangement of the songs is somewhat different from the Bear Family set, and Martin Hawkins's notes include informative discussion of all the songs, with only a handful of photos thrown in. The sound lacks presence and clarity compared to the Bear Family issue, but the price is right, and if you care about rockabilly at all, you've got to have these classic sides in some form.

CARL PERKINS and NRBQ

COLUMBIA 9981 (L)
Boppin' the Blues
An idea this crazy just had to work out: wacky bar band meets rockabilly legend a few years after the fact for 13 fun-filled tunes. Carl fronts six cuts, including "All Mama's Children," "Sorry Charlie," "Allergic to Love," "Boppin' the Blues," and provides a cheery Chet Atkins-flavored guitar instrumental to close the disc. The remaining six selections feature NRBQ only.

THE PERSUADERS
New York R&B/soul group formed in 1969. Their 1971 recording "Thin Line between Love and Hate" was a Number 1 R&B hit. They had several more hits through the '70s for Atco, Win or Lose, and Calla.

COLLECTABLES 5139 (RC)
Thin Line between Love and Hate
Includes the 1971 title hit plus 11 more. Blood Brothers/Thanks for Loving Me/Love Gonna Pick Up and Walk Out/Mr. Sunshine/Can't Go No Further and Do No Better.

THE PERSUASIONS

The best-known and most popular a-cappella group. They were born and raised in the Bed-Stuy section of New York, home for so many street-singing aggregations of the '50s. Formed in 1962, the group included Jerry Lawson, a church-edged "rough" tenor lead, Joseph "Jesse" Russell and Jay Otis Washington (tens), Herbert "Tubo" Rhoad (bar), and Jimmy "Bro" Hayes, the outstanding and sometimes awesome bass. They started their recording career in 1962 without much impact. After recording their first album for Frank Zappa's Straight label in 1969 (*A Capella*), The Persuasions became favorites of the "hip" white crowd. They subsequently recorded for Capitol, MCA, A&M (with backup instrumentation, yielding their only two R&B chart hits in 1974–1975), Elektra (where in 1977 they recorded *Chirpin'*, generally considered their finest recording), Flying Fish, and, most recently, Rounder. In addition to their own recordings they are much in demand as studio backup singers having recorded behind Don McLean, Stevie Wonder, Paul Simon, and Joni Mitchell. Baritone Herbert Rhoad died in 1988 and the group continues as a quartet.

COLLECTABLES 5234 (CL)
We Came to Play
Reissue of the quintet's excellent early '70s Capitol album (originally 791), which includes superb a-cappella renditions of Sam Cooke's "Chain Gang," Curtis Mayfield's "Gypsy Woman" and "Man Oh Man," The Beatles's "Let It Be," Joe South's "Don't It Make You Want to Go Home?," The Drifters's "Another Night with the Boys," plus boss renditions of "It's You That I Want," "The Sun," "Don't Know Why I Love You," and "Walk on the Wild Side." Ten flawless, breathtaking performances from the bandless boys from NY. Highly recommended.

COLLECTABLES 5235 (CL)
Street Corner Symphony: Golden Classics
Reissue of Capitol 872 from 1972, a fine companion to *We Came to Play*. Features peerless, close-harmony a-cappella renderings of "Buffalo Soldier," Sam Cooke's "Good Times," a Temptations medley, the best rendition to date of Curtis Mayfield's "People Get Ready," a righteous version of The Dixie Hummingbirds's "Christian Automobile," plus six

other winning selections sung in superb street corner fashion. Good clean sound.

ELEKTRA 1099 (L)
Chirpin'
A superb collection, including perfect renditions of "Moonlight and Music," "Women and Drinking," "Johnny Porter," Tony Joe White's "Willie and Laura Mae Jones," the doo-wop singers' anthem "Looking for an Echo," Sam Cooke's "Win Your Love (for Me)," and a cover of a gospel song recorded by Chas Johnson with The Sensational Nightingales in 1972, "It's Gonna Rain Again."
Unsurpassable a-cappella singing. Highly recommended.

FLYING FISH 70093 (CL)
Comin' At Ya
1979 album.

HAMMER 'N NAILS 1988 (L)
Live in the Whispering Gallery

RHINO 70362 (CL)
A Cappella
Reissue of their first album from 1969 (Straight 1062), including live and studio recordings. Searchin' for My Baby/Old Man River/Don't Look Back/Drip Drop/Up on the Roof/Since I Fell for You.

ROUNDER 3053 (CL)
Good News
Ten a-cappella classics, with emphasis on Sam Cooke material ("Cupid," "Ain't That Good News," and "I'll Come Running Back to You"), and The Heartbeat's "I Won't Be the Fool Anymore." All I Have to Do Is Dream/Swanee River Medley.

ROUNDER 3083 (CL)
No Frills
You Can Have Her/Sand in My Shoes/I Woke Up in Love this Morning/Still Ain't Got No Band/Treasure of Love/What Are You Doing New Year's Eve?

BOBBY PETERSON

Philadelphia pianist Peterson started out as "Bobby Charles—Ray Charles's Nephew," acknowledging the influence of the master R&B vocalist/pianist on his style. He joined sax blower Joe Pyatt's Combo, cutting six singles for the Philly label V-Tone between 1960–1962, before Pyatt quit to join Dave "Baby" Cortez.

RELIC 8007 (R)
Bobby Peterson Quintet: Piano Rock
All 12 sides of the singles recorded by Peterson with saxophonist Joe Pyatt, including the title hit, with five

tracks featuring Peterson's bluesy vocals. The Hunch/Rockin' Charlie, Pts. 1 and 2/Smooth Sailin', Pts. 1 and 2/Mama Get Your Hammer.

RAY PETERSON

Texas pop-rock singer who started singing during a long stay in the hospital while recovering from polio. He subsequently performed in Los Angeles clubs where he was discovered in 1958 and signed by RCA. Peterson was an impressive singer with a four-and-a-half octave range, which he used to good effect on pop-rock ballads. After a year of going nowhere, he finally hit the big time with the impassioned "The Wonder of You," and a year later had an even bigger hit with the morbid car-crash ditty "Tell Laura I Love Her." He left RCA and formed his own label, Dunes, where he had a few minor hits. After the label folded in the mid-'60s, he moved to MGM where he recorded in a more country-flavored vein with little impact.

BEAR FAMILY 15245 (R)
All His Hits

Ray's best from RCA and Dunes. The 1957–1959 RCA sides include his huge hit "Tell Laura I Love Her" (which Bear Family follows on this LP with Skeeter Davis's answer song "Tell Tommy I Miss Him"!), plus the original version of "The Wonder of You," "Fever," and the never-before released "Doggone It." His 1960–1963 tunes for his own Dunes label include his hit version of "Corrine, Corrina" produced by Phil Spector, and the original version of "Give Us Your Blessing," later a huge hit for The Shangri-Las.

DEWEY PHILLIPS

ZU ZAZZ 2012 (RC)
Red Hot and Blue

Absolutely hilarious madness from the Memphis DJ who, according to Sun's Sam Phillips (no relation) "was responsible for Elvis." His "Red Hot and Blue" show on WHBQ was the happening thing in '50s Memphis, blending R&B, blues, country, gospel, and pop music into a mixture seldom heard before or since. What really makes this a treat are the many, many advertisements, station IDs, plugs, and general nonsense interspersed throughout the programs, all delivered in Dewey's unique down-home, breathless, manic style. He talks a mile a minute, all the while doing his homespun character impersonations when he's not making mincemeat out of his sponsors' commercials by trying to read a page in two seconds!

LITTLE ESTHER PHILLIPS

Excellent R&B singer turned smooth jazzster, born Esther Mae Jones. Esther was discovered by Johnny Otis at the age of 13; she recorded with his band on Savoy from 1949–1952, and had a Number 1 hit with "Double Crossin' Blues" (with The Robins), and Top 10 duets with Mel Walker. In 1952, she moved to the King subsidiary label, Federal, where she recorded a lot of great Leiber-Stoller material, and had a major hit with "Ring-a- Ding Doo." In 1954, she retired due to illness brought on by heavy drug use. She returned to recording in 1962, and had a big chart hit with her soulful rendition of the country standard "Release Me" on Lenox. Over the next two decades she performed a wide variety of material—country, jazz, pop, and blues—with her distinctive smooth but nasal intonation, for a number of labels. Continuing problems with drug addiction took their toll and in August 1984 she died from liver and kidney failure at the age of 48.

ATLANTIC JAZZLORE 90670 (CL)
Confessin' the Blues

Reissue of Atlantic 1680 from 1975, which coupled two previously unissued sessions. The first side offers a wonderful combination of Esther backed by a 17-piece big band including Sonny Criss, Al Porcino, and Herb Ellis, recorded on October 2, 1966. It's full of wonderful blues including "Cherry Red," "I Wonder," and "Romance in the Dark." Side 2 has live recordings from 1970, done at the same time as her *Burnin'* LP with a four-piece electric rhythm section led by pianist Jack Wilson, highlighted by an 11-minute medley of "Blow Top Blues," "Jelly Jelly Blues," and "Long John Blues." New liner notes by Leonard Feather.

CBS ASSOCIATED 40710 (L)
What a Difference a Day Makes

Reissue of her Kudo/CTI LP from 1975. After making some fine LPs for CTI subsidiary Kudo that just didn't sell, Esther was forced to record a disco LP, featuring a disco-fied version of the title cut, originally the biggest hit by her idol Dinah Washington. She didn't want to make the LP, but it was her biggest seller ever, and she scored a massive disco hit with the title tune! The band is led by Joe Beck and includes David Sanborn and The Brecker Brothers. Even Eric Weissberg shows up on steel guitar! One Night Affair/Turn Around, Look at Me/I Can Stand a Little Rain.

CBS ASSOCIATED 40935 (L)

From a Whisper to a Scream

Reissue of CTI label recordings (originally Kudo 09 from 1971) remastered for CD. Thirteen tracks including four previously unreleased.

CHARLY 248 (L)

Better Beware

Fifties Federal recordings, including "The Deacon Moves In" recorded with Clyde McPhatter and The Dominoes, Mel Walker, Bobby Nunn (of The Robins), and Little Willie Littlefield. Featured songs include the fabulous mid-tempo "Ramblin' Blues" with its choice Ben Webster tenor break; the atmospheric "Storm" (blues) with thunder and rain sound effects; the hard-driving, tempo-changing "Cherry Wine"; plus other scorchers ably supported by the likes of Pete "Guitar" Lewis, James Von Streeter on tenor, and Preston Love on alto sax.

KING 622 (RC)

The Best Songs Little Esther Ever Recorded

More early '50s Federal recordings. Choice cuts here include the bluesy "I Paid My Dues," "Street Lights," "Aged and Mellow," and "Sweet Lips," plus the atmospheric "Storm," and novelty jump song "The Deacon Moves In." Some duplication with Charly 248.

MUSE 5302 (L)

A Way to Say Goodbye

Her last recordings.

BOBBY (BORIS) PICKETT and THE CRYPT-KICKERS

Early '60s outfit whose sole hit was "Monster Mash."

DERAM 844 147 (CL)

The Original Monster Mash

The problem with popular novelty songs is that they breed incestuously in the dead of night. "Monster Mash" is fine, once, especially if the listener is about 13 years old. But an entire album of 16 songs that repeat in some way the elements of "Monster Mash"? Well, even 13 year olds have their limits. The main idea of this album (originally Garpax 67001, recorded in 1962) was to poke fun at pop music by using the word "monster" a lot. One song is called "Rabian: The Fiendish Idol." Ha Ha. "The Sinister Stomp" is a goof on "Runaround Sue," for whatever that's worth. "Monster Minuet" is not too bad, and "Monster's Holiday" provides that much sought-after cross between a Christmas and Halloween novelty record.

WILSON PICKETT

One of the most exciting soul singers of all time, "The Wicked Pickett" started out as lead singer of The Falcons. He was "discovered" by Lloyd Price and recorded for Price's Double L label, scoring hits with "If You Need Me" and "It's Too Late." In 1964 he signed with Atlantic and recorded a decade-long string of classic hits in his fervent gospel style, mostly songs written by himself ("In the Midnight Hour," "Ninety-nine and a Half Won't Do," and "I'm a Midnight Mover"). Other recordings include buddy Bobby Womack's "I'm in Love," songs associated with The Falcons ("I Found a Love" and "If You Need Me"), and a song written by Falcon-mate Mack "Bonny" Rice, "Mustang Sally." In the '70s and '80s, he recorded for Big Tree, RCA, his own Wicked label, and EMI America. He recently made a comeback LP for Motown after a decade off the performing trail.

ATLANTIC 501 (RCL)

Greatest Hits

The definitive two-LP/cassette/CD set. Mustang Sally/In the Midnight Hour/Ninety-nine and a Half Won't Do/I'm a Midnight Mover/A Man and a Half/634–5789/Land of 1000 Dances/Sugar Sugar.

ATLANTIC 81283 (F) (CL)

The Best of Wilson Pickett

Twelve great Atlantic sides. In the Midnight Hour/634–5789/Mustang Sally/I Found a Love/Ninety-nine and a Half Won't Do/Funky Broadway.

ATLANTIC (JAPAN) 67 (L)

Hey Jude

Reissue of 1969 album produced by Rick Hall and Tom Dowd. Save Me/Back in Your Arms/Night Owl/A Man and a Half/Search Your Heart/People Make the World.

ATLANTIC (JAPAN) 2371 (L)

In the Midnight Hour

Reissue of Pickett's first LP, Atlantic 8114 from 1965, remastered in original mono. Besides showing off The Wicked One's masterful voice, Pickett's songwriting really shines, as shown not only on the two huge hits "Don't Fight It" and the title cut, but also such tasty LP cuts as "That's a Man's Way," "I'm Gonna Cry," and "I Found a Love." This last song is one of three classic remakes of tunes he originally did with The Falcons, along with "Let's Kiss and Make Up" and "Take this Love I've Got."

ATLANTIC (JAPAN) 2372 (L)

The Exciting Wilson Pickett

Reissue of Wilson's second LP, Atlantic 8129 from 1965. Land of 1000 Dances/Something You Got/ 634-5789/Barefootin'/Ninety-nine and a Half Won't Do/She's So Good to Me.

ATLANTIC (JAPAN) 2379 (L)

The Wicked Pickett

Reissue of Atlantic 8138 from 1966. Mustang Sally/ Ooh Poo Pah Doo/Knock on Wood/You Left the Water Running.

ATLANTIC (JAPAN) 2380 (L)

The Sound of Wilson Pickett

One of the all-time great soul LPs put together by the brain trust of Jerry Wexler, Rick Hall, and Tom Dowd (originally Atlantic 8145 from 1966). The Muscle Shoals crew really shines on this one, perfectly complementing The Wicked One's almost out-of-control soul style. Includes three big dance hits—"Mustang Sally," "Everybody Needs Somebody to Love," and "Knock on Wood"—plus lots more great soul like the Penn/Oldham penned "Up Tight Good Woman." Essential. New Orleans/She Ain't Gonna Do Right.

MOTOWN 6244 (C)

American Soul Man

The Wicked One's back with a vengeance on his first LP since his mostly ignored stint with EMI America, 1979–1981. What can I say: He looks great, and his voice is as good as it's ever been. The music, unfortunately, is a bit disappointing. As Wilson says in the liner notes: "This album was made in a contemporary and synthesized manner and conducted with a select few." Five programmers are listed, with electronics and sax by Robert A. Martin, and guitar by studio hacks Buzzy Ferten and Gary Myrick. Some of the music is sterile but most is soul deep, and wait till you hear Pickett's scream on the new seven-minute "In the Midnight Hour."

✪ RHINO 70287 (CL)

A Man and a Half

Two-CD set spanning Pickett's entire career. Right from the start, as shown by his sweat-inducing lead on The Falcon's "I Found a Love" (the first cut here), Wilson Pickett pushed soul music to its extremes. His gospel schooling with The Violinaires stamped that explosive voice for all time; listen to the pure revival spirit of "It's Too Late," "I'm Not Tired," "That's a Man's Way," "I Found a True Love," and even the non-LP "Mini-Skirt Minnie." He even rivaled James Brown on "Three Time Loser," "Ninety-nine and a Half Won't Do," and "She's Looking Good." But Wilson was more than just a gospel-bred screamer. When a song demanded subtlety, he was right on the money, especially on "Let Me Be Your Boy," "Jealous Love," "I've Come a Long Way," and "You Keep Me

Hangin' On." Even the vapid "I'm in Love" is rescued by his marvelous delivery.

The second CD contains post-1967 successes like "She Said Yes," "Don't Let the Green Grass Fool You," "Funk Factory," "Don't Knock My Love," "Call My Name, I'll Be There," and the psychedelic funk of "Get Me Back on Time, Engine Number 9." These years also spawned some regrettable cover versions, along with formularized but gritty southern soul, often driven by a ragged, road-weary voice. Occasional cuts do sound unusually harsh, but most of these 44 tracks are clear and punchy. Shortcomings aside, this is still an incredible collection that, like Pickett's best songs, rarely loses touch with his gospel roots. One of the best soul sets ever. In the Midnight Hour/Don't Fight It/634-5789/Land of 1000 Dances/Mustang Sally/ Funky Broadway.

GENE PITNEY

Pitney comes from middle-class Hartford, CT. He started his career in the late '50s as a songwriter for popsters Ricky Nelson, Tommy Edwards, and Roy Orbison. A student of electronics, he produced his own first hit single, "I Wanna Love My Life Away" featuring his voice overdubbed seven times! This recording opened the door to a long association with Musicor records, in pop, rock, and later country styles. Pitney is best remembered for his melodramatic movie themes, including "Town without Pity" and the Bachrach-David composition "The Man Who Shot Liberty Valance." By the late '60s, Pitney was more popular in England than his native US. He briefly retired, re-emerging in 1975 with a comeback LP only to retire again into the shadows of pop history.

COLLECTABLES 5084 (CL)

His Golden Classics

Twelve of Pitney's '60s dramas recorded on 45s for the Musicor label. Stock up on Kleenex and dig these crazy grooves! Town without Pity/Love My Life Away/Every Breath I Take/Mecca/24 Hours from Tulsa/It Hurts to Be in Love/The Man Who Shot Liberty Valance/Only Love Can Break a Heart/Half-Heaven, Half-Heartache/I'm Gonna Be Strong/True Love Never Runs Smooth/She's a Heartbreaker.

INSTANT 5051 (L)

Big Forty

Forty Musicor Records tracks by Gene at a very low price. If you can't imagine living in a town without Pitney, this one is for you. Plenty of hanky soakers, plus some of his later country waxings. Love My Life

Away/Every Breath I Take/Town without Pity/The Man Who Shot Liberty Valance/Mecca/24 Hours from Tulsa/That Girl Belongs to Yesterday/Something's Gotten Hold of My Heart.

RHINO 5896 (C)/75896 (L)
Anthology 1961–1968
Sixteen selections recorded for the Musicor label. Love My Life Away/Town without Pity/The Man Who Shot Liberty Valance/She's a Heartbreaker.

SEE FOR MILES 313 (L)
The EP Collection
Pitney's pop picks, taken from UK Stateside label EPs. Twenty-six dramatic ballads, with his trademark big production, including four songs in Italian! Interesting notes, taken from a recent Pitney interview. Every Breath I Take/Town without Pity/The Man Who Shot Liberty Valance/Mecca/True Love Never Runs Smooth/24 Hours from Tulsa/That Girl Belongs to Yesterday/I'm Gonna Be Strong.

BARBARA PITTMAN
One of the few female singers to record for Sun. She was a featured vocalist with The Snearly Ranch Boys singing country tunes, and made her exciting solo sides in 1956. She made a comeback in the mid-'80s.

BEAR FAMILY 15359 (R)
I Need a Man
Beautiful packaging of Pittman's known Sun recordings in a deluxe gatefold sleeve with great photos and liner notes by Hank Davis. There's some fairly pedestrian outings included, as well as several alternate takes. Nothing here is as rocking as her famed "I Need a Man"; but "I'm Getting Better All the Time" (three great takes, one with Jack Clement accompanying her on acoustic guitar), "Everlasting Love," and "Sentimental Fool" (three takes) rock like crazy with that good ol' Sun rhythm. It's funny how she sounds so amateurish at times, and, at other times, like on "Two Young Fools in Love" and "Handsome Man," she's really great.

THE PLATTERS
Ultra-smooth vocal group that was the most successful black group of the '50s. Led by the gorgeous voice of Tony Williams, The Platters recorded for King subsidiary Federal from 1953–1955, cutting some great sides including the original version of "Only You," but they had no hits. Their manager, Buck Ram, also managed The Penguins who were hot with "Earth Angel."

Mercury wanted The Penguins, but Ram wouldn't let them sign unless Mercury also signed The Platters. They remade "Only You," and the rest, as they say, is history. The group added Zoal Taylor from the girl group The Queens and scored an even bigger hit with "The Great Pretender." They continued to score hits well into the '60s after Williams left in 1961. Over the years, many groups calling themselves The Platters have appeared, though most have no connection with the original group.

INSTANT 5045 (L)
Smoke Gets in Your Eyes
Twenty memory makers. A quick listening reveals that at least some of these are remakes, but they are very similar to the original hits, and probably were recorded around the same time. The Great Pretender/Only You/Harbor Lights/Smoke Gets in Your Eyes/Red Sails in the Sunset/Crying in the Chapel.

KING 651 (RCL)
The Platters
Reissue of Federal 651, containing some of their finest pre-Mercury, gospel-inspired ballads and jumps recorded between 1954–1956 when Paul Robi sang with the group. Includes the fine original version of "Only You" without the whistling background. This is The Platters at their least commercial best.

MERCURY 314 510 314 (CL)
The Magic Touch: An Anthology
The definitive collection of The Platters's Mercury recordings featuring 50 songs on two cassettes or CDs. All their Mercury chart hits plus some B-sides and EP/LP-only cuts are here, plus the previously unissued "Hula Hop," and a rare solo recording by lead singer Tony Williams. The accompanying booklet features detailed annotation, a historical essay, and rare photos.

⊕ MERCURY 314 510 317 (CL)
The Very Best of The Platters
Yet another hits package from The Platters triumphant career with Mercury, featuring 12 of their biggest smashes. The Great Pretender/My Prayer/The Magic Touch/On My Word of Honor/Twilight Time/You'll Never Never Know/Only You/I'm Sorry/Smoke Gets in Your Eyes/If I Didn't Care/Enchanted/Harbor Lights.

RHINO 71495 (C)
Anthology
Twenty-four track, double cassette featuring all their Mercury and Musicor hits from 1955–1967. Only You/Winner Take All/You'll Never Never Know/

One in a Million/My Dream/Twilight Time/Smoke Gets in Your Eyes.

THE PLAYMATES

The Playmates trio hailed from Waterbury, CT, and came together when they were U of CT undergraduates. Donny Conn, Chic Hetti, and Morey Carr cut a slew of mindless pop tunes in the late '50s. Formerly The Nitwits, the group's harmonies resembled a crazed version of The Four Lads.

COLLECTABLES 5418 (CL)

At Play with The Playmates: Golden Classics

The group's most bearable side, "Darling," their first for Roulette, is sadly excluded from this collection. "Jo Ann," their third effort, hit the charts in 1958, followed by the dumb "Beep Beep," for which a multitude of subhumans shelled out good coin. In fairness though, the ballad "Your Love" is pleasing to the ear, as is "Jo Ann." This is a reissue of a long out-of-print Roulette LP, with 12 selections. Good average sound.

DOC POMUS

Jerome "Doc" Pomus (Jerome Felder) is best known as a songwriter. His collaborations with Mort Schuman were recorded by Elvis (who recorded 20 of their songs), The Drifters, Dion, Fabian, and many others. He had an abiding interest in jazz and blues from his youth and started playing saxophone and singing in his early teens. He recorded for a number of small independent labels in the late '40s and early '50s, excellent sides that met with little success. In the mid-'50s he concentrated on his songwriting, initially writing for R&B greats like Joe Turner and Ray Charles. He turned his attention to rock 'n roll and pop when he teamed up with Schuman. The two split in 1965 with Schuman moving to France, and Pomus became relatively inactive. In the late '70s he returned to songwriting and wrote the Grammy winner "There Must Be A Better World Somewhere" for B.B. King. In 1991, Pomus was the first white to receive the Rhythm and Blues Foundation Pioneer award. He died of lung cancer later that year.

WHISKEY, WOMEN AND ... 713 (RL)

It's Great to Be Young and in Love

The Doctor shouts, moans, and hollers 19 blues and jump tunes. Includes some rare live performances from The Musicale Club, NY, recorded in the mid-'50s, and at the Pied Piper Club, NY, from 1947. Both outings feature some fine, unrestrained singing from Pomus backed by cookin' little bands featuring cats like Rex Stewart (cnt), Jimmy Jones (pno), King Curtis (ten sax), and Mickey Baker (gtr)! The sound quality isn't half bad and the performances are wild and exciting. If that isn't enough R&B history for you, several informal demo-like sessions with longtime songwriting partner Mort Shuman (vcl, pno) present fascinating insight into how the dynamic duo's worked up a tune. Can you believe tapes of Pomus and Shuman working on a tune for Dion called "It's Great to Be Young and in Love"? Yep, it's the original version of "Teenager in Love"! Pool Playing Baby/Too Much Boogie/Jelly Jelly/Pomus Blues.

THE PONI-TAILS

Toni Cistone (lead vcl), Karen Topinka (b), and LaVerne Novak (high harmony) were high-school buddies in Lyndhurst, OH when they performed their own composition "Que La Bonenza" for a local music publisher. The group went professional, but Karen's parents didn't approve of her hitting the big time, so she was replaced by Patti McCabe. After a couple of duds, they scored big with 1958's "Born Too Late." After two years of fruitless follow-ups, the group disbanded.

TEENAGER 607 (R)

Born Too Late

If you like their slice-of-Wonderbread title hit, there's enough here to fill you up. Malt shop sentiments abound! It's Just My Luck to Be 15/Close Friends/Come on Joey Dance with Me/Seven Minutes in Heaven.

GROOVY JOE POOVEY

Excellent '50s rockabilly artist from Fort Worth, best known for "Ten Long Fingers."

DEE JAY JAMBOREE 2054 (R)

Yesterday and Today

Eighteen cuts recorded by Poovey from the '50s to the '80s, most with producer Joe Shell. Lots of great rockabilly and rockin' country, including his Dixie classics "Ten Long Fingers," "Careful Baby," and "Move Around" (an alternate take), three demos recorded before he signed with the Dixie label ("Nursery

Rock," "Silence Baby," and "Don't Blame It on Me"), and his 1981 and 1984 reunions with producer Shell ("Baby Let's Rock," "A Cold Margarita," "Boogie Woogie Weekend," "Lost in the Shuffle," and five more). Detailed liner notes by Adam Komorowski and Dick Grant.

SUNJAY 562 (R)
The Two Sides
Early rockabilly and country sides, including his classic "Ten Long Fingers." Move Around/Ole Louella/Jamaica Jill/What Have I Got to Lose?/My Life's Ambition.

BOBBY POWELL

Veteran New Orleans soul/blues singer and keyboard player who recorded for Jewel and Whit from the mid-'60s through the early '70s.

ACE (US) 2047 (L)
Especially for You
An album's worth of pure blues, with Powell at the top of his form. He comes to praise women, not to condemn them, as many a bluesman has done. His version of "The Glory of Love, Pts. 1 and 2" proves it, as do other covers like Ray Charles's "A Fool for You" and Don Gibson's "I Can't Stop Loving You." One of the greatest moments here is Powell's cover of "Lucille," not the B.B. King tune, but the Kenny Rogers hit! Most of the originals were written by producer Senator Jones, including the great "When You Move You Lose," the soulful "Let Me Love You," and the churchy "All My World Is Wrapped Up in You." A powerful singer, Powell resorts to emotionally charged flights of falsetto at the drop of a note, and shares his piano and organ duties with Dr. John. A find!

P-VINE 2156 (L)
In Time
Twenty excellent tracks recorded for the Whit and Jewel labels in the mid-to-late '60s. The material is varied, including scorching soul ballads ("Our Love," "In Time," and "Hold My Hand"), loping R&B rockers ("Straighten Up and Fly Right," "It's Getting Late in the Evening," and "I'm Gonna Leave You"), novelty songs ("That Little Girl of Mine"), and effective versions of Hank Williams's "Your Cheatin' Heart" and The Beatles's "A Hard Day's Night."

JIMMY POWELL

Jimmy Powell was a blue-eyed soul singer from Birmingham, England, who was one of the earliest British R&B singers, having a hit with "Sugar Babe" in 1962. He had a fairly good singing voice, gruff but tender, although he did tend to push things a bit with his mannerisms, usually coming off like one of those hard-rock singers from the '70s. His band, The Five Dimensions, was a crack outfit, although their greatest fame came as the backing group for Millie Small's hit "My Boy Lollipop."

SEE FOR MILES 337 (L)
The R&B Sensation
Twenty-two cuts including R&B covers like "Nine Live Wire" and "Sugar Baby," and rock tunes like the excellent "Out of Time" and the so-so "House of the Rising Sun." Some stuff, like "Hipster" and "Progressive Talking Blues," is pretty good, quirky rock.

JOHNNY POWERS

Legendary Detroit rockabilly star who recorded for Sun and Fortune, and was the first white person signed to Motown.

ROLLER COASTER 2010 (R)
Rock! Rock! Rock!
Nice set of 20 rockers done for Sun, Hi-Q (owned by Fortune), and Fox. Long Blond Hair/With Your Love, with Your Kiss/Seventeen/Be Mine.

ROLLER COASTER 2017 (R)
Can't Resist That Rock and Roll
Twenty more classic cuts from Powers, beginning with Johnny's killer, Australian-only release, "Mama Rock" b/w "Indeed I Do," released in 1958 under the name of Johnny "Scat" Brown; it's some of the most savage rockabilly you'll ever hear. Another 1958 session also yielded some strong material. "Trouble (I'm Evil)" and "Don't Lie To Me" are especially good. His deep, rich voice, sounding a lot like Conway Twitty, served him well on ballads too; "The Rest of My Days Are Lonely Ones" is the best of these. Most amazing of all is Johnny's appearance in the Motown studios in the early '60s cutting demos in a variety of styles, working with producer Andre Williams on "Rosalee" and Marvin Gaye on "It's Now or Never Little One"! Twenty big ones.

SUNJAY 587 (R)
Let It Rock
Powers refuses to hang up his rock-and-roll shoes. This recently recorded album was produced in Sheffield, AL, with a pretty good band. Of course, he had to send the goods to Sweden to get a release because no one but a handful of crackpots (like us) care about rockabilly anymore. Johnny sounds good and proves he can still shake it up. Too bad the guitar is so understated in the production, because guitarist John Willis knocks out some nice licks. I could have done without the sax though; it's not really needed here. Let It Rock/Just

Lovin' You/That's Alright Mama/Please, Please Do/
The Way I Walk/Jailhouse Rock.

ELVIS PRESLEY

Elvis, The King of Rock and Roll. Always was and always will be. There have been many pretenders to the throne through the years, but no one had the complete package like Elvis. He had the looks, the style, the excitement, the management, and, of course, one of the greatest voices in popular music. He didn't invent rock and roll but he certainly put it on the map.

Growing up poor in Tupelo, MS, he was listening to blues and country music at an early age. He moved with his family to Memphis in 1948 and five years later he walked through the doors of Sam Phillips's Sun Studios to record an acetate as a birthday present for his mother. The rest, as they say, is history. He was called back by Phillips in 1954 and with Scotty Moore (gtr) and Bill Black (b), he cut loose on "That's All Right Mama," a rockin' blues originally recorded by Arthur "Big Boy" Crudup. Phillips released it, with a rockin' version of Bill Monroe's bluegrass standard "Blue Moon of Kentucky" on the flip. Sun 209 became a big local hit and, after four more brilliant releases and a series of tumultuous live shows, Phillips sold Elvis's contract to RCA for $35,000. The paltry sum in retrospect sounds like the sale of Manhattan by the Indians, but Elvis was getting too big for a small label and, besides, Sam needed the dough.

Elvis's career took off like a rocket with RCA behind him and, even though a few of his rough rockabilly edges were polished off, he still rocked like no one before. He took on the shrewd, Svengali, Col. Tom Parker, as his manager and the fabulous Jordanaires as backup singers. The hits piled up—"Hound Dog," "Blue Suede Shoes," "Heartbreak Hotel," "Jailhouse Rock," and dozens more. His face peered out from dozens of mags and his "scandalous" TV appearances garnered both praise and scorn. It didn't hurt that he could also sing a ballad with conviction, pulling in millions more who may have been less susceptible to this rocker. And, as if all this weren't enough, Elvis also hit the big screen.

There were no Brandoesque pyrotechnics in his films, but his smoldering presence was a natural for the entertaining vehicles he was offered. *Love Me Tender, Loving You, Jailhouse Rock,* and *King Creole* were all bolstered by some classic rock-and-roll tunes.

But the fame and fortune had to be put on hold in 1958 when he was drafted into the army. His legions of fans counted the days until The King's return like a hostage situation. When he was discharged in 1960, he returned as a more mature force. No longer was he the wild rebel rocker. Hollywood saddled him with a series of fun-but-dumb movies and the Colonel turned him into a lounge act in Las Vegas. However, all was not totally lost; for every bit of campy fluff like "There's No Room to Rhumba in a Sports Car," "Yoga Is as Yoga Does," and "Do the Clam," he could also come up with classics like "Viva Las Vegas," "Suspicious Minds," "Such a Night," and "Burning Love." His 1968 comeback TV special also showed that he could rock with the best of them and, for a few years thereafter, the standard of his recordings improved.

By 1973 his marriage was over, he lost interest in performing, became overweight, and started using a wide range of drugs. Eventually it all took its toll and he died of a heart attack in August 1977.

Elvis's record label RCA has long cashed in on his musical legacy, often shamelessly packaging and re-packaging and re-re-packaging the same material, without bothering to improve sound quality or sometimes even using tacky, artificially enhanced stereo masters. In the last decade, the situation has improved with a number of significant pacakges, usually originating in Europe, and eventually released in the USA. If you can afford it, the magnificent *King of Rock and Roll* box set (RCA 60050) is the way to get his classic '50s recordings. A similar box set covering the '60s is in the works at the time of writing and may be available by the end of 1993.

In order to bring some semblance of sanity to Elvis's available recordings, we have divided them into four sections covering the most significant releases, albums released during his lifetime in chronological order, posthumous releases, and miscellaneous goodies.

Important Releases

🌐 RCA 2023 (CL)
The Million Dollar Quartet
Elvis dropped in on a December 1956 Carl Perkins's session at Sun Studios and created a myth known as The Million Dollar Quartet. The music, performed by Presley, Perkins, Jerry Lee Lewis, and Johnny Cash, is casual, spontaneous, and free. Elvis dominates this mostly country and gospel jam (no surprise), but young Jerry Lee holds his own on nearly every song! This is a touchstone in American music and in the roots of rock and roll, sounds great (especially on CD), and should be in everyone's collection. As an added bonus, you get revelatory liner notes by Sun researcher Colin Escott.

RCA 2227 (RCL)
The Great Performances
This 20-song set was released along with a two-volume video collection, documenting some of the man's finest performances, with mixed results. No offense, but how many different versions of "Heartbreak Hotel" (along with the other usual suspects) does even the most devout fan want in his or her collection? Of prime interest is Elvis's first recording, "My Happiness," made as a $4.00 take-home acetate in the summer of 1953 at Sun Studios (solo, with guitar); it is stunning, a pure vocal/guitar performance containing all the elements that would make him rock's first superstar in less than 36 months. Collectors may also enjoy a true stereo version of "Treat Me Nice" and, finally, an undubbed version of Elvis at the piano, again solo, performing "Unchained Melody" on his final tour in June 1977. This rendition strips to the very soul of the man, and actively refutes tired theories (like those in Albert Goldman's bio) that Elvis could

no longer sing. This one track is worth the cost of the entire release.

RCA 2229 (CL)
Essential Elvis, Vol. 3: Hits Like Never Before
Presley fans can be eternally grateful to RCA UK compilers Ernst Jorgensen and Roger Semon for their efforts in this brilliant retrospective. Like the previous two volumes, the focus is on Presley's 1950's studio work, when the man and the music were equally alive and vibrant. Elvis worked as the de facto producer and session leader on these recordings, and was backed by great musicians like Hank Garland, Chet Atkins, and, of course, Scotty Moore. Alternate takes (and studio chatter), all in superb fidelity, enhance dynamic songs from Presley's 1950's oeuvre like "I Got Stung," "King Creole," and "A Big Hunk o' Love." The highlight of this release is his duet with Kitty White on "Crawfish," the full-length version left officially unreleased until now. Recommended for true rockers only. Twenty-four cuts on CD, 20 on cassette.

RCA 2231 (L)
Elvis Is Back
Elvis's first album after being discharged from the army in March 1960. Though he had mellowed a litle, he was singing with as much fire as ever on this selection of often bluesy songs. Make Me Know It/ The Dirty Dirty Feeling/Soldier Boy/It Feels So Right/ Reconsider Baby.

RCA 3894 (R)/RCA 61021 (CL)
NBC-TV Special
Newly restored, this is the soundtrack to Elvis's comeback TV special (originally issued as RCA 4088 in 1968), his first live performance in ten years, proving that he was still a powerful performer. The program included a series of medleys incorporating his own hits "Heartbreak Hotel," "All Shook Up," "Jailhouse Rock," and "Blue Suede Shoes"; golden oldies like "Lawdy Miss Clawdy," "Little Egypt," "One Night," and "Big Boss Man"; three mini- versions of "Guitar Man" and more Leiber and Stoller tunes; and other rockin' numbers. Lots of bang for the buck here.

RCA 5418 (CL)
Reconsider Baby
Although it's the third LP to feature Elvis singing the blues, this has the long-lost, undubbed Sun version of "Tomorrow Night," with Elvis backed only by syncopated electric guitar and soft string bass—it's almost a cappella, and its great! Also includes a great, previously unissued take of "Ain't that Lovin' You Baby" from 1959, plus Arthur Crudup's "So Glad You're Mine," Billy Emerson's "When It Rains It Really Pours," Chuck Willis's "I Feel So Bad," and seven more bluesy numbers.

RCA 5486 (CL)
Elvis' Christmas Album
Reissue of classic 1957 album (originally RCA 1035), featuring eight Christmas songs and four sacred songs. At the time, some folks objected to the king of pelvis-shaking crooning these holiday faves, and the LP was banned on several radio stations, but still was a Number 1 seller. Digitally remastered in original mono. Santa Claus Is Back in Town/Here Comes Santa Claus/Blue Christmas/Oh Little Town of Bethlehem/Peace in the Valley.

RCA 6221 (CL)
The Memphis Record
The '68 special brought Elvis back into our hearts, but it was *Elvis in Memphis* (originally RCA 4155 from 1969) that brought him back onto our turntables. This collection should have included all 32 Memphis recordings, but we only get 23 of 'em. Includes the entire *Elvis in Memphis* LP; all the hits from the January and February 1969 sessions not on LP, including "In the Ghetto," "Suspicious Minds," "Kentucky Rain," "Don't Cry Daddy," and "Mama Like the Roses"; along with the best of the rest, which were originally on the *Back in Memphis* LP (RCA 4429 from 1970). This unfortunately has the overdubbed strings, horns, and background vocals, but it is still an exceptional set. Stranger in My Own Hometown/Long Black Limousine/Without Love/Who Am I/Any Day Now.

⚙ RCA 6382 (RCL)
Elvis: The Number 1 Hits
Excellent set with all 18 of Elvis's Number 1 hits, 17 from 1956's "Heartbreak Hotel" to 1961's "Good Luck Charm," plus his final Number 1, "Suspicious Minds." Check your collection before buying this one, because all 18 tracks are also on *The Top Ten Hits*. Jailhouse Rock/A Big Hunk o' Love/Teddy Bear/Stuck on You/Hound Dog.

RCA 6383 (CL)
The Top Ten Hits
Every single Elvis placed in the Top 10 of the Billboard singles chart. The remastered sound in the original mono and stereo is incredible, the packaging is complete with chart information and songwriting credits, and the material is indispensable.

⚙ RCA 6414 (CL)
The Complete Sun Sessions
This set is an Elvis lover's dream and is a must for everyone who even pretends to like rock and roll, though the mastering isn't totally satisfactory. These recordings are all on *The King of Rock and Roll* set in better-sounding versions. Includes all issued Sun sides, unissued gems, and alternate takes.

RCA 9589 (CL)
Stereo '57: Essential Elvis, Vol. 2
These two-track stereo tapes cut in three sessions from January 1957 were long thought to have been destroyed. The majority of the takes have never been heard before, even on bootleg, and most of them end with Elvis cracking up! They have breathtaking sound quality; you can hear the individual voices of Elvis and The Jordanaires in harmony like never before! A major revelation is "I Beg of You," initially recorded here but never released (it was re-recorded a few months later). Takes 1, 6, 8, and 12 of this tune reveal a much harder edge than in the version that was released. Also from the January 12 and 13 sessions are "Mean Woman Blues" (the issued take), "Peace in the Valley," and "That's When Your Heartaches Begin." Included from the January 19 session are "It Is No Secret," "Blueberry Hill," "Have I Told You Lately That I Love You," and "Is It So Strange." A CD-only bonus is the inclusion of the other five session tunes recorded only in mono: "I Believe," "All Shook Up," "Got a Lot of Livin' to Do," "Tell Me Why," and "Take My Hand Precious Lord."

RCA 61024 (CL)
The Lost Album
Presley was so busy in the early '60s that the follow-up album to *Pot Luck* (RCA 2523 from 1962) was passed over in the rush, even though his big hit "Devil in Disguise" seemed to prime the pump for a long player. A lot of these tracks, recorded in Nashville in 1963 and 1964, were later plundered for B-sides and soundtrack filler. Elvis sounds great on these 15 tunes, a mixture of ballads and sophisticated rockers backed by The Jordanaires, Scotty Moore, and D.J. Fontana, as well as top sessionmen like Floyd Cramer, Boots Randolph, and Grady Martin. Formerly reissued on RCA (UK) 90513. Devil in Disguise/Witchcraft/Western Union/Blue River/Echoes of Love/Ask Me.

RCA 66050 (CL)
The King of Rock and Roll: Complete '50s Masters
Just when we thought that the "keepers of the books," oops, I mean the "keepers of the flame," couldn't find one more way to re-reissue another compilation by Elvis, they've gone and done it again. The surprising thing is that this time they appear to have done it pretty much right. The general approach to this five-cassette/disc set is rather like Bear Family's, that is, each disc contains over an hour's worth of music with 24 to 31 tracks. The first four discs contain the studio versions of every song that was cut in the '50s, even the relatively obscure cuts that some of us didn't buy originally because they were issued only on LPs with titles like *A Date with Elvis*. "Is It So Strange," a great number, fits into that category. On the other hand, the track order on the first four discs is determined by

recording date, which occasionally produces some mildly jarring juxtapositions. "It Is No Secret (What God Can Do)," for example, is followed in short order by "Blueberry Hill." The Christmas and soundtrack cuts pop up unexpectedly in a sea of studio-cut rock and roll. For completists and hard-core fans, there are various outtakes and previously unreleased versions to pique your interest. The 1953 acetates of "My Happiness" and "That's When Your Heartaches Begin" recorded as gift for his mother are here, as is his Presto acetate of The Clovers's "Fool, Fool, Fool." And the entire fifth disc, subtitled "Rare and Rockin'" is composed of alternate takes, live performances, and soundtrack material. Worthy of comment here are Elvis's clear discomfort during his 1956 performances at Las Vegas's New Frontier Hotel, and the arguably superior versions of "Shake, Rattle and Roll" and "Ain't That Loving You Baby" that surface on this last disc. All in all, a quality job. No mindless repeating of the same song over and over again. Lengthy booklet with solid notes by Pete Guralnick and loads of photos. Fine sound, picture discs, and—saving the best (silliest) for last—a collectible set of Elvis stamps featuring LP and EP covers and various picture sleeves (not to be confused with Uncle Sam's Elvis stamp). Wow! I'll trade you my "All Shook Up" picture sleeve stamp for your "Hound Dog." *Vinyl fans, please note*: RCA (UK) 90689 is the British LP version of this box. It has the same musical selection, and includes eight-by-ten photos, an LP-size book, photo sleeves for each LP, and of course a 12-by-12 box to put it all in.

RCA 6738 (CL)
Essential Elvis: The First Movies
Elvis fans have long known that the music in Elvis's movies contain different versions of tunes than what were released on the soundtrack LPs by RCA at the time. RCA has done a tremendous service by issuing all the music from Elvis's first three movies, the studio and the movie versions. *Love Me Tender* includes the version of the title cut with strings and extra lyrics; *Loving You* has unreleased fast versions of the title tune and unissued versions of "Party" and "Got a Lot of Livin' to Do"; and *Jailhouse Rock* includes the title tune with background vocals and a new alternate take of "Young and Beautiful." The CD adds four tracks, the slow "Loving You" take 1, fast "Loving You" take 8, and the studio versions of "Mean Woman Blues" and "Treat Me Nice."

Reissues of Original Releases

RCA 5198 (CL)
Elvis Presley
Elvis's classic first LP, originally RCA 1254 from 1956. Twelve great songs. Blue Suede Shoes/I Got a Woman/ I Love You Because/Tutti Frutti/I'm Gonna Sit Right Down and Cry/Blue Moon.

RCA 5199 (CL)
Elvis
Reissue of Elvis's classic second LP (RCA 1382 from 1956) with 12 great tracks digitally remastered in mono from the original master tapes. Rip It Up/When My Blue Moon Turns to Gold Again/First in Line/So Glad You're Mine/Ready Teddy/How's the World Treating You.

RCA 1515 (CL)
Loving You
Budget reissue of Elvis's best soundtrack LP originally issued in 1957. The packaging is minimal, with no writers' credits or song timings, the playing time is under a half hour, and the cuts are remastered in electronic "stereo." Still, the music transcends it all. Teddy Bear/Got a Lot of Livin' to Do/Party/Don't Leave Me Now.

RCA 5196 (CL)
Elvis' Golden Records
Fourteen of Elvis's first million sellers, originally released as RCA 1707 in 1958. Hound Dog/All Shook Up/Jailhouse Rock/That's When Your Heartbreak Begins/Love Me Tender/Anyway You Want Me.

RCA 3733 (RCL)
King Creole
Originally issued as RCA 1884 in 1958. Eleven songs (averaging roughly two minutes each), including "King Creole" and "Hard-headed Woman," on this extremely short release with restored mono sound.

RCA 5197 (CL)
Elvis' Golden Records, Vol. 2: 50,000,000 Elvis Fans Can't Be Wrong
More often-repackaged gold, originally issued as RCA 2075 in 1959. I Need Your Love Tonight/Wear My Ring around Your Neck/I Got Stung/A Big Hunk o' Love/A Fool Such as I.

RCA 1990 (CL)
For LP Fans Only
Originally issued in 1959. Ten cuts for cassette and CD fans only, restored to original mono from phony stereo.

RCA 2011 (CL)
A Date with Elvis
RCA gets the prize for squeezing every cent they can out of Elvis's material, AND for bleeding the customer dry by putting out outrageously short CDs like this one, a reissue of a 1959 LP. For your bucks, you get ten songs that range in length from 1:55 to 2:37; and this label has the audacity to put this miserly offering in its "Best Buy" series! Urrgh. Blue Moon of Kentucky/Good Rockin' Tonight/Baby Let's Play House.

RCA 3935 (RCL)

His Hand in Mine

Reissue of 1960 LP, originally RCA 2328, his first all-gospel album, often with a rockin' flavor. Milky White Way/I Believe in the Man in the Sky/Mansion over the Hilltop/Joshua Fit the Battle/I'm Gonna Walk Dem Golden Stairs.

RCA 3735 (CL)

GI Blues

Elvis is back in the Army and onto your CD players! This is the American version of the soundtrack LP (originally RCA 2231 from 1960) with "Tonight Is So Right for Love" instead of the European "Tonight's All Right for Love." Wooden Heart/Blue Suede Shoes/Doin' the Best I Can.

RCA 3683 (RCL)

Blue Hawaii

Elvis's most popular soundtrack LP, originally RCA 2426 from 1961. Fourteen tunes, for 32 big minutes of playing time! Can't Help Falling in Love with You/Rock-a-Hula Baby/Hawaiian Wedding Song/It Eats/Beach Boy Blues.

RCA 2370 (CL)

Something for Everybody

1961 album. There's Always Me/It's a Sin/Starting Today/I'm Coming Home/Put the Blame on Me/I Want You with Me.

RCA 2523 (CL)

Pot Luck with Elvis

1962 album featuring 11 songs from 1961 and 1962 Nashville sessions plus an outtake from *Blue Hawaii.* Kiss Me Quick/Gonna Get Back Home Somehow/Steppin' Out of Line/Something Blue/Suspicion.

RCA 2765 (RCL)

Golden Records, Vol. 3

Originally issued in 1963, featuring 12 hits from the early '60s. It's Now or Never/Fame and Fortune/Surrender/Are You Lonesome Tonight/Little Sister/Anything That's Part of You.

RCA 3450 (R)

Elvis for Everyone!

Reissue of 1965 LP. Twelve tracks drawn from various '50s and early '60s studio recordings including the first appearance on record of the previously unissued Sun recording, "Tomorrow Night." Your Chearin' Heart/Finders Keepers, Losers Weepers/Memphis, Tennessee/Forget Me Never.

RCA 3338 (L)

Girl Happy

The 1965 film soundtrack. Mediocre material from a mediocre film.

RCA 3758 (RCL)

How Great Thou Art

1967 gospel LP. Thirteen songs, mostly from 1966 studio sessions along with a few older recordings. Includes his version of "Crying in the Chapel" which was a big single hit in 1965. In the Garden/Farther Along/Without Him/Where Could I Go but to the Lord/If The Lord Wasn't Walking by My Side.

RCA 1297 (CL)

Elvis' Gold Records, Vol. 4

1968 release with 12 cuts. Love Letters/Witchcraft/You're the Devil in Disguise/A Mess of Blues.

RCA 1456 (CL)

From Elvis in Memphis

Elvis returned to Memphis in 1969 and was in fine form on a lengthy series of sessions. This release (originally RCA 4155 from 1969) features twelve, mostly country cuts. Wearin' That Loved On Look/Long Black Limousine/It Keeps Right On a- Hurtin'/I'm Movin' On/Gentle on My Mind/Any Day Now/In the Ghetto.

RCA 61081 (CL)

Elvis: Back in Memphis

1969 album, originally RCA 4429 from 1970. Inherit the Wind/Stranger in My Own Home Town/And the Grass Won't Pay No Mind/From a Jack to a King.

RCA 4362 (CL)

On Stage, February 1970

Ten-cut live show from the International Hotel in Las Vegas. C.C. Rider/Release Me/Sweet Caroline/Runaway/The Wonder of You/Polk Salad Annie/Yesterday/Proud Mary/Walk a Mile in My Shoes/Let It Be Me.

RCA 4114 (C)

That's the Way It Is

Elvis performs with Walter Cronkite (just kidding!). Originally issued in 1970 as RCA 4405, this featured live recordings included as part of a documentary movie about Elvis. I Just Can't Help Believing/How the Web Was Woven/Mary in the Morning/You've Lost That Lovin' Feeling.

RCA 3892 (CL)

Elvis in Person at
The International Hotel, Las Vegas

1970 album (originally 4428) previously issued as part of the 1969 double album, *From Memphis to Vegas* (RCA 6020). A collection of mostly old favorites along with a couple not previously recorded. Blue Suede Shoes/All Shook Up/Hound Dog/My Babe/ Words/Suspicious Minds.

RCA 4350 (CL)
Love Letters from Elvis
Weak album from 1971. Love Letters/If I Were You/Heart of Rome/This Is Our Dance/I'll Never Know.

CAMDEN 2472 (L)
You'll Never Walk Alone
Reissue of 1971 budget album with nine gospel greats. Let Us Pray/We Call on Him/It's No Secret/Take My Hand, Precious Lord.

RCA 1936 (RCL)
The Wonderful World of Christmas
Originally issued in 1971 (RCA 4579). Elvis sings mostly Christmas favorites. O Come All Ye Faithful/On a Snowy Christmas Night/The Wonderful World of Christmas/I'll Be Home on Christmas Day.

RCA 4776 (CL)
As Recorded at Madison Square Garden
Recorded June 10, 1972; pretty much the usual fare.

CAMDEN 2595 (L)
Burning Love and Hits from His Movies, Vol. 2
Reissue of 1972 budget album. Am I Ready/Guadalajara/No More/We'll Be Together.

RCA 2642 (CL)
Elvis: Aloha from Hawaii
1973 set taken from a TV broadcast, originally issued as a double LP, RCA 6089. Mostly pretty familiar material. C.C. Rider/Something/Steamroller Blues/Love Me/It's Over/I'm So Lonesome I Could Cry/Hound Dog.

RCA 0341 (C)
Legendary Performer, Vol. 1
Originally issued in 1974, this one's a potpourri of the familiar and the obscure from the '50s and '60s, along with some interviews. That's Alright/Heartbreak Hotel/Don't Be Cruel/Trying to Get to You.

RCA 0606 (C)
Recorded Live on Stage
1974 album recorded in Memphis. C.C. Rider/Love Me/Why Me Lord/Help Me.

RCA 3732 (CL)
Pure Gold
1975 album, originally RCA 0971. Another throwaway collection, featuring ten fine songs that have been issued many times before. Kentucky Rain/It's Impossible/Don't Be Cruel/All Shook Up/In the Ghetto.

RCA 1039 (CL)
Today
Originally issued in 1975, these are his last official studio recordings; later recordings were done at Graceland or live. Though Elvis was not in good shape, he does a decent job on rockers like "Trouble" and ballads like "Pieces of My Life."

RCA 0873 (RC)
Promised Land
1974 album. Help Me/Love Song of the Year/Your Love's Been a Long Time Coming/Thinking About You.

RCA 1506 (CL)
From Elvis Presley Boulevard
A 1976 LP recorded at Graceland, including a fine version of the old Timi Yuro hit "Hurt" that was a modest hit as a single. Blue Eyes Crying in the Rain/The Last Farewell/Bitter They Are, Harder They Fall.

RCA 2274 (RCL)
Welcome to My World
Originally issued in 1977. A compilation of mostly country material from various '70s sessions. Welcome to My World/Release Me/For the Good Times/Gentle on My Mind/Your Cheatin' Heart.

RCA 2428 (CL)
Moody Blue
Originally issued in 1977. This was the last album released in Elvis's lifetime and featured some of his final recordings made at Graceland filled out with heavily overdubbed live recordings from April 1977. Includes both sides of the "Way Down"/"Pledging My Love" single that gave Elvis his last Top 20 hit.

Posthumous Releases

RCA 2587 (CL)
Elvis in Concert
Double cassette (single CD) of the last live recordings of Elvis made for a CBS-TV show two months before his death. He was in pretty bad shape and these recordings, rushed onto the market immediately after his death, do not serve him well.

RCA 2772 (C)
He Walks beside Me
Originally issued in 1978. Twelve gospel songs mostly recycled from previous gospel albums. He Is My Everything/Where Did They Go Lord/An Evening Prayer/If I Can Dream.

RCA 3026 (CL)
Sings Leiber and Stoller
Aside from one unreleased cut, a duet with Ann-Margret from the film *Viva Las Vegas*, this is just

another rehash of some familiar Leiber and Stoller classics and less auspicious soundtrack stuff from the '60s. For my money, Leiber and Stoller tunes like "Girls Girls Girls," "Bossa Nova Baby," and "Little Egypt" were done best by The Coasters and The Clovers, but you might get a kick out of these versions. Twenty-one cuts on CD, 15 on cassette. Hound Dog/Love Me Tender/Jailhouse Rock/Treat Me Nice/Baby I Don't Care/King Creole/Trouble.

RCA 3114 (CL)
Collector's Gold
The first thing any fan can appreciate about this triple CD/cassette release is that it thankfully omits the usual dozen cuts found on most reissues. The songs, mostly all unreleased takes or cuts, cover his 1960s Nashville, Hollywood, and Las Vegas recordings, with varying results. Hot rockers are contrasted with lousy songs like "What a Wonderful Life," "So Close Yet So Far," and "Gently." The truth is that El's '60s recordings had great vocals and tough backup musicians but often suffered from poor material. However, if you're someone who already has completed your essential Presley purchases but wants more, this set will certainly curl your upper lip!

RCA 4031 (C)
This Is Elvis
Originally issued in 1981. Selections from the motion-picture soundtrack about his life, with several unreleased songs and interviews. Includes selections from the Dorsey, Milton Berle, and Ed Sullivan TV shows.

RCA 4395 (CL)
Memories of Christmas
1982 release, mostly drawn from previous Christmas albums. RCA doesn't believe in being too generous, so there is a grand total of eight songs on this disc! O Come, All Ye Faithful/I'll Be Home on Christmas Day/Santa Claus Is Back in Town/If Every Day Was Christmas.

RCA 4941 (CL)
Gold Records, Vol. 5
A great album if you have nothing since Vol. 4 (released in 1968), otherwise, a total ripoff. A good selection, but only ten songs, and some of them have already been released on two or more LPs. Burning Love/In the Ghetto/Suspicious Minds.

RCA 5182 (CL)
Rocker
Twelve classic rockers from 1956–1957 digitally remastered from the original, mono master tapes. Jailhouse Rock/Tutti Frutti/I Got a Woman/Ready Teddy/Shake, Rattle and Roll/Baby I Don't Care.

RCA 5353 (CL)
A Valentine Gift for You
Originally released to celebrate Elvis's 50th birthday, the LP was pressed on red vinyl (!). Fifteen love songs, including the first US LP appearance of the 1957 B-side "Tell Me Why," a few obscurities ("Give Me the Right" and "I Need Someone to Lean On"), and the millionth reissue of "Are You Lonesome Tonight" and "Can't Help Falling in Love."

RCA 5430 (CL)
Always on My Mind
Thirteen songs about breakups which, when it first appeared on LP, was pressed on purple vinyl. Separate Ways/Don't Cry Daddy/Hurt.

RCA 6985 (CL)
The Alternate Aloha
On January 14, 1973 Elvis performed live worldwide via satellite; the show and consequent double LP were called *Aloha from Hawaii* (released as RCA 6089 in 1973). As has been known for some time, RCA taped a complete dress rehearsal two days earlier, in case anything happened to prevent the live telecast. That show, only slightly shorter than the broadcast, is featured here in its entirety (minus "Hound Dog"). This collection includes the version of "Steamroller Blues" previously available only on *Greatest Hits Vol. 1*, "Burning Love," "You Gave Me a Mountain," "Fever" (from *Leaving It Up to You*), and 14 other performances never before available legitimately. The album closes with a studio version of "Blue Hawaii" that has appeared a few other places. It's Over/American Trilogy/Big Hunk o' Love.

RCA 9586 (CL)
Known Only to Him:
Elvis Gospel 1957–1971
Fourteen songs. Peace in the Valley/I'm Gonna Walk Dem Golden Stairs/Joshua Fit the Battle/Stand By Me/Where Could I Go but to the Lord/We Call on Him/Lead Me, Guide Me.

RCA 9800 (CL)
Blue Christmas

RCA 9801 (CL)
Christmas Classics

RCA (UK) 90642 (RL)
From the Heart
The cover says these 24 love songs (19 on LP) have been digitally remastered, for what that's worth. Lots of favorites here in a pretty, cool-looking color jacket, so snap it up collectors. Good Luck Charm/Suspicious Minds/Love Me Tender/Loving You/It's Now or Never/The Wonder of You.

Other Issues

MAGNUM FORCE 074 (L)

The '50s Interviews

Ten interviews from 1955–1956, compiled chronologically by Nigel Molden, featuring detailed liner notes by astute *Now Dig This* beat reporter Gordon Minto. When it comes to interviews, Elvis is no John Lennon, but anyone interested in a glimpse of what it's like to go from dirt-poor poverty to worldwide fame at 21 will be fascinated by this release. Includes a visit to local television station KLAC-TV and host Wink Martindale (!) that I've never heard before.

REDWOOD 1 (L)

The Elvis Tapes

JIMMY PRESTON

Dynamic vocalist/alto saxman and leader of The Prestones. Preston's 1949 platter "Rock the Joint" is often referred to as the first "rock-and-roll beat" record. "Joint" predates Jackie Brenston's groundbreaking "Rocket 88" by two years, and became a hit when covered by Bill Haley a few years later. Preston's mix of jump and blues never saw much chart action, but is notable for the presence of solid sidemen like tenor saxophonist Benny Golson and guitarist Bill Jennings.

FLYRIGHT 33 (L)

1948–1950

Twenty rockin' postwar tracks, culled from Krazy Kat 806 and 827.

KRAZY KAT 827 (R)

Vol. 2: Rock the Joint

Includes Preston's big hit and "Hucklebuck Daddy," later the basis for The Five Keys's "Hucklebuck with Jimmy." This album also features three never-released alternate takes from 1950 with future jazz star Benny Golson on tenor: "Let's Hang Out Tonight" (with Tiny Grimes) and two takes of "They Call Me the Champ."

JOHNNY PRESTON

Preston was a protege of J.P. "Big Bopper" Richardson. His number-one hit, "Running Bear" from 1959, was penned by The Bopper and includes his background vocals; The Bopper's death helped propel it into smash-hit status on both sides of the Atlantic. After hitting it big, Preston had some lesser hits for Mercury such as "Cradle of Love," "Feel So Fine," and "Leave My Kitten Alone" (later covered by The Beatles).

BEAR FAMILY 15473 (L)

Running Bear

All the Johnny Preston you could want on one CD. Charming Billy/Chief Heartbreak/That's All I Want/Leave My Kitten Alone/I Want a Rock and Roll Guitar/Do What You Did.

THE PRETTY THINGS

High-powered British R&B band formed in 1963 by Dick Taylor, original bassist for The Rolling Stones. Led by vocalist Phil May, the band started off as a wilder version of The Stones, taking their name from the Bo Diddley song. In the mid-'60s, they went psychedelic, releasing the first rock opera, *S.F. Sorrow* in 1968, influencing The Who's *Tommy*. With personnel changes, they became an excellent hard-rock band in the '70s, recording for Led Zeppelin's Swan Song label before finally disbanding in 1977. They reformed in 1984, returning to their roots in R&B.

SEE FOR MILES 103 (RL)

The Pretty Things: 1967–1971

Reissue of *The Pretty Things' Singles As and Bs* (EMI Harvest [UK] 2022 from 1976), consisting of both sides of their three 1967–1968 Columbia singles and three 1970–1971 Harvest singles. Some are re-recordings of tracks from their opera *S.F. Sorrow* ("Private Sorrow") or from their Harvest LP *Parachute* ("The Good Mr. Square"), and others were never issued on LP ("Defecting Grey," "Mr. Evasion," "Circus Mind," and "Blue Serge Blues"). A fine collection.

JESSE PRICE

Memphis-born drummer Jesse Price had an impressive pedigree. He began his career touring the US with legendary blues songwriter/bandleader W.C. Handy. The tour ended in Kansas City, where he joined Count Basie's band as its first drummer, but he quit before the orchestra moved to New York. He led an orchestra with Buster Smith featuring 17-year-old Charlie Parker, was with Harlan Leonard and The Rockets, and joined Chick Webb's band when Chick died, touring with Ella Fitzgerald. Eventually, he moved to LA, and even recorded with Stan Kenton!

JUKEBOX LIL 620 (R)

Jump It with a Shuffle

Seventeen tunes from 1946–1948 Capitol recordings with small all-star combos, with Jesse on drums and/

or vocals on a fine mixture of blues, R&B, and Kansas City Jazz. Includes his big hit, "I Ain't Mad at You," later covered by Count Basie. Musicians include Snooky Young, Buddy Tate, Red Nichols, Dexter Gordon, and Red Norvo. Nagasaki/Big Town Blues/Kansas City Mama.

LLOYD PRICE

Excellent New Orleans R&B singer. Price began his career by writing radio jingles, one of which featured Fats Domino on piano. When Specialty Records heard it in 1952, they transformed it into the hit "Lawdy Miss Clawdy." Price stayed with Specialty until he was drafted in 1953. When he was discharged in 1956, he began his own record label KRC; he scored a local hit with "Just Because" which was leased to ABC-Paramount. He later signed with ABC in 1958, and had a long string of pop hits including "Stagger Lee," "Personality," and "I'm Going to Get Married." He started another label in 1962, Double L, signing The Falcons's lead singer Wilson Pickett to a solo contract.

MCA 1503 (CL)
Lloyd Price
Ten late '50s hits from ABC/Paramount. Stagger Lee/ Lawdy Miss Clawdy/Personality/Just Because.

SPECIALTY 2105 (RCL)
Lloyd Price
Fourteen great Specialty sides, recorded in the early '50s and originally issued on LP in 1959, including the original recordings of many of his biggest hits. Lawdy Miss Clawdy/Mailman Blues/I Wish Your Picture Was You/Chee-Koo Baby.

SPECIALTY 2156 (RC)
Personality Plus
Besides alternate takes of "Carry Me Home" and the immortal "Lawdy Miss Clawdy," this has eight never-before-issued tunes, including such great tunes as "Mailman Boogie," "Woe Ho Ho," "Oh Love," and "Lloyd's Lament (Old Echo Song)." And just to be nice, Specialty has leased Lloyd's three biggest ABC hits for this package: "Personality," "Stagger Lee," and "Where Were You (on Our Wedding Day)." Excellent sound quality and lots of studio chat.

SPECIALTY 2163 (RC)
Walkin' the Track
More unreleased and alternate sides from the Specialty sessions cut between 1952–1953 at the famous J&M studios in New Orleans. Includes the rollicking "Barnyard Rock" from a 1952 demo tape, the bootin' "Frog

Legs" issued in 1953, "If Crying Was Murder," a low-down blues, a powerful alternate version of "Forgive Me Clawdy," plus ten other hard-driving, slow-burning rockers. No duplication with Specialty 2156. Highly recommended.

🄲 SPECIALTY 7010 (CL)
Lawdy!
Twenty-five stompin', wailing sides, backed by J&M Studio's Crescent City sessions royalty Dave Bartholomew (tpt), Herb Hardesty (ten sax), Fats Domino (pno), Ernest McLean (gtr), Frank Fields (b), and Earl Palmer (dms). CD release contains nine bonus cuts, eight of which appear on LPs 5007 (UK), 2156, and 2163. Solid, unadulterated R&B. Lawdy Miss Clawdy/Mailman Blues/So Long/Operator/ Laurelle/What's the Matter Now/If Crying Was Murder/Walkin' the Track/Carry Me Home.

LOUIS PRIMA

Wild Italian bandleader from New Orleans, best-known for his Vegas lounge act and novelty songs. Though he began his career as a hot jazz trumpeter in the '20s, and worked as an adult pop performer, his wildness and his excellent backup band, The Witnesses led by tenor saxman Sam Butera, earned him credit as one of the founders of rock and roll. He is also an excellent songwriter, known for the medley of "Just a Gigolo"-"I Ain't Got Nobody" (covered by David Lee Roth for the younger generation), plus the rock standard "A Sunday Kind of Love." The first collection of his original hits was reissued by Rhino, but is sadly out-of-print; many of these tracks are duplicated on the Capitol and Charly reissues.

CAPITOL 94072 (CL)
Collector's Series
Primo Prima, featuring 26 finger-poppin' picks. Many Keely Smith vocals are featured ("The Lip"-"Baby, Won't You Please Come Home"-"Embraceable You" medley, "That Old Black Magic," "Hey Boy! Hey Girl!," and "I've Got You under My Skin"), plus unreleased versions of "The Music Goes 'Round and 'Round," "Lazy River," and "Sing, Sing, Sing." Just a Gigolo/Buona Sera/Jump, Jive, and Wail/Zooma Zooma.

CHARLY 252 (L)
Jump, Jive, and Wail
Louis is at his wildest on these 16 Capitol recordings taken from 1956–1958, including four extended medleys, the most famous, of course, being "Just a Gigolo"-

"I Ain't Got Nobody." Also includes the self- penned "Angelina" and "Zooma Zooma." If you've already got the Rhino or Capitol compilations, there'll be some duplication, however. Fee Fie Foo/Gotta See Baby Tonight/Oh! Marie/I've Got the World on a String/ Buona Sera.

JAZZ BAND 406 (R)
Plays Pretty for the People
Two exuberant 25-minute radio broadcasts from the Hotel Sahara in Las Vegas from mid-1963 and New Year's Eve 1964. Wife Number 4 Keely Smith is gone, replaced by future wife Number 5 Gia Mione on vocals. Great backing is provided by The Witnesses boasting the big-sax sound of Sam Butera. Everybody gets a chance to stretch out, with some particularly fine blowing by Butera on "Night Train" and "Georgia on My Mind." Robin Hood/Oh! Marie/Sing, Sing, Sing/Up Jumped the Rabbit.

THE PRISONAIRES
Excellent group composed of inmates from the Nashville, TN, state penitentiary. Led by Johnny Bragg, they recorded the original version of "Just Walkin' in the Rain" for Sun at a session surrounded by prison guards! (The song later sold millions for Johnny Ray.) They were modeled on The Inkspots, singing some of the most heart-rending songs ever recorded like "A Prisoner's Prayer" and "No More Tears," as well as more upbeat material. They also showed a lot of promise with the emerging rock-and-roll/R&B style on tunes like "That Chick's Too Young to Fry," "Lucille, I Want You," and "Rockin' Horse." When they were released from the big house, most of the band's members became The Marigolds, who had a big hit on Excello with "Rollin' Stone," covered by The Jacks. Bragg later returned to prison because of a parole violation.

BEAR FAMILY 15523 (L)
Just Walkin' in the Rain
Twenty-six tunes comprised of every song The Prisonaires recorded for Sun Records from 1953–1955. A sharp, 28-page booklet with discography and many photos make this the definitive package of Prisonaires recordings. Wonderful.

P.J. PROBY
In the early '60s, Texan James Marcus Smith moved to England and became the blue-eyed rock/soulster P.J. Proby of ponytail and split pants fame. He had several UK hits, but his only stateside record to hit the charts was "Nikki Hoeky."

SEE FOR MILES 82 (RL)
P.J. Proby at His Very Best, Vol. 2
Volume 1 of this series (SFM 72, now unavailable) had all the wimpy ballads, and this one's got the hard stuff. Most of the material comes from three LPs: I Am P.J. Proby (Liberty 1235 from 1964); Enigma (Liberty 1361 from 1967); and Phenomenon (Liberty 83045, also from '67). Also features non-LP 45 and EP sides, including his first big hit "Hold Me" and his US hit "Nikki Hoeky," backed by writers Pat and Lolly Vegas of Redbone fame. Rockin' Pneumonia and the Boogie Woogie Flu/Don't Worry Baby/I'll Go Crazy/Pretty Girls Everywhere.

WHITEY PULLEN
Dwight Pullen (aka Whitey), who in photos looks about as wild as Pat Boone's tamer cousin, recorded rockabilly and country songs between 1959 and 1964 on a variety of labels. His best-known number, "Sunglasses after Dark," sounds a little like "Blue Suede Shoes" and sports a dangerous guitar break. "Sunglasses" was credited to him, as was the equally great "Teenage Bug."

REVIVAL 3014 (R)
Whitey Pullen
Wild rockabilly and straight country tunes, all in the original mono. The country numbers aren't bad, but sound a bit bloodless next to the hot rockin' numbers. Moonshine Liquor/Let's All Go Wild/Walk My Way/ Everybody's Rockin'/Drinkin' Wine Spo-Dee-O-Dee/ Tuscaloosa Lucy.

?QUESTION MARK and THE MYSTERIANS
ROIR A 137 (C)
The Dallas Reunion Tapes '84: 96 Tears Forever!
The Tex-Mex punk sound of Rudy (?) Martinez lives on, courtesy of this excellent reunion concert from the Arcadia Theater in Dallas. Features the original quintet with Frank Rodriquez on Vox organ (or is it Farfisa?) and Bobby Balderama, now with Joe "King" Carasco Y Los Coronas, on lead guitar. All 14 tunes are originals or were originally recorded by The Mysterians, and all their hits (and you thought they just had one) are included. Performances and sound quality are excellent; Dave Marsh and Question Mark wrote the

informative liner notes. Smokes/Can't Get Enough of You Baby/Girl (You Captivate Me)/Do Something to Me/96 Tears.

THE QUOTATIONS

Yet another white, doo-wop revival quartet from Brooklyn that recorded for Verve in 1961–1962. Members were Larry Kassman (lead), Richie Schwartz (1st ten), Lew Arno (2nd ten), and Harvey Hershkowitz (bar).

CRYSTAL BALL 134 (R)

Time Was: 1959–1963

This set spans the group's entire four-year existence. Features covers, standards, and pop-oriented tunes of minor significance, plus a German cover of the dreadful pop-dirge "Imagination" sung by an unnamed female soloist. For those who like it light and white.

TEDDY RANDAZZO

Teen popster best-known for composing "Going Out of My Head." He recorded from the late '50s through the mid-'60s for ABC-Paramount, Colpix, MGM, and Vik.

DOMINO 1003 (R)

We're Gonna Rock Tonight

Sixteen sides, including the hits "Little Serenade" (1958), "The Way of a Clown" (1960), and "Big Wide World" (1963). Twistin' to the Locomotion/Bo Diddley/Teenage Senorita/Next Stop Paradise.

BOOTS RANDOLPH

Nashville's most popular saxophonist, famous for "Yakety Sax."

BEAR FAMILY 15459 (L)

Yakety Sax

Twenty-six tracks recorded for RCA between 1958–1960, mostly instrumentals along with a couple of dispensable vocals. Sidemen include Hank Garland, Floyd Cramer, Bob Moore, and Grady Martin. Excellent sound, detailed notes by Rich Kienzle, and full discographical information. Percolator/Hey Elvis/I'm Getting the Message Baby/Big Daddy/Greenback Dollar/Red Light/Temptation.

THE (YOUNG) RASCALS

Excellent New York rock band who recorded their best material for Atlantic in the mid-to-late '60s. With two talented lead singers, Eddie Brigati and Felix Cavaliere, they first scored with

their blue-eyed soul versions of Wilson Pickett's "Mustang Sally" and 1965's "Good Lovin'" (originally recorded by The Olympics). By 1967, they were writing their own material, and had hits in a softer vein with "Groovin'" and "How Can I Be Sure." By the end of the decade, they were performing hippie anthems, scoring hits with "A Ray of Hope" and "People Got to Be Free." In the '70s, they regrouped and became a jazz band, recording for Columbia with guest artists like Alice Coltrane!

RAVEN 1015 (R)

Rascals in Retrospect

The definitive Rascals collection, including 20 tunes recorded for Atlantic 1966–1970, compiled by Glenn A. Baker. Nothing particularly special or rare here, but, because their only hits package came out in 1968, this is the only hits LP with their 1969 and 1970 hits. Side 1 has the gritty, blue- eyed soul of their early greats including "Good Lovin'," "Come on Up," "You Better Run," and my two favorites, "Baby Let's Wait" and "I Ain't Gonna Eat Out My Heart Any More," both written by Pam Sawyer and Lori Burton. Side 2 features the "mature" Rascals sound of "Groovin'," "How Can I Be Sure," and "People Gotta Be Free."

JAMES RAY

New York-based singer who had a couple of hits for Caprice in the early '60s.

COLLECTABLES 5199 (CL)

Golden Classics

Twelve cuts. Itty Bitty Pieces/The Old Man and the Mule/Lazy Bones/St. James Infirmary.

JOHNNY RAY

Before Elvis Presley, there was Johnny Ray: a young white singer strongly influenced by black blues and R&B who performed his material in an emotional and uninhibited manner. Although producer Mitch Miller sanitized Ray's music for an early '50s pop audience with orchestras and choruses, the basic power of Ray's singing still shines through on his recordings, including the mega-hits, "Cry" and "Just Walkin' in the Rain." In fact, "Cry" was the first recording by a white artist to top both the pop and R&B charts. It's futile but interesting to speculate what would have happened if Johnny's recordings had been produced by Sam Phillips rather than Mitch Miller! Johnny died in 1991, and remains a pioneering performer whose importance deserves re-evaluation.

BEAR FAMILY 15450 (L)

Cry

A fine cross section of Ray's recordings for Okeh and Columbia between 1951–1960 though, unlike some Bear Family productions, it is not quite the definitive collection it could have been. His important first recording "Whiskey and Gin" and early hits such as "Please Mr. Sun," "Walkin' My Baby Back Home," and "All of Me" are curiously absent. We do, however, get both sides of his monster first hit "Cry" b/w "The Little White Cloud That Cried" which also went to Number 1 on the R&B charts. Included are his provocative (for the time) hit "Such a Night," some fine versions of blues and R&B songs—"Flip, Flop, and Fly," "Just Walkin' in the Rain" (his biggest hit), "How Long, How Long Blues," and "Endlessly"—along with pop standards, country songs, duets with Frankie Laine and Doris Day, and even a version of Sister Rosetta Tharpes's "Up above My Head." Sound quality is, of course, superb, and there is a 24-page booklet with biographical information (much of it based on an interview with Johnny), photos, and discography of all the tracks on the disc. This is not really rock and roll, but with stripped-down production it most certainly would be.

BEAR FAMILY 15666 (L)

Live at The London Palladium

While today's fans of rock and roll will likely find Ray to be timid and tame, audiences like the one at The London Palladium on April 5, 1954 thought he was a wild man. This 32-minute CD reissue of the original British Philips LP includes the hits "Walkin' My Baby Back Home," "Glad Rag Doll," "I'm Gonna Walk and Talk with My Lord," "With These Hands," "Cry," "A Hundred Years from Today," and five others. The 20-page booklet is filled with vintage photos and contemporary *New Musical Express* articles.

THE REBEL ROUSERS

WHITE LABEL 8963 (R)

Rock from Missouri, Vol. 1

I guess just about every state in the '50s had a band called The Rebel Rousers but no one had a Rebel Rousers this hot. Derek "Bebop" Dickinson (Untamed Youth guitarist and *Show Me Blowout* fanzine publisher) tracked down Rebel Rousers's guitarist Jackie Lee Blount a few years back and got a lot of folks excited by his tales of tons of way-cool acetates. Well, here 'tis and it's fabulous stuff. The seven instrumentals rock like crazy with some very sophisticated arrangements for the era. They don't use a sax on these 1959 Jan Records recordings, just their blazin' guitars. The other eight tunes are covers of rock- and-roll standards with mucho hot guitar. If you like 'em crude and rude, this one will flat git it. Fat Man's Walk/Guitar Boogie Rumble/Night Train Stomp/Bo Diddley/Leroy.

OTIS REDDING

Perhaps the most popular and respected soul singer of all time. From Macon, Otis started out imitating another Georgia peach, Little Richard, on an excellent 1962 flop, "Shout Bama Lama." He later became Johnny Jenkins's band's chauffeur and, at the end of one of their sessions, asked if he could record a song. It was the classic "These Arms of Mine," which established Otis as a master ballad singer. Stax even started a subsidiary label, Volt, just for Otis's releases. He hooked up with Steve Cropper from the MGs and wrote a score of soul classics including "Mr. Pitiful," which also showed him to be a master of the fast stuff, "Respect" (later covered by Aretha), "I've Been Loving You Too Long," and "Can't Turn Ya Loose." He also had a good ear for covers, waxing standards ("Try a Little Tenderness"), white rock ("Satisfaction"), and lots of Sam Cooke; he's probably the only artist who could cover James Brown and beat him (check out his version of "Papa's Got a Brand New Bag" on *In Person at the Whiskey au Go-Go*, reissued by Rhino). Just when he was starting to break into the white market, beginning with his now-legendary performance at the Monterey Pop Festival in 1967, he was killed in a plane crash that also killed most of The Bar-Kays. His then-current single "Dock of the Bay" subsequently became his only Number 1 record and remains popular today (lately covered moan for moan by whitebread teen star Michael Bolton).

Atlantic's *Otis Redding Story* is probably the best place to begin, although almost everything he recorded is worth hearing. Most of his '60s LPs have been reissued in their original formats.

ATCO 33261 (C)
The History of Otis Redding
Reissue of his first greatest hits package, Volt 418 from 1967, featuring 12 of his classic sides in "reprocessed" stereo. Respect/Pain in My Heart/Mr. Pitiful/I've Been Loving You Too Long/Try a Little Tenderness.

ATCO 80253 (CL)
Pain in My Heart
Reissue of Atco 161 from 1965, a total of 12 songs including Otis's first hit singles, the deep-soul senders "These Arms of Mine" and the title cut, along with an eclectic assortment of early '60s sides. The cover versions are a "hit-or-miss" proposition: Little Richard's "Lucille," Sam Cooke's "You Send Me," plus "The Dog," "Louie Louie," and "Stand by Me," but fortunately the set is rounded out by Redding's sharp originals "Security," "Something Is Worrying Me," and "Hey Hey Baby." With session notes and original liner information.

ATCO 80254 (CL)
The Dock of the Bay
Another fine reissue in the Atlantic Re-Masters Series, this album was originally released in February 1968, two months after Redding's death at age 26. Ironically, it contains the country-flavored song that became his biggest hit, "(Sittin' on) The Dock of the Bay," the song that brought him the attention and respect from the American public he deserved, albeit posthumously. (He made the R&B charts no fewer than ten times after his death!) The album collects various singles from 1965–1967, including the great ballad "I Love You More Than Words Can Say," and the best thing he recorded with Carla Thomas, "Tramp." Other great moments include the then unreleased Redding-penned "Open the Door," the rocking "Don't Mess with Cupid," the soulful "The Glory of Love," and absolutely everything else on the album. Did Otis ever make a bad record? I don't think so. If you don't have this music, you gotta-gotta-gotta get it.

ATCO 80270 (CL)
The Immortal Otis Redding
Reproduction of Atco 252, released in June 1968, and drawn from many of the same sessions represented on Redding's other posthumous LPs, *The Dock of the Bay* and *Love Man*. Otis was looking to extend his range on these 1967 sessions, on hits like "I've Got Dreams

to Remember," "Hard to Handle," "Amen," and "The Happy Song." On less-known songs like "Nobody's Fault but Mine" and "Champagne Wine," he was pushing his form by incorporating rock and pop elements into the mix. These 11 selections suggest a performer and writer about to come up with something new and unprecedented. And how can you argue with an Otis Redding record produced by Steve Cropper? Highly recommended.

ATCO 80318 (CL)
Otis Blue: Otis Redding Sings Soul
Reissue of Otis's second LP, Volt 412, featuring 11 wonderful, mostly up-tempo tunes from 1965. Includes only three Redding originals, all hits: "Respect," "Old Man Trouble," and "I've Been Loving You Too Long" (cowritten with Jerry Butler). Covers include the obligatory Sam Cooke tunes "Shake," "Wonderful World," and "Change Is Gonna Come"; his hit cover of "Satisfaction"; and such greats as "You Don't Miss Your Water," Solomon Burke's "Down in the Valley," and even "Rock Me Baby."

ATCO 90395 (CL)
Live in Europe
Reissue of Volt 416 from 1967, featuring ten of Otis's biggest hits recorded live. A classic soul show. Can't Turn You Loose/I've Been Loving You Too Long/These Arms of Mine/Shake/Satisfaction/Sad Song/Try a Little Tenderness.

ATCO 91705 (CL)
The Soul Album
This isn't Otis's best album by any means, but there are still some wonderful tunes here like the soulful ballad "Cigarettes and Coffee" and the frantic "634-5789." Otis relies too heavily on recognizable cover versions like Smokey Robinson's "It's Growing" and Sam Cooke's "Chain Gang," but maybe, like me, you'll dig some of them just the same. Scratch My Back/Treat Her Right/Good to Me/Any Old Way.

ATCO 91706 (CL)
The Great Otis Redding Sings
Soul Ballads
Reissue of Volt 411 from 1965, Otis's first. It's full of incredible ballads, both original ("Chained and Bound," "Come to Me," and "Your One and Only Man") and covers (O.V. Wright's "That's How Strong My Love Is," Sam Cooke's "Nothing Can Change This Love," Chuck Willis's "It's Too Late," and The Impressions' "For Your Precious Love"). Interestingly enough, the only up-tempo song here, "Mr. Pitiful," gave Otis his first pop hit.

ATCO 91707 (CL)

Complete and Unbelievable: The Dictionary of Soul

Another great reissue, with Otis in his red and white suit and red mortarboard on the cover! Fa-Fa-Fa-Fa-Fa-Fa (Sad Song)/My Lover's Prayer/Try a Little Tenderness/I'm Sick Y'all/Hawg for You/Sweet Lorene/She Put the Hurt on Me/Tennessee Waltz/Day Tripper.

ATLANTIC 81762 (CL)

The Otis Redding Story

Originally packaged as a beautiful four-LP box set, this set is now available on two double cassettes or CDs with 60 classic tunes. Though not perfect (we still don't get the entirely different single versions of "I've Been Loving You Too Long," "Respect," or "Old Man Trouble"), this sampler is excellent in all ways. Included are the never-before-issued "You Left the Water Running" done as a demo for Wilson Pickett with Otis accompanying himself on acoustic guitar, and the incredibly rare "Stay in School" from the Stax promo LP of the same name. The single "Merry Christmas Baby" b/w "White Christmas" from the *Soul Christmas* LP is featured along with a few non-LP B-sides like "Mary's Little Lamb." The remaining tunes contain huge portions of *Soul Ballads, Otis Blues, The Soul Album, Dictionary of Soul, King and Queen,* and *Immortal,* along with representative tunes from his other LPs. Includes a fact-packed eight-page booklet by Rob Bowman. Highly recommended.

ATLANTIC (JAPAN) 40 (L)

Great Soul Ballads

Seventeen soulful ballads. These Arms of Mine/Chained and Bound/Keep Your Arms around Me/For Your Precious Love/Pain in My Heart/Old Man Trouble/My Lover's Prayer/(I've Got) Dreams to Remember/Think About It.

ATLANTIC (JAPAN) 64 (L)

Groovin' Time

Complementing Atlantic (Japan) 40, this one features the upbeat groovin' side of Otis. Respect/Security/Mr. Pitiful/My Girl/I Can't Turn You Loose/I'm Coming Home/You Left the Water Running/Groovin' Time/The Happy Song.

RHINO 70294 (CL)

Love Man

Reissue of Atco 289 from 1969, featuring 12 songs with backup by Booker T & The MGs and production by Steve Cropper. I'm a Changed Man/Your Love Has Lifted Me Higher and Higher/Lover Man/A Lover's Question.

RHINO 70295 (CL)

Tell the Truth

These are not Redding's best sides, but still they're better than most other soul singers' recordings. Origi-nally issued posthumously as Atco 333 in 1970, this material was drawn from unissued recordings not originally intended to be made public, which explains the unpolished feel to songs like "Wholesale Love" and "Give Away None of My Love." But make no mistake, Otis sings full throttle, and you can almost see him working up a sweat by the end of songs like "Demonstration" and "Snatch a Little Piece." And when he shouts "I Got the Will," who the hell is gonna argue?

RHINO 70380 (CL)

In Person at The Whiskey au Go-Go

If you could own only one live Otis album, the nod would clearly go to *Live in Europe,* one of the greatest live rock/soul releases ever, but this 1966 Los Angeles show is well worth picking up. Originally released (posthumously) in 1968 as Atco 265, these recordings feature Redding in front of a ten-piece band including four saxes, a pair of trumpets, and trombone. He shouts his way through a heavy dose of heart pounders. I Can't Turn You Loose/Papa's Got a Brand New Bag/Respect/Satisfaction/Pain in My Heart/Just One More Day/Mr. Pitiful/I'm Depending on You/Any Old Way/These Arms of Mine.

STAX 8572 (CL)

Remember Me

Fourteen previously unreleased songs are issued here for the first time, selected and annotated by Rob Bowman. This set includes righteous covers ("Cupid," "Send Me Some Lovin'," and "There Goes My Baby"), unheard classics ("Trick or Treat," "You Got Good Lovin'," and "Gone Again"), deep soul shredders ("Remember Me," "I'm Coming Home," and "Little Old Me"), and some oddballs that are fully realized, but didn't quite have the Redding sound. This is not bottom-of-the-barrel stuff; you might hear a ragged passage here and there, but if anything these have gotten better with age, and every one adds to Otis's rich legacy. Only slightly less essential (although soul fans will love them) are unreleased alternate takes of "Dock of the Bay," "Respect," "Open the Door," "I've Got Dreams to Remember," "Come to Me," "Try a Little Tenderness," and the rare "Stay in School" (did Bowman forget that this is also on the Atlantic box?). It's easy to reach saturation with all the Stax/Volt reissues coming out lately, but if you get just one soul disc all year, get this one.

✪ WARNER BROS. 27608 (L)

The Ultimate Otis Redding

Twenty Volt and Atco recordings with wonderful sound, so brilliant that you can almost taste the horns! Fifty-five minutes of gritty soul, including a booklet that gives recording dates and tells which LP originally featured each song. Dock of the Bay/Respect/Can't Turn You Loose/Tramp/Open the Door/Try a Little Tenderness/Pain in My Heart.

OTIS REDDING and CARLA THOMAS

ATLANTIC 82256 (CL)
King and Queen
Eleven of the finest soul duets ever, including the hit version of Lowell Fulsom's "Tramp." The best part is the liner notes, that include a letter from Howard Baker, then Senator from Tennessee, and later Reagan's Chief of Staff. After talking about Tennessee's contributions to music, from Tennessee Ernie Ford to "The Tennessee Waltz" and Elvis, he talks about Stax-Volt and how they helped to ease the tensions of the Cold War! (So that's why the Berlin wall came down. . .) Ooh Otis, Ooh Carla/Tell It Like It Is/Bring It on Home to Me/When Something Is Wrong with My Baby/It Takes Two.

TEDDY REDELL

Teddy Redell is an Arkansas-born piano pounder who recorded quite extensively during the brief rockabilly boom of the '50s for labels like Vaden, Rimrock, and Hi. He even recorded six songs at Sun studios, although none were released. He began his career in 1953 with Wayne Raney's band and has kept up his recording and touring ever since. His piano playing is excellent, covering boogie woogie, rock-and-roll, and country styles, however his singing isn't anything special.

COLLECTOR 4406 (L)
Rockin' Teddy Redell
Thirty tunes, most of them recorded recently. Knocking on the Backside/Judy/I'll Sail My Ship Alone/Saddle Rag/Pipeliner/Brain Cloudy Rock.

WHITE LABEL 8813 (R)
The Teddy Redell Sound
A dozen tunes featuring Redell's hot piano with good backing too. Knocking on the Backside/Gold Dust/Pipeliner/Crawlin' Back to You.

WHITE LABEL 8815 (R)
Teddy Redell Is Back
In 1979, White Label honcho Cees Klop persuaded Teddy Redell to return to the studio to record a new LP; this is it! His original drummer, Carl Stevens, and bassist, Fred Douglas, join him, in addition to an unnamed standup bass player. The result is a pleasant romp through some old favorites like "Pipeliner," "Cow Cow Blues," and "Back in the USA" as well as some familiar sounding "originals" like "Teddy's Boogie," "California Blues," and "China River," a blatant copy of Hank Williams's "Kaw-Liga."

WHITE LABEL 8933 (R)
Rockin' on the "88" in '88
A live LP recorded in Holland on March 26, 1988, with backing by the ubiquitous Dave Travis Band. Teddy shines on versions of his own compositions "Judy" and "I Want To Hold You"; Moon Mullican's "Pipeliner" and "I'll Sail My Ship Alone"; instrumental versions of "Cow Cow Blues," "Pinetop's Boogie Woogie," and "Tumblin' Tumbleweeds"; old rock tunes; and some new originals.

LULA REED

The wife of bandleader Sonny Thompson, Reed was one of the best vocalists to record for King in the mid-'50s. Her sultry, delicate, and sometimes gospel-tinged vocals set her apart from most others in the field.

KING 604 (RL)
Blue and Moody
This reissue offers R&B aficionados one of the rarest and most important albums in the King catalog. It gathers some of Reed's best sides culled from singles released between 1951–1956. Included are her best-known efforts: "Watch Dog," the original "I'll Drown in My Own Tears," "Rock Love," and "Bump on a Log," along with the lesser-known, but by no means less important, "Last Night" and "Jealous Love." This is Lula's best album, with able backup provided by her husband Sonny Thompson's band.

THE REGENTS

Bronx doo-wop group best-known for their hits "Barbara Ann" and "Runaround" released on Gee records in 1961. Originally known as The Desires, the group formed in 1958 with Guy Vilari on lead vocals, backed by Sal Cuomo, Charles Fassert, Don Jacobucci, and Tony "Hot Rod" Gravagna. They had disbanded by the time "Barbara Ann" scored as a hit; later, it was covered by The Beach Boys in 1966 on their *Party* LP, charting at Number 2. In the mid-'60s, The Regents reunited as The Runarounds trio. Although the harmonies on most of their recordings in this later incarnation are sung well, their choice of material will please only the avid fan of insipid pop music.

COLLECTABLES 5403 (CL)
Barbara Ann
Barbara Ann/Your Love Captured Me/Sunday Kind of Love/Lonesome Boy/Run Around/I'm So Lonely.

CRYSTAL BALL 123 (R)
The Runarounds aka The Regents
Mid-'60s recordings. Amid sounds reminiscent of The Belmonts and The Four Seasons is the pleasant a-cappella rendition of "A Lovely Way to Spend an Evening." Includes much previously unissued material.

JOHNNY RESTIVO
"Oh Johnny!" Restivo was a 16-year-old somewhere between Elvis and Fabian in style, who put out a few 45s and an LP for RCA in 1959–1960.

BEAR FAMILY 15171 (R)
The Shape I'm In
Sixteen sides taken from his LP and 45s, plus four unissued tracks. Backing is provided by studio whizzes, including Mundell Lowe, Sheldon Powell, and Al Caiola; one session of four songs features a band led by King Curtis. The teen songs are wonderfully dated, including the title track and even a remake of the old 1920s song, "Last Night on the Back Porch." I Like Girls/I Make the Love.

PAUL REVERE and THE RAIDERS
Perhaps the best-known and loved of the Pacific Northwest bands, led by organist Revere (his real name) and singer/saxophonist Mark Lindsay. Based in Portland, OR, they started as a Johnny and The Hurricanes-type group, featuring piano/sax instrumentals on the local Gardena label, having a regional hit with "Like Longhair." They later cut a party-type LP for Sande that was reissued in the '60s on Jerden. In 1963, the band signed with Columbia, who issued their version of "Louie Louie" as a single. The Kingsmen's version beat it to the punch, and Lindsay split from the rest of the band who moved to LA. They met up with Dick Clark who liked their sense of humor and Revolutionary War garb. Lindsay rejoined and the group became regulars on Clark's TV show *Where the Action Is.* They were soon teenybopper idols, having high-powered hits including "Kicks," "Just Like Me," and "I'm Not Your Stepping Stone" (later covered by The Monkees). They went through about a dozen members and, by the '70s, had a soft-pop sound, as well as a new TV show, *What's Happening.* They scored a Number 1 hit with John D. Loudermilk's "Indian Reservation." Lindsay soon split, had some minor solo hits, but both his solo career and the group soon fizzled out. Revere still leads a group of Raiders that play lounges and amusement parks.

COLUMBIA 9308 (CL)
Midnight Ride
Bargain-priced reissue of The Raiders's third CBS release from 1966. The epic smash hit "Kicks" is the cornerstone of this collection, with the excellent garage-band cover fodder "I'm Not Your Stepping Stone" placing second. Except for a trio of ballads (for the girls who read *Tiger Beat*), the balance of this 11-tune disc rocks like nobody's business. Some people dug the psych-rock arrangement of "Louie, Go Home," and others liked the rock-hard folk-rock of "Ballad of a Useless Man" and "There She Goes." They're all real fine rockers, but the Stones-like piledriver called "Get It On" gets my pulse racing the most. Besides a solid groove and stinging guitar work, this tune has the classic couplet: "Don't listen to them chatter/You've got to use your own gray matter." Roll over Nietzsche and tell Kierkegaard the news.

JODY REYNOLDS
Jody was a mighty fine singer with some great material, especially his big hit, "Endless Sleep" and the equally fine "The Fire of Love." What really catapults his tunes into another league is the great backing by The Storms featuring Howard Roberts on rhythm guitar and Al Casey on atmospheric lead guitar, not to mention the occasional use of Max Roach (drm) and Plas Johnson (ten sax).

SUNJAY 579 (R)
Endless Sleep
Jody was good in a variety of styles: rockabilly ("Beulah Lee"), twist ("Come on Twist"), ballads, and even

duets. In 1967, he recorded two wonderful tunes with a soon-to-be-famous Bobbie Gentry ("Requiem for Love" b/w "Stranger in the Mirror" [Titan 175]), which remind me of the best of the Nancy Sinatra/Lee Hazelwood songs. Includes his two brilliant instrumentals (originally Sundown 114): "Thunder" and "Tarantula." Not to be forgotten is his song about Delaware, "The Whipping Post." Very impressive.

TODD RHODES

Rhodes was the original pianist in McKinney's Cotton Pickers, staying with the band throughout its entire career. In 1947, after a brief retirement, he formed the jazz-R&B group The Toddlers, recording for Vitacoustic and Sensation (1949–1951) and King (1951–1953), becoming King's house band.

JUKEBOX LJL 615 (R)
Todd Rhodes and His Toddlers: Your Daddy's Doggin' Around
Covers 1947–1953, featuring LaVern Baker on vocals on "Pig Latin Blues," "Lost Child," and "Must I Cry Again." Flying Disc/Your Mouth Got a Hole in It/Hot Maw and Cabbage.

CHARLIE RICH

Rich is an outstanding singer/songwriter/pianist who recorded rockabilly and rockin' country sides for Sun in the '50s. He went to Sun subsidiary Phillips International and, in 1960, had his first big hit with "Lonely Weekend." No hits followed until 1965, when he signed to Mercury subsidiary Smash where he had a hit with "Mohair Sam." After that, he recorded for RCA and then Epic. In the early '70s, he teamed up with producer Billy Sherill to record a string of MOR country ("country-politan") hits including "The Most Beautiful Girl" and his biggest hit, 1973's "Behind Closed Doors." This success led many labels to reissue their entire Rich catalog in the early '70s. However, today there is only one mid-'60s session available!

HI (UK) 418 (R)
I'll Shed No Tears
Fourteen unissued tracks, mostly from Charlie's blue-eyed soul session for Hi in 1966. If you're a Rich fan, you can't help loving this album. I just hope some of you soul fans happen to read this review, because you really should hear it. Granted, Charlie is no Elvis or

Lonnie Mack, but his soulful vocals are much more than adequate, and the Hi arrangements and playing are superb, creating some of the greatest white soul ever recorded, including "When Something Is Wrong with My Baby" (recorded before Sam and Dave's version!) Also includes five tunes from Charlie's Hank Williams tribute session. Don't Tear Me Down/I'll Shed No Tears/Pass On By.

CLIFF RICHARD (and THE SHADOWS)

Born in India as Harry Roger Webb, young Richard was intoxicated by the English skiffle sound (a wedding of folk, blues, and a jazz/rock rhythm) like so many of his peers. In 1958, he attracted the attention of London music mogul Carroll Levis who introduced him to EMI Records. At about the same time, Richard met an instrumental group known as The Shadows (led by guitar whiz Hank Marvin). They formed a new group called The Drifters, but soon reverted to using The Shadows name, scoring many vocal hits with Richard, as well as instrumental hits (see the separate Shadows listing). The group stayed together until 1968, and Richard has continued as a very successful solo artist since the '70s. While the hits kept coming on the British charts, Richard never really made it big in America after his 1959 single, "Living Doll," released stateside on ABC/Paramount.

EMI (UK) 792 421 (L)
20 Original Greats

EMI (UK) 792 425 (L)
40 Golden Greats
British hits from the late '50s and early '60s. On the Beach/Lucky Lips/A Voice in the Wilderness/Fall in Love with You/Mean Streak/Move It/Dancing Shoes/Willie and the Hand Jive/I'm the Lonely One/Time Drags By/We Say Yeah!

MUSIC FOR PLEASURE 6005 (L)
Rock On with Cliff Richard

SEE FOR MILES 280 (L)
Ballads and Love Songs
Twenty tracks from EMI EPs.

TOMMY RIDGELEY

New Orleans balladeer/blues shouter who's been recording on his own since signing to Imperial in 1949; these first recordings featured backing by Dave Bartholomew's band. In the mid-'50s, he recorded for Atlantic backed by pianist R.C. Robinson (who was given his own contract as Ray Charles). He recorded for Ric in the early '60s and, because his style was similar to the late Chuck Willis, he was given the title the "New King of the Stroll." He continues to record occasionally.

ROUNDER 2079 (CL)
The New Orleans King of the Stroll
Fifteen fine cuts. While best at heartfelt ballads like "Should I Ever Love Again," "I've Heard that Story Before," or Bullmoose Jackson's "I Love You Yes I Do," he also can pull off such novelties as "Double Eyed Whammy" or "The Girl from Kooka Monga." Also includes two rare 1964 cuts from Watch subsidiary Johen, notably the wicked soul number "I Want Some Money Baby."

THE RIGHTEOUS BROTHERS

The kings of "blue-eyed soul," bass Bill Medley and tenor Bobby Hatfield began their career in 1962 on Moonglow as The Paramours, scoring hits covering '50s R&B songs including Little Walter's "My Babe," as well as Medley's original "Little Latin Lupe Lu." They signed to Phil Spector's Philles label in 1964, and Spector produced their soulful versions of standards including "Unchained Melody" and "Ebb Tide," plus the classic "You've Lost That Lovin' Feeling." Regular appearances on TV's *Shindig*, coupled with their show-stopping acrobatic act, where Bill lifted up Bobby to "reach" those high notes, made them teen sensations. Dissatisfied with Spector, they signed to Verve, producing the beautiful Spectorian "(You're My) Soul and Inspiration." The pair broke up in 1968; Medley went solo, recording for MGM, while Hatfield kept the RB name going with Jimmy Walker of The Knickerbockers. Hatfield and Medley reunited in 1974, scoring a hit with "Rock and Roll Heaven," a tribute to legendary, deceased rock and roll stars, and they still occasionally perform together on Dick Clark's shows. Medley scored a comeback hit on a duet with Jennifer Warnes, "The Time of My Life," featured in the movie *Dirty Dancing*.

LIVE GOLD 30003 (L)
Live 1967
Recorded live at the Anaheim Stadium in Orange County, CA, on May 8, 1967. The RBs split in 1968, so this 35-minute set covers material from one end of their career to the other. The oldies medley was a good idea, but with only a few bars of each song included, it's hard to get too excited about it. Likewise, the two-song gospel medley that closes the show sounds wonderful but only lasts about three minutes. Sound quality is pretty good and the Brothers sound as Righteous as they ever did. Skimpy notes are marred by mistakes! Little Latin Lupe Lu/Let the Good Times Roll/You've Lost that Lovin' Feelin'/Unchained Melody.

◉ RHINO 71488 (CL)
Anthology 1962–1974
Very nice 28-tune collection. Rhino goes way back to 1962, diggin' up the Brothers's first single "There She Goes (She's Walking Away)" (Moonglow 214). The Moonglow phase is represented here by some tough R&B numbers like "Little Latin Lupe Lu" (a garage band favorite), "Koko Joe" (written by Sonny Bono), "Justine," "My Babe," as well as a selection of the lovely ballads that would later propel them to fame and fortune. Their big Philles hits recorded under the guiding hand of Phil Spector are all here: "You've Lost that Lovin' Feeling," "Ebb Tide," "Just Once in My Life," "Unchained Melody," plus three others. Verve picked them up in 1966 for a reported cool million and were immediately rewarded with the Number 1 smash hit "(You're My) Soul and Inspiration." The collection is rounded out with three of their solo efforts and a couple of tunes from their 1974 reunion including the big hit "Rock and Roll Heaven."

VERVE 314 511 157 (CL)
The Moonglow Years
Twenty-eight songs from 1962–1964, ranging from the doo-wop influence of "For Your Love," "I'm So Lonely," and "My Prayer" to the straight-gospel of "In That Great Gettin' Up Mornin'" and "Something's Got a Hold of Me." How many duos could cover Willie Dixon's "I Just Want to Make Love to You" and The Everly's "Bye Bye Love" and sound at home on both?

VERVE 847 248 (L)
Unchained Melody: The Very Best of The Righteous Brothers
Twelve hits, half of them produced by Phil Spector! Minimal packaging and no notes, which seems a little chintzy for the price, but that's life. You've Lost That Lovin' Feeling/Unchained Melody/(You're My) Soul and Inspiration/Little Latin Lupe Lu/On This Side of Goodbye.

BILLY LEE RILEY

The most talented of the second-string Sun artists, Arkansian Riley was adept at guitar, piano, bass, drums, vocals, and songwriting; in fact, he cut tracks as early as 1956 playing all of the instruments himself! When he recorded with a band, he used the cream of the Sun sessionmen, including Jerry Lee on piano. He's best known for his cover of "Billy the Kid" Emerson's "Red Hot" and the novelty classic "Flying Saucers Rock and Roll." His band was called The Little Green Men. In the '60s, he moved to Los Angeles where he worked extensively as a session musician as well as releasing a number of albums under his own name. He returned to the south in the '80s and put out a number of releases, some on his own label. He was recently signed by Hightone Records to record a new album.

BEAR FAMILY 15272 (R)

And The Little Green Men

Only eight of these 15 sides recorded for Riley's and Roland Janes's Rita label were originally issued. This set not only contains sides by Riley, but also his sidemen. It opens with a session with Billy sounding like Jimmy Reed, with the single "Repossession Blues" b/w "Dark Muddy Bottom" originally released as by "Lightnin' Leon." Billy's performance on these two blues songs was so convincing that many blues collectors assumed that this disc was by a black artist! Saxist Martin Willis (aka Cattywampus and Tuff) is heard on his instrumental 45 "Columbus Stockyard Blues" b/w "San Antonio Rock," and drummer J.M. "Jimmy" Van Eaton is featured on five tunes, including his single "Beat-Nik" b/w "Foggy," and three from an unissued session with Travis Wammack on guitar, including "Out-Standing" (this title got left off the cover!), plus six more unissued Riley sides.

BEAR FAMILY 15444 (L)

Classic Recordings, 1956–1960

Excellent double-CD retrospective. The first CD features all of his most memorable Sun rockers such as "Rock with Me Baby," "Flying Saucer Rock and Roll," "Red Hot," and "Pearly Lee," where he is accompanied by such terrific sessionmen as Roland Janes (gtr), Martin Willis (b), and J.M. Van Eaton (drm). It also includes the fine bluesy harmonica instrumentals "Itchy" and "Thunderbird" that were originally issued under Sonny Burgess's name, his relatively undistinguished Brunswick single, and his two singles issued on the Rita label. The second disc features 28 tracks not originally issued, including alternate takes of some of his best Sun songs plus quite a few excellent covers

of blues and R&B favorites like "Your Cash Ain't Nothin' but Trash," "Betty and Dupree," "Saturday Night Fish Fry," and the particularly fine "When a Man Gets the Blues." There is also a brief parody of Johnny Cash's "Folsom Prison Blues," and a 1960 remake of one of his most popular Sun songs "Red Hot," which is given a very different treatment. The sound is superb, and there is a 40-page booklet with fine notes by Rob Bowman and Ross Johnson, much of it based on an interview with Billy. Also included are great '50s photos of Billy with his band The Little Green Men, and full discographical details. Highly recommended.

SUN (UK) 3 (L)

Rockin' with Riley

This three-CD box set is said to include Riley's complete Sun recordings, but given Sun/Charly's reputation of late, I wouldn't count on it. We do get 75 cuts from one of the wildest of the rockabilly wildmen, many of which did emanate from the Sun Studios in Memphis. Later cuts, mostly '60s vintage, come from Phillips International and Checker Records, plus smaller labels like Mojo, Myrl, and Dodge. Judge for yourself whether The Megatons's Checker LP, originally released in very shady fashion as a Bo Diddley "Surf" album, is worth having on CD. But there's no arguing that "Flying Saucers Rock and Roll" (three versions), "Red Hot" (three interesting variations) and the similar "She's My Baby," "Pearly Lee" (three versions), "College Man," and the Little Richard-styled "Got the Water Boilin'" (two versions) are genuine '50s classics. Includes some solid blues with Chicago and Louisiana overtones like "Baby Please Don't Go." Billy Lee's life story is a tragic case of misfortune and double-dealing, told succinctly by Adam Komorowski in the accompanying booklet. A discography is also included, but as usual, trying to match it to the track listings makes calculus look easy. Caveat emptor.

THE RIP CHORDS

REQUEST 13501 (L)

Hey Little Cobra

Eighteen surf and drag-strip numbers. 4:09/She Thinks I Still Care/Shut Down/Three Window Coupe/Hot Rod USA/Surfin' Craze.

JOHNNY RIVERS

Born John Ramistella in New York, Rivers's family relocated to Louisiana when he was three; by age eight, he was playing guitar and mandolin. In the late '50s, he met legendary DJ Alan Freed who changed his last name to Rivers and got him a contract with Gone. In 1959, after graduating from high school, he moved to Nashville, befriending another young unknown songwriter/performer, Roger Miller. The duo cut demo records together. Relocating in the early '60s to LA, Rivers became the lead act at the new Whisky-a-Go-Go club, helping establish it as a center for young rock acts. He signed with Imperial records in 1964 and scored his first hit with a remake of Chuck Berry's "Memphis." He continued to record and score hits through the '60s, including 1966's "Secret Agent Man" and "Poor Side of Town." He befriended songwriter Jimmy Webb, promoting his songs, and discovered The Versailles, molding them into The 5th Dimension, and giving them Webb's "Up, Up and Away" to record for his Soul City label. Rivers linked up with guru Ram Das in the early '70s, and continued to record, achieving only sporadic hits. He has performed on the oldies circuit through the '80s.

EMI 99900 (CL)
Changes/Rewind
Two mid-'60s Rivers LPs on one cassette/CD. *Changes*, originally released in 1966 (Imperial 9334), is one of those "sensitive," introspective deals that is perfectly suited for people who likes to drift in and out of comas while listening to music. Boredom-a-go-go! By comparison, 1967's superior followup, *Rewind* (9341), picks up its feet once in a while, but (hint, hint) both its hits are Motown covers, "The Tracks of My Tears" and "Baby I Need Your Lovin'." The strings have been replaced or at least supported by horns on a few tracks, the background vocals by The Blossoms sound good, and seven songs are Jim "By the Time I Get to Phoenix" Webb compositions. Dig the found sounds on "Sweet Smiling Children."

RHINO 70793 (CL)
Anthology, 1964–1977
I guess I'd forgotten how many great songs Johnny Rivers did during the 13 years covered here. But who can forget the gritty, white-soul sound and evocative imagery of hit songs like "Poor Side of Town," "Baby I Need Your Lovin'," and "Secret Agent Man," or his lighter smashes "Rockin' Pneumonia" and "Swayin' to the Music"? In addition to his chart successes, there are plenty of worthwhile blues and R&B standards, and a whole spectrum of rock, folk, and even country covers. Obviously, JR tried a lot of different strategies along the way, and scored more often than many pop singers of his generation. Thirty-six cuts on CD, 30 on tape. Memphis/Maybelline/Midnight Special/Parch-

man Farm/Do You Want to Dance/The Tracks of My Tears/Sea Cruise.

SUEDE 5787 (R)
Rock and Roll Years
Sixteen rarities by Rivers, most making their first LP appearances. Mainly rockabilly and Johnny Burnette-ish teen rock, these cuts were recorded between 1958–1961, including his first single "Two by Two" b/w "Little Girl," which was released under his real name, Johnny Ramistella. Also featured are his great Gone and Cub sides, with quite a few originals including "Baby Come Back," a rewrite of "Santa Claus Bring My Baby Back to Me," as well as rockin' versions of "White Cliffs of Dover," "Long Black Veil," and "Oh What a Kiss."

THE RIVIERAS
The Rivieras had a smooth sound along the lines of The Platters, mixing pop and big-band style harmonies. Led by tenor Homer Dunn, they recorded for Coed records in the late '50s and early '60s, scoring a hit with 1958's "Count Every Star." Not to be confused with the California pop group (see separate listing).

RELIC 5092 (R)
The Best of The Rivieras
Fifteen Coed cuts, two previously unreleased. Count Every Star/Moonlight Serenade/Our Love/Since I Made You Cry/Moonlight Cocktails.

RELIC 7025 (L)
Moonlight Cocktails
Recorded between 1958–1961 for Coed Records. The title track is one of my personal favorites, but too many of the remaining 17 cuts lack the interesting vocal interplay of good doo-wop and instead aim for a more pop-ish, latter-day Mills Brothers sound. And, the instrumentation is often uncomfortably violin-laden. The better tracks are "El Dorado," "Count Every Star," "True Love is Hard to Find," and "Moonlight Serenade." The Rivieras are a polished and classy group who might well have produced more interesting music if they'd been signed by a label like Vee Jay or Atlantic. Nonetheless, Relic has done an excellent job of preserving their output here. Remastered from the original session tapes, some in stereo.

THE RIVIERAS
Early '60s organ-based rock band who recorded for Chicago's USA label. They're best known for their anthemic cover of Joe Jones's "California

Sun," released in 1963, which was knocked off the charts by the British invasion.

STAR CLUB 8034 (R)

Let's Have a Party

Fantastic LP collecting a dozen killer dillers from the all-too-short career of The Rivieras, who produced two LPs and a few singles. Great liner notes by *Kick's* contributor Miriam Linna. California Sun (1965 remake)/Church Key, Part 2/Bug Juice/Rip It Up/Let's Have a Party.

THE RIVINGTONS

The Rivingtons were four exceptionally talented singers: Carl White, John "Sonny" Harris, Turner "Rocky" Wilson Jr., and Al Frazier. All had sung as The Sharps (Frazier was also in The Lamplighters), and all had cut fine vocal sides for other labels. As The Rivingtons, they scored a huge success with the classic novelty, "Papa-Oom-Mow-Mow."

EMI 95204 (CL)

The Liberty Years:
EMI Legends of Rock and Roll

Contains all the outfit's singles plus album cuts. Now here's the bright side: the flip sides of most of the group's early throwaway numbers were exceptional deep-soul masterworks. Gutwrenching ballads like "Deep Water," "Cherry," "Waiting," and "I'm Losing My Grip" indicate how fine this quartet could be. Too bad none of these gems caught fire; the group could have reached great heights. Book contains thorough discography.

THE ROB ROYS/THE FASCINATORS

CAP 1008 (R)

The Rob Roys Meet The Fascinators

The Fascinators and Rob Roys are perhaps two of the finest mixed-race vocal groups from the late '50s. The Rob Roys started recording on Don Robey's Houston-based Backbeat label in 1957, and their most memorable sides, "Dream Girl" and "My Dearest One," are included here. The Fascinators featured the legendary Tony Passalasqua, whose sad soulful voice graced songs like "Chapel Bells" and "Oh Rose Marie." Twelve issued cuts, plus six unreleased sides and demo versions. Good overall sound, nice pix, no sleeve notes. Very fine doo-wop.

MARTY ROBBINS

Like many other country artists, Robbins cut rockabilly sides in the mid-'50s before achieving fame and fortune on the C&W charts. In the late '50s, he recorded for Columbia, produced by mainstream pop producer Ray Coniff, and then continued in a teen-pop mode through the mid-'60s on a variety of other labels. His biggest pop hits were 1956's "Singing the Blues" and "Knee Deep in the Blues" and 1957's "A White Sport Coat (and a Pink Carnation)."

BEAR FAMILY 15566 (L)

Marty Robbins Sings:
Rockin' Rollin' Robbins, Vol. 1

This is basically a reissue of Bear Family 15212 with two more songs ("Call Me Up" and the earliest track here, "It's a Long, Long Ride"), covering his rockabilly, rock, and up-tempo country material recorded from 1953–1958. These 19 tracks concentrate on the hard rockers, such as his hit cover of Elvis's "That's All Right (Mama)," and his covers of "Maybelline," "Long Tall Sally," and Bill Monroe's "Footprints in the Snow" (from 1958). "Pain and Misery," his 1954 duet with Nashville session guitarist Ray Edenton, is here along with other Marty originals like "Mean Mama Blues" and the chaotic "Tennessee Toddy." To round it out are Marty's 1956 crossover hits "Singing the Blues" and "Knee Deep in the Blues," both Melvin Endsley compositions. Unlike the LP version, this includes notes by Colin Escott and complete discographical data.

BEAR FAMILY 15567 (L)

The Story of My Life:
Rockin' Rollin' Robbins, Vol. 2

Marty Robbins was steamed when Columbia Records New York A&R man Mitch Miller had pop singer Guy Mitchell cover two of his hits, "Singing the Blues" and "Knee Deep in the Blues," denying Marty the vast pop success that could have been his. Known for his hot temper as a teenager, this time he got mad with a purpose. The result? He came to New York in January 1957 to record with Miller, with arrangements by former big-band trumpeter Ray Conniff, Guy Mitchell's arranger! The first session produced the megahit "A White Sport Coat (and a Pink Carnation)." Over the next year and a half, he would do four more sessions for Columbia, yielding a total of 16 songs, all of them compiled here as they were on the LP version (15105). Among them are "The Story of My Life," one of the first hits for the legendary pop songwriting team of Hal David and Burt Bacharach. Most of this material was softer-edged teen fare, including the hits and "Just Married," "Stairway of Love," "She Was Only Seventeen" and Melvin Endsley's "Ain't I the Lucky One." "The Hanging Tree," from the movie of the same name, was recorded at Robbins's final Columbia session in LA. Sound is excellent, as you'd expect from Bear Family, and the notes include new interviews with both Miller and Conniff and complete discographical data. Jazz buffs will recognize these names among the backup players: guitarists Bucky Pizzarelli, Allan Reuss, and Tony Rizzi, and trumpeter Billy Butterfield, among others.

BEAR FAMILY 15569 (L)
Ruby Ann: Rockin' Rollin' Robbins, Vol. 3
CD reissue of Bear Family 15184, which brings together rock and pop tunes from Robbins's post-rockabilly and Ray Conniff periods. The material here was recorded between 1959–1966 and wasn't quite on the level of the earlier sides, but rounds out the other two volumes. Several titles such as "Sweet Cora," "Ain't Life a Cryin' Shame," and "Silence and Tears" were on Volume 5 of the *Marty Robbins Files* series. Two versions of his 1962 hit "Ruby Ann," the hit and an alternate slower version with horns, are included, as is "Teenager's Dad." More importantly, this CD also adds a number of songs not on the LP, including an entire unissued 1959 session with Mitch Miller not included on Vol. 2 (with another unissued version of "Cap and Gown," for those who have to have it all). Also featured are: "A Whole Lot Easier" and two takes of "Hello Baby (Goodbye Baby)" from 1964; "Baby's Gone" from 1965; and "You've Been So Busy Baby" from 1966.

THE ROBINS

Originally called The Robbins, this LA group featured the bass lead of Bobby Nunn and were part of The Johnny Otis Show, often singing behind Little Esther. By the mid-'50s, they lost a "b" to become The Robins, and added Carl Gardner on lead vocals. They were signed to Leiber and Stoller's Spark label, having novelty hits with "Riot in Cell Block Number 9" (with guest vocalist Richard Berry) and "Smokey Joe's Cafe," both leased to Atco records. Atco bought their catalog, and wanted to keep the group with Leiber and Stoller. There was a split, however, with Nunna and Gardner staying on to become The Coasters. The other four Robins returned to LA where they added future soul producer H.B. Barnum to the group and signed to Whippet, where they had a hit in 1956 with "Cherry Lips." They signed to Knight in 1959 before breaking up.

CROWN 1000 (R)
The Best of The Robins, Vol. 2
A reissue of the earlier Crown 1000, with the addition of two previously unissued cuts: "My Baby Done Told Me" and "You Don't Want My Love." The remaining 14 tracks, dating from 1952–1954, are first-rate R&B from Crown and other labels. The material ranges from blues ballads to raucous jump tunes featuring honking sax, with Bobby Nunn occasionally taking a bass lead. Great music, but no notes at all. A Fool Such As I/How Would You Know/Ten Days in Jail/All I Do Is Rock.

SPARK 1000 (R)
The Best of The Robins, Vol. 3
More madness from the group who spawned The Coasters. The fare on these 14 cuts is almost all Leiber and Stoller material, including all the faves. Riot in Cell Block Number 9/Smokey Joe's Cafe/Framed/If Teardrops Were Kisses/Loop-de-Loop Mambo/One Kiss.

SMOKEY ROBINSON and THE MIRACLES

The most talented of the Motown groups, led by vocalist/songwriter/producer Robinson, who has an instantly identifiable falsetto, highly influenced by Nolan Strong of The Diablos. The Miracles started on Chess in 1958, recording an answer song to "Get a Job" called "Got a Job," penned by their manager Berry Gordy. Their next hit, "Bad Girl," came out nationally on Chess but locally on Gordy's new Tamla label (a division of the new Motown company). Their next on Tamla, "Shop Around" (written by Robinson), went to Number 1. Smokey also penned such Motown classics as "My Girl," "Get Ready," "I'll Be Doggone," "You Really Got a Hold on Me," "The Tracks of My Tears," and just about every thing The Miracles recorded from 1964 until he went solo in 1973.

❂ MOTOWN 793 (CL)
Anthology
Handsome two-CD/cassette package featuring 45 songs from throughout their career plus a 32-page booklet. Got a Job/Way Over There/Shop Around/What's So Good about Goodbye/I've Been Good to You/Mickey's Monkey/I Like It like That/Tracks of My Tears.

MOTOWN 3762 (C)
The Season for Miracles

MOTOWN 5136 (CL)
Away We A Go Go
Reissue of Tamla 271 from 1965, with twelve cuts. Whole Lot of Shakin' in My Heart/You Don't Have to Say You Love Me/Beauty Is Only Skin Deep.

MOTOWN 5156 (CL)
The Tears of a Clown
Reissue of Tamla 246 from 1965. My Girl/It Will Be Alright/We Had a Love So Strong/More, More, More of Your Love/I'm the One You Need.

MOTOWN 5160 (CL)
Hi! We're The Miracles
Reissue of their first LP, Tamla 220 from 1961. Incredible early Smokey, bridging the gap between doo-wop and modern soul. Includes the hit "Shop Around." Who's Lovin' You/Depend on Me/After All.

MOTOWN 5254 (L)
Christmas with The Miracles
Originally Motown 236 from 1964.

MOTOWN 5269 (CL)
Going to a Go-Go
Reissue of Motown 267 from 1964. The Tracks of My Tears/My Girl Has Gone/Going to a Go-Go.

MOTOWN 5282 (CL)
What Love Has Joined Together
Reissue of Tamla 301 from 1970. The pickings are starting to get a little slim. Not only are there only six songs, but only one new Smokey song (the title track), along with covers of three Motown songs ("My Cherie Amour," "If This World Was Mine," and a cover-of-a-cover—Blood, Sweat, and Tears's version of "You've Made Me So Very Happy"!), the obligatory Beatles wimp song ("And I Love Her"), and even "This Guy's In Love with You"!

MOTOWN 5360 (C)
Motown Legends
Fourteen early sides. Tears of a Clown/More of Your Love/You've Lost That Lovin' Feeling/Save Me/The Hunter Gets Captured by the Game.

MOTOWN 5437 (CL)
Time Out
Reissue of Gordy 295 from 1970.

MOTOWN 5439 (L)
Doin' Mickey's Monkey
This was the Miracles's groovy "dance-craze" album, originally Motown 245 from 1965, with 11 guaranteed crowd-pleasers for your next mini-skirt party. The Wah-Watusi/Land of 1000 Dances/The Monkey Time/Twist and Shout/The Twist/Do You Love Me?

THE ROCKIN' BERRIES
British invasion pop group led by Geoff Turton who released solo recordings under the name of Jefferson.

SEQUEL 180 (L)
The Best of The Rockin' Berries featuring Jefferson
Twenty-two tune collection covering the '60s recordings of The Rockin' Berries, as well as Geoff Turton's solo releases as Jefferson. These Pye and Piccadilly recordings (1965–1970) are pure British invasion pop but Turton did have a fine voice and carved a niche for the band by putting a beat to the high-register American pop songs he covered. He really soars on the two Goffin/King tunes, "You're My Girl" and "He's in Town," that they covered. They even occasionally rocked a bit, on "Shade of Blue" and the great previously unissued psychedelic tune "Yellow Rainbow." The Jefferson tunes cross the boundaries into pure pop music for the mums and dads. Dawn/Midnight Mary/Mr. Blue/Poor Man's Son.

THE ROCKIN' Rs
Four flipped-out cats from Metamora (sounds like somewhere in outer space to me), IL, who drove the local hubcap-snatchers wacko in the late '50s.

NORTON 205 (R)
Crazy Baby
The Rockin' Rs had one of the most rhythmic approaches goin'; just listen to the manic strummin' on "Crazy Baby," "Heat," and above all, "The Beat." Also included are tunes from a 1958 TV show and a party tape from around the same time. Mustang/Gonna Snatch Me a Satellite/Ron's Raunch/Ready Teddy.

JIMMIE RODGERS
Washington-born pop/folk singer who had a long string of hits on Roulette (from 1957–1961). With the aid of producers Hugo and Luigi, Rodgers scored with "Honeycomb," "Kisses Sweeter Than Wine," and "Oh Oh I'm Falling in Love Again." He signed with Dot in 1962, recording for four years without a hit, but he scored a comeback with "Child of Clay" in 1967 on A&M. Two months later, he was found in his car with a severely fractured skull. He attempted a comeback in the mid-'80s, even appearing in the San Francisco area on Carpeteria commercials!

DOMINO 1005 (R)
Woman from Liberia
Fifteen of the most popular songs of this lightweight pop rocker. Liza/The Wizard/The Girl in the Wood/Kisses Sweeter Than Wine/English Country Garden/Honeycomb/Oh Oh I'm Falling in Love Again.

RHINO 70942 (CL)
The Best of Jimmie Rodgers
Eighteen cuts on CD, 14 on cassette. Kisses Sweeter Than Wine/Secretly/Are You Really Mine/Ring-a-Ling-a Lario/Tucumcari/Women from Liberia.

TOMMY ROE
Buddy Holly-influenced singer from Atlanta who first hit in 1962 with "Sheila," a very Holly-ish sounding song that originally flopped in 1960. He recorded a string of folky-type hits for ABC until 1964, and then came back in 1966 as a bubblegum singer with "Dizzy" and "Jam Up Jelly Tight." He stayed with ABC until 1972, when he signed with MGM.

JUDD 75100 (R)
Hits and Rarities
Includes his Holly-esque hits "Sheila" and "Susie Darling." The rest of the 18-cut LP is comprised of the "rarities" I guess, mostly teen-torment chart chasers. Piddie De Pat/Little Hollywood Girl/Sensations/Kiss and Run.

THE ROLLING STONES
The original bad boys of rock and roll. Group originally consisted of Mick Jagger (vcl), Brian Jones and Keith Richards (gtrs), Bill Wyman (b), and Charlie Watts (drm). The band began its life as an R&B cover outfit, working London's blossoming blues clubs. Their first LPs were heavy on blues and R&B covers, although their first hit was the Lennon/McCartney song "I Wanna Be Your Man." Jagger's and Richards's songwriting talents soon manifested themselves in early hits including "The Last Time," the risque (for the time) "(I Can't Get No) Satisfaction," and "Get Off My Cloud." Brian Jones's influence waned as his growing drug addiction took its toll on his creativity, leading ultimately to his ouster from the band. He was first replaced by Mick Jones in the late '60s/early '70s, fol-

lowed by Ron Wood from The Faces, who remains with the band.

The Stones's '60s catalog is controlled by their ex-manager, Allan Klein, and has been rereleased by his Abkco label in the US. This discography covers their work to 1970 in chronological order, when the band's image as the daredevils of rock started to overwhelm the music.

ABKCO 7375 (RCL)
The Rolling Stones
US version of their first LP, with a more acoustic-blues sound than their later offerings. Carol/King Bee/Route 66.

ABKCO 7402 (RCL)
12 X 5
Chuck Berry and Bo Diddley influences come to the fore on this rockin' LP of R&B and blues covers.

ABKCO 7420 (RCL)
Now!
More blues covers, with Jagger's vocals reaching new heights and the band continuing to tighten up.

ABKCO 7429 (RCL)
Out of Our Heads
America-only LP made up of live and studio cuts from all over the place. "(I Can't Get No) Satisfaction" is the hit here.

ABKCO 7451 (RCL)
December's Children (and Everybody's)
"Get Off My Cloud," other singles, and odd session tracks make up this LP, a move in the arty direction that The Stones would perfect on *Aftermath* and *Between the Buttons.*

ABKCO 7476 (RCL)
Aftermath
First LP to take a turn away from R&B/blues towards more progressive-rock sounds, and the first to feature only Jagger/Richards originals, including the hits "Paint It Black" and the Eastern-influenced "Mother's Little Helper."

☻ ABKCO 8001 (RCL)
High Tide and Green Grass
First hits collection.

ABKCO 7493 (RCL)
Got Live If You Want It
First live LP by Stones, including hits and covers.

ABKCO 7499 (RCL)
Between the Buttons
The Stones continue their move towards artrock, showing the influence of their rivals The Who, The Beatles, and The Kinks. Includes the hits "Let's Spend the Night Together" (which became on Ed Sullivan's show "Let's Spend Some Time Together") and the trippy "Ruby Tuesday."

ABKCO 7509 (RCL)
Flowers

ABKCO 8002 (RCL)
Their Satanic Majesties Request
Their psychedelic LP, either a serious career blunder or an important expansion of their sound, depending on your point-of-view. Includes the hit "She's a Rainbow" and the spacey "2000 Light Years from Home," revived during The Stones's 1992 tour.

ABKCO 7539 (RCL)
Beggars Banquet
A return to the Stones's minimalist roots, setting the stage for their sound for the next two decades. Includes "Sympathy for the Devil" and "Streetfighting Man."

ABKCO 7004 (RCL)
Let It Bleed
Stones first LP with Mick Taylor replacing Brian Jones on lead guitar. Includes "You Can't Always Get What You Want" and "Gimme Shelter."

THE RONETTES
One of the most loved girl groups of all time, led by Ronnie Bennett, her older sister Estelle, and cousin Nedra Talley. After a flop single ("I'm on the Wagon") and LP (*Presenting The Ronettes*) on Colpix in 1962, they were discovered by Phil Spector and given the best of his material and production, including "Be My Baby," "Baby I Love You," and "(Best Part of) Breaking Up." In 1968, Phil and Ronnie got married, and Phil forced her to become a virtual recluse, not allowing her to record; they were divorced in 1974. She went on to record for Buddah with a new set of Ronettes, and, over the last decade, Ronie's made a few solo comebacks.

SEQUEL 620 (L)
The Colpix and Buddah Years
In 1961, before they climbed Phil Spector's "wall of sound" and found fame on the other side, The Ronettes recorded a handful of sides on the Colpix label. This CD contains all 11 of these, including the fabulous "My Guiding Angel," "Silhouettes," "He Did It," and "I Want a Boy." Joey Dee's "Getting Nearer" from 1963, which features The Ronettes on back up vocals, has been added for fun. All four Ronettes cuts on Buddah (1973) follow, and, although Nedra and Estelle had been replaced, these songs, especially "I Wish I Never Saw the Sunshine," have no trouble pleasing the ears. Finally, an overdub session from "Silhouettes" offers a brief glimpse behind the scenes. Ear candy.

RONNY and THE DAYTONAS
ARISTA (JAPAN) 2032 (L)
Landlocked: The Best of Ronny and The Daytonas

THE ROOMMATES
This Long Island group started their career backing singer Cathy Jean on her big hit "Please Love Me Forever." They also recorded under their own name and had a hit with "Glory of Love."

RELIC 5041 (R)
The Roommates Greatest Hits
Eighteen Valmor sides recorded in the early '60s by this white New York vocal group. Includes their only US hit, "Glory of Love" and their local NY hit "Band of Gold." Gee/Please Don't Cheat on Me/Sunday Kind of Love.

ROSIE and THE ORIGINALS
Rosie Hamlin was a 14-year-old skinny thing when she auditioned for David Ponci and his band, The Originals. She wrote a poem and set it to a variation of the chord changes for "Heart and Soul"; this became their one-and-only classic hit, "Angel Baby." Distressed when Ponci took credit for the composition, Rosie set out on her own, recording for Brunswick a series of floparoos backed by syrupy strings, as opposed to the minimalist bar-band sound of The Originals. Rosie has appeared in oldie shows since 1984 around her current hometown of San Bernardino, CA.

BRUNSWICK 754102 (R)
Lonely Blue Nights with Rosie
I've heard that this LP is treasured by the "lowriders" on the West Coast, probably because of the classic status of the timeless 1961 hit, "Angel Baby," on Highland Records. Rosie's gorgeous haunting vocals on that one still bring a chill to this old geezer's spine. While an entire LP of "Angel Baby" sound-alikes might

be a bit much for some, it sure sounds like heaven taken in the right doses. Rosie's voice soars majestically on these fourteen teen classics. I Found a Dream/My Darling Forever/Angel from Above/No Other Love Will Do.

DIANA ROSS and THE SUPREMES
See THE SUPREMES

THE ROYAL TEENS

NY rock group led by pianist Bob Gaudio, and featuring Joe Villa on vocals, who had sung on the NY doo-wop classic "Blanche" by The Three Friends. They had a top-10 hit with the perennial novelty favorite "Short Shorts" in 1958 for ABC, but the remainder of their recordings flopped. They moved by year's end to Capitol, and stuck it out through the end of the decade, adding a young Al Kooper on bass. When they broke up, Gaudio joined The Four Lovers (who became The Four Seasons), and Kooper took up songwriting ("This Diamond Ring," a hit for Gary Lewis and The Playboys), before playing some influential sessions with a young Mr. Bob Dylan and forming The Blues Project and the first incarnation of Blood, Sweat, and Tears.

COLLECTABLES 5094 (CL)
Short Shorts: Golden Classics
Twelve songs, some not originally released.

THE RUNAROUNDS
See THE REGENTS

BOBBY RYDELL

One of the only Philadelphia "pretty-boy" singers of the late '50s/early '60s who was more than a handsome face. Robert Ridarelli was a child prodigy on drums and was a regular on Paul Whiteman's TV show for three years starting when he was nine years old. (Whiteman couldn't pronounce his last name, so he changed it to Rydell.) In 1957, Rydell was a drummer for the local band Rocco and the Saints, which also featured young Frank Avalonne (later Frankie Avalon) on trumpet. He was discovered by manager Frankie Day, who put him up front as a singer because of his good looks. Rydell had

dozens of hits for the Philadelphia Cameo label with help from constant appearances on *American Bandstand*. The British invasion ended his pop-music career, so Rydell moved on to acting, appearing in *Bye Bye Birdie* and recording more mainstream pop for Capitol.

CAMEO 2001 (R)
18 Golden Hits
Exact repro of his 1963 hits package. Eighteen of the biggest Cameo hits by this clean-cut young Philadelphia singer—from 1959's "Kissin' Time" to 1963's "Wildwood Days." Wild One/Volare/Dream Baby/Cha Cha Cha/Sway/I Wanna Thank You/Hey Baby.

CAMEO 8025 (R)
Good Time with Bobby Rydell
Rydell's first record, "Fatty Fatty" (Venise 201) is included along with other hits and misses. Good Time Baby/Lovin' Doll/Cherie/The Third House/Little Queenie.

TREASURE 1058 (R)
All the Hits
Sixteen cover tunes recorded for Cameo between 1962–1964, most taken from his two *All the Hits* LPs. Includes his final Cameo hit "A World without Love" from 1964, vocal versions of "Alley Cat" and "Telstar," plus "Remember Then" (check out the "bass" vocal!), "C.C. Rider," "Him," and "I Know." In mono, though the label says stereo.

THE SAFARIS

The Safaris, from LA, had a big, worldwide hit with 1960's "Image of a Girl," but didn't go on to proverbial fame and fortune. The group originated with Marv Rosenberg and Richard Clasky, two aspiring songwriters. Their first number was called "Touch of Love," and was recorded under the name of The Enchanters, with the pair joined by female vocalist Sandy Weisman. Soon after, Sheldon Briar joined the group, now called The Dories; they recorded "I Love Him So" and "A Lover's Prayer" issued as by "The Angels" on the Tawny label. When Sandy decided to quit the group to get married, local DJ Jim Stephens was brought in to handle lead vocals. The group signed to Eldo records, and recorded their big hit "Image of a Girl." (It's clocklike sound effects were supposedly inspired by Marv's girlfriend's leaky faucet!) A followup, "Girl with a Story in

Her Eyes," was issued, but the majority of the group decided pop music was not the way to make a buck, and so headed off to the halls of academe. Stephens recorded a few singles, followed by a group reunion in 1963 under the new name The Suddens, before the entire enterprise bit the dust. Today Dr. Marv Rosenberg (a psychologist), Sheldon Briar (a lawyer), Richard Clasky (a market researcher), and Jim Stephens (now selling bottled water) continue to sing together occasionally.

IMAGE 1000 (R)

Image of a Girl

Nineteen tunes, including a dozen Safaris tunes, done in an airy doo-wop style typical of the white groups of the era. Almost every song is about the good and bad points of teen love. The balance of the LP collects tracks by The Dories (who record for Dore, of course), The Suddens, and The Enchanters (featuring Sandy Weisman). In addition to the original title hit, there's a fine 1989 remake called "Image of a Girl (Is You)." Four Steps to Love/Touch of Love/Summer Nights/Shadows/Garden of Love/Tragedy of Love.

DOUG SAHM

The King of Tex-Mex rock, and leader of the fabled Sir Douglas Quintet in the '60s and again in the '80s (with time off for good behavior during the '70s). Sahm started playing in 1957 at age 15 in such local bands as The Markays and The Spirits, before putting together his first quintet in 1965 along with fabled organist Augie Meyer on Vox and Farfisa organs. They had a decidedly Tex- Mex sound but, in light of the success of British-invasion groups, producer Huey Meaux tried to pass them off as Brits. He bathed their first cover photo in shadows, hoping to hide the fact that many of the band's members were Chicanos! They had two hits on Meaux's Tribe label, the classic rewrite of "What'd I Say" called "She's About a Mover" and "The Rains Came." When the hits stopped, the band relocated to LA, picking up two hornsmen along the way. They signed to Mercury's Smash subsidiary, recording the excellent *Honky Blues* LP and their last hit single "Mendocino." Since then, Doug has dropped in and out of the band, and the band itself has ranged through a variety of styles, including country, Western swing, conjunto, blues, and rock. In the '80s, the band returned with Sahm to its rockin' roots. Sahm currently performs along with Meyer, Freddy Fender, and Flaco Jimenez as a member of The Texas Tornados (see separate listing).

ANTONES 008 (CL)

Juke Box Music

The Texas Tornado is back with a vengeance! The focus this time out is rockin' R&B; even the ballads have an edge with long-time amigo Rocky Morales blowin' tenacious tenor sax throughout this jumpin' platter. There are affectionate tip-of-the-hats to Johnny Adams ("I Won't Cry"), Etta James ("My Dearest Darling"), Otis Redding ("She Put the Hurt on Me"), and Guitar Slim ("It Hurts to Love Someone"). The tight ensemble Doug has assembled never overplays, but when their time comes they don't miss a beat, especially bassist Jack Barber and drummer/producer George Rains (both veteran band members).

BEAR TRACKS 943401 (L)

Live

Fifteen songs from a mid-'70s show taped by Huey Meaux shortly before Doug made his Atlantic LP *Doug Sahm and Band.* With Augie Meyer on organ, Rocky Morales on tenor sax, and an unknown rhythm section, Doug turns in great versions of his own "She's About a Mover," "Mendocino," "Dynamite Woman," and "The Rains Came." The rest of the material is a mixed bag of covers (some of which work better than others) ranging from Charlie Pride's "Is Anybody Going to San Antone?" to James Brown's "I'll Go Crazy" to Procol Harum's "Whiter Shade of Pale."

EDSEL 154 (L)

Doug Sahm and Band

Early '70s super-session with Augie Meyer, Bob Dylan, Dr. John, David Bromberg, David "Fathead" Newman, Andy Statman, and Flaco Jimenez among the stellar supporting cast. Originally issued as Atlantic 7254 from 1973. Twelve tunes. San Antone/Wallflower/Dealer's Blues/Faded Love/Blues Stay Away from Me/Papa Ain't Salty/I Get Off.

⊗ EDSEL 255 (R)

Sir Doug's Recording Trip

Very impressive two-LP collection culled from Doug Sahm's Mercury/Philips period, 1968–1972. The gatefold sleeve contains an exhaustive appraisal of Sahm's career by Ed Ward, photos, and musicians lowdown. There's no unreleased material here; apparently all that was salvageable was released on the *Rough Edges* LP (Mercury 655) in 1973. That was the album that unleashed the marvelous "Dynamite Woman," a tune that Sahm still plays live, personifying the Doug Sahm sound with soaring vocals and Augie Meyers's galloping Farfisa organ. Also includes his version of Ray Sharpe's Texas barroom classic "Linda Lou," the Mercury 45 "Michoacan" b/w "Westside Blues Again," as well as six cuts from *The Return of Doug Saldana,* Doug's "Chicano album," including "Wasted Days and Wasted Nights" and "Stoned Faces Don't Lie." Recommended for fans and tyros alike. Sahm and his talented bands cross so many musical borders they need passports!

MERCURY 846 586 (L)

The Best of Doug Sahm and The Sir Douglas Quintet 1968–1975

Fabulous 22-track collection. All but about a half-dozen tunes here are also on the excellent Edsel 255, but the tracks really flow together nicely here. Highlights include the previously unreleased "Sunday Sunny Mill Valley Groove Day," a very poppy outing that fits right in following the infectious "Mendocino." After listening to the spine-chillingly beautiful "I Don't Want to Go Home" what else could you follow it with but the magnificent country tune "Be Real"? Also includes one of the best numbers from Sahm's time with the Casablanca label, "I'm Not that Kat Anymore" with a psychedelic phased guitar introduction. While not quite up to Sahm's other organ-chuggin' classics, the previously unreleased "Baby, Let's Go to Mexico" is a real treat for fans.

RHINO 71032 (CL)

Doug Sahm and Friends: The Best of the Atlantic Sessions

Nineteen-song collection (14 on the cassette) combining issued and unissued tracks from Sahm's two 1973 Atlantic LPs *Doug Sahm and Band,* recorded in New York, and *Texas Tornado* (Atlantic 7287), cut in San Francisco. The New York sessions mixed Tex-Mex, R&B, and country played by Doug's regular crew of Texas musicians (Augie Meyer, a then-obscure Flaco Jimenez, and saxophonist Rocky Morales) with Dr. John and some New York studio players along with an inconsequential cameo by Bob Dylan. They mixed Sahm originals like "I Get Off," the R&B stomper "Dealer's Blues," and Bobby Bland's "Your Friends," with covers of Dylan's "Wallflower," Charley Pride's "(Is Anybody Going to) San Antone," and Johnnie and Jack's "Poison Love." The CD includes five outtakes from the New York sessions, among them Sahm's own "Box Car Hobo" and the Conway Twitty weeper "The Image of Me." The second album concentrated largely on Sahm originals, "San Francisco FM Blues," "Hard Way," the Tex-Mex flavored "Nitty Gritty," and a big-band arrangement of Sahm's moody "Blue Horizon." Notes by Chet Flippo, who covered Sahm extensively for Rolling Stone in the '70s, are authoritative and atmospheric.

SAMMY SALVO

Sammy Salvo recorded for various labels during the late '50s and early '60s. He says he styled himself after Bobby Darin but his Alabama roots place him more firmly in the pop/rockabilly mold. His biggest hit in that vein was his version of The Crescendos's "Oh Julie," a haunting, catchy tune that should've done better.

EAGLE 309010 (R)

Here I Go Again

Sixteen pop-rock tunes, including his big hit "Oh Julie." His version of Wayne Handy's "Say Yeah" was quite good and features some fine backing. "One Little Baby" was about the closest he got to out-and-out rockabilly, along with the equally cool "Here I Go Again." The Boudleaux Bryant penned "Wolf Boy" is also very interesting with a fairly tough (for pop-rock) arrangement.

SAM and DAVE

The most energetic and popular soul duo of the '60s, Sam Moore and Dave Prater teamed up in Miami in 1958. After several flops on the Roulette label in the early '60s, they signed to Stax in 1965. They were teamed with producer/songwriters Isaac Hayes and Dave Porter, and with Isaac's gospel piano in the front of the arrangements, and Sam and Dave's exciting performances (they were nicknamed Double Dynamite), they tore up the R&B and pop charts throughout the '60s. The duo remained with Stax through 1968 and went to Stax's distributor, Atlantic, in 1969. They broke up in the early '70s, had a comeback in 1975 with an LP on United Artists, and split up again in 1979. In the same year, The Blues Brothers (aka John Belushi and Dan Ackroyd) had a hit with "Soul Man" that brought Sam and Dave together again, even though they weren't speaking to each other. They quickly broke up again, with Sam performing solo and Dave forming The New Sam and Dave Revue with a substitute Sam, Sam Daniels.

ATLANTIC 80255 (CL)

Hold On, I'm Comin'

Sam and Dave's first album (Atlantic 8708) from 1966. They burst on the soul scene and defined the term "soul duo" with their dynamic singin' and preachin' routines backed by the talented Stax session-men, songwriters (especially Porter and Hayes), and producers. Includes their first Stax hit "You Don't Know Like I Know" and the monster title tune. I Got Everything I Need/Ease Me/I Take What I Want/It's a Wonder.

ATLANTIC 80305 (CL)

Double Dynamite

Reissue of Stax 712 from 1966, their third LP (the second one on Stax). A dozen classics, most written by Isaac Hayes and Dave Porter, along with a couple by Booker T. Jones. I'm Your Puppet/Soothe Me/You Got Me Hummin'/Said I Wasn't Gonna Tell/When Something Is Wrong with My Baby.

✪ ATLANTIC 81279 (CL)

The Best of Sam and Dave

The best of their Atlantic/Stax sides. LP was originally issued in 1969 with 13 cuts; CD has an additional eight tracks, including their first single ("A Place Nobody Can Find" b/w "Good Night Baby") and "Sweet Home," "I Take What I Want," and two other single tracks never before on LP. Slipshod WEA mastering has so much hiss on "When Something Is Wrong with My Baby" and "Sooth Me" that they sound like they were taken from worn 78s! Soul Man/Hold On, I'm Comin'/Wrap It Up/I Thank You/Soul Sister/Brown Sugar.

RHINO 70296 (CL)

Soul Men

Reissue of Double Dynamite's fourth LP, originally Stax 725 from 1967, including 11 great songs. Soul Man/Broke Down Piece of Man/May I Baby/Let It Be Me/Don't Knock It/Hold It Baby/I'm with You.

RHINO 71012 (CL)

I Thank You

The title track was a huge Top 10 hit for Mr. Moore and Mr. Prater. But instead of being one of those albums where the hit is surrounded by filler, this reissue of Atlantic 8205 (released in 1968) features great music surrounded by more great music. "You Don't Know What You Mean to Me" and "Don't Turn Your Heater Down" are soul songs to write home about. Their version of "Wrap It Up" not only taught The Fabulous Thunderbirds how to do it, but beat Archie Bell and The Drells to the punch by two years. "Talk to the Man," "Love Is after Me," "Ain't That a Lot of Love," and the cover of Otis Redding's "These Arms of Mine" are also satisfying grooves.

SAM THE SHAM and THE PHARAOHS

Led by Domingo "Sam" Samudio, this '60s Texas rock band with a sax-organ lead brought the three-chord Tex-Mex sound to new heights. The band had a local hit on Dingo with a cover of Johnny Fuller's "Haunted House," which helped get the group signed to MGM in 1965. The Pharaohs, all decked out in turbans, first scored with the rock classic "Wooly Bully," and had a string of novelty hits with MGM through 1967, including "JuJu Hand," "Ring Dang Doo," and their other giant smash, "Li'l Red Riding Hood." Anti-Egyptian sentiment due to 1967's Arab-Israeli War led Sam to change the name of the band to The Sam the Sham Revue, but their popularity had fizzled out by the decade's end. The group reunited in 1981 to appear on the Ry Cooder's soundtrack for the film *The Border.*

POLYDOR 827 917 (CL)

The Best of Sam the Sham and The Pharaohs

Exact repro of MGM 4422 from 1967, without the original issue's gatefold cover. It's great to have this LP available again at a budget price. This has all the hits ("Wooly Bully," "Li'l Red Riding Hood," "Ring Dang Doo," and "JuJu Hand"), plus eight great LP cuts, including "Mystery Train," "Red Hot," and "I Wish It Were Me."

TOMMY SANDS

Teen rocker who was active in the late '50s and early '60s; later he became Mr. Nancy Sinatra. He made his first recording in 1949 when he was only 12, and subsequently recorded for RCA as a country singer, finally hitting it big after performing "Teenage Crush" (released on Capitol) on an NBC TV movie. He had several more hits for Capitol through the '50s and also appeared in a number of movies. In the '60s. he recorded for several labels with minimal impact. He moved to Hawaii in the late '60s to open a club and occasionally still performs.

BEAR FAMILY 15643 (L)
The Worryin' Kind
Thirty tracks from this teen rocker, some previously unissued.

REVIVAL 3001 (R)
Tommy Sands
Eighteen Capitol recordings, full of teen jive and jump, from 1957–1961. There's lots of hot guitar licks (played by Buck Owens?, Merle Travis?), and lots of covers of R&B tunes. Cover says stereo, but it's not. Hep-Dee Hoodie/Ring-a-Ding-a-Ding/Oop Shoop/ Honey Love/Maybelline/Hearts of Stone.

THE SAPPHIRES
The (Philly) Sapphires sound has been likened to that of The Orlons. Two male singers (George and Joe) remain very much in the background while the female (Carol) takes the shrill- pitched, commercially oriented solo lead.

COLLECTABLES 5007 (C)
Who Do You Love
Twelve-tune collection, including their 1965 chart hits "Gotta Have Your Love" and "Who Do You Love" that are firmly planted in the same groove as The Chiffons and New York's own Shirelles. From their Swan and ABC period, circa 1963–1965. Good sound quality.

FREDDIE SCOTT
Born in 1933 in Providence, RI, Scott worked as a songwriter for Columbia Music in the '60s. He scored a Top 10 hit with "Hey, Girl" in 1963 and had a Top 40 hit in the late '60s with "Are You Lonely for Me."

COLLECTABLES 5413 (CL)
Sings and Sings and Sings
This does not include his hits, but is a collection of pop and folk songs. If I Had a Hammer/Where Have All the Flowers Gone/Days of Wine and Roses.

JACK SCOTT
Detroit-area rocker, originally from Canada, Scott (born Jack Scafone) produced some wonderful Memphis-influenced sides in the late '50s and early '60s. His songs have a hypnotic quality enhanced by his deep voice and an excellent backup band, The Chantones. He started on ABC-Paramount in 1957, having mild success with "Two Timing Woman." In 1958, he went to Carlton, staying there until 1960, and having hits with "Leroy," "My True Love," and the classic "The Way I Walk," his biggest hit. In 1960, he went to Top Rank and had hits with "Burning Bridges" and "What in the World's Come over You." In 1961, he was on Capitol with "My Dream Come True," and in 1963 he was on the RCA subsidiary label Groove. He remains active today. His early Carlton and ABC-Paramount recordings have been reissued on Rollercoaster and are probably among his best. For the completist, all of his recordings have been reissued on Bear Family 15534, a boxed CD set.

BEAR FAMILY 15005 (R)/15445 (L)
Jack Scott on Groove
Twenty songs recorded between 1963–1965 for the RCA subsidiary Groove, including four never-before-issued sides. A mixture of rockers, ballads, and country songs, featuring excellent sound, a 12-page booklet with notes by Colin Escott, and full discographical information on the recordings. There's Trouble Brewing/I Knew You First/I Prayed for an Angel/Wiggle On Out/Flakey John/Tall Tales/The Road Keeps Winding/Gone Again/Standing on the Outside Looking In/This Is Where I Came In.

BEAR FAMILY 15534 (L)
Classic Scott
Includes early demos plus all his recordings for ABC, Carlton, Top Rank, Capitol, Groove, and Jubilee through the early '70s. Includes unissued songs, alternate takes, and the rare stereo versions of ten Carlton songs.

BISON BOP 2022 (R)
Jack Scott
Fourteen big hits. The Way I Walk/My True Love/ Leroy/Geraldine/Midgie/Go Wild Little Sadie.

BISON BOP 2035 (R)
Jack Scott: Picture Disc
Picture disc version of Bison Bop 2022.

BUFFALO BOP 2050 (R)

Greaseball

Twelve great '50s sides, featuring four previously unissued, including the rockin' "Lonesome Mary" and a moving version of the spiritual "Precious Lord." Leroy/Trouble's Brewing/Bella/Good Deal Lucille/Baby Baby.

MUSIDISC 107292 (L)

The Legendary

Twenty-four, French-label collection of Scott's Carlton recordings from 1958–1959. The liner notes call him "un important challenger d'ELVIS PRESLEY" (mais oui!), and while Scott was never massively popular, he did have his share of loyal followers. The country-trained Scott moves easily from rocker to ballad, from original to cover; the set even includes a version of "Apple Blossom Time" with the fabulous Chantones chanting fabulously in the background. Partially duplicates the collection on Roller Coaster. Leroy/The Way I Walk/My True Love/Goodbye Baby/Save My Soul/Go Wild Little Sadie.

⊙ ROLLER COASTER 3002 (L)

The Way I Walk

Twenty-six marvelous songs recorded for ABC-Paramount and Carlton between 1957–1960, including all his early hits like "Leroy" (and an early unissued version of the song called "Greaseball"), his intense ballads "My True Love" and "With Your Love" (which meant a lot to me when I was a teenager about a thousand years ago), the gospel-flavored "Save My Soul," the incessant "Geraldine" (plus a previously unissued alternate take), the wonderful minor-key and very ethnic-sounding "Bella," and covers of Hank Williams's "I Can't Help It" and Chuck Willis's "What Am I Living For." The recordings have been remastered from original master tapes wherever possible, and the set comes with a 16-page booklet with informative notes by Rob Finnis. Highly recommended.

LITTLE JIMMY SCOTT and THE PAUL GAYTEN BAND

Jimmy's professional stage career started in the '40s with shake dancer Estelle "Caldonia" Young. In 1949, he signed with Lionel Hampton and cut his most successful record "Everybody's Somebody's Fool." Then, in 1951, he joined the band of singer/talent scout/pianist/bandleader Paul Gayten. Jimmy sings in a sweeping high tenor, weaving in and out of tempo with ease and grace. His best recordings were made for King in the late '50s.

SPECIALTY 2170 (CL)

Regal Records: Live in New Orleans

This session was recorded live in 1951 at Rip's Playhouse, and came from a tape found in Gayten's garage. The most exciting cut on this nine-song set is "Dueling Tenors," featuring "Wildman" Sam Butera (of Louis Prima fame) honking in mortal combat with Ray Abrams. CD also contains two other fine sax instrumentals by Abrams.

LINDA SCOTT

Linda Scott had a big Number 3 hit with her first release in 1961, a version of the Hammerstein and Kern standard "I've Told Every Little Star." At 17 years of age, she was voted "Most Promising Singer" by *Cashbox*, but her subsequent releases didn't do nearly as well.

CANADIAN AMERICAN 1007 (R)

Great Scott!

Starry-eyed singer who looked for every little star that could follow her single big hit. Starlight, Starbright/Little Star/Count Every Star/Catch a Falling Star.

RAY SCOTT

Rockabilly and rockin' country artist, best known for his often reissued "Kaw-Liga" takeoff called "Boppin' Wig Wam Willie," as well as for writing "Flying Saucers Rock and Roll."

WHITE LABEL 8913 (R)

The Real Memphis Sound, Vol. 2: Ray "Mr. You Drive Me Crazy" Scott

Excellent rockabilly and rockin' country. This release is drawn from demos and alternate takes drawn from sessions for: Marshall Ellis's Erwin label with The Four Recorders, including an alternate of "Boppin' Wig Wam Willie"; Jim Stewart's Satellite label (later Stax) with The Demons; later Erwin recordings with The Monarchs engineered by Scotty Moore; and Stompertime-label (owned by Ellis and Eddie Bond) recordings. Includes the title track, his second big hit.

THE SEARCHERS

The Searchers were an extremely successful Liverpool group (three of their first four singles went to Number 1 in England, and they had 13 chart records in the US in two years). Most of their hits were covers of US artists: Jackie DeShannon ("Needles and Pins" and "When You Walk in the Room"), The Clovers ("Love Potion Number 9"), The Coasters ("Ain't That Just Like Me"), and

The Drifters ("Sweets for My Sweet"). They were also in the forefront of the folk-rock movement, having hits with "What Have They Done to the Rain" and P.F. Sloan's "Take Me for What I'm Worth."

RHINO 70162 (CL)
Greatest Hits
Excellent collection of 14 hits recorded between 1963–1965. Many songs appear in true stereo, and the set includes beautiful color photos and excellent liner notes.

BIG AL SEARS
A major tenor-sax player of both the big-band and '50s rock-and-roll eras. Sears began his professional career in the late '20s, while still in his teens, and, during the '30s and '40s, he lent his blues-based style of playing to various jazz ensembles, including Chick Webb's orchestra, Andy Kirk and his Cloud of Joy, and, after World War II, Duke Ellington's orchestra. In the '50s, he was both a session musician and a leader of his own recording aggregations for Coral, RCA, and Herald.

BEAR FAMILY 15668 (L)
"Sear-iously"
Twenty-five fine tracks, recorded between 1949–1956, evenly split between a big-band jazz feel and songs that lean toward rock and roll. Six of the cuts feature vocals. Highlights include "Brown Boy" (the forerunner of The Jive Bombers later hit retitled "Bad Boy"), "Mag's Alley," "Fo-Yah," "Goin' Uptown," "Come and Dance with Me," and "Love Call." Typical Bear Family quality with excellent sound, great photos, and an informative 28-page booklet. My only regret, a minor one, is that Sears's lead performance on Johnny Hodges's 1951 hit "Castle Rock" is not included.

NEIL SEDAKA
Sedaka was one of the foremost "Brill Building" NY writers of the late '50s and early '60s who went on to become a highly successful solo performer. He started writing with Howard Greenfield when he was only 13; they formed the group The Tokens to sing their songs. He signed on as a writer for Don Kirshner's Aldon Music Publishers, writing such hits as "Stupid Cupid" and "The Diary." He decided to try singing some of them himself, resulting in '60s hits for RCA including "Calendar Girl," "Breaking Up Is Hard to Do,"

and "Happy Birthday, Sweet Sixteen." His high tenor voice, teeny-bopper lyrics, and syrupy arrangements made him one of the most cloying of all the pop vocalists. In the mid-'70s, he retuned again to the charts with a number of big hits on the Rocket label, and continues to tour and perform regularly.

RCA 2406 (CL)
All Time Greatest Hits, Vol. 2
Oh boy, twenty more Sedaka hits! Stupid Cupid/Sunny/The Closest Thing to Heaven/The Diary/The Same Old Fool/Bad Girl.

RCA 53465 (L)
Sings His Greatest Hits
A straight CD reissue of a frequently issued LP originally put out in the early '60s. The CD features only 12 cuts, but every one of them is an exuberant chartmaker by The Juilliard School of Music's revenge on the world of rock and roll. No real liner notes, but fine sound, and a nice cover photo in keeping with the period of this retrospective. Individual tastes vary, of course, but, for me, 12 cuts by Mr. Sedaka are more than enough. Next Door to an Angel/Oh! Carol/Run Samson Run/Calendar Girl/Breaking Up Is Hard to Do/Happy Birthday, Sweet Sixteen.

RONNIE SELF
Wild rockabilly artist from Missouri known as "Mr. Frantic." He started recording for ABC-Paramount in 1956 before going over to Columbia to record a series of classic rockers, including the marvelous "Ain't I'm a Dog" and "Bop-a-Lena," plus a wild adaptation of Bill Monroe's "Rocky Road Blues" later covered by Gene Vincent. He was also a successful songwriter, penning "I'm Sorry" and "Sweet Nothin's" for Brenda Lee. He went to Decca in the late '50s, where his career finally petered out. He died in 1981.

BEAR FAMILY 15436 (L)
Bop-a-Lena
Thirty tunes taken from master recordings done for ABC, Columbia, Decca, and Kapp between 1956–1963, including seven previously unissued. With a 24-page booklet by Colin Escott. Ain't I'm a Dog/Petrified/Flame of Love/Rocky Road Blues/Instant Man/Ugly Stick/Go Go Cannibal/Houdini.

REDITA 139 (R)
Rockin' Ronnie Self

Eighteen tunes, 17 previously unreleased. Mostly taken from demo tapes (recently discovered) and acetates, these tunes find Ronnie doing mostly self-penned, country-flavored tunes. Almost every song seems aimed at the Roger Miller audience (Roger had a hit with Self's "I Ain't Comin' Home Tonight"), so unless you like that kind of country tune, you'd best steer clear of this. Home in Your Hand/Biggest Dog in Town/Hair of the Dog/Wild and Wooly Life.

THE SENSATIONS

The Sensations were led by female vocalist Yvonne Baker with a male backup trio. The group formed in 1954 in Philadelphia as The Cavaliers. When they signed to Atco, they were renamed The Sensations, and scored a few near-hits, including a doo-wop version of "Yes Sir, That's My Baby" and "Please Mr. Disk Jockey." Yvonne retired to get married, but was coaxed out of her retirement during the 1961 doo-wop revival by bass singer Alphonso Howell to re-form The Sensations. This group consisted of Baker, Howell, baritone Sam Armstrong (formerly of The Rays), and tenor Richard Curtain (a founding member of The Hide-a-ways). Their sole hit, 1962's "Let Me In," released on Argo, is memorable for its nonsense chorus with the immortal words "We-oop, we-oop, ooo-we-oop-we-oop." Followups failed to chart, with various incarnations of Sensations coming and going, and Baker recording as a solo act.

REVIVAL 3009 (R)
Let Me In

Almost all you ever wanted to hear from the period 1956–1962, embracing all the group's major successes: "Yes Sir, That's My Baby" (1956), "Music, Music, Music" (1961), and "Let Me In" (1962). Eighteen crisp and clean sounding cuts in stereo, including the beautiful "My Debut to Love," plus a couple of rare boy/girl duet cuts made by Baker for Aladdin in 1958.

THE SHADOWS

One of the most important instrumental bands ever, and one of England's most successful bands. They started in 1958 as Cliff Richard's backup band, The Drifters (see separate Richard listing), but changed their name to avoid confusion with the US doo-woppers. The original group consisted of guitarists Hank Marvin and Bruce Welch, bassist Jet Harris, and drummer Tony Meehan. In 1960, they had their first solo hit, the original version of the instrumental classic, "Apache." Meehan left in 1961, and was joined by Harris in 1962 for solo hits; they were replaced by Brian Bennett (drm) and Brian Locking (b). Locking left in 1963 to become a Jehovah's Witness, and was replaced by John Rostill. This lineup remained stable until 1968 when Marvin decided that ten years was enough and dissolved the band. In 1970, he got back together with Welch and John Farrar to form a vocal-harmony group! In 1973, The Shadows re-formed with Marvin, Welch, Farrar, and Bennett.

EMI (UK) 48278 (L)
String of Hits

CD issue of EMI 3310 from 1979. The Shads were down to a trio led by guitarists Hank Marvin and Bruce Welch with Brian Bennett on drums, joined by Alan Jones (b), Alan Hawkshaw (pno), and Dave Lawson (syn). Sound quality is great, tunes are '70s fare. Theme from *The Deerhunter*/Don't Cry for Me, Argentina/Rulers in the Sky/Classical Gas/Heart of Glass/Bridge over Troubled Waters/Parisienne Walkways.

EMI (UK) 746 243 (L)
20 Golden Greats

Columbia (UK) recordings from 1960–1967. Beautiful sound, much in real stereo. Apache/Man of Mystery/FBI/Wonderful Land/The Rise and Fall of Flingel Bunt/The Savage/Geronimo.

EMI (UK) 797 171 (L)
The Early Years: 1959–1966

Monster 120-track, six-CD box set featuring every Shadows number recorded from 1959–1965, plus a bunch of singles from 1966. Almost everything here is instrumental, and it's a good thing, too, because their vocals sound like The Four Freshmen. As it is, most of the instrumentals sound like soundtrack music for cheesy European movies. But don't let that stop you from considering a purchase, because the Shads had a unique slant on every tune. And, with the sheer bulk of material, there are plenty of tunes that were right up there with The Ventures, especially in The Shads's mid-'60s recordings. Includes a 24-page booklet with notes by John Tobler. Stingray/A Place in the Sun/Blue Shadows/Fandango/Dakota/Ranka Chank/Shindig/Shazam/Les Girls/Guitar Tango/The Bandit/Kinda Cool/The Savage/Shadoogie/Jet Black.

MUSIC FOR PLEASURE 6002 (L)
Another String of Hot Hits (And More)
Twenty-song CD lasting nearly an hour, divided between their original '60s hit records ("Kon-Tiki," "Apache," "Wonderful Land," and "FBI"), and '70s and '80s cover tunes ("Something," "Good Vibrations," "Goodbye Yellow Brick Road," "Pinball Wizard," and "Black Is Black").

SEE FOR MILES 246 (RL)
The EP Collection
Twenty-two tracks. Perfidia/All Day/Lady Penelope/Thunderbirds Theme/Mustang/Giant/Las Tres Carabellas/Valencia/Tonight/Little Princess/Jet Black.

THE SHANGRI-LAS

One of the most famous and "toughest" of the girl groups, the group consisted of two sets of sisters from NY: lead singer Mary Weiss, her sister Betty (who dropped in and out of the group) and the identical twins Mary Anne and Marge Ganser. They signed to Leiber and Stoller's Red Bird label in 1964 and had classic hits that were more like playlets than songs, little slices of teen-age angst. These were produced and arranged by the legendary Shadow Morton and written by the team of Ellie Greenwich and Jeff Barry, and Morton. Most of the songs were maudlin, ranging in topic from breakups ("Remember [Walking in the Sand]"), teen rebellion ("Out in the Streets"), the death of a boyfriend (their biggest hit, "Leader of the Pack," complete with real motorcycle sound effects!), the death of a young couple ("Give Us Your Blessing"), and perhaps the ultimate tragedy, the death of mom ("I Can Never Go Home Anymore"). The hits stopped when Red Bird and the group folded in 1967. Interest in their music among Britain's punk rockers encouraged them to re-form in the late '70s, but without Marge Ganser who had died of a drug overdose.

CENTURY (JAPAN) 00295 (L)
Greatest Hits and More
Twenty-four hits and lots more chewing-gum smackers for bad girls. Leader of the Pack/Give Him a Great Big Kiss/Remember (Walking in the Sand)/Twist and Shout.

COLLECTABLES 5011 (CL)
Remember The Shangri Las
Twelve cuts. Leader of the Pack/Give Him a Great Big Kiss/Give Us Your Blessing.

DEL SHANNON

One of the brightest stars of early '60s rock, Del was from Grand Rapids, MI, where he was discovered in 1960 by famed Ann Arbor producer Ollie McLaughlin, who had him audition for the Detroit label Big Top. He was sent to NY to record and, with his self-penned tunes, strong voice with a highly distinctive falsetto, and a driving backup band featuring Max Crook on the high-pitched Musitron, he produced hits for the label from 1961–1963, including his biggies "Runaway" and "Hats Off to Larry." While touring England, he met the fledgling Beatles, and became the first American artist to cover a Lennon-McCartney song with his mid-1963 version of "From Me to You." He had legal troubles with Big Top and went over to Amy in 1964, scoring more huge hits with covers of "Handy Man" and "Do You Wanna Dance?" and his own "Keep Searchin'" and "Stranger in Town." He went to Liberty in 1966, recorded a good version of "The Big Hurt," and reverted to his real name of Charles Westover to record in a more country vein. He turned to producing at the end of the decade, having Top 10 hits with Smith's "Baby It's You" and Brian Hyland's version of "Gypsy Woman." He remained big in England, recording an excellent live LP there in 1972. By the '80s, he made a wonderful comeback LP backed by Tom Petty and The Heartbreakers, making the Top 40 in 1982 with his cover of "Sea of Love." He committed suicide in 1990 while preparing to record another comeback LP with Petty producing.

EDSEL 121 (RLC)
Runaway Hits
British edition of the LP that originally was issued on Del's own Bug records (Bug 1, 1983). Sixteen of Del's biggest hits cut for Big Top (1961–1963) and Amy (1964–1965). Detailed liner notes and complete discography. Runaway/Keep Searchin'/Hats Off to Larry/Stranger in Town/Little Town Flirt/Sue's Gonna Be Mine.

EMI 95842 (CL)

The Liberty Years

After his early smash hits on Big Top and Amy, Del hitched up with Liberty records in 1966. But times had changed, and of the 26 cuts here, only "The Big Hurt," "Under My Thumb," "She," and "Runaway '67" brushed the bottom of the charts. Also includes some unreleased material.

LINE 9.00252 (L)

Hats Off to Del Shannon

Twelve songs, none over three-minutes long (reflecting the demands of AM radio). The Swiss Maid/Cry Myself to Sleep/Hats Off to Larry/So Long Baby.

LINE 9.00436 (L)

The Del Shannon Collection

Another collection of early '60s tracks as they were issued in Germany. Highlight is the fun flipside to "Little Town Flirt," "The Wamboo," which sounds like the African-pop music of its time, and is making its first CD appearance. All tunes in mono. Runaway/From Me to You/She's Gotta Be Mine/Hats Off to Larry/Don't Gild the Lily, Lily/Jody.

✪ RHINO 70977 (CL)

Greatest Hits

Twenty of Del's greatest taken from the original master tapes. Runaway/Hats Off to Larry/Little Town Flirt/Handy Man/Do You Wanna Dance/Sue's Gotta Be Mine.

RHINO 70982 (CL)

Del Shannon Sings Hank Williams: Your Cheatin' Heart

Reissue of Amy 8004 from 1965. Del pays tribute to his main man with 12 Hank Sr. tunes. Your Cheatin' Heart/Kaw-Liga/That Lonesome Whistle/You Win Again/Hey Good Looking/Cold Cold Heart.

RHINO 70983 (CL)

Little Town Flirt

Reissue of his second album, a hits collection originally issued as Big Top 1308. Twelve tracks, with his early smash hits, including the title track. Hats Off to Larry/Runaround Sue/Go Away Little Girl/Dream Baby/Runaway.

THE SHELLS

Excellent New York doo-wop group who originally formed in 1957, and recorded a number of fine singles for Johnson and various other labels without much success. In 1960 doo-wop collectors Don Fileti and Wayne Stierle encouraged the owner of Johnson to repress the 1957 recording of "Baby Oh Baby," which subsequently became a Top 30 hit. The group re-formed and started recording again, but "Baby Oh Baby" remained their only moment of glory.

COLLECTABLES 5077 (CL)

Golden Classics

Twelve songs. Baby, Oh Baby/A Toast to Your Birthday/Pleading No More/Happy Holiday/My Cherie/Don't Say Goodbye.

THE SHEPPARDS

Late '50s/early '60s Chicago R&B vocal group who bridged the gap between '50s doo-wop and '60s soul. Their most well-known song is the beautiful 1959 doo-wop ballad, "Island of Love."

COLLECTABLES 5078 (CL)

Island of Love: Golden Classics

Eighteen tracks. Island of Love/Loving You/Meant to Be/Feel Like Lovin'/Queen of Hearts/Tragic/So In Need for Love/Just When I Needed You Most.

TONY SHERIDAN

Tony Sheridan was a big star in Hamburg, whose spot in rock history is assured because his rockin' 1962 covers of "My Bonnie" and "When the Saints Go Marchin' In" were backed by The Beatles (credited as The Beat Brothers, the name used by all of Sheridan's many backup bands) with original drummer Pete Best.

BEAR FAMILY 15249 (R)

Ich Lieb Dich So

Sixteen of Sheridan's German-language hits recorded for Polydor between 1962–1965, with backing by The Beat Brothers, The Big 6, and the orchestras of Bert Kampfert and Hort Wende. The title tune is his version of Ben E. King's "Ecstasy." La Bamba/Ya Ya, Pts. 1 and 2/Hey Ba Ba Re Bop/Let's Slop.

BILLY SHERRILL

Unsuccessful rockabilly singer who later became one of country music's most successful producers.

DOMINO 1010 (R)

Rock On Baby

All of Sherrill's good rockabilly numbers are here, as well as a few awful ones. Rock On Baby/Rock and Roll Teenager/Teen Hop Rock/Cadillac Baby/Kool Kat/Don't You Rock Me Daddy-O.

THE SHIRELLES

One of the earliest and most successful girl groups, named after group member Shirley Owens, and including original lead singer Doris Kenner, Beverly Lee, and Addie ("Micki") Harris. The high-school quartet from Passaic, NJ, was discovered by a classmate whose mom owned a local label, Tiara (later Scepter Records). In 1958, they recorded their first single "I Met Him on a Sunday," which was leased to Decca. Group member Shirley Owens wrote the group's third hit, "Tonight's the Night," that she wanted to sing herself; after it hit big, she became the group's lead singer. All their Scepter material was produced by Luther Dixon of The Four Buddies. Only the best songwriters were used, including Bacharach/David ("Baby It's You"), Goffin/King ("Will You Love Me Tomorrow?"), and Dixon himself ("Soldier Boy" and "Boys"). They were one of the few black groups to score consistently higher on the pop, as opposed to the R&B, charts. The Shirelles remained extremely popular until Dixon left in 1963, and their hits stopped coming. Their hits were covered by many British invasion groups including The Beatles ("Boys" and "Baby It's You") and Manfred Mann ("Sha-La-La"). Doris finally left in 1968, and they soldiered on as a trio known as Shirley and the Shirelles, until Shirley went solo in 1975. Doris returned, and the group continued to perform in oldies shows until the death of Micki Harris from a heart attack.

ACE 356 (L)
The Best of The Shirelles
Thirty-two cuts in chronological order. Includes all of their Top-40 Scepter sides, as well as their less-successful singles and a few album-only cuts. The non-single "Putty in Your Hands," with its "abuse me but don't refuse me" story line is as good as it is politically incorrect. And surely no one has ever sung about Armageddon as sweetly as The Shirelles on "Doomsday." Tonight's the Night/Will You Love Me Tomorrow/Dedicated to the One I Love/Mama Said/Foolish Little Girl/Soldier Boy.

COLLECTABLES 5247 (CL)
Golden Classics
Twelve-tune set embraces the moody "Baby It's You" (1962) and their first four big hits, duplicating a slew of other reissues. Average sound quality and, for once from Collectables, decent sleeve notes by Kevin Thomas Tong.

⊛ IMPACT 011 (L)
The Shirelles Greatest Hits
Twenty-two hits and more, superior in all ways to the Rhino issue. All but "Dedicated to the One I Love" is in real stereo. Tonight's the Night/Boys/Baby It's You/Foolish Little Girl/Soldier Boy/Sha La La/Mama Said.

RHINO 75897 (L)
The Shirelles Anthology
CD issue of Rhino 1101 is a bit of a ripoff. The LP was a two-record set with 28 cuts, but the CD has only 16 cuts, with a total playing time of 40 minutes! This has the cream of the crop (though missing such greats as "Putty in Your Hands") and excellent sound, with the unmixed master tapes used to make the digital transfer. "Dedicated to the One I Love" is in original mono; everything else is in stereo. Soldier Boy/Sha-La-La/Will You Love Me Tomorrow/Boys/Baby It's You.

SHIRLEY and LEE

"The Sweethearts of the Blues," the New Orleans duo of Shirley Pixley (age 14) and Leonard Lee (age 15) first recorded for Aladdin in 1952 and had a local hit with "I'm Gone." In 1955, they had a rock hit with "Feel So Good," and they hit their peak in 1956 with the all-time classic "Let the Good Times Roll." Aladdin capitalized on their "Sweethearts" image by releasing a soap opera on successive singles, including "Shirley Come Back to Me," "Shirley's Back," "Lee Goofed," and "Lee's Dream." They went to Warwick in 1960 where they recut "Let the Good Times Roll," and then split up. Shirley went to LA where she teamed up with Jessie Hill as Shirley and Jessie, later performing with Breton Wood as Shirley and Alfred, and with Maurice Rodgers as Shirley and Shep. Shirley and Lee re-formed in the early '70s for rock-revival shows and, in 1975, Shirley (now Shirley Goodman) became a disco queen with "Shame Shame Shame" released as by Shirley and Company (the "Company" was Cuban singer Jesus Alvarez). Leonard Lee died of a heart attack in October 1976.

EMI 92775 (L)

Legendary Masters Series: Shirley and Lee, Vol. 1

Twenty Aladdin recordings with backup by top New Orleans sessionmen, including their hits "I'm Gone," "Let the Good Times Roll," "Feel So Good," "I Feel Good," and "When I Saw You." Excellent sound and nicely packaged with fold-out booklet with detailed notes, photos of memorabilia, and a nice reproduction of the Aladdin label on the disc. Baby/Confessin'/Comin' Over/Deed I Do/I Want to Dance/Don't You Know I Love You.

THE SHOWMEN

General Norman Johnson and The Showmen came to New Orleans from Norfolk, VA, in 1961 and recorded for Joe Banashak's Instant and Minit labels. They had a distinctive sound showcased on their all-time classic, "It Will Stand," which has become a rock-and-roll anthem. Johnson left the group shortly after this hit and later joined the popular '70s soul group, Chairman of the Board.

COLLECTABLES 5162 (CL)

It Will Stand

Country Fool/Valley of Love/39-21-40 Shape/True Fine Mama.

JUMPIN' GENE SIMMONS

Jumpin' Gene (no relation to the Kiss tongueman) had a lengthy career that only produced one hit, "Haunted House," and one LP, of the same name, both in 1964.

HI (UK) 416 (R)

Goin' Back to Memphis

This LP compiles Simmons's single sides, including the title tune (his first song recorded for Hi, but leased to Checker in 1960), and 15 Hi sides cut between 1961–1967, including "Haunted House." Highlights

are two excellent previously unissued tunes—"Come on Over Put Some Love on Me" and a cover of The Clovers's "Down in the Alley"—plus such excellent "flops" as "Skinny Minny," "Bossy Boss," "Keep That Meat in the Pan," and "The Shape You Left Me In."

JOE SIMON

New Orleans-area soulster who moved to Oakland, CA, at age 15, and recorded for a number of local labels. After some songs were picked up nationally by Vee Jay, he signed to Sound Stage 7 in 1966, having a long string of hits until 1970, including the soul classic "The Chokin' Kind." He went to Spring in 1970, and he continued to score hits, including the classic "Drowning in the Sea of Love."

CHARLY 144 (L)

Lookin' Back: The Best of 1966–1970

Sixteen Sound Stage 7 hits. Chokin' Kind/No Sad Songs/Message from Maria/Baby Don't Be Lookin' in My Mind/Nine Pound Steel/Put Your Trust in Me.

SOUTHBOUND 954 (L)

The Sounds of Simon/Simon Country

Reissue of two early '70s LPs, featuring 19 country standards. With these efforts, Simon joined a handful of R&B/soul singers (Ray Charles, Percy Sledge, and Joe Tex) who put on Stetsons for a while to bolster their careers. Help Me Make It Through the Night/My Woman, My Woman, My Wife/Before the Next Teardrop Falls/Kiss an Angel Good Morning.

SOUTHBOUND 971 (L)

Mood, Heart and Soul/Today

Two mid-'70s albums on one CD, totaling 18 cuts. Simon's Southern soul was tempered by covers of mainstream pop songs. Neither One of Us Wants to Be the First to Say Goodbye/Good Time Charlie's Got the Blues/Let's Spend the Night Together/I Just Want to Make Love to You/Let the Good Times Roll/What a Wonderful World/Carry Me/The Best Time of My Life/Come Get to This.

ED SIMPSON/MARCELL STRONG

RED LIGHTNIN' 0039 (R)

Two Soul Chiefs

Recent recordings by two obscure but good St. Louis soul singers. Simpson is more low down and bluesy, while Strong has a more mainstream funk sound. The record is marred by primitive arrangements.

NANCY SINATRA

Frank's daughter and the subject of the pop standard "Nancy with the Laughing Face." She is either loved or loathed, but somehow still retains her popularity. She began recording for dad's Reprise label in 1961, but it wasn't until 1964 when she teamed with former Duane Eddy producer Lee Hazelwood that the hits started, from 1964's "So Long Babe" to 1969's "Drummer Man." Her megahit "These Boots Are Made for Walkin'" topped the charts in 1966, and her duet with dad on "Something Stupid" put Frank back on the pop charts in 1967. She also recorded several duets with Hazelwood, including the original versions of "Jackson" (later covered by Johnny Cash) and "Some Velvet Morning" (covered by Vanilla Fudge and Lydia Lunch).

RAVEN 1012 (R)
Lightning's Girl
The ultimate Nancy LP, lovingly compiled by Glenn A. Baker. Side 1 has the solo sides, including "These Boots Are Made for Walking," "How Does That Grab You," "Darlin'," "Sugar Town," and the title hit. Side 2 has the duets with Lee Hazelwood including "Jackson" and "Some Velvet Morning," plus her Number 1 duet with dad, "Something Stupid." Gatefold cover has dozens of photos including lots of Nancy with Elvis.

RHINO 70166 (L)
Fairy Tales and Fantasies:
The Best of Nancy and Lee
This collection of hit duets draws heavily on the 1968 LP, *Nancy and Lee* (Reprise 6273), with the addition of "Did You Ever?" from their 1972 reunion album *Nancy and Lee Again* (RCA 4645), a Bobby Braddock tune recorded by George Jones and Tammy Wynette in 1976. The sweet pop vocals of Sinatra contrasted nicely with Hazelwood's gruff, world-weary singing (if you could call it that) making them a hot duo for a while. Jackson/Some Velvet Morning/Sand/Summer Wine/I've Been Down So Long (It Looks Like Up to Me).

RHINO 70227 (C)/75885 (L)
Nancy Sinatra's All Time Hits: Boots
Fourteen Reprise singles, from her 1965 flop "So Long Babe" to her final 1970 single "Hook and Ladder," written by Norman Greenbaum. In between, there are lots of real hits, not only "These Boots Are Made for Walkin'" but also "Sugar Town," "Lightning's Girl," "How Does That Grab You, Darlin'," "Something Stupid," and her movie themes "You Only Live Twice," "The Last of the Secret Agents," and "Tony Rome." Comes with a photo-filled insert.

TEENAGER 605 (R)
Like I Do
There are some gorgeous photos on this collector's package as well as a great selection of scarce cuts. "Your Groovy Self," the song she sang in *Speedway*, and the duet with The King on "There Ain't Nothin' Like a Song" are here. "Back on the Road," a duet with the brilliant Lee Hazelwood is a pleasant surprise, a ramblin' country tune with steel guitar, as is Nancy's solo "Get While the Gettin's Good." Also includes a couple more duets with Hazelwood and some covers of pop classics. Is Anybody Goin' to San Antone/On Broadway/Call Me/To Know You Is to Love You.

JOHNNY SKILES

WHITE LABEL 8967 (R)
The Original
Johnny Skiles, from Monroe, LA, settled in Oregon after World War II where he recorded these 17 tunes. He never left his roots though. His hillbilly-flvaored rockabilly sides, like "Rockin' and Rollin'," "Hard Luck Blues," "Come Paddle Footin' Down," and "Is My Baby Comin' Back" catch that fleeting primitive sound we love. Seven of the tunes are instrumentals especially made for country DJs, a clever idea that netted Skiles some handy pocket money when the DJs segued from one thing to another. The LP is rounded out by some very rare, unreleased country-rock demos.

THE SKYLINERS

Excellent white doo-wop group from Pittsburgh best known for their classic "Since I Don't Have You." Led by Jimmy Beaumont, perhaps the finest white doo-wop singer, the group was composed of three members of The Crescents and two members of The El Rios, including wonderful tenor Janet Vogel. They signed with the local Calico label in 1958, and had several hits through 1960 including "Since I Don't Have You" and "This I Swear," with their excellent doo-wop harmonies put in front of lush orchestrations. They moved to Colpix before splitting up, due, in part, to Janet's struggles with recurring periods of depression. Beaumont went solo for a while, forming a new Skyliners in the mid-'60s. Four of the five original members re-formed in 1970 to play the rock revival circuit, staying together until 1979. Janet committed suicide in 1980.

ACE 78 (L)
Since I Don't Have You
Twenty-one Calico and Laurie-label vocal gems. This I Swear/It Happened Today/Lonely Way/Pennies from Heaven.

ORIGINAL SOUND 8873 (L)
Greatest Hits
Twenty original hits. Since I Don't Have You/Stardust/When I Fall in Love/This I Swear/Pennies from Heaven.

RELIC 5053 (R)
Pre-flight
Showcases lead singer Jimmy Beaumont, including seven sides with The Skyliners (three are a cappella, including a gorgeous practice version of "Since I Don't Have You"), five a-cappella sides with his first group, The Crescents, both sides of The Skyliners rare 1962 45 on Viscount ("Tell Me" b/w "Comes Love"), and four a-cappella sides by labelmates, The Centuries.

PERCY SLEDGE

One of the best of the Atlantic soul singers, Sledge specialized in the slow, heavily gospel-flavored ballad style known as deep soul. After years with The Esquires combo in Alabama, Percy went solo; his first record was the ethereal "When a Man Loves a Woman," his best-known hit, recently covered by white clonester Michael Bolton. Sledge recorded at Rick Hall's Fame Studio in Muscle Shoals, utilizing the studio's all-star sessionmen, including Dan Penn, Spooner Oldham, and Chips Moman. He had three solid years of hits, from 1966–1969, including many songs written by the Muscle Shoals team, such as "It Tears Me Up," "Out of Left Field," and "Cover Me." He also covered Mitty Collier's "I Had a Talk with My Woman Last Night," James

Carr's "Dark End of the Street," and Chuck Jackson's "Any Day Now." He stayed with Atlantic until 1973, scoring a minor hit in that year with "Sunshine," which later was a smash for The O'Jays. He went to Capricorn in 1974, scoring with "I'll Be Your Everything." The late '80s found him back in the studio recording soul classics and even C&W!

✪ ATLANTIC 80212 (L)
The Ultimate Collection
One of the best single-artist, soul collections I've heard. Originally issued on vinyl, the CD adds four cuts, "Sudden Stop," "That's How Strong My Love Is," "You Really Got a Hold on Me," and "Put a Little Lovin' on Me." (As far as I know these haven't been reissued anywhere else.) Twenty cuts in all, nearly an hour of playing time. When a Man Loves a Woman/Cover Me/Warm and Tender Love/Dark End of the Street/You're Pouring Water on a Drowning Man.

ATLANTIC (JAPAN) 68 (L)
Take Time to Know Her
Reissue of Atlantic 8120 from 1968, featuring 12 cuts. Baby Help Me/Out of Left Field/Cover Me/Sudden Stop.

ATLANTIC (JAPAN) 2368 (L)
When a Man Loves a Woman
Reproduces Sledge's first LP (Atlantic 8125 of 1966), including the title hit and ten more. You're Pouring Water on a Drowning Man/Put a Little Lovin' on Me.

BULLDOG 3007 (R)
Out of Left Field
Twelve remakes of Sledge's big Atlantic hits, plus other fine deep-soul songs. Unfortunately, the disc is marred by poor recording quality and overly prominent girlie choruses. When a Man Loves a Woman/Out of Left Field/Cover Me/Warm and Tender Love/It Tears Me Up/My Adorable One/Thief in the Night/You're Pouring Water on a Drowning Man.

DEMON 140 (RL)
Wanted Again
Percy's country sessions from 1986–1987 recorded at Quin Ivy's Broadway Sound Studio in Sheffield, AL. He sings ten C&W tunes in his inimitable deep-soul style. It might be stretching the country/soul connection a bit thin by having Percy doing straightforward versions of "Hey Good Lookin'" and "Wabash Cannonball" (I mean, would you want to hear Roy Acuff doing "The Funky Chicken"?), but the ballads work really well. On tunes like "Keep the Fire Burning," "Today I Started Loving You Again," and "Kiss an Angel Good Morning" Percy really gets to show off his talent. The band, led by living legend Travis

Wammack on guitar, is excellent in the classic deep-soul, understated way. For the Good Times/He'll Have to Go.

INSTANT 5041 (L)
Warm and Tender Love
Twenty recent recordings of uncertain origin. If Loving You Is Wrong/When a Man Loves a Woman/Behind Closed Doors/Dock of the Bay/You Send Me.

RHINO 70285 (CL)
It Tears Me Up
Twenty-three picks from his Atlantic years, 1966–1971. Not all the songs are gold; there is some pop drivel, as well as bold ideas that missed the mark. Dark End of the Street/Warm and Tender Love/It Tears Me Up/Kind Woman/I'm Hanging Up My Heart for You/Bless Your Sweet Little Soul/It's All Wrong but It's Alright/Out of Left Field/Take Time to Know Her/When a Man Loves a Woman.

HUEY "PIANO" SMITH

One of New Orleans's best-known pianists, Huey spent years with Earl King, and played on countless sessions. He backed Little Richard on his first Specialty sessions, and also played the famous piano introduction for Smiley Lewis's "I Hear You Knocking." For his own recordings, he used an all-star session lineup with vocals by The Clowns, including lead vocalists Bobby Marchan and Gerri Hall. He had novelty hits on Ace, including "Rockin' Pneumonia and the Boogie Woogie Flu" and "Don't You Just Know It." In 1960, he went to Imperial where Marchan was replaced by Curley Moore, but a legal technicality brought Smith back to Ace where he had another hit with "Pop-Eye," which started that 1962 dance craze. Huey never even got credit for his biggest hit, "Sea Cruise"; Ace erased the original lead vocal by Gerri Hall and overdubbed Frankie Ford, issuing the record as "by" Ford! Huey spent the '60s recording excellent soul under a number of different names (The Pitter-Pats and The Hueys on Instant, and Shindig Smith and The Soulshakers on his own Pitter-Pat label), but got no hits. He is now a Jehovah's Witness minister.

ACE (US) 1027 (R)
'Twas the Night Before Christmas
Reissue of the 1962 New Orleans Christmas classic finds Huey and The Clowns backed by Dr. John's band. Includes Earl King's "Rock and Roll Santa Claus," six Smith originals, and Christmas favorites.

ACE (US) 2021 (RCL)
Huey "Piano" Smith's Rock and Roll Revival
Sixteen-tune collection of Huey and The Clowns, including their hits "Rockin' Pneumonia" and "Don't You Know Yockomo," as well as some of the tunes they played on. There's some excellent material here that didn't show up on Ace 9 from some years back. "I'll Be John Brown" and "Having a Good Time" are both wonderful tunes with trademark piano from Huey. "Honey, Honey," "Tiddley Wink," "Loberta," and "Sea Cruise" (the original version with Gerri Hall's vocal) are all previously unissued! Indispensable, I would say.

ACE (US) 2038 (RCL)
Good Ole Rock and Roll
Beautiful recreation of the Crescent City's piano-boogie glory days, ably supported by Lee Allen (ten sax), Dr. John (gtr), Alvin Tyler (bar sax), plus the legendary Big Boy Myles (trb), with background vocals by The Clowns and an impressive female, gospel-tinged group, The Heartbeats. Sixteen cuts, with great fidelity. Huey and the boys at their best. Gee Baby/Love Letters/The Ending of Love/Educated Fool/Second Line/Bashful Bob/That Will Get It.

MACK ALLEN SMITH

Mississippi rock and roller who recorded for Sun in 1959, but these recordings were never released. He subsequently recorded for several tiny local labels, including Vee Eight, Delta Sound, and Statue. He was rediscovered in England during the mid-'70s rockabilly revival, and made some recordings there.

REDITA 105 (R)
The Sound of Mack Allen Smith
Eighteen tunes from 1976, originally recorded for Redneck Records in England, including four previously unreleased tracks. Lonely Weekends/Red Rooster Blues/Free, Single and Disengaged/Guess I've Been a Fool.

RAY SMITH

Kentucky singer/guitarist/pianist whose finest work was for Sun and Judd, including his 1960 hit "Rockin' Little Angel." Through the '60s, he recorded for a number of labels, including Warner Bros., Smash, and Goldband. He spent the '70s recording country music for a number of small labels, including Cinnamon, Zirkon, and Wix, and then relocated to Germany. He committed suicide in 1979.

JUDD 75002 (R)
It's Great, It's Ray Smith
Reissue of twenty '50s–'60s recordings. You Made a Hit/Why, Why, Why/Rockin' Bandit/So Young/Right behind You Baby/Sail Away.

REVIVAL 3004 (R)
The Rockin' Bandit: Rare Items
Seventeen incredibly rare sides by Rockin' Ray, with a heavy emphasis on his Sun sides, but with a few Judds thrown in. Most of these tunes are unreleased alternate takes, including the title classic. Willing and Ready/Why, Why, Why/Break Up/Forever Yours/Swingin' Boogie/Gone Baby Gone.

RUNDELL 003 (R)
Rockin' in Germany
A selection of the usual '50s rockers recorded during Ray's years in Germany during the '70s. His performances are OK, but the sound quality is awful. For completists and diehards only.

SUN (UK) 32 (L)
Rockin' with Ray
His Sun label recordings.

JIMMY SOUL
Producer Frank Guida, the brains behind Gary "U.S." Bonds, was mad about calypso music. He brought Bonds the song "If You Wanna Be Happy" to record, a revved up version of the Calypso song "Ugly Woman," but Bonds passed on it because he didn't think it was soulful enough. So, Guida found an unknown singer named Jimmy McCleese, renamed him Jimmy Soul, and had him record the song. The song sold a million, and Guida built the label SPQR around Soul. His next big hit, "Twistin' Matilda," was a rockin' ripoff of Harry Belafonte's hit "Matilda." Between 1961–1964, Soul did some classic sides with the patented handclappin', sing-along, party sound, and another great calypso spinoff, "A Woman Is Smarter in Every Kinda Way." He was also a decent straight R&B singer. When Soul went into the army in 1964, his recording career ended.

RHINO 70527 (CL)
The Best of Jimmy Soul
Eighteen cuts on CD, 14 on cassette. Includes his calypso-flavored hits, party numbers ("My Baby Loves to Bowl," "Change Partners," "Food of Love," and "Hands Off"), and even some soulful R&B (the beautiful "I Know Why Dreamers Cry" and "One Million Tears").

SPQR 2000 (R)
Greatest Hits
Fourteen biggies for Frank Guida's label, some in stereo for the first time. If You Wanna Be Happy/Twistin' Matilda/Treat 'Em Rough/Take Me Back to New Orleans.

THE SPARKLETONES
Teenaged rockers from South Carolina, led by guitarist/vocalist Joe Bennett. They recorded for Am-Par, a subsidiary label of ABC-Paramount, from 1957–1959, and were best known for "Black Slacks," a song widely covered by US new-wave bands in the '70s.

PARIS 7281 (R)
The Sparkletones
Fourteen fine rockin' sides, including their big hit "Black Slacks," and other hot items featuring the group's distinctive vocals and driving instrumental work.

BENNY SPELLMAN
New Orleans singer known initially for providing the bass vocals on Ernie K-Doe's classic "Mother-in-Law." He recorded the original version of "Lipstick Traces" for Minit in 1962, which later became The O'Jays first major hit. His next hit, "Fortune Teller," has become a rock standard.

COLLECTABLES 5165 (CL)
Fortune Teller
Sixteen Minit, Alon, and Bandy tunes, recorded 1959–1966. A nice cross section of Spellman's gently rolling numbers, spiced by his always pleasing voice. Includes his big hits "Fortune Teller" b/w "Lipstick Traces" (Minit 644), which has to be one of the best two-sided R&B 45s ever. The Word Game/T'Ain't It the Truth/Talk about Love/Life Is Too Short.

THE SPIDERS
New Orleans's The Spiders began as the gospel-singing Zion City Harmonizers in the '40s. The group centered around the brothers Leonard

"Chick" and Hayward "Chuck" Carbo. In 1950, they changed their name to The Delta Southernaires, but called themselves The Spiders when they started recording secular music for Imperial in 1953. Both sides of their first single ("I Didn't Want To It" and "You're the One") were R&B hits, and their next few releases also did very well. In 1955 Chuck left for a solo career, and a year later Chick left too. The group disbanded in 1957.

BEAR FAMILY 15673 (L)
The Imperial Sessions
Two-CD set. Everything is here: the hits—"I Didn't Want to Do It," "You're the One," "I'm Slippin In," "Twenty-one," and "Witchcraft"—as well as less-popular but great numbers such as "Why Do I Love You," "I'll Stop Crying," "Bells in My Heart," and "Better Be on My Way." Also included are "John the Revelator" and "Bye and Bye" which were recorded using the name The Delta Southernaires and were probably never previously issued. Includes an informative, photo-packed 36-page booklet.

THE SPOTNICKS

Sweden's premier instrumental group from 1960 until at least the late '70s, with Bo Winberg on lead guitar and, on most sides, Bob Lander on rhythm.

STAR CLUB 8028 (R)
Rarities
Eighteen incredibly rare sides, from their first-ever recording, "Home on the Range" to 1979's "Indigo," most never before on LP, taken primarily from Swedish EPs and 45s, Japanese 45s, French EPs, and compilation LPs. Included are Bo's solo single, "Telstar," rush released for the Scandinavian market, and a fine version of Frank Zappa's "Lumpy Gravy." On two tracks, the drummer is Jimmy Nicol, who toured with The Beatles when Ringo had appendicitis.

DUSTY SPRINGFIELD

Big-voiced British chanteuse known for her breakable-looking hair. Born Mary O'Brien, she began her career as a member of the British folk band The Springfields. After being bitten by the Motown bug, she changed her name and her appearance and recorded covers of US soul hits and big ballads, producing a long string of hits for Philips between 1964–1967, including "I Only Want to Be with You," "Wishin' and Hopin'," and "The Look of Love." In 1968, she went to Atlantic and, with producer Jerry Wexler, recorded the classic LP *Dusty in Memphis*, which included the hits "Son of a Preacher Man" and "Windmills of Your Mind." After that, she worked only occasionally as a session vocalist, and made several unsuccessful comeback attempts in the '70s and '80s.

MERCURY 824 467 (C)
Dusty Springfield's Gold
Reissue of Philips 600-220 from 1966, including ten classic tracks in real mono. Wishin' and Hopin'/All Cried Out/You Don't Have to Say You Love Me/I Only Want to Be with You/I Just Don't Know What to Do with Myself.

RHINO 71035 (CL)
Dusty in Memphis
Reissue of her 1968 classic, originally Atlantic 8214. CD version has three bonus tracks from rare singles.

RHINO 71036 (CL)
A Brand New Me
1970 soul album, originally Atlantic 8249. CD has nine bonus tracks!

CLYDE STACY

Late-'50s/early-'60s rockabilly, sometimes teen-pop, artist from Lubbock, TX. Clyde recorded some fine sides that for some reason became big hits in Canada. Clarence Stacy and Clint Stacy may be other names that he used on some recordings, or two other (unrelated and unknown) artists.

HYDRA 7707 (R)
Rockin' Around
Includes his 1957 Candelight-label sides, featuring a fantastic version of "Hoy Hoy," along with "So Young," which was later banned because of its suggestive lyrics. In 1958, Clyde went to Bullseye Records where Little Willie Littlefield, his labelmate, supplied him with "Baby Shame." He also covered "Honky Tonk Hardwood Floor" and Bobby Lee Trammel's "I Sure Do Love You Baby." A short stint on Len followed in 1961, which gave us "You're Satisfied" b/w "Sittin' Down Cryin'" written and backed up by the fantastic Poe Kats (Big Al Downing, Bobby Poe, and Vernon Sandusky). Rounding out the collection are three Clarence Stacy sides from 1959–1960, which are in much more of a pop mold.

TERRY STAFFORD

One of the few Elvis imitators to make the charts, reaching Number 3 in 1964 with "Suspicion," a cut from Elvis's 1962 *Pot Luck* LP.

CRUSADER 1001 (R)
Suspicion
Reissue of 1964 album that mixes rockers and ballads.

JOE STAMPLEY and THE UNIQUES

Louisiana band active from the mid-'60s through the early '70s. While they never burned up the charts, they did have a strong Southern following. Their biggest numbers were "Not Too Long Ago" and "All These Things" from 1966. Stampley went on to a career as a country singer, performing honky-tonk songs as one half of the duo Moe and Joe (with Moe Bandy).

PAULA 2208 (L)
Golden Hits
Twelve songs, half originals and half covers, recorded between 1964–1971. The Uniques chose their covers carefully, turning in fine versions of William Bell's "You Don't Miss Your Water" and the David Huff tune, "Fool Number 1."

THE STANDELLS

One of the first and best LA punk groups, which started off as an organ-based cover band, recording for Vee Jay and Liberty in the early '60s. Original drummer Gary Leeds went to England, achieving fame as one of The Walker Brothers. With Leeds's replacement, Dickie Dodds (an original Mousketeer) on vocals and some great organ by Larry Tamblyn (whose brother Russ starred in the film of *West Side Story*), the group teamed with producer/writer Ed Cobb on the Capitol subsidiary Tower. Their Top 10 hit, "Dirty Water," was inspired by a trip to Boston, where Cobb was mugged while walking by the Charles River! They had trouble with their follow-up, "Try It," which was banned. Other minor hits include "Why Pick on Me" and the punk classic, "Sometimes Good Guys Don't Wear White." By 1967, the band's popularity had faded, although one late lineup included a young Lowell George (later of Little Feat).

RHINO 70176 (CL)
The Best of The Standells
Eighteen classic tracks. Sometimes Good Guys Don't Wear White/Medication/Riot on Sunset Strip/Don't Say Goodbye/Dirty Water.

THE STAPLE SINGERS

Gospel-tinged R&B vocal group, led by Roebuck "Pops" Staples. Pops was born in Mississippi, and his guitar playing shows the influence of the great Delta bluesmen. He performed with several gospel quartets in his home state before relocating to Chicago in 1941. Ten years later, he formed a family gospel group featuring his daughters Mavis and Cleotha and his son Pervis. In the '50s, the group recorded gospel in a bluesy style for United and Vee Jay. Late in the decade, they signed to Riverside, a jazz label, that tried to market them to the growing "folk revival." There followed a few years in the '60s on Epic, before they signed with the famous Memphis soul label, Stax, in 1968, where the group pursued a more pop-soul sound. Pervis left in 1970, replaced by another daugther, Yvonne. The group's repertoire switched from gospel and folk-blues to social-protest songs set in a funky groove. They scored a series of hits before the Stax label folded. Through the mid-'70s and '80s, they continued to record sporadically, charting occasionally with covers of rock and soul songs. For purposes of this book, we are concentrating on the group's R&B offerings.

STAX 4116 (CL)
Be Altitude: Respect Yourself
Reissue of 1972 album. Ten great cuts. Respect Yourself/I'll Take You There/Who Do You Think You Are/I'm Just Another Soldier.

STAX 8532 (RC)
We'll Get Over
Reissue of Stax 2016 from 1969, their second Stax LP, recorded when they were a quartet with brother Purvis still in the group. Produced, arranged, and engineered by Steve Cropper. Tend to Your Own Business/Give a Damn/Everyday People.

STAX 8553 (RCL)
Be What You Are
Contains the chart hits, "If You're Ready (Come Go with Me)," "Touch a Hand, Make a Friend," and the title cut.

STAX 8561 (CL)
Soul Folk in Action
Interesting reissue of 1968 recordings, with Pops, Mavis, and the other Staples in front of the unbeatable Stax rhythm section and horns. As with Mavis's solo LPs, Steve Cropper's production efforts are a little too psychedelicized to stand the test of time; but still the music carries the moment. The CD features two unissued bonus tracks "The Lady's Letter" and "Pops's Instrumental," which are equally strong as the 11 issued tracks. We've Got to Get Ourselves Together/Dock of the Bay/The Weight/I See It/The Ghetto.

STAX 60-007 (L)
The Best of The Staple Singers
All their hits and three LP tracks.

MAVIS STAPLES

Pops's daughter has pursued a sporadic solo career, suffering from a poor choice of material and poor production.

STAX 8539 (RC)
Only for the Lonely
Reissue of Volt 6010 from 1970. Since I Fell for You/You're the Fool/It Makes Me Wanna Cry/Endlessly.

STAX (UK) 014 (RCL)
Don't Change Me Now
Highlights from Ms. Staples's two solo albums on Volt, *Mavis Staples*(Volt 6007, produced by Steve Cropper) and *Only for the Lonely*(Volt 6010, produced by Don Davis), plus three unreleased cuts. Mavis's voice comes right out of the earth—gritty, breathy, and pungent—and it grabs and lifts you straight up to sweet soul heaven. The unrestrained sensuality of her vocal delivery, tinged with heartache, sass, and wisdom, is easily on par with the greatest church-bred '60s soul sisters. Too bad she was generally smothered in lame, unsympathetic production, and made to sound more derivative than divine. If you can put up with some sappy strings, clumsy horns, smack-dab-in-your-face background singers, and other dated dese-

crations, you'll be delighted by the more subtle treats this collection offers.

ANDY STARR

Andy Starr (born Franklin Delano Gulledge; he also recorded as Frank Starr) from Arkansas, had his own radio show on KWAL in Wallace, ID, in 1956. He was primed and ready for the rockabilly explosion that followed Elvis's success, recording some hot sides for MGM, Lin, and Holiday Inn.

REVIVAL 3012 (R)
Rockin' Rollin' Stone
Twenty cuts, featuring his four great MGM releases (the title cut, "She's a Going Jesse," "Round and Round," and "One More Time"), two of his three Lin releases, and the fabulous Holiday Inn release, "Knees Shakin'." Unlike other less-worthy rockabilly cats, Starr really can provide an entire LP of quality material. Give Me a Woman/I Wanna Go South/Evil Eye.

JACK STARR

Starr began his career in the '50s playing primitive rock and roll and rockabilly (some songs were cut as soundtracks to his homemade monster movies!). Jack didn't hot foot it to Nashville to record country when the '60s rolled around, like most of his rockabilly brethren. No sir, our boy fronted a series of wild garage-punk bands, recording some absolute killers. This deranged entrepreneur even found time to work as a magician.

NORTON 204 (R)
Born Petrified
Recent recordings by Starr, including a couple of his wacky radio spots. Crazy Rock (Bald Headed Woman and a Long Haired Man)/Born Bad/My Love for You Is Petrified/Rumble at Flagpole Hill/I Love My Baby/My Baby Don't Care/I Need Your Lovin.'

TOMMY STEELE

British teen popster who later had a career as an actor. In his early career in the '50s, he performed as a country singer, going by the name Chick Hicks (his real name is Tommy Hicks), and performed in a comedy troupe (The Cavemen). He became the UK's first serious rocker when he released "Rock with the Caveman" in October 1956, continuing with further rockin' hits through the '50s. By the late '50s, he had shifted from rock and roll to being a family entertainer, and his jovial cockney persona enlivened several of London's West End musicals.

SEE FOR MILES 203 (RL)
The Rockin' Years

Excellent retrospective of Steele's 1956–1961 rockin' sides, thanks mainly to exhaustive notes and research by Roger Dopson. Tommy, in the Merchant Navy, had actually been to the US and seen Elvis on TV. However, Steele was much more influenced by Bill Haley than Elvis, and the tunes are more on the "jive" side. Twenty-four UK Decca tracks, with solid covers of US hits, even his cover of The Fireflies's "You Were Mine" and his first big hit, "Rock with the Caveman." Tallahassee Lassie/Come On Let's Go/Butterfly/Singin' the Blues.

DODIE STEVENS

Born Geraldie Ann Pasquale, Dodie was discovered while performing in a talent show at age 10. She recorded her big hit "Pink Shoelaces" when she was 11 for Crystallette Records, who also gave her a new, whitebread name. Despite her fluffy discography, the youngster was more into rock and roll than dreamy teen ballads: "I didn't like the song, [and I] didn't like the name [Dodie Stevens]. I thought it was dumb." Still, it was a big hit, and Dodie continued to record until 1961, appearing in a number of films including such classics as 1959's *Hound Dog Man* with Fabian and (who can forget?) 1961's *Alakazam The Great*, featuring Frankie Avalon. Geri (as she prefers to be called) retired and married at age 16, but when her marriage ended in 1968, she returned to singing, performing as one of the two girl singers in a later incarnation of Sergio Mendes and Brasil '66, in revival shows, and as a backup for Mac Davis.

CRYSTALETTE 728 (R)
Pink Shoelaces

Who can ever forget Dodie's big 1959 hit "Pink Shoelaces"? Now, who would like to forget it? If any guy at my high school had worn "tan shoes and pink shoelaces with a polka dot vest," he would've lost enough lunch money to the local hoods to set them up in an auto-repair business. But Dodie's world was one of cotton candy, puppy love, and prom dresses, so she probably thought it was cute to sing "Mairzy Doats," "Steady Eddy," and "Let Me Tell You 'bout Johnny." Her version of Spector's "To Know Him Is

to Love Him" is the best thing here, and "Candy Store Blues" shows a surprising sophistication considering the rest of the fluff. Sailor Boy/The Gypsy No/Just a Dream.

SHAKIN' STEVENS and THE SUNSETS

Michael Barratt, aka Shakin' Stevens, led one of many British rockabilly bands to emerge in the late '60s. In the late '70s, he appeared in the stage musical *Elvis* and started recording for Epic under the guidance of Stu Coleman and Dave Edmunds. He was rewarded with a series of single and album hits in the early/mid-'80s, and, as a result, many of his earlier recordings were reissued. By the mid-'80s, his success faded and his recordings started disappearing from the market.

COLLECTOR SERIES 153 (RL)
Shakin' Stevens and The Sunsets Collection

Original mid-'70s recordings by Stevens with his first band, The Sunsets. This two-LP/CD set has only 20 tunes, with most cuts under three minutes, and could easily have fit on a single disc. Still, it's fine, early British rockabilly revival music. Sweet Little 16/Rock Around with Ollie Vee/Baby I Don't Care/Jungle Rock/Reet Petite.

ROCK AND COUNTRY 1005 (R)
Come On Memphis

1975–1976 recordings by one of Britain's better rockabilly revival bands, performing mostly cover versions of rock standards. Honey Hush/Oakie Boogie/Reet Petite.

SUNROCK 832 (R)
Lonesome Town

Early sides. Queen of the Hop/California Cowboy/You Talk Too Much/Punk/Hop, Rock, Bop.

BILLY STEWART

Incredible Chicago R&B/soul singer who recorded some fantastic sides for Chess in the mid-'60s. He started out in The Rainbows, a vocal group from his hometown of Washington, DC, that had a hit in 1955 with "Mary Lee." (Don Covay was another group member.) He was discovered by Bo Diddley and played in Bo's band for a couple of years. In 1961, he signed with Okeh, and soon after went to Chess. He had hits with "Reap What You Sow" and the classic "I Do

Love You." In 1966, he recorded a version of "Summertime" that featured him singing in a very dadaesque scat style, doing for "Summertime" what The Marcels had done for "Blue Moon." The song went into the Top 10 and earned Billy the moniker "Motor Mouth." His follow-up, "Secret Love," was done in the same way. He also had a hit with the Chicago soul classic, "Sitting in the Park." He was killed in a car crash in 1970, along with two of his band members.

CHESS 6027 (CL)
One More Time
Long overdue collection of Stewart's best Chess sides (excluding "Wedding Bells" and "A Fat Boy Can Cry"), spanning 1956–1969. Hits "I Do Love You," "Sitting in the Park," and "Summertime" are included, along with seven other charted sides. Learned sleeve-notes by Adam White. Great fidelity.

CHESS 9104 (RC)
The Greatest Sides
Fourteen of the most popular sides by this vastly underrated R&B/soul singer. Summertime/A Fat Boy Can Cry/Sitting in the Park/I Do Love You

THE STRAWBERRY ALARM CLOCK
The Strawberry Alarm Clock was a strange group. Best known for "Incense and Peppermints," their music, full of sitars and bongos, and their song's subject matter ("Sit with the Guru," "Rainy Day Mushroom Pillow," and "Black Butter-Present") were all extremely psychedelic, but their vocal arrangements were straight out of The Association!

BIG BEAT 56 (L)
Strawberries Mean Love
Thirteen tunes, mostly from their first two LPs, plus the original A-side of "Incense and Peppermints," "Birdman of Alkatrash," never on LP before. Features plenty of beautiful searing guitar solos from Ed King, later in Lynyrd Skynyrd!

THE STRING-A-LONGS
The String-A-Longs were a Norman Petty discovery. He recorded them in the early '60s in his Clovis studio, selling some tunes to the big instrumental label, Warwick. Their sound was a subtle

one, based on a quirky little riff or odd tone that often made their tunes sound like incidental film music, calling forth visions of young girls running through a field of flowers. "Wheels" was a big hit for them in 1961.

NOR-VA-JAK 810 (R)
Rare Tracks
Like the title says; does not include their hit "Wheels." Blue Love/Places I Remember/Black Grass/Hound Dog/Woodpecker/Blue Guitar.

NOLAN STRONG and THE DIABLOS
Highly influential Detroit doo-wop group who recorded for Jack and Devora Brown's Fortune Records throughout the '50s and into the '60s. The Diablos were the most popular group to come out of Detroit, and many local singers were influenced by Strong's beautiful falsetto, his most famous disciple being Smokey Robinson. In the '60s, the group made some wonderful a-cappella recordings under the pseudonym of The Velvet Angels (see separate listing). The group's biggest hit was the ethereal "The Wind," recorded in 1954, which was a giant hit five years later when it was covered by The Jesters.

FORTUNE 8010 (R)
Fortune of Hits
Twelve incredible, influential Fortune sides, including the classic "The Wind." If I/A Teardrop from Heaven/(I Want) an Old Fashioned Girl/The Way You Dog Me Around.

FORTUNE 8012 (R)
Fortune of Hits, Vol. 2
Twelve more great Fortune sides, including two standards ("Danny Boy" and "White Christmas") and ten originals. Adios My Desert Love/Daddy Rocking Strong/Baby Be Mine/Hold Me until Eternity.

FORTUNE 8015 (R)
Mind over Matter
Twelve more hot sides. (You're Not Good Lookin') You're Presentable/Are You Sincere/A Lil Coochie.

FORTUNE 8020 (R)
Daddy Rock: The Legendary Nolan Strong with The Diablos
Twelve sides, ten never previously issued, including seven by the original mid-'50s group, four by the early-'60s group, and one solo cut. Includes an alternate take of their classic "The Wind," an alternate of

"Daddy Rocking Strong" called "Daddy Nolan Strong," and a great a-cappella medley of "Since I Don't Have You" and "Rockin' Robin."

NOLAN STRONG and THE DIABLOS/THE FIVE DOLLARS

FORTUNE 8016 (R)

From the Beginning to

Five classic Fortune sides, including The Diablos's "You Are" and "Wild Side of My Baby," and The Five Dollars's "The Bells," "Weekend Man," and "Dr. Baby."

GENE SUMMERS

Gene Summers, from Dallas, TX, wasn't one to give up easily, never leaving his rockin' roots and recording dozens of tunes spanning over 30 years and 20-plus labels!

STAR CLUB 8011 (R)

The Texas Rebel

Twelve fine '50s and '60s sides, and four tunes from his out-of-print 1977 album for Lake County.

SUNROCK 841 (R)

Live in Scandinavia

Recorded live in Sweden in 1983 with a nondescript Swedish band. An unexceptional performance of mostly rock-and-roll standards.

WHITE LABEL 8826 (R)

Early Rocking Recordings

Fourteen rockin' numbers from the '50s and early '60s, including six previously unissued tracks, notably the fantastic instrumental "Loco Cat" from 1959. Check out the incredibly cool "Turnip Greens" from 1962. School of Rock and Roll/Nervous/Alabama Shake/Straight Skirt.

THE SUN RHYTHM SECTION

FLYING FISH 445 (RC)

Old Time Rock and Roll

THE SUPREMES

The most popular female vocalists of all time. They started out as a quartet called The Primettes on Lupine records, featuring Florence Ballard on lead vocals backed by Diane Ross, Mary Wilson, and Betty Travis. The girls signed to Motown in 1961, and produced nine flops in a row (including the original version of "Baby Love"), until

they finally hit it big with "Where Did Our Love Go?," which went to Number 1. They had five Number 1 hits in a row, and 20 chart hits between 1964–1967. There was a growing rift between Diana (as she was now called), whom Berry Gordy selected to be lead singer because he thought she was sexy, and original leader Ballard. In between sets during a Las Vegas performance, Ballard was forced out of the band; she died on welfare of cardiac arrest at age 32 in 1976. The band was now called Diana Ross and The Supremes, with Cindy Birdsong from Patti LaBelle and The Bluebelles replacing Ballard. The hits kept coming, but Ross was being groomed for superstardom and, in 1968, she left the band after a final hit, "Some Day We'll Be Together." The band kept going with replacement Jean Terrell, and the seemingly impossible happened: Ross's solo singles flopped while The Supremes continued to have hits ("Stoned Love," "Up the Ladder to the Roof," "Nathan Jones," and "Floy Joy"). But, Motown dropped all support for the band and concentrated on Ross, who finally hit Number 1 with an overly dramatic version of Marvin Gaye's "Ain't No Mountain High Enough." The Supremes kept going, although Terrell was replaced by Shari Payne in 1973. After a number of personnel changes and one more chart hit ("You're My Driving Wheel"), the group finally disbanded. Diana, Mary, and Cindy reunited for the Motown 25th Anniversary Show.

✪ MOTOWN 794 (CL)

Anthology

Three cassette/two CD set covering all of their big hits with Ross.

MOTOWN 5441 (CL)

Floy Joy

Reissue of Motown 751 from 1972; the gals without Ross.

MOTOWN 5442 (CL)

Right On

First post-Ross LP, originally Motown 705 from 1970.

MOTOWN 5447 (CL)

Touch

Originally Motown 737 from 1972.

MOTOWN 5487 (CL)
Greatest Hits and Rare Classics
Seventies hits by the Rossless Supremes, and solo tracks by Jean Terrell and Shari Payne.

MOTOWN 5497 (CL)
New Ways, But Love Stays
Originally Motown 720 from 1971.

MOTOWN 8151 (L)
More Hits by The Supremes/ Sing Holland-Dozier- Holland
Two LPs (originally Motown 627 from 1965 and 650 from 1967) on one CD.

THE SUPREMES/THE FOUR TOPS

MOTOWN 5491 (CL)
Best Of

THE SUPREMES/STEVIE WONDER

MOTOWN 8141 (L)
Merry Christmas/ Someday at Christmas
Two LPs of Christmas stands on one CD, The Supremes's Christmas record from 1965 (originally Motown 638) and Wonder's 1969's Christmas outing.

SCREAMIN' LORD SUTCH

Crazed English rocker who started his career in the early '60s under the guiding hand of the legendary producer Joe Meek. Sutch was noted for his wild stage act, which owed something to Screamin' Jay Hawkins and to the many luminaries who passed through his bands. Though never achieving much musical success, he is a beloved figure on the British scene, possibly more for his persona than his musical abilities. He has even run for Parliament as the leader of the Monster Raving Loony Party.

ACE 65 (RL)
Rock and Horror
Recorded in 1981–1982, Sutch goes beyond just being another novelty act because his band is very good, featuring well-known Brit rockers like Freddie "Fingers" Lee on piano and Bob Burgos on guitar. The naughty Lord howls his way through a dozen grizzly tunes like "Screem and Screem," "All Black and Hairy," "Jack the Ripper," "Monster Rock," and "Murder in the Graveyard." Just the thing to listen to on a dark, foggy night. One of my faves; it really rocks.

THE SWALLOWS

The Swallows have remained primarily a collectors' vocal group, because their best ballad sides were blue and moody and did not have great commercial potential. However, their novelty sides "Bicycle Tillie" and "It Ain't the Meat" found a broader market. Led by tenors Eddie Rich (on jumps) and string-bass player Herman "Junior" Denby (on ballads), the group had a rich earthy blues style all their own. Other original members included tenor Earl Hurley (bongos), baritone Fred "Money Guitar" Johnson (gtr), and bass Norris "Bunky" Mack (pno, gtr, drm). Formerly known as The Oakaleers, they came out of the "swing in rhythm" quartet tradition of The Spirits of Rhythm. They first recorded for King in 1950–1954.

CHARLY 287 (L)
Dearest
Twenty-four cuts, covering their four-year King contract, with learned notes and discography by Tony Watson and two rare pics. Harmony in the classic Orioles and Ravens tradition.

DOO WOP DELIGHTS 101 (C)
The Best of The Swallows
Covers most of their long out-of-print, early '50s recordings (many of which are extremely rare and fetch astronomical prices), plus their first waxing shared with The Strangers in 1950, solo efforts by lead singer Junior Denby, and recent sides made by the group led by Eddie Rich. Thirty-four songs in all.

BETTYE SWANN

Fine Louisiana soul singer who moved to Los Angles and started recording for the Money label in the early '60s. She topped the R&B charts with the beautiful "Make Me Yours." She later moved to Atlantic and had a number of hits with country/soul songs like "Today I Started Loving You Again".

COLLECTABLES 5177 (CL)
Make Me Yours: Golden Classics
Twelve soulful gems. Make Me Yours/Don't Look Back/Don't Take My Mind/I Think I'm Falling in Love/The Heartache Is Gone/What Is My Life Coming To.

THE SWEET INSPIRATIONS

Influential backup group who worked behind many '60s soulsters (and even Elvis!) The group began in Newark's New Hope Baptist church, centering on Emily "Cissy" Houston (mother of Whitney). They worked as backup singers for Ronnie Hawkins and The Hawks (later The Band); at this time, the group consisted of Cissy, Sylvia Guions (aka S. Shemwell), Estelle Brown, and Myrna Smith. They became the house backup singers for Atlantic, and were given their name by Jerry Wexler, after their big hit, the Penn/Oldham number "Sweet Inspiration," released in 1968. Cissy left the group to tour as a backup singer for her niece Dionne Warwick, while the remaining trio continued to record as backup singers and produced occasional projects under their own name through the '70s. Myrna Smith cowrote Carl Wilson's first blue-eyed soul LP with the Beach Boy.

STAX 8565 (L)
Estelle, Myrna, and Sylvia
The group after Cissy left.

TARHEEL SLIM and LITTLE ANN

Tarheel Slim (born Allen Bunn) had a long career in blues and early rock. In 1957, he met his future wife "Little Ann," and they began recording as a duo. Their big hit was "It's Too Late." Slim also recorded as a member of the vocal group The Larks.

COLLECTABLES 5159 (CL)
The Robin and Fire Years
Fifteen rockin' R&B and lowdown blues sides, including the deadly duo, "Wildcat Tamer" and "Number 9 Train." Average sound quality. Much Too Late/It's Too Late/Can't Stay Away, Pts. 1 and 2/It's a Sin.

BUDDY TATE/FRANK CULLEY

Tate was a Texas tenor saxophonist originally with The Terrence Holder Band in the '40s, whose alumni also include Jesse Stone, Earl Bostic, and Lloyd Glenn. He found fame in the Count Basie Orchestra, and, in the '50s, made some great honking rock-and-roll sides for NY's Baton Records.

KRAZY KAT 784 (R)
For Dancing the Lindy Hop
Reissue of Baton 1201 from 1955 with two extra cuts by Tate. Instrumental rock and roll. Nothing profound here, but some lively dance music.

JOHNNIE TAYLOR

Excellent, gritty-voiced soulster who became Stax Record's top-selling male vocalist after Otis Redding died. Taylor began his career as a member of the vocal group The Five Echoes who recorded for Vee Jay in 1955. He replaced Sam Cooke as lead vocalist of The Soul Stirrers in 1958, but soon left to tour with Cooke. On a whim, he auditioned for Stax in 1965, but it wasn't until 1967 that the smash hits started coming, including "Who's Makin' Love," "I Got to Love Somebody's Baby," and a hit cover of Parliament's "Testify (I Wanna)." He remained a steady hitmaker for Stax until the label died in 1975. Their distributor, Columbia, picked up his contact, and Taylor scored one of his first platinum hits with "Disco Lady." By the '80s, he had lost his US contracts but put out some "sexy soul" LPs in Japan. He's recently signed to Malaco for more excellent recordings.

ATLANTIC 82253 (CL)
Wanted One Soul Singer
Reissue of fine, bluesy 1972 album.

MALACO 7446 (RCL)
In Control
Recent LP from Johnnie finds him moving away from the beat-heavy, dance floor emphasis of some of his other Malaco albums. There is some solid soul singing here, most notably on the ballad "It Don't Hurt Me Like It Used To," and his cover of Wilson Pickett's "I Found a Love." The arrangements are often too cluttered, and some were designed with the disco crowd in mind, but this is nonetheless Johnnie's best record in quite a while.

MALACO 7452 (CL)
Crazy 'bout You
1991 release with nine roots-blues numbers.

MALACO 7463 (CL)
Best Of

STAX 8508 (RL)
Raw Blues
Reissue of Johnnie's first Stax LP, 2008, from 1969, produced by Al Jackson and engineered by Steve

Cropper. Lots of great blues and soul shouting. Hello Sundown/Part Time Love/That Bone.

STAX 8520 (RC)
Super Hits
Ten great Stax sides recorded between 1968–1974. Who's Makin' Love/Testify/Steal Away/I Am Somebody.

STAX 8563 (CL)
The Johnnie Taylor Philosophy Continues
Despite the uninviting title, this reissue of Taylor's 1969 Stax album (originally 2023) is great soul. Backed by three-quarters of The MGs (Marvell Thomas replaces Booker T on keyboards). Testify/ Separation Line/I Had a Fight with Love/It's Your Thing/Who Can I Turn To/I Could Never Be President/Love Bones/Love Is a Hurting Thing.

STAX 60-006 (L)
Chronicle: The Twenty Greatest Hits
Twenty Taylor triumphs for the Stax label, totaling over an hour of music. Who's Makin' Love/Steal Away/Cheaper to Keep Her/Just Keep on Lovin' Me.

LITTLE JOHNNY and TED TAYLOR

PAULA 503 (L)
The Super Taylors
Originally released in 1973 as Ronn 7533, featuring the unforgettable voices of Ted and Little Johnny (no relation) together and separately. And, despite the truly ugly vintage cover art, all 12 tracks are straight-ahead, solid soul. The only chart success was Johnny's "Everybody Knows about My Good Thing," but "I Can't See Myself as a One Woman Man," "When Are You Coming Home?," and "Make Love to Me Baby" are every bit as good. Ted's cuts include the excellent "Only the Lonely Knows," "Gonna Find Me a New Love," "Honey Lou," and the metaphorically strained "(I'm Just a Crumb in Your) Bread Box." Of the four duets, only "Funky Ghetto" feels like filler; "Walking the Floor," "Cry It Out Baby," and "Pretending Love" all sparkle. Unfortunately, no notes, session information, or extra tracks are included.

TED TAYLOR

Southern soulster with a distinctive tenor voice. Ted was a member of The Cadets/Jacks, and later had a fairly successful solo soul career on the Jewel/Ronn labels, including his hits "How's Your Love Life Baby?" and "Something Strange Is Going On at My House."

MR. R&B 1005 (R)
Somebody's Always Trying
A finger-poppin' feast of 18 superb single sides that Ted made for the Duke, Gold Eagle, Warwick, Laurie, Atco, and Okeh labels, including the fiery "Dancin' Annie" and the tonsil-twisting "Can't Take No More." Swooping falsetto with solid grit. A perfect companion to the out-of-print Charly 1011 (that reissued his early sides). Detailed notes by Luciano Federighi.

VINCE TAYLOR

Vince Taylor was a '50s British rocker who left the old sod to conquer France, showing the Frenchies what rock and roll was all about. Unlike the vast majority of British "rockers," Taylor and his Playboys knew you had to really cut loose to play authentic rock and roll.

EVA 11 (L)
I'll Be Your Hero
Includes six excellent tunes from 1958–1959 including "I Like Love," "Move Over Tiger," and "Jet Black Machine," plus six more tunes from 1973. Taylor and the boys blast through "Say Mama," "Kansas City," "Rock Island Line," and "Brand New Cadillac 73," with Vince in fine voice and some guitar work that could cut through iron bars.

THE TEDDY BEARS

Early vocal group led by a young Phil Spector, formed while he was a student at LA's Fairfax High. Their big hit was 1958's "To Know Him Is to Love Him," a teen ballad written and produced by the talented Phil. (The tune's title line was taken from Spector's father's gravestone!) The group included lead vocalist Annette Kleinbard, guitarist and tenor vocalist Marshall Leib, and bass singer Harvey Goldstein (although he was gone by the time of their hit). They took their name from Elvis's big hit, "Teddy Bear." After their initial hit, disagreements flared up between Phil and their label, Dore, so they switched to Imperial where they were unable to reproduce their original fame. In 1960, Kleinbard was seriously injured in an automobile accident, and her performing days ended, although she went on to become a talented songwriter under the name Carol Connors, writing and cowriting numerous hits and movie themes, including "The Night the Lights Went Out in Georgia" and theme songs for *Rocky, Sophie's Choice*, and *Mr. Mom.* Marshall Leib formed his own label, played second guitar on many of Duane Eddy's hit recordings, and went on to score a number of country-esque films, including *Ode to Billy Joe* and *Take This Job and Shove It.* Phil went to NY and fame as a producer!

TREY 20207 (R)

My Little Pet

Sixteen tracks. Don't You Worry My Little Pet/Till You'll Be Mine/Oh Why/My Foolish Heart/Severe Lonely Days.

THE TEENBEATS

The Teenbeats were the top band in Las Vegas from 1962–1966. They didn't record all that much, but they played the clubs every weekend, building up a big local following. Like many teen bands of the era, The Teenbeats were heavy on instrumentals, because their singers Larry and Don had more enthusiasm than talent.

NORTON 220 (R)

Surf Bound

All of Side 1 and part of Side 2 feature a fantastic live show recorded in 1962 at the Knights of Columbus Hall in Vegas. Led by Jim Logue's sax and Larry Chernoff's lead guitar, they really rip it up, especially on "Caterpillar Crawl," where they gradually speed up the tune to increase the excitement. Also includes their great first single "Live Like a King," as well as other singles and some outtakes. Surfbound/Mr. Moto/Stalkin'/Slinky/Russian Roulette.

THE TEMPREES

Excellent '70s soul trio featuring the sweet falsetto lead of Jabbo Smith.

STAX 8524 (RCL)

The Best of The Temprees

Twelve fine singles recorded for the Stax subsidiary, We Produce, from 1972–1976, including beautiful remakes of "Dedicated to the One I Love" and "A Thousand Miles Away." Love Maze/Explain It to Her Mama/At Last/My Baby Love.

THE TEMPTATIONS

One of the most popular, longest-lasting, flashiest-looking, and best-dancing groups of all time. The original group featured lead vocalist Elbridge "Al" Bryant, Otis Williams, Mel Franklin, Eddie Kendricks, and Paul Williams. Originally called The Primes (whose "sister" group, The Primettes, went on to become The Supremes) and The Elgins, the group signed with the fledgling Motown label in 1960. They spent three years releasing flops produced and written by Berry Gordy, first on Motown subsidiary Miracle and then Motown. By 1963, David Ruffin replaced Bryant, the group switched to Motown's Gordy label, and they teamed up with writer/producer Smokey Robinson who gave them their first hit in 1964, "The Way You Do the Things You Do," and their first Number 1 hit, 1965's "My Girl." With Ruffin's raspy baritone, Kendrick's silky tenor, and Robinson's incredible songs, The Temps hit for two more years with "Get Ready," "Since I Lost My Baby," and "Don't Look Back." In 1966, Norman Whitfield, together with Eddie Holland of Holland-Dozier-Holland fame, supplied the hits, including "Ain't Too Proud to Beg" and "(I Know) I'm Losing You." Ruffin was showcased on these tunes and, soon after, went solo, being replaced by former Contours's lead vocalist Dennis Edwards in 1968. In the late '60s/early '70s, influenced by the success of Sly Stone and Curtis Mayfield, the group produced a number of hits reflecting the new black consciousness, including "Cloud Nine," "I Can't Get Next to You," "Psychedelic Shack," and "Ball of Confusion." In 1971, they hit with a Kendricks-led ballad in their classic style, "Just My Imagination." Kendricks left soon after for a solo career, and was replaced by Damon Harris, and Paul Williams also left due to "illness" (he committed suicide two years later). Williams was replaced by Richard Street from The Monitors. The new group scored with 1972's "Papa Was a Rolling Stone" and 1973's "Masterpiece." Harris left in 1975, and was replaced by Glenn Leonard. Though off the pop charts, The Temps hit the soul charts regularly until they left Gordy for Atlantic in 1976. After a few hitless years, they returned to Gordy and more hits in 1980. In 1982, Kendricks and Ruffin rejoined the group, and, in 1985, the duo hitched up with blue-eyed soulsters Hall and Oates.

MOTOWN 782 (CL)
Anthology
Handsome package with three cassettes or two CDs, featuring 42 songs plus a 32-page booklet. The Way You Do the Things You Do/My Girl/Get Ready/Ain't Too Proud to Beg/All I Need/Runaway Child, Runnin' Wild/Cloud Nine.

MOTOWN 5140 (CL)
Meet The Temptations
The Temp's debut, originally Gordy 911 from 1964, features "The Way You Do the Things You Do," "Farewell My Love," and ten more.

MOTOWN 5144 (CL)
Masterpiece
Reissue of Gordy 965 from 1973.

MOTOWN 5159 (CL)
Cloud Nine
Reissue of Gordy 939 from 1969. I Heard It Through the Grapevine/Runaway Child, Running Wild/Hey Girl (I Like Your Style)/I Need Your Lovin'/I Gotta Find a Way.

MOTOWN 5164 (CL)
Psychedelic Shack
The Temps tribute to the summer of love, originally Gordy 947 from 1970, with "Take a Stroll through Your Mind," "War," "Friendship Train," and the monumental title track. Eight mind-expanding soul classics.

MOTOWN 5172 (CL)
Puzzle People
Originally issued as Gordy 949 in 1970. I Can't Get Next to You/Don't Let the Joneses Get You Down/It's Your Thing/You Don't Love Me No More/Running Away (Ain't Gonna Help You).

MOTOWN 5205 (CL)
Sing Smokey
Smokey Robinson-penned hits and misses; originally Gordy 912 from 1965. Way You Do the Things You Do/Baby, Baby I Need You/What Love Has Joined Together/Who's Lovin' You/What's So Good about Goodbye.

MOTOWN 5235 (CL)
In a Mellow Mood
Reissue of Gordy 924 from 1967. The Temps in transition as Ruffin was about to be replaced by Dennis Edwards and the group is forced to put out an LP of standards. Only their incredible voices save this one. The liner notes are by Soupy Sales!! Hello Young Lovers/Old Man River/Try to Remember/Who Can I Turn To/A Taste of Honey.

MOTOWN 5251 (CL)
Christmas Card
Ten tracks, originally Gordy 951 from 1970. Rudolph, The Red Nosed Reindeer/Santa Claus Is Coming to Town/Someday at Christmas/Let It Snow/The Christmas Song.

MOTOWN 5272 (CL)
A Song for You
Reissue of Gordy 969 from 1975.

MOTOWN 5276 (CL)
I Wish It Would Rain
Reissue of Gordy 927 from 1968.

MOTOWN 5279 (CL)
Give Love at Christmas

MOTOWN 5299 (CL)
With a Lot of Soul
Reissue of Gordy 922 from 1967, the last really strong LP with Eddie Kendricks and David Ruffin. There are lots of great hits here. (I Know) I'm Losing You/All I Need/(Loneliness Made Me Realize) It's You that I Need/You're My Everything.

MOTOWN 5306 (CL)
Live at The Copa
Reissue of Gordy 921 from 1967. Kendricks and Ruffin lead the band through the usual Motown melange of medleys and pop standards. They are in great voice on "Ain't Too Proud to Beg," "Get Ready," "Don't Look Back," and "My Girl," but did they really have to do "Old Man River"?

MOTOWN 5373 (CL)
Gettin' Ready
Reissue of Gordy 918 from 1966.

MOTOWN 5374 (CL)
Temptin' Temptations
Reissue of Gordy 914 from 1966.

MOTOWN 5411 (CL)
Greatest Hits, Vol. 1
Twelve early Temps classics. My Girl/Ain't Too Proud to Beg/The Way You Do the Things You Do/Get Ready.

MOTOWN 5412 (CL)
Greatest Hits, Vol. 2
Twelve cuts of choice Temps from their later years. Cloud Nine/Ball of Confusion/Psychedelic Shack/Runaway Child.

MOTOWN 5417 (CL)
All Directions
Reissue of Gordy 962 from 1972.

MOTOWN 5474 (CL)
The Sky's the Limit
Reissue of Gordy 957 from 1971.

MOTOWN 5480 (CL)
Solid Rock
Reissue of Gordy 961 from 1972.

MOTOWN 6331 (CL)
Milestone

TAMMI TERRELL

Tammi, under her real name Tammi Montgomery, started out in the early '60s as part of The James Brown Revue, having an occasional solo spot. She signed with Motown in 1966, and had a few solo releases before teaming up successfully with Marvin Gaye for a long series of highly popular duets on Tamla, including "Ain't No Mountain High Enough," "For Your Precious Love," and "Ain't Nothin' Like the Real Thing." In 1967, Tammi collapsed in Gaye's arms onstage, and it was discovered she had a brain tumor. Tamla continued to release some previously recorded tunes ("You're All I Need to Get By"), but the hits stopped in 1970 when Tammi died at age 26.

MOTOWN 5231 (CL)
Irresistible
Reissue of Motown 652 from 1969, her only solo LP. Includes her hit "Come On and See Me." I Can't Believe You Love Me/This Old Heart of Mine/Can't Stop Now.

JOE TEX

"The Rapper," Joe was one of the first R&B artists to combine his gospel roots with C&W. He started out on King (1955–1957), went to Ace (1958–1960), Anna, Parrot, Checker, and Jalynne. In 1964, he signed to Buddy Killen's Dial label (based in Nashville and distributed by Atlantic) and the hits, mostly country and novelty tunes, came regularly until 1969 ("Hold What You've Got," "Show Me," and his biggest hit "Skinny Legs and All"). He also had a hit in 1972 with "I Gotcha." In that same year, Tex (real name Joe Arrington Jr.) converted to the Muslim faith and changed his name to Joseph Hazziez and retired. He made a comeback in 1976 with "Ain't Gonna Bump No More (with No Big Fat Woman)." He died of a heart attack in 1982 at age 49.

ATLANTIC 81278 (C)
The Best of Joe Tex
Twelve of his best Atlantic/Dial sides. SYSLJFM (The Letter Song)/Show Me/Hold What You've Got/I've Got to Do a Little Bit Better/Papa Was Too.

CHARLY 133 (L)
The Very Best of Joe Tex
Twenty-five great Dial sides from the mid-'60s including all his chart hits. In-depth notes by soul expert Barney Hoskins. Hold What You've Got/A Woman (Can Change a Man)/Don't Make Your Children Pay (for Your Mistakes)/The Love You Save (May Be Your Own)/I'm a Man/SYSLJFM (The Letter Song)/Papa Was Too (Tramp)/Show Me/A Woman's Hands/Men Are Gettin' Scarce/You Need Me Baby/You're Right, Ray Charles.

CURB 77520 (CL)
Greatest Hits
Five of his soulful ballads recorded for Dial are featured on this 12-song collection: "Hold What You've Got," "A Sweet Woman Like You," "I Want To (Do Everything for You)," "I Believe I'm Gonna Make It," and "The Love You Save (May Be Your Own)." The remainder is made up of funk-junk chart fodder drawn from material cut before Joe became a Muslim in 1972. Scant notes, average sound.

RHINO 70191 (CL)
I Believe I'm Gonna Make It: The Best of Joe Tex
Eighteen of The Rapper's best Dial sides, 1964–1972. All of Joe's biggest and best are here (except "Men Are Gettin' Scarce"), along with a few great LP tracks. Excellent sound, and an eight-page booklet with liner notes by Mike McDowell. I Gotcha/SYSLJFM (The Letter Song)/Skinny Legs and All/Hold What You've Got/Show Me/A Sweet Woman Like You.

THE TEXAS MAVERICKS

NEW ROSE 112 (L)
Who Are These Masked Men?
Late '80s recordings by Doug Sahm and friends. Cover photo shows them sitting at a bar wearing Mexican wrestling masks to "disguise" their true identities! Ten tunes with a heavy rockabilly feel, featuring five new originals including "Hillbilly Soul and a Rockabilly Mind" and "Lovin You Best," plus covers of Van Morrison's "Brown Eyed Girl," Roy Head's "One More Time," Junior Parker's "Mother-in-Law Blues," "I Fought the Law," and "Rock and Roll Ruby."

TEXAS TORNADOS

Super group made up of Doug Sahm and Augie Meyers (of the original Sir Douglas Quintet), Freddy Fender, and accordion ace Flaco Jimenez.

REPRISE 26251 (CL)
Texas Tornados
Disappointing debut offering.

REPRISE 26472 (CL)
Los Texas Tornados
Rockin' hits in Spanish!

REPRISE 26683 (CL)
Zone of Our Own
Far superior to their first (English-language) outing. Opening with Sir Doug's delivery of the border anthem "Is Anybody Goin' to San Antone," the Tornados blow through these ten good-timin' tunes with youthful spunk. You'll be hankerin' for a Lone Star beer to wash down Sahm's "I'm Not That Kat Anymore," "He Is a Tejano," and "Just Can't Fake It." And it's great to hear these radio-ready roots rockers perform genuine Tex-Mex fare like "Bailando," "La Mucura," and the old favorites "El Pantalon Blue Jean" and "Volver." Good clean fun, Texas style.

REPRISE 45058 (CL)
Hangin' on a Thread

THE 13TH FLOOR ELEVATORS

One of the most tripped-out, punked-out groups ever, led by Roky Erickson.

COLLECTABLES 505 (L)
Roky Erickson and The 13th Floor Elevators: The Magic of Pyramids
CD issue of the exciting 13-tune live tapes that were rediscovered in 1988. Roky and the boys are heard performing in late 1965 or early 1966 at Houston's La Maison club. This show was recorded for Roy Ames, who soon lost the Elevators to Leland Rogers and International Artists, where they recorded four LPs plus some singles. Even at this early date they had all of the trademark Elevator traits together: Tommy Hall's electric jug, the mystical lyrics, spacey guitar work, and Roky's dynamic vocals. Fire in My Bones/ Roller Coaster/Reverberation/Monkey Island/Levitation/Fire Engine.

DECAL 2 (L)
The Collection
Four-CD box set of The 13th Floor Elevators's LPs on the International Artists label out of Houston, TX. Taken as a whole, these discs represent a major masterpiece of psychedelia. Forty-two mind benders in a small format slipcover box.

B.J. THOMAS

Sixties vocalist best-remembered for his hit cover of the Bachrach-David classic "Raindrops Keep Fallin' on My Head."

COLLECTABLES 5099 (CL)
Raindrops Keep Fallin' on My Head: Golden Classics
This one would make great music for a late '60s theme park; remember "Rock and Roll Lullaby," "Hooked on a Feeling," "I Just Can't Help Believing," and "The Eyes of a New York Woman"? Twelve tracks in all, including the title hit.

RHINO 70752 (CL)
Greatest Hits
Fourteen tracks on cassette, 18 on CD; duplicates the Collectables reissue, with better sound and packaging.

CARLA THOMAS

The daughter of Rufus Thomas, Carla was one of the first stars of the fledgling Satellite label, recording a duet with her father on "Cause I Love You" and her first solo outing, the teenybopper "Gee Whiz (Look at His Eyes)." Satellite soon transformed itself into Stax, and Carla became the label's reigning Queen of Soul, charting 22 times as a soloist and in a duet with Otis Redding on "Tramp."

ATLANTIC 80329 (CL)
Comfort Me
Reissue of Stax 706, recorded in 1964–1965, including 12 gorgeous soul tunes. The song selection is all over the place; she covers everyone from Holland-Dozier-Holland to Bacharach-David, as well as the expected slew of Steve Cropper and Hayes-Porter tunes. Unlike her next LP (Carla), Comfort Me didn't spawn any big hits. Solidly recommended. Yes, I'm Ready/Lover's Concerto/What the World Needs Now/Let It Be Me/Will You Love Me Tomorrow.

ATLANTIC 82340 (CL)
Carla
This repro of Stax 709 (1966) is even better than her first LP, because Thomas had become a much more assured interpreter. There are some groundbreaking R&B hits ("B-A-B-Y" and "Let Me Be Good to You"), as well as even wilder song choices: imagine a record that includes soul versions of Willie Dixon's "Little Red Rooster," Jimmy Reed's "Baby What You Want Me to Do" and Hank Williams's "I'm So Lonesome I Could Cry"! Highly recommended.

RHINO 71015 (CL)

The Queen Alone

Reissue of Carla's third solo LP for Stax (7718), originally issued in 1967. It's not bad stuff, but it's not great either. Original cover art and notes. Decent stereo sound. Twelve cuts providing 31 minutes of music. Any Day Now/I Take It to My Baby/When Tomorrow Comes/Unchanging Love/Lie to Keep Me from Crying.

STAX 8538 (RC)

Memphis Queen

Reissue of Stax 2019 from 1969. Features fine Memphis soul, including her last big hit, "I Like What You're Doing (to Me)," and the obligatory tune from *Hair*, "Where Do I Go." Precious Memories/Strung Out/Guide Me Well/More Man than I Ever Had.

IRMA THOMAS

Excellent New Orleans soulstress. Born Irma Lee, she was discovered in 1962 while working as a waitress by bandleader Tommy Ridgeley, who worked for Ron Records. He was so impressed that he took her into the studio the next day to record the classic "You Can Have My Husband (but Please Don't Mess with My Man)." She signed with Minit in 1963, where producer Allen Toussaint had her record "It's Raining" and "Time Is on My Side" (covered by The Rolling Stones). She signed with Imperial in 1964 and finally hit the national charts with "Wish Someone Would Care." She's still very active, mostly playing New Orleans and touring occasionally. She recorded for Rounder in the '80s.

CHARLY 195 (L)

Ruler of Hearts

Twenty-four tracks, including 16 great Minit recordings from the early '60s and eight songs recorded live at The New Orleans Jazz and Heritage Festival in 1976.

CHESS 93004 (CL)

Something Good:
The Muscle Shoals Sessions

Twelve great sides from 1967 featuring backup by the fabulous Muscle Shoals studio musicians. Only three singles were originally issued; the rest were unreleased until their appearance on a Japanese LP some years ago. The recording of "Cheater Man" here is a different mix from the Japanese set. The CD has two extra tracks, including a second, different mix of "We Got Something Good."

⊙ EMI 97988 (CL)

Time Is on My Side:
The Best of Irma Thomas, Vol. 1

This compilation is the best thing since walking upright. Twenty-four tracks, documenting Irma's career at Minit and Imperial Records between 1961–1966. Six songs were written by Minit man Allen Toussaint, including "Ruler of My Heart" (which Otis Redding reworked as "Pain in My Heart") and "It's Raining." Her biggest chart success "Wish Someone Would Care" and its original flip side, the double-time "Break a Way," are exceptional, but then so are all four of the previously unreleased cuts, "Think Again," "Long after Tonight Is Over," "Maybe," and "Live Again." The Rolling Stones copied her version of "Time Is on My Side"—and had the hit that she deserved—but their version pales in comparison. "He's My Guy" and "It's Starting to Get to Me Now," both penned by Van McCoy, are worthy of special attention, as is the Randy Newman composition "While the City Sleeps." Highly recommended.

KENT (UK) 010 (R)

Time Is on My Side

Sixteen sides recorded for Minit and Imperial between 1964–1965, duplicating the EMI reissue.

RCS 1004 (L)

Safe with Me/Irma Thomas Live

CD reissue of a 1980 studio album and 1977 live set. The studio LP is OK; Thomas sounds good on "Don't Stop," "Safe with Me," "Zero Willpower," and "What's the Matter Baby," but the band is nothing special. The reason to get this disc is the live set from 1977, recorded in Baton Rouge at The Kingfish Club. Originally intended as part of a TV series on R&B, this recording finds Irma in excellent voice, with a suitably exuberant band. To make matters even better, the songs are mostly classics, including six by Allen Toussaint, starting with "Cry On" and moving through masterpieces like "It's Raining," "Two Winters Long," and "Ruler of My Heart." Even new ones like "Friendly" and "Don't Blame Him" are memorable. My thumb is up.

ROUNDER 2046 (RCL)

The New Rules

This 1986 release was her first in a number of years.

ROUNDER 2058 (RCL)

The Way I Feel

Irma's second record for Rounder finds her again updating her classic New Orleans sound, with mixed but better results. Her voice is as good as ever and shines on great tunes such as "You Can Think Twice," "Dancing in the Street," and Allen Toussaint's "Old Records." Often, however, she is done in by a plodding band and stilted drumming. Still, when she sinks into a tune like Bobby Bland's "I'll Take Care of You," aided by Ron Levy's piano, there are few who can touch her.

ROUNDER 2110 (CL)
Simply the Best
1991 live album.

ROUNDER 2117 (CL)
True Believer

RUFUS THOMAS

Former Memphis DJ best-known for his novelty and dance hits. He recorded sporadically for Sam Phillips and Sun Records, scoring his first hit with 1953's "Beat Cat," an answer song to "Hound Dog," and "Tiger Man," which was successfully revived by Elvis during his 1968 comeback. In 1961, he and his daughter Carla (see separate listing) auditioned for Satellite Records; their duets, including "Cause I Love You," were the label's first hits. In 1963, national fame came with his three dance records: "The Dog," "Walking the Dog," and "Can Your Monkey Do the Dog." He had dance hits into the '70s, including 1970's "Do the Funky Chicken" and 1972's "Do the Push" and "Do the Funky Penguin." He stopped recording when Stax went under in 1975, but still performs. He made a comeback recording for Alligator in the '80s.

ALLIGATOR 4769 (CL)
That Woman Is Poison!
A mostly blues-oriented set from 1988. Big Fine Hunk Woman/The Walk/Blues in the Basement/All Night Worker.

ATLANTIC 82254 (CL)
Walking the Dog
Reissue of Stax 704 from 1963, which was released to capitalize on Thomas's unlikely dance hit. Not only did he follow up "The Dog" with "Walking the Dog" but he followed both up with the outrageous concept of "Can Your Monkey Do the Dog." Rufus keeps the dancers on the floor with some good covers of "Mashed Potatoes" and "Land of 1000 Dances," as well as versions of Lee Dorsey's "Ya Ya" and Jessie Hill's "Ooh-Poo-Pah-Doo." Good clean fun by the world's oldest teenager.

STAX 8569 (CL)
Can't Get Away from This Dog
Twenty unreleased songs recorded between 1963–1967. The selections are heavy on the R&B dance music that made Thomas famous, "Walking the Dog" being the best known. An alternate version of that hit is here, along with other doggie songs like "Can Your Monkey Do the Dog," "Stop Kicking My Dog Around," and the title track. The latter is the best cut, and was, according to Rufus, written by Sam Cooke. Of the three duets with daughter Carla, the best is their version of "Don't Mess Up a Good Thing," though "Reconsider Baby" is no slouch. The backing band is none other than Booker T and The MGs and the Mar-Key Horns (Wayne Jackson and Andrew Love; later known as The Memphis Horns).

RUFUS and CARLA THOMAS

STAX 4124 (CL)
Chronicle: Their Greatest Stax Hits
Fifteen soul duets and solo outings, including Rufus's hits "Do the Funky Chicken," "Push and Pull," "Sixty Minute Man," "The Breakdown," and "Do the Funky Penguin."

HAYDEN THOMPSON

Hard rockin' Memphis artist who recorded for Sun in the '50s. He switched to Kapp in the '60s where he had a career as a country singer. In the '80s, he returned to performing rockabilly and touring Europe. Sunjay has issued these more recent recordings, along with the definitive reissue of his early material (Sunjay 569).

BEAR FAMILY 15263 (R)
Fairlane Rock
Rockabilly and country cuts. Some hot rockabilly on 1956 Sun sides featuring Roland Janes, including Thompson's only Phillips International release, "One Broken Heart" b/w "Love My Baby." Also included are newly discovered, earlier recordings of both tunes, plus a couple of never-issued tunes recorded for Fernwood. None of the country material has been previously issued, though some have appeared on Sunjay label compilations. Includes a fun anti-British-invasion cut "I Need a Break" (including the immortal couplet, "Herman's got four ol' Hermits to help him/I've just got little ol' me"), and a nice guitar-only demo session.

KAPP 3507 (R)
Here's Hayden Thompson
Twenty-track collection featuring material Hayden recorded between 1961–1975 for various labels. Mystery Train/That's Alright/Good Rockin' Tonight/I'm Left, You're Right, She's Gone/My Baby Left Me/Be-Bop-a-Lula/These Boots Are Made for Walkin'.

SUNJAY 589 (R)/SUNJAY-SPARK 13 (L)

The Time Is Now

1990 recordings find Thompson singing better than ever and sticking to straight-shooting rockabilly and country with wonderful authentic backing. Hayden wraps his rich baritone around some great rockers like "Ain't That Loving You Baby," "At the Party Tonight," and "I Ain't Takin' No Prisoners." The country songs are fine as well, especially his versions of Wynn Stewart's "Wishful Thinking" and Johnny Cash's "I Still Miss Someone." Hayden's excellent 1987 tribute to you know who, "The Boy from Tupelo" (dig that guitar), rounds out an impressive collection.

SUNJAY 563 (R)

The Rockin' Country Man

Recent recordings by rockabilly legend.

SUNJAY 569 (R)

Early Days

The definitive early Hayden set. An amazing 22-song LP, with only four tunes released: his 1954 Von single ("I Feel the Blues Coming On" b/w "Act Like You Love Me") and his 1962 Arleen single ("Queen Bee" b/w "Pardon Me"), the latter also appearing in two alternate versions. Most of the 18 previously unissued tracks were recorded between 1958–1962 with a solid trio of Thompson (pno), Travis Westmoreland (gtr), and Bob Miller (drm). Mostly from original master tapes.

JOHNNY TILLOTSON

Highly successful pop/country artist from Florida who signed to Cadence Records in 1959 and had huge hits with 1961's "Poetry in Motion" and 1962's "It Keeps Right on a-Hurtin'." Johnny entered the army and, when he returned, Cadence had gone under, so he signed with MGM, recording a series of country-oriented sides. His MGM hits include "Send Me the Pillow You Dream On" and "Heartaches by the Number." He later recorded for Ampex and Buddah, and still performs.

ACE 331 (L)

Talk Back Trembling Lips/
The Tillotson Touch

Two early '60s LPs on one CD. Blue Velvet/Danke Schoen/Blowin' in the Wind/This Old House/Cold, Cold Heart/Jailer Bring Me Water.

ACE 345 (L)

She Understands Me/That's My Style

Reissues two complete MGM albums from 1964–1965 and contains his last two chart successes, "She Understands Me" and "Heartaches by the Number." Most of the material here is marred by strings and background singers. Johnny's smooth voice deserved better, but he still shines on "Busted," "I've Seen Better Days," "Oh, Lonesome Me," and "Me, Myself and I." He even rocks a little on "The Race Is On" until the Anita Kerr singers swoop in. Twenty-four songs in all.

ACE 946 (L)

All His Early Hits: And More!

Thirty-track CD, including his Cadence hits. Many of these cuts were previously reissued on two Japanese CDs that are no longer available. Poetry in Motion/It Keeps Right on a-Hurtin'/Send Me the Pillow You Dream On/I Can't Help It/Funny How Time Slips Away/Earth Angel/Pledging My Love.

TREASURE 1059 (R)

All the Hits

Sixteen MGM recordings made between 1963–1965, mostly in true stereo. Heartaches by the Number/Angel/She Understands Me/Raining in My Heart/Only the Lonely/Rhythm of the Rain/Blue Velvet.

TINY TIM

Novelty star of the late '60s who became a freak hit thanks to TV exposure on *The Smothers Brothers* and *Johnny Carson* shows. He even made his own film, *You Are What You Eat*, which also featured Paul Butterfield, The Electric Flag, and Barry "Eve of Destruction" McGuire! He performed under the names Herbert Khaury in the '50s and Darry Dover and Larry Love in the mid-'60s to the Greenwich Village coffeehouse crowd. After recording for Reprise through 1972, Tim has resurfaced occasionally to make recordings that are truly terrible!

BEAR FAMILY 15409 (L)

Tip Toe Through the Tulips/
Resurrection

Sixteen truly horrible recent recordings done for Playback Records in Nashville. While there was a certain charm to his original Reprise recording of the '60s, these, complete with orchestral background, are just plain lousy. Tip-Toe through the Tulips/Bill Bailey/Pennies from Heaven/Baby Face.

TOMMY TOLLESON

Gulf Coast piano player who's best known for his rockin', Kool disc, "A Gal Named Sue."

COLLECTOR 4407 (L)

Rockin' the Boogie

Twenty-four cut mixture of old and new tunes. The '50s and '60s recordings are very good for the most part, including his hit "A Gal Named Sue," but there are only nine of them. The rest were recorded in the late '70s in Tommy's living room and are of only minor interest. To the Dance/The Gulf Coast Twist/Carla Blues/Stompin' the Boogie/Wild Leg Boogie.

ALLEN TOUSSAINT

One of the most important producer/arranger/songwriter/pianists from New Orleans. A devotee of Professor Longhair, Toussaint formed his first group when he was 14, and later became a session pianist in the late '50s, appearing on some Fats Domino sessions as well as a lot of Ace sides. In the late '50s, he also hooked up with Joe Banashak's Minit label, producing most of the classic sides by Ernie K-Doe, Jessie Hill, Irma Thomas, Lee Dorsey, and Barbara George. After a two-year stint in the army in 1963–1965, Toussaint rejoined Banashak at the Alon label, where he worked with Esquerita and put out records by The Stokes, a group he had formed a few years earlier. Later in 1965, he teamed with Marshall Seahorn, creating Sansu Productions and the Sea-Saint Studios. He was responsible for the growth of interest in New Orleans music in the late '60s, producing hits for Lee Dorsey and Betty Harris. In the '70s, he worked with The Meters (the Sansu house band) and such old-timers as Ernie K-Doe, Earl King, and Benny Spellman. Soon he was "discovered" by hip white artists, and he sessioned with The Band, Paul Simon, and Paul McCartney. Self-described as "easy-listening soul," his own recordings aren't nearly as interesting as his productions, but are definitely worth a listen. Don't expect raucous New Orleans R&B; he's closer in style to the '70s singer/songwriter crowd.

BEAR FAMILY 15641 (L)

The Complete 'Tousan Sessions

Reissues Allen Toussaint's 1958 instrumental LP for RCA *The Wild Sound of New Orleans* (RCA 1767), and throws in the rare recordings he cut for the Seville label between 1960–1963. The RCA stuff is good, not great, with only "Whirlaway," "Tim Tam," "Nashua," and "Pelican Parade" deserving of the titular adjective

"wild." The rest is pleasant if somewhat undistinguished despite featured artists like Alvin "Red" Tyler (bar sax), Roy Montrell (gtr), and Frank Fields (b). The Seville material includes all four singles, a few unreleased songs, and a couple of alternate takes from various sessions. Some songs suffer from an ice-rink organ sound that is far, far from wild. Excellent notes and pix.

EDSEL 275 (RL)

The Wild Sound of New Orleans by Tousan

Reissue of Allen's first LP, RCA 1767, from 1958. Duplicates the Bear Family reissue.

KENT (UK) 036 (RL)

From a Whisper to a Scream

Reissue of what some consider to be Allen's best solo LP. The songs have been rearranged so that Side 1 has all the vocal sides and Side 2 has the instrumentals. Originally released in 1970, the music sounds somewhat dated, but fans will want this. Includes personnel listing, LP discography, and liner notes. Sweet Touch of Love/What Is Success/Chokin' Kind.

REPRISE 26549 (CL)

The Allen Toussaint Collection

Sixteen '70s solo waxings by Toussaint, including some smooth soul senders among these 16 cuts. From a Whisper to a Scream/Southern Nights/What Do You Want the Girl to Do/Night People/With You in My Mind.

REPRISE (JAPAN) 4415 (L)

Southern Nights

Reissue of his 1975 Reprise LP (2186). Ten beautiful cuts that flow like an extended suite, featuring Toussaint's grand piano chordings backed by The Meters and a seven-piece horn section. The title track became a big hit for Glen Campbell, and "What Do You Want the Girl to Do" has often been covered. Last Train/Worldwide/Back in Baby's Arms/Country John/Basic Lady/You Will Not Lose/When the Party's Over/Cruel Way to Go Down.

WARNER BROS. (JAPAN) 4414 (L)

Life, Love and Faith

Reissue of Reprise 2062 from 1972, on which Toussaint is backed by a sizable New Orleans studio cast, including The Meters and Red Tyler. Twelve cuts. Victims of the Darkness/Goin' Down/Out of the City/Soul Sister/Fingers and Toes/Gone Too Far/Electricity.

WARNER BROS. (JAPAN) 4416 (L)

Motion

Toussaint's 1978 LP (Warner Bros. 3142) was one of the better efforts of the disco-dominated era. It was a bit of a departure for him, with production duties relinquished to Jerry Wexler, and was recorded in Hollywood, far from his New Orleans turf. But the sound is solid, and, in some ways, stronger than his usual homegrown solo projects. The opener "Night People" is one of Toussaint's best tracks. Guests include Etta James, Bonnie Raitt, and Paulinho Da Costa. Just a Kiss Away/Motion/Viva La Money/Happiness/The Optimism Blues.

TRAFFIC

Progressive British rock band of the '60s, formed around ex-Spencer Davis Group vocalist/keyboardist Steve Winwood, with guitarist/vocalist Dave Mason, Chris Wood (sax), and Jim Capaldi (drm). The original band's pop psychedelia was greatly influenced by Mason, who was present on the group's first three LPs, released in 1968–1969. Winwood jumped ship in 1968 to perform with the supergroup Blind Faith, but that band succumbed to internal tensions almost immediately. Returning to the studio to record a solo LP, Winwood sought the help of ex-Traffic mates Wood and Capaldi, eventually releasing the LP as 1970's folk/rock/jazz fusion, *John Barleycorn Must Die*, Traffic's best-known effort. The band soldiered on through the early '70s, augmented by various studio musicians, with Mason briefly rejoining them for a 1971 tour. Their last LP came out in 1973.

ISLAND 510 553 (L)

Smiling Phases

Two-CD anthology of Traffic's best, newly remastered for much-improved sound.

ISLAND 842 417 (CL)

Welcome to the Canteen

Reissue of 1972 live set, with Mason back in the fold, along with an expanded rhythm section. Includes a remake of the old Spencer Davis chestnut, "Gimme Some Lovin'," that was a minor chart hit.

ISLAND 842 590 (CL)

Traffic

Their second, trippy effort. Feelin' Alright/Pearly Queen/Vagabond Virgin/40,000 Headmen.

ISLAND 842 779 (CL)

Low Spark of the High Heel Boys

Highlight is the 12-minute jam on the title cut, a favorite of early '70s FM radio.

ISLAND 842 780 (GF) (CL)

John Barleycorn Must Die

It's still okay to like Traffic, isn't it? Six classics of the era. Glad/Freedom Rider/Empty Pages/Stranger to Himself/John Barleycorn/Every Mother's Son.

ISLAND 842 781 (CL)

Shoot-out at the Fantasy Factory

Things are winding down on this 1973 release, as the boys attempt to regain steam by recording in Muscle Shoals.

ISLAND 842 783 (CL)

Mr. Fantasy

Reissue of their first LP, with some spacey masterpieces accompanied by twanging sitars.

ISLAND 842 787 (CL)

Last Exit

Studio outtakes and live tracks put together after the band originally split in 1969.

ISLAND 842 893 (RCL)

On the Road

1973 live recordings.

THE TRAITS

The Traits featured Roy Head, best-known for his minor hit "Treat Her Right." They were from San Marcos, TX, and hitched up with TNT records out of San Antonio around 1956.

DOMINO 1011 (R)

Rebel Rock

If you like well-recorded, slick rock and roll, then step aside, because this stuff is as raucous as a Texas roadhouse at 2 AM. Twenty tunes, divided into two sides: the 1956–1958 originals and the 1962–1963 second versions. The rerecorded versions don't suffer by comparison, and are actually a bit better if you like the heavier guitar and some Tex-Mex organ. Beware though, the track listing on the cover for Side 2 is screwy and so are the track times (maybe the dates, too). Curiously, "Treat Her Right," Head's biggest hit, is not here. Recommended. One More Time/Summertime Love/Live It Up/Yes I Do/Night Time Blues.

BOBBY LEE TRAMMEL

Arkansas rocker who turned country singer. He recorded for a number of small labels as well as Atlantic and Decca, and, in 1978, he joined the revived Sun label. He's probably best-known for his song "Shirley Lee," later a hit for Ricky Nelson.

BISON BOP 2039 (R)
Bobby Lee Trammell
Fourteen sides, with hot guitar on some cuts. Shirley Lee/Open Up Your Heart/My Susie Jane/You Mostest Girls/Hi Ho Silver/Come On.

DEE JAY JAMBOREE 2036 (R)
Arkansas Twist
Fourteen late '50s/early '60s sides. Come On Baby/Sally Twist, Pt. 1/Watch Me Do the Twist/Bobby Lee Needs Love/Carolyn.

DEE JAY JAMBOREE 2040 (R)
Toolie Froolie
More '50s-'60s rockers. The title track is a variation on "Papa-Oom-Mow-Mow." Other wild ones include "I Can't Sit Still" and a cover of Jerry Lee's "Whole Lotta Shakin' Goin' On." Several of the other tracks are rather more restrained, and the LP as a whole has a '60s feel to it.

THE TRASHMEN
Wild Minneapolis garage band who recorded for the Garrett label in 1962–1963. The group consisted of ace lead guitarist Tony Andreason, Dan Winslow (gtr, vcl), Bob Reed (b), and Steve Wahrer (drm, vcl). They recorded one single under the name of Jim Thaxter and The Travelers before taking their more funky moniker. Who would ever think there'd be a surf group from Minnesota, but with the remarkable "Surfin' Bird" (a mixture of The Rivingtons's "Papa Oom-Mow-Mow" and "The Bird's the Word"), they were one of the most successful. They re-formed to play some local shows in the '80s.

GARRETT 300 (R)
Bird Dance Beat
Fourteen trashy tracks by the titans of twang. Many of these tracks are on the Request CD. A-Bone/Walkin' My Baby/Whoa Dad/Bird '65/Ubangi Stomp/Sally Jo.

✪ REQUEST 13502 (L)
Surfin' Bird
Twenty-six rockin' tracks. Surfin' Bird/Bird Bath/Misirlou/Malaguena/A-Bone/Bird Dance Beat/Whoa Dad/Ubangi Stomp/New Generation.

SUNDAZED 5002 (R)/11006 (L)
Live Bird 1965–1967
Who woulda thunk it? After all these years, the Sundazed crew have unearthed and released some primo vintage Trashmen captured live in their Midwest habitat. Landlocked they might have been, but The Trashmen certainly didn't let the lack of surf stop them from churnin' up a tidal wave of super-wet, reverb-drenched surf tunes. The first eight tracks are from a 1965 gig at Proaches Popular Ballroom. They blast through Dick Dale's "Let's Go Trippin'" as well as surfin' standards like "Baja" and "Malaguena." Jerry Lee's "Lovin' Up a Storm" gets the full treatment, and, of course, they can't fly the coop until they've ruffled a few feathers with "Surfin' Bird," all five minutes and 49 seconds worth! "Bird Dance Beat" and "King of the Surf" were recorded in 1966 at a girls reform school (the mind boggles), and "Mashed Potatoes" and "Ubangi Stomp" at St. Paul's version of Whiskey A-Go-Go. Throw in a couple more from a 1967 gig and some short interviews and you've got one essential collection. CD includes two bonus tracks, "Henrietta" and "Rumble."

SUNDAZED 5003 (R)/11007 (L)
Unreleased Studio Recordings, 1964–1966
Their complete second LP, which went unreleased at the time, along with some later recordings. There's a hefty dollop of surf music with cool versions of "Stick Shift," "Havah Nagila" and even "Be True to Your School." Lead guitarist Tony Andreason really has that wet sound down pat using it to great effect on everything from "Ghost Riders in the Sky" to "Greensleeves" to "Green Onions." "Mind Your Own Business" and "Bird Diddley Beat" come from a 1966 session recorded for Huey Meaux. A couple of 1966-era tunes close things out, recorded at the legendary IGL Studios in Iowa. CD has two bonus tracks, "Lucille" and "Green Onions."

THE TREMELOES
These British invaders began in 1959 as Brian Poole's backup band. After Poole went solo, The Tremeloes tried their hands at hitmaking, and for a short while were quite successful, but more so in England than America. Their biggest US hits (all from 1967) include a very close cover of The Four Seasons's "Silence Is Golden," "Even the Bad Times Are Good," and "Here Comes My Baby" written by a young Cat Stevens. At heart, The Tremeloes were a blue-collar club band who made surprisingly polished and energetic, if minor, pop music.

RHINO 70528 (CL)
The Best of The Tremeloes
Twenty-song collection, including the band's top UK chart singles, selected album cuts, and two tracks previously unissued in the US ("Do I Love You" and "Alley Oop"). Eclectic cover songs include "Show

Me" by Joe Tex, "Too Many Fish in the Sea" by The Marvelettes, and Dylan's "I Shall Be Released" recorded with the Keith Manfield Strings!

THE TRENIERS

Wild R&B nightclub group led by twin brothers Claude and Clifford Trenier, who could not only sing but were also talented dancers and comedians. Claude started out singing with Jimmy Lunceford's band in 1944, and, when he was drafted, he was replaced by Clifford. When they went solo as The Trenier Twins for Mercury in the late '40s, they were as well-known for their comedy act as for their incredible scat singing. In 1951, brothers Buddy and Milt joined and, as The Treniers, they made lots of great, raucous R&B sides for Okeh in 1951–1956, with their biggest hits being 1951's "GoGoGo!" and 1955's "Get Out of the Car."

BEAR FAMILY 15418 (L)
Cool It Baby

BEAR FAMILY 15419 (L)
Hey Sister Lucy
Two CDs reissuing all the group's Mercury and RCA recordings, plus all the solo Milt Trenier recordings.

DR. HORSE 803 (RL)
You're Killin' Me
Sixteen cuts from 1947–1956 in a party mood, with clean sound and brief, but good notes. Buzz, Buzz, Buzz/Why Did You Get So High, Shorty/Flip Our Wigs.

T.N.T. TRIBBLE

Trumpeter/bandleader famous for playing two instruments at once.

KRAZY KAT 828 (R)
Vol. 2: Red Hot Boogie
Fourteen, mostly previously unreleased cuts drawn from Gotham sessions from the early '50s. Tribble and band are, by turns, swingin', jumpin' and smoky-sounding. Even the Krazy Kat sleuths are at a loss to pin down many of the band members, including the dynamic guitar player on "Red Hot Boogie" and "Rockin' Mama," although their best guess is that it is Mauzette Graham. Vol. 1 is out of print. Hey Everybody/Cadillac Blues/T.N.T. Stroll/She Walked Right In.

THE TROGGS

Tough, leather-clad English punkers best-known for the immortal three-chord crunch, "Wild Thing." While most of the bands of this era could rightfully be called one-hit wonders, The Troggs presented strong, menacing material throughout their career. They seemed to disappear in the '70s, but lead vocalist Reg Presley has kept different versions of the band going, touring and recording (for the French New Rose label).

MERCURY 512 936 (L)
Archeology 1967–1977
Their classic tracks from the original master tapes.

RHINO 70118 (RC)
Best of The Troggs
Fourteen tracks by England's only true '60s punk band. A decade before Elvis Costello, Reg Ball changed his name to Reg Presley and led these tough leather boys through their all-time classics. Wild Thing/With a Girl Like You/Love Is All Around/From Home/Night of the Long Grass.

RHINO 71064 (CL)
Athens Andover
The Troggs meet a Michael Stipe-less R.E.M. (!) on these 1992 recordings.

SEE FOR MILES 256 (R)
Wild Things
A compilation taken from their mid-'70s comeback LPs, and I'm sure it sounded a lot better then than it does now. There are lots of over-the-top Presley vocals and way too much hard rock/heavy metal ('70s style) guitar noise but, if you like The Troggs and aren't afraid of this kind of thing, you might dig it. Includes a reggae version of "Wild Thing" and scads of trashy cover versions. Satisfaction/Walkin' the Dog/Peggy Sue/Good Vibrations/No Particular Place to Go.

THE TURBANS

Excellent group from Philadelphia featuring the expressive soaring lead of Al Banks. Their first record for Herald in 1955, the catchy mambo flavored "When You Dance," was a gigantic hit. Although they recorded more fine sides, they never dented the charts again and, after recording for several other labels, they disbanded in 1961.

COLLECTABLES 5019 (C)

The Best of The Turbans
Twelve mid-'50s Herald sides, all also on the Relic LP. When You Dance/Wadda-Do/Sister Sookey/Valley of Tears.

RELIC 5009 (R)

The Turbans Greatest Hits
Same track line up as Collectables cassette, though this came out first.

IKE and TINA TURNER

Although Tina Turner is now a superstar, the Ike and Tina story goes back to the late '40s, when Ike ran the great Kings of Rhythm (their recordings are listed in our companion book, *The Down Home Guide to the Blues*). Ike did some singing himself and, with his first wife, he made duo recordings under the name Ike and Bonnie. In a St. Louis club in the mid-'50s, he met Annie Mae Bullock, who insisted she was a singer. She sang with the band, and Ike liked what he saw and heard, and asked her to join them. The two were married in 1958. Ike formed The Ike and Tina Turner Revue out of the remnants of The Kings of Rhythm, playing lead guitar in the new eight-piece band, with Tina out front and backup vocals by The Ikettes. They signed to Sue Records in 1960, having a major pop hit with "A Fool in Love." They had hits throughout the early '60s, and, in 1966, they recorded the immortal "River Deep, Mountain High," produced by Phil Spector. Ike and Tina signed with Liberty, scoring a number of small hits. Their big break came in 1969 when they were asked to open The Rolling Stones's US tour, where they gained massive exposure before a white audience both during the tour and in the film of the tour, *Gimme Shelter*. They subsequently scored a number of hits—mostly covers of white rock songs, including "Come Together," "Proud Mary," and "I Want to Take You Higher"—on various Liberty and United Artists labels, including subsidiaries Minit and Blue Thumb. Their stage show included Tina's high-energy vocals and famous high-heeled dancing. Their career sputtered throughout the '70s, with a little interest rekindled by Tina's role as the Acid Queen in the movie *Tommy*. The pair split. Tina was "rediscovered" in the early '80s after appearing on a satellite broadcast of a Rod Stewart concert, leading to her 1982 megahit, "What's Love Got to Do With It." Meanwhile, Ike has battled a cocaine addiction, his prized home studio burned down in the year of Tina's massive solo success, and he has made a few, abortive comebacks.

CEMA 57362 (L)

The Best of
The millionth time these songs have been reissued by Capitol. Ten megahits, including Tina's solo version of "The Acid Queen" from *Tommy*. A Fool in Love/Proud Mary/Nutbush City Limits/Workin' Together/I Idolize/It's Gonna Work Out Fine/Honky Tonk Women/Sexy Ida, Pt. 2/River Deep, Mountain High.

COLLECTABLES 5107 (RCL)

Golden Classics

COLLECTABLES 5137 (RCL)
It's Gonna Work Out Fine
Two collections of early Sue classics, recorded between 1960–1962. It's Gonna Work Out Fine/A Fool in Love/Poor Fool/Tra La La La La/I Idolize You.

⊛ EMI 95846 (CL)
Proud Mary: The Best of Ike and Tina Turner
Twenty cuts from Sue, Minit, Liberty, and United Artists. Includes the early R&B classics like the sassy "A Fool in Love," the oft-covered "It's Gonna Work Out Fine," "River Deep Mountain High," and "Ooh Poo Pah Doo," plus the rocked-out soul of "Come Together," "Honky Tonk Women," "I Want to Take You Higher," "Proud Mary," "Acid Queen," and "Nutbush City Limits."

KENT (UK) 065 (L)
The Ike and Tina Turner Sessions
Reissue of the out-of-print LP Ace 065, featuring 20 of their best 1964–1965 Kent/Modern recordings, including five in real stereo and seven never issued previously. Track listing is identical to the LP; you'd think with only 46 minutes playing time they could've added more! Excellent sound, although a couple cuts sound a bit echoey. Goodbye So Long/Lose My Cool/I Need a Man/He's the One/If I Can't Be First.

LIBERTY (JAPAN) 6597 (L)
You've Got Too Many Ties That Bind
In 1970, the hell-raising Ike and Tina Turner Revue was at their peak and were unsurpassable in professional polish and raw excitement. This 16-song collection contains their three charted hits for Liberty: "I Want to Take You Higher," "Workin' Together," and their best rendition of John Fogerty's "Proud Mary." Also features the stompin' "Honky Tonk Woman" and their tear-stained rendition of the Mophead's "With a Little Help from My Friends." The Turners at their mean and dirtiest. Music to be played loud through giant speakers. Booklet contains lyrics to all songs.

MOBILE FIDELITY 849 (L)
River Deep, Mountain High
A reissue of Philles 4011 from 1966 in Mobile Fidelity's high-priced, gold-plated series. This legendary Phil Spector-produced masterpiece sounds magnificent. Contains the title classic, along with other Ike and Tina greats. A Fool in Love/It's Gonna Work Out Fine/I Idolize You.

SAJA 91223 (L)
Greatest Hits, Vol. 1

SAJA 91224 (L)
Greatest Hits, Vol. 2

SAJA 91228 (L)
Greatest Hits, Vol. 3
Releasing three volumes of this stuff and calling it "Greatest Hits" is an insult to the performers, serious collectors, and the record-buying public in general. This label would be well advised to avoid conflict with truth-in-advertising laws by renaming this series "Ike and Tina Turner Play Other People's Greatest Hits." Many inferior covers of such familiar tunes as "Louie Louie," "It's My Own Fault," "Knock on Wood," "Money," "Get Back," "Woke Up this Morning," and "Got My Mojo Working," often performed in a tacky disco/funk style with whining synthesizer. The dregs.

TOMATO 70382 (L)
The Great Rhythm and Blues Sessions
Thirteen cuts from sessions conducted in Memphis at The Royal Recording Studios (1967–1968). Nothing from this period sold well for the duo, although they deserved heftier sales with winners like the raunchy "Rock Me Baby," blues downer "I Smell Trouble," hard-driving "Crazy 'Bout You Baby," and tearful weeper "It Sho' Ain't Me." Heavy participation by The Ikettes, who solo on the magnificent "Poor Little Fool." Nice arty pix and detailed sleeve notes by Rob Bowman.

JESSE LEE TURNER
Texas-born rockabilly and teen-pop star, whose one hit was the novelty "The Little Space Girl" (1959), complete with sped-up, Chipmunk-style vocals, and the immortal lines she has "four arms, the better to hold you/Three lips, the better to kiss you."

TURNER 8011 (R)
Shake Baby Shake
Fourteen sides, including his hit "Little Space Girl," the two follow-up singles ("That's My Girl" and "The Elopers"), plenty of fine rockabilly and '50s teen-pop, and some '60s tunes like "The Ballad of Billy Sol Estes." The title tune is a fine wild ripoff of "Sexy Ways." Baby Please Don't Tease/Shotgun Boogie/Teen Age Misery/The Voice Changing Song/Thinkin'.

TITUS "TEE" TURNER
Turner, who sang briefly with the Count Basie band, wrote songs for Little Willie John, Ray Charles, and Elvis Presley.

COLLECTABLES 5160 (CL)
Golden Classics: Soulville
Fourteen cuts produced by Bobby Robinson.

TITUS TURNER/TOMMY TUCKER

RED LIGHTNIN' 86 (L)

Titans of R&B

CD reissue of the Tommy Tucker album on Red Lightnin' (022, *Mother Tucker*), teamed up with 14 tracks by songwriter/singer Titus Turner. Of Turner's mid-'60s efforts here, "Leave My Kitten Alone" is probably his best known. Tommy Tucker is responsible for "Hi-Heel Sneakers" and other soulful blues numbers. Twenty-five cuts in all.

THE TURTLES

Long-lived LA band that started out as the surf band The Nightriders. When Mark Volman joined on vocals and sax, they changed their name to The Crossfires (their early recordings under that moniker were reissued on Rhino 019). In 1965, when the folk-rock boom hit and The Byrds were LA's most popular band, their manager changed their name to The Tyrtles, although the band insisted on the normal spelling. They hitched up with the small White Whale label, scoring a Top 10 hit with a cover of Dylan's "It Ain't Me Babe." They stayed in the folk-rock vein for a while, with lead vocals by Howie Kaylan and Volman on harmony. After a near hit with P.F. Sloan's "Let Me Be," they teamed up with pop-rock tunesmiths Bonner and Gordon from the group The Magicians, who gave them their biggest hits with "You Baby," "Happy Together," and "She'd Rather Be with Me." Joining the band were Jim Pons, former bass player from The Leaves (famous for "Hey Joe"), and Johnny Barbatta from The Sentinels. They started writing their own material ("Elenore"), and their bizarre sense of humor started appearing in their songs ("Umbassa and the Dragon" and their entire *Battle of the Bands* LP). Barbatta was replaced by John Seiter from Spanky and Our Gang, and the group finally broke up in 1971, with Kaylan, Volman, and Pons joining Frank Zappa in The Mothers of Invention. Because of litigation against The Turtles by White Whale, Kaylan and Volman recorded under the pseudonym The Phlorescent Leech and Eddie, shortened to Flo and Eddie. They've become masters of satirical rock, and they always do Turtles material in their act.

RHINO 5160 (L)

20 Greatest Hits

Thanks to Rhino's extensive reissue program, I've revived a childhood love of these guys. This 20 tracker has 53 minutes of their best in fine sound from the folk-rock period ("It Ain't Me Babe" and "Let Me Be") to power pop ("You Baby," "Happy Together," and "She'd Rather Be With Me"), into my favorite era, psychedelic pop ("She's My Girl Sound Asleep" and "You Know What I Mean") through the tongue in cheek of "Elenore" and "You Don't Have to Walk in the Rain." Extensive liner notes by Rhino's Harold Bronson.

RHINO 70159 (CL)

The Best of The Turtles, Vol. 2

Minor hit singles, B-sides, and other goodies gathered together under the dubious banner "Best of ... Vol. 2." References to The Kinks, The Zombies, and, of course, the LSD-era Fab Four crop up on many cuts, particularly "Outside Chance," "Somewhere Friday Night" and the enigmatic "House on the Hill." Their hard-edged "Goodbye Surprise" goes even further into Anglophilia/psychedelia, conjuring up the spirit of Arthur Brown. Other winners are "We Ain't Gonna Party No More," the best anti-war rock opus ever done on a seven-inch record; the simply beautiful "Lady-O"; and one of the many ultra-demented no-commercial-potential singles, a psychotic waltz entitled "Grim Reaper of Love." "Guide for the Married Man" and the brilliant Beach Boys spoof "Surfer Dan" round out the collection nicely, making it well worth the price.

RHINO 70177 (C)

Best of The Turtles

All 14 White Whale hits from 1965's "It Ain't Me Babe" to the Ray Davies-produced "Love in the City" from 1969. Lots of great fun. You Baby/Happy Together/Elenore/She'd Rather Be with Me/She's My Girl/You Know What I Mean.

CONWAY TWITTY

Twitty was one of the most successful country stars in the world in the '70s and '80s, but in 1955 he was just Harold Jenkins, a guy who loved country but knew he had to rock in order to record. He didn't start out well, as none of the sides he cut for Sun in 1956–1957 were released initially. He changed his name to Conway Twitty and signed to Mercury in 1957, having a minor hit with "I Need Your Lovin'." However, once he signed to MGM in 1958, he had perfected a rock-a-ballad style that gave him a long string of rock hits, including "It's Only Make Believe," "Danny Boy," and "Lonely Blue Boy." With his pop hits drying up, Twitty signed with Decca in 1965 and recorded in a straight country style. Twitty died of a heart attack after a performance in 1993.

BEAR FAMILY 15174 (9) (R)
Rock and Roll Years, 1956–1963
Amazing nine-LP box set featuring everything recorded by Harold Jenkins, later known as Conway Twitty, for Sun, Mercury, and MGM. Altogether, there are 144 songs, including seven never on LP and 23 never released. This beautiful box set comes with gorgeous laminated covers for each LP and also includes a book by Colin Escott.

SPECIAL MUSIC 837 668 (L)
It's Only Make Believe
All in all, this disc makes a convincing case that Old Conway, now the king of country tease, was once a pretty fair rocker. The major hits are here, such as the title track, "Lonely Blue Boy," and "Danny Boy." But most of the others are less well known, including "Goin' Home," "Hey Miss Ruby," "I Vibrate from My Head to My Feet," and "My One and Only You." All 12 clearly come from early in his career, drawn from his MGM cuts recorded in the late '50s. My only real complaint is that there are so few songs here to enjoy, plus no notes at all.

THE UNIVERSALS

RELIC 5006 (R)
The Universals
Fourteen a-cappella sides from the early '60s.

RITCHIE VALENS

One of the most influential Chicano rockers (born Richard Valenzuela), Ritchie first recorded for Del-Fi in 1958 at the age of 17. His first hit was the rockin' "Come On Let's Go," which charted in September 1958. In November, he put out the classic "Donna" which hit the Top 10. On the flip side, was his megahit "La Bamba," which hit the charts in January 1959. By February 3rd, he was dead, a victim of the same crash that killed Buddy Holly and The Big Bopper. Ritchie can be seen performing in the movie *Go Johnny Go*, and his life story was immortalized in the 1987 film, *La Bamba*, featuring music by Los Lobos.

ACE 317 (L)
The Lost Tapes
Forty selections from unreleased tapes discovered in 1990. The first selections are just Ritchie and electric guitar on "We Belong Together," "Let's Rock and Roll," and "Ritchie's Blues." There are many pre-Del-Fi cuts, mostly demos and auditions. For anyone who appreciates music in the making, the "La Bamba" rehearsals are most noteworthy, although Ritchie's vocals are barely discernible. There are many other multiple takes of his best-known songs. Donna/Cry Cry Cry/Dooby Dooby Wah/In a Turkish Town/Bluebirds over the Mountain/La Bamba.

ACE 387 (L)
The Best of Ritchie Valens
Includes the obvious hits "Donna," "Come On Let's Go," and "La Bamba," plus a cross section of lesser-known and often less-successful tunes such as "Dooby Dooby Wah" and "Ooh My Head." Ace's sound quality standards are high, as one would expect, but pictures are few and notes are brief.

ACE 953 (L)
Ritchie Valens/Ritchie
Two LPs on one CD, originally Del-Fi 1201 and 1206. That's My Little Suzie/Come On Let's Go/Donna/Bony Moronie/La Bamba/Stay Beside Me/Rockin' All Night.

RHINO 70178 (CL)
Ritchie Valens
Excellent collection of 17 Del-Fi sides. Informative notes, including interviews with his producer Bob Keene and Ritchie's girlfriend Donna Ludwig, and excellent sound thanks to the Sonic Solutions No Noise process. Includes "Fast Freight," released as by "Arvee Allens," and all of his all-time greats. La Bamba/In a Turkish Town/The Paddi-Wack Song/Malaguena/Come On Let's Go/Donna/We Belong Together/That's My Little Suzie.

RHINO 70231 (C)
Ritchie Valens
Reissue of Ritchie's first LP. That's My Little Suzie/Come On Let's Go/Boney Moronie/La Bamba/Hi-Tone/Dooby Dooby Wah.

RHINO 70232 (C)
Ritchie
Reissue of Ritchie's second (and posthumous) LP, Del-Fi 1206 from 1959. There are a few complete tracks, some completed after his death, and many beautiful demos with just Ritchie and his guitar. Includes his rare "Fast Freight" instrumental single released as by Arvee Allens, and "Hurry Up" written by Sharon Sheely and taught to Ritchie by Eddie Cochran. The Paddi-Wack Song/Ritchie's Blues/Now You've Gone.

RHINO 70233 (C)
Ritchie Valens in Concert at Pacoima Jr. High
Reissue of Del-Fi 1214 from 1961, complete with narration by Del-Fi's Bob Keene. Side 1 has Ritchie performing at his alma mater, his only live recording. Includes the hits "Come On Let's Go," "La Bamba," "Donna," the instrumental "From Beyond," and "Summertime Blues." Side 2 has five incomplete Valens studio tracks: "Rhythm Song," "Guitar Instrumental," the instrumental tracks for "Malaguena," plus incomplete tracks with vocals for two new songs, "Rock Little Darlin'" and "Let's Rock and Roll."

THE VALENTINES
"Richie" Barrett and The Valentines were a short-lived Philly-Sugar Hill group beloved by hard-core doo-wop aficionados. But to me they sound like the adult equivalent of Frankie Lymon and The Teenagers, who also recorded for George Goldner in East Harlem. The quintet is backed by the extremely impressive Jimmy Wright Combo.

COLLECTABLES 5405 (CL)
Best of The Valentines: Rama Recordings 1955–1957
Fifteen-cut set, including jumpers and moderately pleasing ballads. One of their uptempo numbers—"Woo Woo Train"—became Boston D.J. Arnie Ginsberg's theme song. Ballads include 1956's "Why" and 1955's "Hand Me Down Love," along with the previously unreleased "Sweetheart of Mine," also from 1956. Good sleeve notes.

BOBBY VEE
Long-lasting teen idol whose good looks helped him have a tremendous string of hits on Liberty through the '60s. Bobby was discovered when his band, The Shadows, replaced Buddy Holly after the plane crash during the rest of the winter 1959 tour. Bobby was signed to a solo contract, groomed to become a pretty boy, and given excellent material to sing, including The Clovers's "Devil or Angel" and Goffin and King's "Take Good Care of My Baby" (listen to the way he enunciates "don't ever" in that song, one of my favorite rock moments). The hits dried up with the British invasion, but by 1967 he was back for another string of hits, including "Beautiful People" and the million-selling "Come Back When You Grow Up." In the 1970s, balding and sporting a beard, he made "relevant" recordings, returning to his real name of Robert Thomas Velline. More recently, he resurrected the Bobby Vee name and hit the oldies circuit.

EMI 92774 (CL)
Legendary Masters
A solid, 26-track collection of hits and obscurities, including a one-minute radio spot. Includes all of his Top-10 hits. Devil or Angel/Rubber Ball/Take Good Care of My Baby/Run to Him/The Night Has a Thousand Eyes/Come Back When You Grow Up.

EMI 96054 (CL)
Bobby Vee Meets The Crickets
Reissue of Liberty 7228 from 1962, with nine unreleased tracks from the same period, plus a 1989 reunion performance of a Buddy Holly medley. Could Vee, a squeaky clean teen idol accustomed to being swamped in strings, hold his own on classic material identified with Buddy Holly, Chuck Berry, and Little Richard? Listen to these 22 cover versions and decide for yourself! Peggy Sue/Bo Diddley/Well All Right/Sweet Little Sixteen/Lucille/Little Queenie.

EMI 96057 (CL)
I Remember Buddy Holly
Essentially a reissue of the 1963 LP of the same name (Liberty 7336), with ten "bonus tracks" of other Holly or related material, including "Buddy's Song," penned by Holly's mother after his tragic death. Good sound, photos, and notes. For confirmed fans only. That'll Be the Day/It Doesn't Matter Anymore/Peggy Sue/Maybe Baby/Everyday.

THE VELOURS

Jerome Ramos and The Velours got together in 1956 and started recording for Jerry Winston's Onyx label. They sang smooth, pretty, soulful ballads like "Can I Come Over Tonight," "Romeo," and "My Love Come Back," all unforgettable classics of the late '50s doo-wop genre. One of Brooklyn's finest groups whose style was both polished and professional.

ONYX 201 (R)
Best of The Velours
Fourteen cuts, ten of which duplicate those on Relic 5005 and 5050 (see R&B anthology listings). The remaining four songs from Cub appear in album format for the first time and include the classic novelty jump "Tired of Your Rock and Rollin'."

THE VELVET ANGELS

The nom-de-disc of Nolan Strong and The Diablos (see separate listing) used for their a-cappella sides.

RELIC 5004 (R)
A Cappella Showcase
One side features a group rehearsal recorded in a hotel room, the other side is their 1963 studio session. For Sentimental Reasons/Be Ever Wonderful/I'm in Love/It's Too Soon to Know.

THE VELVETS

Fine, pop-flavored R&B group that was championed by Roy Orbison. Before connecting with Orbison, they had recorded for Red Robin, Fury, and a handful of other small labels in the late '50s. Orbison brought them to the attention of his label, Monument, in 1961, and composed many of their songs, including their big hit "Lana." They stayed with Monument until 1964. Their most successful single "Tonight (Could Be the Night)" hit Number 26 in the 1961 pop charts, but didn't dent the R&B chart. Virgil Johnson's beautiful lead vocals were a hallmark of their sound.

CBS SPECIAL PRODUCTS 21475 (L)
Tonight Could Be the Night
A meager, 12-song reissue. Their entire output could have been issued on one CD, so why CBS chose to include just 12 songs is a mystery (CBS's parent company, Sony/Japan, managed to fit 30 songs on their CD!). And, since photos of the group exist, I can't see the point of the horrible cover painting. A frustrating collection. Still, no complaints about the music or the sound. Lucky Old Sun/Crying in the Chapel/Kiss Me/Time and Again/Lana.

SONY (JAPAN) 5646 (L)
The Velvets
Includes all eight of their Monument singles. Ballads like "If" and "Dawn" are unambiguously pleasing, but some songs are too cute and suffer from violin flourishes. "Spring Fever" is a fine song, but it sounds like something Ricky Nelson should have sung. Aside from the singles, the collection includes 14 other songs, presumably unreleased Monument material. The liner notes probably give more information, but they're in Japanese! Some of the extra tracks like "Be Evermore," "Alicia," and the stunning ballads "I'm Trusting in You" and "Who Has the Right" are actually much better than the singles. Go figure.

THE VENTURES

The most successful and most prolific instrumental group ever. With the long-lasting lineup of Nokie Edwards and Don Wilson (gtrs), Bob Bogle (b), and Mel Taylor (drm, who replaced original drummer Howie Johnston in 1963 after an auto accident), the Ventures have been plugging away steadily since 1959. They recorded a demo of jazz-guitarist Johnny Smith's tune, "Walk Don't Run," and, when no one would release it, Don's mom put it out herself, creating the Blue Horizon label. Liberty later picked the song for its Dolton subsidiary, and it reached Number 2. Their long string of hits on Dolton and later Liberty, and the series of instruction records they released (*Play Guitar with The Ventures*), influenced thousands of kids who wanted to learn rock guitar. Their influence was especially strong on the San Francisco psychedelic bands, who emulated their guitar playing during their legendary "jams." In 1968, keyboard player Johnny Durrill joined the crew. They continue to perform today, enjoying huge success in Japan.

COLLECTOR SERIES 156 (RL)

The Ventures Collection

Two-LP set with 27 original Dolton/Liberty recordings. Hawaii Five-O/Walk Don't Run/Walk Don't Run '64/Slaughter on Tenth Ave./Secret Agent Man/ Apache/Wipe Out/Telstar/Pipeline/Memphis/ Rebel Rouser/Tequila/Sleepwalk.

🌑 EMI 93451 (CL)

The Best of The Ventures

Twenty-six tunes, along with three radio spots and a long interview. A worthy replacement for those scratchy, well-played LPs. Walk Don't Run/Perfidia/ Ram-Bunk-Shush/The 2000 Pound Bee (Pts. 1 and 2)/ The Savage/Slaughter on Tenth Avenue/Hawaii Five-O.

LIBERTY (JAPAN) 7129/32 (L)

The Ventures History Box, Vol. 1

LIBERTY (JAPAN) 7121/24 (L)

The Ventures History Box, Vol. 2

This four-CD box features the contents of eight albums from the '60s plus a few tracks that were only on singles and EPs, for a total of 106 twangy tunes. LPs included are *The Ventures Play Telstar/The Lonely Bull* (Dolton 8019, 1963), *Surfing* (Dolton 8022, 1963), *Bobby Vee Meets The Ventures* (Liberty 7289, 1963), *The Ventures Play Country Classics* (Dolton 8023, 1963), *Let's Go* (Dolton 8024, 1963), *In Space* (Dolton 8027, 1964), *The Fabulous Ventures* (Dolton 8029, 1964), and *Walk Don't Run, Vol. 2* (Dolton 8031, 1964).

SEE FOR MILES 292 (RL)

The EP Collection

Wow! Twenty-four tracks from the band that launched 10,000 instrumental bands. You would need two lifetimes and a Savings and Loan bailout check to complete a Ventures record collection. But now you can at least get a leg up for a pittance with this selection of tunes taken from nine different EPs released in England on London and Liberty between 1960–1966. No Trespassing/Night Train/Torquay/ Bulldog/Guitar Twist/Moon Dawg/Secret Agent Man/Man from U.N.C.L.E.

THE VIDELS

Early '60s white doo-wop group from Rhode Island featuring Pete Anders and Vinnie Poncia, who split off as a duo in the mid-'60s to record as The Trade Winds and Innocence.

MAGIC CARPET 1005 (R)

A Letter from The Videls

GENE VINCENT

One of the best of the original '50s rockers, and one of the few who didn't "turn country" during the '60s. Gene wrecked a leg in a motorcycle accident (he told everyone he was shot in Korea), causing him so much pain that he found it hard to work. Reportedly, his mom suggested a recording career, and he won an audition with Capitol Records who was looking for a "new Elvis." His first record consisted of two of his own compositions. The original A-side, "Woman Love," was considered by the label's brass too lewd to be the lead title, so they decided to put it out as the B-side. The original B-side was a song that Gene had written about comic-strip star Little Lulu called "Be-Bop-a-Lula." The song hit the Top 10 and has become a rock and roll standard. Gene formed his best group, The Blue Caps (named after Eisenhower's golf cap!) in 1956, with Cliff Gallop (lead gtr), Wee Willie Williams (rhythm gtr), Jack Neal (b), and Be-Bop Harrel (drm). With Paul Peek replacing Williams, the band stayed together until 1958 when Gene formed his second great Blue Caps, featuring the great Johnny Meeks (lead gtr), Bobby Jones (b), Harrel (drm), and Peek and Tommy Facenda (later famous for "High School USA"; see separate listing) as clapper boys (backup singers and dancers). Rhythm guitar was handled by sessionmen, usually Buck Owens or Grady Martin. Gene toured with buddy Eddie Cochran, traveling to England in 1960 where they recorded some great stuff for the BBC (available on Rockstar 1004). While abroad, Cochran and Vincent were in a car crash that killed Cochran and further damaged Gene's leg. Gene turned to alcohol and drugs to relieve his pain. His hits at home dried up, but he was still very popular in England and France. He cut an LP for British Columbia in 1964; in 1966 he cut some single sides for Challenge. His popularity rose in the late '60s with the rock revival. He cut three good LPs in 1970–1971: *I'm Back and I'm Proud* for John Peel's Dandelion label and two others for Kama Sutra (reissued by See For Miles). His drinking caught up with him and he died later in 1971 from bleeding ulcers at the age of 36.

Vincent's classic Capitol sides have finally been reissued by Capitol US on an excellent CD, and also are available on Rockstar and See For Miles. See separate Eddie Cochran and Gene Vincent listing for their BBC recordings.

✪ CAPITOL 94074 (L)
Collector's Series
Twenty-one tracks that remain undiminished by the passing of more than a generation's time. Gene's raw vocals are backed by the biting lead guitar of Cliff Gallop or Johnny Meeks. Highlights abound, from the perfection of "Be-Bop-a-Lula" to the exquisite harmonies in "Get It," aided by buddy Eddie Cochran. Discover the rocker the English still pray to on Saturday nights. Don't miss the expletive Gene utters in the midst of "Woman Love"! Rockin' good news! Race with the Devil/Bluejean Bop/Crazy Legs/Lotta Lovin'/Dance to the Bop/I Got It/Rocky Road Blues/Say Mama.

CAPITOL (UK) 1 (L)
The Gene Vincent Box Set
Six-CD set featuring all of Gene's Capitol and Columbia recordings made between 1956–1964. A total of 151 tracks, including 29 previously unreleased outtakes. Superb sound courtesy of Bob Jones. Includes a 48-page booklet with rare and previously unpublished photos from the Capitol archives.

MUSIDISC 107382 (L)
Mister Gene Vincent
Eighteen later recordings, consisting of remakes of his hits and covers of other rockin' standards. Be-Bop-a-Lula/Say Mama/Pistol Packin' Mama/Bird Doggin'/Rocky Road Blues/Ruby Baby/Love Is a Bird.

SEE FOR MILES 233 (RL)
Into the Seventies
Gene's final two LPs, done for Kama Sutra. Contains eight tracks from the rare Gene Vincent LP (Kama Sutra 2019 from 1970), with backing by Augie Meyers

from The Sir Douglas Quintet on organ, along with Blue Cap Scotty McKay on lead guitar. This material ranges from the countryish "Sunshine" and "500 Miles Away from Home" to long '70s-style jams on "Slow Times Comin'" and "Tush Hog," complete with rambling guitar solos and wah-wah pedals. Also contains nine of the 11 tunes from *The Day the World Turned Blue* (Kama Sutra 2027 from 1971). This is a much more satisfying LP, emphasizing country and rockabilly, with covers of Ronnie Self's "High on Life," and other '50s standards such as "Oh Lonesome Me," "Boppin' the Blues," and "There Is Something on Your Mind." Some good new material is included as well: "How I Love Them Old Songs," "The Woman in Black," and the title tune.

SEE FOR MILES 253 (RL)
EP Collection
Twenty-two cuts from Vincent's nine Capitol UK EPs. Race with the Devil/Crazy Legs/Dance to the Bop/She She Little Sheila/Crazy Beat/Gone Gone Gone.

ROCKSTAR 1007 (R)
Gene Vincent
Nineteen classic Capital sides recorded between 1956–1959, remastered in beautiful mono by Bob Jones. Also includes the 1968 Jim Pewter interview available on a few other LPs. Hold Me, Hug Me, Rock Me/Jump Back, Honey, Jump Back/Pink Thunderbird/Jumps, Giggles and Shouts/Pretty Pretty Baby.

THE VIPERS SKIFFLE GROUP
The Vipers (Wally Whyton, Johnny Martyn, Jean Van den Bosch, [gtrs, vcls], John Pilgrim, [wshbd], and Tony Tolhurst [b]) were one of Britain's first and most-popular skiffle bands, second only to Lonnie Donnegan. Their residence at Soho's "2 I's" coffee bar established it as the first British teen mecca. George Martin discovered the group there, and signed them to Parlophone, producing their recordings at Abbey Road studios. This set contains 20 Parlophone recordings from November 1956 through July 1957.

ROLLER COASTER 2011 (R)
Coffee Bar Session
Side 1 contains ten singles and EP cuts, including their two big hits "The Cumberland Gap" and "Don't You Rock Me Daddy-O." Side 2 contains their entire, rare ten-inch LP *Coffee Bar Session*, with its original cover used for this set's front sleeve. Maggie May/Pick a Bale of Cotton/10,000 Years Ago/If I Had a Hammer/This Land Is Your Land/John B. Sculs.

FRANK VIRTUE and THE VIRTUES

Philadelphia-based band in the Freddie Bell/Bill Haley vein, but without their spirit. Lead guitarist Virtue (born Virtuoso), along with south Philly buddy Johnny Bruno, formed a Nat King Cole style trio after his discharge from the navy in 1946. They remained a local phenomenon for the next 12 years, until they covered a piece Frank learned while in the navy from Arthur "Guitar Boogie" Smith. Called "Guitar Boogie Shuffle," it was a Number 5 hit for them on the Philadelphia Hunt label in 1959. The band now consisted of Virtue (b), Bruno (gtr), Dave Raplin (vcl), John Renner (ten sax), and Joe Vespe (drm). They tried in vain to equal their first hit, even trying to cash in on the twist craze with 1962's "Guitar Boogie Shuffle Twist." The band disbanded after this last feeble attempt to reach the charts, and Virtue went on to lead various combos, and to produce records including Eddie Holman's Number 2, 1970 hit, "Hey There Lonely Girl."

PRESIDENT 16 (R)
Guitar Boogie Shuffle
Thirteen late '50s sides, about half instrumental.

THE VISCOUNTS

New Jersey instrumental combo that hit it big in 1960 with their atmospheric version of "Harlem Nocturne" (which charted again in 1965!). Harry Haller's sax was raunchy and moody, but what set them apart was the dirge of Larry Vecchio's organ coupled with the weird, treble-heavy meandering of Bobby Spievak's guitar playing.

AMY 8008 (R)
The Viscounts Rock
They put the "Harlem Nocturne" touch on "Summertime," "September Song," and "The Touch" just to show it was no fluke. Of course, they could rock, too, as "Viscount Rock," "Dig," and "Night Train" show. A must for instrumental fans, even if the sound quality on some cuts is questionable.

THE VOCALEERS

One of the best vocal groups to record for Bobby Robinson's early '50s New York label, Red Robin, led by high tenor and songwriter Joe Duncan.

RELIC 5094 (R)
Is It a Dream?
Absolutely dynamite material, featuring the group's 12 released sides with excellent sound, plus two previously unreleased cuts from rather scratchy acetates. A fine doo-wop showcase with nice notes by Phil Groia. Highly recommended. I Walk Alone/Angel Face/Be True/How Soon/Will You Be True/Hear My Plea.

THE VOCALTONES

Major '50s, Harlem, street-corner vocal quintet who fostered a sound of their own, excelling on ballads.

RELIC 5082 (R)
Our Version of Love
Long overdue, complete collection of their work, including the hit ballads "My Girl" and two versions of "My Version of Love." Other notable cleffings include the jumping "I'm Gonna Get That Girl" and two stunning performances by the group led by Brenda Lee (no, not that one!). Great sound clarity and unusually informative sleeve notes.

THE VOGUES

The Vogues had two distinct career phases. From 1965–1968, they were a high-energy pop band led by Bill Burkette's strong voice. In 1968, they signed to Reprise and became a smooth-as-silk harmony group in The Four Lads mold.

RHINO 70245 (CL)
The Best of The Vogues
Both sides of The Vogues career is covered on this collection, including their 1965–1968 rockin' hits, originally issued by Co & Ce ("You're the One," "Five O'Clock World," "Magic Town," and "Land of Milk and Honey"), and their vocal-harmony hits, originally released between June 1968 and June 1969, including covers of Glen Campbell's "Turn Around, Look at Me," Bobby Helm's "My Special Angel," The Angels's "Till," and The Four Lads's "Moments to Remember."

THE VOLUMES

Black doo-woppers from Detroit, MI, including Eddie Union (lead), Elijah "Tennie" Davis (1st ten), Larry Wright (2nd ten), Joe Trevillion (bar), and Ernest Werson (b). The group formed in 1961 and recorded for the Chex label, having a modest hit with "I Love You." The original lineup lasted until 1965, and various members came and went through 1968, when their recording career ended. They continued to perform in oldies shows through at least the mid-'70s.

MOTOWN 5465 (CL)
Junior Walker and The All-Stars "Live!"
Originally Soul 725 from 1970. Hey, this is great! Eight live cuts delivered with a soulful punch, good vocals, surprisingly sharp sound, not to mention Walker's distinctively searing tenor sax. A forgotten classic. Something You Got/Come See about Me/Shotgun/What Does It Take.

COLLECTABLES 5032 (CL)
I Love You: Golden Classics
Angel/You Put a Spell on Me/Miss Silhouette/Bells/I Love You.

RELIC 5062 (R)
Chex Records Presents The Volumes

JUNIOR WALKER and THE ALL STARS

Autrey deWalt Walker Jr. (aka Junior Walker) leads this ultra-tuff combo, playing a mean tenor sax and singing in his trademark raspy style, along with Willie Woods (gtr), Vic Thomas (org), and James Graves (drm). Originally signed to ex-Moonglow Harvey Fuqua's Harvey label, The All Stars had a local hit with "Cleo's Mood" in 1962. Berry Gordy, Fuqua's brother-in-law, purchased the label and put The All Stars on Motown's Soul subsidiary label, where they scored hits with "Shotgun," "High Heeled Sneakers," and "Do the Boomerang." By 1969, Walker mellowed out with his biggest hit "What Does It Take (to Win Your Love)." Though his hits stopped by 1972, he recorded for Motown through 1978, leaving briefly for a stint with the Whitfield label, returning to the Motown fold for 1983's *Blow the House Down*. He continues to play on the oldies circuit, and work as a sessionman on mainstream rock releases.

MOTOWN 786 (C)
Anthology
Two-cassette compilation of '60s through early '70s hits and LP tracks originally issued in 1974.

MOTOWN 5141 (CL)
Shotgun
Reissue of Soul 701 from 1965, featuring 11 hot cuts. Shotgun/Shoot Your Shot/Cleo's Mood.

MOTOWN 5208 (CL)
Greatest Hits
Reissue of Soul 718 from 1969. Shotgun/Do the Boomerang/Cleo's Mood/High Heeled Sneakers.

MOTOWN 5297 (CL)
All the Greatest Hits

TRAVIS WAMMACK

Guitar picker extraordinaire Travis Wammack occupied the mysterious time zone (late '50s-early '60s) that separated rockabilly from the British invasion and American garage punk. Wammack grew up right outside of Memphis, and cut his first record at the age of 12. Producer/guitarist Roland Janes took a likin' to the boy and let him do some recordings, too. They went nowhere at the time, but anyone fortunate enough to have stumbled upon a copy of the "Scratchy" b/w "Firefly" 45 realizes what a mind-boggling guitar-wrestler Travis was.

BEAR FAMILY 15415 (L)
That Scratchy Guitar from Memphis
Essential Wammack instrumentals recorded between 1961–1967, plus some not-so-special vocal numbers. If you like whacked-out, whammy-bar garage grunge, you have no choice but to pick this one up, even if you have to sell a few Link Wray records to do it. You won't miss 'em.

THE WANDERERS

The New York-based Wanderers quartet has always been popular with East Coast fans, due in part to the fact that the group still performs. The group is led by the dynamic tenor pipes of Ray Pollard; other original members included Frank Joyner (2nd ten), Robert Yarborough (bar), and Sheppard Grant (b). The group originally formed as The Barons in 1952 and over the years had several personnel changes, subsequently becoming The Larks, The Singing Wanderers, and finally The Wanderers.

ONYX 202 (R)
The Best of The Wanderers
Eighteen tracks recorded in the late '50s-early '60s, including their best-loved ballad "Thinking of You." Other fine tracks include the pretty, lung-stretching "If

I Could Make You Mine" and "I'll Never Smile Again," plus the soulful "I'm Not Ashamed."

ROBERT WARD

Influential, but long-forgotten, guitarist/singer, originally heard on guitar behind Wilson Pickett's "I Found a Love" and later in the seminal soul group, The Ohio Untouchables.

BLACK TOP 1063 (CL)

Fear No Evil

Ward emerged from 20 years of obscurity in Dry Branch, GA, on this 1991 release, with his powers, not to mention the incredibly funky tone he gets from his old Magnatone amp, still intact. Backed by George Porter of The Meters, he coaxes lightning-fast runs and raunchy blues. His patented harp-like vibrato bursts from his guitar, perfectly accentuating his husky, impassioned vocals on a selection of fine originals. Snatch this up, and catch him if he comes to your town. Your Love Is Amazing/Fear No Evil/Forgive Me Darling.

BILLY WARD and HIS DOMINOES

Billy Ward formed The Dominoes in 1950, drawing on students in his class at NY's The Juilliard School of Music where Ward worked as a vocal coach. The original group consisted of Clyde McPhatter (lead voc), Charlie White (ten), Joe Lamont (bar), Bill Brown (b), and Ward (pno). The group signed with King/Federal Records that same year, and their third release, "60 Minute Man," in 1951, skyrocketed them to stardom, and they continued with a string of hits over the next couple of years. In 1953, McPhatter left The Dominoes to form his own group, The Drifters, and was replaced as lead by Jackie Wilson. The Dominoes continued to record for King and Federal, though by 1954 the hits had stopped coming and the group signed with Jubilee. They moved to Decca and then Liberty, and were rewarded with more hits on their renditions of standards like "Stardust" and "Deep Purple." In 1957, Wilson left the group and was replaced by Eugene Mumford (formerly with The Larks), and the group remained active until the early '60s.

❂ CHARLY 242 (L)

60 Minute Man

Twenty of the group's jumps and ballads, including seven of their nine charted sides from the 1950–1953 period. Clyde McPhatter takes the lead on three classic

cuts: the haunting "Weeping Willow Blues"; the doom-laden "Bells"; and the beautiful "Do Something for Me" with its tortured blues-guitar accompaniment. Jackie Wilson, who came on board in 1953 and stayed for two years, belts out "If I Never Get to Heaven," "You Can't Keep a Good Man," "Tenderly," and "I'm Gonna Move to the Outskirts of Town." Accurate, concise sleeve notes by Tony Watson. Includes rare pix and discography.

KING 733 (RL)

Clyde McPhatter and Jackie Wilson

This collection embraces the pop-oriented ballads and occasional standards recorded by The Dominoes between 1950–1955, fronted by McPhatter and Jackie Wilson, Clyde's successor. Some great vocal acrobatics, especially on "When The Swallows Come Back to Capistrano." Jackie's only claim to lead work on this collection is his reading of "Tenderly." Duplicates the 1977 Gusto reissues King 5005X and 5008X.

DIONNE WARWICK

Before Diana Ross, the Grande Dame of white-sounding black pop was Dionne Warwick. She began her career as a member of the gospel group The Drinkard Sisters, but by the early '60s she was singing back up for major pop acts, including The Shirelles. Their label, Scepter, signed her as a solo star, and she connected with the then-unknown songwriting team of Burt Bacharach and Hal David. In 1963, she had her first hit by them, "Don't Make Me Over." She recorded dozens of their classic hits, before she left Scepter for Warner Bros. in 1971. Though she floundered around for a while, in 1975 she had her first Number 1 hit, "Then Came You," featuring The Spinners. She signed with Arista in 1979, and continues to record in a pop style. After hosting TV's *Solid Gold* program, Warwick stooped to new lows when she signed on as TV host for the "Psychic-Friend" network! She's also Whitney Houston's cousin.

RHINO 70329 (CL)

Hidden Gems

When someone has more charted singles than Chuck Berry and Michael Jackson put together, it's no surprise that an album called *Hidden Gems* would be wonderful. "Hidden" refers to the fact that this compilation features largely unavailable material—most of the songs have been out of print for 20 years—and only "Make It Easy on Yourself," "Who Is Gonna Love Me," and "This Girl's in Love with You" were actual hits. All 20 tracks are from Scepter Records, and nearly every one was written by Bacharach/David. A notable exception is the excellent gospel standard "This Little Light" (culled from her 1967 *The Magic of Believing* LP, originally Scepter 567), with Ms. Warwick accompanying herself on piano. The powerful "Many Days of Sadness" with sister Dee Dee and aunt Cissy Houston providing backup vocals is another neglected gem. Wishin' and Hopin'/I Cry Alone/Here I Am/I Smiled Yesterday.

RHINO 71100 (CL)
Anthology, 1962–1971
Double CD/cassette set with 28 cuts, giving a complete survey of her Scepter years, with all her hits and most of her near misses from 1963's "Don't Make Me Over" to 1971's "Amanda." All but three cuts were written by Burt Bacharach and Hal David. Includes extensive liner notes by Mike McDowell of *Blitz* Magazine and a "suitable for framing" photo. Anyone Who Had a Heart/Do You Know the Way to San Jose?/Walk on By/I Say a Little Prayer.

JUSTINE "BABY" WASHINGTON
Fine R&B/soul singer Justine "Baby" Washington started her career in Harlem in 1956 performing with the groups The Hearts and subsequently went solo. She recorded for Neptune (1959–1962) and Sue (1963–1966) in an upbeat R&B style and had a number of hits. The late '60s were slow for her, but she revived her career in the early '70s having several minor hits on the Master 5 label, including a version of The Marvellettes's "Forever" with Don Gardner.

COLLECTABLES 5040 (CL)
The Best of Baby Washington
Twelve 1963–1965 Sue sides. The Time/Move on Drifter/You Never Could Be Mine/That's How Heartaches Are Made/Leave Me Alone/Let's Love in the Moonlight.

COLLECTABLES 5108 (CL)
Only Those in Love
Twelve 1963–1965 Sue sides, including the rare Christmas coupling of "White Christmas" and "Silent Night." Only Those in Love (also on Collectables 5040)/Who's Gonna Take Care of Me?/Your Fool.

COLLECTABLES 5124 (CL)
That's How Heartaches Are Made
A reproduction of the long out-of-print LP, Sue 1014 from 1965, containing three of her finest post-Neptune ballads: "Careless Hands"; "Standing on the Pier" (with tasty guitar fills); and "Go On." "Doodlin'," one of her best up-tempo efforts, is included, along with a

smattering of not-so-hot Dionne Warwick-type production efforts. Good, but uneven collection produced by the great Juggy Murray.

NOBLE "THIN MAN" WATTS
Fine New York R&B sax blower. His bluesy rockin' instrumental "Hard Times" was a hit for Baton in 1957. His classic early recordings are currently unavailable.

ALLIGATOR 4785 (CL)
Return of The Thin Man
Reissue of his Kingsnake album recorded in the early '90s.

MARY WELLS
Motown's first female superstar. In 1961, 16-year-old Mary brought Berry Gordy a song she had written for Jackie Wilson. When Gordy heard her sing it, he signed her immediately, and the song, "Bye Bye Baby," became a hit. Next, she teamed up with Smokey Robinson (as producer/songwriter) and came up with such gems as "My Guy" and "You Beat Me to the Punch." In 1964, she achieved even more fame by opening shows for The Beatles. She left Motown when she reached the legal age of 21, and signed to 20th Century, where she recorded the collectible LP *Love Songs to the Beatles* (20th Century 4178), but nothing else hit. After a few minor hits for Atco in the mid-'60s and some more for Jubilee, she retired in the '70s to raise a family (she married Cecil Womack, Bobby's brother). Since her divorce, she attempted a comeback in the '80s, managed by Cecil's brother Curtis! Wells succumbed to throat cancer in 1990.

MOTOWN 5161 (CL)
Bye Bye Baby
Reissue of Wells's first LP, Motown 600 from 1961 (also the first Motown LP release).

MOTOWN 5167 (CL)
My Guy
Reissue of Motown 617 from 1964.

MOTOWN 5221 (CL)
Two Lovers
Reissue of Motown 607 from 1962, with the original artwork. Two Lovers/My 2 Arms – You=Tears/Goody Goody/Operator.

MOTOWN 5233 (CL)
Greatest Hits
Reissue of Motown 616 from 1963.

JOEY WELZ
Original pianist with Bill Haley and The Comets.

HYDRA 7713 (R)
Rockabilly Years
Fourteen tunes showcasing Welz's early years. Eight of these songs have never been released; numbers like "You Drive Me Wild," "Mrs. Lindy," and "Crazy Mixed Up Baby" were probably too wild for most record companies to release. The low-fi production didn't help his cause any, either, but what does that matter if it rocks? Nice collection with cool vintage photos.

SONNY WEST

TOLAKAI 5690 (C)
Ride: Featuring His '50s Clovis Sessions

THE WHO
One of the most influential of all British rock bands, known for their stage antics (including the destruction of their instruments), their sneering, bad-boy attitude, and leader/guitarist Pete Townsend's anthemic songs. The original group consisted of Townsend, John Entwistle, and Roger Daltrey; legendary drummer Keith Moon came on board soon after. Beginning their life as an R&B outfit, they evolved into one of the most powerful rock bands, linking up with the growing Mod movement thanks to their manager/producer, Kit Lambert. Townsend penned some of the '60s most memorable songs, including "My Generation," "The Kids are Alright," "Won't Get Fooled Again," and the legendary rock-opera, *Tommy*. Their US popularity was cemented by a memorable appearance at the Monterey Pop Festival, and a legendary guest shot on the Smothers Brothers show, during which drummer Moon set off a keg of explosives in his bass drum, nearly blowing the band off the stage! From the early '70s, the group's work dropped in intensity and quality, and the death of drummer Keith Moon in 1978 ended the group for all intents and purposes, although they soldiered on through the early '80s and reunited in the late '80s for a 25th-anniversary tour. We've listed their recordings through the early '70s in chronological order.

MCA 4068 (C)
Magic Bus/The Who Sings My Generation
Two early Who LPs. *Sings My Generation* features their first big hit, along with some early R&B covers. *Magic Bus* was their second stateside LP.

MCA 4067 (C)
Quick One (Happy Jack)/Who Sell Out
Their third and fourth stateside LPs, featuring the mini-rock opera "A Quick One," plus the wonderful concept LP, *The Who Sell Out*, featuring great parodies of '60s rock radio spots and the powerful "I Can See for Miles."

MCA 10005 (RCL)
Tommy
The greatest rock opera of all time, despite its somewhat dated story line. "Pinball Wizard" and "Acid Queen" were the hits off this one. Now a major Broadway musical.

MCA 1577 (RC)/31196 (L)
Live at Leeds
Following the pretention of *Tommy*, this live LP captured the stripped-down sound of the band at their primal best. Some say this LP created the "heavy metal" sound.

MCA 1691 (RC)/37217 (L)
Who's Next
Perhaps their greatest LP, featuring Townsend's blistering "Won't Get Fooled Again."

MCA 1578 (RC)/37001 (L)
Meaty Beaty Big & Bouncy
Retrospective LP of the band's hits and other odds and ends through 1972.

MCA 25892 (RC)/31221 (L)
Who's Missing
B-sides and R&B covers from the group's early years through 1972.

MCA 5172 (RC)/31222 (L)
Two's Missing
Another volume of early takes, 1964–1973.

MCA 6899 (RCL)
The Kids Are Alright
Soundtrack to retrospective film, including their big hits and odd tracks.

SPENCER WIGGINS

VIVID SOUND 003 (L)
Soul City U.S.A.

THE WILD TCHOUPITOULAS

Classic New Orleans band led by the late Big Chief Jolly (born George Landry), with backing by members of The Meters and The Neville Brothers.

MANGO 9908 (CL)
The Wild Tchoupitoulas
Reissue of classic LP of New Orleans Indians originally issued as Island 7052. Hey Pocky A-Way/Hey Hey (Indians Comin')/Indians Here Dey Come/Brother John.

MARTY WILDE

Good British rocker active since the '50s, a veteran of the Larry Parnes's stable of stars. The Wildman, decked in leather, mostly covered US hits, so he made virtually no impact here. In fact, his daughter Kim is probably better known. Still, he cranked out some great sides; his biggest hit was "Bad Boy." Many sides feature Big Jim Sullivan on guitar.

STAR CLUB 8007 (R)
The Wildcat Rocker
Sixteen cuts recorded between 1957–1961, consisting of mostly cover versions of US hits of the time. Wilde was a pretty good singer, but the arrangements are a little square.

ANDRE WILLIAMS

Intense Detroit singer, originally the lead singer of The Five Dollars. Williams went solo, and the rest of the band ended up backing him under the name The Don Juans.

FORTUNE 8019 (R)
Jail Bait
Twelve tracks, including the great title song, all from the late '50s. Going Down to Tia Juana/The Greasy Chicken/Tossin' and Turnin' and Burnin' All Up Inside.

LARRY WILLIAMS

Black rock-and-roll shouter from New Orleans, later based in Oakland, CA. He started out as a session pianist at Cosimo Matassa's studio, and joined Lloyd Price's band in 1955, and also worked as Price's valet and chauffeur. When Price left Specialty, label owner Art Rupe had Williams record Price-like material with Price's band. He also recorded a number of Little Richard-style novelty hits including "Dizzy Miss Lizzy," "Bony Moronie," and "Short Fat Fannie." Williams moved back to Oakland when the hits dried up, making money by pimping and dealing drugs. The '60s found him as staff producer for the newly revived Okeh label, producing Little Richard and leading his own revue featuring Johnny "Guitar Watson." He gained great popularity in England and even recorded with the strange LA band Kaleidoscope featuring David Lindley (see separate listing). In 1978, Larry made an unsuccessful comeback on Berkeley's Fantasy label, and committed suicide two years later.

ACE 129 (R)
Dizzy Miss Lizzy
Incredible LP with 16 Specialty sides, including ten of 12 from *Here's Larry Williams* (Specialty 2109), digitally remastered from the master tapes for incredible sound. Recorded in New Orleans at Cosimo Matassa's studio and in Specialty's LA studios from 1956–1959. Bad Boy/Bony Moronie/Short Fat Fannie/Lawdy Miss Clawdy/Slow Down.

ACE 917 (L)
The Best of
The ultimate Williams collection, 22 tunes recorded for Specialty between 1957–1958. Thirteen tunes were originally released, and the remainder come from recently discovered master tapes that have been released on Specialty (2158, 2162) and Ace (129) in 1987. Comes with notes and photos, including a great picture of Williams with Buddy Holly and Alan Freed. Exceptional sound. Dizzy Miss Lizzy/Bony Moronie/Bad Boy/Slow Down/Short Fat Fannie/Just Because/She Said "Yeah"/Baby's Crazy/Jelly Belly Nellie/Hocus Pocus/You Bug Me Baby.

EDSEL 119 (L)
The Larry Williams Show
Reissue of excellent live LP, originally issued as British Decca 4691 in 1965. Features Williams on vocals, Johnny "Guitar" Watson on guitar and vocals, with backup by the British R&B group The Stormville Shakers. There are even some Williams-Watson duets, and a cover of the Yardbird's "For Your Love"! Slow Down/Two Hours Past Midnight/Out of Tears/

Whole Lotta Shakin' Goin' On/Sweet Little Baby/Stormsville Groove.

FANTASY 9553 (R)
That Larry Williams
His 1978 comeback attempt. Times had changed, the people wanted a new sound, and that's what they got. Bony Moronie (Disco Queen)/The Resurrection of Funk/Funky Force/Can't Dance to the Music (If It Ain't Got That Funky Rhythm).

SPECIALTY 2109 (RCL)
Here's Larry Williams
Reissue of his classic 1959 LP, originally issued under the same catalog number. Bony Moronie/Lawdy Miss Clawdy/Dizzy Miss Lizzy/You Bug Me Baby/Hootchy-Koo.

SPECIALTY 2158 (RC)
Unreleased Larry Williams
Larry's really wild on these 14 unissued tunes. There are four alternate takes of "Bad Boy," "Slow Down," "Just Because," and "High School Dance" many with different lyrics. Includes a fast version of "You Bug Me Baby" and a wild "Rockin' Pneumonia" with Art Neville. Highly recommended. Zing Zing/Marie Marie/Iko Iko/Jelly Belly Nellie.

SPECIALTY 2162 (RC)
Hocus Pocus
A second volume of rare and unreleased Larry, featuring 16 more alternate takes and non-LP B-sides. One of the finest moments is the beginning of an alternate of "Short Fat Fannie" where Larry shouts in disbelief "You want me to whistle intro"?! Includes an alternate of "Dizzy Miss Lizzy," a version of "Iko Iko" called "Hey Now, Hey Now," an energetic cover of Little Richard's "Heebie Jeebies," the wild title tune, and a reworking of "Bad Boy."

⊕ SPECIALTY 7002 (RCL)
The Legends of Specialty: Larry Williams, Bad Boy
Twenty-track, two LP/cassette or single CD, featuring some solid high-octane burners. A virtual "who's who" of great sessionmen back up Williams's vocals, including Lee Allen, Earl Palmer, Plas Johnson, Roy Montrell, and Harold Battiste. All these tracks have been out before, but this set is beautifully remastered. Includes brief but informative notes by Gene Sculatti and full discographical information. The CD features three additional tracks, one of which, "Marie, Marie," is an interesting alternate. Bony Moronie/Hocus Pocus/Dizzy, Miss Lizzy/Rockin' Pneumonia/Heebie Jeebies/Short Fat Fannie/Slow Down.

STAR CLUB LIVE 1 (R)
Larry Williams on Stage
Reissue of the very rare Larry Williams Live LP, issued only on British Sue (922) and Swedish Sonet in 1965. An entire 42-minute 1965 London performance of 13 tunes including all his hits, four Little Richard tunes, and three James Brown tunes: "Try Me," "Think," and "Please Please Please." Bony Moronie/Short Fat Fannie/Dizzy Miss Lizzy.

OTIS WILLIAMS and HIS CHARMS
Cincinnati vocal group that was best known for its covers of other artists' songs. According to legend, they were discovered by King owner Syd Nathan while they were playing stickball across the street from his offices, although they had already recorded for Rockin' Records in 1953. Nathan had them cover The Jewels's "Hearts of Stone" for his DeLuxe subsidiary; their version went to Number 15 on the pop charts and topped the R&B charts. They also covered "Ko Ko Mo" and "Ling Ting Tong." However, when they covered Cathy Carr's "Ivory Tower," their version was covered by Gale Storm on Dot. The same thing happened with "Two Hearts Two Kisses"; it was covered by Frank Sinatra! In the 1960s, Williams led a black country band, The Midnight Cowboys.

KING 570 (R)
Sing Their All-time Hits
Ballads like "Walking After Midnight" and "Creation of Love" are two of the group's best sides. So much of the Charms's best material is still, alas, unavailable after 30 years. Duplicates half of King 5015X issued by Gusto in 1978.

PAUL WILLIAMS and HIS HUCKLEBUCKS
Wild baritone saxman best known for his up-tempo instrumentals, including "The Hucklebuck" and "35–30."

SAXOPHONOGRAPH 510 (R)
Spider Sent Me
Sixteen Savoy tracks featuring Williams blowing some exciting but never excessive baritone. "Cranberries" and "Swingin' for Pappy" are screamers in "The Hucklebuck" mold. The influences of big band jazz (listen to "Blues at Daybreak") and the baritone sax of

Leo Parker are obvious throughout. There are four nice vocals, particularly two by Nancy Cobb. A solid and exciting album.

COOTIE WILLIAMS and ORCHESTRA

Former Ellington trumpeter who led his own jumping band in the late '40s–early '50s.

JUKEBOX LIL 623 (R)
Things Ain't What They Used to Be
Fifteen tunes recorded from 1944 through the early '50s. Includes Ellington-esque jazz pieces along with jumpin' R&B. Highlights are a wild, live version of Willis Jackson's (who played in the band for a time) signature tune "'Gator Tail," with Bill "Weasel" Parker taking over the pyrotechnic tenor-sax solo duties; the title tune, a sophisticated city blues number, sung by Eddie Mack; and the swinging, live cuts "Ooh La La" (with vocals by Bob Merrill) and "Across the Alley from the Alamo" (with the great Ella Fitzgerald singing). Recording quality varies.

MAURICE WILLIAMS and THE ZODIACS

Excellent Lancaster, SC, vocal group best known for their Herald classic "Stay," later a hit for The Four Seasons. They started out recording gospel under the names of The Junior Harmonizers and The Royal Charms. They switched to performing original material in a pop vein, recording the classic "Little Darlin'" for Excello under the name of The Gladiolas (which they used from 1956–1957); the song later was copied note-for-note by The Diamonds. They changed their name to The Excellos and finally, in 1960, to The Zodiacs. At this time, the group consisted of Maurice Williams (lead vcl), Henry Gaston (ten), Wiley Bennet (ten), Chas Thomas (bar), Albert Hill (b), and Little Willie Morrow (drm). This incarnation of the group recorded some jumping sides, many of which became regular beach-dance classics in the Carolinas.

COLLECTABLES 5021 (RC)
The Best of Maurice Williams and The Zodiacs
Twelve classic Herald recordings from the early '60s. Stay/Always/May I/High Blood Pressure.

RELIC 5017 (R)/7004 (L)
Stay: The Best of Maurice Williams and The Zodiacs
Twenty-one early '60s Herald recordings. CD has the beautiful "Dearest Baby" as a bonus track, which recently was reissued on Stay 301, a fabulous collection of Gladiolas and earlier Zodiacs cuts from the '50s. I Remember/Do I/Come Along/Someday/Little Mama/Come and Get It/It's Alright/Stay.

CHUCK WILLIS

The Sheik of Shake; The King of The Stroll. Excellent R&B singer from Atlanta, who was discovered by a local DJ in 1952, and taken to Columbia Records where his first recordings appeared on their Okeh subsidiary. Most of the tunes were written by Chuck, including "Don't Deceive Me (Please Don't Go)" and "Feel So Bad," later covered by Elvis. He became known for his wardrobe of turbans (some say they hid scars from brain-tumor operations) and his dance The Stroll. In 1956, he went to Atlantic, where he crossed into the pop charts with "C.C. Rider" (covered by Mitch Ryder as "Jenny Take a Ride"), "Betty and Dupree," and "It's Too Late" (covered by Derek and The Dominoes). He died of peritonitis in 1958, and had two posthumous hits, "What Am I Living For?" and "(Don't Wanna) Hang Up My Rock and Roll Shoes."

CBS SPECIAL PRODUCTS 36389 (L)
My Story
Fourteen great early Okeh sides. Don't Deceive Me/I Feel So Bad/Two Spoons of Tears/You're Still My Baby/Going to the River/I Rule My House/It Ain't Right to Treat Me Wrong/Salty Tears.

DON WILLIS

Obscure rockabilly star who auditioned for Sun but finally recorded for Jackson, TN's Satellite Records (not the same label that later became Stax) in 1957, cutting his one hit "Boppin' High School Baby."

WHITE LABEL 8965 (R)
Boppin' High School Baby
Do we really need a whole LP by such an obscure cat? Includes all four numbers he recorded for Satellite Records, and alternate takes of "Warrior Sam" and "Boppin' High School Baby" that have more echo than the originals! The other eight tunes are taken from an

acetate in Don's collection and are pretty good rockers, although they are marred by uninspired sax leads replacing the rockin' guitar.

THE WILLOWS

Tony Middleton and The Five Willows hail from Lenox Ave. in Harlem, and are best remembered for the commercial-sounding "Church Bells May Ring," recorded for Melba in 1956. The group also waxed some very fine jump and ballad tunes like the tearful "My Angel," the stomping "Do You Love Me," and the mournful "My Dear, Dearest Darlin'." The Willows were one of Harlem's best quartets but they never gained the recognition that they deserved and disbanded in 1965 after recording for many small labels with little success.

ELDORADO 1001 (R)
The Church Bells May Ring Forever
Nineteen cuts reissued for the first time. Includes informed sleeve notes, great pix, and discography.

JACKIE WILSON

One of the greatest R&B singers and showmen of all time. Detroiter "Sonny" Wilson started out as a boxer at age 16, but later he turned to singing. In 1951, he was discovered by Johnny Otis while performing in a talent show, and, in 1953, he replaced Clyde McPhatter in Billy Ward and The Dominoes (see separate listing). After four years, he went solo. His first single, "Reet Petite," was written by his buddy Berry Gordy, and it became a hit. Gordy continued to write for Wilson, creating smashes "To Be Loved," "I'll Be Satisfied," and the Top 10 "Lonely Teardrops." Gordy used his income from this last hit to finance his Motown label. The hits, all recorded for Brunswick in their New York studios, continued until 1961 when Jackie, while trying to stop a female fan from shooting herself, was shot in the stomach himself. With the exception of 1963's Number 1 "Baby Workout," the hits were fewer and not as high in the charts. In 1966, Brunswick moved their studios to Chicago, to be run by famed Okeh producer Carl Davis. The marriage of Chicago soul with Jackie's R&B resulted in his two biggest hits, "Whispers (Gettin' Louder)" and "(Your

Love Keeps Liftin' Me) Higher and Higher." After that, Jackie turned to a more pop style, but still produced some fine, underrated soul sides. He hit the oldies circuit in the mid-'70s, and, while playing on a Dick Clark tour in 1975, suffered from a massive heart attack on stage. (According to legend, he was singing "Lonely Teardrops" and reached the line "My heart is crying, crying" when he was stricken.) He lapsed into a coma, and never recovered consciousness. He died nine years later in 1984.

ACE 902 (L)
Reet Petite
Eighteen-track CD reissuing the out-of-print LP, Ace 125, with these differences: "Yeah! Yeah! Yeah!" and his fine duet with Linda Hopkins on "Shake a Hand" are replaced by four great tunes: "Talk That Talk," "I'll Be Satisfied," "That's Why (I Love You So)," and "You Better Know It." This is the best of Jackie's 1957–1965 Brunswick recordings all done in New York, with lots of hits and tunes from early LPs. Highlights include a great early version of "Danny Boy" that shreds the 1965 hit version, and a version of "Do Lord" with Linda Hopkins. Great digital sound and fact-filled booklet.

✪ ACE 913 (L)
The Very Best of Jackie Wilson
Twenty-four of Jackie's best New York and Chicago Brunswick hits from his first ("Reet Petite") through 1972's "You Got Me Walking." All the greats, remastered by Adam Skeaping. No Pity in the Naked City/Higher and Higher/Lonely Teardrops/Baby Workout/I'll Be Satisfied.

RHINO 70574 (CL)
Merry Christmas from Jackie Wilson
Reissue of 12-song, 1963 Brunswick LP 754112. Silent Night/White Christmas/Deck the Hall/Joy to the World/God Rest Ye Merry Gentlemen.

RHINO 70775 (CL)
Mr. Excitement!
Three-CD, 72-song set, revealing why performers from Van Morrison to Aretha Franklin count Wilson as an influence. He was incredibly versatile, approaching the century-old Irish song "Danny Boy" and the Berry Gordy, Jr. tunes "Lonely Teardrops" and "Reet Petite" with equal ease. The set covers Wilson's lengthy career at Brunswick Records, throwing in "St. Louis Blues" and "St. Therese of the Roses" with Billy Ward and The Dominoes on Decca for starters. From there it covers early hits (and a few non-hits) of the late '50s, including "To Be Loved," "Talk That Talk," "You Better Know It," and "I'll Be Satisfied"; '60s

successes like "A Woman, a Lover, a Friend," "Baby Workout," and "Higher and Higher"; up to his final chart success from 1975 "Don't Burn No Bridges" with The Chi-Lites. The later material—though not Wilson's voice—runs a bit thin, but don't let that dissuade you from picking up this classy tribute to a hugely talented singer. Booklet includes great pix, discography, and notes from Robert Pruter.

BOBBY WOMACK

Excellent Cleveland soulster who's been going strong since the '50s. He started out in a gospel group with his four brothers, called The Womack Brothers (what else?). Bobby replaced Sam Cooke as lead singer in The Soul Stirrers when Cooke went solo. In 1962, when Cooke started his Sar label, he signed up Bobby and his brothers, who were now an R&B group; Cooke renamed them The Valentinos. They had several hits on the label, including two much-covered classics written by Bobby: "It's All Over Now" (covered by The Rolling Stones and the J. Geils Band, to name two) and "Lookin' for a Love." After Cooke's death, Womack shocked the soul world by marrying his widow. The Valentinos signed to Chess where they had no hits (1965–1966), and Bobby left soon after to pursue a solo career. He hooked up with Wilson Pickett, writing hits for him ("I'm in Love" and "I'm a Midnight Mover") and leading Pickett's band, while also recording as a solo artist for United Artists subsidiary label Minit. His hits dried up in the '70s, but he made a major comeback in the early '80s with a Number 3 R&B hit "If You Think You're Lonely Now." Later in the decade, he worked with The Rolling Stones, appearing on their *Dirty Work* LP and producing a solo album for guitarist Ron Wood. His brother Cecil and sister-in-law Linda (Sam Cooke's daughter) formed the popular songwriting/performing duo, Womack and Womack.

EDSEL 172 (R)
Home Is Where The Heart Is
Reissue of Columbia 34304 from 1976, a mid-'70s funk LP recorded mainly in Muscle Shoals. Low points include covers of "How Long" and "Close to You." However, a great Eddie Hinton tune called "A Little Bit Salty," and a beautiful version of "A Change Is Gonna Come" make up for these more disappointing sides. Backup vocals by The Valentinos.

EDSEL 291 (R)
Looking for a Love Again
Reissues Bobby's 1974 United Artists LP (199), containing a funky/disco-esque remake of his 1962 hit with The Valentinos, "Looking for a Love." An LP of primarily funk bordering on disco. For Womack fanatics only.

LIBERTY (JAPAN) 6596 (L)
Looking for a Love
Most of Bobby's finest Minit single sides, including "Baby, I Can't Stand it" (his finest effort on the label), "Somebody Special," "Love, the Time Is Now," "I'm a Midnight Mover" (covered by Wilson Pickett), "I'm in Love," and a remake of "Looking for a Love" supported by The Valentinos. Great soul grit from the dusk of the era. Booklet contains lyrics to all songs.

STEVIE WONDER

One of today's most respected artists. Little Steveland Judkins Morris was discovered by Ronnie White of The Miracles when the 8-year-old was playing harmonica on his front porch. Ronnie brought him to Motown where Berry Gordy proclaimed him "a little wonder." After four years of Motown training, the "12-year-old genius" recorded his first records. The first few singles flopped, but the fourth, "Fingertips, Pts. 1 and 2," hit Number 1 on both the pop and R&B charts. He spent the next few years searching for a style, mixing light jazz and tributes to Ray Charles with covers of pop material like Dylan's "Blowin' in the Wind" and "A Place in the Sun." Beginning in 1966, he was finally allowed to focus on his own material, beginning with the energetic "Uptight (Everything's Alright)." 1967's "I Was Made to Love Her," featuring Stevie's distinctive harmonica, hit big, and from then on he was allowed to do his own songs, with almost all of them becoming massive hits. In 1971, he renegotiated his Motown contract when he turned 21. He was the first Motown star to be given total control over his material, from song selection to production. He produced several classic LPs and singles in the '70s, becoming a megastar in the '80s. Even if his recent material doesn't appeal to you, you owe it to yourself to discover (or rediscover) his classic early Motown sides.

⚫ MOTOWN 282 (CL)
Greatest Hits, Vol. 1
Hits from 1963–1968, when this was originally issued on LP. Shoo-be-doo-be-doo-da-day/Uptight/High Heel Sneakers/Kiss Me, Baby/Fingertips, Pt. 2/Contract on Love.

⚫ MOTOWN 313 (CL)
Greatest Hits, Vol. 2
Hits from 1968–1972. Signed, Sealed, Delivered (I'm Yours)/For Once in My Life/You Met Your Match/My Cherie Amour/Never Had a Dream Come True.

MOTOWN 314 (CL)
Music of My Mind
Reissue of 1972 LP, the first under Stevie's new contract giving him total artistic control. Rather than a collection of singles and filler tracks, Wonder produced a coherent series of songs, playing most of the instruments himself. This lay the basis for his classic LPs of the '70s.

MOTOWN 319 (CL)
Talking Book
Wonder's breakthrough LP, originally issued in 1972. Includes the Number 1 hits "Superstition" and "You Are the Sunshine of My Life." Maybe Your Baby/Tuesday Heartbreak/Big Brother/Lookin' for Another True Love.

MOTOWN 326 (C)/MOBILE FIDELITY 554 (L)
Innervisions
1973 LP of more politically oriented material, including monster hits like "Higher Ground," "Don't You Worry 'Bout a Thing," and "Livin' for the City." The Mobile Fidelity version has superior fidelity at the cost of a higher price.

MOTOWN 332 (CL)
Fulfillingness First Finale
1974 album, including two Number 1 R&B hits: "You Haven't Done Nothin'" (with background vocals by The Jackson 5) and "Boogie on Reggae Woman." Smile Please/Too Shy to Stay/Creepin'.

MOTOWN 5150 (CL)
With a Song in My Heart
Reissue of Motown 250 from 1965, a collection of popish standards. When You Wish Upon a Star/Make Someone Happy/Put on a Happy Face/Get Happy/Without a Song.

MOTOWN 5166 (CL)
Down to Earth
Reissue of Motown 272 from 1966.

MOTOWN 5176 (CL)
Signed, Sealed and Delivered
Reissue of Tamla 304 from 1970, including the title hit and his hit cover of The Beatles's "We Can Work It Out." Never Had a Dream Come True/Heaven Help Us All/Joy.

MOTOWN 5179 (CL)
My Cherie Amour
Reissue of Motown 296 from 1970 with the title hit. At Last/Shadow of Your Smile/Pearl/Yester-Me Yester-You, Yesterday/I've Got You.

MOTOWN 5183 (CL)
Uptight
Reissue of Motown 268 from 1966, featuring the self-penned title hit. Love A Go Go/Blowing in the Wind/Teach Me Tonight/Ain't That Asking for Trouble/Pretty Little Angel/With a Child's Heart.

MOTOWN 5219 (CL)
Jazz Soul of "Little" Stevie Wonder
Jazz-styled cuts, originally issued as Motown 233 in 1963. Fingertips/Soul Bongo/Paulsby/Wondering/Barn.

MOTOWN 5234 (CL)
For Once in My Life
Reissue of Motown 291 from 1969 with the title hit. You Met Your Match/I'm More than Happy (I'm Satisfied)/Sunny/Ain't No Lovin'/Do I Love Her.

MOTOWN 5255 (CL)
Someday at Christmas
1969 LP, also reissued as on a CD along with The Supremes Christmas effort (see separate listing).

MOTOWN 5273 (CL)
I Was Made to Love Her
Reissue of Motown 279 from 1967. Includes the title hit plus quite a few covers of R&B and soul hits. Send Me Some Lovin'/I'd Cry/Respect/Baby Don't You Do It/Can I Get a Witness/Please, Please, Please.

MOTOWN 5274 (CL)
Where I'm Coming From
Reissue of Motown 308 from 1971. This was the beginning of Stevie's quest for a personal musical identity and pointed the way to his groundbreaking releases a year later. Look Around/Think of Me as Your Soldier/If You Really Love Me/Take Up a Course in Happiness.

MOTOWN 6002
Original Musiquarium I
This 1982 double set was mostly a hits package covering the period 1972–1982 along with three new songs. Isn't She Lovely/Higher Ground/Send Me Your Love/Superstition/Front Line/Sir Duke/Masterblaster.

BRENTON WOOD

Shreveport, LA-born vocalist who enjoyed brief success in the late '60s. Wood originally formed a vocal group called The Quotations in college, but soon split for a solo career. He linked up with producers Joe Hooven and Hal Winn of LA's Double Shot records, producing three self-penned hits: the novelty "The Oogum Boogum Song," the ska-ish "Gimme Little Sign," and "Baby You Got It" in 1967–1968. After this initial success, however, he quickly dropped off the charts into obscurity.

RHINO 70223

The Best of Brenton Wood

Twelve of Brenton's best sides. Includes his three big hits, plus more great tunes that he wrote or cowrote, including "Best Thing I Ever Had," "I Think You've Got Your Fools Mixed Up," "I'm the One Who Knows," and an excellent cover of "A Change Is Gonna Come." Double Shot's other hit act was the San José-based group Count Five. To save money, they took a backing track from Count Five's hit "Psychotic Reaction" and overdubbed a new vocal by Wood along with some hilariously cheesy Hammond organ. This must be heard to be believed!

LINK WRAY

Highly influential guitarist, born Lincoln Wray, Wray invented fuzztone by sticking a pencil through his speaker, and, in the '50s, pioneered the "power trio" (some people call him "The Father of Heavy Metal"). In 1958, Wray with his trio The Wraymen (also spelled Raymen) came up with the classic instrumental "Rumble" on Cadence and, the next year, they waxed "Rawhide" on Epic. "Rumble" introduced fuzztone and distortion, using these effects to simulate a barroom brawl. Wray's next big hit was "Jack the Ripper" on Swan in 1965. He moved near Washington, DC, and set up a home studio in a shed, behind his home (calling it The Three Track Shack) where he spent the next several years, issuing material sporadically. In the mid-'70s, punk performers rediscovered early rockabilly. One of them, New York's Laughing Dogs's vocalist Robert Gordon, switched to a '50s look and covered many early classics. He brought Link out of retirement and had him lead his band through

two LPs, always giving Link a solo spot during his shows. Wray swaggered around in leather clothes and masterfully blasted out his earlier hits.

You can't go wrong with any Link Wray purchase. The three-volume "Missing Links" series on Norton is a must-have, covering a good slab of his guitar-burning career. Sony/Epic has finally seen fit to re-release his early '60s Epic waxings, and Ace has several LPs of his early and mid-period recordings for various labels. Ace has also released recent recordings, showing that Link can still make a string twang!

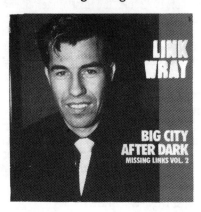

ACE 006 (R)

Early Recordings

Actually from his middle period, 14 Swan sides from 1963–1964. Jack the Ripper/Ace of Spades/Fat Back/I'm Branded/Scatter.

ACE 069 (R)

Good Rockin' Tonight

Besides his hits "Rumble" and "The Swag," this includes eight previously unissued early '60s sides. A real treat. Mustang/Law of the Jungle/Run Boy Run.

ACE 266 (R)

Rumble Man

Recent self-produced LP by Link Wray, and it's a hot one. Link proves he can still play that low-down and dirty sound. Although he loses steam on the final four tunes, most of these cuts rank a ten on the scorchin' scale. Draggin'/Street Beat/Aces Wild/The Rumble Man/I'm Gonna Sit Right Down and Cry over You.

ACE 286 (R)

Apache

Recorded in London in October 1989. I'm glad to say it's a killer and a half; peel me from the wall, somebody. The Wild One/Dallas Blues/Big Boss Man/

Shawnee/The Joker/Apache/Green Hornet Theme/ Dick Tracey, Private Eye.

ACE 296 (R)
Wild Side of the City Lights
This appears to be from the same October 1989 session as *Apache*, recorded in London with help from Bruce Brand only. Brand plays rhythm guitar, drums, harmonica, bass guitar, univox, and piano (it's not known whether he swept out the studio afterwards). This is the guitar-playing equivalent to the lonely jazz genius blowing a solo midnight horn. Hotel Loneliness/The Flying Wedge (Drag Race)/Don't Leave Me/Viva Zapata.

✪ ACE 924 (L)
The Original Rumble
Twenty-three track, hour-long CD compilation of early instrumental classics, along with recent recordings. This is great if you don't have the early Ace LPs, otherwise there is quite a bit of duplication. No unreleased cuts, as far as I can tell, just a lot of gritty gonzo guitar from the master. Rumble/Ace of Spades/Jack the Ripper/Run Chicken Run/Deuces Wild/That'll Be the Day/Rawhide.

ACE 931 (L)
Apache/Wild Side of the City Lights
Two recent LPs collected together on one CD.

BIG BEAT 972 (L)
Live in '85/Growling Guitar
Two Ace LPs on one CD. *Live in '85* is a collection of raw, live recordings, featuring Link's power trio. *Growling Guitar* is more to our liking, comprised of great mid-to-late '60s sides. In keeping with the times, there is some delightfully over-the-top psychedelia, done as only the Linkster could.

EPIC 47904 (CL)
Walkin' with Link
Includes the entire rare Epic LP 3661, with the Okeh single "Rumble Mambo" and the Epic 45 "Ain't That Lovin' You Baby" b/w "Mary Anne." There's lots of hilarious studio chatter leading into the tunes. In addition, there are five previously unissued tunes, including a savage "Dance Contest" and a pair of alternate takes, making 20 cuts in all. Comes with a cool little booklet with boss pix and notes by *Kicks* university dean Billy Miller. Slinky/Ramble/Hand Clapper/Comanche/Radar/Walkin' with Link.

HANGMAN HANG 31 UP (R)
The Swan Demos, 1964
Not only are these tunes raw, unreleased demos, there are many here that he didn't re-record at the time! Essential, oily rockin' grunge! Bo Diddley/Ace of Spades/Rumble/Mustang/Deuces Wild/Frenchy/ Law of the Jungle.

HANGMAN HANG 33 UP (R)
Jack the Ripper
Classic '50s and '60s Link Wray tunes. Hard-to-come-by items are presented along with the standards. Ace of Spades/Jack the Ripper/Run Children Run/My Beth/Deacon Jones/Steel Trap/Dinosaur/Big Ben.

LINE 9.00690 (L)
Born to Be Wild (Live)
Typical gnarly live recording of a hot 1987 gig, with Link in top form. On the seven-minute opener "Born to Be Wild," he lets loose with a mind-numbing psychedelic barrage that takes the guitar to previously uncharted realms. Recommended for diehard fans and anyone else who can stomach lo-fi live CDs.

NORTON 210 (R)
Hillbilly Wolf: Missing Links, Vol. 1
Incredibly cool collection of early recordings including four previously unissued cuts! Features Link's brothers Lucky on vocals and Doug on drums on several cuts. All three volumes in this series come with incredibly cool color photos, front and back. Teenage Cutie/I Sez Baby/Johnny Bom Bonny/Flirty Baby Number 1/Danger One Way Love Ahead/Hillbilly Wolf/Got Another Baby/I'm Gonna Sit Right Down and Cry over You/Lawdy Miss Clawdy/Vendetta.

NORTON 211 (R)
Big City After Dark: Missing Links, Vol. 2
Not only are there two more unissued cuts here, but almost all of Side 2 features a great live set from 1961. Walkin' down the Street Called Love/The Bad and the Good/The Outlaw/Baby What You Want Me to Do/Rawhide '63.

NORTON 212 (R)
Some Kinda Nut: Missing Links, Vol. 3
Collects the mid-'60s monsters that Link and the brothers were churning out to deaf ears during the British invasion. A couple of Bunker Hill tunes are included because Link and The Wraymen were his backing band. Drag Strip/XKE/Baby Doll/Please Please Me/Genocide/Growling Guts/The Earth Is Crying.

RUMBLE 1 (R)
Link Wray Sings and Plays Guitar
Great collection of classic rumblin', growlin', and howlin' Link Wray monsters! This one includes the good ones you might already have as well as a few not on any of the recent compilations. Twin Exhaust/Goose Bumps/School Girl/Mash Potato Party/ I'll Do Anything for You/Genocide/Growling Guts/ Johnny Bom Bonny.

RUMBLE 2 (R)
Hold It

Sixteen grungy, guitar-packed tunes, including a trio of tunes not readily available: "Trail of the Lonesome Pine," sounding like background music for a horse opera; "Night Life," a late-night groover; and "It's the Music She Says," a straight-ahead, rockin', hillbilly boogie number with brother Lucky on great vocals.

THE WRENS

The Wrens sounded much like Willie Winfield and The Harptones, which probably accounted for their lack of commercial success.

COLLECTABLES 5404 (CL)
The Best of The Wrens Featuring Bobby Mansfield

Their best-known sides, including "Beggin' for Love" and "Hey Girl," plus 12 other pleasers, backed by the irrepressible Jimmy Wright Band. Originally issued on LP as Murray Hill 199.

BETTY WRIGHT

Miami, FL, soulster who first sang with her family in The Echoes of Joy, a gospel group. At 13, she cut her first solo single, and signed to Henry Stone's Alston label in 1968 at age 18. She had a number of pop and R&B hits, beginning in 1968 with the tough "Girls Can't Do What Guys Do" and "He's Bad Bad Bad," followed in 1971 by the ultimate get-your-act-together-before-that-tramp-steals-your-man ballad, "Clean Up Woman." Wright left Alston in 1981 for Epic, where she recorded in a funk/disco vein, cutting a duet with Stevie Wonder on "What Are You Going to Do with It." In 1988, she returned to the R&B charts on her own Ms. B label, with "No Pain, No Gain" and "After the Pain." Continuing with the "pain" theme, she had a further hit with the upbeat "From Pain to Joy" in 1989.

COLLECTABLES 5118 (CL)
Golden Classics

A reissue of Betty's great Alston sides, recorded between 1968–1975. Unfortunately, this Collectables reissue provides only cheesy graphics and no song information. Her two classics are here, "Girls Can't Do What Guys Do" and "Clean Up Woman," but perhaps even better is "The Wrong Girl," a sordid tale of incest, with these immortal words: "He married a young girl/They really really loved each other/But oh was he surprised/To find they had the same mother."

All the tunes here were cowritten by Clarence "Blowfly" Reid. Some duplication with the superior Rhino reissue. Baby Sitter/He's Bad Bad Bad/It's Hard to Stop (Doin' Something When It's Good to You/The Best Girls Don't Always Win.

RHINO 70796 (CL)
Live

Reissue of Alston 4408 from 1978. A neglected classic.

RHINO 71085 (CL)
The Best of Betty Wright

Collects many of her best Alston sides from 1968–1980, where she specialized (thanks to writer Clarence Reid, aka Blowfly) in soulful, provocative other-woman songs like "Clean Up Woman," "Baby Sitter," "Outside Woman," and "Secretary." While the disco wave did affect her music, Wright usually managed to avoid drowning in the din of aimless synthesizers. Still, it's no accident that only three of the songs here were recorded after 1975. Soul fans, especially those of Laura Lee, Ann Peebles, and Millie Jackson, will not be disappointed.

DALE WRIGHT

Dale Wright was a pop rocker from Ohio who charted in the late '50s with his Fraternity Records waxings "She's Neat" and "Please Don't Do It." Wright generally opted for a pop-rock, malt-shop bopper sound. While his voice was pretty bland, somehow he sounds intriguing on the hypnotic-styled boppers built around a catchy, tough riff like his big hits.

ACE 402 (L)
She's Neat: The Fraternity Sides

Includes his big hits and eighteen other tracks. Two of the best tunes were never originally released; "I Hate to Go to School" and "She's a Killer" probably were felt to be bad for Dale's clean-teen image, but they are decent rockers. "Show Biz" is a nice novelty item with a funny lead-in where innocent Dale is shown the door by a hard-nosed record executive. Dance with Me/You're the Answer/I'm the Lovin' Type/Walk with Me.

HYDRA 7710 (R)
She's Neat

Eighteen of Wright's Fraternity sides, largely duplicating the Ace reissue. There's an interesting version of "Hound Dog" from 1964, that surprisingly owes more to Big Mama Thornton than to Elvis. A cool poster is included of Wright posing with the 'Vette he bought with his first big royalty check.

JIMMY WRIGHT

Jimmy Wright (not to be confused with the sax player of the same name who recorded for Rama) was a hip, white drummer whose band cut some wild, driving sides for a number of West Coast labels.

SAXOPHONOGRAPH 131 (R)
Let's Go Crazy Crazy Baby

Fifteen attention-grabbing sides, fueled by Wright's drumming, Porky Harris's frenzied guitar, and some thunderous honking by Chuck Higgins, Art Reed, and Boogie Daniel. Music, photos, and notes are uniformly excellent. If you're a fan of Big Jay McNeely and Joe Houston, then don't pass this one by.

O.V. WRIGHT

Overton Vertis Wright was an excellent deep-soul singer from Memphis who was never able to break into the pop charts. Like many of his Hi labelmates, O.V. started out recording gospel, at first with The Sunset Travellers for Peacock. (A later unrecorded quartet, The Harmony Echoes, also included James Carr!) He missed a chance for a smash hit in 1965 when Otis Redding covered his "That's How Strong My Love Is," beating him to the charts. O.V. recorded great sides for Backbeat between 1965–1973, including the modern classic "A Nickel and a Nail." He went to Hi Records in 1975, where he became good friends with labelmate Otis Clay, staying with the label until his death in 1980. Now that the deep-soul style that Wright helped pioneer is popular, Clay has been preaching O.V.'s gospel, recording his "A Nickel and a Nail" on both his *Live in Japan* LP and Roy Buchanan's comeback LP on Alligator.

HI (UK) 103 (L)
The Wright Stuff/Live

Two great, late-'70s LPs, totaling 20 tracks, complete on one CD. Precious, Precious/Trying to Live My Life without You/I'd Rather Be Blind, Crippled and Crazy/Love and Happiness/That's How Strong My Love Is/You're Gonna Make Me Cry.

HI (UK) 108 (L)
That's How Strong My Love Is

Essential 1976–1980 recordings. Into Something (I Can't Shake Loose)/I Feel Love Growing/Precious, Precious/God Bless Our Love—When a Man Loves a Woman—That's How Strong My Love Is (medley)/A Little More Time.

HI (UK) 414 (R)
The Wright Stuff

A dozen incredible Hi sides recorded between 1976–1980. Wonderful, gospel-drenched, deep soul. Includes his versions of "Precious, Precious" and Otis Clay's "Trying to Live My Life Without You." Rhymes/The Bottom Line/Your Good Thing Is About to End/Into Something (I Can't Shake Loose).

HI (UK) 426 (R)
Live

Excellent live show of O.V. from 1979, recorded in Japan with the Hi backup band of the Hodges Brothers on bass, guitar, and piano, and Howard Grimes on drums. I'd Rather Be Blind, Crippled and Crazy/Eight Men and Four Women/Ace of Spades/That's How Strong My Love Is.

GENE WYATT

Wyatt was a good, but obscure, Louisiana rockabilly artist who recorded in the '50s and '60s, best known for his Edd-label tunes "Lover Boy" and "Love Fever," and "Prettiest Girl at the Dance" issued by Lucky Seven.

WHITE LABEL 8887 (R)
Gene Wyatt Rocks Again

Sixteen tracks from the '50s and '60s, including 13 never released and three alternate takes from White Label 8874. Includes backing by The Peermonts, The Louisiana Boys, and Reuben Bell and his Band. Twistin' Bones (two takes)/The Contest (two takes)/1-2-3 Little Kisses/Grandpa's Teaching Grandma the Limbo Rock.

GENE WYATT and TOMMY BLAKE

WHITE LABEL 8874 (R)
Gene Wyatt/Tommy Blake

Wyatt's most famous numbers, along with 11 others, all previously unissued. Except for "Rock and Roll Guitar" and "One Love," they should've stayed in the can. The hot guitarist on these sessions was "James Burton," but I'm not sure if it's *the* James Burton! Tommy Blake originally recorded for Sun, and later had a release on Recco records called "$ F-olding Money $," a great stop-start bopper. A very rare and early recording on Buddy Records, "Koolit," is also included, as well as a pair of very nice previously unissued tunes from 1958–1959.

THE YARDBIRDS

The premier British R&B group. The original band featured Keith Relf (vcl, hca), Top Topham (lead gtr), Chris Dreja (rthm gtr), Paul Samwell-Smith (b), and Jim McCarty (drm). Initially a blues band, Topham left in 1963 when the group turned professional, and was replaced by a young guitarist named Eric Clapton, previously of The Roosters. The group was managed by Giorgio Gomelsky, and they frequently backed Sonny Boy Williamson when he toured England. Their popularity led them to replace The Rolling Stones as the house band for The Marquee Club, where their first LP, *Five Live Yardbirds*, was recorded. By 1965, they scored a pop hit with "For Your Love," but Clapton, wanting to play only blues, quit to join John Mayall's Bluesbreakers. With Clapton's replacement, Jeff Beck, the group produced classic recordings through the mid-'60s. When Samwell-Smith quit to go into producing, Dreja took over on bass, and session guitarist Jimmy Page joined the group. Both Beck and Page played lead guitar, as immortalized in the film *Blow Up*, featuring a crazed version of "Train Kept A-Rollin'" called "Stroll On." Beck left the group, which continued as a quartet, now managed by pop wunderkind Mickie Most (who handled The Animals, Herman's Hermits, and Donovan, amongst others). They scored a few pop hits before dissolving in 1968. Page kept the name, and formed The New Yardbirds, which eventually evolved into Led Zeppelin. Relf and McCarty teamed up with Samwell-Smith to form the classical-rock group, Renaissance. Chris Dreja went into photography, taking the cover photo for the first Led Zeppelin LP. In 1975, Relf formed the heavy-metal group, Armageddon, and, a year later, was found dead by his son, electrocuted by his own guitar. In 1983, the surviving members of The Yardbirds re-formed to play The Marquee Club's 25th Anniversary party, and Dreja, McCarty, and Samwell-Smith decided to form a new group, A Box of Frogs.

CHARLY 8 (L)
Greatest Hits
Sixteen songs. For Your Love/Got to Hurry/Good Morning Little Schoolgirl/Still I'm Sad/Jeff's Blues/Steeled Blues/A Certain Girl/Train Kept A-Rollin'.

CHARLY 187 (L)
The Studio Sessions 1964–1967
Comprehensive reissue, in chronological order, of all the completed studio recordings done for Columbia/Epic in 1964 and 1965. Twenty-two tracks, including eight with Eric Clapton before his departure and replacement by Jeff Beck. Includes the obvious hits, plus obscurities like "Stroll On" from the *Blow Up* soundtrack and the sitar version of "Heartful of Soul." A must for 'Birds lovers. Good Morning Little Schoolgirl/I Ain't Got You/For Your Love/Evil Hearted You/Train Kept A-Rollin'/Shapes of Things.

DECAL 1 (L)
Shapes of Things
An essential addition to any rock-and-roll fan's collection. It's the same package as the old Charly LP Box 104, but with a slightly different track running order. The big, beautiful LP-sized booklet is replaced by a mini CD-sized booklet; except for a different layout, it has most of the same photos, clippings, and information. Some of the best British-invasion rockin' blues featuring Beck, Page, Clapton, and company on four nice-sounding CDs.

EMI 98213 (L)
Little Games Sessions and More
At long last, EMI has dusted off the *Little Games* LP sessions (issued stateside as Epic 26313 in 1967), featuring the incinerating guitar of Jimmy Page, on a double-CD set. At the time, no one had ever heard such a distorted, fuzzed-out guitar sound, and the LP bombed because there was no hit single. But the big story is the inclusion of some of the unreleased stuff: the acoustic version of "White Summer"; a mindnumbing raver called "You Stole My Love"; instrumental versions of "Ten Little Indians" and "Tinker, Tailor, Soldier, Sailor"; a short instrumental workout called "L.S.D."; a heavily phased and looped tune called "De Lane Lea Lee"; a second version of the extremely trippy "Glimpses"; and a straight-ahead guitar romp for Page called "Never Mind." The 28-page booklet is loaded with a discography, pix, and info.

L+R 4400 (L)
The First Recordings
Mostly blues and R&B covers from 1963. Includes one track with Sonny Boy Williamson. Smokestack Lightning/Take It Easy Baby/Let It Rock/Boom Boom/Who Do You Love.

⊙ RHINO 70128 (R)/75895 (L)
Greatest Hits, Vol. 1, 1964–1966

Fourteen tracks (18 on CD) that have been reissued many times before. Still, if you have nothing at all, or have worn out your earlier LPs, you might want this. Remastered from the original master tapes, with the cuts about equally divided between Clapton and Beck. Includes a beautiful color photo on the front cover and track-by-track notes. I'm a Man/Smokestack Lightning/For Your Love/Shapes of Things/Heart Full of Soul/Train Kept A-Rollin'.

RHINO 70189 (CL)
Five Live Yardbirds

Reissue of Columbia (UK) 335X 1677 from 1964. It's hard to believe that this all-time classic LP has never been issued in the US before now. This monster blues-rock LP, recorded live at the Marquee Club, unleashed Eric "Slowhand" Clapton onto the world. Most of the tunes here would become staples of US and UK garage bands, especially "I'm a Man," "Smokestack Lightning," and "Good Morning Little Schoolgirl." The original recording was sped up to fit the whole thing on one LP, but is now remastered at the correct speed. Here 'Tis/Pretty Girl/Too Much Monkey Business/Louise.

SONY MUSIC 48655 (CL)
Vol. 1: Smokestack Lightning

SONY MUSIC 48658 (CL)
Vol. 2: Blues, Backtracks and Shapes Of Things

Two-CDs sets duplicating the Decal CD box. Vol. 1 reissues 28 cuts from *Having a Rave Up with The Yardbirds* (issued in the US in 1965 as Epic 26177) and *For Your Love* (Epic 26167, also from 1965), along with some of the great live material from the Sonny Boy Williamson show and the *Five Live Yardbirds* LP. If you don't have it, you need it. Vol. 2 brings together *Little Games* (Epic 26313 from 1967) and *Over Under Sideways Down* (Epic 26210 from 1966). There's some more manic material from the *Five Live Yardbirds* album, and various takes of "Good Morning Little Schoolgirl," "Got to Hurry," and "Heartful of Soul" (including the sitar version).

MALCOLM YELVINGTON

One of the original Sun rockabilly stars.

COLLECTOR 4403 (L)
A Tennessee Saturday Night Fever

A fine 1988 live set. He's backed by a top-notch English band led by ace guitarist Dave Travis, given an appropriate country flavor by the addition of Terry Keating on steel guitar. Malcolm croaks his way through a mixture of his old rockabilly favorites like "Drinkin' Wine Spo-Dee-O-Dee," "Gonna Have My-self a Ball," and "Yakety Yak," and country crowd pleasers like "Hey Good Lookin'" and "Mr. Blue."

RUSTY YORK

Rusty cut some of the very best rockabilly of the '50s. He was a pretty good singer and a dynamite guitar player, usually backed by a powerful band. Best known now for his rockin' cover version of Marty Robbins' "Sugaree," York suffered from an over-reliance on cover versions.

EAGLE 901008 (R)
Sweet Love

Eighteen rockin' tracks, including ten outtakes and demos of some of his hottest tunes (although some of the demos are pretty shaky). If you don't already have the Jewel release from 12 years ago, grab this and get hip to Rusty's savage attack of "Sweet Love," "The Girl Can't Help It," "Great Balls of Fire," and "Shake 'Em Up Baby."

YOUNG-HOLT UNLIMITED

Bassist Eldee Young and drummer Red Holt were two-thirds of the Ramsey Lewis Trio during their golden days of the early '60s. They split off and formed their own group, originally a trio, and had a long series of hits on Brunswick from 1966–1974.

KENT (UK) 062 (R)
Wack Wack

A fine cross section of hits and LP cuts, most produced by Carl Davis and Eugene Record. Includes the title hit; "Soulful Strutt" (originally the backing track of Barbara Acklin's "Am I the Same Girl"); "Who's Making Love"; a live medley of their two biggest Ramsey Lewis hits, "In Crowd" and "Wade in the Water"; and even a cover of Donovan's "Mellow Yellow"!

THE ZOMBIES

One of the most advanced British groups of the '60s. They were originally formed as The Sun-downers by schoolchums Rod Argent (pno), Paul Atkinson (gtr), Hugh Grundy (drm), and Colin Blunstone (vcl). They changed their name to The Mustangs and, finally, The Zombies in 1962, adding bassist Chris White to the lineup. The original band had hits with 1964's "She's Not There," featuring Blunstone's breathy lead vocals; the US Top 10 "Tell Her No" from 1965; and "Time of the Season," a 1969 release that hit it big stateside after the band had split up. They briefly reunited to capitalize on the hit, but quickly dissolved. Argent formed his own self-named group, which lasted until 1976. Blunstone recorded as a solo artist through the '70s and '80s.

RHINO 70186 (CL)

Odessey and Oracle

Reissue of Date 4013 from 1968 that was only the second LP recorded by The Zombies (besides the first, the rest were compilations); it was originally released after the group broke up. It has remained on my Top 10 list of great rock LPs since. Includes the hit "Time of the Season." This Will Be Our Year/Maybe After He's Gone/Care of Cell 44/Butcher's Tale (Western Front 1914).

SEE FOR MILES 30 (RL)

The Zombies

Beautiful LP featuring the A and B-sides of their ten (UK) Decca 45s recorded between 1964–1967, plus one 45 released only on US Parrot and never before on LP ("I Want Her Back" b/w "I Remember When I Loved Her"). Includes their US smash "She's Not There," and the followup "Tell Her No," plus other unrecognized classics. Is This a Dream/You Make Me Feel Good/I Love You.

ROCK ANTHOLOGIES

❂ ABKCO 7118 (CL)

Phil Spector:
Back to Mono (1958–1969)

Phil "Wall of Sound" Spector was a legendary and probably the most influential of all early rock producers. This set gathers 73 of his classic sides, including the famous *Christmas* LP, by The Teddy Bears, Ben E. King, Bob B. Soxx and The Blue Jeans, The Crystals, The Ronettes, Darlene Love, The Righteous Brothers, Ike and Tina Turner, and many more. The sound is spectacular; Hal Blaine's drum intro to "Be My Baby," for example, never sounded sharper. Includes a 96-page booklet, with two profiles of Spector (including Tom Wolfe's famous 1965 essay), as well as song lyrics overlaid on large photos. A testament to one man's unique vision.

ACE 1 (RL)

Hollywood Rock and Roll

Twelve rompin', stompin' rockabilly cuts from the Era label by Glen Glenn, Dorsey Burnette, Don Deal, Dick Bush, Ben Joe Zeppa, and Alis Leslie (the female Elvis Presley).

ACE 25 (R)

Teenage Rock and Roll Party

Fourteen sides, mostly from the '50s, a mixture of R&B, rockers, and ballads by Hershel Almond, Jesse Belvin, The Chanters, Frankie Ford, Joe Houston, Jimmy and Johnny, Lee Kristofferson, Oscar McLollie, B. Milton, Roy Perkins, The Teen Queens, Johnny "Guitar" Watson, and Young Jesse.

ACE 45 (R)

The Best of Ace Rockabilly

Fourteen fine cuts drawn from various Ace albums by Hershel Almond, Link Davis, Sonny Fisher, Glen Glenn, Sonny Hall and The Echoes, Hal Harris, Jimmy and Johnny, George Jones, Sleepy LaBeef, and Danny Reeves.

ACE 191 (RL)

Rockabilly Shakeout

Mid-to-late '50s tracks mostly from the Houston-based Starday label. Everything from classic "wild man" sides by Benny Joy and Sonny Hall to more sedate hillbilly rock. Highpoint: Glenn Barber's "Atom Bomb," which recommends dancing during total annihilation. CD features nine additional cuts by Tommy Spurlin, Charlie Feathers, and Ray Scott.

❂ ACE 218 (RCL)

The Fifties: Rockabilly Fever

Extremely hot collection of 22 Starday/Dixie sides. No losers, but some have been on other Ace LPs, and many are on the budget-priced Cascade 1003 and 1009. Includes Hal Harris, Sonny Hall and The Echoes,

Pat Cupp, Link Davis, and Ray Scott's oft-reissued "Rockin' Wig Wam Willie."

ACE 264 (R)

Dance Baby Dance:
Glo-lite Rockabilly from Memphis

❂ ACE 288 (RCL)

Another Saturday Night

Originally issued on Charlie Gillet's Oval label in 1974, this has been newly remastered with several additional tracks. Swamp pop, R&B, and cajun music by Tommy McClain (solo and with Clint West), Cookie and The Cupcakes, Vin Bruce, Gary Walker, Rufus Jagneaux, Belton Richard, Margo White, and Johnnie Allan. The CD adds Carol Fran and Donnie Jacobs. Terrific!

ACE 289 (L)

Golden Age of American Rock and Roll

Thirty pre-British-invasion era tracks recorded between 1954–1963. Includes expected classics by The Penguins, Bobby Day, The Skyliners, and The Crests, along with less often collected tracks by The Jaynetts, The Jive Five, The Genies, and The Paris Sisters. Over 78 minutes of great music, with excellent liner notes that provide the US and UK labels, catalog numbers, and peak chart position for every cut.

❂ ACE 303 (L)

32 Hot Rod Hits

The Deuce Coupes and The De-Fenders provide enough fuel-injected guitar playing, squealin' slicks, and roaring engines to please just about anybody. Road Rattler/Gear Masher/Top Eliminator/Taco Wagon/ Drag Beat/Alky Burner.

❂ ACE 311 (L)

Rarest Rockabilly and Hillbilly
Boogie/Best of Ace Rockabilly

Oldtimers and newcomers alike should go ape over this CD pairing two of the finest rockabilly LP collections ever released: *The Best of Ace Rockabilly* and *Rarest Rockabilly and Hillbilly Boogie*. All but two of the 28 tracks were originally released on the Starday label in the '50s. George "Thumper" Jones, Sonny Hall, Glen Glenn, Sonny Fisher and The Rocking Boys, Sleepy LaBeef, Link Davis, Hal Harris, Hershel Almond, Bill Mack, and Jimmy Stewart and His Night Hawks are among the luminaries. Git it cats.

ACE 313 (L)

The Del-Fi and Donna Story

Bob Keane founded Del-Fi Records after a short but successful stint with his first company, Keen. Ritchie Valens and The Bobby Fuller Four were his big acts, but for the most part this 31-tune compilation checks out the rest of the Del-Fi and Donna stable. Includes the fabulous Latino rocker Chan Romero who garnered a flash of fame with "Hippy Hippy Shake," Rene Hall, and a young Dick Dale before his surf-guitar days. The local surf scene is represented by The Lively Ones, The Sentinals, and Bruce Johnston, while the low-ridin' scene is covered by cool cats like Johnny Flamingo and The Shadows. Except for a few pop tunes by Johnny Crawford and The Addrisi Brothers, this collection is top-flight rock and roll and R&B.

ACE 316 (L)
All American Rock and Roll from Fraternity Records
Blonde bombshell Sparkle Moore, Carl Dobkins, Jr., Dale Wright, Jesse Lee Turner, and Bill Parsons are among Fraternity's acts who tried to mix rockabilly with pop rock. My favorite Fraternity disc, Robin Hood Brians's rampage through "Dis a Itty Bit," is the highlight here.

🟤 ACE 319 (L)
Big Surf
The five bands featured on this 32-track CD drawn from Del-Fi label recordings—The Lively Ones, Dave Myers and The Surftones, The Impacts, The Sentinals, and The Centurions—are among the very best. Plus, there's no dopey lyrics or teen-pop crooners to set your teeth on edge! Pipeline/Church Key/Surf Rider/Steel Pier/Impact/The Pipe/Surfin' at Mazatland/Surf Beat/Wipe Out/Latin'ia.

ACE 347 (L)
Radio Gold
Thirty "golden oldies" mostly from the mid-'50s and '60s. About 75 minutes of music, almost no notes. Dion, The Everly Bros., The Jive Five, Larry Williams, The Chordettes, Bobby Fuller, The Mystics, The Shirelles, The Chiffons, Sam Cooke, Jessie Belvin, and Aaron Neville are among the hitmakers.

ACE 933 (L)
The Laurie Records Story
Fine 29-track compilation drawn from Laurie's successful pop efforts from the late '50s to nearly a decade later, with all the label's hitmakers, including Dion and The Belmonts, The Chiffons, The Barbarians, The Music Explosion, The Passions, The Jarmels, The Four Pennies, Dean and Jean, The Royal Guardsmen, and The Balloon Farm.

ACE (US) 2026 (RL)
The Greatest Rockabillies
Sixteen wild Louisiana rockabilly sides from the Ace and Vin labels; no recording information other than title and artist, but the music's great. Includes Mickey Gilley, Charlie Rich, Charlie Feathers, Johnny and The Wildcats, Dick Holler, Danny Ray, Narvel Felts, Mack Allen Smith, Eddy Seacrest, and Hershel Almond.

ATOMIC PASSION 1957 (R)
Teenage Riot
Here's some rock and roll with a bad attitude that you won't hear on your poodleskirt-shakin', oldies radio station. Besides the obvious choices, such as Phil Johns and The Lonely Ones's "Ballad of a Juvenile Delinquent" and Portuguese Joe's "Teenage Riot," there are many oddities that are sure to please. There are also some great movie adverts for classic juvenile delinquent films like *Highschool Hellcats*, *Hot Rod Gang*, and *Girls on the Loose*.

BEAR FAMILY 15111 (R)
Rockin' Rollin' High School, Vol. 3
Sixteen pop and rock-and-roll rarities from RCA recorded between 1958–1962, including cuts by The Sprouts, Roy Orbison (with one previously unreleased cut), Ric Cartey, Jack Clement, Sonny James, The Lane Brothers, The LeGarde Twins, and Don Robertson.

BEAR FAMILY 15115 (R)
Rockin' Rollin' High School, Vol. 7
Sixteen more rarities from RCA including some unreleased Teen Queens's tracks recorded as The Teeners, along with Jimmy Dell, Dave Rich, Floyd Robinson, Dave Burton, and The Nite Rockers.

BEAR FAMILY 15218 (R)
Elvis Hits in Deutsch, Vol. 1
BEAR FAMILY 15219 (R)
Elvis Hits in Deutsch, Vol. 2
BEAR FAMILY 15220 (R)
Elvis Hits in Deutsch, Vol. 3
Although Elvis is all over the beautiful foldout covers of these three 16-track LPs, he's nowhere in the grooves. These are German-language covers of Elvis's hits, recorded for various German labels between 1956–1961. Backups vary from Germanic orchestras to jazzy combos to some legitimate rockin' outfits. Artists are all unknown in the US, and they perform such hits as "Hotel zur Einsamkeit" ("Heartbreak Hotel"), "Total Verrukt" ("All Shook Up"), "Wunderbar Wie Du Heut' Wieder Kusst" ("I Got Stung"), and "Tutti Frutti" ("Der Frutti mit der Tutti" ... just kidding!). Rock trivia fans will enjoy Gus Bakus's cuts on Vol. 2; he was one of the original Del Vikings who later hit it big in Germany.

BEAR FAMILY 15233 (R)
Rock and Roll Cannibals
Rock and teen jive from Gene Autry's Challenge label released in 1958–1959. Wynn Stewart, Big Al Downing, the Everly-esque Barker Brothers, rocker-turned-preacher Kimball Cobern, and Kip Tyler (whose backup band The Flips included Steve Douglas, Bruce Johnston, Jim Horn, Larry Knechtal, and Sandy Nelson) are among the stars.

BEAR FAMILY 15250 (R)

Surfin' Germany

We know the surfin' craze provoked seemingly normal teenagers to truck around surfboards in the landlocked Midwest, but who could have guessed that the teens of the Fatherland would also respond like termites to a woodie and gobble it up as well? Mostly sung in German, bands like Die Crazy Girls, The Magnets, and Die Blue Brothers perform such well-known surfin' classics as "Lass Dir Zeit," "Eine Reise Nach New York," and "Kleine Kiddio" (these three are loosely based on "Walk Don't Run," "Fun, Fun, Fun," and "G.T.O.") A nice bonus is the German language version of "In My Room," entitled "Ganz Allein," done by The Beach Boys for the German market. Beautiful, colorful packaging too!

BEAR FAMILY 15533 (L)

Let's Go Jivin' to Rock and Roll

Twenty diverse tracks from the RCA archives, including pop rock, hillbilly rock, and R&B-styled rock, mostly from the mid-'50s. Includes Perry Como, The Davis Sisters, The Mike Pedicin Quintet, Pee Wee King, Sammy Salvo, Jimmy Dell, The Sons of the Pioneers (!), The Morgan Twins, Johnny Restivo, Neil Sedaka, Janet Baker, Mickey and Sylvia, and Wade Ray. Some tracks are presented in real stereo for the first time. Excellent sound and 20-page booklet with detailed notes by Rob Finnis, lots of photos, and full discographical information.

⊙ BEAR FAMILY 15623 (L)

That'll Flat Git It!, Vol. 2

Dynamite 30-tune collection from the Decca vaults featuring a solid lineup; many tracks include backup by the fantastic Decca session cats led by guitarist Grady Martin. Fine rockabilly by Johnny Carroll, Roy Hall, Eddie Fontaine, Jackie Lee Cochran, and Terry Noland, along with more obscure acts including Peanuts Wilson, Johnny Bell, Billy Harlan, and The Five Chavis Brothers. Heck, even country legend Webb Pierce sounds OK on his "Teenage Boogie." You gotta have it!

⊙ BEAR FAMILY 15624 (L)

That'll Flat Git It!, Vol. 3

Another fantastic 30-tune collection, this time from the Capitol vaults. Many of these tracks have a strong country flavor but, if you don't mind a bit of downhome twang with your rockin', you'll be richly rewarded. Includes The Louvin Brothers, Dub Dickerson, Faron Young, Ferlin Huskey, Simon Crum, Tommy Sands, Skeets McDonald, and The Farmer Boys. Scoop it up.

BEWARE 001 (R)

Wavy Gravy:
Plants Can Read Our Minds

First of a great new series that intersperses weird tunes with radio ads for all those great, terrible teen and monster flicks of the '50s and '60s. Song selection is eclectic, including rock, R&B, and country. Dig Porter Waggoner's "Rubber Room," Eddie Noack's cover version of Jack Kittel's "Psycho," Selwyn Cox's yodelin' "His Name Is Jesus," "Wild Thing" by Senator Everett McKinley (the flip side of Senator Bobby's version), Wendell Austin's "LSD," and the wild "Ho Ho Laughing Monster," plus more inspired madness.

BEWARE 666 (R)

Psycho Serenade

This one comes with wild graphics on the album cover and even wilder music (for want of a better word) in the grooves. Highlights include Nanine's very downhome, hog callin' "Souie Baby Souie," Red River Dave's incredible "California Hippy Murders," "Mad" by The Social Outcasts, "Chickie Run" by Homer Denison, and the legendary "Evil Dope" by swamp-popster Phil Phillips. There's much more, including some very filthy interludes. Wooooweee!!

BEWARE 999 (R)

Wavy Gravy

A bizarre conglomeration of reggae, '60s garage rock, instrumentals, C&W, and you-name-it interspersed with commercials, movie ads, and general madness. Highlight is Autry Inman's unconsciously nutty patriotic twanger, "The Ballad of Two Brothers," about a good boy who goes to 'Nam and a bad one who joins the protest movement! Add to this a mess o' radio ads from flics like *The Tingler, Astro Zombies,* and *Women in Cages* and you have more hoots than a political convention.

BIG BEAT 18 (L)

Rockabilly Psychosis and
The Garage Disease

There are rowdy CDs and then there are *really* rowdy CDs; this release falls into the second category! Within this impressive 16-cut compilation of garage-cum-psychabilly rockers are 25 years worth of wild, demented songs by Hasil Adkins, The Gun Club, The Sonics, The Trashmen, The Novas, Link Wray, The Legendary Stardust Cowboy, and nine others. Recommended, if your heart can stand it!

⊙ BIG BEAT 90 (RL)

The Wild Wild World of
Mondo Movies Music

SEE one of the most exciting, alluring displays of mondo movie mania graphics ever to grace an LP (or CD) cover. HEAR the sickest, wildest, craziest '50s teenage performers playing the monster soundtrack masterpieces from their earth-shattering movies. THRILL to the naked lust and driving rock-and-roll beat on radio promos for classics like *Wild Guitar, She Devils on Wheels,* and *The Incredibly Strange Creatures who Stopped Living and Became Mixed Up Zombies.* GYRATE to the grooviest rockin' sounds ever made by Arch Hall Jr., Ron Haydock and The Boppers, Carol Kay and The Stone Tones, Rocky Roberts and The Airedales, and a cast of dozens. BUY the LP/CD release of the decade! You Is a Rat Pfink/Twist Fever/The Bird's the Word/Big Boss a Go-Go Party.

⚫ BIG DADDY 501 (R)

Sin Alley

Considered by many to be the finest and wildest rockabilly compilation ever! Eighteen ravers so wild it's lucky that the needle stays in the grooves. Highpoints include Roy Gaines's "Skippy Is a Sissy," Rudy Green's "Juicy Fruit," Pico Pete's "Chicken Little," Terry and The Tune Tones's "She's My Baby Doll," and Dave Travis's "I Don't Like Him." Enough to drive a cool cat wild!

BISON BOP 2000 (R)

The Bop That Never Stopped, Vol. 1

Nice collection of '50s and '60s rockers by Art Adams, Jerry Adams, Lonnie Allen, The Dazzlers, Gary Engel, Jackie Gotroe, Johnny Powers, Tommy Smith, and Bob Vidore.

BISON BOP 2001 (R)

The Bop That Never Stopped, Vol. 2

Art Adams, Ray Campbell, The Country GJs, Bill Davenport, The Dazzlers, Harold Jackson, The Morris Brothers, Johnny Powers, Billy Tidwell, Carl E. Tyndal, and Bob Vidore.

BISON BOP 2002 (R)

Strictly Instrumental

The Crowns, Glynn Hipp's Jokers, The Millionaires, The Ramblin' Ramblers, The Rhythm Rockers, The Rockaways, The Rocket City Rockets, King Rock, The Rockin' Rs, The Royal Jokers, and Will Treamain's Thunderbirds perform songs without words.

BISON BOP 2005 (R)

The Bop That Never Stopped, Vol. 3

Gary Andrews, Lloyd Arnold, The Chaperrals, Webb Foley, Tommy Lam, The Loafers, Buddy Love, Jackie Morningstar, Merle Richardson, The Rock-A-Tones, and Jack Winston.

BISON BOP 2006 (R)

The Bop That Never Stopped, Vol. 4

Pat Davis, Barry Etris, Jimmy Lester, The Moonlighters, Cliffie Nash, The Rebelaires, Mike Ryan, Speck and Doyle, Tennessee Thompson, and Val Volk.

BISON BOP 2007 (R)

The Bop That Never Stopped, Vol. 5

Buck and The Premiers, Benny Cliff, Sonny Deckelman, The Imps, Walley Jeffrey, Cliffie Nash, Ronnie Ray, Mel Robbins, and Herbie Smith.

BISON BOP 2008 (R)

The Bop That Never Stopped, Vol. 6

More bop from Chuck Brooks, Cheek-O-Vass, Jimmy Ford, Don Head, Dennis Hunt, Curtis Lee, The Orbits, Dennis Wayne, and Jimmy Williams.

BISON BOP 2009 (R)

The Bop That Never Stopped, Vol. 7

Stop already! Fred Carter, Jimmy Copeland, Lee Dorn, Vern Edwards, Troy Ferguson, Glen Garrison, Junior Gravely, Bob Hicks, Dennis Puckett, and The Three Clicks.

BISON BOP 2010 (R)

The Bop That Never Stopped, Vol. 8

Jeff Daniels, Carlos Diaz, Eddie Eay, Don Glenn, B. Goode, Carl Groves, Linc Jeffries, Jack Lane, Gray Montgomery, D. Tacker, and The Three Clicks.

BISON BOP 2011 (R)

The Bop That Never Stopped, Vol. 9

Lonnie Anderkin, Phil Barclay, Bobby Green, Jimmy Grubbs, Lloyd Harp, Red Moore, Tex Neighbors, Ray Smith, and Lanie Walker.

BISON BOP 2012 (R)

The Bop That Never Stopped, Vol. 10

Six tracks each by Mickey Hawks and Chuck Wiley.

BISON BOP 2014 (R)

The Bop That Never Stopped, Vol. 11

Jackie Gotroe, Don Hager, Glenn Johnson, Alan Lee, Charles Looper, Carl Mann, The Jimmie Martin Combo, Howard Mayberry, and Darrell Speck.

BISON BOP 2015 (R)

The Bop That Never Stopped, Vol. 12

Danny Dell, Bubba Ford, Billie J. Killen, Curtis Long, Ray McCoy, The Moonlighters, Carl Newman, Tyrone Schmidling, Jimmy Stringer, and Larry Terry.

BISON BOP 2016 (R)

The Bop That Never Stopped, Vol. 13

Glen Bland, Harmon Boazeman, Bill Gaida, Chester McIntyre, The Moods, Jeff Store, and Al Urban.

BISON BOP 2017 (R)

The Bop That Never Stopped, Vol. 14

Jim Burgett, The Dusters, Jimmy Gray, Wayne Hammond, The Jiants, J. Kirkland, Keith McCormack, Arlie Miller, The Prowlers, The Three Aces, and Rod Willis.

BISON BOP 2018 (R)

The Bop That Never Stopped, Vol. 15

Billy and Mickey, Don Dell, Jerry Dell, The Dusters, The Fireflies, Willie Goodson, Kimble Janes, Ken and Roy, The Love Brothers, The Maddy Brothers, and Pete and Jimmy.

BISON BOP 2019 (R)

The Bop That Never Stopped, Vol. 16

Art Adams, Eddie Dugosh, Curtis Hobeck, Jerry Ross, The Sabres, and Andy Starr.

BISON BOP 2020 (R)

The Bop That Never Stopped, Vol. 17

Jack Baley, Villas Craig, Hank Davis, Jimmy Dempsey, Larry Derieux, Tom Dorsum, Sanny Mayo, Eddie Ringo, Bill Roberts, Frankie St. John, and The Teen Tones.

BISON BOP 2021 (R)

The Bop That Never Stopped, Vol. 18

George Darro, Jimmy Dempsey, Ralph Lane, Len and Judy, Lonnie Miley, Turner Moore, Jim Morrison, The Orbits, The Rock-A-Tones, Joey Vee, Rod Willis, and Jimmy Woodall.

BISON BOP 2023 (R)

The Bop That Never Stopped, Vol. 19

Floyd Mack, Plez Gary Mann, Darwin Nelson, Bill Pollard, Johnny Reed, Ronny and Johnny, Orden Sexton, Gus Talburt, and Frankie Taro.

BISON BOP 2024 (R)

The Bop That Never Stopped, Vol. 20

Twelve rarities including three incredibly bizarre cuts by Maynard Horlick, as well as Bob Bowman, Johnny Conville, Jim Foley, Gene Norman, Cliff Nash, The Rockaways, and Jim Warfield.

BISON BOP 2025 (R)

The Bop That Never Stopped, Vol. 21

Stop! Stop! Bob Calloway, Ed Faucett, Harry Lee, Kenny Owens, The Pedigo Brothers, Bobby Wayne, and Chuck Wheeler.

BISON BOP 2026 (R)

The Bop That Never Stopped, Vol. 22

Parker Cunningham, Ray Darden, The Dawnbeats, Chuck Dockery, Jerry Parsons, Doug Powell, The Runabouts, and Dick Seaton.

BISON BOP 2027 (R)

The Bop That Never Stopped, Vol. 23

Mike Fern's "A Bomb Bop" and the bizarre "Cranberry Blues" by Robert Williams are the highlights of this collection, also including Billy Childs, Jimmy Lambreth, Roy Moss, Rex Qual, and Rodney Scott.

BISON BOP 2028 (R)

The Bop That Never Stopped, Vol. 24

Country boogie rather than rockin' cuts by The Dixieland Drifters, James Dotson, Jay Earls, Bill McMakin, The Stoltz Brothers, Hank Spurling, Lanie Walker, and Dave Wilburn.

BISON BOP 2029 (R)

The Bop That Never Stopped, Vol. 25

Jim Alley, Peter Concillo and The Cool Notes, Skip Goodspeed, Curley Griffin, The Hi-Tombs, Paul Keppler and The Hi-Tombs, and Bill Woods.

BISON BOP 2030 (R)

The Bop That Never Stopped, Vol. 26

Tommy Boyles, Don Hart, Grady Lewis, Buddy Miller and The Rockin' Ramblers, Pete Nantz, Curtis Potter, The Richard Brothers, The Sabres, and Billy Smith.

BISON BOP 2031 (R)

The Bop That Never Stopped, Vol. 27

Highlight: "Stanky Woman" by the trio of Harold Lee, Bob Fackler, and Kenny Welch, along with cuts by Tommy Duncan, Lucky Moore, Tyrone Schmidling, Monte Meade, Johnny Elmore, Johnny Fraser, Kim Erwin, and Jerry Lando.

BISON BOP 2032 (R)

The Bop That Never Stopped, Vol. 28

Six cuts each by two bands: Andy Anderson and The Dawn Breakers, and Steve Call and The Jaggs.

BISON BOP 2033 (R)

The Bop That Never Stopped, Vol. 29

Dean Beard, The Blue Echoes, Russ Brian, The Crowns, Jackie Gotroe, Bobby Mack, Curtis Potter, and Wallace Waters.

BISON BOP 2034 (R)

The Bop That Never Stopped, Vol. 30

The Royal Dukes accompany both Don Ellis and Harold Shutters (the latter under the name of "The Rocats") on four cuts each, along with eight cuts by Jimmy Reed.

BISON BOP 2037 (R)

The Bop That Never Stopped, Vol. 31

Red Berry and The Berry Brothers, Billy Bonny, Vern Clark, Jerry Dorn, Gil Gilroy, Lonnie Lillie, Don Murphy, Ray Titze and The Rollettes, and Link Wray.

BISON BOP 2038 (R)

The Bop That Never Stopped, Vol. 32

Ralph Banks, Tommy Beckham, Ross Cook and The Jay Rockers, Bobby Everhart, Jess Hooper, Johnny Maupin, Johnny Roane, Al Runyon, Jimmy Staggs and The Jay Rockers, and Joey Welz and The Rock-a-Billies.

BISON BOP 2041 (R)

The Bop That Never Stopped, Vol. 33

Ronnie Speaks, Johnny Earl, Grady Lewis, Clinton Brooks, Tommy Lee, and John Kirby.

BISON BOP 2042 (R)

The Bop That Never Stopped, Vol. 34

L.C. Smith, Leon Holmes, Clyde Owens, Jerry Arnold, Lee George, Billy Hogan, and Nelson Ray.

BLUBBA 484848 (R)

Fat! Fat! Fat!

Apparently our rockabilly and R&B brethren found never-ending amusement over the sight of a Rubenesque-figured gal shakin' on the dance floor. These 18 tunes are just a sampling of the 1950s rock and roll heavyweight division. Tunes include "Too Fat" by Little Freddy and Don, "Fatty Patty" by Lee Pickett and The Screamers, and "Fat Mama" by Ronnie Moleen. Get the idea? To be fair though, some of these studs are also strainin' the scales, but they're proud of it, like Big John Greer, who boasts "I'm the Fat Man," and Phil Barclay's pal "Short Fat Ben." Have another jelly donut 'cause you can really work off a few pounds dancing to this.

BOPCAT 400 (R)

Goin' Back to Memphis

Rare, unissued '50s and early '60s cuts by Tommy Blake, Ernie Chaffin, Jack Clement, Hardrock Gunter, Glenn Honeycut, Randy Lee, Carl Perkins, Earl Peterson, Slim Rhodes, Billy Riley, Gene Simmons, Onie Wheeler, and Malcolm Yelvington.

BOPCAT 700 (R)

Rock around the Town

Sixteen unreleased or alternate Sun-label sides by Dean Beard, Sonny Burgess, Jack Earls, Curtis Hoback, Patsy Holcomb, Glenn Honeycut, Charlie Rich, Warren Smith, and Junior Thompson.

BUFFALO BOP 2045 (R)

The Bop That Never Stopped, Vol. 35

It's back! Five good cuts by Jackie Lee Cochran, including two previously unreleased, along with four each by Bill Love and John Worthan, and one by The Love Brothers.

BUFFALO BOP 2046 (R)

The Bop That Never Stopped, Vol. 36

The Varitones, Don Coates, The Corvettes, Al Dean, Marvin Jackson and The Rockin' Aces, Larry Kirk, Merle Matts, and The Rockers.

BUFFALO BOP 2047 (R)

The Bop That Never Stopped, Vol. 37

Terry Ray Bradley, James Brink, Al Davis and The Blackouts, Truitt Forse, John Henry, Ralph Jerome, Jim McBride, Joe Moon, Eldon Rice, and The Volk Brothers.

BUFFALO BOP 2048 (R)

The Bop That Never Stopped, Vol. 38

Mike Cushman and The Interludes, Larry Donn, Jim Elk's Rhythm Rousers, Mike Fern and The Del Royals, Donald Hanchey and The Marauders, Kenneth Hunt, Melvin Morris, The Pearlescents, Hiram Philmon, and LaVerne Stovall.

BUFFALO BOP 2051 (R)

The Bop That Never Stopped, Vol. 39

Fourteen unknown rockers including a very early cut by Ronnie Dove, later of "Right or Wrong" fame. Some stuff is OK, but Gene Jenkins's "Short Stuff" is one of the worst records ever made! Includes The Emanons, Ray Burden, Jimmie John and The Rockin' Rangers, and Ken Darrow.

BUFFALO BOP 2052 (R)

The Bop That Never Stopped, Vol. 40

Unreleased material by Arlie Miller and Arlie Neaville recorded at Miller's home in Danville, IL, in 1958-1959. Most of these tunes are originals, either by Miller, or Miller and Neaville, with backup by The Varitones featuring Miller and Jim Foley (gtrs), and The Studio Band.

BUFFALO BOP 2053 (R)

The Bop That Never Stopped, Vol. 41

Mostly cowboy acts performing Western-flavored material. Willie Phelps is the main rustler here, along with Jay Chevalier and Alden Holloway.

BUFFALO BOP 2055 (R)

The Bop That Never Stopped, Vol. 42

Bop and teen rock by Bob Bowman, The Hodges Brothers and Al Sweatt, Darwin Nelson, Andy and The Live Wires, The Raiders, Tommy Palm and The Rockers, Skeet Williams, and Donnie Martindale and The Starfires.

BUFFALO BOP 2056 (R)

The Bop That Never Stopped, Vol. 43

Fourteen unknown and, for the most part, mediocre rockers, along with a few country folk, including The

Swanks, Frankie Taro, Jerry Grimes, Frank Cathey, and Jackie Benson.

BUFFALO BOP 2057 (R)
The Bop That Never Stopped, Vol. 44
Is it my imagination or is this series actually getting better? The spirit of Gene Vincent pervades these tracks by Buddy Dean and The Enchantments, Bobby Martin and The Tune Twisters, and Leroy Bowman and The Arrows.

BUFFALO BOP 2058 (R)
The Bop That Never Stopped, Vol. 45
Bruce Porter and The Bellhops, Bob Butler, Renaud Veluzat, and Dale Thomas and The Bandera Boys.

BUFFALO BOP 2059 (R)
The Bop That Never Stopped, Vol. 46
Mostly country tunes mascarading as rock, though Tommy Jackson's "Flat Top Box" is quite good. Lenny and The Star Chiefs, The Wild Childs, Lee Wagoner and The Echomores, The Titzie Brothers, and Steve Bledsoe.

BUFFALO BOP 2061 (R)
The Bop That Never Stopped, Vol. 47
Fourteen rare rockabilly and rockin' country tunes, including five by Bill Sherrill, as well as Deacon and The Rock'n'Rollers, The Temptations, Bobby Tidwell, and Amos Greer.

BUFFALO BOP 2062 (R)
The Bop That Never Stopped, Vol. 48
Fine set highlighted by two strong rockers by Joe Castle. The rest is mostly rockin' country, but these are also strong selections by John Worthan and Mackey Hargett.

BUFFALO BOP 2065 (R)
The Bop That Never Stopped, Vol. 49
Fourteen rarities including excellent instrumentals by Don and The Galaxies, lots of fine rockabilly, and a couple rockin' country tracks. Ronnie Knull, Deacon and The Rock'n'Rollers, Hunter Watts, and Jim McCrory.

BUFFALO BOP 2066 (R)
The Bop That Never Stopped, Vol. 50
Fourteen rarities topped by three unissued rockabilly sides by The Sabres, along with Hank Mizell, Terry and The Pirates, and The Rebel Rowsers.

BUFFALO BOP 2067 (R)
The Bop That Never Stopped, Vol. 51
Hot, if not well-recorded, scorchers. My fave is Randy Luck's "I Was a Teen-Age Caveman," similar in sound to "Teen-Age Werewolf." Also includes four rockers by Wally Deane and The Flips, as well as Kent Westbury, Jimmy Gale's Imperials, Wesley Hardin and The Roxters, and Jimmy Voytek and The Velvetones.

BUFFALO BOP 2068 (R)
The Bop That Never Stopped, Vol. 52
Rare rockabilly and jive, highlighted by Buck Trail's "The Knocked Out Joint on Mars." Thirteen other tracks by Dale Thomas, The Four Unknowns, Johnnie Kaye, The Roxters, Tommy Spurlin, and Bobby Gray.

BUFFALO BOP 2069 (R)
The Bop That Never Stopped Vol. 53
Thirteen good rockers by Leon and James, Buddy White, Little Lawrence Shaul, Darrell Rhodes, and Rikki and The Rikatones.

BUFFALO BOP 2070 (R)
The Bop That Never Stopped, Vol. 54
Ten standard rockabilly numbers and four country boppers by Jimmie Patton, Happy Wainwright, The Chieftones, and Jesse Lee King.

BUFFALO BOP 2071 (R)
The Bop That Never Stopped, Vol. 55
Lloyd McCullough, Little Man Henry, Frankie and Margie, and Mic's Masters on a solid set of rockin' sounds.

BUFFALO BOP 2072 (R)
The Bop That Never Stopped, Vol. 56
Fourteen strong cuts by Billy Mache, Bobby Brown, Keetie and The Kats, Don Feger, and Buddy Miller.

BUFFALO BOP 2073 (R)
The Bop That Never Stopped, Vol. 57
Bobby and Boobie, The Carpenter Brothers, The Senders, Jerry Coulston, Gene Terry, Ira Allen, and J. Gale Kilgore.

BUFFALO BOP 2074 (R)
The Bop That Never Stopped, Vol. 58
Wayne Whorley and The Whorley Birds, Charles Jones, Artie and The Mustangs, Jerry and The Del-Fis, Hal Payne, The Night Hawks, Clyde Arnold, and Jimmy Stewart. Another must have for diehard rockabilly fans.

BUFFALO BOP 2075 (R)
The Bop That Never Stopped, Vol. 59
Fourteen, so-so, medium-paced rockabilly tunes by Big Jeff, The Teen Rockers, Jimmy Chambers, Gary Leath, and Jan Doss. Highpoint: Charlie Pack's "Fluffy Dog," a crazy love song to a mutt, featuring the little mongrel barking along right on the beat!

BUFFALO BOP 2076 (R)
The Bop That Never Stopped, Vol. 60
Average 14-tune selection by Mike McAllister, Bobby and The Rhythm Rockers, Danny Zella, Jan Davis, and Bonnie Blue Bell.

BUFFALO BOP 2077 (R)
The Bop That Never Stopped, Vol. 61
Fourteen cuts, about half duds. The more inspired outings are by Ron Berry and Andy Sanders, Gene Davis, Jerry Bradford, Ray Hudson and The Rhythmaires, The Twiliters, and Johnny Champion.

CADENCE (JAPAN) 25CP-33 (L)
20 Top Teen Favorites
Hits and misses by Cadence stars Lenny Welch, Eddie Hodges, Johnny Tillotson, The Chordettes, and Jean Thomas. Only Welch's "A Taste of Honey" is in stereo. For the completist.

CADILLAC 1958 (R)
Boppin' Cadillac
Twenty '50s rockers about cars, including ten about Cadillacs, by The Aquatones, Doug Bowles, Jimmy Carroll, Jackie Lee Cochran, Rocky Davis, Mel Douglas, Larry Dowd, Jim Flaherty, Val Hughes, Jan and Arnie, Baker Knight, Bob Luman, Sammy Masters, Jim McCrory, Bill Sherrill, Howie Strange, Sonny Wallace, H. Weston, Rick West, and Hal Willis.

✪ CANDY 001 (R)
At the Party
This one's subtitled "16 Rompin' Stompin' Lease Breakin' Tunes," and it lives up to its name. Black rock and roll, rockabilly, and screamin' instrumentals, including the title blaster by Big Sambo and The House Wreckers, Dee Clark with backing by The Upsetters, Don Covay (recording as Pretty Boy), Scott Wood, The Saxons, Rex Garvin and The Mighty Cravers, and Doc Harvey.

CANDY 002 (R)
Too Much Goin' On
According to cover credit this features "16 Yellpin' Scalpin' Pow-Wowing Tunes" (!) by Mickey Lee Lane, Joe McCoy and His Real McCoys, Red (Hot) Russell, and Fred Hughes.

CANDY 003 (R)
Whip It On 'Em:
16 Soul Stirring Stompers
Sixteen '60s dance tunes guaranteed to get the whole crowd shakin' and shimmyin' by Harvey Scales and The Seven Sounds, Bobby Davis, Don Gardner, and R.T. and The Pot Lickers. It'll be mighty hard to top this one.

CANDY 004 (R)
Bug Out, Vol. 1
Loony anthology of 16 dance tunes by '50s and '60s groups including Johnny Ray Gomez and The U-Neeks, Gene The Hat, The Sierras, Sonny Bloch's Elephants, and The Seven Teens. So bad, it's good!

CANDY 005 (R)
Bug Out, Vol. 2
Another fantastic collection of party tunes that'll surely cause your living room to be wrecked. Wacky monstrosities by The Galaxies and The Regulars, The Warner Brothers, and Kenny and The Fiends. One dance I wouldn't recommend is "Twistin' in the Tub" by Damal and Rasheed. Don't try this at home!

CANDY 006 (RL)
Shakin' Fit
Wacked-out collection of dance-floor soul music, most of it as scarce as cogent quotes by Dan Quayle. Only "Love-Itis" by Harvey Scales and the 7 Sounds has been previously reissued. The Five Du-Tones, The Fabulous Playboys, Willie Parker, The Shells, and The Ideals gyrate like mad. If you can sit still through Junior and the Classics's "The Dog," may your soul rest in peace. CD adds the 13 cuts from *Whip It On 'Em* (Candy 003).

✪ CAPITOL 96861 (CL)
Wild Surf: Monster Summer Hits
Probably the best surf collection yet, with 26 tunes from the Capitol/EMI valuts. You know you're gonna hear The Beach Boys, but how about some lesser-known tunes by Mr. Gasser and The Weirdos ("Finksville U.S.A." and "Doin' the Surfink"), along with the underrated Jerry Cole and His Spacemen ("Surf Age" and "Pipeline"). Also includes faves by The Marketts, The Fantastic Baggys, and The Trashmen, plus a Big Daddy Roth-style print suitable for framing. Catch a wave!

✪ CAPITOL 96862 (CL)
Drag City: Monster Summer Hits
Twenty-six hot rod classics from Capitol/EMI, including Robert Mitchum's wonderful "The Ballad of Thunder Road." Also featured: corny, but fun numbers by Bert Convy and The Cheers; the ancient but fast "Hot Rod Race" by Jimmy Dolan; the mighty, stompin' "Brontosaurus Stomp" by The Piltdown Men; and more by Jerry Cole and His Spacemen, The Super Stocks, and The Gants.

CAPITOL 98138 (CL)
Spring Break, Vol. 1:
Hot Rods and Hard Bods
All-time classics thrown together to make a buck. Pop this on and pop a top with The Rivingtons, The Human Beinz, Johnny Otis, The Beach Boys, Gene Vincent, Eddie Cochran, and The Exciters.

CAPITOL 98139 (CL)
Spring Break Vol. 2:
Cold Kegs and Tan Legs
More faves by Gene Vincent, Eddie Cochran, The Outsiders, The Classics IV, The Beach Boys, Johnny

Rivers, and Billy "Crash" Craddock. We even get into the '70s with Grand Funk Railroad, The Raspberries, and Katrina and The Waves. Go figure.

CASCADE 1002 (RC)

Twenty Great Rock and Roll Hits of the '50s

Excellent budget collection taken from the Ace, Cadence, and Modern catalogs. Includes Jessie Belvin, The Cadets, The Chordettes, Jimmy Clanton, The Everly Brothers, Frankie Ford, The Jive Five, Bobby Lewis, Little Richard, Oscar McLollie, Johnny Olenn, The Olympics, Chan Romero, Huey "Piano" Smith and The Clowns, Jeff Stone, Joe Tex, The Teen Queens, Richie Valens, and Link Wray.

CASCADE 1003 (RC)

20 Great Rockabilly Hits of the '50s

Hershel Almond, Benny Barnes, Don Cole, Les Cole, Jimmie Dale, Sonny Fisher, Glen Glenn, Hal Harris, Jesse James, George Jones, Benny Joy, Sleepy LaBeef, Chester McIntyre, Matchbox, The Poorboys, Rock Rogers, Johnny Todd, Al Urban, and Gene Wyatt mostly from previous Ace LPs.

CASCADE 1006 (RC)

20 Great Guitar Instrumentals

Excellent LP featuring old and new recordings by The Shades, The Geezers, The Meteors, Link Wray, The Milkshakes, Kid Rogers and The Henchmen, The De-Fenders, The Raiders, Arvee Allens (aka Ritchie Valens), Alden Holloway, The Bill Smith Combo, Bob Millsap, Jimmy Heap, The Bill Wimberly Band, and The Steve Diver One Man Band.

CASCADE 1009 (RC)

20 Great Rockabilly Hits of the '50s

Glenn Barber, Dick Busch, Fred Crawford, Dee and Patty, Eddie Dugosh and The Ah-Ha Playboys, Charlie Feathers, Sonny Fisher, Glen Glenn, Sonny Hall and The Echoes, Hal Harris, B.J. Johnson, George Jones, Sleepy LaBeef, Bill Mack, Wayne McGinnis, Danny Reeves, Rock Rogers, Junior Thompson, and Johnny Todd.

CASCADE 1012 (RC)

20 Great Teen Ballads of the '50s and '60s

Excellent set with all styles represented and lots of rarities. Features The Passions, Glen Glenn, Frankie Avalon, The Jive Five, Little Richard, and The Everly Brothers. Special bonus for collectors: "The Way You Look Tonight" by The Lonely Guys, Neil Diamond's first recording.

CASCADE 1014 (RCL)

20 Great Crusin' Favorites of the '50s and '60s

Twenty "oldies" to play in your low-rider by Little Richard, Larry Williams, Sam Cooke, The Everly Brothers, The Chordettes, Johnny Tillotson, The Cadets, Marvin and Johnny, Dion, and The Chiffons.

CASCADE 1015 (RL)

20 Great Crusin' Favorites, Vol. 2

Dion, The Ernie Fields Orchestra, Bobby Day, The Mystics, Eddie Hodges, Randy and The Rainbows, Eugene Church, The Everly Brothers, The Chiffons, and Art Neville.

CASCADE 1016 (RCL)

20 Great Cruisin' Favorites, Vol. 3

An excellent collection of well-known numbers by Dion, The Everly Brothers, Big Boy Myles and The Shaw-Wees, The Chiffons, Lloyd Price, Little Richard, Sam Cooke, Dean and Jean, Bobby Day, and Oscar McLollie.

CASCADE 1018 (CL)

20 Great Love Songs of the Rock and Roll Era

Kissy face music from 1954-1961 performed by the usual suspects: The Penguins, The Skyliners, The Crests, The Paris Sisters, The Capris, The Pentagons, Dion and The Belmonts, The Shadows, The Safaris, Jesse Belvin, The Dreamlovers, Richie Valens, The Belmonts, The Fiestas, and the Everly Brothers. Collectors should note that "So Tenderly" by The Mystics and "This Is My Love" by The Passions appear in stereo for the first time.

CBS SPECIAL PRODUCTS 37618 (L)

Rockabilly Stars, Vol. 1

CBS SPECIAL PRODUCTS 37621 (L)

Rockabilly Stars, Vol. 2

Reissue of great two-LP sets of hillbilly bop, country, and rockabilly from the '50s and '60s. Twenty-four cuts from Carl Perkins, The Everly Brothers, Marty Robbins, Johnny Horton, Link Wray, The Collins Kids, Scotty Moore, Johnny Cash, Mac Curtis, and Charlie Rich.

CHAM 18177 (R)

Rockin' Rollin' Vocal Groups

Nice set by John Ashley, The Bay Bops, The Bell Notes, Ritchie Cordell, The Dal Raneys, The De-Villes, The Equadors, The Four Counts, Frankie and The Echoes, The Lark Tones, Mark Four, The Morgan Twins, The Nobles, Eddy Reynolds, The Slates, The Temptations, The Valaires, and The Velvets.

CHAM 80423 (R)

Rockin' Rollin' Vocal Groups, Vol. 2

Andy and The Gigolos, The Aquatones, The Bell Notes, Billy and Mickey, The Blue Jays, Bob and Ray, The Carroll Brothers, The Cavaliers, Dickie Doo and The Don'ts, The Ebb Tides, The Equadors, The Eternals, Mark Four, Lowell McGuire, The Montereys, The Satellites, The Seniors, The Strange Lovers, Roy Teo, and The Tri Tones.

CHAM 80430 (R)

Rockin' Rollin' Vocal Groups, Vol. 3

Excellent '50s collection by The Aquatones, Dick Campbell, Jackie Carbone, The Contenders, Phil Gary, The Genies, The Genos, The Hollywood Playboys, The James Boys, The Lafayettes, Jerry Landis (aka Paul Simon), Scotty McKay, The Sinceres, The Solitaires, The Sophomores, and Tyron and the Newports. Highpoint: the classic "Martian Hop" by The Ran-Dells.

CHAM 80505 (R)

Rockin' Rollin' Vocal Groups, Vol. 4

Fifteen more big ones, featuring Billy Ward and The Dominoes, The Accents, The Day Brothers, The Ding Dongs, Don and The Roses, The Earls, The Equadors, The Jarmels, Willie Lofton and The Discords, Ronnie Price and The Velvets, Rick and The Rockers, The Saints, and The Velours.

CHAM 80635 (R)

Rockin' Rollin' Vocal Groups, Vol. 5

Sixteen eclectic rockabilly, rock and roll, and R&B sides by The Fretts, The Argyles, The Cables, The Untouchables, The Ds, The Royal Teens, The Kings, The Val-Chords, The Visuals, The Del Chords, The Gems, The Larados, and The Philharmonics. Highlights are two jumping pre-Jan and Dean sides by Jan Betty and Arnie Ginsberg, as well as Andre Williams's timeless classic "Bacon Fat," wrongly ascribed as "Diddlee Diddlee Womp Womp." Nice pics. Great party wax.

CHARLY 16 (L)

The Best of Sun Rockabilly

Twenty-two great tracks by Little Junior's Blue Flames, Sonny Burgess, Ray Smith, Jack Earls, Carl Perkins, The Miller Sisters, Slim Rhodes, Dean Beard, Warren Smith, Ray Harris, and Billy Lee Riley.

CHARLY 36 (L)

The Best of Sun Rockabilly, Vol. 2

Twenty-five of the more obscure Sun rockers on one disc. Well-known stars Carl Perkins, Jerry Lee Lewis, and Charlie Rich are joined by lesser luminaries Sonny Burgess, Warren Smith, Mack Self, Jimmy Wages, Barbara Pittman, Billy Lee Riley, Glenn Honeycutt, Jack Earls, Harold Jenkins (aka Conway Twitty), and

Hayden Thompson. Fifty-seven powerful minutes with fine sound quality.

CHARLY 296 (L)

The Red Bird Story

Red Bird, a label owned by songwriters/producers Leiber and Stoller and record executive George Goldner, was actually four labels—Red Bird, Blue Cat, Tiger, and Daisy—with Red Bird epitomizing the girl group sound, thanks to producers/songwriters Jeff Barry, Ellie Greenwich, and Shadow Morton. This four-disc set, an expanded version of the out-of-print two-LP Red Bird sets (Charly 15 and 19), is loaded with the finest girl-group sounds by The Dixie Cups, Ellie Greenwich, The Shangri-Las, The Jelly Beans, The Ad-Libs, and The Butterflies. Soul and R&B fans will also find lots to chirp about here, with appearances by Alvin Robinson, Linda Jones, Bessie Banks, Sidney Barnes, Bobby Moore and The Fourmosts, Sam Hawkins, and The Soul Brothers. Ninety-six songs, with info-laden booklet.

❸ CHIEF 1156503 (L)

Ultra Rare Rockabillys, Vol. 3

Thirty uptempo rockabilly tunes from a variety of small and mid-sized labels. Not exactly "ultra rare," but "well-done" just the same! Includes Billy Barrix, G. "Davy" Crockett, Art Adams, The Phantom, Billy Carroll, and Ray Cole and His Skyrockets. Sound quality is great, so you are really blasted by all of the hot guitar breaks on these tunes! Absolutely the best rockabilly CD compilation I've heard so far.

CLUB 006 (R)

Grab This and Dance, Vol. 6

Eighteen hot rockabilly tracks from the '50s by Gene Watson and The Rockets, Bob Luman, Merrill Moore, Micky Hawks and The Night Raiders, Joyce Green, Jet Powers, Billy Barrix, and The Rockin' Rs.

COLLECTOR SERIES 145 (R)

Hits of the Fifties

Two-LP set with 24 pop hits from the Columbia/Epic labels. Mostly "adult" (pre-rock) pop by Patti Page, Doris Day, Sal Mineo, Guy Mitchell, Rosemary Clooney, Vic Damone, Johnny Mathis, and Judy Garland. There's also country pop by Johnny Horton, Stonewall Jackson, and Johnny Cash, and even (who knows why) Link Wray's fabulous "Rawhide."

COLLECTABLES 503 (L)

Acid Visions: Best of Texas Punk and Psychedelic, Vol. 1

Fourteen powerful tunes by Amos Boynton and The ABCs (featuring Johnny and Edgar Winter), The Scotty McKay Quintet, Satori, Roy Head, The Pandas, and The Bad Roads.

COLLECTABLES 504 (L)

Acid Visions: Best of Texas Punk and Psychedelic, Vol. 2

Fourteen by The Fanatics, The Sherwoods, BLC, The Warlocks (a Dallas band that included Frank Beard and Dusty Hill, who wound up in ZZ Top a few years later), and Homer (a band that is now favorably compared with early Quicksilver).

⚙ COLLECTOR 4402 (L)

Fantastic Rock and Roll

The title does not lie! Twenty-five hot tracks by The Lonesome Drifter, Charlie Brown, Micky Hawks and The Nighthawks, Eddie Gaines, Dwain Bell, Joe Griffith, and Jimmy Roby. Highly recommended.

COLLECTOR 4404 (L)

Original Memphis Rock and Roll and Country

Great 30-track collection of rockabilly and country rockers by Eddie Bond and The Stompers, Marlon Grisham, B.B. Cunningham Jr., Joe E. May, Tiny Fuller, Bud Deckleman, Ray Scott, and Don Willis and The Orbits.

COLLECTOR 4409 (L)

Great Rockin' Girls

Thirty gal rockers, from boppin' hillbillies like Doris Hubbard and Betty Jo, through out-and-out rockers like Tonya Dee and The Dischords, Connie and The Cytations, The Browning Sisters, and Sandy Lee.

⚙ COLLECTOR 4410 (L)

Dixie Rock and Roll

Dixie Records was formed as an offshoot, custom label for Houston's Starday Records in the '50s. This 30-tune collection gives a good overview of their many releases in the rockabilly vein. There's some real raw stuff here to be sure, including two of the only tunes that feature a banjo in a rock-and-roll lineup: Jessie Floyd's "Satan's Wife" and Pete Peters's "Rockin' in My Sweet Baby's Arms." Also includes tracks by Alden Holloway, Tommy Nelson, Bill Carroll, and Eddie Skelton. Highly recommended.

COLLECTABLES 5414 (CL)

Carole King—Plus The Cookies and Little Eva

More bubble gum from the songwriting pens of Carole King and Gerry Goffin performed by The (reconstituted) Cookies, King herself, and chipper Little Eva. Reissue of 12-song Dimension album. Some duplication with Collectables 5407, sketchy sleeve notes, and usual disregard for the intelligent collector. Average sound.

COLLECTABLES 5416 (CL)

Murray The K's Sing Along with Original Golden Gassers

A Murray Kaufman "oldies" reissue extravaganza of pop and R&B hits by Crescent City Joe Jones, James Sheppard with The Heartbeats, Buddy Knox, Sonny Til and The Orioles, Herbie and The Cleftones, The Crows, Jimmie ("Honeycomb") Rodgers, The Continentals, Frankie Lymon, Jimmy Bowen, The Channels, and The Playmates. No pics or decent notes.

⚙ COLLECTABLES 8807 (L)

Acid Visions: The Best of Texas Punk and Psychedelic

Earthshaking three-CD set containing the first two *Acid Visions* LPs (Collectables 503 and 504), plus an additional 42 tracks, at least half of which have never beeen issued on compilations before (I checked!); the rest are pretty hard to find anymore. You'll see colors while you groove to The Great Believers, The Scotty McKay Quintet, The Pandas, The Bad Roads, The Fanatics, The Weavils, The Black Sacks, Johnny Winter, Sabana Breeze, The Pearl Divers, The Purple Haze, The Surf Knights, Pure Jade Green, Lunar Madness, The Sherwoods, The Interns, Saddlesore, Thursday's Children, The 13th Floor Elevators, SJ and the Crossroads, and The Lemon Fog. You also get a pretty decent booklet for a change from Collectables. Texas punk rules, partners.

CONNOISSEUR COLLECTION 134 (L)

Goffin and King Songbook

Twenty-four classics by 23 artists, including The Cookies, The Shirelles, The Chiffons, Dusty Springfield, Maxine Brown, The Byrds, The Monkees, The Righteous Brothers, The Crickets, Laura Nyro, Bobby Vee, Betty Everett, and Little Eva. You know the titles.

CORNBALL 1958 (R)

Shake Shake Shake It Baby: Sin Alley, V

Twenty-one of the strangest things ever to pass for rock and roll. Not for the faint-of-heart.

COUNTRY ROUTES 06 (L)

Rockin' at Town Hall

Callin' all rockabilly fans. You just can't live without this fabulous live material recorded for the *Town Hall Party* TV show between 1959-1961. Can you believe Carl Perkins doing seven of his classics live, including "Blue Suede Shoes," "True Love," "Matchbox," and "Boppin' the Blues." Or dig Bob Luman at his peak with either James Burton or Roy Buchanan on mind-boggling lead guitar doing "Milkcow Blues," "I Got a Woman," and "Oh Lonesome Me." The sound quality ain't so hot, but so what. You'll play this one over and over again.

COUNTRY MUSIC FOUNDATION 014 (CL)

Vintage RCA Rockabilly

The first domestic RCA rockabilly anthology ever: 33 songs on two cassettes or one CD, expertly assembled and annotated by the Foundation's Jay Orr, featuring Joe Clay, Janis Martin, Dave Rich, Tommy Blake, Ric Cartey, Pee Wee King, David Houston, Jimmy Dell, fiddler Gordon Terry, Martha Carson, Hoyt Johnson, The Morgan Twins, and Milton Allen. A beautiful job. CD includes all of the tracks from the cassettes, except Joey Castle's "That Ain't Nothin' but Right."

CRYSTAL BALL 105 (R)

From the Vaults of Laurie Records

Fourteen fine and very rare sides issued by Laurie in the early '60s by The Continentals, The Del-Rios, The Delltones, The Holidays, The Monograms, The Montclairs, The Motions, The Mystics, The Ovations, The Paramounts, The Premiers, The Regents, and The Teenagers.

CRYSTAL BALL 106 (R)

A Full House

Fourteen unreleased cuts from the Laurie label by The Bon-Aires, Carlo, Dean and Jean, The Del-Satins, The Four Graduates, The Modern Ink Spots, The Mystics, and The Skyliners.

CRYSTAL BALL 110 (R)

The Best of Mowhawk Records

Fourteen sides from the New York label that first recorded Dion and The Belmonts and The Demensions. Good stuff, though the orchestrations are a bit heavy. Includes demos and previously unreleased material by The Belmonts, The Companions, The Del-Terriers, The Demensions, Dion and The Belmonts, The Intruders, Joey and The Ovations, Lonnie of The Carrolons, Marco, The Mello-Kings, The Radiants, and Ricky Reynolds.

CRYSTAL BALL 112 (R)

There's No Place Like Rome

Eighteen early '60s sides (including 11 previously unreleased demos) from Trade Martin's Rome label, best known for white, doo-wop groups like The Earls. Includes The Del-Escorts, The Glens, Johnny and The Jokers, The Pretenders, and The Prince-Tones.

CURB 77402 (CL)

All-Time Great Instrumental Hits, Vol. 2

Really fine selection of boss '50s and '60s instrumentals. Walk Don't Run/Hawaii Five-O (The Ventures)/ Topsy, Pt. 2 (Cozy Cole)/Peter Gunn (Ray Anthony)/ Let There Be Drums (Sandy Nelson)/Blues Theme (Davie Allan and The Arrows)/The Green Mosquito (The Tune Rockers)/Surfer's Stomp (The Marketts).

DCC COMPACT CLASSICS 043 (L)

Toga Rock II

Fourteen-cut, frat-rock compilation. Get a case of Old Milwaukee, put on your laurel wreath, and get obnoxious to the stompin' sounds. Shout/Do You Love Me/ Money/Papa-Omm-Mow-Mow/Gloria/Shake a Tail Feather/Dance to the Music.

DCC COMPACT CLASSICS 050 (L)

Monster Rock and Roll Show

A terrific collection of classic monster songs, interspersed with trailers from horror movies like *The Haunted Strangler, Horror of Dracula, The Amazing Colossal Man,* and *The Astro Zombies.* Excellent sound courtesy of Steve Hoffman and detailed notes by Alan Warner. Monster Mash (Bobby "Boris" Pickett)/Midnight Stroll (The Revels)/Frankenstein of '59 (Buchanan and Goodman with Count Dracula)/ Screamin' Ball (at Dracula Hall) (The Duponts)/ Haunted House (Johnny Fuller)/Witch Queen of New Orleans (Redbone)/The Green Slime (The Green Slime)/I Ain't Superstitious (Howlin' Wolf)/Morgus the Magnificent (Morgus and The Ghouls).

DELUXE 1041 (L)

King-Federal Rockabillies

Fourteen great tracks by Charlie Feathers, Mac Curtis, Hank Mizell, and Bob and Lucille.

DOWN SOUTH 9211 (R)

Rock from the Other Side

DOWN SOUTH 9212 (R)

Rock from the Other Side, Vol. 2

DOWN SOUTH 9213 (R)

Rock from the Other Side, Vol. 3

DOWN SOUTH 9215 (R)

Rock From the Other Side, Vol. 5

Before there was The Bee Gees, before there was Air Supply ... there were these rare rockabilly and rock and roll discs from New Zealand and Australia. Each volume includes eighteen sides recorded in the late '50s through early '60s, by bands that even today aren't household names.

EDSEL 145 (R)

The Autumn Records Story

Pioneering San Francisco label owned by DJs Big Tom Donahue and Mighty Bob Mitchell. Early recordings by The Charlatans, The Beau Brummels, Bobby Freeman, The Great Society, Sly Stewart (aka Stone), and The Tikis (later called Harper's Bizarre), many reissued elsewhere.

EDSEL 270 (L)

This Is Merseybeat

CD reissue of a couple of rare Oriole LPs recorded live in July 1963 at Liverpool's Rialto Ballroom utilizing a primitive mobile recording unit. Twenty-nine tracks by Rory Storm and The Hurricanes, Sonny Webb and The Cascades, Ian and The Zodiacs, The Nomads, and other groups that put the more-commercial Liverpudlians to shame. Recommended.

EMI 96268 (CL)

24 Greatest Hits of All Time

A nice "golden oldies" collection, presenting rock, R&B, vocal groups, and pop performers from EMI's vast holdings. We could do without even the best efforts by Cher, Bobby Goldsboro, Vicki Carr, and Slim Whitman, but the majority of these are pure gold nuggets from The Clovers, Eddie Cochran, Fats Domino, The Ventures, Little Anthony and The Imperials, Shirley and Lee, The Exciters, The Five Keys, and Jan and Dean.

EMI 99987 (CL)

Legends of Christmas Past

Twenty Xmas rockers, from white artists like Bill Haley, The Beach Boys, The Ventures, Canned Heat, and even The Chipmunks, and R&B greats Amos Milburn, The Five Keys, Charles Brown ("Merry Christmas, Baby"), and Baby Washington. So whether you prefer Jan and Dean, or Marvin and Johnny, there's something here for you. And if you don't like either, how about Lon Chaney doing "Monster's Holiday"? A sense of fun makes this one stand out from the pack.

EMI (UK) 798130 (L)

British Rock and Rollers

Eighteen British rock songs recorded between 1956-1961 that are often just pale covers of American hits. But among the dross is some first-class stuff. Johnny Kidd and The Pirates's hit "Shakin' All Over," later covered by The Who, is a classic, and Vince Taylor and The Playboys's "Brand New Cadillac" (later cut by The Clash) is a stunner. Other worthwhile artists include Adam Faith, Screamin' Lord Sutch, Shane Fenton and The Fentones, Dave Sampson and The Hunters, and Helen Shapiro.

EMI (FRANCE) 798131 (L)

Rock and Roll Instrumentals

Eighteen American and British tunes recorded between 1957–1963, with a few previously unreleased cuts. The best- known US artists are Johnny and The Hurricanes, Ernie Freeman, Sandy Nelson, Phil Upchurch, and The Ventures. Though most of the English cuts lack the hard edge of their earlier U.S. counterparts, The Krew Kats's "Samovar" and Bert Weedon's "Sorry Robbie" are particularly effective. All in all, an interesting collection, with good sound and fair notes.

ERA 840 (L)

Rock and Roll Guitar Classics

Guitar grinders leaning toward the surf end of the musical spectrum. The serious collector will already have the hits by The Ventures, Duane Eddy, Link Wray, and Dick Dale contained in this digitally remastered collection covering the late '50s to early '60s. But wait, there's more: You also get Santo and Johnny's atmospheric "Sleepwalk" and Lonnie Mack's high energy "Wham."

ERNIE DOUGLAS 66 (R)

Shutdown '66

A collection of '60s garage rockers who cut some of the most woeful, tear-drenched ballads ever waxed. Eighteen tunes so loaded with teen angst that you'll probably sprout a zit or two just listening to them. Features The Crucibles, The Royal Coachmen, The Avantis, The Hearts of Stone, and The Rockers.

ESOLDUN 2221 (L)

Texas Rockabilly and Hillbilly Boogie, Vol. 1

ESOLDUN 2222 (L)

Texas Rockabilly and Hillbilly Boogie, Vol. 2

Two twenty-one cut CDs. Vol. 1 features boppers by Jimmy Patton, Alvis Wayne, Lee Finn, Gene Chapman, Lucky Boggs, Lone Star Playboys, and the great Bennie Hess. Vol. 2 has Jerry Irby, William Pennix, Hank Stanford, Al Epp and The Pharaohs, The York Brothers, Hoyle Nix, and Joe D. Gibson.

EVA 2 (L)

Texas Punk from the '60s, Vols. 1 and 2

Previously issued as two LPs, this is a prime collection of '60s punk by The Undertakers, Kempy and The Guardians, The Chessmen, Mouse and The Traps, The Outcasts, and The Coastliners. Highest recommendations.

EVA 3 (L)

The Sound of the '60s

Twenty-eight '60s punk/garage classics previously issued as two LPs. Well-known groups like The Count Five, Creation, The Animals, The Yardbirds, and ?Question Mark and The Mysterians doing mostly lesser-known tunes are interspersed with great unknowns like The Shake Spears, Sir Henry and His Butlers, The Hairy Ones, and The Ingoes. The sound is pretty good, and there's a nice booklet with pics and info on the bands, but it's in French (mais naturellement!).

EVA 7 (L)
Louisiana Punk from the '60s, Vols. 1 and 2

Twenty-nine rockers by Dr. Spec's Optical Illusion, The Bad Roads, The Moon Dawgs, and The Satans. Originally reissued on two LPs. Get it, it's great!

FINK 1 (R)
It's Finking Time!: '60s Punk vs. Dancing Junk

Eight slabs of hot '60s punk by The Underworld, The Twiliters, The Pastels, and The Hunted, and eight shakin' and shimmyin' dance classics, including the legendary tune "Baby Let Me Bang Your Box" by The Bangers, Alf Newman's "Let's Do the Fink," and The Underbeats's "Annie Do the Dog." It's a winner.

FLAME 001 (R)
Desperate Rock and Roll! Vol. 1

Twenty wild rockabilly and rockin' country tracks. My favorites are the space rock numbers: Deacon and The Rock'n'Rollers's "Rockin' on the Moon," Terry Dunavan's "Rock It on Mars," Casey Grams's "Countdown," Nelson Young's "Rock Old Sputnick," and Don Winters's "Pretty Moon."

FLAME 002 (R)
Desperate Rock and Roll! Vol. 2

Another 20 obscure, wild-and-crazy rockabilly, rock and roll, and rockin' country sides by The Musical Linn Twins, Screamin' Joe Neal, The Alabama Kids, Eddie Kirkland, The Hamptones, and Butch Paulson.

FLAME 003 (R)
Desparate Rock and Roll! Vol. 3

Twenty wild ones performed by total unknowns, including Tommy Genova, Kai Ray, and W.L. Horning, along with a few slightly more familiar names like Danny Ezba and Sax Kari.

FLAME 004 (R)
Desperate Rock and Roll! Vol. 4

Twenty wild rockabilly, rock-and-roll, and R&B "classics," even including the original Sonny Boy Williamson doing "Polly Put the Kettle On"! Fredale Mannew's "It's a Gas" was originally issued as a free cardboard record by *Mad* magazine! Inspired cuts by Teddy McRae (aka Mr. Bear), Kenny McKennon, Sandy Lee, and Maynie and Howie.

FLAME 005 (R)
Desperate Rock and Roll! Vol. 5

Surreal rock by Ray Vernon (aka Vernon Wray, Link's brother) and Randy Hobbs (The McCoys's bassist), and total trash by Icky Renrut (Ike Turner?), Vic Thomas, Joe McCoy (Kansas Joe?), and The Black Albinos.

FLAME 006 (R)
Desperate Rock and Roll! Vol. 6

Not as far-out as previous volumes, this release focuses on raw, but not real raw, rockabilly. The novelties are OK, including the kid rock of Little Jacky Wayne, and foreign-language cuts by Kanui and Lula (in Hawaiian) and Henry Cording (in French). Other goodies from Lightnin' Hopkins, Ric Carty, Rufus Shoffner, and The Sly Fox.

FLAME 007 (R)
Desperate Rock and Roll! Vol. 7

A return to crazy and raw rock and roll, R&B, rockabilly, and novelty tunes by Dick Robinson, Willy Whack and The Thumpers, Slim Watts, Munroe Moe Jackson, and Dave Bartholomew.

FLAME 008 (R)
Desperate Rock and Roll! Vol. 8

Solid rockabilly with some great R&B thrown in, but not as wild as previous releases. Highlights are Jesse Knight's raucous "Nothin' but Money" done to the tune of "Shake, Rattle and Roll," and Dewaine Olby's "Iron Worker Blues." Also includes Junior Wells, Prince Arky, Bob Cass, and Steve Bledsoe.

FLAME 009 (R)
Desperate Rock and Roll! Vol. 9

Los Boppers, Jimmy Franklin, Shakey Jake, Bobby Page, Steve Alaimo, The Vice-Roys, Lattie Moore, and Lonesome Lee.

FLAME 010 (R)
Desperate Rock and Roll! Vol. 10

Dennis Smith, Billy Miranda, Gene Morris, "Sandman" Howard, Piano Red and Bertha Colbert, Frank Motley, and Bobby Hodge.

FLAME 011 (R)
Desperate Rock and Roll! Vol. 11

Twenty solid rockabilly and rock-and-roll tunes by The Ray-O-Vacs, Jack Jolly, The Bop Kats, Wild Bill Taylor, and Eddie Con Los Shades.

FLAME 012 (R)
Desperate Rock and Roll! Vol. 12

The desperados are Little Ernest Tucker, Tommy Martin and The XLs, Merv Benton, Ronnie Self, Charles Walker, Vince Maloy, and Bunker Hill.

FLAME 013 (R)
Desperate Rock and Roll! Vol. 13

Sixteen hot rockabilly numbers, mostly previously reissued, which feature blazin' guitar solos. "Crazy Little Woman" by The 3-Ds and Johnny McAdam's nice Spade release "Nine O'Clock Blues" are new to vinyl. Also includes Rod Willis, Tommy Danton, The Seniors, and Morty Marker.

FLAME 014 (R)

Desperate Rock and Roll! Vol. 14

Sixteen crazy, pop-chart losers by Dean Beard, The Creep, Conny and The Bell Hops, Ron and Jo, Lanny Duncan, The Rhythm Rocker, Kenny Lund, and Eddie Angel.

FLYRIGHT 21 (L)

Louisiana Swamp Pop

Twenty classics from Jay Miller's Louisiana studio. This is the cream of the swamp-pop crop. Doug Charles, Warren Storm, Katie Webster, Lazy Lester, and Guitar Gable and King Karl.

⚙ FLYRIGHT 27 (L)

Louisiana Rock and Roll

Twenty rockabilly, rock-and-roll, and R&B tunes recorded by Jay Miller back in the '50s and early '60s. Al Ferrier, Rocket Morgan, Tommy Strange, Johnny Jano, Honey Boy Allen, Katie Webster, and Slim Harpo are among the standouts.

FLYRIGHT 37 (L)

Talk to Me Daddy

A gaggle of groovy gals including Thelma (Dolly) Cooper, Camille Howard, Ella Johnson, blues vet Lil Armstrong, Agnes Riley, Dorothy Donegan, Millie Bosman, Fay Simmon, and Daisy Mae. Twenty-one outstanding cuts, with encapsulated notes by Tony Burke.

FLYRIGHT 516 (R)

Tag Along

Fifties Louisiana rockabilly and rock and roll from the Jay Miller archives, almost all previously unissued, by Honey Boy Allen, Joe Mayfield, Rockey Morgan, Warren Storm, Pee Wee Trahan, and Wonder Boy Travis.

FLYRIGHT 554 (R)

Boppin' It

Previously unissued rockabilly recorded by Jay Miller, including tracks by Edwin Babin, Johnny Bass, Allan Broussard, Al Ferrier, Johnny Jano, Frankie Lowery, Tommy Strange, and Pee Wee Trahan.

FLYRIGHT 557 (R)

Bayou Boogie

Rare, unissued rockabilly and rockin' country sides, along with a few straight country recordings by Johnny Bass, Ronald Bezette, Alex Broussard, Don Ray Coates, Benny Fruge, Joey Gils, Mack Hamilton, Bill Ray, Smokey Stower, Al Terry, Pee Wee Trahan, and P.V. Whitewing.

FLYRIGHT 598 (R)

Rock and Roll Beat

Fourteen rockers produced by Jay Miller, ten previously unreleased, featuring Johnny Winter's first band (The Coastaleers), and Frankie Lowrey, Rick

Johnson, Tony Perreau, Arnold Broussard, Peto Marlow, Guitar Jeff, Erwin Babin, and Ken Lindsey.

FLYRIGHT 616 (R)

Louisiana High School Hop

Fourteen cuts, primarily unreleased or alternate takes, from the Jay Miller vaults. The emphasis is on mid-tempo swamp pop, with some interesting exceptions. Johnny Jano turns in a rockabilly raver with "Havin' a Whole Lot of Fun," and The Tune Tones cook up sort of a zydeco-billy gumbo on "Won't Somebody Love Me." Also includes Classie Ballou, The Gaynotes, The Dukes of Rhythm, Jerry Starr, and Henry Clement.

GAL 201 (R)

Cough Syrup for Elvis Impersonators

Another one of those collections of wacky, nutty tunes interspersed with the usual (or unusual) madness, like advertisements for "Chicken Doodee" and "Motion Lotion" and bits on mass murderers and striptease ministers. Highpoint is Dr. Cough's unintentionally funny anti-drug speech, "Pot Party," accompanied by a cool jazz score. Other "thought-provoking" cuts by Mickey Lee Lane, Al Hendrix, Mad Jack, Andre Williams, Groundhog Richardson, Charlie Feathers, and The Tune Rockers.

⚙ GLOBAL VILLAGE 2001 (C)

Flying Rock: South African Rock and Roll, 1950-1962

Absolutely terrific and fascinating collection of 16 ultra-rare, South African, rock-and-roll 78s recorded by black groups (with a possible wild Boer or two). An amazing amalgam of hillbilly, blues, R&B, rock and roll, and Latin music blended with local traditions. The basic rockin' beat is solidly laid down, a Zulu musical sensibility is added, and then the lyrics are changed and languages mixed together. Includes King's Brothers, The Bogard Brothers, Benoni Rocket, and The Pretty Dolls.

GMG 3 (R)

Madness Invasion, Vol. 3

Sixteen "classics" from the '50s and '60s that you won't want to miss (though the best have been around on other compilations before). (I Was a) Teenage Creature (Lord Luther)/The Creature (from Outer Space) (The Jay-Hawks)/Bop Diddlie in the Jungle (Tommy King and The Starliters)/Double Mirror Wrap Around Shades (Andy and The Manhattans)/Loud Mufflers (Robert Williams)/I Was a Teenage Cave Man (Randy Luck)/Speed Queen (The In Crowd).

GMG 400 (R)

The Madness Invasion

Sixteen extremely weird ones. Nina-kocka-nina (The Dinks)/Like Thunder (The Rialtos)/The Three Little Pigniks (The Caps)/The Vampire (Archie King)/50

Megatons (Sonny Russell)/There's a Fungus Among Us (Hugh Barrett and The Victors).

GMG 75030 (R)

Madness Invasion, Vol. 2

Sixteen monster tunes, beatnik ravings, and utter nonsense! Jerry Neal's "Hate Rabbits" is the highlight with guitar and weird mutterings by Eddie Cochran. Other great tracks include: Billy Taylor's "Wombie Zombie"; The Statesmen's "Roo-Buh-Doo-Buh-Doo"; The Crestone's classic "She's a Bad Motorcycle"; and Kip Tyler's "Rumbler Rock."

GMG 75031 (R)

Swing for a Crime

Instrumentals that sound like they could have been theme music for '50s cop shows or juvenile delinquent and beatnik movies. Real jazzmen like Barney Kessel, Art Van Damre, and Cozy Cole are joined by schlock-meister Lex Baxter, Ric Gary, and even James Brown and The Fabulous Flames in disguise as Nat Kendrick and The Swans. Highlights are The Viscounts's "Harlem Nocturne" and The Vikings's "Nicotene."

GNP CRESCENDO 2152 (RCL)

Bustin' Surfboards

Fourteen rockin' instrumentals, mostly from the early-to-mid-'60s, along with a couple from the '70s and '80s by some of the legends of surf music. Notes by Jim Pewter. Includes The Beach Boys, The Challengers, Dick Dale, Bobby Fuller, The Gamblers, The Lively Ones, The Marketts, Jim Messina and the Jesters, Jack Nitzsche, Neil Norman, The Rockin' Rebels, The Surf Raiders, The Tornadoes, and Ritchie Valens.

HEE HEE HEE (R)

I Was a Teenage Brain Surgeon!

Seventeen crypt kickers, including two different tunes claiming the rights as the title tune, one by Eddie Davis and the other by Jack the Ripper. You decide which one tickles your brain cells! High camp by The Emersons, Tony Carr, The Raiders, The Vogues, Bobby Please, The Brassets, and Round Robin. If you're not already reaching for your checkbook when you see a collection with a title like this, then you're beyond my help.

HI (UK) 101 (L)

The Hi Records Story

Twenty-four cuts spanning the entire history and stylistic range of Hi Records, beginning with the early '60s instrumental sounds of Bill Black and Ace Cannon, and ending with the smooth soul of O.V. Wright in 1977. Along the way we hear from rocker Gene Simmons, Charlie Rich, label founder Willie Mitchell, stars Ann Peebles and Al Green, soul veterans Otis Clay and Syl Johnson, and relatively obscure acts like

Jean Plum, Quiet Elegance, Jerry Jaye, and Murray Kellum.

HI (UK) 434 (R)

Hi Records: The Early Years

Although today Hi Records is associated with Memphis soul, the label began its life recording rockabilly, country pop, and straight pop. These 29 tunes recorded between 1957-1964 focus on this aspect of the label's activities, including the label's debut, Carl McVoy's "Tootsie," through hits by Bill Black's Combo ("Smokie, Pt. 2"), Ace Cannon's "Tuff," and Jumpin' Gene Simmon's smash hit "Haunted House." Also includes Teddy Redell, Tommy Tucker, Bill Reeder, Jay B. Lloyd, Kimball Coburn, and The Charmettes.

HI (UK) 442 (R)

Hi Records: The Early Years, Vol. 2

Two-LP set of late '50s through mid-'60s rockabilly and country-flavored material. Favorites include four previously unissued tunes by the ill-fated Tommy Tucker, and an entire side of great tracks by Jerry Jaye. Sadly, the material from Bill Black's Combo focuses on their campy instrumentals that recall the soundtracks of early '60s B-movies.

HOBO BOP 1180 (R)

Hobo Bop

Twenty fine '50s rockabilly and rock songs about trains by Sonny Anderson, H. Davis, Jimmy Farmer, Lloyd George, Leon James, Stan Johnson, Lonnie Nye, Frank Lowery, Curley Money, Tommy Nelson, Gene Norman, Danny Reeves, Bob Riley, Ray Scott, Frankie Stewart, Norman Sullivan, Vernon Taylor, and Johnny Wallen.

HO-DAD 4002 (R)

Ho-Dad Hootenanny: Beer Blast '65!

Eighteen cuts of assorted '60s teenage craziness. Mix in equal parts rampaging hormones, bad attitude, and inebriation and you'll be ready to appreciate these gems by The Madmen, The Rangers, Them (not those Them), The Mysterians, and even a tune by The Sonics made for their loyal fan-club members.

HOLLOWBODY 12001 (L)

Wild Men Ride Wild Guitars!

Twenty Challenge-label rock and rockabilly tracks from 1958-1960, including a couple of unissued songs, some unissued demos, and a stereo version of Joe Maphis's "Water Baby Boogie." It also includes Big Al Downing's classic "Down on the Farm," plus tracks by Huleyn Duvall, George Weston, Dean Beard, and Kip Tyler. Fold-out booklet with detailed notes by rockabilly guru Colin Escott and some nice photos.

HOLLOWBODY 12002 (L)
Rockin' in the Farmhouse: Rockabilly, Vol. 2

Solid, 20-track collection of primo '50s era rockabilly from Roulette Records and George Goldner's Gone and Rama labels. Highlights include four early Johnny Rivers numbers, revealing that he was a fine rocker before he became a teen idol. Also includes five cuts (four unreleased) by The Rock-A-Teens, Jimmy Lloyd's "Rocket in My Pocket", Roc LaRue's "Baby Take Me Back," and Jimmy Bowen's "My Baby's Gone." Beaucoup rockin' guitars and even some fascinating studio chatter, along with a nice illustrated booklet by Billy Miller.

HOT ROD ASSOCIATION 1 (R)
Boss Drag '64

Eighteen, super-charged, nitro-burning numbers, mostly drawn from rare LPs. The selection is top-notch, with an ear to the hottest sounds avaialble. Hear the boss sounds of burning rubber, whining engines, and roaring exhaust pipes (not to mention crashing drums and churning guitars) on The Deuce Coupes's "Gear Masher," Jim Messina and The Jesters's "Suspense Run," The Vibrasonics's "Drag Race," The Kickstands's "Scrambler," and The Blasters's "Oil Burner."

HOT ROD ASSOCIATION 2 (R)
Surfin' Wild

Hot new surf compilation with 18 boss tunes. Highlight is "Ghost Guitars" by Baron Daemon and The Vampires, featuring mucho tremolo and one of those goofy Transylvanian-accented vocals. Don't miss the novelty surf tunes, including The Deadly Ones's "Creature in a Surfer's Lagoon," Mr. Gasser's "Phantom Surfer," and The Silly Surfers's "A Woodie on a Surfari." Other surfmaestros include the great Dave Meyers and The Surftones, Scott Engel, and The Frantics.

HYDRA 7702 (R)
Like Wow

Sixteen pieces of wild, wild rockabilly, highlighted by the extremely rare "Bertha Lou" b/w "'Til the Law Says Stop" by The Rock and Roll Trio, a 1955 demo cut at Sun studios, later issued on Surf. Also includes Tony Conn, Little Denny, Morty Marker, and some extremely wild unknown demos that make The Cramps sound like Kenny Rogers.

HYDRA 7703 (R)
Dance to the Bop

Eighteen rare rock, R&B, and jive tunes. The few recognizable names include Louis Prima's sax blower Sam Butera, Scott Engel (later of The Walker Brothers), The Bell Notes, and a pre-Diamonds Dave Sommerville. Collectors' note: A really rare Five Keys

single on Seg-Way released under Rudy West's name, "You're the One," is included.

HYDRA 7705 (R)
Teenage Dance Party

Eighteen rare teen jive tunes from the '50s. Highlights are Marlene Paula's "I Want to Spend Christmas with Elvis," Donna Dameron's "Big Love" (produced, written, and guest starring The Big Bopper), The Jodimars's rare "Shoo Sue" b/w "Story Telling Baby" done for President in 1957, and Gerry Granahan's (later of Dickie Doo and The Don'ts) "No Chemise Please."

HYDRA 7711 (R)
Teenage Dance Party, Vol. 2

Nice selection of 18 boppers and pop rockers by The Four Aces, The Rock Brothers, The Southerneers, John Fred, Clarence Garlow, Mike Pedicin, The Red Tops, and Jeri Lynn.

HYDRA 7714 (R)
Teenage Dance Party, Vol. 3

A more appropriate title would be "Adult Dance Party," because this album collects 18 heavily orchestrated examples of what the old folks deemed rock and roll. It's still loads of fun to listen to these rockin' chair rockers. Homer Esk was a member of Cliffie Stone's country band, but he shakes the hay out of his hair on "Please Please." Cab Calloway rocks it up good on "Chigger Chigger Wa Wa." Even Patty Andrews from The Andrews Sisters gets in the act doing a nice "Music Drives Me Crazy." Also includes Jack Hammer, Hank Penny, The Flairs, Johnny Angel, and Butch Stone. Roll back the carpets, lindy hoppers.

IMPACT 001 (R)
Stop, Look and Listen

Sixteen rare girl-group records originally on Laurie and related labels. Includes Les Girls, Julie and The Desires, Bernadette Carrol, The Delrons, The Cheese Cakes, Beverly Warren, The Four Pennies, The Chiffons, Marie Antoinette, The Jeans, The Charmers, The Summits, and Gloria Dennis.

INCREASE 1964 (L)
Cruisin' 1964

Mostly R&B cuts on this best-of-'64 collection, 12 songs alternating with radio jingles, commercials, and other radio broadcast tidbits. Harlem Shuffle/Nitty Gritty/Chapel of Love/It's All Right/Ain't It Funny.

INCREASE 1965 (L)
Cruisin' 1965

Ten chart-toppers from 1965, interspersed with genuine radio commercials and announcements for those who crave that "you-are-there" feeling. Wooly Bully/You've Lost That Lovin' Feelin'/The Birds and the Bees/It Ain't Me Babe/Eve of Destruction.

INCREASE 2000 (R)
Cruisin' 1955

Recreation of a radio show with "Jumpin'" George Oxford on KSAN, San Francisco. Commercials include Acme Home Modelers and Rogers Men's Store; acts include Ray Charles, Hank Ballard and The Midnighters, The Charms, Little Willie John, The Penguins, Chuck Berry, The Platters, Fats Domino, The Nutmegs, and Bill Haley.

INCREASE 2001 (R)
Cruisin' 1956

Recreates a radio show by Robin Seymour from WKMH, Dearborn, MI. Includes "The Robin Seymour Theme" and a Ford commercial, both by The Four Lads, and a Budweiser ad by The Crew Cuts, as well as cuts by Chuck Berry, The Teen Queens, The Mello Kings, Little Willie John, The Platters, Little Richard, The Cadets, Otis Williams, The Five Satins, and Bill Doggett.

INCREASE 2002 (R)
Cruisin' 1957

Recreates the Joe Niagra Show from WIBG, Philadelphia, including Ford and Muntz TV commercials and discs by Jimmy Dorsey, The Coasters, Chuck Berry, Buddy Knox, The Spaniels, The Diamonds, Larry Williams, The Five Satins, Jimmie Rodgers, and Bill Justis.

INCREASE 2003 (R)
Cruisin' 1958

Jack Carney from WIL, St. Louis spins hot platters by Danny and The Juniors, The Champs, Jimmie Rodgers, Little Richard, The Coasters, Jimmy Clanton, Bobby Freeman, Bobby Day, The Silhouettes, and Duane Eddy, interspersed with Gilette, Old Spice, Chevy, and Mercury commercials.

INCREASE 2004 (R)
Cruisin' 1959

Legendary DJ Hunter Hancock's show from KGFJ, Los Angeles. Includes ads for Robert Hall, Champion Spark Plugs, and the *Saturday Evening Post*, along with hits by The Olympics, Big Jay McNeely, The Coasters, Chuck Berry, Dinah Washington, The Crests, Lloyd Price, Brook Benton, Phil Philips, and Wilbert Harrison.

INCREASE 2005 (R)
Cruisin' 1960

Wildman Dick Biondi from WKBW, Buffalo, hosts this show, with songs by Mark Dining, The Drifters, Jack Scott, Hank Ballard and The Midnighters, Ray Peterson, The Hollywood Argyles, Maurice Williams and The Zodiacs, Toni Fisher, Duane Eddy, and Buster Brown. Also includes Budweiser, Genesee Beer, L&M, and Wardynski Sausage ads.

INCREASE 2006 (R)
Cruisin' 1961

Radio show hosted by the great Arnie "Woo Woo" Ginsberg from WMEX, Boston. Ads include Adventure Car Hop (featuring the Ginsburger), and Pall Mall Cigarettes. "The Arnie Ginsburg Theme" is performed by both Freddie Cannon and The 3-Ds. Also includes hits by The Marcels, The Jive Five, Chuck Berry, Clarence "Frogman" Henry, Sheb Wooley, Bobby Lewis, Del Shannon, The Regents, Lee Dorsey, and Freddie King.

INSTANT 5040 (L)
Rockabilly Rhythm: The Sun Story, Vol. 2

Twenty-nine hot, boppin' hits from Sun Records by Carl Perkins, Jerry Lee Lewis, Johnny Cash, Billy Riley, Roy Orbison, Carl Mann, Warren Smith, and Bill Justis.

INSTANT 5052 (L)
Girls on Top: A Collection of Girlie Group Smash Hits

Surprisingly enough, this budget-priced, 17-song CD is an almost perfect selection of girl-group tunes, including "Mr. Lee" by The Bobbettes, "Will You Still Love Me Tomorrow" and "Dedicated to the One I Love" by The Shirelles, "He's So Fine" by The Chiffons, and "Da Doo Ron Ron" by The Crystals. Only The Ronettes are missing, and a couple of the tracks sound like later remakes. Despite the fact that the Cedar system was used to remaster these babies, the sound is kinda funky.

INSTANT 5053 (L)
Surf's Up

This budget-priced CD isn't aimed at the collector's market, but it does provide a nice selection of surfin' tunes for penny-pinching party animals. Ten hot hits by The Beach Boys and Jan and Dean, along with such classics as "Surfin' Bird" by The Trashmen, "Pipeline" by The Chantays, "New York's a Lonely Town" by The Tradewinds, and "Little Honda" by the Hondells.

JIN 9013 (R)
Golden Dozen, Vol. 3

Reissues from the Jin, Sun, SSS, Plantation, and Phillips International labels by Jeannie C. Riley, Rod Bernard, Jerry Lee Lewis, Clint West, Johnny Cash, Tommy McLain, Johnny Allen, Charlie Rich, John Wesley Ryles, and Rufus Jagneaux.

JIVIN' 182 (R)
14 Great All-time Jivers, Vol. 1

Rare '50s rockers by Jim Alley and the Alley Cats, The Bay Bops, Jimmy Breedlove, Ned Coster, Pat Flowers, Gary Hodge, Chuck Miller, Orlie and the Saints, Hal

Page, The Royal Jokers, Jim Shaw, Ruckus Tyler, and Jim Wilson.

JIVIN' 183 (R)

14 Great All-time Jivers, Vol. 2

Lillian Briggs, The Carroll Brothers, Dorothy Collins, The Creel Sisters, Ravon Darnell, The Four Mints, Rudy Greene, Jimmy Kelly and The Rock-A-Beats, Chuck Miller, Roy Milton, and Jimmy Thompson.

JIVIN' 184 (R)

14 Great All-time Jivers, Vol. 3

Wynona Carr, Dorothy Collins, The Evans Sisters, The Lancers, Snooky Lanson, The Palais Royals, The Pitch Pipes, Real George, Mike Sarge and The Sargents, Ray Scott, The Skee Brothers, and Billy Williams.

JIVIN' 185 (R)

14 Great All-time Jivers, Vol. 4

Lillian Briggs, Jay Brinkley, Dorothy Collins, The Four Tophatters, The Gaylords, The Goofers, B.B. King, Bunny Paul, Teddy Randazzo, The Schooners, The Treniers, and Millie Vernon.

JIVIN' 186 (R)

Jive Jive Jive, Vol. 1

Fourteen obscurities by Joe Barone, Bob Braun, Jo Ann Campbell, Lilyan Carol, Lee Chandler, Jeff Daniels, Mari Jones, Ronnie Love, Jimmy Maddin, Tony Nicholas and The Hazeltones, Al Pittman, Don Rogers and Ann Tanner, and The Tyrones.

JIVIN' 187 (R)

Jive Jive Jive, Vol. 2

Fourteen cuts by Eileen Barton, The Bluenotes, Lillian Briggs, Lee Chandler, The Danleers, The Dawn Breakers, Chuck Dean, Rusty Draper, Steve Drexell, The Gaylords, Charles Gully, The Skyliners, and The Wailers.

JIVIN' 188 (R)

Jive Jive Jive, Vol. 3

Twelve cuts by Al Alberts, Sandra Alfred, Little Marie Allen, Pearl Bailey, Lillian Briggs, Johnny Carson, The Strangeloves, Tom Swift, Vera and The Three Jays, Sonny Wilson, and Nat Wright.

JIVIN' 189 (R)

Jive Jive Jive, Vol. 4

Fourteen jivers, mostly from the pop side of the charts, by Bill Carey, Eddie Cole, Don Cornell, The Four Tunes, Buddy Greco, Roy Hamilton, The Lancers, The Prophets, The School Belles, Jack Teagarden, Jon Thomas, and Titus Turner.

JIVIN' 190 (R)

Jive Jive Jive, Vol. 5

Molly Bee, The Belairs, Jimmy Breedlove, The De Castro Sisters, Zig Dillon, Helen Grayco, Dick Lory,

Johnny Maddox, The Modernaires, Buddy Morrow, and Billy Williams.

JIVIN' 191 (R)

Jive Jive Jive, Vol. 6

Brook Benton, Lillian Briggs, The Capitols, Scott Engel, Paul Gallis, Barbara Green, Sandra Grimms, Dick Hyman, Louis Jordan, and Arthur Prysock.

JIVIN' 192 (R)

Jive Jive Jive, Vol. 7

The Beverly Sisters, Beverly Bluff, The Bobettes, Lola Dee, The Field Brothers, Jim Francis, The Gainors, The Jaye Sisters, Pat Kelly, The King Brothers, Jackie Lee, Lorry Raine, and The Red Caps.

JIVIN' 193 (R)

Jive Jive Jive, Vol. 8

Annette, Honeyboy Bryant, Dea Doll, Joe Gene, Scatman Crothers, Marie Knight, Sabby Lewis, The Manin Brothers, Clarence Samuels, Sandy Shaw, Olie Sheppard, The Staffords, and Jimmy Thomason.

JIVIN' KING 1287 (R)

The Rockin' Jivin'

One of the better jive compilations, thanks to the inclusion of such gems as Amos Milburn's "Chicken Shack Boogie," Louis Jordan's "Bills," Louis Prima's wild, wild "I Wanna Be Like You," and a fun "Rock 'n' Rollin' Santa Claus" by Benny Lee. Also includes Rodney Scott, Mike Pedicin, The Elchords, and The Boptones.

JUKEBOX SATURDAY NIGHT 1005 (R)

Rock and Roll Fever, Vol. IV

Fourteen primarily lovey-dovey, soda-pop, teen-rock tracks. Includes Boyd Ingram, Freddy North, Dick Lory, Mike Leeds, Mel Albert, and Paul Evans.

JUKEBOX SATURDAY NIGHT 1006 (R)

Rock and Roll Fever, Vol. V

Rockin' and pop-rock compilation with Dean Beard, Carl Perkins, Dave Burgess, Barry Mann, Vince Everett, Billy Cee, Veline Hackert, and Frank Pizani.

JUKEBOX SATURDAY NIGHT 1007 (R)

Rock and Roll Fever, Vol. VI

Fourteen pop rockers by George Walsh, Johnny Burnette, Millie Vernon, Kenny Lozan, The Swingin' Conners, Paul Hampton, and Buzz Clifford.

KEY 1590 (R)

Ten Long Fingers

Excellent collection of 20 cuts of '50s rock and roll featuring hot piano work. Includes Arlin and Earl, Donnie Bowshire, Mike Cain, Everett Carpenter, The Catalinas, Jimmy Dee, Bobby Denton, Don Eee, Mickey Gilley, Jimmy Gone, The Hiliters, Tommy Hudson, Ronnie Keenan, Bob Miller, Groovey Joe

Poovey, The Rave Ons, Pat Richmond, Al Sims, and Don Wayne.

KRAZY KAT 819 (R)
Have Yourself a Ball
Fourteen sides from the Gotham label's rock-and-roll subsidiary, 20th Century. Most of the tunes are in a Bill Haley-ish rockaphilly jive style featuring brass sections, sax solos, and forced-sounding, "teenaged" lyrics. Highlights are the five earliest Charlie Gracie sides backed by The Wildcats, including Charlie's great guitar solos. Also features Bobby Boyd's Jazz Bombers, The Playboys, Don Haven and The Hi-Fis (which may also be The Playboys), The Nutones, and The Mike Pedicin Quintet, including his hit cover of "Shake a Hand."

KRAZY KAT 826 (R)
Be Bop Boogie
Second volume of rock and roll from the Gotham vaults, mostly tracks that owner Ivin Ballen bought for possible release. Features Don Hager and The Hot Tots, Rockin' Ronnie, The Acorns, Bobby Green and The Sportsmen, Dudley Callicutt and The Go Boys, and The Derocher Sisters.

LAURIE (JAPAN) 22057 (L)
Dream Girls: Gems of Girl Group Sound
Twenty-three hits and rarities from the early '60s by The Chiffons, Bernadette Caroo, Cathy Carr, The Charmers, Dawn, Gloria Dennis, The Summits, Juanita Nixon, and Les Girls.

LAURIE (JAPAN) 22058 (L)
Laurie Rare Masters, Vol. 1: Carnival Girl
Eighteen teen-pop tracks by Frank Cherval, The Tokens, The Mystics, The Del-Satins, Carlo, The Demilles, Lenny Coleman, Jimmy Curtiss and The Regents, and Gene Bua.

LAURIE (JAPAN) 22059 (L)
Laurie Rare Masters, Vol. 2: Geraldine
Eighteen-track collection, though not all are rarities, by Boots Walker, The Passions, Randy and The Rainbows, The Jarmels, Kenny Chandler, Carlo, The Motions, Dean and Jean, The Five Discs, and The Teardrops.

LEGEND 1002 (R)
Rock It!
Fourteen rare rockabilly cuts by Carl Cherry, Buddy Howard, Linda Burnette, The Stripes, J. Mikel and The Hepcats, Junior Dean, and Little Joey Farr.

LEGEND 1003 (R)
Grand Daddys Rockin', Vol. 2
Pricey but essential compilation of great rockabilly tunes, most never before on any LP. Sixteen tracks by Kenny Brown, Buck Trail, Joe Tate, Lennie Lacour, Billy Adams, and Ebe Sneezer.

LEGRAND 1000 (R)
Rock's World Revolution
Early '60s hits produced by Frank Guida by Gary "U.S." Bonds, Gregory Cafone, Daddy G and The Church Street Five, Tommy Facenda, Lenis Guess, Frank Guida, and Jimmy Soul.

LIBERTY (JAPAN) 5876 (L)
Golden Summer, Vol. 1
Twenty-two tracks by The Beach Boys, The Ventures, Jan and Dean, The Markettes, Frankie Avalon, The Surfaris, The Trashmen, The Tradewinds, and Annette Funicello.

LIBERTY (JAPAN) 5877 (L)
Golden Summer, Vol. 2
Twenty-seven tracks, including some hot rodders, by The Beach Boys, The California Suns, The Powder Puffs, The Honeys, The Survivors, The Zip-Codes, Jill Gibson, Gary Lewis, Jan and Dean, The Ventures, The Eliminators, The Hornetts, and The Fantastic Baggys.

LIBERTY (JAPAN) 5878 (L)
Golden Summer, Vol. 3
Twenty-six tracks by The Beach Boys, The Ventures, Jan and Dean, The Rally Packs, Shutdown Douglas, The Powder Puffs, The Fantastic Baggys, The Legendary Masked Surfers, The Ho-Dads, The Cheers, Sandy Nelson, and Glen Campbell.

⊕ LINK 1 (R)
Strummin' Mental, Vol. 1
⊕ LINK 2 (R)
Strummin' Mental, Vol. 2
⊕ LINK 3 (R)
Strummin' Mental, Vol. 3
⊕ LINK 4 (R)
Strummin' Mental, Vol. 4
⊕ LINK 5 (R)
Strummin' Mental, Vol. 5
Five volumes of the wildest instrumentals ever assembled. The spirit of Link Wray pervades these records, not only in the label name, but also in the cover photos, though he's not in the grooves. Each set has 20 (well, Vol. 1 has 19) raw, exciting, garage-rock instrumentals recorded between 1957-1965. This is all, and I mean ALL, primo, poundin', rock-and-roll guitar and drums (and some wailin' sax), the cream of the crop, mostly from rare and obscure groups, along

with the occasional better-known names. Absolutely essential.

LIVE GOLD 6000006 (RL)

The Real Buddy Holly Story

Mostly tribute songs and interviews. The only tracks actually featuring Buddy are two 20-second jingles for radio station KLLL to the tune of "Everyday," and three familiar songs ("Well All Right," "You're So Square," and "Heartbeat") with backups overdubbed by The Picks in 1984. Includes tributes by Familee, The Picks, The Pilot, and The Rubettes. Interviews are conducted by Red Robinson, Alan Freed, and Dale Lowery, and some of them are new to this release. An interesting release, if not quite what it appears to be.

LIVE GOLD 1000010/11 (L)

To Elvis, with Love:
40 Rare Elvis Presley Tributes

LIVE GOLD 40004/5 (L)

Elvis Mania:
52 Elvis Novelty and Tribute Songs

Two double-CD sets featuring a total of 92 Elvis novelty and tribute songs by Roy Hall, Otto Bash, Lalo Guerrero, Janis Martin, Peter De Bree and The Wanderers, The Holly Twins, Genee Harris, Steve Schickel, The Greats, Bill Parsons, Dodie Stevens, LaVern Baker, Betty Riley, Gary Lewis and The Playboys, and Johnny Wakelin.

MACOLA 6002 (R)

East Side Story, Vol. 2

Ten, prime, low-rider tunes by the original artists! When We Get Married/Catch You on the Rebound/ Angel Baby/Where Lovers Go/For Your Precious Love/ Who Do You Love.

MAGNUM FORCE 034 (L)

Hillbilly Rock:
20 Rare Tracks from the Hickory Vault

Twenty tunes, more in a hillbilly vein than rock, recorded in the '50s for Wesley Rose's Hickory label, with backup by those great Nashville cats Floyd Cramer, Hank Garland, Chet Atkins, Grady Martin, and Harold Bradley. Includes Al Terry, Rusty and Doug, Joe Melson, Bill Carlisle, Melvin Endsley, and Wiley Barkdull.

MAGNUM FORCE 043 (R)

Red Hot Rockabilly 2

A dozen raw rockers by eight artists, with Eddie Bond's "One Way Ticket" and "Tore Up" and Vern Pullens's "Rock on Mabel" from the '70s, the rest cool '50s recordings by Jerry Irby, Ray Doggett, Tony Snider, Larry Brinkley, Kenny Parchman, and Jack Earls.

MAGNUM FORCE 048 (R)

The Rockin' '50s

Sixteen ravers from the Capitol Records vaults by Tommy Sands, Skeets McDonald, Gene Vincent, Wanda Jackson, The Jordanaires, Bob Luman, Del Reeves, and Hank Thompson.

MAGNUM FORCE 055 (R)

Red Hot Rockabilly 3

A dozen, fine, old and new selections. Most of the '50s recordings are great tunes by unknowns including Ray Doggett, William Pennix, and Jimmy Craig (with backing by The Fireballs). These are accompanied by '70s recordings by Vern Pullens and Eddie Bond.

MAGNUM FORCE 056 (R)

Red Hot Rockabilly 4

Fine LP of '50s-'70s rockabilly, highlighted by Barbara Pittman's 1954 Sun demo of "I'll Never Let You Go" and some wild Johnny Powers sides from 1958. Also includes vintage recordings by Jack Earls, Don Rader, Ray Doggett, and Tony Snyder, and '70s sides by Eddie Bond and Vern Pullens.

MAGNUM FORCE 069 (RL)

Red Hot Rockabilly 7

Sixteen rockin' tracks from Dwain Bell, Gene Sisco, Joyce Green, The Carpenter Brothers, Paul Chaplin, and The Van Brothers.

MAGNUM FORCE 075 (L)

Rock and Roll Dance Party

Twenty-seven live cuts drawn from Alan Freed's package tours by The Johnny Burnette Trio, Chuck Berry, Bill Haley, Clyde McPhatter, Gene Vincent, Frankie Lymon, The Platters, Etta James, LaVern Baker, The Penguins, The Jacks, The Flairs, and The Drifters. A pleasant trip down memory lane, if you can take the almost nonstop screaming!

MAGNUM FORCE 082 (L)

Red Hot Rockabilly 8 (Best Of)

Twenty-five cuts from the old vinyl volumes 2, 3, and 4.

MAGNUM FORCE 1.058 (R)

Live at The Star Club

Hamburg's Star Club was one of the best showcases of British beat music in the '60s. On Feb. 8, 1980, the Club was reopened with two all-star shows featuring some of the pioneering rockers who originally played the club in the early '60s, some coming out of retirement to perform. Includes Screamin' Lord Sutch, Tony Sheridan, Wee Willy Harris, Johnny and The Hurricanes, Lee Curtis, Beryl Marsden, Cliff Bennett, and Rock Island Line.

MCGARRETT 5-0 (R)
Waikiki Surf Battle
Welcome reissue of a boss surf-band competition held at the Waikiki Shell in Hawaii in 1963-1964 culled from three LPs released at the time on the Sounds of Hawaii and Star labels. Even at this early date, the bands all had the wet, pounding sound down to a tee! A big 18 cuts by The Spiedels, The Originals, The Vaqueros, The Royal Malads, The Renegades, and The Statics.

MERCURY (JAPAN) 454 (L)
Girl Girl Girl
Beautiful-sounding, 20-track compilation, half in real stereo, of '60s Mercury girl singers and groups. Better-known acts include Dusty Springfield, Lesley Gore, and The Angels, with more obscure performers like The Honey Bees, Judy Thomas, The Pixies Three, The Secrets, and Cathy Carroll.

MR. MANICOTTI 328 (R)
The Big Itch
A feathers-flyin' salute to the greatest rock-and-roll record ever: "Surfin' Bird" by The Trashmen. Bird-esque numbers include "Toolie Froolie" by Bobby Lee Trammell, "Olds-Mo-William" by Gregory Dee and The Avantis (an R&B bird-dance record), "Nina Koka Nina" by The Dinks, and "Bird '65," in which The Trashmen rip off themselves! Also includes Freddy and The Ravens, The Deacons, Arch Hall, Jr., and Glenn Mooney and The Ferraris.

MR. MANICOTTI 329 (R)
Diggin' Out
Eighteen rare, small-label surfing instrumentals by sundry reverb-crankin' kahunas from California to Rochester, NY. Most unusual surf-band award goes to The Goldtones from Riverside, CA, who feature Glenn Campbell (no, not that one) on wild steel-guitar! Their selection, "Gutterball," is also an homage to bowling, so it's double cool. More standard surf fare comes from The Rockin' Shadows, The Gestics, and The Lonely Ones. I'm stoked.

MR. MANICOTTI 340 (R)
A Memorial to Joe E. Ross
Eighteen horrendous cuts in loving tribute to Joe E. Ross, who played Gunther Toody on *Car 54*, and was famous for his fine "singing" on his signature tune, "Ooh Ooh." When you see song titles like "Fried Chicken Baby" and "Tamales and Rock 'n' Roll," you know you've got something, er, special. Other stinkers are performed by The Rocky-Fellers, Jimmy Knight, Tommy Hancock, The Metropolitans, and George Ross and The Red Tops.

MR. MANICOTTI 341 (R)
The Big Itch Three
Amazing collection of some of the nuttiest records you'll ever hear, all encased in an eyepoppin' cover featuring wrestling photos from the '50s. Who can forget these dance crazes: Glenn and Christy's "Wombat Twist," Gary Shelton's "The Trance," or "The Temper Tantrum" by The Warlocks? And, if these get you limbered up enough, you can move on to "The Weasel," the "Mexican Stretch," the "Graveyard Cha Cha," the "Moon Step Twist," and the "Cave Man Hop."

MR. MANICOTTI 342 (R)
Concussion!!!
Eighteen raw, wailin' instrumentals from the '60s by groups that ate Link Wray 45s for breakfast. Rare stuff from small labels like Doll, Reo, Cool, and Conbie, along with some ultra-rare acetates like the legendary "Nautiloid Reef" b/w "Nautiloid Surf" by The Downbeats, "Yukkum Yukkum" by Punk Carson and The Chucklers, "Look Out" by The Bop-Kats, and "Heart Attack" by Jack and The Rippers. Full speed, pedal-to-the-metal rock and roll at its best!

MSI (JAPAN) 10037 (L)
Cucamonga Years:
The Early Works of Frank Zappa
Long before the Mothers of Invention unleashed their madness on an unsuspecting rock audience, Frank Zappa was busily creating some pretty bizarre music. These 13 tracks give an overview of his inspired output in doo-wop, R&B, and instrumental styles. The most famous of these early recordings is The Penguins's "Memories of El Monte," a song written by Zappa. Also includes R&B by Baby Ray and The Ferns, "monster" rock by Bob Guy, and two boss instrumentals by The Hollywood Persuaders, who also did the classic "Drums a-Go-Go" (unfortunately not included).

NO HIT 003 (R)
Desperate Dallas Demos
Sixteen mid-'50s rockabilly and rock-and-roll thumpers from the ultra-cool Dallas scene. All but three cuts are scratchy, half-out-of-tune demos capturing the true teenage rockin' spirit. Includes Ronnie Dawson, Gene Rambo and The Flames, Carl Canida, Casper and The Ghost, The Starcombo, and The Catalinas. With liner notes by Billy Miller, lots of photos, and a dozen repros of "Big D Jamboree" adverts (the lineups will make you drool).

OLDE 003 (R)
Ye Olde Jive Master, Vol. 3
Sixteen examples of the stuff they call jive, rock and roll's well-mannered cousin, the kind of music Dobie Gillis probably dug. The coolest tune is Sax Kari's

"Disc Jockey Jamboree," where Kari spins a jive-talkin' rap, droppin' the names of most of the big rock jocks of the day like "Moondog" Freed, Poppa Stoppa, Symphony Sid, Big Daddy Sears, and Dewey Phillips, just to name a few! The rest of the cuts are in a Bill Haley or Crewcuts style featuring Mike Pedicin, The Tyrones, The Dawnbreakers, and Larry Ragon.

ORB 1001 (R)
Universe Rocketin'
Ultra-cool production with a great cover and 22 hot tunes dealing with one of rockabilly's favorite subjects: outer space. A host of unknowns work up some witty variations on this theme: "Orbit Twist," "Rock Old Sputnick," "The Martian Band," "Light My Rockets," and "Creature from Outer Space." Blast off cats!

ORIGINAL SOUND 8881 (L)
Oldies but Goodies: 21 Number 1 Hits
Mixture of rock, soul, and R&B smash hits. Classic tunes by Dion, The Shirelles, Bobby Lewis, The Everly Brothers, Jerry Lee Lewis, Del Shannon, Jerry Butler, The Dixie Cups, and Johnnie Taylor. Generous, but typical oldies selection, no surprises (except the inclusion of "Do the Hustle"!).

PELVIS 1 (R)
Big Beautiful Guitars
Fast and raw rockabilly by unknown artists, plus a great trashy cover. Includes The Jet Tones, Billy Lanthrem, The Rockin' Hi-Lows, Bob Buster, and Harry Carter.

PLANET 01 (R)
Monster a Go Go!: Teen Trash from Psychedelic Tokyo, 1966-1969

PLANET 02 (R)
Big Lizard Stomp!

PLANET 03 (R)
Slitherama!
Three volumes, beautifully presented in red, green, and yellow vinyl, with gorgeous "Destroy All Monsters" covers. About half the tunes are originals, and, even when these far-out Japanese bands do cover versions, the interpretations are usually fresh and interesting. If you like tough guitar with a psychedelic edge, you'll love The Beavers, The Spiders, The Mops, The Bunnys, and The Golden Cups. How do you say "mindblowing" in Japanese?

REGENCY 101 (R)
20 Rock and Roll High School Rarities, Vol. 1
Twenty pop-rock tracks from the '50s. A highlight is "Suspeto," the Italian version of Terry Stafford's "Suspicion." Also includes long-in-the-tooth R&B queens Vareta Dillard and Savannah Churchill, chasing the teen buck; popabilly greats Conway Twitty, Tommy Sands, and Ersel Hickey; and teen gods Bobby Darin, Connie Stevens, Bobby Curtola, and Buzz Clifford.

REGENCY 102 (R)
20 Rock and Roll High School Rarities, Vol. 2
Twenty more freshly popped corn kernels from the '50s. Hear Donna Douglas sing "All the Other Girls" (say, wasn't that the gal who played Ellie Mae on *The Beverly Hillbillies*?), plus Al Saxon, Roy Lee, Jerry Angelo, Ricky Stevens, and Tim Connor.

RHINO 70025 (C)
Nuggets: The Hits, Vol. 1

RHINO 70033 (C)
Nuggets, Vol. 9: Acid Rock
Late '60s psychedelic and garage-rock hits. Only two volumes are available on cassette, but selections from the entire series is available on CD (Rhino 75892, 75777, 75754).

RHINO 70087 (CL)
Summer and Sun
Eighteen hot summer hits by Mungo Jerry, The Lovin' Spoonful, Eddie Cochran, Annette Funicello, The Beach Boys, Lesley Gore, and Billy Stewart. But how did The Ramones, Blondie, and War get on here?

RHINO 70089 (CL)
Surfin' Hits:
The Ultimate Surf Compilation
Eighteen board-waxers by Dick Dale, The Beach Boys, Jan and Dean, The Surfaris, The Trashmen, and The Belairs.

RHINO 70136 (C)
Frat Rock! The Greatest Rock and Roll Party Tunes of All
A dozen loud, simple, moronic, three-chord wonders. Not only did these tunes launch a million parties, but the songs were so easy, any idiot could play them, so they also launched a million bands. Series continues on Rhino 70183/84 and 70190 on cassette, and 75778, 75772, and 70732 on CD. Louie Louis (The Kingsmen)/Wooly Bully (Sam the Sham and The Pharaohs)/Twist and Shout (The Isley Brothers)/Wild Thing (The Troggs)/Hang on Sloopy (The McCoys)/Wipe Out (The Surfaris).

RHINO 70179 (C)
Best of the Girl Groups
Fourteen by The Shangri-Las, The Shirelles, The Chiffons, The Jaynettes, Betty Everett, and Claudine Clark.

RHINO 70180 (C)
Best of The Teen Idols
Get out the Brylcreem, run on down to the malt shop, and dig these discs by Bobby Vee, Fabian, Paul Anka, Frankie Avalon, Del Shannon, and Tab Hunter.

RHINO 70183 (C)
Frat Rock, Vol. II
Vol. 1 was essential three-chord boomers, but this set stretches the definition a bit to include some favorite East LA Chicano rock in honor of the film *La Bamba.*

RHINO 70184 (C)
Frat Rock, Vol. III
Rhino's really stretching the "Frat Rock" tag to include stuff like Ray Charles's "What'd I Say" and The Midniter's "Whittier Blvd." Also includes Chuck Berry, James and Bobby Purify, The Beach Boys, Cannibal and The Headhunters, The Guess Who, and The Trashmen.

RHINO 70187 (CL)
Golden Throats:
The Great Celebrity Sing-Off!
Some of the worst and funniest recordings of all time by Hollywood celebrities desparately trying to cash in by crossing over to the rock-and-roll market. Not only does Capt. Kirk (aka William Shatner) overact his way through a hilarious "Lucy in the Sky with Diamonds" and "Mr. Tamborine Man," but Mr. Spock (Leonard Nimoy) souls it up on "Proud Mary" and "If I Had a Hammer." And that's just the beginning! How about Sebastian "Mr. French" Cabot reciting "It Ain't Me Babe" and "Like a Rolling Stone," or Eddie "Oliver" Albert tunelessly wading through "Blowin' in the Wind," Joel Grey giving that old Broadway try to Cream's "White Room," or Jack Webb doing his best Joe Friday monologue on "Try a Little Tenderness." Volume 2 is Rhino 71007.

RHINO 70190 (C)
Frat Rock, Vol. IV
More party time from the good folks at Rhino.

RHINO 70192 (CL)
Christmas Classics
Twelve rock Xmas classics, including less-common songs such as Boris Pickett's "Monsters' Holiday," Santo and Johnny's "Twistin' Bells," and The Barron Knights's "Merry Gentle Pops." Features Bobby Helm, Brenda Lee, The Cadillacs, Aretha Franklin, Roy Orbison, The Ventures, Charles Brown, James Brown, The Drifters, and Chuck Berry. CD has four extra cuts.

RHINO 70193 (C)
Cool Yule, Vol. 2
Second fab collection of hip Xmas tunes from the '50s and '60s.

RHINO 70291 (CL)
Bo Diddley Beats
The famous Bo Diddley "shave and a haircut, two bits" beat finally gets its own album. Luckily, the wide variety of musical styles keeps it from being monotonous. What other collection would dare contain The Blue Rockers's 1955 version of "Calling All Cows," The Strangeloves's "I Want Candy," Donovan's "Hey Gyp (Dig the Slowness)," and Ghanaian drummer Oboade's "Ma-Mi Ayiko (Well Done, Mama)"? Disco is proudly represented by Shirley And Company's Number 1 groove "Shame, Shame, Shame," and elevator music by Joe Reisman's Orchestra and Chorus doing "Bo Diddley." And yes, Bo also does "Bo." The CD has four bonus tracks. Where diversity meets perversity. Big fun!

RHINO 70319 (CL)
The British Invasion:
History of British Rock, Vol. 1
Twenty-track CD/14-track cassette, focusing on recordings from 1964-1966, primarily of EMI/Brian Epstein-managed artists. Comes with 16-page booklet by rock guru Parke Puterbaugh, and some rarities among the better-known cuts. Includes Peter and Gordon, The Kinks, Gerry and The Pacemakers, Freddie and The Dreamers, The Zombies, Billy J. Kramer with The Dakotas, and The Swinging Blue Jeans.

RHINO 70320 (CL)
The British Invasion:
History of British Rock, Vol. 2
Twenty CD/14 cassette tracks, with a similar lineup to Vol. 1.

RHINO 70321 (CL)
The British Invasion:
History of British Rock, Vol. 3
Ibid, with similar groups to Vols. 1 and 2 with the addition of Donovan, The Yardbirds, The Seekers, and Manfred Mann.

RHINO 70322 (CL)
The British Invasion:
History of British Rock, Vol. 4
Similar selection of groups to previous three volumes.

RHINO 70323 (CL)
The British Invasion:
History of British Rock, Vol. 5
Actually includes The Beatles (though in their pre-Capitol days performing the oft-reissued "Ain't She Sweet" in a session recorded while backing pop crooner Tony Sheridan), along with a wider palette of groups than the previous volumes, including Lulu and The Luvers, Georgie Fame and The Blue Flames, Petula Clark, Wayne Fontana and The Mindbenders,

Them, The Bachelors, The Moody Blues, Tom Jones, Dusty Springfield, and The Fortunes.

RHINO 70324 (CL)

The British Invasion: History of British Rock, Vol. 6

We're moving into the mid-'60s on this collection of groovy mindblowers. Imagine yourself skipping down Carnaby St. listening to The Hollies, Them, Dusty Springfield, The Mindbenders, Lulu, Dave Berry, The Small Faces, Manfred Mann, The Walker Brothers, and Unit 4+2.

RHINO 70325 (CL)

The British Invasion: History of British Rock, Vol. 7

More later Brit rock, including Los Bravos, Donovan, Jonathan King, The Bee Gees, Eric Burdon and The Animals, The Hollies, The Easy Beats, Wayne Fontana, Dusty Springfield, Petula Clark, Gerry and The Pacemakers, The Small Faces, The Walker Brothers, and my personal favorite "Winchester Cathedral" by The New Vaudeville Band.

RHINO 70326 (CL)

The British Invasion: History of British Rock, Vol. 8

Psychedelic classics by Donovan, Cream, The Status Quo, Eric Burdon, The Moody Blues, Spencer Davis, and Procol Harum. Interesting rarities include early recordings by Cat Stevens, Marc Bolan (later of T-Rex), and Steve Howe (later of Yes).

RHINO 70327 (CL)

The British Invasion: History of British Rock, Vol. 9

More later '60s classics, with a similar lineup to Vol. 8.

RHINO 70515 (RCL)

The Best of Louie Louie, Vol. 2

More covers of the song that launched a hundred garage rockers. First volume issued as Rhino 70605.

RHINO 70535 (CL)

Halloween Hits

Ten budget-priced tracks, including old favorites like "Monster Mash," "Haunted House," and "Purple People Eater," as well as great mood music like "The Blob" by The Five Blobs, "Twilight Zone" by Neil Norman and His Cosmic Orchestra, and "The Addams Family" by Vic Mizzy. There are even a couple of recent classics, such as "Ghostbusters" and "Attack of the Killer Tomatoes."

RHINO 70536 (CL)

San Francisco Nights

All your favorite turned-on bands, including Country Joe and The Fish, Blue Cheer, Quicksilver Messenger Service, The Sopwith Camel, The Great Society, The Beau Brummels, and Sly and The Family Stone.

RHINO 70561 (CL)

Legends of Guitar—Rock: The '50s, Vol. 2

If the sound of a twanged guitar string makes you weak in the knees, get this one and grab a chair pronto! Eighteen boppers, benders, and flat-out blisterers (14 on tape), featuring guitarists Roland Janes, Ike Turner, Scotty Moore, Willie Joe Duncan, Paul Burlison, Cliff Gallup, Santo and Johnny, Frannie Beecher, Chuck Berry, Duane Eddy, James Burton, and Ritchie Valens. Collectors' note: includes Sonny Curtis's clean pickin' on Buddy Holly's rarely-heard "Blue Days." Vol. 1 is Rhino 70719.

RHINO 70588 (CL)

Rockin' and Rollin' Wedding Songs, Vol. 1

Pop mush, R&B, and doo-wop prevail on this mishmash of tributes to wedlock. Good fold-out book notes and promo glossies from Richard Henderson.

RHINO 70589 (CL)

Rockin' and Rollin' Wedding Songs, Vol. 2

Sentimental slushers and gushers, some more candied than others, along with a few rarities. Decent fold-out booknotes with publicity shots from Richard Henderson.

RHINO 70593 (CL)

There's A Riot Going On! Classics of Leiber and Stoller

Eighteen great songs (14 on cassette) written by two of the most important pop songwriters of the '50s and early '60s. Great sound and informative 12-page booklet.

RHINO 70598 (CL)

Top Rock'n'Roll Hits: 1955

Each volume in this series (Rhino 70598-99 and 70618-35) presents the Top Ten pop chart hits of the year, based on the *Billboard* charts. Many are issued in true stereo for the first time. Rock Around the Clock (Bill Haley and the Comets)/Maybelline (Chuck Berry)/Earth Angel (The Penguins).

RHINO 70599 (CL)

Top Rock'n'Roll Hits: 1956

Don't Be Cruel (Elvis Presley)/Be-Bop-a-Lula (Gene Vincent and His Blue Caps)/Blue Suede Shoes (Carl Perkins).

RHINO 70605 (CL)

The Best of Louie Louie

Includes the original version by Richard Berry, along with covers by Black Flag, Les Dantz and His Orchestra, The Impossibles, The Kingsmen (the one you know), The Last, The Rice University Marching Owl

Band, Rockin' Robin Roberts, The Sandpipers, and The Sonics.

RHINO 70611 (C)

Teenage Tragedy

In the words of the Rhinettes, "all the best teen-death sagas are lumped together in a package that doubles as a tissue dispenser." Highlight: Julie Brown's "Homecoming Queen's Got a Gun."

RHINO 70617 (CL)

The Best of La Bamba

Ten Bamba-ettes, including Ritchie's original hit, a traditional Mexican version by Conjunto Medellim de Lino Chavez, a modern Mex version by Mariachi Vargas, heavy metal by Drive, doo-wop from Daddy Cool, Tonio K's La Bamba, and of course, versions by The Rice University Marching Owl Band and The Mormon Tabernacle Choir. (They did leave off my faves, though: The Plugz great punk version and Los Lobos traditional version from the movie.)

RHINO 70618 (CL)

Top Rock'n'Roll Hits: 1957

All Shook Up (Elvis)/Wake Up Little Susie (The Everly Brothers)/Diana (Paul Anka).

RHINO 70619 (CL)

Top Rock'n'Roll Hits: 1958

At the Hop (Danny and the Juniors)/Tequila (The Champs)/To Know Him Is to Love Him (The Teddy Bears).

RHINO 70620 (CL)

Top Rock'n'Roll Hits: 1959

Mack the Knife (Bobby Darin)/Venus (Frankie Avalon)/Lonely Boy (Paul Anka).

RHINO 70621 (CL)

Top Rock'n'Roll Hits: 1960

It's Now or Never (Elvis)/Cathy's Clown (The Everly Brothers)/The Twist (Chubby Checker).

RHINO 70622 (CL)

Top Rock'n'Roll Hits: 1961

Tossin' and Turnin' (Bobby Lewis)/Runaway (Del Shannon)/Blue Moon (The Marcels).

RHINO 70623 (CL)

Top Rock'n'Roll Hits: 1962

Big Girls Don't Cry (The Four Seasons)/Duke of Earl (Gene Chandler)/Soldier Boy (The Shirelles).

RHINO 70624 (CL)

Top Rock'n'Roll Hits: 1963

Sugar Shack (Jimmy Gilmore and The Fireballs)/Surf City (Jan and Dean)/He's So Fine (The Chiffons).

RHINO 70625 (CL)

Top Rock'n'Roll Hits: 1964

Bread and Butter (The Newbeats)/Do Wah Diddy Diddy (Manfred Mann)/I Get Around (The Beach Boys).

RHINO 70626 (CL)

Top Rock'n'Roll Hits: 1965

Hang on Sloopy (The McCoys)/Mr. Tambourine Man (The Byrds)/This Diamond Ring (Gary Lewis and The Playboys).

RHINO 70627 (CL)

Top Rock'n'Roll Hits: 1966

I'm a Believer (The Monkees)/Summer in the City (The Lovin' Spoonful)/Wild Thing (The Troggs).

RHINO 70628 (CL)

Top Rock'n'Roll Hits: 1967

Little Bit o' Soul (The Music Explosion)/The Letter (The Box Tops)/Happy Together (The Turtles).

RHINO 70629 (CL)

Top Rock'n'Roll Hits: 1968

I Heard it Through the Grapevine (Marvin Gaye)/Judy in Disguise (with Glasses) (John Fred and The Playboys)/Yummy Yummy Yummy (Ohio Express).

RHINO 70630 (CL)

Top Rock'n'Roll Hits: 1969

Aquarius (The Fifth Dimension)/Dizzy (Tommy Roe)/Sugar, Sugar (The Archies).

RHINO 70631 (CL)

Top Rock'n'Roll Hits: 1970

Venus (Shocking Blue)/Mama Told Me (Not to Come) (Three Dog Night)/I Think I Love You (The Partridge Family).

RHINO 70632 (CL)

Top Rock'n'Roll Hits: 1971

Joy to the World (Three Dog Night)/Maggie May (Rod Stewart)/One Bad Apple (The Osmonds).

RHINO 70633 (CL)

Top Rock'n'Roll Hits: 1972

Alone Again (Naturally) (Gilbert O'Sullivan)/I Can See Clearly Now (Johnny Nash)/Black and White (The Osmonds).

RHINO 70634 (CL)

Top Rock'n'Roll Hits: 1973

Crocodile Rock (Elton John)/Bad, Bad Leroy Brown (Jim Croce)/Midnight Train to Georgia (Gladys Knight and The Pips).

RHINO 70635 (CL)

Top Rock'n'Roll Hits: 1974

Bernie and The Jets (Elton John)/The Loco-Motion (Grand Funk Railroad)/Nothing from Nothing (Billy Preston).

RHINO 70636 (CL)

Billboard Greatest Christmas Hits (1955-Present)

Novelty and rock Christmas hits from then to now with Elvis, Bobby Helms, Brenda Lee, the Chipmunks, The Harry Simeon Chorale, Harry Belafonte, Charles Brown, Elmo 'n Patsy, The Drifters, and Barry Gordon.

RHINO 70719 (CL)

Legends of Guitar—Rock: The '50s

Fine, if incomplete, collection of rock-guitar classics, mixing instrumentals and accompaniment. Includes Chuck Berry, Bo Diddley, Danny Cedrone, James Burton, Frank Virtue, Luther Perkins, Eddie Cochran, Les Paul, Link Wray, Cliff Gallup, The Crickets featuring Buddy Holly, Jimmy Nolan, Jimmy Spruill, and Carl Perkins. Vol. 2 is Rhino 70561.

RHINO 70720 (CL)

Legends of Guitar—Rock: The '60s

Surf, British invasion, psychedelia, Memphis Soul, and barroom rock styles from all parts of the decade. Great material and fine Dan Forte notes.

RHINO 70724 (CL)

Legends of Guitar—Surf, Vol. 1

OK guitar players: Turn up the reverb unit and get ready to play along with Dick Dale, The Chantays, The Astronauts, Eddie and The Showmen, The Ventures, Jim Messina and The Jesters, Bobby Fuller, and The Crossfires (later known as The Turtles). CD has four bonus tracks. Fab liner notes by the man who wrote the book on surf music, John Blair.

RHINO 70732 (L)

Grandson of Frat Rock (Vol. 3)

See Rhino 75778.

RHINO 70734 (CL)

Songs of Protest

Rockers with a conscience! Includes The Turtles, Barry McGuire, The Rascals, Country Joe and The Fish, Edwin Starr, and The Temptations. Four CD bonus tracks feature folkie protesters The Kingston Trio, Donovan, and Phil Ochs, along with Manfred Mann.

RHINO 70741 (CL)

Rock This Town: Rockabilly Hits, Vol. 1

Eighteen-song collection (14 on tape) collecting rockabilly's bestsellers, including tracks by The Johnny Burnette Trio, Billy Lee Riley, and Jerry Lee Lewis.

Besides the other big names, you'll also find a few great semi-obscure tunes too, like Sonnee West's "Sweet Rockin' Baby," Jimmy Edwards's "Love Bug Crawl," and Jimmy Lloyd's classic "I Got a Rocket in My Pocket."

RHINO 70742 (CL)

Rock This Town: Rockabilly Hits, Vol. 2

Eighteen '50s hits and modern classics (14 on cassette), including original discs by Eddie Cochran, Wanda Jackson, Ronnie Dawson, and The Collins Kids. Also includes more modern sides by Commander Cody and His Lost Planet Airmen, Robert Gordon with Link Wray on sizzling guitar, Tex Rubinowitz, and The Blasters.

RHINO 70743 (CL)

Dr. Demento's 20th Anniversary Collection

In the early '70s, DJ Barry Hansen realized that nothing made his request lines light up like those kooky, krazy novelty records, and so Dr. Demento was born. Dementia is now 20 years old, and Rhino Records is celebrating with this double CD/cassette set of straitjacket screamers, poignant parodies, stinging satires, and psycho psingles. Classic loonies like Spike Jones, Tom Lehrer, Stan Freberg, Allen Sherman, Nervous Norvus, and Bobby "Boris" Pickett figure prominently, along with one-hit wierdos like The Playmates ("Beep Beep"), Frank Gallop ("The Ballad of Irving"), Barnes and Barnes ("Fish Heads"), The Trashmen ("Surfin' Bird"), and Napoleon XIV ("They're Coming to Take Me Away"). Some of the newer stuff is too cute for me, but among these 36 cuts there's more than enough inspired lunacy to go around.

RHINO 70896 (CL)

Sound of the Swamp: The Best of Excello Records, Vol. 1

RHINO 70897 (CL)

Southern Rhythm 'n' Rock: Best of Excello Records, Vol. 2

Two CDs documenting the diverse mixture of blues, doo-wop, country boogie, rockabilly, and swamp pop recorded for Lousiana's Excello label in the '50s and '60s. Great stuff.

RHINO 70912 (CL)

Bummed Out Christmas

Some of the strangest and most cynical Xmas discs ever. Don't miss "Xmas Eve Can Kill You" by The Everly Brothers, Johnny and Jon's "Xmas in Viet Nam," Sherwin Linton's "Santa Got a DWI!," Clyde Lasley's "Santa Came Home Drunk," plus other goofy tracks by George Jones, The Sonics, The Staple Singers, and Ron Holden.

RHINO 70988 (CL)
The Best of the Girl Groups, Vol. 1
Eighteen (14 on cassette) songs, spanning half a decade (1961-1966) of heartaches, longing, and loneliness, buoyed by bright, energetic production, unrestrained vocals, and terrific songwriting. Highlight: the debut solo single from Cherilyn (Cher!), "Dream Baby."

RHINO 70989 (CL)
The Best of the Girl Groups, Vol. 2
Eighteen more classics (14 on tape) from 1958-1966.

RHINO 70992 (CL)
Groove 'n' Grind: '50s and '60s Dance Hits
The dances for a decade of teenagers (1957-1967), including The Jerk, The Twist, The Monkey, The Bird, The Hully Gully, The Swim, The Locomotion, and The Stroll. Four extra tracks on CD.

RHINO 70995 (CL)
Dick Bartley Presents One Hit Wonders of the '60s, Vol. 1
Twelve cuts in a variety of styles (but mostly middle-of-the-road pop) by the groups and acts "we forgot to remember."

RHINO 70996 (CL)
Dick Bartley Presents One Hit Wonders of the '60s, Vol. 2
Twelve more hits from groups that (mostly) soon fell from glory to playing the lounges at Holiday Inns. This one is much better than Vol. 1 if you like your pop with more of a rockin' beat. Tunes like "Gimme Gimme Good Lovin'" by Crazy Elephant, "Hang on Sloopy" by The McCoys, and "Let It All Hang Out" by The Hombres still sound great after all of these years.

RHINO 71007 (CL)
Golden Throats 2: More Celebrity Rock Oddities!
Oh no! Those cutups at Rhino, who defined the "so-bad-it's-good" esthetic are at it again. More Hollywood squares take a stab at the '60s and '70s pop market. Leonard Nimoy, Sebastian Cabot, and the histrionic William Shatner all have return engagements, securing their reputations as the most unlikely rock stars ever. But they get some heavy competition from Phyllis Diller, who serves up a burnt "(I Can't Get No) Satisfaction," Watergate panel member Senator Sam J. Ervin's massacre of "Bridge over Troubled Water," Cassius Clay's not-quite-all-there version of "Stand by Me," the surreal sing-along version of "Give Peace a Chance" from Mitch Miller's Gang, Mae West on the nearly extinguished "Light My Fire," and B-B-Bing Crosby's "Hey Jude." Fourteen tacky treasures.

RHINO 71103 (C)/75884 (L)
The Sun Story
Twenty-five cuts on two cassettes or twenty cuts on one CD, making the most complete Sun hits collection ever. As far as I know, this is the only compilation to include the A-sides of Elvis's first and second singles, "That's All Right" and "Good Rockin' Tonight." Includes all the rockin' and R&B Sun hits, and even some great doo-wop, but no blues or country. Also features some tunes not usually found on compilations, such as Roy Orbison's "Devil Doll" and Johnny Cash's "Straight A's in Love," along with lesser artists Bill Justis, Charlie Rich, Carl Mann, and Warren Smith. Comes with four-page booklet with photos and James Austin liner notes; CD has awesome digital sound.

RHINO 71106 (C)
Summer of Love
Put the flowers in your hair and relive the late '60s in this 25-track collection, featuring Scott McKenzie, The Youngbloods, Donovan, The Strawberry Alarm Clock, Canned Heat, The Fifth Dimension, Spanky and Our Gang, The Sunshine Company, and even Petula Clark!

RHINO 75754 (L)
Even More Nuggets: Psychedelic Sixties, Vol. 3
See Rhino 75892.

RHINO 75755 (L)
Dr. Demento Presents the Greatest Novelty Records of All Time, Vol. 6: Christmas
Sixteen tracks by The Chipmunks, The Singing Dogs, Gayle Peevey, Tom Lehrer, Yogi Yorgesson, Stan Freberg, Kip Addotta, Weird Al Yankovic, and other certifiable characters.

RHINO 75767 (L)
The Best of Cool Yule
CD combines nine cuts each from Cool Yule, Vols. 1 and 2 (Rhino 70192/70193), guaranteeing that you'll be the hippest cat in Yulesville.

RHINO 75772 (L)
Son of Frat Rock (Vol. 2)
See Rhino 75778.

RHINO 75777 (L)
More Nuggets
See Rhino 75892.

RHINO 75778 (L)
Frat Rock (Vol. 1)
Compilation from cassette series (see Rhino 70136/183/184/190).

RHINO 75892 (L)

Nuggets: Classics from the Psychedelic '60s

Eighteen cuts distilled from the Rhino LP series of the same name (70025 and 70033 are the only releases still available from the original series; CDs 75777/754 present more cuts from this same series). Sound quality is exceptional, with a 12-page booklet with band photos and biographies, as well as reproductions of '60s magazine ads (remember Zappa's Hajstrom guitar ad, "Folk Rock is a drag"?)

ROCK AND COUNTRY 1006 (R)

Rock and Country Rockabilly

Nice collection of rare rockabilly and rock-and-roll cuts by Bob Calloway, Ric Cartey, Royce Clark, Mason Dixon, Orville Fox, Jim McDonald, Gene McKnown, Dan Nirva, Larry Philipson, Joe South, The Van Brothers, and Don Wade.

ROCK AND COUNTRY 1007 (R)

Spade Rockabilly

Rockabilly and rockin' country recorded in the '50s for the Spade label. Vern Pullens is featured with nine cuts, along with a couple of cuts by Bennie Hess and Royce Porter.

ROCK AND COUNTRY 1009 (R)

Dore Rock and Roll, Vol. 1

Twelve rock and pop cuts from the late '50s through the early '60s cut for the Dore label by Tony Casanova, Johnny Coley, Ronnie Cook, Darwin, Johnny Durain, Glen Glenn, Larry Harmon, Deane Hawley, Frankie Lee, The Tides, Tony and Joe, and Freddie Weller.

ROCK AND COUNTRY 1010 (R)

Yucca Rockabilly

Nice collection of rockabilly, rock and roll, and rockin' country from this El Paso label. Includes the first recordings of The Bobby Fuller Four, along with cuts by Bill Chapell, Larry Dalton, Long John Hunter, Don Orr, Hal Smith, Bob Taylor, and Sonny Wallace.

ROCK AND COUNTRY 1011 (R)

Spotlight on Crest Records

Twenty western-swing, rockabilly, and white-pop cuts from this fine LA label that boasted such sessionmen as Eddie Cochran, Buck Owens, and Glen Campbell. Includes Tony Dee, Frank and Ernie, Bobby and Terry Caraway, and Tom Reeves.

ROCK AND COUNTRY 1012 (R)

Ace Rock and Roll

Twelve rock-and-roll and R&B recordings from the famed Ace label, featuring Hershel Almond, Narvel Felts, Frankie Ford, Dick Holler, Scotty McKay, Big Boy Myles, Eddie Seacrest, Huey "Piano" Smith, and Ron Willis.

ROCK AND COUNTRY 1015 (R)

Goldband Rockabilly

Fourteen '50s rockabilly sides recorded for Eddie Shuler's famed cajun label, including a great early Rockin' Sidney cut, plus tracks by Little Billy Earl, Al Ferrier, Guitar Junior, Larry Hart, Johnny Jano, Don La Fleur, Little Miss Peggie, and Gene Terry.

ROCK AND COUNTRY 1016 (R)

Jin Rock and Roll

Twelve swamp-pop and rockabilly sides from Floyd Soileau's famed Louisiana label by Red Smiley, Billy Lewis, Rod Bernard, Phil Bo, Prentice Thomas, Mary McCoy, Johnnie Allen, and Rockin' Sidney.

ROCK AND COUNTRY 1017 (R)

Dore Rock and Roll, Vol. 2

Tony Casanova, Jim Ratterree, Johnny Day, Doug Hansen, The T-Shirts, Bobby Mell, Glen Glenn, Frankie Lee, Freddy Weller, Darwin, The Capers, and Rodney and The Blazers.

ROCK AND COUNTRY 1018 (R)

Razorback Rock and Roll

Twelve sides from Bobby Crafford's famed Arkansas label, including Crafford, Sonny Burgess, The Five Roughes, Jimmy Luke, Rick Durham, and Teddy Redell.

ROCK AND COUNTRY 1019 (R)

Vin Rock and Roll

Sixteen tunes from the rockabilly subsidiary of Johnny Vincent's Ace label. Lots of this stuff has been on Ace compilations, but this is a fine, solid set featuring such rarities as unissued demos by Charlie Feathers and Charlie Rich, and great cuts by Al Vance, The Phaetons, Jimmy Ford, and Alton and Jimmy.

ROCK AND COUNTRY 1020 (R)

The Buddy Holly Sound

Sixteen tracks from the '50s and '60s by performers influenced by Holly, including Bobby Jameson, The Muleskinners, The Hollyhawks (produced by Norman Petty), Bobby Fuller, David Box, Tommy Roe, Royce Clark, and J.R. LaRue.

ROLLER COASTER 2008 (R)

Roller Coaster Rockers

Eighteen rockin' cuts, some from other Roller Coaster LPs, by Niki Sullivan, Bill Haley and His Comets, Groovy Joe Poovey, George Browning and The Echo Valley Boys, Hardrock (Gunter) and The Rhythm Rockers, Charlie Gracie, Sid King and The Five Strings, Alvis Wayne and The Rhythm Wranglers, Marvin Rainwater, Sidney Jo Lewis, Shirly Caddell and The Aristocrats, Kenny Lord and The Statesmen (Mike Berry), Chip and The Chimes, The Crickets, and Tony Morra and The Belltones.

ROLLER COASTER 3003 (L)
Hep Cats from Big Spring
Twenty solid tracks of Texas rock and roll recorded in the '50s and early '60s by artists influenced by, or in some way connected with, Buddy Holly. Includes Ben Hall, David Box, Bob Osburn, Bobby Allison, and The Teen Kings (not Roy Orbison's backup band!).

ROMULAN 03 (R)
Girls in the Garage, Vol. 2
Sixteen cuts by girl garage groups of the '60s, who generally sound tough vocally but rather tentative on the instrumental side. Exceptions are Kathy Lynn and The Playboys, The Chimes of Freedom (who waxed an amazing "Jungle Rock" complete with screams and raw fuzz guitar), The Girls, and The Whyte Boots.

ROMULAN 04 (R)
Girls in the Garage, Vol. 3
Fifteen tunes by 12 girl bands, ranging from the truly inept to the ineptly charming. Highlights include the ultra-cool Jacqueline Taieb (who asks the musical question, "Which mini skirt shall I wear today?" in her song "7:00 AM"), Jean and The Statesiders, The Tone Benders, and San Francisco's Ace of Cups.

ROMULAN 06 (R)
Girls in the Garage, Vol. 4
Eighteen songs by girl groups and soloists. Features Cher's immortal single, "Ringo, I Love You," released under the name Bonnie Jo Mason and produced by the great Phil Spector! Who can resist such cool rockin' mod sounds as Minnie and The Kneebones doing "Me and My Miniskirt," or the Zappa understudies, The GTOs, singing "Love on an 11-Year-Old Level"? Extensive liner notes.

ROMULAN 08 (R)
Real Gone Garbage
Eighteen wacky 45s recorded in the '50s and '60s, rescued off the trash heap no doubt.

ROMULAN 09 (R)
Frolic Diner: 18 Wild Instros fer Eatin' and Strippin' To
One side of instrumentals named after your favorite foodstuffs (including The Sandabs's "Crab Louie," Paul Gayton's "Hot Cross Buns," The Don Thompson Quartet's "Cheese Blintzes," and Felix and His Guitar's "Chili Beans"), and a flip with the kind of slow-grinding, saxy instros associated with strip shows including sleazemeisters like The Premieres, The Xterminators, and The Contrails.

ROMULAN 12 (R)
Girls in the Garage, Vol. 6
Perhaps the best in the series, this heapin' platter contains hot cuts by Kari Lynn, The Cupons (performing the wonderful "Turn Her Down," recently covered by The Pussywillows), Ellaine and The Shandells, Joanna Gault, The Fatimas, and Karen Verros.

ROMULAN 14 (R)
Surf Creature, Vol. 2
Fifteen rare surf tunes from the '60s by Zorba and The Greeks, The Silvertones, The Velvetones, Manuel and The Renegades, The Truants, and Dave Meyers and The Surf Tones. Many cuts feature unusual rhythms and sounds, particularly for this era.

ROMULAN 15 (R)
Frolic Diner, Vol. 2
OK, gang, pile in the car: We're headin' off to our favorite eating spot again, Frolic Diner, where the food is greasy and the music is even greasier. Let's check out the menu today. I'll have "Chili with Honey" (by Danny Bell and The Bell Hops), "Enchilada" (by The Scamps), and "Two Tacos" (by Felix and His Guitar). For you, I'd recommend "Succotash" (by Roy Milton and His Orchestra) and "Bullfrog" (by Johnny Moore and His Blazers). We'll wash it down with a "Screwdriver" (by Michael and The Jesters) and some "Apple Cider" (by the great Doc Starkes and His Nightriders.) Still hungry? Well, there's plenty more; eighteen mouthwatering cuts, all told.

ROUNDER 37 (RCL)
Sun Rockabilly: The Classic Recordings
No surprises here, just a great collection of 14 classic rockabilly cuts from Sun by Billy Riley, Gene Simmons, Ernie Barton, Warren Smith, Hayden Thompson, and Harold Jenkins (later Conway Twitty). Superb sound, full discographical details, informative notes by Colin Escott, and some great liner photos.

ROUNDER 1031 (RC)
Wild Wild Young Women
Fourteen fine rockabilly and rockin' country sides from the '50s by Jean Chapel, Alvaden Coker, The Collins Kids, The Davis Sisters, Joan King, Linda and The Epics, Rose Maddox, Janis Martin, Sparkle Moore, and The Nettles Sisters.

❂ ROXY 100 (R)
Mayhem and Psychosis, Vol. 1: 20 Psych Punk Classics of the '60s
Twenty, wild, acid-punk tunes, by The Jelly Bean Bandits, The Galaxies, The Beatin' Path, and The Hysterics.

❂ ROXY 101 (R)
Mayhem and Psychosis, Vol. 2: 20 Psych Punk Classics of the '60s
The Other Half, The Chocolate Moose, The Spades (with Roky Erickson), Calico Wall, The Leaves, and We The People.

ROXY 102 (R)

Lookin' for Boys:
16 Girl Group Classics of the '60s

Spector-ish girl-group tunes produced by such seasoned hands as Goffin and King, Jeff Barry, Shadow Morton, Brian Wilson, Lori Burton and Pam Sawyer, and Jimmy Bowen. A highlight is Earl-Jean's incredible original of the classic song "I'm Into Something Good," as well as tracks by The Honeys, The Whyte Boots, The Ribbons, Ellie Greenwich, and The Darlettes.

❀ ROXY 104 (R)

Mayhem and Psychosis, Vol. 3

The baddest of the bad in '60s punk. If you don't already have The Fanatics's "I Can't Believe", believe me, it's worth the price of the album; what a killer rave up sound! The Wanted do the best version of "In the Midnight Hour" that I've ever heard. Lots more psychotic reactions from The X-Treems, The Bedlam Four, The Clue, and The Ugly Ducklings. Great sound quality, too.

ROXY 106 (R)

Beyond the Wall of Sound:
18 Girl Group Classics

Many of the recording techniques pioneered by the tortured genius of Phil Spector, including miniature orchestral arrangements, are demonstrated in these eighteen back-to-mono classics. Includes the underrated Jackie DeShannon, Shelley Fabares, The Raindrops (aka Jeff Barry and wife Ellie Greenwich), Donna Loren, Sadina, The Bonnets, The Donays, The Bobbi-Pins, Shirley Matthews and The Big Town Girls, and Reparata and The Delrons.

RRDP 1 (R)

Rock and Roll Dance Party, Vol. 1

Sixteen dance tunes, not quite up to the standard, but still a solid, rockin' mix. Includes V. and B.B., The Melo-aires, Bob Carter, and Joe Benson.

RRDP 202 (R)

Rock and Roll Dance Party, Vol. 2

The X-Cellents, Veline Hackert, Guitar Red, The Jackson Brothers Orchestra, Florian Monday, The Kents, Bobby Parks, and Pat the Cat and His Kittens will get you up on the dance floor.

RUNDELL 001 (R)

Rock and Roll Meeting

Twelve rockabilly sides, including two '50s Charlie Gracie sides, two '60s Ray Smith sides, and two '80s sides by Belgian revivalists The Black Caps. Others include Lloyd Arnold, Colt Davis, Bob Gifford, and Joe D. Johnson.

RUNDELL 005 (R)

Rockabilly Heroes

Mixed bag of '80s recordings by Jackie Lee Cochran, Bob Luman, and Groovy Joe Poovey.

RYKODISC 20074 (L)

Big Guitars from Texas

Twenty-one contemporary guitar instrumentals by Evan Johns and many others, originally issued (with fewer tracks) on Jungle Records.

RYKODISC 20126 (L)

Get with the Beat:
A Lost Decade of Rock and Roll

Twenty-seven sides recorded for Harry Glenn's Marvel and Glenn label in the '50s and early '60s. A fine mixture of rockin' country and rockabilly from mostly obscure performers like Shorty Ashford, Chuck Dollis, Ginny Carter, Harold Allen, Bill Ferguson, and Herbie Duncan, along with a few slightly better-known names like Bobby Sisco, Jack Bradshaw, and Rem Wall. These recordings were previously issued on the now defunct Cowboy Carl label run by Carl Schneider who provides the informative notes on this nicely produced collection.

RYKODISC 40032 (L)

The Cruisin' Series

Fifteen hits from the '50s and early '60s (original recordings by the original artists) with radio station jingles, DJ patter, and commercials from the era. Includes hits by Chuck Berry, The Cadets, The Big Bopper, The Hollywood Argyles, The Kingsmen, The Turtles, and The Seeds.

SATAN MVI (R)

Gamma Knee Kappa:
The Best in Frat Rock, Vol. 1

Seventeen great unknowns with names like The Del Counts, The Buggs, The Jerms, and The Loafers who cover "standards" and "substandards" like "High Blood Pressure," "Shake a Tail Feather," and "You Can't Sit Down." Boss, man, boss!

SATAN 1003 (R)

Riot City

Sixteen cuts of maniacal '60s garage punk. Includes an early P.F. Sloan (of The Fantastic Baggys) group, The Street Cleaners, on the anthemic "That's Cool, That's Trash," one of the best party records ever.

SATAN 1004 (R)

Wail on the Beach!

Sixteen worthy additions to the libraries of surf and instrumental fanatics, though there are vocal and hot-rod tunes here as well.

SATAN 1313 (R)
What A Way to Die
All killer, no filler '60s garage-rock anthology. Includes The Pleasure Seekers (with young Suzi Quatro) and Lou Reed's pre-Velvets studio group, The Beech-Nuts.

SATAN 2120 (R)
Bo Did It!
Eighteen Bo Diddley-inspired tunes, in rockabilly, R&B, and '60s garage rock styles.

SD 810 (R)
Rockin' Daddy
Rockabilly from Sonny Fisher, Sleepy LaBeef, Glen Barber, and Amos Como (not Perry's brother!).

SD 820 (R)
Rock It
Sixteen rockabilly gems. George "Thumper" Jones, Fred Crawford, Bill Mack, Bob Doss, Alden Holloway, Hoyt Scoggins, Lou Walker, and Arlie Duff.

SD 830 (R)
Let's Get Wild
Good boppin' hillbilly rock. Rudy "Tutti" Grayzell, Rock Rogers, Rocky Bill Ford, Lattie Moore, Lonnie Irving, and Jack Kingston.

SD 840 (R)
Sixteen Chicks
Sixteen, mostly obscure rockabilly gems by Link Davis, Eddie Skelton, Fuzzy Whitener, Lonnie Smithon, Andy Doll, Lloyd McCollough, Sleepy Jeffers, Arnold Parker, and Buddy Shaw.

SD 850 (R)
Chicken Bop
More obscure rockabilly. Truitt Forse, Dave Brockmann, Jimmy Johnson, Sonny Burns, Larry Nolan, Dave Woolum, Bill Floyd, and Johnny Tyler.

SD 860 (R)
Teenage Cutie
Sixteen rockabilly obscurities. Lucky Wray, Les Chambers's plight, Eddie Noack, Hal Harris, Bill Nettles, Darnell Miller, and Bill Parsons.

SEE FOR MILES 58 (R)
Recorded Live at the Cavern
Reissue of Decca 4597 from 1964 featuring 16 cuts by various Liverpool groups recorded at the Cavern Club (where The Beatles got their start), plus The Big Three's legendary four-cut *Live at The Cavern* EP. Includes The Marauders, The Fortunes, The Dennisons, Heinz, Dave Berry and The Cruisers, Lee Curtis, Ben Elliot and The Fenmen, and Beryl Marsden.

SEE FOR MILES 72 (R)/226 (L)
The British Psychedelic Trip, Vol. 2
Twenty turn-ons (25 on CD) from the vaults of EMI, recorded between 1967–1969. A neat treat is a young David Bowie leading Davy Jones and The Lower Third on "You've Got a Habit of Leaving." The Gods, who rip up "Hey Bulldog" and "Real Love Guaranteed," evolved into Uriah Heep. The Idle Race, blissed out on "Skeleton and the Roundabout" and "Worn Red Carpet," were led by Jeff Lynne of The Move, ELO, and later still of The Traveling Wilburys. LP is pressed on psycedelic blue vinyl.

SEE FOR MILES 73 (R)
The R&B Scene, Vol. 2 (1963–1969)
Twenty obscure and interesting tracks from the Decca vaults, including instrumental B-sides by The Bread and Beer Band—with a young Reg Dwight (aka Elton John)—and pianist Ian Stewart (who toured and sessioned with The Rolling Stones) and The Railroaders (featuring Keith Richards, Bill Wyman, and ex-Shadows drummer Tony Meehan)! Also includes Them, The Graham Bond Organization with John McLaughlin, Ginger Baker and Jack Bruce, The Cruisers, Dave Berry, and The Fairies.

SEE FOR MILES 86 (R)
The British Psychedelic Trip: 1966–1969, Vol. 3
Twenty rarities from the UK Decca/Deram/Philips/Fontana/Track vaults. You'll groove to forgotten psychedelic bands such as John's Children, Kaleidoscope, The Open Mind, Turquoise, Human Instinct, The Californians, Crocheted Doughnut Ring, Tinkerbell's Fairydust, The Cuppa T, Virgin Sleep, and even an early tune by Al Stewart.

SEE FOR MILES 123 (R)
Sixties Lost and Found, Vol. 2
Twenty British-rock obscurities from the mid-'60s recorded for British Decca, including lots of early cuts by future stars: Zoot Money, The Graham Bond Organization, Joe Cocker, Rod Stewart, Nero and The Gladiators, The Zombies, Bern Elliot and The Fenmen, Screamin' Lord Sutch, The Snobs, Them, The Outer Limits, David Bowie, Marianne Faithful, Denny Laine, George Bean, Lulu and The Luvvers, The Beat Chics, The Vernon's Girls, The Applejacks, and The Gonks.

SEE FOR MILES 125 (R)
Liverpool 1963–1964
Twenty Merseybeat obscurities recorded for British Decca. The Big Three, The Dennisons, The Mojos, The Coasters, Beryl Marsden, Freddie Starr and The Midnighters, The Pete Best Four, Lee Curtis and The All-Stars, The Orchids, and Chick Graham.

SEE FOR MILES 126 (R)
Sixties Lost and Found, Vol. 3: 1962–1969

Twenty more rarities from the vaults of British Decca. The Crying Shames, The Birds (with Ron Wood), Peter Jay and The Jaywalkers, Heinz, Billy Boyle, and Marianne Faithful.

SEE FOR MILES 202 (R)
Ready Steady Win! Plus ...

Reissue of the extremely rare Decca (UK) 4634 LP from 1964 with six additional tracks. In 1964, the British TV fave *Ready Steady Go* ran an amateur rock-group contest; the best 16 tunes appeared on LP, and the best group was awarded a Decca contract with further TV appearances. The 16 groups from the original LP were a mix of (even today) unknown Merseybeat and British R&B groups. The winners were the wild Bo Street Runners, a legendary band that never had an LP release, and later featured Mick Fleetwood on drums.

SEE FOR MILES 204 (R)
Decade of Instrumentals

Twenty-two rock instrumentals from 1959–1967 from the Decca (UK) vaults, with the majority from the early '60s. The 1967 single "Curly" by The Blues Breakers features John Mayall with backup by Peter Green (gtr), John McVie (b), and Mick Fleetwood (drm), who soon after became Fleetwood Mac. Big Jim Sullivan plays on "Grumbling Guitar" by The Other Two, and Jimmy Page is on "Pop the Whip" by Wayne Gibson and The Dynamic Sound. Also includes tracks by Tony Meehan, and Nero and The Gladiators.

SEE FOR MILES 206 (R)
The British Psychedelic Trip, Vol. 4

Another 20 psychedelic sides from British Decca and Deram. Tinkerbell's Fairydust, Pacific Drift, Amazing Friendly Apple, The Majority, Toby Twirl, The (UK) Chocolate Watchband, and Cherry Smash.

SEE FOR MILES 223 (L)
The Sixties Explosion, Vol. 1

Thirty tracks recorded between 1961–1967 for Decca; over 70 minutes playing time! Zoot Money, Joe Cocker, Nero and The Gladiators, Bert Elliot and The Fenmen, The Snobs, The Outer Limits, Denny Laine, and Lulu and The Luvvers.

SEE FOR MILES 224 (L)
The British R&B Explosion, Vol. 1

Twenty-two tracks recorded between 1962–1968, including Graham Gouldman, Pete Kelly's Solution, Zoot Money's Big Roll Band, Joe Cocker, Jimmy Powell, and Duffy's Nucleus.

SEE FOR MILES 225 (L)
The Great British Psychedelic Trip, Vol. 1

Twenty-six tracks recorded between 1966–1969, featuring Turquoise, The Poets, The World of Oz, End, Tintern Abbey, and Toby Twirl.

SEE FOR MILES 243 (R)
Pop Inside the Sixties

Twenty-two unabashed stabs at the British pop charts by a legion of young mod hopefuls. Rolling Stones's producer Andrew Loog Oldham arranged two of the best tracks here: "Just Sticks In Your Mind" by Vashti and "(Walking through the) Sleepy City" by The Mighty Avengers, both written by "The Glimmer Twins" (aka Mick Jagger and Keith Richards). Also includes Olivia Newton John, David Essex, Steve Marriott, Jon Anderson of Yes (performing with The Warriors), and Graham Gouldman and Kevin Godley of 10CC (performing with The Mockingbirds).

SEQUEL 102 (RL)
Some Other Guys: 32 Merseybeat Nuggets 1963–1966

Two-LP set containing the best of Pye's and Piccadilly's contributions to the British invasion. The Searchers are the best-known of the Pye groups, though who can forget The Undertakers, who dressed in black and traveled to gigs in a hearse! Also includes Tommy Quickly, The Chants, The Wackers, and The Trends.

SEQUEL 103 (RL)
Dance On: Youth Club Classics 1961–1963

Two-LP set of early British teen music. The best things here are the instrumentals by The Eagles and The Saints, but even these barely transcend their teen-pop roots. Of historical interest only.

SEQUEL 106 (RL)
A Shot of Rhythm and Blues: The R&B Era, Vol. 1

Maximum R&B from a lineup of mostly second-tier groups that recorded for Pye Records between 1963–1966. These are some of the rawest, most savage British recordings made in the '60s. Cyril Davies and His Rhythm and Blues All Stars, Tony Jackson and The Vibrations, The Brand, The Primitives, The Clique, The Riot Squad, The Sorrows, and The Kinks shake 'em down but good.

SEQUEL 107 (RL)
Watch Your Step: The Beat Era, Vol. 1

Lesser-known British-beat groups, including The Honeycombs, The Rockin' Berries, The Sorrows, and The First Gear. "Zulu Stomp" by The Brand is incredible.

SEQUEL 108 (RL)

Quick Before They Catch Us: The Pop Era, Vol. 1

Sixteen British pop tunes from the mid-'60s. Includes "Creeping Jean," one of Dave Davies's non-Kinks singles. Other popsters are The Sorrows, The Searchers, The Chapters, The Riot Squad, and Don Crain of The Downliners Sect.

SEQUEL 109 (RL)

Soul Source: The Soul Era, Vol. 1

Sixteen cuts of British blue-eyed soul. Sandra Barry, A Band of Angels, The Spectres, Timebox, and Kenny Bernard.

SEQUEL 110 (RL)

The Immediate Alternative: A Collection of Rarities

Immediate Records was formed in 1965 by Tony Calder and Rolling Stones's manager Andrew Loog Oldham, and lasted until 1970 with a few successful groups like The Small Faces and The Nice. This LP digs up some buried treasure from the Immediate vaults, including tons of finely crafted pop by Les Fleurs de Lys, Goldie (of Goldie and The Gingerbreads), The Mockingbirds (who later became 10CC), The Poets, Billy Nichols, and The Outer Limits.

SEQUEL 111 (RL)

Here Come the Girls: British Girl Singers of the '60s

Sixteen tracks by British female vocalists in The Chiffons, Ronettes, and Crystals mold, including The Breakaways, Sandra Barry, and Sandie Shaw.

SEQUEL 149 (L)

British '60s Instrumentals (1961–1964)

Twenty-two British instrumentals originally recorded in the early '60s. Although well played, this is fairly tame stuff, sounding more like soundtrack music than rock and roll. The Fentones show more power than the other groups on this anthology, including The Boys, The Scorpions, The Cougars, The Planets, and The Outlaws.

SEQUEL 150 (L)

Highly Strung: Instrumental Diamonds, Vol. 2

More early '60s instrumental releases, with considerably more grungy spirit than the first volume. With a generous 25 tracks by The Sons of The Piltdown Men, The Eliminators, Ahab and The Wailers, The Honeycombs, Peter Jay and The Jaywalkers, The Blackjacks, and The Ravens.

SEQUEL 171 (L)

The Joe Meek Story: The Pye Years

This two-CD set documents English producer Joe Meek, who has garnered a cult following, often being called the English Phil Spector because of his groundbreaking arrangements. He is best known for the hit "Telstar," not included here. Many of these forty-eight tracks are standard teen-pop fare, although there's also a fair share of good beat music by groups like The Honeycombs, The Riot Squad, and The Blue Rondos, and some excellent numbers by instrumental bands, especially The Flee-Rekkers.

SEQUEL 177 (L)

Here Come the Girls, Vol. 2: Take Three Girls

Twenty-three pop tunes from the top three gals who recorded for Pye/Piccadilly: the ever-popular Helen Shapiro; the perky Julie Grant; and the mod's pin-up girl, Billie Davis.

SEQUEL 193 (L)

Run Mascara: Here Come the Girls, Vol. 3

Twenty tunes from the Roulette/Jubilee/Colpix/Dynavoice labels recorded between 1962–1966, featuring energetic, sweet-voiced ladies who are either romantically troubled or elated—often both! The Essex, The Exciters, The Raindrops, The Girlfiends, Toni Wine, Earl-Jean, The Toys, Shelley Fabares, The Carolines, and Elena.

SEQUEL 619 (L)

Roulette Rock and Roll Collection

Most of the best Roulette singles, along with gems from George Goldner's Gone, End, and Rama labels. Andy Dio, Bob Davis, Roc Larue, Jimmy Lloyd, The Chapparals, and Jimmy Isle.

SLASH 25605 (CL)

La Bamba Soundtrack

Exceptionally fine LP featuring music from the Ritchie Valens's biopic. The show belongs to Los Lobos, who perform five Valens's classics: "Ooh My Head," "Come On, Let's Go," "We Belong Together," "Goodnight My Love," and the title tune. There's one tune each from guest stars Bo Diddley, Howard Huntsberry, Brian Setzer, and the set's only real loser, a slick, almost technopop "Crying Waiting Hoping" by Marshall Crenshaw.

SLEAZE 5562 (R)

Sin Alley, Vol 4: Filthy, Sleazy '50s Trash

Rockin' and often weird tracks from the glory days of our youth. McKinley Mitchell, Phil Campos, Jay Blue, Tarantula Ghoul and Her Gravediggers, and Mad Man Jones.

SONY MUSIC SPECIAL PRODUCTS 47348 (CL)

Stroll On: The Immediate Story

Repackaging of the Immediate *Blues Anytime* collection, plus other material from this fledgling British blues-rock label. Features a surprisingly bluesy Rod Stewart, Eric Clapton, Jimmy Page, Albert Lee, The Yardbirds, Savoy Brown, John Mayall, Tony McPhee, and Jo Ann Kelly.

SONY MUSIC SPECIAL PRODUCTS 47351 (CL)

The Immediate Singles Collection, Vol. 1

Twenty masterpieces of '60s mod-rock from Andrew Oldham's Immediate label. The Small Faces were the most successful band on Immediate; their masterful "Itchycoo Park" is an acknowledged classic. Their other tunes show a lot of verve as well, including "Wham Bam Thank You Mam" and "My Mind's Eye." Also includes The McCoys, Chris Farlowe, P.P. Arnold, Nico, and The Mockingbirds. A nice surprise is Fleetwood Mac, using the name Earl Vince and The Valiants, performing the immortal classic, "Somebody's Gonna Get Their Head Kicked In Tonight."

SONY MUSIC SPECIAL PRODUCTS 46994 (CL)

The Immediate Singles Collection, Vol. 2

Twenty more trippy, mid-'60s, London sounds. The Small Faces, Charles Dickens (aka David Anthony), Goldie (aka Genya Ravan), The Factotums, The Apostolic Intervention (basically The Small Faces under a different name), and The Excelsior Spring.

SONY MUSIC SPECIAL PRODUCTS 47894 (CL)

Dealing with the Devil: Immediate Blues Story, Vol. 2

More limey blues rockers, recorded 1963–1966. Fifteen early cuts by Eric Clapton, John Mayall, Tony McPhee, Albert Lee, Cyril Davies, Jeff Beck, and Savoy Brown.

SONY MUSIC SPECIAL PRODUCTS 47897 (CL)

Down and Dirty: Immediate Blues Story, Vol. 3

For my money, this is the best volume so far, with 14 cuts featuring true blue Brits Jo Ann Kelly, Jeremy Spencer (later of Fleetwood Mac), Eric Clapton, and Jimmy Page.

STAR CLUB 8017 (R)

All American Rock, Vol. 1

Sixteen cuts from Ray Bishop's Bishop label from Pittsburgh, featuring local rockabilly recorded between 1957–1981 by Donna Danger, George Darro, The Fortunes, Chuck Owston, Howard Perkins, Rick Rickels, Buddy Sharpe and The Shakers, Pat Wallace, and Tennessee Slim.

STAR CLUB 8019 (R)

All American Rock, Vol. 2

Sixteen wild rockers from the '50s featuring Hasil Adkins's immortal "She Said," plus hot tracks by Frank Triolo, The Jokers, D. Fearsley, Bradd Suggs, The Rock-A-Beats, The Rockits, Gene Davis, The Discords, Wild Child Gibson, Benn Joe Zeppa, The Noise Makers, and Howard Brady.

STAR CLUB 8027 (R)

All American Rock, Vol. 4: Rockin' Record Hop

Eighteen rockin' teen-jive tunes from the Columbia vaults, recorded between 1957–1959. Nine cuts by actor/jiver Paul Hampton, along with single cuts by Carl Perkins, Billy "Crash" Craddock, John D. Loudermilk, Mel Tillis, and Dick Lory.

STAR CLUB 8037 (R)

All American Rock, Vol. 5: Rockin' Rollin' Groups

Fine rock and roll and rockabilly by '50s white vocal groups, featuring tough guitar and/or sax-led bands. Sixteen crazy, raw rockers by The Castle Kings, The Deans, The Seniors, and Kent Perry and The Rogues.

STAR CLUB 8038 (R)

Rock and Roll Christmas

Sixteen fun, rockin', rollin' Xmas ditties including "Rock and Roll Christmas" by Cordell Jackson, "The St. Nick Rock" by Gary Reno, "Papa Noel" by Brenda Lee, "Rock 'n Roll-y Poly Santa Claus" by Lillian Briggs, "New Baby for Christmas" by George Jones, "I Wanna Spend Xmas with Elvis" by Little Lambsie Penn, and "Snow in the North" by The Spotnicks.

STAR CLUB 8099 (R)

Rock and Roll Party

Sixteen rare '50s rockabilly and rock and roll sides by Phil Barclay, Jane Bowman, Gene Davis, Benny England, Bob Hicks, The Interludes, Gene Lewis, Little Jerry, Long Tall Marvin, Lee Mitchell, The Night Owls, Wesley Reynolds, Brad Suggs, Al Sweatt, and Toby and Ray.

STRIP 001 (R)

Las Vegas Grind

Twenty warped tunes, mostly sax-led instrumentals featuring weird spoken bits. The Wildtones's "Shut-up" ("I don't wanna go to Europe."/"Shut-up and keep swimming") is typical. This is the weirdest and most fun record I've heard in a while, with lots of great '50s photos of a sleazy stripper on the cover.

STRIP 002 (R)

Louie's Limbo Lounge
(Las Vegas Grind, Vol. 2)

More uncatagorizable musical mayhem. Jack Hammer, The Noisemakers, Frank Motley and His Motley Crew (no, not those jokers), The Rhythm Addicts, and The Periscopes tear up the place.

STRIP 003 (R)

Las Vegas Grind, Vol. 3

Hubba, hubba! Check out the measurements on this baby: 20 lewd and lascivious morsels to raise your blood pressure higher than a cornered wampus cat. "Riding By" sounds like The Champs at 78 rpm and shouldn't be danced to without permission from your chiropractor; however, Jack Hammer's absolutely manic "Wiggling Fool" is just what the ol' sawbones ordered. Bob and Don's "The Beat Generation" is music-minus-one for bongos!

STRIP 004 (R)

Las Vegas Grind, Vol. 4

Believe it or not, there were even more sleazy, greasy, kooky 45s made in the '50s and '60s than you or I ever imagined. Jack Ross, Edgar Allen and The Po' Boys, The Gee-Cees, The Charts, The Crescendos, The Playboys, and The Egyptians.

STRIP 005 (R)

Jungle Exotica

The closest these guys ever got to a jungle was a trip to the local Tiki lounge or watching Tarzan reruns. You won't want to miss "The Jungle" by Diablito, "Kookie Limbo" by Kookie Joe, "Watusi Zombie" by Jan Davis, and "Congo Mambo" by Guitar Gable! Something like "Hi Yo Camel" by The Peeple might set back "world beat" about 20 years. The cover art is so colorful, beautiful, and bizarre that it will make you weep with pleasure.

SUN (UK) 33 (L)

Those Rockin' Gals

The Miller Sisters, The Kirby Sisters, Barbara Pittman, Maggie Sue Wimberly, Wanda Ballman, Jean Chapel, and Patsy Holcomb are represented by some fine rockabilly and honky-tonk cuts. The same can't be said for Elvis's old flame Anita Wood on the dire "I'll Wait Forever" or Bobbie Jean Barton "singing" "Just Discovered Boys," which is actually so bad that it's good.

SUNDAZED 5001 (R)

The Best of Metrobeat

Minneapolis-area rockers of the late '60s who recorded for the Metrobeat label, including The Trashmen, The Cornerstones, Jokers Wild, and The Underbeats.

SUNDAZED 11003 (L)

Surf and Drag, Vol. 1

Twenty boss sounds from the beach and dragstrip! Mostly rubberburners by The Knickerbockers, The Four Speeds, Gene Moles, and Don Brandon, with surfin' sides from Jan and Dean, and The Champs.

SUNDAZED 11010 (L)

Oh Yeah! The Best of
Dunwich Records

Thirty-one track CD (counting five short radio spots) brings together most of the best tracks, including some fine unreleased demos, from Chicago's seminal garage-band label. The Shadows of Knight, The Del-Vetts, Saturdays Children, The Knaves, The Mauds, and the rest of the Dunwich stable were marked by a tendency toward the more melodic, well-produced side of '60s punk, but still performed with a power and urgency that is compelling. Comes with a 20-page, fully illustrated booklet by Jeff Jarema. Originally released as a Voxx LP, with fewer tracks, in 1990.

SUNJAY 568 (R)

Memphis Rockabilly

Sixteen sides recorded for Marshall Ellis's labels in the mid-to-late '50s, including Erwin, Clearmont, E&M, Rivermont, and Zone. The most famous name here is Eddie Bond, heard on "Here Comes That Train." Jimmy Luke, Jimmy Evans, Ray Scott, Merdel Floyd, and Hoyt Johnson.

SUNJAY 578 (R)

Memphis Rockabilly, Vol. 2

Rare material from Buford Cody's labels, Memphis, Co, and Wi, released in the late '50s/early '60s. Features a rare surf record from Memphis, "Night Surfin'" by The Rebel Rousers, who also contribute "Thunder and The Zombie Walks," along with tracks by Charlie Feathers, Eddie Bond, Jody Chastain, Lloyd Arnold, Thomas Ingle, and Ramon Maupin.

SUNJAY 582 (R)

California Rockabillies

Great collection of previously unissued material by Tommy Brooks, Gary Lambert, Glen Glenn, and Eddie Cochran! This LP isn't for the casual fan, but for rockabilly buffs it's a must.

SUNJAY 588 (R)

Big D Jamboree

Twenty-two cuts from tapes made by Ed McLemore in the late '50s and early '60s. The two Gene Vincent demos will surely excite his many fans, even though "Lonesome Boy" and "Lady Bag" aren't really very exciting tunes. Also includes Johnny Carroll, Ronnie Dawson (as Ronnie Dee), Mitchell Torok, and unknowns Eddie McDuff, Billy Jack Hale, and Jay Hawkins (not "Screamin' Jay") who create some primal rockabilly.

SUNROCK 822 (R)

Rock and Roll Jamboree

Twelve rare rockabilly and rock-and-roll sides from the '50s. Art Adams and The Rhythm Kings, Gene Dunlap and The Jokers, Mickey Hawks and His Night Raiders, Hank Mizell, Jerry Parsons and The Blue Jeans, Lynn Pratt and His Rhythm Cats, The Rockers, Johnnie Strickland, Hank Swatley, and Dale Vaughn and The Starnotes.

SUNROCK 831 (R)

Rock and Roll Jamboree, Vol. 2

Fourteen '50s rockabilly and R&B obscurities performed by Bobby Mitchell, Eddie Palace, Dixie Dee/Wade Curtis and The Rhythm Rockers, Jimmy Pritchett, Curley Coldiron and The Circle "C" Boys, G.L. Crockett, Hoyt Johnson and The Four Recorders, Wally Lewis, Chuck Barr, and Lynn Pratt and His Rhythm Cats.

SUPERSONIC 1169 (R)

Hot Boppin' Girls, Vol. 1

SUPERSONIC 1170 (R)

Hot Boppin' Girls, Vol. 2

SUPERSONIC 1171 (R)

Hot Boppin' Girls, Vol. 3

SUPERSONIC 1173 (R)

Hot Boppin' Girls, Vol. 5

SUPERSONIC 1174 (R)

Hot Boppin' Girls, Vol. 6

SUPERSONIC 1175 (R)

Hot Boppin' Girls, Vol. 7

SUPERSONIC 1176 (R)

Hot Boppin' Girls, Vol. 8

Each volume in this series features 16 sides of '50s rockabilly and rock-and-roll by well-known and lesser-known female artists. Sleeve features eye-poppin', girly graphics (for the discriminating listener). Artists include Patsy Cline, Dorothy Collins, JoAnn Campbell, Georgia Gibbs, LaVern Baker, Teresa Brewer, Eartha Kitt, The Melody Maids, Laura Lee Perkins, Jackie DeShannon, Dolly Parton, Barbara Pittman, Debbie Stevens, Ruth Brown, and Katie Webster.

TEENAGER 5917 (R)

Let's Go Rocking at the High School Hop Again

Sixteen '50s numbers, a mixture of rockin' doo-wop, jivers, rockabilly, and country boppers. Chubby Checker, The Impacts, Warner Mack, Wink Martindale, The Fireballs, Trini Lopez, Mel Tillis, Mack Vickery, and Jim Alley.

TEICHIKU 25846 (L)

Surfin' and Hot Rod: The Endless Summer Hit Graffiti 30

Like the title sez, ya get 30 rubber-burnin', wave-churnin' twangers that stoked all the locals, customizers, gremmies, and sand baggers back in the JFK years. Jan and Dean, The Chantays, The Ventures, The Ripcords, The Hondells, and Santo and Johnny are among the stars of our youth captured on this anthology.

TORTURE 000-NO (R)

Bent, Batty and Obnoxious

The most demented, warped, and, yes, truly awful slabs o' wax ever unleashed on an unsuspecting public. Ranging from a hilarious tribute to a Philadelphia cheese steak house called "Pat's Steaks" (easily my favorite recitation record of the year), to Johnny Buckett's hippy-bashing country crooner "Hippy in a Blender." Not recommended for the squeamish.

UNION PACIFIC 004 (R)

Transfusion

Excellent collection of rare '50s rockers performed by The Band, The Del Vikings, Al Downing, The Everly Brothers, Johnnie Greer, Ronnie Hawkins, Nervous Norvous, Ronnie Self, Vince Taylor, and Conway Twitty.

UNION PACIFIC 005 (R)

Loose Ends

Fine selection of mid-'50s to early '60s rock-and-roll instrumentals by B.B. Cunningham Jr., Duane Eddy, The Fendermen, The Fireballs, The Hawk (aka Jerry Lee Lewis), The Scotty Moore Trio, Ronnie and The Rainbows, Eddie Skelton, The Vigilantes, The Virtues, The Viscounts, and Young John Watson.

UNLIMITED PRODUCTIONS 715 (R)

Surfin' in the Midwest, Vol. 2

Sixteen land-locked surf and surf-influenced classics by The Titans, The Four Wheels, The Venturas, The Enchanters Four, and The Crestones, with extensive notes on each band.

White Label

Cees Klop in Holland is a man with a mission: trying to unearth just about every obscure, '50s rockabilly and rock-and-roll recording. He started White Label a dozen years ago or so, and since then has issued nearly 200 LPs of unissued songs, alternate takes, demos, and home recordings. In 1991, he began issuing material on CD on the Collector label, including material previously issued on White Label along with newly unearthed material. The majority of the White Label releases are anthologies, often with a regional or label-based theme. There are also some single-artist issues and a few recent recordings of old rock-and-roll performers. Almost every LP has some material that is superb, but almost every LP also has some material that is truly dire. The diehard collector will want them all; the less dedicated will hopefully find some useful comments here to separate the wheat from the chaff. Good luck!

WHITE LABEL 8801 (R)

Rock and Rhythm

Fourteen cuts, ten previously unreleased, by Alton Lott, James Truck, Denny White, Lou Millet, and Johnny Angel.

WHITE LABEL 8802 (R)

Kentucky Rockabilly

Thirteen rare rockabilly gems by Eddie Gaines, Gus Pate and The Jokers, Tag and Effie, and Dwain Bell and The Turner Brothers.

WHITE LABEL 8805 (R)

Rock, Rock, Rock

Fourteen rockin' tracks by Dick Holler, Alton Carroll, Charlie Feathers, Al Vance, and Mack Allen Smith.

WHITE LABEL 8806 (R)

Rockabilly from Tennesse

Taps the archives of the Jackson, TN-based Hillcrest and Westwood labels. Half of these 14 tunes were never originally released, for good reason. The highlight is Larry Brinkley's big bad "Jackson Dog," a sound with such a bite that it's brought back for an encore on "Move Over Rover" and "Tornado."

WHITE LABEL 8807 (R)

Virginia Rockabilly and Country

One dozen cuts drawn from Virginia's Liberty and Mart labels, which released the first recordings of Micky Hawks and The Night Raiders, one of the wildest groups of the '50s. Featuring a sledgehammer beat, wailin' sax, and savage guitar, "Bip Bop Boom" and "Rock and Roll Rhythm" are all-time classics. Hender Saul, Leon and Carlos, and The Martin Brothers are also featured.

WHITE LABEL 8808 (R)

Rockabilly from Tennessee

Thirteen fairly lame tunes recorded in Fayetteville for the Linco label. The best material here is by Curtis Long, Clyde Owens, Hollis Champion, and The Four Sons. Also of interest is a cut by Alton Delmore, of the legendary Delmore Brothers, who performs a chipper C&W tune, "Good Times in Memphis," from 1959.

WHITE LABEL 8810 (R)

Rockabilly from Tennessee

Side 1 features Joe Griffith, a fairly weak singer who was accompanied by some legendary guitarists, including Chet Atkins. Side 2 is a real treat: a live show from Memphis recorded in 1954 and featuring the obscure Red Rolison and his band. The tape isn't in great shape, and the band is as raw as sushi, but they really rock.

WHITE LABEL 8811 (R)

The Rocking Dees and Poor Boy Labels

Thirteen tunes by Little Donnie Bowshier, Roy Boy Baker, Gene Cisco, Evelyn White, The Ramblin' Rebels, The Van Brothers, and Norman Witcher.

WHITE LABEL 8812 (R)

Unknown Rock and Roll

Interesting, although spotty release; half of the 14 tunes here were previously unissued. The best artists are Jesse Stevens, Joe Moon, The Boppers and Bob, and Orville Fox.

WHITE LABEL 8814 (R)

The Island Recordings

Uneven collection from Cleveland, OH, label, including recordings by Bill Browning and His Echo Valley Boys, Rudy Thacker and His String Busters, and Lou and The Monarchs.

WHITE LABEL 8816 (R)

10 Years of Collector Records

Sixteen-cut anthology of recordings reissued by Collector and White Label, including The Lonesome Drifter (Thomas Johnson), Jimmy Roby, Billy Wayne, Bobby Lollar, Charles Dean, and Teddy Redell.

WHITE LABEL 8818 (R)

Rock from Arkansas

Twelve tracks. The highlights are the four Bobby Brown cuts, with hot guitar, fine vocals by Bobby, and knocked-out 88-ticklin' by Teddy Redell. Teddy also cuts loose on a solo "Saddle Rag." Includes Joyce Green, Johnny Moore, Bill Duniven, and K. Owens.

WHITE LABEL 8819 (R)

More Real Rockabilly and Country

Solid LP of rockabilly and uptempo country. Hollis Champion is the standout, performing "Big Beat" and "Long Gone Lonesome Blues" in a style that would make wild man Hasil Adkins sit up and stare. Other super rockabilly tracks are provided by Johnny Scoggins and Henry McPeak, while Chandos McRill checks in with some uptempo country numbers. Doyle Madden and The Oklahoma Nightriders, Bill and Bink, Paul Durham, June Draper, and Deral Clour also contribute some fine tunes.

WHITE LABEL 8820 (R)
Tennessee Rockin'
Rockabilly and rock and roll from Don Wade's Tennessee-based San label. Wade, Ronnie Allen, and piano pounder Preston Lipford are the featured artists.

WHITE LABEL 8821 (R)
Aaahhh Rockabilly
Fourteen cuts by Tom James, Lee Ebert, Rikki and The Rikatones, Virgil Bozman, and Jim Owen. James's "Track Down My Baby" and "Hey Baby" are both relentless rockers with great vocals and red-hot guitar work, too.

WHITE LABEL 8822 (R)
Rock and Rockabilly
Must-have rockabilly collection featuring Brownie Johnson, Ray Awalt and The Bi-Stone Playboys, Jimmy Witter and The Shadows, Boliver Shagnasty, Ray King and The Kingsmen, The Chancellers, Jimmy Wayne and The Galaxies, and Jerry Lott (aka The Phantom).

WHITE LABEL 8823 (R)
The Cozy Label
John Bava's Cozy label from WV started in the '40s and recorded country and rockabilly sides well into the '50s. These seventeen cuts feature a cross section of both styles, with Keith Anderson and The Showmen, Johnny Watson (not Guitar Watson) and his Night Owls, Dorsey Lewis (aka The Scared Coal Miner), Butch Lester, and Hank The Cowhand.

WHITE LABEL 8824 (R)
Rockabilly Rock
Detroit-based (!) rockabilly by Lafayette Yarborough and The Rim Shots, along with Texans Orville Couch and The Troublemakers, Bob Calloway and The Clicks, and Don Gilliland. Highlight is a rare and great Jimmy Murphy tune, "There's No Use in Me Loving You" done for Midnite.

WHITE LABEL 8827 (R)
The Best of Linn and Kliff
Sixteen tracks culled from these rockabilly labels from Gainesville, TX, with artists David Ray, Buck Griffin, Don Terry, and Don Curtis (aka Butch McClarey).

WHITE LABEL 8828 (R)
More Rockabilly
Fourteen raucous tracks by Bob Luman with The Mac Curtis Band, Pete and Jimmy, The Reekers, Slim Dortch, Rudy Hansen, Bobby Carter and The Spotlites, and Ty B. and Johnny.

WHITE LABEL 8829 (R)
Wild Rockin'
Side 1 is devoted to Florida rockabilly singer Gene Watson and His Rockets, Side 2 to Bob Calloway and The Spiro Hep Cats and Rodney and The Blazers. Sound quality varies.

WHITE LABEL 8830 (R)
Primitive Sound
Fifteen cuts, including some mildly interesting demo takes, by Darrell Speck and The Rebel Rousers, Norman Bullock and The Southerneers, The Renfro Brothers, Jerry Cox, and Joey Castle. A couple of late '60s recordings by Ray Scott (remember "Boppin' Wigwam Willie" from the '50s?) are surprisingly great with a very straight-forward rockin' sound.

WHITE LABEL 8831 (R)
Tank Town Boogie
Fifteen tunes from the vaults of Hank Harral's Caprock label, active in Big Springs, TX, in the late '50s. Nothing much here for hard-core rockabilly fans, but lovers of country, boogie, and Western swing will have a good time. Hank performs the title cut; also included are Max Alexander, Hoyle Nix, Jimmy Haggett, Ace Ball, and Jack Tate.

WHITE LABEL 8832 (R)
Rockin' Rockin'
Side 1 features Andy Doll and his band on nine boppin' hillbilly tunes recorded for Doll's own AD label from Iowa. Side 2 is all rockabilly, with Blacky Vales, Jimmy Dane and His Great Danes, Phil Cay, and four others.

WHITE LABEL 8833 (R)
More Primitive Sound
Side 1 features Jerry Woodard, a talented rockabilly singer/guitar player from Alabama who made a go of it in the mid-to-late '50s. Includes released sides and some scratchy acetates. Side 2 has eight tunes, ranging from decent (Wayne Newman and The Torques) to abysmal (Bill Duncan).

WHITE LABEL 8834 (R)
Great Labels of the South
Side 1 collects titles from Rupert McClendon's Trepur label from LaGrange, GA. Jaybee Wasden is the highlight here, performing a wonderful "Elvis in the Army," and a bizarre tune called "De Castrow" about a Cuban rebel who tried to steal his girl! Side 2 gives a quick look at the Ridgecrest label, also from LaGrange. Rockabilly performers include The Carpenter Brothers and The Rhythm Boppers, and Red Melson and The Missouri Nighthawks.

WHITE LABEL 8835 (R)
Southern Rockin'
Lonnie Allen, Lanier Smith, and Dewey Guy are artists from LaGrange, GA. Jim Wilson, Lawrence Shaul, and Mason Dixon all recorded for the Reed label out of Alabama. Shaul's version of "Tutti Frutti" is a real hoot; he sounds like a 14-year-old in front of a wild rockin' band.

WHITE LABEL 8836 (R)
Yucca Records and Others
Sixteen tunes mostly recorded for Calvin Boles's Yucca label out of beautiful Alamogordo, NM. Boles, Al Sims, Bob Taylor and The Counts, Steve Cooper and The Avantis, Jerry Bell and The Original Rockets, Lewis Pruitt, Dappa Smith, The Renaults, and Jerry Bright and The Embers are the stars.

WHITE LABEL 8837 (R)
Still Going Strong
Contemporary recordings by '50s rockabilly performers, including Buddy Miller, Jerry Arnold, The Sabres, Gray Montgomery, and Tommy King and The Starliters.

WHITE LABEL 8838 (R)
Rockabilly Souvenir
Fifteen vocals and instrumentals by Bud Landon and The Rhythm Masters, Bill Blevins, The Raper Brothers, Jorris Hennessee, Roy Moore and The Tennessee Drifters, and Ray Clark and The Demons.

WHITE LABEL 8839 (R)
Rockin' in the '50s
Mixed bag of 15 tunes by Wisconsin's Marv Blihode, and Jack Roubik and The T-Js, along with Ronnie Hanson and The Super-Phonics, Harvey Hurt, Tommy Faile, and Johnny Ramistella.

WHITE LABEL 8840 (R)
More Tennessee Rockin'
Rare rockabilly from Dubb Pritchett, Cliff Blakley, Bubba Ford and The Sounds, Little Joe Allen and The Off Beats, and a duet by Phil Beasly and Charly Brown.

WHITE LABEL 8841 (R)
Rock Originals
Unique songs (each with a special gimmick) by Charles Senns, The Nomads, Ron Hall, Kenny Smith, Wink Lewis, Howie Stange, and The Satellites. This is probably the best White Label collection so far.

WHITE LABEL 8842 (R)
Rockabilly Boppin'
Fifteen tunes by Ray Campi, The Slades, Bozo Ratliff, R. Dean Taylor, and Gene Ray.

WHITE LABEL 8843 (R)
Let's Rock Tonight
Sixteen hot numbers, including the title cut by Jimmy Grubbs and The Music Makers, one of the most powerful rockabilly recordings ever waxed with driving guitar over a pounding beat. Also includes Gene Ski and The Troubadours, Larry Phillipson and his band, The Rollettes, Jerry and The Silvertones, Johnny Waleen, and Bobby Lane.

WHITE LABEL 8844 (R)
Rock Originals, Vol. 2
Fifteen numbers by Jimmy Woodall, Jerald Boykin and The Three Ramblers, T.K. Hulin, and Jack Reno, along with hot, guitar-powered instrumentals by The Shifters, The Teen Tones, and The Storms.

WHITE LABEL 8846 (R)
Rock from East to West
Bobo Baxter, Jerry Raines, Rudy Preston, Bill James and The Hex-O-Tones, Leo Gosnell and The Drifters, Chuck Harrod and The Anteaters, Billy Hogan and The Twi-Lighters, and The Rockabilly Three provide the fun. You just have to love a tune like "Shake It Over Sputnik" by Hogan; it's as '50s as a kidney-shaped coffee table.

WHITE LABEL 8847 (R)
The Cuca Records Rock Story, Vol. 1
First in a three-LP series that digs into the archives of Cuca Records, based in Sauk City, WI. "Mule Skinner Blues" by The Fendermen was the most famous record to come out of James Kirchstein's operation, but the rockers came from far and wide to lay down a track or two. Instrumental thunder from Willie Tremain's Thunderbirds, The Rock-a-Fellers, and The Montereys.

WHITE LABEL 8848 (R)
The Cuca Records Rock Story, Vol. 2
Sixteen more tough rockers from the Cuca archives. If you like rockin' instrumentals from the late '50s and early '60s, then you'll get a real charge out of the tracks by The Orbits, The Zircons, The Teen's Men, The Furys, The Nighthawks, and The Phaetons. Bud Squires and Bob Mattice are the best of the vocal brigade, although it's impossible to find fault with Ray Kannon and The Corals, either.

WHITE LABEL 8849 (R)
The Cuca Records Rock Story, Vol. 3
Marv Blihovde and The Vanguards perform the first half dozen tunes of this 19-tracker. The Teen Tones, Bobby Smith and The Neat-Beats, The Catalinas, and

The Mule Skinners are among the great guitar twangers featured.

WHITE LABEL 8850 (R)

Great Rarities from Various Labels

Fourteen rockin' numbers by: Johnny Dove; Bobby Wayne; The Warriors (Wayne's backup band); Joe, Ron and George; Al Oster; The Oxtones; Duke and Null; and The Emanons.

WHITE LABEL 8851 (R)

Great Rarities from Various Labels

Johnny Denton, Johnny Worthan, Jay Brown and The Jets, The Royal Lancers, and Wynn Stewart perform fifteen rockers and instrumentals.

WHITE LABEL 8852 (R)

Minnesota Rockabilly Rock

Fantastic 14-track selection of rock and roll recorded for the cool Soma label, as well as happening labels like Gaity and Hep (along with their custom releases). Features cuts by Tommy Scott, Ronnie Ray and The Playboys, Jim Thaxter and The Travelers (three of these guys went on to form The Trashmen!), Hal Fritz and The Playboys, Ron Thompson and The Broughams, and The Orbits.

WHITE LABEL 8853 (R)

Minnesota Rockabilly

Fifteen slabs of rockabilly furor by Terry Lee and The Poorboys, The Sonics, and Myron Lee and The Caddies. They'll bludgeon you over the head with their power—and you'll love it too. Highly recommended.

WHITE LABEL 8854 (R)

Minnesota Rockabilly Rarities, Vol. 2

Fifteen '50s and early '60s rock-and-roll tracks from Minnesota. DJ and The Cats (aka DJ and The Runaways), The Inn-Truders, The Galaxies, and The Jades are here to rock the house. There's even a cranked-up, western-swing number by Les Tucker called "Wrong Kinda Lovin'."

WHITE LABEL 8855 (R)

Minnesota Rockabilly Rarities, Vol. 3

Highlights one of the more popular Minneapolis-area bands of the '50s and '60s, Mike Waggoner and The Bops, with recordings taken from recently discovered demo tapes. The sound is quite good and the guitar is ferocious. A couple of hot numbers by Eddie Barkdall and The Corvets plus three other bands round out the action.

WHITE LABEL 8856 (R)

Rockin' Rufus

The title tune is a good rocker by Ramon Maupin originally out on Memphis's Fernwood label. Also includes Gary Hodge, Jerry Dean and The Shades, Steve Purdy and The Studs, The Emcees, Ronnie D'Valiant, Willie Ward, Ray St-Germaine, and a cat called Mondo.

WHITE LABEL 8857 (R)

The Lucky Records Label

Cinncinati's Lucky label released a string of good recordings during the late '50s and early '60s. Most of these 15 tunes are solid rockabilly, but they all show some strong rural roots. Includes Bill Watkins, Nelson Young, Larry Dale, Bobby Grove, and all four of Bill Browning's Lucky sides.

WHITE LABEL 8858 (R)

More Wild Rockin'

Featured singers include Bobby Lawson, Marlon Grisham, The Cheerleaders, Dinky Harris and The Spades, Rabon Sanders, and Chuck Bowers. Instrumental fans won't be disappointed either with Bob Vidone and The Rhythm Rockers, and The Dick DeWayne Combo.

WHITE LABEL 8859 (R)

Mister Rock and Roll

Fifteen primitive tracks by Dennis Volk, Paul Ballenger and The Flares, Leon Bowman, Kenny Owens, Johnny Boni and His Triumphs, and The Kilgore Brothers.

WHITE LABEL 8860 (R)

Rare Rock from Canada

Documents the Canadian rock-and-roll scene of the '50s. Side 1 highlights Banff-label recording artist Ted Daigle, who melts some tundra with his self-penned "Mary Lou" and some rockin' covers. Other artists include Bob and Lucille (aka The Canadian Sweethearts), Reg Smith, Scotty Stevenson with The Edmonton Eskimos, and Bob King.

WHITE LABEL 8861 (R)

Rare, Primitive Early Rock and Roll

If you like blazing guitars and wailin' saxes (with an occasional boogie-woogie piano), then this 17-track, smokin' collection of instrumentals is for you! The Swanks, The Phantom Five, The Dissonaires, The Vulcans, and The Princeton Five are the acts. Turn up the volume and break out those dancin' shoes!

WHITE LABEL 8862 (R)

Gotta Rock Me Daddy

Fifteen rockin' numbers by Richie Deram and The New Tones, Paul Wheatley, The Shades, Arnold Wheatley, and Bobby Rutledge. Deram echoed the sentiments of many a red-blooded '50s teen with his awesome "Girl and a Hot Rod."

WHITE LABEL 8863 (R)

Tooter Boatman and Friends

Fourteen, mostly unissued '50s rockers from Tooter, Danny Wolfe, Johnny Duncan, Huelyn Duvall, and the rest of this rowdy Texas crew.

WHITE LABEL 8865 (R)
Rock-on Roll-on
The Vi-Kings, Mack Vickery, The Gamblers, Bob Vidone and The Rhythm Rockers, and Bailey's Nervous Cats scratch out 16 hot tracks. The Gamblers cashed in with the original version of "Moon Dawg," a much-covered instrumental.

WHITE LABEL 8866 (R)
Rock and Roll Girls
White Label's first foray into the rockin' gals genre, and it's a corker. Seventeen rockers by Betty Nickel and The Rockets, Linda and The Epics, Betty Jo, Penny Candy, and Brenda Darlin'.

WHITE LABEL 8867 (R)
Home Made Early Rock and Roll
Fifteen, small-label, demo-quality custom pressings. Jimmy Holder and The Chevells, The Tornados, Steve Kingsmill, Bobby Smith, and Sonny Freeze are among the acts.

WHITE LABEL 8868 (R)
More Home Made Early Rock and Roll
Uneven collection of 15 tracks, featuring Hugh Friar and The Virginia Vagabonds, and Kip Tyler.

WHITE LABEL 8869 (R)
Swinging the Rock
A string of second-rate popabilly performers, with the exception of Ronnie Braham, Donny Lee Moore, Little Richard Moreland, and Sherree Scott.

WHITE LABEL 8870 (R)
More Rare Rock
Eddie McKinney, Johnny Lane and The Hot Rodders, The Duals, Don Duncan, Lucky Boggs, and Jerry Woodard provide some real '50s flavor on these tracks.

WHITE LABEL 8871 (R)
Lot of Rockin'
Fifteen tunes, featuring boppin' hillbilly by Tommy Trent, Al Winkler, and Retus Blair; Bill Haley-type rock and roll by Jimmy Cavallo, Charlie Aldrich, and Eddie Lee; piano pounding by Piano Slim; and Texan instrumentalists The Royal Jokers.

WHITE LABEL 8872 (R)
Reed Recordings
Seventeen mid-'50s recordings from Homer Milam's Reed label of Birmingham, AL. Bill Perry, Mason Dixon, Larry and The Loafers, and The Starliners are the standouts on this collection of otherwise rather bland material.

WHITE LABEL 8873 (R)
Alabama Rocks
Tim Bowman, who recorded under the moniker of Tiny Tim (no jokes please), performs his awesome "I've Gotta Find Someone." His band The Tornadoes contribute some absolutely savage guitar playing to this cut. His cousin Leon Bowman does three country rockers, too. Johnny Cook, Sammy Salvo, The Epics, and Jimmy Holder and The Chevells are also included on this 14-cut collection.

WHITE LABEL 8875 (R)
I Want Rock
Leon and James, Rick Tucker, Chuck Jones and The Stardusters, Claude King, Roger Stafford and The Royal Monarchs, Wesley Reynolds, D.C. Rand and The Jokers, and Larry O'Keefe perform 14 rockin' tracks.

WHITE LABEL 8877 (R)
The Crazy Alligator
Irvin Russ turned out a great rocker in "The Crazy Alligator," based on Johnny Horton's "Ballad of New Orleans," but told from the gator's viewpoint! Bobby Lumpkin and The Kapers, Mackey Beers and the Rockitts, Billy Taylor, Carl Belew, and instrumentalists The Twisters are the standouts on this 15-cut collection.

WHITE LABEL 8878 (R)
Minnesota Rockabilly Rarities, Vol. 5
This fifth and final volume of Minnesota rock and roll is divided into a vocal side and an instrumental side. Robbie Robbins, The Jades, and Augie Garcia are the vocalists, with Garcia's R&B-tinged vocals the best of the lot. The Flames, The Delricos, The Glenrays, and The Five Spots provide the hot instrumentals.

WHITE LABEL 8881 (R)
Real Rockin' Now
Tommie Tolleson, Johnny Fay and The Blazers, Jessie King and The Crowns, Maximilian, Cuddles C. Newsome, Ray Beach, and Gary and Dick Faulkner are the best acts on this uneven collection.

WHITE LABEL 8882 (R)
Always Rockin'
Features The Astronauts's first release from 1962, "Come Along Baby" (originally on the Palladium label), showing that Stormy and the boys were rockers from the get go. Ray McArthurs's Hill Stompers, Joe Caldwell, Little Ben and The Cheers, Gene Davis, Ray Doggett, Jim Murphy, and Billy Free are all on this 15 tracker.

WHITE LABEL 8884 (R)
Original Early Rock Instrumentals
Eighteen blasters taken from some very scarce and rare small-label 45s like Flame, Flick, Reverb, and Amp. Side 1 has the earlier, primitive numbers, many in a hopped-up country vein, by The Raging Storms, The Earthquakes, and The Tempomen. Side 2 really kicks into high gear with some of the heavier frantic bands of the early '60s, like The Vulcans, The Royaltones, The Dawnbeats, The Noise Makers, The Hollywood Hurricanes, and The Sting Rays. Highly recommended.

WHITE LABEL 8885 (R)
Rare Rockin' Girls
The Carter Kids, J. Aguirre, Rosie Stevens, and Dot Anderson are among the artists on this 16-tracker. Some of these tunes are so bad that they're good, especially Lona Parr's weird, ramshackle "I'm a Bop."

WHITE LABEL 8886 (R)
Rock Along
Eighteen cuts by Ted Newton, Chuck Tharp and The Fireballs, Jimmy Work, The Glentells, Chester Smith, and Bill Royal.

WHITE LABEL 8888 (R)
The Pike Recordings
Seventeen tunes from Roy Flowers's Pike Records out of Bakersfield, CA, many previously unissued. There's nothing to get excited about on the first side, although the tunes by Vancie Flowers and The Rialtos aren't half bad. Highlights of the flip side include plenty of weirdness from the minds of Tommy Dee and Gene Moles on "Sheep," "Bingo's Bongo Bingo Party," and "Bingo." You have to hear them to believe them!

WHITE LABEL 8889 (R)
Rockin' in Louisiana
So-so collection of 15 mostly previously unissued '50s rockabilly recordings including Jay Chevalier and The Long Shots, Benny Barnes, and Happy Wainwright.

WHITE LABEL 8890 (R)
Rock Baby Rock
Eighteen-tune collection boasting two of rockabilly's all-time classics, Joey Castle's "Rock and Roll Daddy-O" and Jett Powers's "Go, Girl, Go," along with some wild, live, lo-fi recordings by The Sundowners. Other acts include Neil Darrow, The Highlights, Thomas Mitchell, and Ricky Roy and The Belaires.

WHITE LABEL 8891 (R)
The Best Original Rock in Town
Uneven collection by Mike Moore, Don Coates, Buddy Phillips and The Rockin' Ramblers, Don Ruby, Jerry and The Del-Fis, and Joey Bellomo.

WHITE LABEL 8892 (R)
Rockin' in Louisiana, Vol. 2
The second volume of Louisiana rock and roll is even weaker than the first. The LP is shared by two minor talents. Johnny Ray Harris had a good record with "Cajun Weekend," but the unissued tunes here are lame except for the funny "Alligator Meat." All of Jimmy Wray and The Shreveport Boys's tracks were initially unissued; you'll see why if you buy this!

WHITE LABEL 8893 (R)
Rockin' in Louisiana, Vol. 3
Bozo Darnell, Louis Hobbs, Jerry Raines, Marvin Kerry, and Lawrence Walker perform rockabilly and cajun numbers on this collection, the best so far in the Louisiana series.

WHITE LABEL 8894 (R)
A Rare Collection of Rock
Glen Goza, Sammy Lara, Jimmie Davis, Henry Levoy, Johnny Angel and The Dodgers, Rebel Wright, Marvin Jackson, and Bobby Dean are some of the names on this 16-tracker.

WHITE LABEL 8896 (R)
The Acetate Sessions
These 14 tunes are all previously unissued, taken from very rare acetates. Includes three of rockabilly's greatest heroes: Johnny Carroll, Sonny Burgess, and Mac Curtis. Carroll and Curtis's selections are OK, although the pressings are noisy, but you wouldn't pay much notice to Burgess's sides if they didn't have his name on them. In fact, the trio of tunes by the unknown Jim and Jenny Aguirre are much better, especially "Oh Look at That Baby."

WHITE LABEL 8897 (R)
Pennsylvania Rocks
Bee label recordings, featuring some outstanding teen bands, including Don Ellis and The Royal Dukes, The Del-Rays, Hermy Herman and The Blue Rays, The Royal Rockers, Chuck Barr and The Rockabillies, and The Genos.

WHITE LABEL 8898 (R)
Rock from Rare Small Labels
Bostonians rejoice!! For the first time in decades, the promo-only single by the great DJ Arnie "Woo Woo" Ginsberg with The 3-Ds has been reissued!! Includes "Arnie's Theme," used as the opening of Arnie's *Night Train* show on WMEX, and "PM Rock," a long commercial for Mel's Men's Wear. Also includes Wayne Parker, terrible Elvis covers by Romy Hines, The Starfires, Macey Ross, Starvin' Marvin, and Curly Rash.

WHITE LABEL 8899 (R)
More Rare Rockin' Girls
"Hey guys, put down those dice/And come listen to this gal's advice!" Twenty rare, girl rockabilly sides,

mostly by deservedly unknown acts. Karen Wheeler (Onie Wheeler's daughter) comes closest to being a "name artist." Along for the ride are Lonnie Mae and The Satellites, Kay Johnson, Bolean Barry, Joyce Poynter, Bunny Paul, and Donna Darlene.

WHITE LABEL 8901 (R)

More Rock from the Great Early Days

Sixteen rock and rockin' country obscurities by Ron Seuderi, Wibby Lee, Berry Smith and The Radio Pals, Don Hopkins, and Al Lee. Not one of White Label's better efforts.

WHITE LABEL 8902 (R)

That Good Ole Rock and Roll Show

Includes "two of the strangest rockers ever issued," by Carroll Linn and The Linn Twins ("Rockin' Out the Blues" and "Indian Rock"). They're headed straight for instant cult status. Keetie and The Kats, Jimmy Clendenning, Charlie O'Bannon, Curtis Long, and The Boys and Girls are the other artists on this above-average collection.

WHITE LABEL 8903 (R)

Rock and Roll Medicine

Side 1 features eight cuts by Tommy Scott and His Ramblers, who've been recording country music and playing medicine shows since 1937. They mostly play uptempo country numbers with steel guitars and fiddles, although rock fans will appreciate Scott's answer song to "Roll with Me Henry" called "Dance with Her Henry." Fred Milton's "Barbie Barbie" and "Hound Dog Boogie" by The Hound Dogs (from the Hound Dog label!!) are really terrible, and make you wonder why White Label reissued them. But there's some good stuff like "Linda Baby" by Sammy Fitzhugh and His Moroccans and "San Antone" by Earl Ball.

WHITE LABEL 8904 (R)

Memphis ... Rock and Roll Capitol of the World, Vol. 1

Sixteen rare tunes from tiny Memphis labels, featuring the work of "famous" (?) Memphis producer Marshall Ellis, owner of Erwin, Rivermont, and Clearmont Records, represented here by The Monarchs and Ray Scott. Tex Dixon and Rex Toran offer some rocking numbers, and there are unreleased cuts, mostly straight country, by Larry Eads, Hoyt Johnson, and Chuck Raleigh. Dig the unissued "Two Timing Lover" by Ben Gattis and The Shorty Ginn Band, a rockabilly romp featuring clarinet lead!

WHITE LABEL 8906 (R)

College Hop: Real '50s Boppers

One of the most solid White Label LPs I've heard in quite a while. Almost everything here is high quality and rockin'. Highlights are by The Northern Lights from Massachusetts, and wild stuff by Sonny Flaherty,

Jim Jordan and The Regents, and Johnny Carlton and The Escorts.

WHITE LABEL 8907 (R)

Real Rock Instrumentals

Garage/grunge instrumental fans will dig these 16 rockers, primarily led by scratchy guitars, although there are some piano pounders here, too. Most are from privately issued singles sold at the bands' gigs. The Rel-Yeas, The Shadows Five, The Polaras, The Rangers, The Carnations, and Alan Pierce and The Tone Kings are the standouts.

WHITE LABEL 8908 (R)

Rockabilly World

Sixteen rare rockabilly and rockin'-country tracks from tiny labels. Link Davis and The Canyons is the "name" group here. Also includes Riley Walker and His Rockin'-R-Rangers, Bill Thomas, Babe Sims, and Dennis McCann and The Cut-Ups.

WHITE LABEL 8909 (R)

Little Jump Joint

Fifteen rare rockers, with some of the most frantic music I've heard, especially "Boppin' Wigwam Willie" by Carl Phillips. Ronnie Pearson, Rocky Bop and The Tonight Boys, Ronnie Oldham and The Encores, and The Rel-Yeas perform rockabilly originals and covers.

WHITE LABEL 8910 (R)

More Pennsylvania Boppers

A spotty LP, but it has one of my favorite songs, "Pizza Pizza Pizza Pie" ("Pizza Pie for you and I/I will drive and you will buy") by Neil Alan and The Cosmos, also heard performing the immortal "Light My Rockets and Send Me to the Moon." Includes the entire output of Norman Kelly's Process and Country Star labels, mostly pleasant tunes with acoustic guitars and harmonica performed by Nick Foley (Red's cousin), and Gordon Sizemore (country singer Little Jimmy Sizemore's dad). Also heard are The Impacts, Jim Hall and His Radio Pals, Buddy Sharpe and The Shakers, and Billy Wilson on a mix of rock and country numbers.

WHITE LABEL 8912 (R)

Rock from the Carolinas

Fourteen rarities, primarily devoted to the five-piece band, Louis Gittens and The Sabres, featuring Pete Deal (gtr) and Bob Nuttall (sax). A standout is their "Take up the Slack Daddy-O," about a hipster learning how to water-ski. Harold Crosby and Don Ray are also heard.

WHITE LABEL 8914 (R)

Memphis: Rock and Roll Capital of the World, Vol. 3

Sixteen mostly previously unreleased tunes, featuring 14 cuts by singer-guitarist Herbert Woolfolk, mostly recorded in the '50s in Herb's garage!

WHITE LABEL 8916 (R)

Memphis: Rock and Roll Capital of the World, Vol. 4

Sixteen recordings (14 previously unissued) from Buford Cody's Memphis and Co&Wi labels by Les Sabres, Lloyd Arnold, Charlie Feathers, The Rebel Rousers, Thomas Ingle, and Jim Shaw and The Starlighters.

WHITE LABEL 8917 (R)

The Lembo Recordings, Vol. 1

Rockabilly and sax rock from Boston, recorded by producer Sam Lembo, best known for discovering Freddie Cannon. My fave is "I Wanna Go" by Jimmy Rhodes, featuring his "girlfriend" whining the title line. Also includes The Allstars, The Satellites, Dwarless Fearsley, Johnny Gamble, and The Dusters.

WHITE LABEL 8918 (R)

Memphis: Rock and Roll Capital of the World, Vol. 5

Seventeen tunes from small Memphis labels including E&M, Light, Shimmy, Honesty, and Marble Hill by Jimmy Evans and The Jesters, Bart Barton, and Macy "Skip" Skipper with Brad Suggs on lead guitar, plus a couple of instrumentals by The Skylarks.

WHITE LABEL 8919 (R)

The Girls Are Rockin'

Seventeen rock-and-roll, rockabilly, and rockin'-country tunes with female vocalists, most of whom started out as straight country artists but rocked it up after Elvis came around. High-quality work by Ardis Wells, Barbara Tennant and The Hindle Butts, Ginny Millay, Sandy Lee, and Barbara Bennett and The Hi-Lites.

WHITE LABEL 8920 (R)

Memphis: Rock and Roll Capital of the World, Vol. 6

Fifteen sides from a variety of small labels. The two best-known names, Travis Wammack and Sun session-pianist Smoochy Smith, also contribute the best tracks. Doug Stone and His Tennessee Mountaineers, Blackie Starks, Shelby Smith, Sonny Blankenship, and Tiny Fuller contribute other rockabilly and rockin'-country numbers.

WHITE LABEL 8924 (R)

Rock Moon Rock

First of three LPs reissuing material from the old Collector label (the original White Label), featuring 16 blistering tunes by Billy Lee and The Rugbeaters, The Fendermen backing Don Stewart, The Jordan Brothers, Jimmy Dale, Buck Fowler, and Daniel James.

WHITE LABEL 8925 (R)

Stop Then Rock

Volume 2 of reissues from the Collector label, with more rock and roll and teen rock than rockabilly sides.

The Corvairs and Bob Jones and The Bob Cats contribute some nice instrumentals, along with tracks by Charlie Herman and The Keytones, Phil Gray, Tony Chick, and Lonesome Long John Roller.

WHITE LABEL 8926 (R)

Super Rock Instrumentals from the Past

Eighteen, wild and sizzling instrumentals. Guitar-led bands like The Fendermen, The Mysterions, The Beltones, and The Hi-Fis contribute some gritty cuts, along with Dumpy "Piano" Rice's rollicking version of "Your Cheatin' Heart."

WHITE LABEL 8927 (R)

Rare '50s Rockers: Busy Rock and Roll

A third volume of Collector label material, with an emphasis on rock and roll rather than rockabilly. Barry Lane, The Night Trains, and Dave Travis and The Premiers are the cream of the crop.

WHITE LABEL 8928 (R)

Wild Original Rock and Roll

Exceptionally strong collection of screaming black rock and roll and drivin' sax instrumentals. There's actually a "name" act here, Don Jullian and The Meadowlarks, along with excellent sides by Bobbie and Boobie, Carmen Taylor and The Buddy Lucas Band, and Curley Hamner and the Cooper Brothers. Don't miss Joe Johnson's rockin', hilarious "Gila Monster" ("No son, that's your mama, the monster's over there").

WHITE LABEL 8929 (R)

Universal Rock and Roll

Seventeen very rare, and mostly quite good rock-and-roll and rockabilly sides by E.C. "Ski-King" Beatty and His Life Boys, The Fallouts, and Jimmy Johnson and Al Casey (THE Al Casey?) and The Arizona Hayriders.

WHITE LABEL 8930 (R)

Monster Hop

Sixteen tunes originally reissued on the limited-edition Collector label. Mostly mid-tempo rockabilly and rockin' country, with the most recognizable name being Herbie Duncan accompanied by The Hurricanes. Other tracks feature vocals by Jimmy Dee and The Meteors, The Blackwell Twins, and Edgel Grooves, and instrumentals by The Nightbeats and The Abstracts.

WHITE LABEL 8931 (R)

Real Fine Primitive Originals

The title says it all! Real rough-sounding records probably cut in garages and living rooms, just bursting with energy, if nothing else (including talent). There's everything here: country boogie, rockabilly, car songs, jive, and instrumentals. Who can forget Lonnie Lillie,

Roger Smith, Doug Harden and The Desert Suns, and Jack and The Ripperz?

WHITE LABEL 8932 (R)

Ordinary Rockin' Girls

Eighteen tunes representing nearly every type of up-tempo '50s music: rock and roll, rockabilly, jive, R&B, rockin' country, honky tonk, even boogie woogie. The only known name here belongs to teen-queen Shirley Gunter, but you'll also hear vocalists Mari Jones, Shirley Jean Wiley, Lee Jones, and Debby Davenport, plus instrumentals by Evelyn and The Ivorytones.

WHITE LABEL 8934 (R)

They Are All Rockin' Kats

Kenny and Doolittle, Clinton O'Neal and The Country Drifters, Tall Paul and The Neighborhood, and Don Agee rock up the grooves on this fine collection. Highlight: Al "Surfin' Hootenanny" Casey picking some great guitar on "If I Told You."

WHITE LABEL 8935 (R)

Original Early Rockers

Jack Day grabs top honors on this one with a pulverizing "Little Joe" featuring a full rockin' sound and hot guitar. Also includes Curley Jim and The Billy Rocks; the Everly-esque Carpenter Brothers and The Nomads; Ronnie Molleen; and John Rocky'rhule (and you think they have crazy names these days).

WHITE LABEL 8936 (R)

Georgia Music

This set of unissued pop-ish or hillbilly material is for completists only or Georgia music enthusiasts. However, there are several good rockers here, including Pat Kelly, The Playtoys, The Cubs, and Mike Cushman and The Interludes.

WHITE LABEL 8937 (R)

Another Collector Release

Don't ya just love this title? Hey, if you released over 150 rockabilly LPs, you'd scratch your head after a while too! This is a pretty eccentric collection, but if you like the backwaters of rockabilly, you'll dig it. Bob and Vic and The Kool Kats, Tommy and The Mighty Four, Skip Stanley, and Mike and Jim and The Billy Rocks are among the big-name acts.

WHITE LABEL 8938 (R)

The Welty Recordings

Quentin Welty was an Ohio record producer who released records on the Hilltop, Z, Prism, and B-W labels between 1958–1962 featuring cuts by The Red Coats, Bobby and The Bengals, Tommy Carpenter and The Rhythm Boys, and The Gudell Brothers.

WHITE LABEL 8939 (R)

Rock and Roll Billy

Average collection of instrumental, rockin' hillbilly, teen hop, and rockabilly by Joe and Ray Shannon, Pete Peters and The Rhythmakers, Joey Warren, and The Cals. "Highlight" is "Nuthin, Man Nuthin," with real party sound effects, by Dick Vance and The Dominos.

WHITE LABEL 8940 (R)

Hot Rod Weekend

An instant party provided by vocalists Donnie and Diane, Jan and Jerry, Sonny Knight, and Butch St. Clair, along with some great instrumentals by The Vibratos and The Breakers.

WHITE LABEL 8941 (R)

Private Rock and Roll

The cover photo shows every record collector's ultimate dream: an old warehouse piled floor to ceiling with shellac treasures. Until you find it, you'll have to make do with these 17 rare rockers. Rick West, Chuck Blevins, J.R. and The Golden Nuggets, The Jet Tones, Russ Parks and The Versatones, and The Warner Brothers Combo are the featured acts.

WHITE LABEL 8942 (R)

More Georgia Music

There are no world beaters here, but there are some good, mostly unreleased rockabilly and R&B tracks recorded for the Super label in the '50s by Little Jimmy Dempsey, Jimmy Myers, Sister Dempsey, and Pete Willis (Chuck's brother), along with more recent outings by The Spades, Dr. Harmonica Zack and The Groovers, and Frans and The Never Mind Band.

WHITE LABEL 8943 (R)

Simply Rockin'

Worthwhile collection of rockin' tracks by Ronnie Wilson, Rocky Davis and The Sky Rockets, Dick Halleman, Gary and The Detonators, Jim Anderson and The Red Scales, and George Brady and The Kingsmen. Also included is the obligatory "previously unissued demo recording": Eldon Rice doing a fantastic rockin' hillbilly number, the great "Hillbilly Swampman."

WHITE LABEL 8945 (R)

Wiggle Walkin' Boogie

Art Buchanan (aka Art Ontario), Wolf Opper, Sandy Scott, Roy Templin and The Credit Cards, King Rock and The Knights, Johnny Dee and The El Dorados, and Vince Maloy on a mixed bag of rockers.

WHITE LABEL 8946 (R)

Bang Bang Rock and Roll

Plenty of hot guitar work by Denny Noie and The Catalinas, The Torquays, and Johnny and The Roccas, along with strong selections by Lee McBride, Don Jobe, Larry Terry, and a cat simply named Ralph. Bobby Hodge and The Rainbow Rangers's "Gonna Take My Guitar" is a tremendous rockin' hillbilly number with a great steel-guitar break.

WHITE LABEL 8947 (R)
Early Rockin' in Arkansas
Includes nine tunes by Wallace Waters, mostly previously unissued, along with ten other cuts by Don Head, Carl Stacey and El Gassaway, and Bill Hardy. There's even an ode to The University of Arkansas football squad by Bob G. Garret: "Arkansas Razorback's No. 1." Is this the only rockabilly "fight song"?

WHITE LABEL 8948 (R)
Bob Mooney and Rem Records
Concentrates on Bob Mooney's Rem label from Lexington, KY, although two of the four Billy Lathrem cuts were actually released on Sun-Ray. Little Jackie Wayne, Little Ennis and The Fabulous Table Toppers, Joe Coleman and The Starlights, Bill Stamper, Jimmy Lee Ballard, The Rhythm Rockers, and Chester and Ruby (a fine hillbilly duo) perform rockabilly and rockin' country numbers.

WHITE LABEL 8949 (R)
Moonlight Rock
Nineteen rockabilly tunes, mostly recorded in the '50s in Kentucky and Tennessee. The Dotson Brothers and The Rockette Band, The Escorts, Rex and Herb, Little Bob and The Night Riders, Norm Seachrist, and Jimmy Wert and The Four Squirts contribute somne boppin' cuts. The real highlight in this lightweight company is the fantastic "Nitebeats Are Rocking" by The Nitebeats, a scorcher with catchy call-and-response singing.

WHITE LABEL 8950 (R)
Rockin' Peg
Sixteen very obscure but very rockin' cuts by Little Monte Jones, Johnny Redd, Jack Gillen, Bobby Ferguson, Bill Meadows, Red Garrison, Ray Storm, Tommy Brown, Rudy and Vince and The Teen Timers, Slim Edwards and The Western Wildcats, The Mysterions, and Charles Glass.

WHITE LABEL 8951 (R)
Rare Rockers from Small 1950s Labels, Vol. 1
The Darts, Lee Harmon and the Circle C Band, Jimmy Dee, 88s cruncher Mickey Gilley with Tracey and Carroll, Bob Hoban and The Midniters, Jimmy Low, and Dennis Smith perform 18 strong rockers and honky-tonk songs.

WHITE LABEL 8952 (R)
Rare Rockers from Small 1950s Labels, Vol. 2
Not nearly as strong as Vol. 1 due to an emphasis on "rare" rather than "rockers" on this collection. But this doesn't mean that there's no meat in the stew. Shorty Long and Bob Norris are the standout vocalists, with Art and The Scioto Rhythm Boys, The Royal Tones, The Cyclones, and Bud Settlemire contributing a quartet of good instrumentals.

WHITE LABEL 8953 (R)
Rare Rockers from Small 1950s Labels, Vol. 3
Bill Carter, Darris Richard, Buddy Watson (with Tommy Riddle's Band), and Melvin Blake and The Star Rockers are the hot vocalists on this collection, with George Torrens and The Maybees, The Rockin' Continentials, The Invaders, The Viscos, and The Titans adding some first-rate instrumentals.

WHITE LABEL 8954 (R)
Rare Rockers from Small 1950s Labels, Vol. 4
Eighteen more rockabilly tunes from extremely rare labels like Zin-A-Spin, Triple A, Provencher, and Skippy. Includes Bruce Marvello and The Red Coats, Joey Mancuso, Earl Mack, The Tren-Dells, The Sultans, Johnny and The Drifters, and William Teller and The Wild Ones. Teller contributes the album's one howler, "Baby Don't," a lowpoint in rockabilly's distinguished history.

WHITE LABEL 8955 (R)
Great Swinging Girls
Eighteen '50s rockers, mostly new to LP. Nancy Day and Glenna Dene contribute a couple of real dogs, but things pick up with Gale Davis, Margaret Lewis, Joyce Lee, Carmela Rosella, Kelly Hart, Jan Moore, and Linda Burnetter. Sue Sinford and Jean Martin can't sing but they turn in a couple of fun, upbeat numbers. There's also some wild novelty tunes, like Ann Castle's "Go Get the Shotgun Grandpa," with blazin' guitar, and "Boogie Woogie Rock," where the cops drive up and knock down the door in the middle of the song.

WHITE LABEL 8956 (R)
Original Early Rockers: Mickey Gilley Was Here
Piano pounding rockabilly (and later C&W) giant Mickey Gilley not only recorded a whole truckload of great tunes, but his prowess on the 88s was much in demand by those in the know, including Jimmy "French" Dee, Johnny Guidry, and Gail Collins. Gilley really shines on instrumentals by Shelton Bissell, The Cajun Combo, and especially on "Hold It, Pts. 1 and 2" credited to Mickey Gilley and Leland Rogers. This is a real nice collection, providing a real service to rockabilly collectors.

WHITE LABEL 8957 (R)
Rare Rockers from Small 1950s Labels, Vol. 5
Maybe these are rare rockers, but some of the best have already been reissued according to my checklist.

Nevertheless there's enough good stuff among these 18 tracks to keep the rockabilly collector satisfied. Gene Parson, The Emanons, Buddy Smith, Jackie Powers, and Billy Craddock are the featured artists. Smith takes top honors in the nuttiest title catagory with the wild "Monkey Singing Baboon What Crazy Crazy Feet."

WHITE LABEL 8958 (R)

Rockin' and Rehearsing

Eighteen cuts by Sam Euggino and The Quotations, Rockin' Sid (a boogie pianist), The Rhythm Kings, Ken Howell, Kookie Jones, teen group Richie and The Reknowns, Montie Jones, Jimmy Patrick, and Pat Kelly and The Shamrocks, and instrumental cuts by The Melotones and Billy Lee and The Ramblers.

WHITE LABEL 8959 (R)

Buddy Holly: His Kind of Music

Eighteen tunes showing the influence of Buddy Holly by Ray Ruff and The Checkmaters, Rich Roman, The Royals, and Chan Romero. Features three previously unissued cuts with Buddy allegedly playing guitar with a fella called Larry Welborn. We'll have to let the Holly experts decide if Buddy's really the string-bender on these sides.

WHITE LABEL 8960 (R)

Dreamboat Rock and Roll

Rockabilly tracks by Fred Sherwood, The Unknowns, The Shadows (NOT those Shadows), Joe Franklin and The Hiliters, Blaze Fury, and Jerry Demar, along with boppin' country numbers by Floyd Fletcher, Tommy Hammond, Earl Aycock, and Connie Dycus. A mixed bag, for sure.

WHITE LABEL 8961 (R)

Dusty but Rockin'

Eighteen big ones by Paul Perry, The Rockers, The Tempests, Lee Pickett and The Screamers, Vinni Vincent, and Carl Hunter and The Mustangs.

WHITE LABEL 8962 (R)

Rock and Roll Hunting

Five hot tunes by The Chavis Brothers are the highlights of this set, which also includes hot instrumentals, some good rockabilly numbers like The Carroll Brothers's manic jive version of "Red Hot," as well as the usual dud or two.

WHITE LABEL 8964 (R)

Missouri Rockers, Vol. 2

Jan Records acetates from the '50s, featuring three local bands. The Krazy Kats are represented by all four tunes that they recorded in 1959, and The Night Rockers contribute a couple of cool instrumentals. The Orbits take over on Side 2, showing some hillbilly influence on tunes like "Frankie and Johnny" and

"Steel Guitar Rag," but still rock out in the classic '50s style on everything they do. Sound quality is uneven.

WHITE LABEL 8966 (R)

Memphis: The Record Label Story

Seventeen tracks from Memphis label Cover Records, run by Buddy Blake Cunningham. Old man Cunningham had a son, B.B. Jr., who played some wicked guitar. He practically burns down the studio on scorchers like "Electrode," "Ivory Marbles," "Trip to Bandstand," and "Tantrum" with Sun legend James Van Eaton pounding the skins. And when B.B. Jr. isn't breakin' strings, Lynn Vernon gives 'em a good wackin' on Marlon Grisham's classic (the best known Cover 45) "Ain't That a Dilly" and his own "Moon Rocket." This is one of the coolest collections I've heard!

WHITE LABEL 8968 (R)

18 Rare Rockin' Jewels

About one-third of these tracks have been reissued elsewhere, but still it's a good collection of rare rock by Marshall Ray Walters, Curtis Lee, Red Lewis and The Rockin' Robins, Ernie Nowlin and The Blue Shadow Boys, Billy Barnett, and Chuck Tyler.

WHITE LABEL 8969 (R)

Memphis: The Stompertime Record Label Story

Memphis rockabilly legend Eddie Bond started his own label in 1957, so he could continue to record even though rockabilly was already sliding in popularity. Stompertime also recorded local artists for label releases as well as vanity recordings and demos for Melvin Endsley, Ray Scott, Eddie by himself and with his band (The Stompers), Leon Starr, Jim Morgan, Doug Stone, and Bud Deckleman. About half of these 19 tunes were never released. For the hardcore rockabilly fan only.

WHITE LABEL 8970 (R)

The Acetate Sessions, Vol. 2

Eighteen extremely rare acetates of varying quality by Bobby Hicks, Dusty Croswhite, The Monarchs, The Unknowns, and Rick and The Rockers. And, of course, the White Label fellers unearthed some great instrumentals by The Rockers, Wally Deane and The Flips, and J.V. and His Band. Bad sound, good fun.

WHITE LABEL 8971 (R)

Rocking Jalopy

Sixteen tracks, with the best by Dave Rogers and The Premiers, Jack Holt, Ray Burden, The Alabama Kid, and The Checkers.

WHITE LABEL 8972 (R)

Frantic Rock and Roll Instrumentals

Eighteen monster workouts originally put out on cool little labels like Star Satellite, Barry, Klub, Sho-Biz, and Fenway with hep titles like "Draggin' Waggin'," "Youngster Meets Monster," "Dragonfly," and "Thunderbird." Ventures wannabes include The Spades, The Marlins, The Thunderbolts, The Bonnevilles, and Blaze Fury.

WHITE LABEL 8973 (R)
Rock and Roll with Piano
Seventeen rare piano-based rockers by some really obscure cats. The best known track is Gene McKown's Aggie-label pounder "Rockabilly Rhythm." Lil' George, Bernie Skelton, The Downbeats, Oscar Neiswander and The Beavers, Rocky Rhule, and Earl Craig are among the keyboard killers.

WHITE LABEL 8974 (R)
Rock to the Bop
Sixteen unjustly obscure rockers. Bill Roberts and The Escorts, Gene Price and The Chordsmen, The Outcasts, The Panting Panther (I'm not making these names up, ya'know), The Stringshifters, Jimmie Fletcher, and Burl Boykin are among the shadowy groups here.

ZU ZAZZ 2005 (R)
Memphis Saturday Night
Diverse collection of '50s Memphis rock and roll and rockabilly. Side 1 opens with a great little jive-talking segment from an old Dewey Phillips radio show, featuring Jay B. Loyd, Ramon Maupin, and Merle "Red" Taylor. Side 2 includes a very early Bill Justis workout, "Instant Crap," and, because Justis was just starting to play rock and roll (coming from a dance-band background), the title's not far from the truth. Billy Riley (under the pseudonym Willie B.) does a couple of Jimmy Reed-sounding numbers, Eddie Bond sings a C&W tune, Ramon Maupin tries to sing on the otherwise fine tune, "Love Gone," and Wink Martindale jumps on the rockin' bandwagon with "Bug-a-Bop."

ZU ZAZZ 2016 (L)
Deep in the Heart of Texas
Texas rock and roll, R&B, and Norteno music from the mid-to-late '80s by Kevin and The Blacktears, Doug Sahm (with Santiago Jimenez), Charlie Beal, Kevin Kosub, Flaco Jiminez, Augie Myers, Dogman and The Shepherds, Toby Torres Y Su Conjunto, and Mike The Lead Singer.

R&B/DOO-WOP ANTHOLOGIES

ACAPPELLA 1001 (R)
New York City to L.A.: A Cappella All the Way!
Despite the title, all of the groups here are from New York or New Jersey: The Variations; The Atlantics; The Hudsons; and The Ad-Libs (formed by John Taylor who wrote "The Boy from New York City"). My guess is that these recordings were made in the '60s.

ACE 87 (R)
West Coast Doo-Wop
Fourteen rarities from 1954 recorded for RPM by The Chanters, The Flairs, The Meadowlarks, Buddy Milton and The Twilighters, The Rocketeers, and The Sounds.

ACE 242 (L)
The Dootone Story, Vol. 1
Dootsie Williams put out some of the finest L.A. and Bay Area doo-wop during the '50s on his Dootone label, including some of the best by The Pipes, The Medallions, The Crescendos, The Silks, The Meadowlarks, The Calvanes, The Romancers, The Penguins, Willie Headen, and The Cufflinx.

ACE 291 (RL)
Specialty Rock and Roll
Sixteen cuts on vinyl, 18 on CD from one of the finest independent record labels of the '50s, Los Angeles's Specialty label. Besides the landmark rock and roll made by Little Richard, Specialty operated the sole recording studio in New Orleans, with a fantastic house band to match. Includes Larry Williams, Don and Dewey, Lloyd Price, Art Neville, Jerry Byrne, Marvin and Johnny, Lil Millet, Roddy Jackson, and The Titans. Great sound.

ACE 309 (L)
Laurie Vocal Groups: The Doo-Wop Sound
Thirty-song CD with some of the finest recordings of the white doo-wop revival of the early '60s. Among the assembled gems are heartaching ballads by Al Mickens and The Orients, Tony Gallagher, and the renowned Passions (see Crystal Ball 138). Also included are the soulfully sensitive Ronnie Premier and The Royal Lancers, Davey Nichols and The Harps (aka The Camelots, whose a-cappella output appears on Relic collections), The Bon-Aires, Dino and The Diplomats, The Jo-Vals, The Criterions, the fabulous Five Discs (who surely deserve better recognition for their work), and The Del Satins (later Dion's backing group). The first 16 cuts appeared on the now out-of-print 1987 Ace album 205.

⊕ ACE 335 (CL)
Jukebox R&B
Treasure trove of 22 R&B, doo-wop, and electric blues tracks from the Los Angeles Bihari Brothers stable of labels (Kent, Modern, RPM, Flair, and Crown). Contains righteous blues oldies by B.B. King, Floyd Dixon, Lowell Fulsom, Elmore James, and Johnny "Guitar" Watson; select R&B servings from Etta James, Earl Curry, Jimmy Beasley, Ike and Tina, and the perky Teen Queens; and doo-wop gems from The Cadets, The Flairs, The Jacks, and The Robins. Personal fave is young Obie Jessie's lung-belter "Hit Git and Split." Fascinating notes by Ted Carroll.

ACE 346 (L)
Laurie's Vocal Groups: The '60s Sound
An amazing 34 cuts totaling over 76 minutes, chronicling the white vocal groups who recorded between 1961–1965 for New York's Laurie label. Most of the songs here are obscure, many showing the influence of the then-popular Four Seasons. The only real hit here is "Denise" by Randy and The Rainbows. Other featured artists include The Tokens, The Bob Knight Four, and The Five Discs.

ACE (US) 2027 (RL)
The Greatest Groups of the '50s
Sixteen fine vocal-group sides from Coaster, Ace, Rex, Twin, and other labels that were part of Johnny Vincent's small company acquisitions. Standouts include the fine "In the Garden of Love" by Dee Thomas backed by The Versatiles, "Please Don't Tell 'Em" by the Crescent City's own Blue Dots, the hit "Lama Rama Ding Dong" by The Edsels, plus the all-time classic whistling doo-wop "Mysterious Teenager" by Tim Whitsett and The Imperials, a gem of much beauty and originality. Recommended.

ACE (US) 2031 (R)
The Ace Story, Vol. 1
Fourteen tracks by Frankie Lee Sims, Frankie Ford, The Supremes, Joe and Ann, Mac Rebennack, Alvin "Red" Tyler, Bobby Marchan, and Morgus and The Ghouls.

ACE (US) 2032 (R)
The Ace Story, Vol. 2
Fourteen tracks featuring Junior Gordon, Mercy Baby, Eddie Bo, The Blue Dots, Little Shelton, Joe Dyson, Charles Brown and Amos Milburn, and Lightnin' Hopkins.

ACE (US) 2034 (R)
The Ace Story, Vol. 4
Sixteen great sides by Johnny Angel, Alvin Tyler, Joe and Ann, Jesse Allen, Huey "Piano" Smith, Floyd Brown, Joe Tex, and Frankie Lee Sims.

ACE (US) 2035 (R)
The Ace Story, Vol. 5
A great collection of mostly New Orleans blues and R&B recorded in the '50s by Johnny Fairchild, Edgar Blanchard, Jesse Allen, Elton Anderson, Calvin Spears, Earl King, Charles Brown, and Eddie Bo.

ACE (US) 2040 (RL)
Rock and Roll Christmas
Includes Huey Smith, Charles Brown, Dr. John, Alvin "Red" Tyler, Lee Allen, Earl King, and James Booker.

ACE (US) 2041 (RL)
The Heartbeat of New Orleans Rock and Roll
Twenty odds and ends, many tracks sounding like unfinished demos, with backing vocals and horns dubbed in years later! If the heartbeat of New Orleans was this weak, it would have been dead and buried long ago. Best cuts are by Jimmy Donelly, Johnny Meyers and Amos Milburn, Lloyd Price, Joe and Ann, Bobby Hebb, and Eddie Bo.

ADAM AND EVE 501 (R)
Girls, Girls, Girls, Girls

ADAM AND EVE 502 (R)
Doo-Wop Honor Roll of Girls

ADAM AND EVE 503 (R)
Girls, Girls, Girls, Girls, Vol. 2

ADAM AND EVE 504 (R)
Girls, Girls, Girls around the World, Vol. 4
Four collections with 14 tunes each featuring rare doo-wop sides from the '50s and early '60s named for girls. Some of the groups sing well and in key, others are of the "painful wince" variety. Many of these cuts are hard-to-find, but the collections are marred by uneven sound, no pics, and no sleeve notes.

ATLANTIC 82218 (L)
The Complete Stax/Volt Singles, 1959–1968
An exhaustive box set compiling every single put out by the independant Stax/Volt labels in their heyday. Known primarily as the home of soul legends like Otis Redding, Rufus and Carla Thomas, Sam and Dave, Eddie Floyd, Booker T and The MGs, William Bell, Johnnie Taylor, The Bar-Kays, and The Mad Lads, the labels also sported blues heavyweight Albert King, New Orleans artists Bobby Marchan and Sir Mack Rice, and a lot of regional one hitters who would be banished to undeserved obscurity if it weren't for this encyclopedic volume. Two hundred forty-four cuts on nine CDs, digitally remastered from original mono masters. An enthusiastic thumbs up for anyone who's yearning to own a big fat chunk of R&B history.

⊙ ATLANTIC 82305 (L)
Atlantic Rhythm and Blues 1947–1974
The original 14-LP version of this set was an immediate classic, a thrilling compilation of this seminal R&B label's most lasting hits, with a sensible emphasis on the Stax/Volt recordings that Atlantic distributed. The original, single-CD versions of the set were somewhat disappointing: some tracks were randomly lopped off, and the sonic impact was diminished from the LPs. Now, Atlantic has done it right, reissuing all of the original LP tracks on eight CDs in an LP-sized case with the original liner notes, along with 17 additional tracks, bringing the total to a whopping 203 songs! From Joe Morris to Major Harris, Atlantic's classic period featured a wide array of performers, writers, and producers whose commitment to soul remains unequalled. Any set that presents—in context—many of the finest recordings of LaVern Baker, William Bell, Booker T and The MGs, Solomon Burke, Ray Charles, The Clovers, The Coasters, Arthur Conley, The Drifters, Aretha Franklin, Chris Kenner, Ben E. King, The Mar-Keys, Clyde McPhatter, Wilson Pickett, Otis Redding, Sam and Dave, Percy Sledge, Carla and Rufus Thomas, Joe Turner, and Chuck Willis belongs on every serious listener's shelf. This is soul of the highest order, and earns our highest recommendation.

ATLANTIC 82316 (CL)
Soul Christmas
Twenty holiday songs from Clyde McPhatter and The Drifters, Clarence Carter, Otis Redding, Rufus and Carla Thomas, King Curtis, Joe Tex, The Sweet Inspirations, and Solomon Burke.

ATLANTIC 82341 (CL)
The Stax/Volt Revue, Vol. 1: Live in London

ATLANTIC 82342 (CL)
The Stax/Volt Revue, Vol. 2: Live in Paris
Reissue of Stax LPs 721 and 722, recorded in March 1967. The performers are among Stax's finest: Booker T and The MGs, The Mar-Keys, Eddie Floyd, Otis Redding, Carla Thomas, and Sam and Dave. My only complaint is that this material could have fit on one CD or cassette. Excellent digital remastering; an essential collection of soul singers at the height of their powers.

ATLANTIC (JAPAN) 25 (L)
Twist and Shout!
Atlantic singles produced by Phil Spector performed by Billy Storm, The Top Notes, Jean Du Shon, Ruth Brown, and LaVern Baker.

BEAR FAMILY 15308 (R)
The Mercury New Orleans Sessions, 1950

Two-LP set documenting Mercury's foray into the rich New Orleans R&B scene, mostly from a momentous two-night session held at National Recorders in February 1950, with the rest from the summer of 1950. Highlights are nine classic Professor Longhair tunes, including three never-before-issued songs, and four alternate takes. Vocalists Alma Mondy (aka Lollypop), Dwine Craven, Little Joe Gaines, Theard Johnson, and George Miller and His Mid Driffs are accompanied by great musicians like Lee Allen and Leroy "Batman" Rankin (ten saxes), and Alex Burrell (pno). With the exception of the abysmal crooning of Johnson, there are some very exciting, mostly uptempo performances. Beautiful sound, gatefold sleeve, vintage photos, discography, and great liner notes by Rick Coleman. Wonderful Crescent City music.

BLACK OUT 1901 (R)
Gonna Party Tonight

Sixteen sides of hard-drivin' rock and roll played by black artists, including Don and Dewey, The Robert "Bumps" Blackwell Band (with Little Richard on piano), James Brown and His Band, Davon Darnell, Mari Jones, Cledus Harrison and the Natural Studio Band, Big Bee Kornegay, Wild Child Gibson, Tommy Brown, Big Bob, The Twilighters, Joe Tex and his Band, and Young Jessie.

CAPRICORN 42003 (L)
The Scepter Records Story

Although the Scepter and Wand label vaults have already been plundered by the Collectables, Ace, and Kent labels, this is the first label-oriented retrospective ever. The story of Scepter and its founder Florence Greenberg is pretty amazing, told with glowing detail in a deluxe 32-page booklet that is also packed with anecdotes, full-color album art, and discographical information. Among the 65 tracks on these three CDs, a few R&B, soul, and pop hitmakers are prominent, including The Shirelles, B.J. Thomas, Chuck Jackson, Dionne Warwick, Maxine Brown, and Tommy Hunt. Most of these selections made chart appearances between 1959–1972. A few rarities by Brown, Jackson, and The Shirelles are included, as well as some star duos by these artists. We also get scattered hits by The Kingsmen, The Isley Brothers, King Curtis, The Rocky Fellers (a Filipino family act!), Roy Head, Ronnie Milsap, The Esquires, Fred Hughes, The Joe Jeffrey Group, and The Buoys, whose "Timothy" was banned because of its alleged references to cannibalism! Even the producers and arrangers on these sessions are stars: Luther Dixon, Carole King, Bacharach and David, and Ashford and Simpson! This is more than just a compilation; it's a lovingly produced time capsule that captures a soulful slice of the '60s.

CBS SPECIAL PRODUCTS 37321 (L)
Okeh Soul

CD reissue of two-LP set featuring '60s recordings by Major Lance, Billy Butler and The Enchanters, Walter Jackson, The Opals, The Artistics, and The Vibrations.

⊛ CBS SPECIAL PRODUCTS 37649 (L)
Okeh Rhythm and Blues

CD reissue of fantastic 2-LP set, showcasing 28 R&B/doo-wop/New Orleans/early rock cuts by Smiley Lewis, Chuck Willis, Big Maybelle, Screamin' Jay Hawkins, Titus Turner, Larry Darnell, The Ravens, Johnnie Ray, The Sandmen, The Marquees, Billy Stewart, The Schoolboys, The Sheppards, The Treniers, Paul Gayten, Little Joe and The Thrillers, Doc Bagby, Red Saunders, and Little Richard! This stompin' comp is a must for all you hep kats and kittens, with great sound quality to boot.

CHARLY 10 (L)
Compact Soul

Twenty-two early soul cuts by The Impressions, Jimmy Hughes, and Bobby Bland. All are available on various Charly LPs.

CHARLY 14 (L)
The Soul of New Orleans

New Orleans R&B drawn from various Charly albums including tracks by Lee Dorsey, The Meters, Lloyd Price, Alvin Robinson, Aaron Neville, Johnny Adams, Fats Domino, Benny Spellman, and Diamond Joe. Some great music, though sound quality could be better.

CHARLY 22 (L)
Honky Tonk Jump Party

Rocking R&B mostly from the Aladdin, Capitol, King, and Vee Jay labels, by Bill Doggett, Louis Jordan, Tiny Bradshaw, Earl Bostic, The Five Keys, Joe Lutcher, Little Esther, The Dominoes, Eddie "Cleanhead" Vinson, and Roy Brown. British band Rockin' Louie and The Mama Jammers on two tracks seem a little out of place in this distinguished company. Better-than-usual sound for Charly.

CHARLY 42 (L)
Soul Deep

Eighteen deep-soul gems, including obscurities as well as hits from the Sound Stage 7/77 labels, including Geater Davis, Sam Baker, Earle Gaines, Toussaint McCall, Big Al Downing, Doris Duke, and Clarence Carter, with complete information in an accompanying eight-page booklet. Highlights include Little Richard's incredible "I Don't Know What You Got but It's Got Me," recorded for Vee Jay in 1965, and Gladys Knight and The Pips's 1965 Maxx single "Either Way I Lose," which got them signed to Motown.

CHARLY 85 (L)
Harlem Shuffle
Solid soul collection by The Capitols, The Shades of Blue, The Soul Survivors, The Esquires, Jackie Lee (actually Earl Nelson of Bob and Earl), Barbara Lewis, Mel and Tim, The Olympics, and Gene Allison.

⬤ CHESS 6022 (C)
The Best of Chess Rhythm and Blues
Incredible two-cassette set with 20 of the best R&B sides from the Chess/Checker/Cadet labels, from 1956's "Please Send Me Someone to Love" by The Moonglows to 1962's "Tell Mama" by Etta James. Includes doo-wop by The Miracles and The Corsairs; R&B by Jimmy McCracklin and Clarence "Frogman" Henry; plus lots of fine Chicago soul by Billy Stewart, Fontella Bass, The Dells, and Bobby Moore and The Rhythm Aces. Highly recommended.

CHESS 6024 (C)
The Best of Chess Rock and Roll
Two cassettes with 20 cuts. Includes hard-driving rock and roll by Chuck Berry, Bo Diddley, and Jackie Brenston; rockabilly by Dale Hawkins; R&B by Johnnie and Joe, and Tommy Tucker; New Orleans R&B by Clarence "Frogman" Henry; and beautiful doo-wop by The Flamingos, and Lee Andrews and the Hearts.

CHESS 6029 (C)
The Best of the Chess Vocal Groups
Two cassettes featuring 20 songs by 17 vocal groups recorded circa 1955–1969. Most of this material, notably cuts by The Flamingos, The Moonglows, The Dells, The Hearts, The Ravens, The Students, and The Marathons, has appeared on other collections, with three exceptions: the classic rendition of "She's Gone" by The Dozier Boys from 1949, plus two previously unreleased but worthwhile sides by The Four Tops (yes, Levi Stubbs's group) and The Lovettes (aka The Gems). Great pics and intelligent notes.

CHESS 9282 (L)
The Best of the Chess Vocal Groups, Vol. 1

CHESS 9283 (L)
The Best of the Chess Vocal Groups, Vol. 2

CHESS 31317 (L)
The Best of Chess Rhythm and Blues, Vol. 1

⬤ CHESS 31318 (L)
The Best of Chess Rhythm and Blues, Vol. 2

CHESS 31319 (L)
The Best of Chess Rock and Roll, Vol. 1

CHESS 31320 (L)
The Best of Chess Rock and Roll, Vol. 2
These individual CDs correspond to the cassette sets described above, with bonus tracks.

CLIFTON 1011 (L)
A-Cappella Showdown: Classic Doo-Wop Harmony, Pt. 1
Twenty-six tracks of latter-day a-cappella groups performing classic songs, mostly from the '50s. With the exception of the previously unreleased "When I Woke Up This Morning" by The Darchaes (1961), all the material was cut in the late '70s and '80s. Includes The Infernos, Now and Then, The Computones, Street Corner Memories, Patty and The Street-Tones, The Chips, Subway Serenade, Retrospect, The Attributes, The Copas, The Splendors, Charm, The Blendaires, Reality, The Endings, and Choice. Who needs instruments?

CLUB 001 (R)
Doo-Wop Fast and Slow, Vol. 1
Eighteen tunes by both white and black vocal groups. Some numbers (and groups) are obscure and some as common as K-tel selections. Among the lesser-known groups are Rico and The Ravens, The Cupids, The Three Friends, The Flaming Hearts, The Accents, and The Gothics.

CLUB 002 (R)
Doo-Wop Jive and Stroll, Vol. 2
A generous 22 tracks featuring a wonderful selection of scarce vocal-group sounds. Each side has seven "jive" (up-tempo) numbers, a trio of "stroll" tunes, and a solitary "smoocher." Get out your dancin' shoes for The Four Most, The Impressors, The Bachelors, The Wheels, and The Cherlos. In the nutty stroll department, there's "Jungle Superman" by The Individuals and "Papaya Baby" by The Jumpin' Jacks.

CLUB 006 (R)
Doo-Wop Jive and Stroll, Vol. 6
Twenty-two tunes. There's more in the smooch department this time around, with some gorgous ballads by The Sheppards, The Zodiacs, and The Imaginations. Opens with one of the wildest falsetto wailers ever waxed: The Cobras doing "La La." Also includes The DuDroppers, The Chords, The Five Masks, The Feathers, Lee Maye, The Suedes, and The Capris.

CLUB 007 (R)
Doo-Wop Jive and Stroll, Vol. 7
Twenty-two more jive, stroll, and smooch tunes, with a Latin ("Dirty Dancing") number snuck in to boot! The Jumpin' Jacks, The Sparks of Rhythm, Gerry Granahan, Dickie Doo and The Don'ts, Frankie and The Echoes, The Dubs, The Jets, The Wrens, and The Zodiacs.

COLLECTABLES 2508 (CL)
WCBS FM 101 History of Rock: The Doo Wop Era, Pt. 2
One of the best collection of '50s doo-wop marred only by Collectables typical low fidelity and inferior packaging. Twenty-four tracks by The Five Satins, The Passions, The Harptones, The Students, The Belmonts, The Eternals, Dion and The Belmonts, The Fireflies, Lee Andrews and The Hearts, The Silhouettes, Randy and The Rainbows, and The Turbans.

COLLECTABLES 5037 (C)
Great Groups of the '50s, Vol. 1

COLLECTABLES 5038 (C)
Great Groups of the '50s, Vol. 2

COLLECTABLES 5039 (C)
Great Groups of the '50s, Vol. 3
Three volumes of all-time best selling doo-wop. Sound quality typical for Collectables's releases (i.e., average), and there are no notes. Each cassette features a few previously unissued cuts, so collectors have to buy all three to get these gems.

COLLECTABLES 5048 (CL)
Dootone Rhythm and Blues
Fourteen vocal-group tracks by The Penguins, Vernon Green and The Medallions, Don Julian and The Meadowlarks, The Pipes, The Calvanes, and The Pearls.

COLLECTABLES 5051 (CL)
Harlem Holiday, Vol. 1: New York R&B

COLLECTABLES 5052 (CL)
Harlem Holiday, Vol. 2: New York R&B

COLLECTABLES 5053 (CL)
Harlem Holiday, Vol. 3: New York R&B

COLLECTABLES 5054 (C)
Harlem Holiday, Vol. 4: New York R&B

COLLECTABLES 5055 (C)
Harlem Holiday, Vol. 5: New York R&B

COLLECTABLES 5056 (C)
Harlem Holiday, Vol. 6: New York R&B

COLLECTABLES 5057 (C)
Harlem Holiday, Vol. 7: New York R&B
Seven-part series focussing on New York small-label doo-wop recordings mostly from the late '50s and early '60s. Average sound quality, and no notes or pictures. Some of this material has been previously reissued by Relic. Of most interest to collectors is the first volume, featuring vocal-group material drawn entirely from singles issued in 1957 on the Holiday label, including two beautiful ballads by The Bop Chords, along with rare cuts by The Thunderbirds, The Harmonaires, The Love Notes, The Ladders, and Jimmy (Handy Man) Jones with The Pretenders. Vols. 2 and 3 collect boss vocal-group material recorded from 1951–1961 for Bobby Robinson's labels—Fire, Fury, Red Robin, Whirling Disc, and Everlast—by The Federals, The Mello Moods, The Whirlers, The Channels, The Topps, The Angels, The Teenchords, The Scarlets, The Quadrells, The Charts, The "C" Tones, The Hemlocks, The Pretenders, and The Extremes. Vol. 4 is a beautiful collection of doo-wop ditties from the Paul Winley and Cyclone labels, recorded between 1956–1960. Unbeatable sides by Julius McMichael and The Paragons, Adam Jackson and The Jesters, The Collegians, The Calendars, The Quinns, and the incomparable Duponts (better known as Little Anthony and The Imperials); duplicates Relic 5019. The final three volumes are drawn from Al Silver's Ember, Herald, and Standard labels recorded between 1953–1962. All of this outstanding material is available on Relic albums 5008/09, 5011, 5015/16, and 5047/48. Includes The Embers, Leroy Griffin and The Nutmegs (aka The Lyres), The Turbans, Fred Paris and The Five Satins, The Thrillers, The Sunbeams, The Smooth Tones, The Rocketeers, The Starlites, The Five Willows, The Colonairs, The Heralds, Maurice Williams and The Zodiacs, The Vocalaires, The Sonnets, The Starlarks, The Desires, The Loungers, The Debonaires, Roger and The Travelers, The Mint Juleps, The Marktones, The Bop-Tones, and The Fabulons.

COLLECTABLES 5071 (CL)
Collectables Rhythm and Blues Christmas
Holiday hummers by Baby Washington, Chuck Berry, The Moonglows, and more!

COLLECTABLES 5123 (CL)
Best of Sue Records
Almost all of this collection has surfaced on other reissues over the past few years. Includes cuts by Ike and Tina Turner, Charlie and Inez Foxx, Baby Washington, The Poets, Bobby Hendricks, The Soul Sisters, Barbara George, Jimmy McGriff, and Wilburt Harrison. Too bad Collectables lacked the foresight to reissue some of the more obscure singles that have never reappeared in any shape or form. No sleeve notes, but good, clean sound.

COLLECTABLES 5208 (C)
Harlem Rock n' Blues, Vol. 1

COLLECTABLES 5209 (C)
Harlem Rock n' Blues, Vol. 2

COLLECTABLES 5210 (C)
Harlem Rock n' Blues, Vol. 3

Three solid collections of recordings from Bobby Robinson's Red Robin, Fire, Fury, and Everlast labels of the '50s and '60s. Many of these sides have been previously reissued by other labels, and the packaging is poor. Includes Champion Jack Dupree (ably assisted by Sonny Terry), Brownie and Sticks McGhee, Red Prysock, "Wild" Jimmy Spruill, Buster Brown, Tiny Grimes, King Curtis, Noble Watts, June Bateman, King Curtis, Hal Paige and The Whalers, and The Chas Lucas Combo.

COLLECTABLES 5224 (CL)
Deep in the Soul of Texas

Obscure Texas soul from Houston, mostly recorded at ACA and Andrus Studios between 1963–1975. Includes Joe Medwick, Al "TNT" Braggs, Ernie K-Doe, Ivory Joe Hunter, Joe Hughes, Bobby Boseman (aka Gashead), O.V. Wright, The Citations, and Oscar Perry.

COLLECTABLES 5409 (CL)
Teenage Party

Exact reissue of Gee 702 featuring five groups from George Goldner's Gee, Rama, and Bruce labels, circa 1953–1956. Even the original album's fluffy and trite sleeve notes are lovingly reproduced for the CD booklet. Most of this material has surfaced on other reissues. Includes The Cleftones, The Crows, The Wrens, The Harptones, and The Valentines.

COLLECTABLES 6004 (L)
The Home of Grand Records

Twelve early-to-mid-'50s doo-wop recordings from this Philadelphia label by The Angels, The Belltones, The Carte-Rays, The Castelles, The Castroes, The Cherokees, George Grant, and The Marquees.

COLLECTABLES 7001 (C)
Harlem, NY: The Doo-Wop Era

Two-cassette set featuring 40 tunes previously reissued on Collectables singles. Though most are from the late '50s, these groups aren't all from New York; for some reason, there are a lot of Chicago sides from Vee Jay. This is, though, the sound that was popular in NY. No smoochy ballads here, it's all high speed with mainly high-pitched or kid leads, by groups like The Chalets, The Pyramids, The Silhouettes, The Edsels, The Dells, and The Kodaks.

COLLECTABLES 7002 (C)
Harlem: The Ballad Era

Two-cassette set of 40 doo-wop ballads recorded in New York on a multitude of small labels. Includes The Spaniels, The Charts, The Jesters, and The Click-ettes. Surprisingly good sound quality, but no notes or pictures. Most cuts have appeared on Collectables singles. A solid selection for the starter collection.

COLLECTABLES 7003 (C)
For Collectors Only, Vol. 1: The Rarities

Two-cassette set of 40 East Coast doo-wop ballads from the '50s, mainly issued on the Grand, Gotham, and Red Robin labels. Includes The Castelles, The Capris, The Vocaleers, and The Flamingos. No pics, minimal notes, and average overall sound quality. Most cuts have appeared on Collectables singles and albums. For hardcore doo-wop fans only.

CRYSTAL BALL 113 (R)
The Best of the U.G.H.A. Groups

Sixteen sides from 1983 by the best bands of the The United in Group Harmony Association, which supports a-cappella music. Includes The Computones, The Emerys, The Endings, Patty and The Street-Tones, Reality, Street Corner Memories, The Uniques, The Valentinos, and Yesterday's News.

CRYSTAL BALL 116 (R)
Al Brown's New York Sound

In the early '60s, Al Brown, a famed New York producer, re-recorded many bands and tunes he had originally cut in the '50s for his Joyce and Aljon labels. This is great stuff, all featuring the fantastic guitar of Robert Ward from The Ohio Untouchables. Includes The Charletts, The Crescents, Donnie and The Chappells, Eddie and The Starlights, The Gaytunes, The Jell Tones, Lunar and The Planets, The Mellow Notes, The Passions, and The Vilons.

CRYSTAL BALL 117 (R)
Al Brown Presents Joyce

Just about the entire output by this famed New York doo-wop label cut during its one-year lifetime (1957). Includes the first recordings by Johnny Maestro and The Crests, along with The Crescents, The Gaytunes, The Love Notes, and The Starlites, along with one track by an unknown group.

CRYSTAL BALL 121 (R)
The Best of Cousins Records: The Bronx

CRYSTAL BALL 122 (R)
Lou Cicchetti's Bronx Classics

CRYSTAL BALL 124 (R)

Unreleased from the Vaults of Lou Cicchetti

Three collections of similar-sounding, white vocal groups recorded by Bronx-based independent record producer Lou Cichetti on his Cousins label. Each LP features ballads and nonsense jump songs by a handful of male aggregations who all seem to sound the same even when they're singing out of tune. Features The Original Camerons, The Regents, The Consorts, Guy Villari and The Dreamers, Lee Mareno and The Runarounds (aka The Regents), Al Reno, The Chuckles, The Dreams, The Dials, Chuck Harper, Sonny Dee, The Bi Tones, The Ruteens, The Orientals, The Excellents, and The Teardrops. Superior in sound quality over earlier collections.

CRYSTAL BALL 128 (R)

They Sang in Brooklyn

A cacophony of Caucasian, Brooklyn doo-wop from rare demos, practice session tapes, and singles by The Mystics, The Bay Bops, The Quotations, The Vocal-Airs, The Bob Knight Four, The Passions, The Zarzano Brothers, and The Ultimates. The great Tony Pasalacqua with The Fascinators perform the album's one redeeming cut: a pretty, almost a-cappella version of "Dear Lord" originally made famous by The Continentals. Produced by Robert Diskin, Adam Pick, and Ed Engel. Painful sound quality on some sides.

CRYSTAL BALL 129 (R)

The Rarest of the Rare: Collectors Showcase, Vol. 1

An assortment of both black and white harmonists warbling both popular standards and originals, with many extremely fine and rare selections. Includes The De Coys, Eric with The Plazas, Bryan Brent with The Cut Outs, The Carvettes, The Mustangs, The Twisters, Dutch London, John Hurley, The Crystalights, The Classics, The Capris, The Cardinals, The Downbeats, and The Dawns.

CRYSTAL BALL 130 (R)

They Sang in Pittsburgh: Great Group Sounds, Vol. 1

CRYSTAL BALL 131 (R)

They Sang in Pittsburgh: Great Group Sounds, Vol. 2

Issued and unissued vocal-harmony material, both a cappella and with rhythm accompaniments. A motley assortment of outfits including The Marcels, The Laurels, The Jets, Fred and The Embers, The Altairs, Lou and The Sensations, The Dynamics, Walt Maddox, The Skyliners, The Del Vikings, The Chi-Tones, The Chapelaires, The Twilighters, and The Fabulous Uptowners. The second volume is made up entirely of old tapes and demos that have never been issued before, drawn from the collections of the groups themselves. Sparse notes, good pics, and reasonable fidelity.

DCC COMPACT CLASSICS 031 (L)

Back Seat Jams

Seventeen doo-wop grinders and smoochers by The Dells, The Capris, The Jive Five, The Skyliners, The Nutmegs, The Paragons, The Shirelles, The Fireflies, Little Caesar and The Romans, Ritchie Valens, The Mello-Kings, and The Pentagons.

DCC COMPACT CLASSICS 033 (L)

Beachbeat Shaggin'

Twenty regional hits from the Southeast Coast. Though there's hits here, this set also includes some great tunes that never got past The Carolinas, including my personal fave, Willie Tee's "Thank You, John." Also includes The Embers, Garnet Mims and The Enchanters, The Drifters, Maurice Williams and The Zodiacs, The Tymes, and The Swingin' Medallions.

DDW 801 (R)

Dangerous Doo-Wop

DDW 802 (R)

Dangerous Doo-Wop, Vol. 2

DDW 803 (R)

Dangerous Doo-Wop, Vol. 3

DDW 804 (R)

Dangerous Doo-Wop, Vol. 4

Generous collections of mid-to-late-'50s doo-wop, mostly to a rockin' beat. The first three volumes rely too heavily on better-known material, although each does feature a few more obscure sides by relatively unknown, but super-fine groups. Serious doo-wop collectors will certainly want to own them. The last volume has the strongest selection of unique material. Among the more obscure names are The King Oden Four, Artie Wilkins, The Blisters, The Sunbeams, The Tantones, The Tune Blenders, The Velvetones, The Re-Vels, The Royal Jokers, The Sharps, The Ly-Dells, The Keystoners, The Senators, The Master-tones, The Five Vets, The Deltas, The Olympics, The Four Clippers, The Moonlighters, The James Quintet, Sonny Stevenson, The Aquatones, and The Rocketeers.

DELMARK 438 (L)

Honkers and Bar Walkers, Vol. 1

DELMARK 452 (CL)

Honkers and Bar Walkers, Vol. 2

Twenty-two swingin' selections of dance-floor crooners and bands who recorded in the '50s for the Apollo label, including Willis Jackson, Morris Lane, famed drummer Panama Francis, Bill Harvey's Orchestra, and King Curtis. Charlie "Little Jazz" Ferguson is the most exciting contestant here, shining on blues and late-night numbers, but he also flaunted his agility on crazy shoe-burners like "Bean Head" and "Hi Beam."

DOOTO 204 (R)

The Best Vocal Groups: Rhythm and Blues

DOOTO 224 (R)

The Best Vocal Groups: Rock and Roll

DOOTO 855 (R)

The Oldies: Great Vocal Groups

Three LPs of '50s vocal sides by The Dootones, The Meadowlarks, The Medallions, The Birds, The Calvanes, The Cuff Links, The Meadowlarks, The Medallions, The Penguins, The Pipes, The Romancers, and The Souvenirs.

DOO WOP DELIGHTS 374 (C)

Sims Records

Thirty-seven classic, hard-to-find '60s soul and rock tracks from The Sims label. Founded in 1955 by the Sims brothers—Russell and Lee—the label's primary focus was recording country and country-rock. However, in between, a handful of mainly Nashville-based soul artists found their way onto the label, including The Wallace Brothers, Don Brantley, Roscoe Shelton, The Kelly Brothers, and Eddie Powers. Rockabilly sides by Bobby Lee Trammell, Jack Cochran, and Wally Lewis are also featured.

DOUBLE TROUBLE 3024 (R)

Texas R&B Cruise

Nice collection of late '50s and early '60s blues and R&B from four Texas musicians: Clarence Green; El Paso blues legend Long John Hunter; veteran piano player Teddy Reynolds; and Big John and The Dallas Playboys. Big John's selections from 1959 are quite a revelation. He's a pretty good singer and the sax player is fine but, oh Lordy, their unknown guitar player sounds as hot and nasty as Sun great Pat Hare. Recommended.

EARTH ANGEL 903 (R)

Music City Records

Twenty-one mid-'50s, rare doo-wops recorded for this important Berkeley label owned and operated by Ray Dobard. Includes The Four Deuces, The Midnights, The Gaylarks, Wanda Burt, and Joe Blackwell and The Five Crystals. First rate sleeve notes by doo-wop expert Jim Dawson.

EARTH ANGEL 906 (R)

Dolphin's of Hollywood: The Doo-Wop Sessions

John Dolphin called his record shop on Central Avenue in Los Angeles "Dolphin's of Hollywood," even though it was miles from that city. He started recording in 1949, and later formed the Money, Cash, and Lucky labels to release product aimed at the new teenage market. Dolphin recorded The Robins (with Mickey Champion taking the lead vocal chores), The Falcons and The Turbans (West Coast groups, not their more famous namesakes), Cry Baby Curtis, and Byrd's Voices. Twenty tunes, with the usual cool photos and packaging.

EARTH ANGEL 907 (R)

Music City Records: California Doo-Wop and R&B (1954–1961)

Volume 2 of California R&B vocal groups who recorded for this seminal label in the '50s, including The Midnights, The Four Deuces, The Rovers, and Wanda Burt and The Crescendos. The still-popular Johnny Heartsman can be heard with his "house-party sound" on four great tunes.

EDSEL 283 (R)

Stewed Moonbeams in Wavy Gravy: Okeh Black Rock and Roll

A boss collection of prime obscurities recorded for the Okeh label in the late '50s. We get two howlers from the Screamin' Jay-styled Hurricane Harry, along with Big John and the Buzzards, Duke Stevens, Tiny and Tim, Bobby Gray, The Honkers, Lloyd Fatman, Billy LaMont, and Dave "Baby" Cortez.

EXPLOSIVE DOOWOPS 100 (R)

Explosive Doo-wops, Vol. 1

EXPLOSIVE DOOWOPS 200 (R)

Explosive Doo-wops, Vol. 2

EXPLOSIVE DOOWOPS 300 (R)

Explosive Doo-wops, Vol. 3

EXPLOSIVE DOOWOPS 400 (R)

Explosive Doo-wops, Vol. 4

Four LPs of commercial, white vocal-group jump sides recorded in the late '50s/early '60s. Although many of these singles are rare, the compilers have chosen to issue only the A-sides, thus frustrating the true vocal-music collector who would want the flips as well. Average sound quality, but no pictures or notes with any of the releases. Groups include The Unique Teens, The Fabulaires, The Cordells, Lonnie Heard, The Elites, The Del-Airs, The Karl Hammel Junior group, The Concords, Lenny Dean and The Rockin' Chairs, The Paramonts, The Dories, The Up Starts, The Royal Lancers, Tiny Tim (NO, not that one!), The Demensions, The Del-Larks, and The Inspirations.

⊙ FLYRIGHT 29 (L)

Thunderbolt: R&B Sax Instrumentals

Twenty super-duper tenor-sax tooters and booters from the golden age of instrumental R&B. These tracks are taken from Krazy Kat 778 and 784 featuring NY dance-floor destroyers, all recorded by Joe Davis for his Baton label. Includes Warren Lucky with guitarist

Mickey Baker, Al King, Buddy Tate, and Frank "Floorshow" Culley. Culley's crazed cuts, along with those by Dizzy Gillespie sideman Warren Lucky, are in the solid sock-hop tradition; King and Tate's contributions are a little more uptown, swingin' and swayin' with jazzy sophistication. In general the tempos are frantic and the blowing is manic, but don't panic; there are still a few slow dancers for you romancers. Guaranteed to turn any party into grounds for eviction; essential listening for sawdust stompers of all ages.

FLYRIGHT 30 (L)
Fine as Wine, 1952–1956

Twenty solid smokers from the mid-'50s, recorded by veteran NY record producer/song publisher Joe Davis on his Beacon, Jay-Dee, and Davis labels, as well as earlier sides leased to MGM. Most of this material was previously reissued on Krazy Kat 797 and 798. Includes Lillian Leach and the underrated Mellows of the Bronx (who are every bit as fine an act today), Dean Barlow with and without The Crickets, The Sparrows, The Chestnuts, and The Scale Tones (who later went on to greater fame as The Dubs), plus the mysterious Chris (?) and his gang. Gilt-edged instrumental support on most sides by Mickey Baker (gtr), Sam "The Man" Taylor (ten sax), Dave McCrae (alto sax), Lloyd Trotman (b), and Panama Francis (drm).

FLYRIGHT 32 (L)
Best of Washington DC R&B

TNT Tribble and Frank "Dual Trumpets" Motley were two of the hottest R&B acts to emerge during the postwar years. The sometimes raucous, but most-times exciting Motley hails from Cheraw, SC, and began performing his two-trumpets-at-once trick in 1949. Tommy Tribble from Ferrel, PA, started drumming during WW II in USO outfits. In 1950 Tribble joined Motley's band for what was to become a jumping sensation. They recorded for Ivin Ballin's Gotham label between 1951–1955, with vocals by Tribble, Jimmy Harris, and "Fat Man" Smith. First issued on wax as Krazy Kat 805, 809, and 828. Great, sock-leaping blues.

FLYRIGHT 42 (L)
Louisiana R&B

Twenty-song collection from the vaults of J.D. Miller recorded from the late '50s to the early-to-mid-'60s. Most of the material, which remained unreleased for decades, is excellent. Acts include Carol Fran, Lester Robertson, The Gaynotes, Lightnin' Slim, and Honey Boy Allen. The only artist with two cuts is Wonder Boy Travis (real name: Travis Phillips), who later played guitar for Clifton Chenier. Good stuff.

FLYRIGHT 46 (L)
I Always Remember

A tasty collection of 20 vocal-group tracks recorded between 1951–1955 either for or by Ivan Ballen's Gotham label. Most of the tracks are alternate takes of released material or, in seven cases, previously unreleased tunes. First-rate doo-wop, with upbeat tunes slightly outnumbering the ballads. Much of the material has a decidedly early '50s feel, particularly the tracks by The Cap-tans. Generally excellent sound, and fine notes by the redoubtable George Monoogian. Also includes The Gazelles, The Capris, The Whispers, The Kings, and The Moonglows. Enthusiastically recommended.

FLYRIGHT 570 (R)
Too Hot to Handle

Twelve rockin', mostly unissued R&B sides from the Miller archives, featuring Classie Ballou, Ken Cameron, Joe Carl and The Dukes of Rhythm, The Good Time Brothers, Little Bob, Little Clem and The Dewnotes, Jay Nelson and The Jumpers, Lionel Torrence, and Sad Leroy White.

GOLDWAX 5004 (L)
Echoes of Yesteryear, Vol. 1

Twelve-tune collection of deep-soul and soul-funk from the vaults of the Doc Russell/Quinton Claunch Goldwax label, founded in 1964 in Memphis to catch part of the Stax action. This clutch of cleffings, although studded with highlights, does not match the glory of Vivid 006. Includes O.V. Wright, James Carr, The Ovations, Percy Milem, Willie Hightower, and Ollie Nightingale.

GREASY R&B 5463 (R)
Talkin' Trash

There's trash talkin' aplenty here, but I'd hardly call gospel shouters like Evelyn Freeman's "Didn't It Rain" and Rev. Lofton and The Holy Travellers's "Look to Jesus" true trash! The rest falls into the "bad" school of novelty knee-knockers, by The Honeybears, The Dorsets, King Coleman, Screamin' Jay Hawkins, John Tee, Rudy Ray Moore, Mr. Wiggles, Earl Curry, and Pigmeat Markham.

HDH 501 (L)
The Hits of Invictus and Hot Wax Records

In the late '60s, after leaving Motown, songwriters Holland-Dozier-Holland started their own Hot Wax and Invictus labels. Their output has never been adequately reissued until now in this strong collection of 21 hits, packaged with a 12-page booklet with bios and color photos of the artists and a listing of US and UK chart positions. Includes The Chairmen of the Board, Freda Payne, Honey Cone, Eighth Day, 100 Proof, Flaming Ember, and Glass House. Standout is Laura Lee's incredible "If You Can Beat Me Rockin' (You Can Have My Chair)."

HI (UK) 430 (R)

320 South Lauderdale Avenue: Green, Wright, Bryant

The title refers to the address of the old Hi recording studio in Memphis, a converted movie theatre with the control room placed in the former projection booth. Colin Escott has sifted through Willie Mitchell's production rejects to discover some interesting rare and unissued takes. Don Bryant provides the best tunes on the LP, perhaps because the expectations are not as high for him as for the other two artists. Green's tracks are mostly in a fervent gospel style, as opposed to the relaxed style shown on his successful later hits. O.V. Wright's songs are among his lesser efforts. For the dedicated collector only.

HI (UK) 439 (R)

Hi Records: The R&B Sessions

HI (UK) 440 (R)

The Soul Years

Two LPs covering the pre-Al Green, Hi years (439) and the soulful '70s (440), that were dominated by Green's success. The first volume features some great gospel-derived soul singing, much of it by little-known artists like James Fry who sang in The Sunset Travelers with O.V. Wright and is represented by two unissued tracks. There are also two songs by the obscure but soulful girl group, Janet and The Jays, and four unissued tracks by Don Bryant. The biggest surprise is the inclusion of two tracks by The Five Royales, titles apparently recorded in the summer of 1967 and never released. The second LP follows Hi into the '70s and, appropriately enough, kicks off with an Al Green single, "Strong as Death (Sweet as Love)," never before available on LP. With the emergence of Green as the superstar of the early '70s soul scene, the sound of the label began to change as well. It moved away from the tougher gospel-influenced, deep-soul sound toward a slicker production complete with added strings and horn sections. Other great artists include Syl Johnson, O.V. Wright, Otis Clay, Ann Peebles, and two groups, The Masqueraders and Quiet Elegance.

HOLLYWOOD 369 (CL)

Rhythm and Blues Christmas

Twenty tracks by Hank Ballard, Amos Milburn and Charles Brown, Freddy King, The Dominoes, Bill Doggett, Lowell Fulson, Gatemouth Moore, and Jimmy Witherspoon.

❸ HONK IT 68 IOU I (R)

Lookey-Doo Key

Roll up the carpet for some real dance rock by The Nightriders, Champion Jack Dupree, Big Maybelle, Piano Red (with a small band), The Continentals, and L.C. McKinley. Many cuts feature some red-hot guitar breaks. Very little duplication with similar LPs on this essential purchase.

INSTANT 5059 (L)

For Sentimental Reasons: 28 Doo-Wop Classics

All the big names (The Flamingos, The Five Satins, The Prisonaires, The Cadillacs, The Monotones, The Dubs, The Cleftones, The Skyliners, The Orioles, The Chantels, The Mello Tones, The Heartbeats, and Shep and The Limelites) are represented by their most popular songs. Nice CD for the budding doo-wop fan.

KENT (UK) 006 (R)

On the Soul Side

Sixteen dance tunes mostly from UA/Liberty/Imperial/Minit labels by Homer Banks, H.B. Barnum, The Exciters, Ellie Greenwich, Jimmy Holiday (one cut with Clydie King), Brenda Holloway, Little Anthony and The Imperials, Gene McDaniels, Garnet Mimms, The O'Jays, Bobby Sheen, The Showmen, Benny Spellman, Ginger Thompson, and Timi Yuro.

KENT (UK) 022 (R)

Club Soul

Sixteen Scepter/Wand label recordings by Big Maybelle, Maxine Brown, Candy and The Kisses, Lee Charles, Johnny Copeland, Nella Dodds, The Esquires, The Honey Bees, Chuck Jackson, Diane Lewis, Jack Montgomery, The Moods, The Shirelles, George Tindley, and Brenton Wood.

KENT (UK) 029 (R)

Kent Stop Dancing

Designed for you dancing fools, Side 1 is programmed for dancin' the frug, Side 2 for the bugaloo! Includes novely dance hits like The Moving Sidewalk's "99th Floor" and The Kingsmen's "Louie Louie," as well as cuts by Barbara Acklin, The Artistics, Maxine Brown, The Esquires, Benny Gordon, Roy Head, The Isley Brothers, Chuck Jackson, The Platters, Rosco Robinson, The Rocky Fellers, The Shirelles, and Jackie Wilson.

KENT (UK) 039 (R)

Right Back Where We Started

Fifteen sides from the Capitol/Liberty labels that have become "classics" in northern soul clubs. One side of "blue-eyed soul" and one side of the regular variety by Herbie Goins and The Nightimers, Thelma Houston, The Human Beinz, Levi Jackson, Jay and The Americans, Little Anthony and The Imperials, Garnett Mimms, Jerry Naylor, Sandy Nelson, Maxine Nightingale, The Outsiders, Billy Preston, Al Wilson, Nancy Wilson, and The World Column.

KENT (UK) 046 (R)
"It's Torture" and
15 Other Great Soul Destroyers

Sixteen soul sides by black and white artists, including unreleased material from Maxine Brown (performing the title cut) and Porgy and The Monarchs. Also includes The Masqueraders, Dean Parrish, Jackie Wilson, Gene Chandler, Charles Lamont and The Extremes, Jerry Fuller, Wally Cox (!), Mel Wynn, Ron Holden, Billy Butler, The Esquires, The Charts, Adams Apples, and B.J. Thomas.

KENT (UK) 051 (R)
The Funk and Soul Revolution

Fourteen great funk riffs from the pre-disco '70s, most of which consist of a great dance groove with some kind of (often political) slogan chanted over it. Includes The Chilites, Bohannon, Alvin Cash, and Ann Bailey. Highlight: Sly and The Family Stone's rare version of "I Ain't Got Nobody."

KENT (UK) 057 (R)
The Magic Touch

Uptown soul from Kent's Northern Soul series, mostly from the Scepter/Wand and Brunswick labels. Lots of previously unissued material by Melba Moore, Porgy and The Monarchs, Candy and The Kisses, and even the rhythm track to Chuck Jackson's "Hand It Over," credited to "The Wand Rhythm and Blues Ensemble." Other artists include Barbara Acklin, The Groove, and The Artistics.

KENT (UK) 064 (R)
Think Smart Soul Stirrers:
Jerk It at the Party in Chicago

Despite the stupid title (based on the titles of five of the tunes on the collection), this is one of the better Kent compilations. Sixteen tunes from the vaults of Old Town and its subsidiary Barry by The Fiestas, Bobby and Betty Lou, The Gypsies, Hector Rivera, Lester Young, Irene Reid, and Thelma Jones.

KENT (UK) 082 (R)
Fast, Funky and Fantastic

Most of this is semi-mindless early disco taken from the Fantasy vaults, recorded in the early-to-mid '70s. The set is mostly listenable, especially Side 2, featuring the hits "Walkin' in Rhythm" by The Blackbyrds and Johnny "Guitar" Watson's comeback "I Don't Wanna Be a Lone Ranger." Also includes some rare tracks by soul greats Laura Lee and Betty Everette.

KENT (UK) 083 (R)
Great Sixties Soul Groups

Sixteen tracks by The Lost Generation, The Diplomats, Johnny Maestro and The Crests, The Visitors, The Chancellors, The Platters, The Jive Five, and The Intruders.

KENT (UK) 084 (R)
Down to the Last Heartbreak

An amazingly fine soul-ballad collection from the music's peak period: the early-to-mid-'60s. Standouts include ex-Drinkard Singers Judy Clay's impassioned "He's the Kind of Guy"; early singles by Wilson Pickett and Ike and Tina Turner; Marvin Preyer's classic soul ballad "Don't Stop Loving Me This Way"; and the tearful "I'm Really Thankful" by J.B. Troy. Includes other deep-soul knockouts by Johnny Moore, Johnny Copeland, L.C. Cooke and The Traits, Little Charles and The Sidewinders, Benny Scott, Walter Jackson, Roscoe Gordon, John Parker, and Irma Thomas.

KENT (UK) 086 (R)
Rhythm and Blue-eyed Soul

Collection of British R&B originally released in the '60s on British Decca and its subsidiary, Deram. Most of these are blue-eyed "soul" singers who sound like Tom Jones or Englebert Humperdink! Some black American soul artists also recorded in England, including The Flirtations, Clyde McPhatter, The Fantastics (originally the doo-wop group, The Velours), Larry Williams and Johnny Watson, and Otis Spann. They provide the best stuff here. Best of the Brits is Chris Farlowe doing "Air Travel" and, with The Blazers, "Blue Beat."

KENT (UK) 087 (R)
The Hurt of the City:
Big City Soul, Vol. 2

Sixteen "big ballads" from the vaults of Brunswick, Musicor, and Scepter/Wand. Includes a few never-before-released gems by The Shirelles, Big Maybelle, Maxine Brown, and The Junior Lewis Trio, along with tunes by Tommy Hunt, Theola Kilgore, Johnny Maestro and The Crests, and Jackie Wilson.

KENT (UK) 089 (R)
Soul Cities

One of the better Kent compilations, thanks to some really good unissued soul recordings. Includes 16 cuts by Sugar Pie DeSanto, Benny Gordon, The Platters, Johnny Copeland, and The Intruders.

KENT (UK) 096 (R)
Trippin' on Your Soul

Fourteen Stax/Volt sides from 1969–1980 by Paul Thompson, Mel and Tim, The Charmels, The Mad Lads, The Newcomers, Shirley Brown, and John Gary Williams.

KENT (UK) 100 (L)
For Dancers Forever

KING 513 (RCL)
All Star Rock and Roll Revue
A dozen well-known, but enjoyable, King cuts. Includes big guns like Billy Ward and His Dominoes, The Charms, and Little Willie John.

KING 528 (RC)
After Hours
It's 3 A.M., and there you are at the Dew Drop Inn: too broke, too drunk, or just too blue to go out and hit that long highway home. Life just wouldn't be worth livin' if it weren't for the cool, after-hours sounds these cats are puttin' down, all blowing soft, sweet, and reet in a solid nocturnal groove. Lots of slinky sax, laid-back ivories, and dreamy guitar on ten all-instrumental cuts, with the original LP cover. Take it from me, you can't get anything this mellow anymore without a prescription. Includes sax blowers Sonny Thompson, Earl Bostic, Todd Rhodes, and guitarists Bill Jennings, Pete Lewis, and Jimmy Nolen.

KRAZY KAT 04 (L)
Best of Gotham R&B
Twenty Gotham-label tracks by The Ernie Fields Orchestra, The Jones Boys, Jimmy Rushing, Johnny Sparrow, Screamin' Jay Hawkins, Bill Jennings, Jimmy Preston, The Three Peppers, Panama Francis, and The Rhythm Rockers.

KRAZY KAT 778 (R)
Thunderbolt!: Honkin'
Fourteen great honkers recorded between 1952–1956 by Haywood Henry, Al "Tenor Sax" King accompanied by His Royal Crowns or His Kingsmen, and Warren "Tenor Sax" Lucky.

KRAZY KAT 791 (R)
Lousisiana Southern Soul
Sixteen great soul sides by Alabama singers from Lee Lavergne's Lanor label from Louisiana (apparently they had no good local soulsters!). The Sam Cooke-influenced Willie Mallory sides were recorded at J.D. Miller's studio with Katie Webster (pno) (also available

on Red Pepper 702). Others include Hugh Boynton, Ella Brown, Willie Mallory, and 1969 sides by Phil Phillips.

KRAZY KAT 796 (R)
R&B from Joe Davis, Vol. 2
Davis and Jay-Dee label material by Erskine Butterfield and His Band, Dean Barlow (lead singer of The Crickets), Ernestina (Ernestine Hassell Abbott), Enyatte Holta (LaVerne Holt), Abner Kenon, and Harlem Harley and Chris and His Gang. Some of the best and last R&B sides recorded by Joe Davis before he switched to cutting more popular music in album format. Intelligent sleeve notes and fine pics.

KRAZY KAT 798 (R)
Vocal Group R&B, Vol. 2
Fourteen group sides recorded by Joe Davis for his Jay-Dee and Davis labels, by The Chestnuts, Goldentone, Lillian Leach and The Mellows, The Pyramids, and The Scaletones. The Mellows's sides are all available on their Relic LP.

KRAZY KAT 833 (R)
J.B. Summers and The Blues Shouters
I confess; I took one look at this and I knew I'd love it. J.B. really has the Wynonie Harris bit down pat, shoutin' out good-time R&B over a blazing band. He is backed up on different occasions by the orchestras of Tiny Grimes, Doc Bagby, and Eddie Woodland. Also includes one of the greatest blues shouters, Jimmy Rushing, backed by The Count Basie All Stars. A very enjoyable collection, with liner notes by super sleuth Bruce Bastin.

KRAZY KAT 838 (R)
Stompin' with Bill
Fourteen Gotham recordings, almost all unreleased takes or previously unissued titles. Includes former Louie Jordan and The Tympany Five guitarist Bill Jennings, Tiny Grimes, pianist Ray Bryant, Billy "Guitar" Davis, and Gay Crosse and His Good Humor Six.

KRAZY KAT 7444 (R)
Howling on Dowling
Companion volume to Krazy Kat 7407 and 7418 (no longer available) documenting the R&B scene of Houston, TX, in the late '40s and early '50s. There are lots of obscurities here, but don't let that scare you. Except for some understandable roughness in the sound quality, the performances are almost all excellent and exciting. Tenorman Ed Wiley, Clarence Samuels, Hubert Robinson, and Little Willie Littlefield are among the stars. The real treat is Big Mama Thornton's first recording (as The Harlem Stars on the E&W label): "Bad Luck Got My Man" b/w "All Right Baby," the former a slow blues, the later a ravin' R&B blaster with hot sax.

KRAZY KAT 7448 (R)
Tough Mamas
Fantastic collection of real tough R&B gals, including Pearl Reaves and The Concords, Big Mama Thornton, Gladys Bentley, and Dorothy Ellis. And, the next time your nerdy friend requests Madonna, you can slap on "Rattlesnakin' Daddy" or "Madonna's Boogie" by Madonna Martin and really rattle their cage. Informative notes by Chris Bentley.

KRAZY KAT 7449 (R)
Pepper Hot Baby
A feast of mainly New York vocal-group sides from Sol Rabinowitz's Baton label, circa 1954–1956. Includes five outstanding sides by Rex Garvin and The Hearts from Harlem featuring Johnnie Richards (who later became Johnnie of Johnnie and Joe fame); the stompin' Big Mike Gordon from New Orleans; the short-lived Delltones; Gene "Thousand Stars" Pearson and The Rivaleers; the excellent Suburbans; a jumpin', unreleased Clippers instrumental; plus two Wynonie-like solo efforts by Milan Brown.

LIBERTY (JAPAN) 6599 (L)
Liberty Soul Survivor
Seventeen soul-dipped renditions interspersed with bad patches of funk and disco. Soulsters include Candi Staton, Rosey Grier, the underrated Sonny Green, Lee "Shot" Williams, and The Living Proof.

LIBERTY (JAPAN) 6600 (L)
52 Minits of Soul
Eighteen immersions into '60s super-soul brings us a galaxy of talent, including the under-appreciated Homer Banks, Mississippi-born Jimmy Holiday, Jimmy Lewis, ex-Raelette Little Clydie King (otherwise known as Brown Sugar), Gloria Jones, Lea Roberts, and Herman Hitson. Some good strong testimony in among efforts of lesser virtue.

MARDI GRAS 1001 (RL)
Mardi Gras in New Orleans
Includes The Dixie Cups, The Meters, The Olympia Brass Band, Jake the Snake, Sugarboy Crawford, and A.J. Loria. CD has one bonus track by The Mardi Gras Big Shots.

MARDI GRAS 1011 (CL)
Best of Jazz Fest 1988:
Live from New Orleans
Twelve songs from the 1988 New Orleans Jazz and Heritage Festival. Includes cajun/zydeco, jazz, and R&B by Dr. John, Allen Toussaint, and Irma Thomas. The sound is good, although the mix is a little off in the beginning.

☺ MERCURY 838 243 (L)
Mercury R&B
This fine two-CD collection gathers several of the hottest Mercury R&B acts. There are eight cuts each by Dinah Washington, Eddie "Cleanhead" Vinson, Buddy and Ella Johnson (including one previously unissued cut), and Louis Jordan; four each by Professor Longhair and Clyde McPhatter; and one by The Eagles. The material is all classic stuff, but the Jordan cuts are mostly remakes of his Decca hits, and Clyde was past his prime when these cuts were made. The sound is very clean, and the packaging great, with a 24-page booklet, including 20 pages of detailed notes by R&B authority Pete Grendysa, several photos, and a complete discography for all the cuts.

MOONSHINE 501 (R)
Soulin', Vol. 1

MOONSHINE 502 (R)
Soulin', Vol. 2

MOONSHINE 503 (R)
Soulin', Vol. 3
Three LPs of obscure mid-'60s soul classics. This is the real thang, with many rare cuts on each LP, but no notes or photos. Includes Andre Williams, Dobie Gray, Fontella Bass and Tina Turner, Tommie Young, Vernon Garrett, Freddy Scott, Wilmer and The Dukes, Sam Dees, George Torrence and The Naturals, Bobby Marchan, Doris Troy, Clyde McPhatter, Ann Mason, Tommy Neal, Bobby Patterson, Leon Haywood, Roy Lee Johnson, Roger Collins, Alvin Cash, Soul Brothers Six, Barbara and Brenda, Jackie Moore, and Tony Alvon and The Belairs. Average sound quality.

MOONSHINE 702 (R)
From San Antonio to
the Gulf of Mexico
Excellent compilation of Tex-Mex rock and swamp pop from San Antonio and the surrounding areas. Includes Barbara Lynn, Big Bud Harper, Maria Elena and The Sunglows, Phil Bo and The Vikings, and Spot Barnett, credited as a huge influence on Sir Doug. Solid LP.

MOTOR CITY 1001 (R)
Vocal Groups, Vol. 1

MOTOR CITY 1002 (R)
Vocal Groups, Vol. 2

MOTOR CITY 1003 (R)
Vocal Groups, Vol. 3
Three LPs of rare Motor City vocal-group recordings from 1954–1962 collected from many small labels. Vol. 1 contains two prime and extremely rare 1960–1961 cuts by The Satintones (one of the finest Detroit records ever recorded), and two by the legendary

Voice Masters (who later became The Originals). Vol. 2 highlights are tracks by David Ruffin (before he hitched up with The Temptations), plus "Just for Your Love" by Joe Stubbs and The Falcons. Vol. 3 highlights the fabulous no-strings version of "My Beloved" by The Satintones, "Everytime" from Ty Hunter (who later became a soul soloist), The Voice Masters, plus the unforgettable "Why Did You Go?" by the Flints. Other Motown harmonizers heard through this series include The Royal Jokers, The Five Emeralds, Cornell Blakely and The Johnson Brothers, The Creations, The Martiniques, The Seminoles, The Five Quails, The Five Dollars, The Downbeats, The Serenaders, The Sierras, The Four Imperials, Eddie Bartel and The Fresandos, The Fascinators, and The Five Scalders. No pics or sleeve notes, and average monaural fidelity; essential collectors' material.

MOTOWN 5249 (L)
16 Number 1 Hits: The Late '60s
The Four Tops, Gladys Knight and The Pips, Diana Ross and The Supremes, Smokey Robinson and The Miracles, The Temptations, and Stevie Wonder.

MOTOWN 5248 (L)
16 Number 1 Hits: The Early '60s
The Contours, The Four Tops, Martha and The Vandellas, The Marvelettes, The Miracles, The Supremes, The Temptations, Jr. Walker and The All Stars, Mary Wells, and Stevie Wonder.

MOTOWN 5256 (RC)
A Motown Christmas
Two records/cassettes with The Temptations, Stevie Wonder, The Jackson Five, and Smokey Robinson and The Miracles.

MOTOWN 5343 (L)
Every Great Motown Song, The First 25 Years, Vol. 1
Fourteen memorable smash sides from the soulful '60s by The Supremes, Smokey Robinson and The Miracles, The Four Tops, Marvin Gaye, and The Marvellettes. Guaranteed to send a "big chill" down your spine.

MOTOWN 37463-6312 (CL)
Hitsville USA: The Motown Singles Collection 1959–1971
It's an endless party with all the hit singles from Motown's glory years on this terrific boxed set. Includes The Contours, The Elgins, The Four Tops, Marvin Gaye, The Isley Brothers, The Jackson Five, Gladys Knight and The Pips, Martha and The Vandellas, The Marvellettes, The Originals, Smokey Robinson and The Miracles, Edwin Starr, Diana Ross, The Supremes, The Temptations, Jr. Walker and The All Stars, Mary Wells, and Stevie Wonder. Comes with an illustrated booklet.

POLYDOR 829 417 (L)
James Brown's Funky People

POLYDOR 835 857 (L)
James Brown's Funky People, Vol. 2
Two CDs of hot funk from the short-lived People Records label, mostly featuring the key members (and unforgettable sound) of the early '70s James Brown band. Includes Bobby Byrd, Marva Whitney, Lyn Collins, and Maceo and The Macks.

P-VINE 1411 (L)
Lover's Prayer: 10 Years of Chicago Streetcorner, Vol. 1

P-VINE 1412 (L)
Boom Diddle: 10 Years of Chicago Streetcorner, Vol. 2

P-VINE 1413 (L)
My Dream: 10 Years of Chicago Streetcorner, Vol. 3
Three great CDs drawn from the vaults of Vee Jay Records, each with excellent sound quality. Vol. 1 includes four previously unreleased cuts by The Orchids from Parrot Records, as well as the latter-day Orioles, The Lyrics, The Highlighters, The Delltones (a white group), and two unreleased, but unimpressive, cuts from The El Cincos. The featured groups on Vol. 2 are The Eldorados, The Magnificents, The Chords, and The Capers. Vol. 3 is the least successful of the group, with tracks from the late '50s through the mid-'60s. High points include four cuts each by The El Tempos and The Dontells. Less successful ensembles include The Golden Rods, The Scientists, and The Twinettes. Unfortunately, the booklet notes are in Japanese!

P-VINE 1612 (L)
Lone Star Gold: White Soul Treasures
Fifteen swamp-pop novelties from the mid-'60s, mostly by unknown bands, but some featuring Johnny and/or Edgar Winter. It's hard to tell which, though, because the liner notes are in Japanese.

P-VINE 1618 (L)
Doo-Wop Christmas
Twenty vintage vocal-group Xmas sides. Includes The Ravens, The Orioles, The Moonglows, The Dominoes, The Penguins, The Falcons, The Marquees, and The Miracles.

P-VINE 2009 (L)
The Beatles Classics
This big 30-track disc features the original versions of songs covered by The Fab Four. The sound is good on most tracks, even though it is a bit uneven, no doubt due to the variety of different source materials. Songs include "Twist and Shout" by the Isley Brothers,

"Hippy Hippy Shake" by Chan Romero, Buck Owens's "Act Naturally," "Devil in His Heart" by The Donays, and three tunes by Carl Perkins: "Matchbox," "Everybody's Tryin' to Be My Baby," and "Honey Don't." Great fun at parties: confound all your friends who thought The Beatles were really great songwriters; win hundreds of dollars on drunken bets!

P-VINE 2121 (L)

Soulful Broadway 1650, Vol. 1: Wand Deep Soul

A fine and powerful collection of deep-soul recorded for NY's Wand label. Artists include The Masqueraders, L.C. Cooke, Marvin Preyer, Benny Conn, Clarence Reid, and an unknown singer. Producers include Chips Moman, Tommy Cogbill, and Buddy Killen so you know it's gonna be good. Sound is a little distorted on some tracks.

P-VINE 2122 (L)

Soulful Broadway 1650, Vol. 2: Wand R&B Groups

The Esquires, Richie's Room 222 Gang, The Tabs, The Diplomats, and a couple of unknown groups from way back in the vaults somewhere, totalling 16 cuts.

P-VINE 2137 (L)

Sea of Love: Louisiana Bayou Hits, 1950s–1960s

A fine, 21-track collection of Louisiana swamp pop, blues, and zydeco. Opening with Cookie and The Cupcakes lovely rendition of the Phil Phillips hit "Sea of Love," it also includes sides by Tommy McClain, Rockin' Sidney, Clifton Chenier, Rockin' Dopsie, Johnnie Allan, Jivin' Gene, Joe Barry, Gary Walker and The Boogie Kings, Otis Smith, and Donnie Jacobs.

P-VINE 2151 (L)

Chicago Deep

A collection of Chicago blues, R&B, and soul recorded in the late '70s or early '80s (I think). Highlights are the Artie White tracks, including hard-driving blues and hard-edged R&B and soul. Lee "Shot" Williams and Cicero Blake offer more mainstream soul efforts.

P-VINE 2153 (L)

We Remember Sam Cooke

Includes tracks by L.C. Cooke, Clay Hammond, Willie Rogers, Little Johnny Taylor, Billy Perry, and The Soul Stirrers.

P-VINE 2155 (L)

Ebb Rhythm and Blues Masters

Twenty-two cut sampler, including Eddie Daniels, Sammy Vance, The Ambers, J.J. Jones, Ted Taylor, and The Hollywood Flames.

P-VINE 2162 (L)

A Woman's Love: Classic Soul Jewelry 1

Twenty soulful '60s sides by Joe Valentine, Billy Keen, Albert Washington, Isaac Taylor, and Buddy Ace from small labels.

P-VINE 2163 (L)

A Man In Love: Classic Soul Jewelry 2

Twenty-one small-label '60s soul selections by George Perkins, Eddie Giles, Joe Perkins, Tommy Ridgley, Johnny Adams, and Clarence Carter.

P-VINE 2173 (L)

Teenager's Dreams: Best of Harlem Vocal Groups, Vol. 1

P-VINE 2177 (L)

Flame in My Heart: Best of Harlem Vocal Groups, Vol. 2

P-VINE 2178 (L)

Goodnite My Love: Best of Harlem Vocal Groups, Vol. 3

Three CDs drawn from Bobby Robinson's stable of labels, with good digital sound and rare pictures. Vol. 1.contains great sides by Lewis Lymon (Frankie's brother) and The Teenchords (who sounded very much like The Teenagers), Pearl McKinnon and The Kodaks (Pearl later replaced Frankie in The Teenagers, The Tellers, and Little Bobby Riviera. Vol. 2 features Herman Dunham and Joe Duncan with The Vocaleers from Harlem's 142nd Street (who recorded some of the earliest examples of street-corner doo-wop for Fury's Red Robin label between 1952–1954); Fred Paris (who later sang lead with The Five Satins) and The Scarlets; Joe Grier and The Charts; and Earl Lewis and The Channels, one of Robinson's more successful outfits. All but The Vocaleers's cuts have been reissued on wax over the last few years. Vol. 3 includes The Mello Moods, The Du-Droppers, The Velvets, The Rainbows, plus 15 others, mostly from the early-to-mid-'50s.

P-VINE 2190 (L)

Slow Motion: P-Vine All-Time Greatest Love Ballads

Thirteen-track '70s soul sampler that's great make-out music! Oddly, the biggest hit here is The Escorts's "Let's Make Love (at Home Sometime)," which stalled at Number 58 on the R&B charts. But that's what makes this collection worthwhile: the songs haven't been compiled to death. One of the best cuts is Bobby McClure's "I Want to Be with You Tonight," which never charted. Likewise, non-hits by Phillipe Wynne (ex-Spinners), George Kerr, First Class, and The Montclairs are winners. And Sylvia's version of

Marvin Gaye's subtle "You Sure Love to Ball" could pass for a porno-movie soundtrack. Lights out!

P-VINE 2295 (L)

The Soul Clan

Powerful 20-track compilation of '60s soul duos from various labels, including the awesome Patterson Twins, Johnny and Jon, The Wallace Brothers, Ted and Little Johnny Taylor, and Lonnie and Floyd.

P-VINE 2320 (L)

This Is How It All Began: Roots of Rock and Roll

Twenty-six cuts offer a chronologically arranged picture of the evolution of the Specialty label's version of the '50s rock-and-roll sound, beginning with the gospel sounds of The Chosen Gospel Singers and The Soul Stirrers, traveling through rural blues, small-combo R&B, and blues balladeers, and ending with rock and rollers Larry Williams, Little Richard, and Don and Dewey. Fine sound quality. Liner notes in Japanese, but full lyrics in English, and quite a few small photos. Originally issued as two Specialty LPs in 1969–1970.

P-VINE 2515 (L)

Houston' Deep Throat: Rhythm and Blues

Seventeen tracks by Al "TNT" Braggs, Gene Allison, Levenia Lewis, Ernie K-Doe, Buddy Ace, Helen Wilson, and Henry Moore.

P-VINE 2517 (L)

Elvis Classics

Twenty-six original versions of songs that tickled The King. To my ears, this is the most satisfying "back to the roots" compilation yet. As our Elvis consultant Johnny "Sideburns" Savage says: "Even if you can't stand Elvis, you'll love this CD: it's a thick slice of American pop culture that's tastier than apple pie a la mode." Sound quality is consistently good throughout. Includes Big Boy Crudup, Big Mama Thornton, Jr. Parker, Roy Brown, Joe Turner, Little Richard, Arthur "Hardrock" Gunter, Ray Charles, Lloyd Price, Smiley Lewis, Ivory Joe Hunter, The Orioles, and Clyde McPhatter, along with more obscure acts like Eddie Riff and The Spiders. Recommended.

P-VINE 3004 (L)

Modern/Kent: The Best of R&B Vocals

Twenty tracks from the Modern/Kent/Crown/ R.P.M. label holdings; most have previously shown up on various Ace reissue packages. Highlights are The Cadet's classic "Stranded in the Jungle," Marvin and Johnny's tasty "Cherry Pie," Richard Berry's entertaining tale "Next Time," The Teen Queens's innocent "Eddie My Love," Oscar McLollie's double-sided jumper "Convicted" b/w "Roll Hot Rod Roll," and Young Jesse's timeless "Mary Lou." Also featured are

The Jacks, The Rams, The Drifters, The Cliques, The Flairs, and Shirley Gunter and The Queens.

RED LIGHTNIN' 0059 (R)

Laff Blasts from the Past

Thirteen sides produced by Atlantic Records founder Herb Abramson between 1958–1965, plus a 1978 cut by Otis Blackwell. All but three tracks are previously unreleased, including the hilarious "Ungawa Twist" by The Ravens from 1962 with King Curtis on sax. Features other hot novelty cuts by Otis Blackwell, The Cashmeres with Eddie Jones, The Chanteclairs, The Clovers, The Dovers, The Essentials, The Jarmolettes, The Magnetics, Sonny Middleton and Jack Hammer, The Ravens, and The Symbols.

RED LIGHTNIN' 0065 (R)

Boss Vocal Groups of the '60s

Amazingly good Atco and Festival label recordings from 1961–1966 by Jimmy Ricks and The Raves, Buddy Bailey and The Clovers, Sonny Til and The Orioles, and The Universals (not Kenny Gardner's group). You will be surprised by the quality of these sides. Good fidelity; recommended.

RED LIGHTNIN' 0069 (R)

Condition Your Heart

Fifteen rare and unissued R&B, blues, and doo-wop recordings cut in St. Louis in the late '50s/early '60s by The Kinglets, Little Herbert and The Arabians, Fred Green, Ike Turner's Kings of Rhythm, Fontella Bass, and Oliver Sain.

RED PEPPER 702 (R)

Louisiana R&B from Lanor

Fourteen R&B sides from this Cajun label, recorded between 1961–1963 at J.D. Miller's studio in Crowley, LA, and Cosimo Matassa's studio in New Orleans. Artists include Elton Anderson (with Dr. John, pno), Drifting Charles, Little Victor, Duke Stevens, and Charles Tyler. Some duplication with Krazy Kat 791.

RELIC 101 (R)

The Best of A Cappella

RELIC 102 (R)

The Best of A Cappella, Vol. 2

RELIC 108 (R)

The Best of A Cappella, Vol. 3

RELIC 109 (R)

The Best of A Cappella, Vol. 7

Four LPs, each with twenty forgettable cover versions of standard doo-wop tunes by uninspiring, mediocre, '60s revival East Coast groups. It's very difficult to distinguish one outfit from the other. The first volume also features original '50s sides by The Nutmegs. Includes The Quotations, The Reminiscents, The

Chevieres, The Creations, The Del-Vikings, The Uniques, The Notations, The Citadels, The Apparitions, and The Vibraharps.

RELIC 5005 (R)
The Golden Groups, Vol. 1:
The Best of Onyx Records
Twenty 1956–1958 sides from Jerry Winston's Manhattan-based Onyx label. Includes The Chordells, The Impressors, The Joyettes, The Marquees, The Montereys, The Pearls, and The Velours.

RELIC 5007 (R)
The Golden Groups, Vol. 2:
The Best of Vita Records
Nineteen sides from this fine Pasadena label, recorded between 1955–1958. Highlight: the original version of "Adorable" by The Colts, later covered by The Drifters. Also The Chavelles, The Squires, and The Vitamins (aka The Titans).

RELIC 5012 (R)
The Golden Groups, Vol. 3:
The Best of Angletone/Atlas
Twenty sides from Harlem's first black-owned R&B label, Thomas Robinson's Atlas Records (1951), later joined by a rock-and-roll subsidiary, Angletone (1957). Includes The Chandeliers, Vic Donna and The Parakeets, The Four Haven Knights, The Gypsies, Little Butchie and The Vells, The Revels, and The Travellers.

RELIC 5014 (R)
The Golden Groups, Vol. 4:
The Best of Celeste Records
Nineteen sides from this New York label, highlighted by a-cappella rehearsal tapes of Lillian Leach and The Mellows. Also includes The Four Sounds and The Minors.

RELIC 5015 (R)
The Golden Groups, Vol. 5:
The Best of Herald Records
Twenty sides from Al Silver's New York label by The Cashmeres, The Concords, The Debonairs, The Five Willows, The Heralds, The Loungers, The Mello-Kings, The Mint Juleps, The Nutmegs, The Premiers, The Royal Holidays, Little Butchie Saunders and His Buddies, The Smart Tones, The Sunbeams, and The Thrillers.

RELIC 5016 (R)
The Golden Groups, Vol. 6:
The Best of Ember Records
Twenty sides from Al Silver's other major label, best known for The Five Satins. Also includes Lee Allen, The Barries, The Camelots, The Edsels, The Embers, The Fabulons, The Illusions, The Marktones, The Silhouettes, The Smoothtones, and The Starlarks.

RELIC 5019 (R)
The Golden Groups, Vol. 7:
The Best of Winley Records
Twenty-two sides from Brooklyn's legendary label, home of The Paragons, The Jesters, and Little Anthony's first group, The Duponts. Also includes The Calendars, The Collegians, The Persuaders, and The Quinns.

RELIC 5021 (R)
The Golden Groups, Vol. 8:
The Best of Red Top Records
Twenty sides from the legendary Philadelphia label by The Quintones, Tony Maresca's Tony and The Twilighters, The Blue Notes, The Ivytones, and The Students.

RELIC 5022 (R)
The Golden Groups, Vol. 9:
The Best of Club Records
Eighteen sides from Carl Edelson's short-lived Club label (1956–1957) and his '60s labels, Michele and Showcase. Features The Cherlos, The Crescents, The Duvals, Little Freddie and the Gents, The Pagents, The Relations, Jay Saunders, and The Willows.

RELIC 5026 (R)
The Golden Groups, Vol. 10:
The Best of Tip Top Records
Eighteen cuts from the seven labels run simultaneously by Leo Rogers, including Tip Top, Bruce, Lido, and Lo Fi. Features The Three Friends, The Creations, The Emblems, The Five Vets, The Jumping Jacks, The Master-tones, The Mistakes, The Performers, Eddie Robbins, and The Versatones.

RELIC 5027 (R)
The Golden Groups, Vol. 11:
The Best of Relic Records
Bits and pieces from various labels, including Onyx, Ancho, and Mali, recorded in the '50s but released for the first time on the original Relic label in the early '60s to cash in on the oldies revival. Includes The Academics, The Darvels, The Four Most, The Illusions, The Martels, The Melloharps, The Skylarks, The Teenos, The Unique Teens, and The Versatones.

RELIC 5028 (R)
The Golden Groups, Vol. 12:
The Best of Beltone Records
Seventeen sides from one of the last doo-wop labels (1961–1963), featuring The Jive Five, Dean Barlow, The Cameos, The Carnations, The Corvairs, The Dontells, The Headliners, George Jackson and The Unisons, Johnny and The Jokers, The Leopards, The Mello-Kings, and The Meteors.

RELIC 5029 (R)

The Golden Groups, Vol. 13:
The Best of Xtra Records

Eighteen sides from this obscure late '50s NY label. Includes The Admirations, The Belaires, The Collegians, The Heartspinners, The Sonics, The Unknowns, and The Youngtones.

RELIC 5031 (R)

The Golden Groups, Vol. 14:
The Best of Johnson Records

Eighteen sides by the NY label best known for The Dubs and the Shells. Includes The Dubs's three-song audition tape. Other acts are The Arcades, The Cameos, Bobby Capri and The Velvet Angels, The Caribbeans, Cleo and The Crystaliers, The Cordovans, and Nate and The Chryslers.

RELIC 5032 (R)

The Golden Groups, Vol. 15:
The Best of Times Square Record

Sixteen sides from the label that was run out of Slim Rose's famed record shop, which sparked the early '60s oldies revival. Teen leads and driving saxes can be heard on these tracks by The Decoys, The Five Sharks, The Jaytones, The Pharotones, The Summits, and The Timetones.

RELIC 5034 (R)

The Golden Groups, Vol. 16:
The Best of Rainbow Records

Eighteen sides from this legendary early '50s NY label that issued the first single by The Clovers and classic sides by Lee Andrews and The Hearts. Also includes The Dappers, The Jets, The Lovenotes, The Marquees, The Startones, The Swans, and The Winners.

RELIC 5036 (R)

The Golden Groups, Vol. 17:
The Best of Relic Records

Eighteen '50s sides, most recorded by Al Brown, that were unreleased until put out on Relic 45s in the early '60s. Many of the groups are unknown or perhaps misidentified.

RELIC 5037 (R)

The Golden Groups, Vol. 18:
The Best of Premium Records

Sixteen rare sides from this short-lived (1955–1957) NY label. Includes The Copesetics, The Escorts, Arthur Lake and The Wheels, The Montclairs, The True Loves, The Wheels, and Paul Winley and the Rockets.

RELIC 5038 (R)

The Golden Groups, Vol. 19:
The Best of Jay-Dee Records

Eighteen sides cut by colorful NY producer Joe Davis, recorded between 1953–1956. Includes The Blenders, The Chestnuts, The Continentals, The Dovers, The Goldentones, The Pyramids, The Romancers, The Scaletones, and The Sparrows.

RELIC 5042 (R)

The Golden Groups, Vol. 20:
The Best of Valmor Records

Eighteen sides from this NY label that had a hit with Cathy Jean and The Roomates's "Please Love Me for Ever." Also includes The Roomates (without Cathy Jean), The Embers, The Paramounts, and The Twilights.

RELIC 5043 (R)

The Golden Groups, Vol. 21:
The Best of Lupine Records

Eighteen sides from Robert West's legendary Detroit labels Flick, Bumble Bee, and Lupine. Features the first records by The Falcons, Marv Johnson, and Brian Holland. Also includes The Conquerors, The Bumble Bees, The Tornadoes, The Rivals, Little Joe and The Moroccos, Sonny Woods's Group, Bob Hamilton's Group, The Five Masters, Professor Hamilton and The Schoolboys, and The Minor Chords.

RELIC 5044 (R)

The Golden Groups, Vol. 22:
The Best of Klik Records

Eighteen sides from the Connecticut Klik label, owned by Marty Kugell, producer of "In the Still of the Nite." Features Nicky and The Nobles, The Centuries, The Shades, The Revlons, The Angletones, and The Memories.

RELIC 5045 (R)

The Golden Groups, Vol. 23:
The Best of Showtime Records

Fifteen sides from this incredibly rare LA label. The cuts by The Feathers are gorgeous, especially "Desert Winds," where they back June Moy. Also includes John and Louis Staton (leaders of The Feathers), The Five Stars, and The Individuals.

RELIC 5046 (R)

The Golden Groups, Vol. 24:
The Best of Bruce Records

Twenty sides from Leo Rogers's many labels including Lido, Bruce, and All Star. Includes the original version of "Baby Talk" by The Laurels, and cuts by The Corvells, Johnny Angel, The Premiers, Eddie Robins, The Four of Us, The Shy-Tones, The Versatones, The Van Dykes, The Five Vets, Herb Lance, The Jumping Jacks, The Kingsmen, and The Creations.

RELIC 5047 (R)

The Golden Groups, Vol. 25:
The Best of Herald, Vol. 2

Twenty rarities by The Debonaires, The Five Willows, The Thrillers, The Rocketeers, The Heralds, The Loungers, The Cashmeres, The Mint Juleps, Little Butchie Saunders and His Buddies, The Sonnets, The Desires, The Smart Tones, Dale and The Del-Hearts, The Dynamics, and The Vocalaires.

RELIC 5048 (R)

The Golden Groups, Vol. 26:
The Best of Ember, Vol. 2

Eighteen real obscurities by The Skarlettones, The Bop-Tones, The Starlites, The Wonders, The Fashions, The Paramounts, The Barries, The Silhouettes, David Clowney, The Concords, The Colonaires, The Wonders, and Roger and The Travellers.

RELIC 5049 (R)

The Golden Groups, Vol. 27:
The Best of Flash Records

Eighteen from Charlie "Flash" Reynolds, who based his label in his LA Flash Record Store. Includes some great stuff from the Jayhawks (later known as The Vibrations and The Marathons), including the original version of "Stranded in the Jungle," later covered by The Cadets. Also includes The Arrows, The Cubans, The Emanon Four, The Hornets, and The Poets.

RELIC 5050 (R)

The Golden Groups, Vol. 28:
The Best of Onyx, Vol. 2

Eighteen fast-paced sides by The Velours, The Pearls, The Impressors, The Montereys, The Wanderers, The Carvels, and The Marquees.

RELIC 5051 (R)

The Golden Groups, Vol. 29:
The Best of Atlas/Angletone, Vol. 2

Little Butchie and The Vels, The Lincolns, The Five Dukes, The Chandeliers, The Charmers, The Angletones, The Travelers, The Parakeets, The Fabulous Fabuliers, The Four Haven Knights, and The Gypsies.

RELIC 5052 (R)

The Golden Groups, Vol. 30:
The Best of Dig Records

Eighteen tracks from Johnny Otis's Dig and Ultra labels, featuring an unreleased Arthur Lee Maye and The Crowns's side. Also The Premiers, Mel Williams and The Jayos, Julian Herrera and The Tigers (with Roy Estrada, later of The Mothers of Invention and Little Feat!), The Tears, Cell Foster and The Audios, Tony Allen and The Night Owls, and The Gladiators.

RELIC 5054 (R)

The Golden Groups, Vol. 31:
The Best of Specialty Records

Sixteen rare group records from Specialty, eight previously unreleased. With The Chimes, The Dukes, Arthur Lee Maye and The Crowns, Tony Allen and The Champs, The Crystals, Ben Zeppa and The Zephyrs, The Crowns, The Metronomes, The Tropicals, The Pharaohs, The Twilighters, and Byron Slick Gipson and The Sliders.

RELIC 5055 (R)

The Golden Groups, Vol. 32:
The Best of Class Records

Sixteen sides from the mid-to-late '50s LA label owned by songwriter Leon Rene and his son Googie. Includes the original version of "Little Bitty Pretty One" by Bobby Day and The Satellites, and other seminal sides by Oscar McLollie, Earl Nelson and The Pelicans (same band as The Satellites), Richard Berry and The Pharaohs, The Blenders, The Classics, Paul Clifton, The Intervals, and The Sputniks.

RELIC 5056 (R)

The Golden Groups, Vol. 33:
The Los Angeles Groups

Sixteen sides from various tiny LA labels including Firefly, Jab, Jan Lar, Eastman, L&M, and Rift. Highlights: The Thrills's sides, featuring Jimmy Nolan (gtr). Also includes The Ebbtides (who later became The Rivingtons), The Cadets, The Castle-tones, The Gassers, The Jayhawks, The Marvells, The Peacocks, The Rocketeers, and The Strands.

RELIC 5057 (R)

The Golden Groups, Vol. 34:
The Best of Class, Vol. 2

Richard Berry and The Pharaohs, The Blenders, Eugene Church and The Fellows, The Classics, Paul Clifton, Bobby Day and The Satellites, The Intervals, Steve Kass and The Lovelarks, Earl Nelson and The Pelicans, The Rollettes, The Searchers, The Sputniks, The Tangiers, and The Titans.

RELIC 5059 (R)

The Golden Groups, Vol. 35:
The Best of Club 51 Records

This legendary Chicago label owned by Jimmie and Lillian Davis released only eight 45s between 1951–1957. Of the 14 tracks here, only four by The Four Buddies (including one each as backup for Bobby James and Rudy Greene) and two by The Kingsmen were ever released. The other eight are audition and demo tapes, one by The Four Buddies and the rest by unknown groups. Also included is a radio promo for the label.

RELIC 5060 (R)
The Golden Groups, Vol. 36:
The Best of Swingin' Records
Fourteen sides from the LA label formed by famed DJ Hunter Hancock, featuring ten great falsetto tunes by Rochelle and The Candles, and The Hollywood Saxons.

RELIC 5065 (R)
The Golden Groups, Vol. 39:
The Best of Nu-kat
Benjamin F. Allen's shoestring label offers us a slew of under-released, raggedy sounding sides by such "notables" as The Continental Five, The Orbits, The Velvatones, and The Five Roses. For collectors only.

RELIC 5066 (R)
The Golden Groups, Vol. 40:
The Best of Len Records
Buddy Caldwell's Len Records was a subsidiary of his V-Tone label out of West Philly, which released about 40 sides between 1958–1960. Contains 16 cuts by eight groups, the most exceptional of whom include The Tops, The Four Bars, The Premiers, and The Marquees. Also features two cuts by The Dreamlovers, one of Philly's most successful outfits during the early '60s.

RELIC 5067 (R)
The Golden Groups, Vol. 41:
The Best of V-Tone
Varied group sounds recorded between 1959–1962, some of which are reissued here for the first time in album form. Highlights: the classic "Did We Go Steady Too Soon?" by The Madison Brothers, and "Wonderful Marvelous," a fine weeper by The Tremains out of Harlem. Also includes four cuts by the ever-popular Dreamlovers, and two outstanding sides by the great ex-gospel veteran, Joe Van Loan, backed by The Parliaments. Recommended.

RELIC 5068 (R)
The Golden Groups, Vol. 42:
The Best of Lummtone Records
A long overdue collection of beautifully recorded ballads and jumps, by Jimmie Smith and The Elgins (later of Motown fame) and The Upfronts led by David Johnson. Lummtone, owned by Lummie Fowler, operated out of South Central LA between 1959–1965. Other examples of the sweet, mellow, Southern California vocal-harmony sound come from The Colognes, The Five Ramblers, and The Troopers. An indispensible collection.

RELIC 5069 (R)
The Golden Groups, Vol. 43:
The Best of Combo Records

RELIC 5070 (R)
The Golden Groups, Vol. 44:
The Best of Combo Records, Vol. 2
Two albums documenting the vocal group sound of Watts, LA, during the '50s. Combo was owned and operated by Oakland-born trumpeter Jake Porter, who recorded during the war with his own band in San Francisco on the Pacific label. Great, jumpin' Latin-flavored sounds and pretty ballads from The Sharps (later The Rivingtons), on their own and backing Carl White, Al Smith and The Savoys, Fred and The Native Boys, The Ko-Kos, The Nutones, The Debonaires, Ray Frazier and The Blenders, Marzetta Freeman and The Echoes, Bobby Relf and The Laurels, The Paramounts, Willard Candy and The Starliters of Oakland, Carl Eli and The Buddies, Delmer Wilburn and The Squires (see Relic 5007), and Gene Moore backed by The Chimes and The Chanters. All groups supported by the well-qualified Jake Porter and Jack McVea Bands. For other recommended related material, see Ace 84 and 104. Many of these tracks have appeared on bootleg issues, but the sound quality is superior here.

RELIC 5071 (R)
The Golden Groups, Vol. 45:
The Best of Timely and Luna
Classic New York street-corner doo-wop from 1954. Timely was owned and operated by Herman Siegal who worked with the Bermans of Apollo Records; Luna was an Apollo subsidiary label. Includes four released singles by The Ambassadors, The Charmers, The Gaytunes, and The Crystals (aka The Opals), and unreleased material including practice sessions and alternates. These are rare sides, long considered collector's items, and never previously reissued in legal form.

RELIC 5075 (R)
The A Cappella Audition Album
First rate, mid-'50s, East Coast street-corner harmony. Exceptional practice tapes by Chester Mayfield and The Casanovas, Miriam Grate and The Dovers, the little known Gentlemen/Avalons, and Sam Kearney with The Keynotes. Some unissued material, and good sound quality throughout. One of the finest Relic collections to date.

RELIC 5076 (R)
The Golden Groups, Vol. 46:
Best of Combo, Vol. 3
Harmony heaven. The Chanters, The Native Boys, The Ebonaires, The Chimes, The Squires, The Echoes, The Debonaires, The Sir Nites, and The Combonettes. A collector's essential, as strong as Relic 5069 and 5070 (Vols. 1 and 2).

⚫ RELIC 5077 (R)

The Golden Groups, Vol. 47: Apollo Records, Vol. 1

An amazing set of vocal-harmony rarities, circa 1952–1954. Made up of ballads and jumps in equal proportion, this is by far the rarest and most interesting Apollo-label compilation. Includes prime tracks by The Mel-o-dots, Billy Austin and The Hearts, The Opals (formerly The Crystals), Eli Spillman and The Jumping Jacks, the sparkling Lydia Larson, the bluesy River Rovers (thought to be one of the first female R&B groups to record), and Eugene Mumford and The Larks.

RELIC 5078 (R)

The Golden Groups, Vol. 48: Apollo Records, Vol. 2

A great collection featuring Ted "Larry" Bogar, The Larks, the fabulous Miriam Grate, Doc Starkes and The Nite Riders, and Eli Spillman and The Romeos (aka The Jumping Jacks).

RELIC 5079 (R)

The Golden Groups, Vol. 49: All A Cappella: Times Square Records

RELIC 5080 (R)

The Golden Groups, Vol. 50: Best of Apollo Records, Vol. 3

Sixteen tracks, including rare and unissued sides from Jimmy "Good Timin'" Jones and The Sparks of Rhythm, including the 1956 original version of "Handy Man," led by bass singer Andrew Barksdale; the newly discovered gem, "Pretty Mama," by The Inspirations; the amazing "So Strange" from a rehearsal tape sung by the great Lillian Leach with The Mellows; plus a righteous a-cappella audition goodie, "Early One Morning" by Floyd Adams and The Keynotes.

RELIC 5081 (R)

The Golden Groups, Vol. 51: Best of Apollo Records, Vol. 4

The Delroys, The Tonettes, The Brochures, two unissued a-cappella warblings by Melvin Stowe and The Casanovas, Little Anthony and The Chesters (later known as The Imperials), The Claremonts, and Ann Ford (aka Annie Alford).

RELIC 5085 (R)/7033 (L)

Unreleased Gems of the 1950s

Features The Belaires, Gene Pitney (who's never sounded better), and Larry Lee backed by The Embers and The Serenaders. Some of the material is in mono, but most is in stereo. Exceptional sound quality and exhaustive notes round out a fine set.

RELIC 5087 (R)

The Golden Groups, Vol. 52: Best of Parrot/Blue Lake Records, Vol. 1

RELIC 5088 (R)

The Golden Groups, Vol. 53: Best of Parrot/Blue Lake Records, Vol. 2

The Parrot/Blue Lake labels were owned and operated out of Chicago's "record row" by DJ/booking agent Al Benson in the mid-'50s. Benson was responsible for the emergence of some of the most important blues, jazz, and doo-wop of the period. Each LP features 17 winning sides by The Orchids, The Flamingos, The Earls, The Five Thrills, The Fascinators, The Swans, The Clouds, The Parrots, The Pelicans, The Fortunes, and The Five Chances. Essential.

RELIC 5089 (R)

The Golden Groups, Vol. 54: The Best of Whirlin' Disc

Great NY doo-wop from 1956–1957 by The Empires, The Pretenders, The Continentals, The Whirlers, The Channels, and The Philly Quadrells. Beautiful clean overall sound on this first legal reissue of classic material.

RELIC 5091 (R)

The Golden Groups, Vol. 55: The Best of Holiday Records

An absolutely unbeatable collection of sixteen uptempo and tender ballad renditions from Danny Robinson's short-lived Harlem waxery. Harmonic blending of the first order by William Dailey and The Bop Chords, the little known Harmonaires, the fabulous Love Notes, Johnny Jackson and The Ladders, and Jimmy "Handy Man" Jones and The Pretenders. Minor duplication with P-Vine 2178.

⊙ RELIC 7005 (L)
The Original Rumble

This is THE original Rumble collection, first put out as part of a tough black vocal-group series on Jubilee Records in the early '60s. The CD adds six extra cuts to the original LP. Contains doo-wop gold by The Bop Chords, The Channels, The Continentals, The Love Notes, plus fourteen others. Great NY doo-wop from the music's twilight years, with two unreleased alternate takes. Definitive sleeve notes by Don Fileti, digitally reconstructed from the original mastertapes.

⊙ RELIC 7009 (L)
Raging Harlem Hit Parade

Fabulous 22-track collection of blues, R&B, soul, and doo-wop from the priceless vaults of Harlem's greatest black-music pioneer, Bobby Robinson, spanning the years 1957–1962. Choice material by Elmore James, Gladys Knight, Bobby Marchan, Buster Brown, Lightnin' Hopkins, Wilbert Harrison, Don Gardner and Dee Dee Ford, King Curtis, Tarheel Slim, The Charts, Red Prysock, Dr. Horse, Les Cooper, The Velvets, Lee Dorsey, and Arthur "Big Boy" Crudup. Digitally transferred from the original session tapes, some of which appear for the first time in real stereo.

RELIC 7027 (L)
Rockin' at Midnight at the Parrot Club

Sixteen blues, R&B, doo-wop, jazz, and comedy sides from the excellent Blue Lake and Parrot catalog. The recording attempts to replicate what a typical Chicago club show might have been in the mid-'50s. Includes The Five Thrills, The Chocolateers, Marvin Phillips, The Five Echoes with Walter Spriggs, Lowell Fulson, Lou Mac, Mabel Scott, The Maples, Browley Guy and The Skyscrapers, The Five Arrows, and The Rockettes. Rich, varied, and important material.

RELIC 8004 (R)/7017 (L)
The Detroit Girl Groups

Eighteen rare girl-group sides from Detroit's Lupine label, featuring two 1960 cuts by The Primettes (later known as The Supremes), and a great cover photo of them, too. Also includes The Kittens, La Dolls, Ruby and Her Swinging Rocks, Clara Hardy, The Corvells, The Clevers, The Taylor Tones, The Conquerors, and The Satin Angels.

RELIC 8008 (R)
Lupine Records Presents a Rock and Roll Party

Lots of rare Detroit R&B and rock from Robert West's Lupine, Flick, Contour, and Kudo labels. There are seminal Motown roots here, with Brian Holland's (of Holland-Dozier-Holland) 1958 solo single "Shock," and early Supremes, in the form of The Primettes, backing Al Garner on "Tears of Sorrow." Also includes Sonny Wood, teen instrumentals by The Vulcans, raw doo-wop with The Majestics, even a raucous "Where You Goin' There Saphire" by the famed Upsetters.

RELIC 8009 (R)/7034 (L)
The Soul of Detroit

Gospel-influenced, early soul tracks by Gene Martin and Don Revel backed by The Primettes, Betty Lavette backed by The Falcons, three future members of The Falcons heard on early solo sides (Mack Rice, Eddie Floyd, and Joe Stubbs), Benny McCain and The Ohio Untouchables (later The Ohio Players), The Minor Chords, The Conquerors, The Majestics, and The Rivals.

RELIC 8011 (R)
Cruisin' the Drag

Fourteen previously unissued (and unknown) sides from Hugh Whitlow's Tulsa-based, tiny Wheel label. Recorded at Perspective Sound between 1959–1961, these doo-wop and rock-and-roll cuts seem muddied, as if recorded in back of a large storm drain. It's a pity, because the doo-wop cuts by The Five Sonics are classics, and the rock-and-roll material by The Vibes, The Crowns, and Flash Terry are also worthwhile.

RELIC 8018 (R)
Goodbye '40s, Hello '50s: Vol. 1

RELIC 8019 (R)
Goodbye '40s, Hello '50s, Vol. 2

Two volumes focusing on vocal groups who span the bridge between the old style of blues and rhythm and the newer, emerging form of R&B. This outstanding collection, put together by Marv Goldberg and Ray Funk, highlights some of the most important East Coast quartets of the time. Vol. 1 includes four knockout close-harmony sides recorded in 1949 by The Striders, two great previously unreleased gospel sides by Eugene Mumford and The Larks, The Melody Masters, the little known Earl Plummer and The Four Blues, The Rivals, plus two Christmas tunes by The Rhythm Kings. Vol. 2 features Apollo vocal-group sides from the 1947–1951 period. Includes The Whispers, The Strider (Brothers), Danny Owens and The Melody Masters, the obscure Rhythm Kings (aka Rhythmasters), The Three Riffs of Cleveland, and four novelty selections by Philadelphia's Four Blues. Informative sleeve notes and good sound.

RHINO 70037 (C)
Soul Shots, Vol. 1: Dance Party

Fourteen tunes that will get ANYBODY onto a dance floor. Includes Jackie Wilson, The Show Stoppers, Dyke and The Blazers, James Brown and The Famous Flames, and Billy Stewart.

RHINO 70038 (C)
Soul Shots, Vol. 2: Sweet Soul
Mellow soul hits by Brenton Wood, The Kars, Dobie Gray, The Esquires, and The Checkmates, Ltd.

RHINO 70039 (C)
Soul Shots, Vol. 3: Soul Instrumentals
If you spent years of your youth trying to master the Farfisa organ, you'll love these soulful cuts by The Mar-Keys, King Curtis, Booker T and the MGs, and The Ramsey Lewis Trio.

RHINO 70040 (C)
Soul Shots, Vol. 4: Screamin' Soul Sisters
Etta James, Aretha Franklin, Koko Taylor, Barbara George, and Maxine Brown.

RHINO 70041 (C)
Soul Shots, Vol. 5: Soul Ballads
Aaron Neville, Billy Stewart, The Deltonics, Lou Rawls, and The Impressions. I've never heard a prettier collection.

RHINO 70042 (C)
Soul Shots, Vol. 6: Blue-Eyed Soul
Fourteen-song selection of Caucasian cacophony of the soul-funk persuasion by Billy Joe Royal, P.J. Proby, The Soul Survivors, The Young Rascals, and Wayne Cochran.

RHINO 70043
Soul Shots, Vol. 7: Urban Blues
Thirteen tracks of soul, blues, and down-home anguish. Little Jr. Parker, Albert King, Tommy Tucker, B.B. King, Junior Wells, Lowell Fulsom, Otis Rush, Little Milton, Buddy Gay, and Little Johnny Taylor. Great collection for those starting out in postwar electric R&B/blues.

RHINO 70044 (C)
Soul Shots, Vol. 8: Sweet Soul Sisters
The Mirettes, Patti Drew, The Flirtations, The Sweet Inspirations, and Barbara Acklin.

RHINO 70045 (C)
Soul Shots, Vol. 9: More Dance Party

RHINO 70046 (C)
Soul Shots, Vol. 10: More Sweet Soul

RHINO 70047 (C)
Soul Shots, Vol. 11: More Ballads

RHINO 70076 (C)
History of New Orleans R&B, Vol. 1 (1950–1958)
Fourteen tunes covering the roots of second-line boogie. Although there are no Fats Domino or Little Richard sides, all the important early hits are here by Huey "Piano" Smith, Earl King, The Hawkettes, Clarence "Frogman" Henry, Sugar Boy Crawford, Bobby Charles, Professor Longhair, Lloyd Price, Shirley and Lee, Lee Allen, and Guitar Slim.

RHINO 70077 (C)
History of New Orleans R&B, Vol. 2 (1959–1962)
New Orleans pop at its peak. The amazing Allen Toussaint wrote, arranged, and played on most of these great tracks by Ernie K-Doe, Art Neville, Aaron Neville, Benny Spellman, Earl King, Barbara George, Jessie Hill, Bobby Marchan, Lee Dorsey, The Showmen, Chris Kenner, Frankie Ford, and Clarence "Frogman" Henry.

RHINO 70078 (C)
History of New Orleans R&B, Vol. 3 (1962–1970)
The highlights are the two hard-to-find Alvin Robinson sides, "Down Home Girl" and "Something You Got for Tiger," and Aaron Neville's wonderful "Tell It Like It Is." Also includes Lee Dorsey, Robert Parker, Irma Thomas, Benny Spellman, Johnny Adams, Barbara Lynn, and The Dixie Cups.

RHINO 70181 (C)
The Best of Doo-Wop Ballads
A nearly perfect collection of mostly well-known late-night smoochers. Includes hits by The Five Satins, The Dells, The Crests, Dion and The Belmonts, The Penguins, and The Mello-Kings.

RHINO 70182 (C)
The Best of Doo-Wop Uptempo
The Five Satins, The Dells, The Crests, The Jive Five, Dion and The Belmonts, The Penguins, Rosie and The Originals, The Mello-Kings, and The Spaniels. See also Rhino 70904/05 (cassettes) and 75763/64 (CDs).

⊕ RHINO 70570 (CL)
Risque Rhythm: Nasty '50s R&B
Hmmm. These songs are supposed to be naughty, explicit, suggestive, and blue. But Wynonie Harris's "Keep On Churnin'" is clearly about butter, The Sultan's "Lemon Squeezing Daddy" is about a father who squeezes lemons, and Dinah Washington's "Big Long Slidin' Thing" is about a missing trombone player. So what's risque about that? Julia Lee may be overly proud of the distinguished fellow on "My Man Stands Out," but what's nasty about that? The folks at Rhino must know what they're doing, though, because they've also included Bullmoose Jackson's "Big Ten Inch (Record)" about a 78 rpm, the space-travel saga "Rocket 69" by Todd Rhodes, The Toppers's "Let Me Bang Your Box," and a lot of other great songs. The CD has four bonus cuts.

⊕ RHINO 70587 (CL)
New Orleans Party Classics
Sixteen Mardi Gras standards, many of which were just local Crescent City favorites. Highlights: the regional hits like Oliver Morgan's "Who Shot the La La," originally recorded as a Crescendo single in 1963 and reissued here for the first time, and the popular instrumental "Peanut Vendor" by saxophonist Alvin "Red" Tyler and His Gyros from 1959. Includes Fats Domino, Frankie Ford, Allen Toussaint, Dr. John, The Neville Brothers, Professor Longhair, The Wild Tchoupitoulas, The Dirty Dozen Brass Band, Stop Inc., Al Johnson, Huey "Piano" Smith and The Clowns, and Li'l Bob and The Lollipops. All in all, it's more fun than twisting the heads off a barrel of crawfish.

RHINO 70638 (CL)
Billboard Greatest R&B Christmas Hits
Ten tunes, including "Merry Christmas Baby" by Johnny Moore's Three Blazers, "Boogie Woogie Santa Claus" by Mabel Scott, "The Little Drummer Boy" by Lou Rawls, "Rudolph the Red-Nosed Reindeer" by The Cadillacs, and "Santa Claus Is Coming to Town" by The Jackson 5.

RHINO 70904 (C)
Best of Doo-Wop Ballads, Vol. 2

RHINO 70905 (C)
Best of Doo-Wop Uptempo, Vol. 2
See Rhino 70181/82 and the CDs 75763/64.

RHINO 71037 (CL)
Atlantic Sisters of Soul
Twenty-three lesser-known female soul numbers recorded between 1965–1973 for the Atlantic, Atco, Cotillion, and Clintone labels. Tempos and moods range from jump-tune intensity to slow and sultry balladry. Includes The Sweet Inspirations, Baby Washington, Dee Dee Warwick, Irma Thomas, and One'sy Mack. Excellent sound quality. A great selection of tracks overall, with an 18-page booklet full of equally great photos. Recommended.

RHINO 71057 (CL)
Doo-Wop Christmas
Eighteen yuletide crooners (14 on tape) from The Penguins, The Drifters, The Harmony Grits, The Falcons, The Five Keys, The Cadillacs, Jimmy Beaumont and The Skyliners, Frankie Lymon, Margo Sylvia, The Marcels, The Uniques, The Moonglows, The Orioles, The Echelons, The Shells, The Statues, and The Heartbeats.

RHINO 71111 (CL)
New Orleans Jazz and Heritage Festival: 1976
Fabulous live sets from America's greatest folk festival by Allen Toussaint, Irma Thomas, Ernie K-Doe,

Lighnin' Hopkins, Professor Longhair, Lee Dorsey, Earl King, and Robert Parker. One instant party record.

RHINO 72006 (L)
Billboard Top R&B Hits 1965–1969
Five-CD box set, documenting the hits of each of these years, many in stereo and on CD for the first time!

RHINO 75757 (L)
Soul Shots, Vol. 3
See Rhino 75770.

RHINO 75763 (L)
Best of Doo Wop Ballads

RHINO 75764 (L)
Best of Doo Wop Uptempo
Drawn from cassette collections 70181/82 and 70904/05.

RHINO 75770 (L)
Soul Shots, Vol. 2
See Rhino 75774.

RHINO 75774 (L)
Soul Shots
CD compilations of cassette-only series (See Rhino 70037-70047).

R&B 401 (R)
Rhythm and Blues
Mixed bag collection of solid, mostly mid-tempo R&B tunes by Paul Bascomb, Jimmy Lee and Artis, Wilbert Harrison, Sonny Parker, H-Bomb Ferguson, and Jewel King. The rest are good if not earth shaking.

R&B 402 (R)
Rhythm and Blues, Vol. 2
Familiar names and tunes combined with some obscure gems. Highlights: both sides of Earl Curry's great 1954 single, "One Whole Year Baby" b/w "I Want Your Lovin'." Also includes Mike Gordon and The El Tempos, Teddy Reynolds, Roy Wright, Joe Thomas, Ella Johnson, Zuzu Bollin, and Bill Doggett.

ROUNDER 2072 (RC)
Modern New Orleans Masters
A sampler from Rounder's New Orleans catalogue, including tracks by The Golden Eagles, Irma Thomas, Earl Turbinton, and Alvin "Red" Tyler, plus a couple of previously unissued tracks by The Dirty Dozen Brass Band and James Booker.

ROUNDER 2075 (RCL)
Carnival Time! The Best of Ric, Vol. 1
Al Johnson, Lenny Capello, Eddie Bo, Joe Jones, Martha Nelson, Johnny Adams, Tommy Ridgley, Edgar Blanchard, and The Velvetiers. Great stuff!

ROUNDER 2076 (RCL)

We Got A Party! The Best of Ron, Vol. 1

Ron, the bluesier brother of Ric, sported such New Orleans legends as Professor Longhair, Irma Thomas, Chris Kenner, Robert Parker, Bobby Mitchell, Warren Lee, and Eddie Lang, and more obscure acts like The Top Notches, Joe "Guitar" Morris, Paul Marvin, Jerry Starr, and The Party Boys.

ROUNDER 2078 (RCL)

New Orleans Ladies: R&B from the Vaults of Ric and Ron

Fine selection of Ric and Ron sides from three spirited women who recorded in the heyday of New Orleans R&B, 1959–1965. Mostly arranged by the colorful and talented Eddie Bo, these cuts are noteworthy for the four first efforts of Irma Thomas, eight excellent songs by Martha Carter, and two Carla Thomas-ish numbers by Leona Buckles.

ROUNDER 2087 (CL)

Keys to the Crescent City

Includes piano wizards Eddie Bo, Willie Tee, Art Neville, and Charles Brown. Good concise booknotes.

ROUNDER 2113 (CL)

The Mardi Gras Indians Super Sunday Showdown

Imagine recording an all-day party for CD release. If your party was in, say, Ho-ho-kus, NJ, forget it. But if the affair was in New Orleans, hosted by the party-mad Wild Magnolias and Golden Eagles Indian groups, you'd have an instant hit! With guests like Dr. John, Champion Jack Dupree, keyboardist Willie Tee, and the irrepressible Rebirth Brass Band, this disc can't miss. Only The Golden Eagles medley was recorded live, but the rest is all-the-way live in the studio, thriving on a very loose collaborative atmosphere.

ROUNDER 11567 (L)

Mardi Gras Party

Fifteen carnival cuts taken from currently available Rounder releases by Professor Longhair, Marcia Ball, Beausoleil, Irma Thomas, Nathan and The Cha Chas, Bo Dollis (chief of The Wild Magnolias), Tuts Washington, The Dirty Dozen Brass Band, The Rebirth Brass Band, Art Neville, and James Booker.

SAVAGE KICK 101 (R)

Black Rock and Roll

SAVAGE KICK 502 (R)

Black Rock and Roll, Vol. 2

SAVAGE KICK 503 (R)

Black Rock and Roll, Vol. 3

SAVAGE KICK 504 (R)

Black Rock and Roll, Vol. 4

SAVAGE KICK 505 (R)

Black Rock and Roll, Vol. 5

SAVAGE KICK 506 (R)

Black Rock and Roll, Vol. 6

SAVAGE KICK 507 (R)

Black Rock and Roll, Vol. 7

Seven LPs primarily of rock and R&B cuts by great unknowns and well-known acts. Vol. 1 features everything from Louis Jordan-inspired swing-jive to fast blues and up-tempo doo-wop by Lord Luther, Calvin Boze, Ike Turner with Icky Renrut, Bo Diddley, Lightin' Hopkins, Peppermint Harris, Harmonica Frank, Betty James, Papa Lightfoot, and Joe Tex. Among the unknowns are Ricky Charles, Big Daddy, Juke Boy Bonner, King Coleman, The Thunderbirds, Johnny Wright, Jimmy Coe, Jumpin' Jay, and Tiny Lewis.

SAVAGE KICK SKVUN (R)

Vicious, Vicious Vocals, Vol. 1

Sixteen great R&B tunes by the famous (The Cadets, The Chips, and The Jay-Hawks) and the obscure (Little Jimmy and The Sparrows, Little Moose and The Hunters, The Composers, and The Kinglets).

SAVOY 1157 (RCL)

Mr. Santa's Boogie

Blues, jazz, and R&B Christmas songs including "White Christmas" by The Ravens, "Trim Your Tree" by Jimmy Butler, "Silent Night" by Big Maybelle, "Christmas Blues" by Gatemouth Moore, "Santa's Secret" by Johnny Guarnieri with Slam Stewart, plus Little Esther Phillips, Charlie Parker, and "Washboard" Pete.

☻ SEQUEL 618 (L)

The Ultimate Doo-Wop Collection

Twenty songs from various labels in the vast Roulette catalog. Collectors will argue about which songs belong on the "ultimate" compilation, but most of the choices here are solid. Acts include The Crows, The Orioles, The Cadillacs, The Chantels, Frankie Lymon, The Miracles, and The Four Tunes. The big reason to get this, though, is the extremely rare "Stormy Weather" by The Five Sharps (1952), which has never been on CD, and, since only two 78 rpm copies have ever turned up, seldom shows up anywhere in any form.

☻ SIRE 26731 (CL)

Sweet Soul Music: Voices from the Shadows

Billed as "a listening companion" to Peter Guralnick's book of the same title, this disc is the best soul collection around. It captures the essence of soul in a way that a package of Top-Ten hits could never do. Biggies like Aretha Franklin, Percy Sledge, and Solomon Burke are here, represented by excellent songs that are not usually reissued. There are also stunning cuts from more minor artists, including Laura Lee, Soul Brothers Six, Arthur Alexander, Judy Clay, Eddie Giles, and The Enchanters. Better than a plane ticket to Memphis.

SKATFISH KICK 01 (L)

Savage Catfish Kick

Sixteen R&B and gospel tunes, about half of which are pretty common and which any self-respecting R&B fan should have already. "Spunky Onions," an instrumental by Billy Davis and The Legends, is the most obscure tune here and is almost worth the price alone. More excitement is generated by Frankie Lee Sims, Guitar Junior, Doctor Ross, The Five Du-Tones, and The Pilgrim Travellers.

SOUL SUPPLY 1 (L)

Rare Soul on CD, Vol. 1: The Vocal Groups

Twenty-three up-beat, danceable rarities. There are a few recognizable names, including Harold Melvin and The Blue Notes, The Showmen, Frankie Beverly and The Butlers, and The Executive Four (aka The Cadillacs). Lesser knowns include Porgy and The Monarchs, The CODs, The Tempos, and The Incredibles. Most of these tunes are lifted from records, so, although digitally remastered, the sound is still fairly weak.

SPECIALTY 2112 (RC)

Our Significant Hits

Solid LP featuring three hits each by Specialty's four biggest stars: Lloyd Price, Sam Cooke, Little Richard, and Larry Williams.

SPECIALTY 2114 (RC)

Doo-Wop

Fourteen great Specialty sides compiled by Dr. Demento. The title is somewhat misleading because one side of this collection features mellow doo-wop, but the second side is totally wild novelty and jump blues numbers. Acts include The Chimes, The Monitors, Larry Williams, Vernon Green and The Phantoms, Jesse and Marvin, Marvin and Johnny, The Four Flames, Roddy Jackson, Bob "Froggy" Landers with Willie Joe and His Unitar, Roy Montrell, Jimmy Liggins and His 3-D Music, King Perry and His Pied Pipers, Rene Hall, and Joe Lutcher.

SPECIALTY 2155 (RC)

The Golden Groups

Sixteen tracks featuring The Chimes, Arthur Lee Maye and The Crowns, The Crystals, The Tropicals, and The Twilighters.

SPECIALTY 2167 (RC)

Lay That New Orleans Rock and Roll Down

Fourteen rare cuts, all with punchy sound from the original session tapes. A few of these songs should have been left in the vaults, but the ratio of diamonds to dung is very favorable. Some of the unreleased gems are unusual variants on the classic New Orleans sound (which may explain why they never saw daylight before) and are truly great. Features Larry Williams, Ernie K-Doe, Bobby Marchan, Lloyd Price, Roy Montrell, Art Neville, and Big Boy Myles.

✪ SPECIALTY 2168 (CL)

Creole Kings of New Orleans

Nothing will get your party jumping more successfully than these R&B stompers from the Crescent City, circa 1950–1958. Twenty-six selections, including five alternates, two unissued, and one demo. Includes Leo Price, Professor Longhair, Lloyd Price, Guitar Slim, mellow thrush Alberta Hall, Ernie K-Doe, Jerry Byrne, Big Boy Myles, Li'l Millet, Roy Montrell, Larry Williams, Percy Mayfield, Joe Liggins, The Royal Kings, The Kings, Clifton Chenier, Lloyd Lambert, and Edgar Blanchard. Get it for Art Neville's stunningly beautiful "I'm a Fool to Care." Lots of rare pics and cameo bios of major acts.

SPECIALTY 2173 (CL)

Doo-Wop from Dolphin's of Hollywood, Vol. 1

Twenty-six cut selection (including nine bonus tracks on the CD version) of wonderful mid-'50s doo-wop recorded for John Dolphin's Cash and Money labels out of LA. I count a lucky 13 tracks listed as previously unissued, making this a worthy addition to every serious vocal-group collection. The unreleased tracks are fine, as a rule, with only a slight lack of polish or originality preventing their release. Includes Bobby Byrd backed by The Voices, Jessie Belvin and The Gassers, The Turbans, The Turks, and The Miracles (later The Jaguars).

SPECIALTY 2174 (CL)

Doo-Wop from Dolphin's of Hollywood, Vol. 2

Twenty-three more great vocal-group tracks (only 16 on cassette). The main man here again is Bobby Byrd with The Hollywood Flames, The Birds, and whoever else was in the studio when he was recording. Also includes Grady Chapman (who once sang with The Robins) and The Suedes, The Ebonaires, The Hollywood Arist-O-Kats, and The Five Bars. Seven unidentified cuts are also included, four of which might very well be by The Hollywood Flames.

STAR CLUB 8026 (R)

All American Rock, Vol. 3: Doo-Wop '50s Style

Great white doo-wop by three of the best groups. There are six Regents's tunes, including their immortal "Barbara Ann"; six by New Haven's Nobles, including two with new lead Nickie Delano released as by Nicky and The Nobles; and four by The Quotations. All of these tracks are also available on Relic or Crystal Ball, but this one's a nice, solid collection.

STARLIGHT DISCS 19901 (L)

Starlight Serenade: 1950s Doo-Wop "A Cappella"

STARLIGHT DISCS 19911 (L)

Starlight Serenade, Vol. 2: 1950s Doo-Wop "A Cappella"

STARLIGHT DISCS 19913 (L)

Starlight Serenade, Vol. 3: 1950s Doo-Wop "A Cappella"

STARLIGHT DISCS 19921 (L)

Starlight Serenade, Vol. 4: 1950s Doo-Wop "A Cappella"

Four generously programmed CDs that offer examples of vocal bravado as pitched on the streets of the Big Apple during the doo-wop heyday of early earth satellites. Clean and sparkling recordings made between 1980–1990 by some of the surviving vets of the genre, including The Tokens, The Street Dreams, The Allures, The Shallows, The Velours, The Four Sevilles, The Originals, A Moment's Pleasure, Dino and The Heartspinners, John Kuse and The Excellents, Lewis Lymon and The Teenchords, Frank Ayala and The Arrogants, The Flipsides, Joe Grier and The Charts, Robert Murphy and Neighbor's Complaint, The Dubs, Street Corner Serenade, Norman Fox and The Rob Roys, Rick and The Masters, The Swallows, The Galls-Tones, Magic Touch, The Ovations, Fred Johnson and The Marcels, Brooklyn Connection, Reminisce, New Image, The Bob Knight Four, The Five Boroughs, The Lar-Kings, The Revelations, The Tycoon, and BQE. Lovingly produced by Bob Kretzchmar and Jerry Zidel.

STAX 8501 (RC)

Stax 15 Original Big Hits, Vol. 1

STAX 8502 (RC)

Stax 15 Original Big Hits, Vol. 2

STAX 8516 (RC)

Stax 15 Original Big Hits, Vol. 3

STAX 8519 (RCL)

It's Christmas Again

Features The Staple Singers, Albert King, and others.

STAX 8535 (RC)

Stax 15 Original Big Hits, Vol. 4

Four collections of late '60s/early '70s soul and R&B sides, the post-Atlantic years from Stax/Volt/Enterprise. Acts include The Bar-Kays, William Bell, Booker T and The MGs, Shirley Brown, The Dramatics, The Emotions, Eddie Floyd, Isaac Hayes, F. Knight, Jean Knight, Little Milton, Mel and Tim, Soul Children, The Staple Singers, Johnny Taylor, Rance Allen, William Bell and Judy Clay, Albert King, The Newcomers, Shack, The Temprees, Carla Thomas, Rufus Thomas, Hot Sauce, and Jimmy Hughes.

STAX 8543 (RCL)

Stax Soul Sisters

Excellent collection of 1968–1975 Stax singles, many never on LP, with a heavy emphasis on deep-soul. Includes well-known Stax stars Carla Thomas, Mavis Staples, Barbara Lewis, Inez Foxx, Jean Knight, Margie Joseph, Mabel John, and Judy Clay.

STAX 8548 (RCL)

The Stax Soul Brothers

Includes William Bell, Isaac Hayes, and Little Milton.

STAX 8549 (RCL)

Sweet Soul Music

Includes The Dramatics, The Lords, and The Leaders.

STAX 8567 (CL)

Funky Broadway: Stax Revue Live at the 5/4 Ballroom

Interesting historically and musically, this Stax revue was recorded in Watts before the 1965 riots. It includes Booker T and The MG's earliest live recordings, including their only live version of "Soul Twist." Also includes William Bell, The Mad Lads, The Astors, The Mar-Keys, Rufus Thomas, and Carla Thomas. DJ "Magnificent Montague" adds words of introduction, uttering his pre-riot trademark "burn, baby burn." Not a perfect live disc, but you'll be happy somebody turned on a tape recorder during this show. Thirteen cuts, with good liner notes, too.

✪ STAX 88005 (RCL)

Top of the Stax: Twenty Greatest Hits

Twenty deep-soul classics with informative liner notes by Lee Hildebrand as well as snazzy little photos of all the artists. Includes both the mid-'60s (Atlantic-owned) and later '60s/early '70s (post-Atlantic) hits.

STAX 88009 (L)

The Stax/Volt Revue, Vol. 3: Hit the Road Stax

More Stax superstar roadshows from London and Paris in 1967. Recording quality varies widely, and makes straight-through listening a little rugged. The best cuts are by Otis Redding, Booker T and The MGs, and The Mar-Keys. Also heard are Carla Thomas and

Eddie Floyd, generally under less-than-ideal circumstances. Still, with 20 songs (and six introductions from the stage!), how can you go wrong?

STAX (UK) 012 (R)
Soul Soldiers
Sixteen upbeat dance-inducing songs from the Volt vaults, circa 1968–1972, featuring Darrell Banks, J.J. Barnes, Major Lance, and Jimmy Hughes. Between the heavy workouts are three outstanding soul-drippers by Darrell Banks and the shamefully underrated Jimmy Hughes. For lovers of hip-jerking northern soul and beach music.

STAX (UK) 013 (RL)
Stax Sirens and Volt Vamps
Sixteen tracks recorded for Stax and Volt in the late '60s and early '70s by Shirley Brown, Mable John, Jean Knight, Judy Clay, The Sweet Inspirations, Veda Brown, Margie Alexander, The Emotions, Margie Joseph, Jackie Ross, Jeanne and The Darlings, The Charmells, Inez Foxx, Carla Thomas, and Kim Weston. For lovers of soul bordering on funk. Literate but microscopic sleeve notes.

STAX (UK) 042 (L)
1000 Volts of Stax: The Stax Sessions
Unreleased '60s soul from deep in the vaults. This collection is a little more uneven than previous releases in this series, but many of the 18 songs here are so spectacular that the inconsistency doesn't really matter. Even if Carla Thomas's exceptional "Run Around" were the only track, no one would feel cheated. Also includes Ruby Johnson, Otis Redding, William Bell, Albert King, The Mad Lads, The Mar-Keys, Eddie Floyd, Rufus Thomas, Bobby Marchan, and Booker T and The MGs.

STAX (UK) 043 (RCL)
Stax Gold
Many of the 24 songs in this set will be instantly familiar, although the artists may evade your memory. Includes Booker T and The MGs, The Emotions, Mavis Staples, The Dramatics, Frederick Knight, Isaac Hayes, Jean Knight, The Staple Singers, Johnnie Taylor, and Shirley Brown. Even if you own the records, this CD offers great sound quality.

STILL 1151 (R)
Long Black Train
Fourteen rare and rockin', early, bluesy R&B recordings by Larry Green, Bobby Van Hook and The Night Owls, The Commandos, Johnny Acey, and Little Willie Littlefield.

STOMPIN' 101 (R)
Stompin'

STOMPIN' 102 (R)
Stompin', Vol. 2

STOMPIN' 103 (R)
Stompin', Vol. 3

STOMPIN' 104 (R)
Stompin', Vol. 4

STOMPIN' 105 (R)
Stompin', Vol. 5

STOMPIN' 106 (R)
Stompin', Vol. 6

STOMPIN' 107 (R)
Stompin', Vol. 7

STOMPIN' 108 (R)
Stompin', Vol. 8
Series of LPs, each with 18 tracks, mostly by either obscure artists or obscure cuts by well-known folks. Highlights on Vol. 1 are songs like "I Had a Little Dog" by Big Jack Reynolds, "Come on Home" by Louis "Blues Boy" Jones, and "My Goose Is Cooked" by Bob Williams that are sure to please the collector. Vol. 2 is a mix of obscurities with better-known tracks. It includes rock by Jesse and Buzzy, J.L. Smith, Bobo Jenkins, and Square Walton; jump blues by Lord Lebby, Pigmeat Peterson, and Ernest Brooks; and stompin' blues by the harp wailin' Cousin Leroy. Vol. 3 returns to an emphasis on obscurities by Harmon "Hump" Jones, The Crawford Brothers, The Table Toppers, Polka Dot Slim, Sherman Evans, Phil Flowers, Freddie Clark, The Bees, and Wally Mercer. Vol. 4 features a rare selection of rockin' blues and stompin' R&B tunes chockful of smokin' guitar and smouldering sax playing. Featured artists are Good Rockin' Sammy T, Pork Chops, K.C. Mojo Watson, Kid Thomas, Little Johnny Cook, Tender Slim, and Big Boy Groves. Stars on Vol. 5 include Gabriel and His Band of Angels, Rayvon Darnell, Gene and Billy, H-Bomb Ferguson and His Mad Lads, Rollee McGill, Lloyd George (no, not the Prime Minister), Lonnie Brooks, Larry Davis, and Rudy Green. Vol. 6 probably has more obscurities than any of the previous LPs, including Johnny Spains, Little Lawrence and The Suspenders, Tye-Tongue Hanley, Rev. Ballenger, Jesse Anderson, and Willard Harris and His Czars of Rhythm. Vol. 7 features Albert Washington, Roy Perkins, Lord Tennyson (no, not the poet laureate!), Sammy Jr. (no, not the Vegas lounge singer!), Freddy Hall and His Aces, Prince Charles (no, not the madly-in-love-with-someone-other-than-his-wife-future-king-of-England!), Smokey Joe, and Willie King. Vol. 8 is devoted to blues shouters like Big Joe Turner, Elmo Nixon, Bernie Hardison, Dr. Gaddy (Bob Gaddy), Jimmy "Mr. Blues" Williams, Max Bailey, Mr. Sad Head, Gene Parrish, Blow Top Lynn, Dave Bartholomew, and R&B DJ Moohah. Any of these LPs would make excellent rug-cuttin' music!

UGHA/RELIC 001 (R)

Rockin' the Blues:
Original Sound Track

All 16 tunes performed in the movie, without the comedy bits. Includes The Harptones, Pearl Woods and The Wanderers, Reese La Rue, Linda Hopkins, and The Hurricanes.

VARRICK 015 (RCL)

Christmas Soul Special

Wilson Pickett, Martha Reeves, Ben E. King, and Mary Wells celebrate a cool yule.

VIVID SOUND 001 (L)

The Goldwax Collection

Nineteen-track collection of classic gospel-derived southern soul from this important Memphis label. Roughly half of the material is available on other reissue LPs. Includes James Carr, Spencer Wiggins, The Ovations, Eddie Jefferson (not the jazz singer), The Lyrics, George and Greer, Willie Walker, and Percy Milem. The sound quality is first rate with exceptional vocal presence. Essential.

VIVID SOUND 006 (L)

Goldwax Collection 2

Hard-to-find singles and unissued cuts, half of which surfaced briefly in the late '70s on two long-gone Japanese album collections. Great speaker-bending sound. Includes the priceless, first 45 released by Goldband, "Darling" b/w "How a Woman Does a Man" by The Lyrics; the classic "Unlovable" by the obscure Barbara Perry; the soul anthem "That's How Strong My Love Is" by the late, great O.V. Wright; "Crying Baby Baby Baby" by the under-recorded Percy Milem; and the impressive "Love Me" by Phillip and The Faithfuls. Gene "Bowlegs" Miller, The Vel-Tones, Eddie Jefferson, Timmy Thomas, and "Wee" Willie Walker add anguish to the set.

VIVID 017 (L)

Soul Sounds of Memphis

Soul stew of Memphis-made music from Spencer Wiggins, Barbara and The Browns, and Ollie Nightingale, recently recorded at the Sounds of Memphis studios. All juice ably supported by staunch rhythm sections and Memphis horns. Notes in Japanese.

WARNER BROS. 27601 (L)

Atlantic Soul Classics

Fifteen winners from the Atlantic/Stax catalogs, perfect for parties. Mastering here is better than on most of the WEA CDs. Though I wouldn't really call The Coasters's "Yakety Yak" "soul," there's no faulting the other fourteen selections. Soul Man/Midnight Hour/Respect/I've Been Loving You Too Long/When a Man Loves a Woman/Sweet Soul Music.

WIZARD 5001 (R)

Angels of the Night

Fourteen sides from the '50s and early '60s featuring female doo-wop groups, including The Antwinetts, The Baby Dolls, The Debutantes, The Dolls, The Fairlanes, The Gales, Ginger and The Chiffons, The Kittens, Beverly Noble and Group, Pearl and Ronnie and Lisa and Lila, The Rubies, The Sharmeers, The Starlets, and The Veneers.

WIZARD 5003 (R)

Rare Doo-Wops

Sixteen cuts of varying quality with some rarities. Highlights: "Praying for You" by The Primes, "I'm a Fool" by The Hy-Tones, the beautiful "My Dear" by The Constellations, The Rendezvous's 1962 "Congratulations Baby," and the jumping "Way to My Heart" by the great Billy Storm and The Valients. Average sound, no notes or pics.

ZU ZAZZ 2009 (RL)

If It Ain't a Hit, I'll Eat My...Baby

First off, if you're under 18, easily offended, or a member of the PMRC, read no further. This LP has a dozen (17 on CD) of the filthiest records ever made, a mixture of blues, R&B, doo-wop, and even zydeco. There have been some fine double-entendre LPs issued before, and a few of these tracks fall into that category, including Roy Brown's "Butcher Pete, Pts. 1 and 2," Chick Willis's "Stoop Down, Pts. 1 and 2," and Bullmoose Jackson's "Big Ten Inch (Record)." The remaining cuts are some of the finest and funniest single-entendre records made by established stars and superstars of the '50s and '60s. including The Clovers's "Rotten Cocksucker's Ball," The Blenders' "Don't Fuck Around with Love," Slim Gaillard's "Fuck Off (The Dirty Rooster)," the triple-X rated "Think Twice" by Jackie Wilson and LaVern Baker, and a couple of accordion classics by Boozoo Chavis including a fine "Deacon Jones." A real "porn-ucopia" of prurient pleasures; highly recommended.

ILLUSTRATION CREDITS

Hasil Adkins, courtesy Norton Records

Hank Ballard and The Midnighters, courtesy King Records

Booker T and the MGs, courtesy Stax Records

The Byrds, courtesy Sony Music

Ray Charles, courtesy Atlantic Records

Joe Clay, courtesy Bear Family Records

Eddie Cochran, courtesy Rockstar Records

Creedence Clearwater Revival, courtesy Fantasy Records

The Crickets, courtesy Relic Records

The Drifters, courtesy Atlantic Records

The Edsels, courtesy Relic Records

Esquerita, courtesy Norton Records

The Everly Brothers, courtesy Magnum Force Records

The Five Royales, courtesy Relic Records

The Flamingos, courtesy Sequel Records

The Four Seasons, courtesy Rhino Records

Aretha Franklin, courtesy Atlantic Records

Charlie Gracie, courtesy Roller Coaster Records

Screamin' Jay Hawkins, courtesy Bear Family Records

Buddy Holly and The Crickets, courtesy MCA Records

The Hollywood Flames, courtesy Specialty Records

The Kinks, courtesy Rhino Records

Gladys Knight and the Pips, courtesy Relic Records

Jerry Lee Lewis, courtesy Rhino Records

Little Richard, courtesy Specialty Records

Frankie Lymon and The Teenagers, courtesy Sequel Records

The Monkees, courtesy Rhino Records

Rick Nelson, courtesy MCA Records

Roy Orbison, courtesy Charly Records

Carl Perkins, courtesy Rounder Records

Elvis Presley, courtesy RCA Records

The Rascals, courtesy Atlantic Records

Paul Revere and The Raiders, courtesy Sony Music

Sam and Dave, courtesy Atlantic Records

The Shirelles, courtesy Rhino Records

The Skyliners, courtesy Relic Records

The Staple Singers, courtesy Stax Records

The Turbans, courtesy Relic Records

Ike and Tina Turner, courtesy Cenco/Spry Records

The Turtles, courtesy Rhino Records

Richie Valens, courtesy Ace Records

Gene Vincent, courtesy Musique et Passions

Link Wray, courtesy Norton Records

The Zombies, courtesy Rhino Records

Bop that Never Stopped, courtesy Bison Bop Records

Minnesota Rock-a-Billy, courtesy White Label Records

Gotham R&B, courtesy Krazy Kat Records

The Golden Groups, courtesy Relic Records

About the Authors

Al Ennis was born in Virginia in 1948 but grew up in Wilmington, Delaware. After a short stint as a singer in a garage band, he joined the Navy in 1967. Upon his discharge, Al attended Orange Coast College and the University of California at Berkeley, majoring in English literature.

He worked in the hotel business for nine years after college, during which time he cofounded the now nationally distributed syndicated radio show, *Maximum Rock and Roll*, as well as contributing to various publications. Al joined Down Home Music (later Roots & Rhythm) in 1985, and has since become the chief rock and roll critic for the newsletter. Al currently lives in Albany, CA with his wife Christina and their seventeen-month-old daughter, Cailen.

Frank Scott was born in London, England in 1942 and has been collecting blues since the early '60s when he was first introduced to the music in London's flourishing club scene. Trained as an aerospace engineer, he moved to Southern California in 1966 to pursue his career and to be closer to the music he loves. In 1978, he moved to Northern California, where he joined Chris Strachwitz of internationally renowned Arhoolie Records to form a mail-order operation as an adjunct to Chris's retail store, Down Home Music. Over the years, this company has acquired a reputation for having the most comprehensive stock of blues and other specialty music. In 1990, Frank and his wife Nancy spun off the mail-order operation into a separate business, renamed Roots & Rhythm in 1992, which continues to serve some 13,000 customers worldwide.

In the '70s and early '80s, Frank also ran a small record company, Advent, that produced a handful of critically acclaimed blues and folk recordings. Besides his contributions to Roots & Rhythm newsletters and catalogs, he has written liner notes and articles for specialty magazines, and has hosted several radio programs. Frank currently lives in El Cerrito, CA with Nancy and their four-year-old son, Benjamin.

- -

Keep Up to Date with Rock and Roll and R&B!

Nearly all the records, cassettes, and CDs in this book are available through Roots & Rhythm, America's leading specialty music mail-order company. If you would like to receive regular newsletters with reviews of new rock and roll and R&B releases (and lots of other music too!), please fill out the coupon below. You will also receive a price list for the releases in this book, along with a 15 percent discount certificate good for your first order.

NAME _____

ADDRESS _____

CITY _____ STATE _____ ZIP _____

MUSICAL INTERESTS: _____

_____

Mail coupon to: ROOTS & RHYTHM
    6921 Stockton Avenue
    El Cerrito, CA 94530

    You may also phone (510) 525-1494 or fax us (510) 525-2904.